THE HOUSE OF THE GOAT

Investigating the murder of a shabby man who had asked directions to the home of Lord Lancroft before being found brutally stabbed, Superintendent Budd has only one clue. Inside the man's jacket is a piece of paper, on which is written the Lord's name and address, and the words 'The House of the Goat' . . . And when an ancient mummy is stolen in the search for a mysterious ring, nothing is as it seems . . . Two stories of mystery and cunning from the pen of Gerald Verner.

GERALD VERNER

◆

THE HOUSE OF THE GOAT

Complete and Unabridged

LINFORD
Leicester

First published in Great Britain

First Linford Edition
published 2014

A catalogue record for this book is available
from the British Library.

ISBN 978–1–4448–2197–0

Published by
F. A. Thorpe (Publishing)
Anstey, Leicestershire

Set by Words & Graphics Ltd.
Anstey, Leicestershire
Printed and bound in Great Britain by
T. J. International Ltd., Padstow, Cornwall

This book is printed on acid-free paper

THE HOUSE OF
THE GOAT

1

The Bald Man of Park Lane

The constable remembered, afterwards, having spoken to the bald man earlier in the evening. He had taken off his shabby hat, to mop the perspiration from his shining head while he put his question, and the policeman had been fascinated by his complete hairlessness.

When he saw him again the bald man was dead.

He was lying on his face, near the railings that divide the park from the roadway, a flabby, huddled heap, and the back of his ragged coat was wet and sticky. The startled constable, confronted with his first murder, acted promptly and intelligently, thereby earning a word of commendation from his immediate superiors, and within forty minutes of the discovery of the body Superintendent Robert Budd had taken charge of the inquiry.

He stood, a fat, sleepy-eyed man, his big face expressionless, while the divisional surgeon made his brief examination.

'The man was stabbed.' The grey-haired doctor rose to his feet and moved out of the circle of light thrown by the lamp in a constable's hand. 'He probably died without knowing what had killed him. The point of the knife, which must have had a long, narrow blade, pierced the heart. That's all I can tell you at present.'

'H'm, thank yer, Doctor.' Mr. Budd yawned and gently massaged the lowest of his many chins. 'You say you saw this man before?' He turned to the constable who had made the discovery.

'Yes, sir. He came up to me at the Piccadilly end of Park Lane, and — '

'What time was this?' interrupted Mr. Budd, and the constable was confused. He had taken no particular note of the time. It was quite a usual thing for people to ask him for information, and he had seen nothing in the incident to impress the time on his memory. The nearest he could swear to was that it had been after eight and before a quarter to nine —

The big man stopped his stammered apologies with a gesture.

'I'm not askin' you for the exact minute,' he said wearily. 'Between eight an' a quarter ter nine, was it? Well, that's good enough. What did 'e want to know?'

'He asked me if I could tell him where a man named Harvey Bradshaw lived, sir,' replied the policeman, obviously relieved that the time question had been so smoothly overcome. ''E said it was somewhere in Park Lane, but I couldn't tell 'im because I'd never heard the name before — '

'Harvey Bradshaw?' broke in the divisional-inspector quickly. 'That was Lord Lancourt's name before he got his peerage, wasn't it?'

'Was it?' grunted Mr. Budd. 'Does 'e live round here then?'

The divisional-inspector pointed into the darkness.

'Over there,' he answered. 'The big house beside the block of flats. It's one of the few old houses left.'

5

'H'm! Interestin' an' perculiar,' murmured the stout superintendent, pinching his lower lip between a massive finger and thumb and staring vaguely beyond the crowd of interested sightseers that the police were vainly trying move on. 'Lord Lancourt, eh? An' this feller was askin' where 'e lived? You're sure it was this feller?'

'Quite sure, sir,' replied the constable confidently. ' 'E took off his hat to wipe 'is head while 'e was talking, and I remember thinkin' how queer 'e looked. You can see for yerself, sir.' He jerked his head in the direction of the dead man.

Mr. Budd nodded thoughtfully.

'Yes, I can see,' he said slowly. 'Bald as a badger.'

'Alopecia,' put in the doctor. 'In a very advanced stage, too. Usually it only occurs in patches.'

'Is that what it is?' said the big man. 'Maybe I'll like to hear more about that, doctor. In the meantime, we'd better get this feller away as soon as we can. Has anybody been through 'is pockets?'

The divisional-inspector, to whom the

question was addressed, shook his head.

'We thought it best not to touch him until after you'd seen him,' he said.

'Very right an' proper,' murmured Mr. Budd, and looked sleepily round. 'Where's that sergeant o' mine? I'll bet 'e's fallen asleep somewhere.'

'I'm 'ere — jest behind you,' came the aggrieved voice of Sergeant Leek, in refutation of the slander. 'What is it?'

'See if you can find anythin' in this feller's pockets that'll tell us who he is,' ordered his superior. 'That's the most important thing at the moment. One of you give him some light, will yer?'

The lean sergeant slouched forward and knelt beside the body of the bald man. With expert fingers he rapidly searched the various pockets in the shabby clothing, but the few articles he found were not very illuminating.

'That's the lot,' he said presently, and Mr. Budd bent down and peered at the meagre collection. It consisted of a dirty handkerchief, eightpence-ha'penny, a nearly empty packet of cheap cigarettes, and a box containing a few matches.

The big man grunted his disappointment.

'Nothin' very helpful there,' he said, straightening up. 'Maybe his clothes'll tell us more. We can look at 'em later.'

The ambulance had arrived, and was drawn up a short distance behind the police-car which had brought Mr. Budd and the lugubrious Leek from the Yard. Under the curious eyes of the watchful crowd, the body of the bald-headed man was lifted on to a stretcher, carried over to the waiting vehicle, and carefully deposited inside. The men were closing the doors when Mr. Budd stopped them.

'Where's his hat?' he demanded suddenly. 'Has anybody seen it?'

There was a general disclaimer.

'Well, 'e had a hat,' grunted the big man. 'We know that, because 'e took it off while he was speakin' ter the constable. It must be here somewhere.'

But a search failed to reveal the missing headgear. It was not on the pavement, nor, as Leek brightly suggested, had it been wafted in some miraculous fashion over the railings into the park.

'Queer,' muttered Mr. Budd, rubbing his large nose irritably. 'Unless some fool 'as pinched it as a souvenir, the murderer must have taken it away with 'im.'

'What for?' asked the divisional-inspector.

'How should I know?' snapped Mr. Budd shortly 'Maybe he collects hats, an' this was a rare specimen!' He lumbered ponderously over to the ambulance. 'All right, you can get off,' he said. 'Have 'is clothes sent along ter the Yard as soon as possible, will yer?'

The ambulance moved away, and the stout superintendent rejoined the little group on the pavement.

'I've got a hunch this is goin' ter be a big job,' he remarked to nobody in particular. 'It's a queer business altogether. Here's an unknown feller killed in the middle o' Park Lane at eleven o'clock at night when there are still a lot o' people about, an' the murderer gets away unseen, takin' with 'im his victim's hat.' He concealed a yawn with a huge hand. 'About two hours before 'e's killed, 'e's tryin' to find out where a feller called

Harvey Bradshaw lives,' he went on. 'When did this Bradshaw become a lord?'

'Eighteen months ago,' said the divisional-inspector.

'Evidently this feller who was lookin' for 'im didn't know,' murmured Mr. Budd. 'H'm! Interestin' an' perculiar. I wonder why 'e didn't know? Well, I think we might 'ave a word with his lordship. P'raps he'll be able to tell us who the dead man was.'

'I'll be getting along,' put in the doctor. 'I'll fix up the post-mortem tomorrow and let you have a report.'

He gave a quick nod to include them all, and went over to his car. As he drove off Mr. Budd, Leek, and the divisional-inspector crossed the road, leaving the three constables to disperse the remainder of the crowd.

Lord Lancourt's house was large and imposing; an eyesore that was rendered impressive only by comparison with the factory-like blocks of flats in its immediate vicinity. In answer to their ring, the door was opened by a thin-faced footman who eyed them superciliously.

10

"Is lordship is not at 'ome,' he said loftily in reply to Mr, Budd's inquiry. "'E and 'er ladyship are in the country.'

He was inclined to refuse all further information, but reconsidered this attitude on learning the identity of his questioner sufficiently to grudgingly impart his master's address.

'Repton House, East Repton,' repeated Mr. Budd, making a note in his book. 'That's in Norfolk, ain't it?'

The footman condescendingly replied that it was.

'Thank you,' said the big man, shutting his notebook and stowing it away in his pocket. 'How long will 'is lordship be stayin' there?'

The servant was vague about this, but he thought it would probably be for several weeks. Mr. Budd thanked him again, and, since there was obviousiy nothing more to be learned, returned to the waiting police car.

One or two patient stragglers still remained, in the hope of further excitement, but the bulk of the crowd had been persuaded to depart on their various ways.

'There's nothin' more to be done here,' said the stout superintendent, fishing one of his foul black cigars out of his waistcoat pocket and sniffing at it delicately. 'I'm goin' back ter the Yard.'

He took his leave of the divisional-inspector, clambered wearily into the car, and settled himself comfortably in a corner.

'Well, what d'yer make of this job?' ventured Leek, as the machine sped along Park Lane. 'Funny business, ain't it?'

'There's nothin' funny about murder!' retorted Mr. Budd severely, applying a match to his cigar. 'But maybe I haven't got your peculiar sense of humour.'

'I didn't mean funny like that,' protested the lean sergeant mournfully. 'I meant, it's queer — '

'Well, why don't yer say what you mean?' grunted his superior, blowing out a cloud of acrid smoke.

Leek coughed.

'It's the same thing — ' he began argumentatively.

'It's not the same thing at all!' broke in Mr. Budd. 'You're queer, but you're not funny. Now keep quiet. I want to think.'

He hunched himself up in his corner and closed his eyes, puffing jerkily at the cigar between his teeth. The long-suffering sergeant sighed, caught his breath, and broke into a violent fit of coughing.

Mr. Budd opened his eyes and shifted irritably.

'Must you do that?' he demanded crossly.

'It's the smoke,' gasped Leek painfully. 'It's a bit strong.'

'Put on yer gas mask!' snarled Mr. Budd, and relapsed once more into meditation.

When they arrived at Scotland Yard, he climbed laboriously out of the car and made his way to his cheerless little office. Here he ensconced himself in the chair behind his desk and remained in an apparent state of coma until a messenger appeared with a bulky parcel, when he roused himself.

'Put it down there,' he ordered, nodding towards the desk, and, when the man had gone: 'Switch on that other

13

light, will yer? We'll have a look at these things. Maybe we'll learn something.'

Leek obeyed, and he opened the parcel, spreading the contents out on the desk before him. They consisted of a thread-bare overcoat, a cheap and well-worn suit of tweed, a shirt with collar attached, darned and mended in several places; a ragged tie; a set of underwear, even older than the shirt, and a pair of thick, woollen socks.

Mr. Budd, with the interested Leek peering over one of his shoulders, examined each garment with care, but there was nothing to supply a clue to the identity of the dead man. There were no laundry marks on the shirt and under-clothes; no tailor's tab attached to either the overcoat or the shabby suit.

'Nothin',' grunted the big man disap-pointedly, when he had finished his inspection. 'It looks as though we'll have ter rely on what Lord Thing-a-me-bob can tell us, or hope that somebody 'ull recognise the circulated description of this feller an' come forward — Hallo! What's this?' He fingered the jacket, and

Leek heard a faint rustle. 'There's somethin' 'ere — a paper or somethin'. Give me your knife, will yer?'

He took the penknife, which the sergeant held out, and carefully slit the lining. Inserting a fat thumb and finger, he withdrew a dirty and crumpled slip of paper on which some pencilled words had been scrawled. With difficulty, for they were very faint, he succeeded in deciphering them:

' . . . Bradshaw, Park Lane. The House of the Goat . . . '

Mr. Budd pursed his thick lips and gently scratched the side of his head.

'The House of the Goat,' he murmured. 'That's a queer name, ain't it? I wonder what it means?'

2

The Girl Who Looked Afraid

Lord Lancourt took the card from the salver which the servant held out, and studied it with a surprised frown. He was a middle-aged man, stout and red of face, with thinning hair that just avoided showing his scalp.

'A police officer?' he muttered. 'What the devil can he want to see me about?' His lips pursed and his pale eyes narrowed. 'Oh, well, I suppose you'd better show him in, Bates.'

The footman bowed and went soft-footed from the room. As the door closed behind him, Lancourt rose slowly to his feet and stood with his back to the fire, twisting the card about between a finger and thumb, the frown still on his face. He was standing thus when Mr. Budd was ushered into the big, book-lined room.

'I'm very sorry to bother yer lordship,' murmured the fat detective apologetically, 'but I believe you may be in position to supply some very important information concernin' an inquiry I'm makin'.'

Lancourt raised his thin eyebrows.

'To what inquiry do you refer?' he asked.

'I'll tell you,' said Mr. Budd, and proceeded to do so, while the other listened attentively.

'There's no doubt that this man was tryin' ter find you, m'lord,' the big man concluded, 'an' I'm hopin' that you can tell us his name.'

Lord Lancourt slowly shook his head.

'I'm afraid I can't help you at all,' he said. 'The description you have given me conveys nothing to me.'

'Maybe you can recognise him better from this, sir?' suggested Mr. Budd, plunging a fat hand into his breast pocket and producing an envelope. 'Here's a police photograph of the feller, taken at the mortuary.'

Lancourt made a gesture of distaste, but he glanced at the picture, which the stout superintendent thrust towards him all the same.

'No,' he declared, shaking his head again, 'I have never seen the man before, to my knowledge.'

Mr. Budd was disappointed, and his feelings showed in his face. The long journey from London to Norfolk appeared to have been a waste of time and energy. An idea occurred to him, and he put it into words.

'P'raps 'e wasn't bald when you knew him, m'lord,' he said hopefully. 'Maybe if I cover the top of his head; it'll make a difference.'

But it made no difference, apparently. Lord Lancourt continued to deny all knowledge of the dead man.

'It's very queer, sir,' sighed Mr. Budd, pinching one of his chins and shaking his head sadly. 'This feller was definitely lookin' for you. He not only asked the constable where you lived, but 'e had your name written on a piece o' paper which was found on 'im. Your name, Park Lane, an' somethin' about 'The House of the Goat' . . . ' His sleepy eyes noted the sudden change in the face of the man before him, and he stopped abruptly. 'Does that convey anythin' to you, sir?' he asked, after a slight pause.

'Extraordinary!' muttered Lancourt, almost to himself; 'Most extraordinary! You are sure those were the words?'

'Quite sure, sir,' replied Mr. Budd. 'The House of the Goat — that was it. Do you know what it means?'

'It refers to a house not very far away from here,' answered the other, fingering his cheek and frowning. 'An old thirteenth-century building, standing on an island in the middle of a broad. 'The House of the Goat' is the local name for it.'

Mr. Budd pricked up his ears. Here was something anyway. Perhaps his journey to Norfolk was going to produce results after all.

'Who lives there, m'lord?' he inquired.

A faint smile hovered for an instant over Lancourt's heavy face.

'Nobody,' he replied. 'You wouldn't get anyone to live there for a fortune. The place has been empty for years.'

'What's the matter with it?' asked the

big man interestedly, and the other eyed him thoughtfully before he replied.

'It's in a shocking state of repair and most inconveniently located,' he said after a while, 'but that's not the reason entirely. As a matter of fact, it has a very bad reputation. Several people have tried to live there, but they none of them stayed very long.'

'Do you mean that the place is s'posed ter be haunted?' said Mr. Budd sceptically.

'That is the general belief,' assented Lancourt, nodding. 'The legend attaching to the house dates back to the period when it was built. In those days it was occupied by an astrologer, or so the story goes, and this man is credited with having had direct intercourse with the devil. Hence the name which the place has acquired locally.' He saw the puzzled look on Mr. Budd's face, and hastily explained. 'Satan is supposed to have appeared to his worshippers at the old Sabbats in the form of a goat,' he added.

The stout superintendent sniffed disparagingly.

'You don't believe all that nonsense, of course, sir?' he said, and the other shrugged his thick-set shoulders non-committedly.

'Perhaps I don't,' he answered, without conviction, 'but the vast majority of the people in this district do. Few would willingly pass within sight of the place after dark, and its history certainly bears out that there is some thing wrong with it. It has been unoccupied for nearly ten years, and the last people to live there left at twenty-four hours' notice.'

Mr. Budd had opened his mouth to reply, when a girl came quickly into the room.

'Have you — ' she began, and stopped suddenly. 'Oh, I'm sorry. I didn't know there was anyone here.'

'It's all right, my dear,' said Lancourt. 'This gentleman is a detective from Scotland Yard. Apparently a man was killed almost opposite our house in Park Lane last night.' Rapidly he explained the situation, while Mr. Budd, with that deceptive sleepy expression that missed nothing, watched the girl. The momentary fear which had flickered in her eyes at the mention of the word 'detective' had not escaped him, and he was wondering what had induced it. What had this slim, pretty girl, with the fair hair, to fear from an officer of the law? Was it merely the natural uneasiness which even the most law-abiding citizen experiences when brought into contact with the police, or was it due to something more potent? Whatever the reason, it did not recur. The big grey eyes were wide and interested, but that instantaneous flash of terror did not appear again.

'How dreadful,' she replied, when Lancourt had finished. 'I wonder who the man could have been?'

'I've no idea,' he said, 'or why he should have been looking for me.'

'It's all very mysterious,' murmured Mr. Budd, shaking his head. 'Very mysterious, indeed. An' the most mysterious bit is this ref'rence to the House of the Goat.'

Again, from under his heavy lids, he saw terror spring up in the girl's eyes. It faded almost at once, but the effort at control drained the colour from her cheeks. This girl knew something. Even if she shared the superstitious fears of the people in the neighbourhood concerning the place, it was unlikely that the mere mention of it, in the prosaic comfort of that cosy, book-lined room, would have brought such a look to her face. It was something worth noting, but nothing more could be done for the present, and Mr. Budd prepared to take his leave.

'Well, sir,' he said slowly, 'it doesn't seem as though you can help me. Maybe what you have told me 'ull turn out useful; it's difficult ter tell at this stage. I'm sorry to 'ave had ter trouble you.'

'I'm sorry that I am unable to be more helpful,' said Lancourt politely, accompanying him to the door. 'But this man is a complete stranger to me, and I cannot even offer a suggestion as to why he should have been carrying my name and the name of this deserted house about with him. If you learn anything, I hope you'll let me know. I'm naturally curious.'

'I will, m'lord,' promised Mr. Budd.

'Good night — good night, miss.'

He made his way ponderously down to the spacious hall where Sergeant Leek was waiting. A footman came forward and let them out, and they set off down the dark drive.

'Well,' asked the lean sergeant, after waiting in vain for his stout companion to say something, 'did yer learn anythin'?'

Mr. Budd produced one of his cigars and lit it carefully before he replied.

'I did, an' I didn't,' he answered. 'This *is* a queer business, an' I've got a hunch that it's goin' ter get queerer.'

Briefly he related what had passed in the house they had just left.

'It seems ter me,' remarked Leek, when he concluded, 'that this 'ere 'ouse has got somethin' ter do with it — '

'You surprise me!' broke in Mr. Budd sarcastically. 'The way your keen brain works these things out is amazin'.'

'I'm pretty good at spottin' things like that,' said the sergeant complacently. 'It struck me at once — '

'It was so obvious,' interrupted his superior, 'that a congenital idiot couldn't

24

'ave missed it! Maybe that accounts for you spottin' it! I think for once you're right, though,' he went on, before the injured Leek could think of a suitable reply. 'It's a pretty long cry between a dead man in Park Lane an' a devil-house in Norfolk, but when we find the connection this business'll be cleared up.'

They had reached the end of the drive, and Leek, who was a few paces ahead, paused.

'Which way d'we go?' he asked.

'We find the quickest way to this place they call the House of the Goat,' answered Mr. Budd promptly. 'I'm very anxious to have a look at that ill-omened buildin' without wastin' any time.'

3

Dead Man's Hat

'Well, I've seen more cheerful-lookin'
places,' remarked Mr. Budd, staring
across the gloomy expanse of water at the
dim smudge which marked the island in
the middle of the broad. 'So that's the
'ouse, is it? No wonder people won't live
in it fer long.'

Sergeant Leek shivered as a chill gust
of wind rippled the surface of the broad.

'I don't know what yer wanted ter
come 'ere for,' he complained, pulling his
overcoat closer round his lean form. 'We
might jest as well 'ave left it till the
mornin'.'

'Never put off till tomorrow what yer
can do terday,' said his superior sententiously. 'My bump o' curiosity is very
highly developed, an' when it starts
workin' overtime it 'as ter be satisfied.'

'Well, now you've satisfied it, what

26

about goin' back ter that there pub?' suggested the sergeant hopefully. 'It don't surprise me this place 'as got a bad name. It's enough ter give anyone the creeps.'

Mr. Budd privately agreed with him. They were standing on the edge of a vast, rush-girt lake, fitfully lit by the appearances of a watery moon. Before and behind them, and on either side, stretched a wild tract of flat marshland, unbroken by house or tree, and with nothing to relieve its sombre monotony except the island, which rose menacing and forbidding from the dark water. Of the house which occupied it very little could be seen, for here, by some curious freak of nature, trees grew thickly, forming an impenetrable screen, so that only a hint of gable and chimney was visible. A lonely and unprepossessing spot at the best of times, thought Mr. Budd. Seen now, in the intermittent light of the waning moon, curiously and definitely sinister.

'The feller at the pub thought we was mad when we asked 'im the way,' grumbled Leek, sniffing pathetically, 'an'

I reckon 'e was right! Fancy walking three miles jest ter take a look at that!'

He swept an arm in the direction of the island with a gesture of disgust.

'The trouble with you — ' began Mr. Budd severely, and stopped suddenly. 'Look!' he breathed quickly. 'Look!'

The scudding clouds had completely obscured the moon, and, in the intense darkness, the surprised sergeant saw a tiny star of light gleam brightly for a second amid the trees on the island.

'There must be somebody there!' he whispered excitedly. 'Look, there it is again!'

The little point of light flashed in a different place, went out, and flashed again.

'There's someone moving about among them trees with an electric torch,' murmured the big man. 'Interestin' an' perculiar. I'd like ter know who it is, an' what they're doin'.'

'Well, I don't see 'ow yer goin' to,' said Leek thankfully. 'There's no way of gettin' over there — '

'That's where you're wrong, as usual,'

grunted Mr. Budd. 'If you'd used yer eyes, same as I did, you'd 'ave seen that boat that's moored a few yards away. I spotted it d'rectly we got here.'

He moved along by the edge of the water, and presently stopped at a place where the rushes grew less thickly. The moon came out from behind the wrack of cloud at that moment, and in its pale, bleary light the lugubrious sergeant saw the dinghy tied up to a stunted bush. It was an ancient boat, half-rotten, and, to judge by the amount of water in the bottom, leaked badly.

'You're not thinkin' of goin' over in that, are yer?' he asked in dismay.

'Maybe you'd prefer to swim?' snarled the stout man. 'What's the matter with yer? Afraid of gettin' yer feet wet?'

'It don't look safe ter me — ' began Leek.

'Don't start an argument!' snapped Mr. Budd irritably. 'I'm goin' over to that island, an' you're comin' with me, an' that's that! Get in!'

With a resigned sigh the lean sergeant stepped gingerly into the little boat and grasped frantically at the gunwale as it rocked violently. The water swirled over his ankles, and he gasped at the sudden chill.

'I shall catch me death of cold,' he said plaintively. 'There's nothin' worse than wet feet — '

'There's hundreds of worse things, an' you'll discover 'em all if you don't stop grumbling!' growled his superior, getting in beside him and untying the painter. 'Sit down, an' give me them oars.'

The unhappy Leek obeyed, and, pushing the dinghy out of the rushes with a thrust from one of the blades, Mr. Budd fitted the sculls into the rowlocks and began to pull towards the island.

It took him longer than he expected, for distances on water are deceptive, but eventually the nose of the boat bumped gently against the bank, and the big man gripped the branch of an overhanging tree.

'Catch hold o' that bush,' he whispered, 'an' hang on while I get out.'

He scrambled ashore, while Leek held the boat in, with an agility that was remarkable for a man of his bulk, and, after tying the dinghy securely to the trunk of a tree, assisted the lean sergeant to join him.

It was very dark and, except for the gentle lapping of the water, completely silent. If there was anyone lurking there, under the trees, he was keeping very still.

For a long time Mr. Budd waited, listening intently, hoping that if there was a third person near at hand, some movement would reveal his presence; but nothing stirred. Darkness and silence brooded over the whole place. It was more than probable that the torch-bearer had heard the approach of the boat and made himself scarce.

The big man, with Leek at his heels, began to move farther inland, forcing his way through the waist-high weeds that grew thickly everywhere. In a little while the trees thinned, and they came out into an open space that had apparently at one time been a lawn and flower-garden. They reached it during a period of brightness which enabled them to see clearly the neglect and ruin on every side. The flowerbeds were a tangled mass of weeds, the lawn a waste of rank grass; and the remains of a pergola lay strewn about, with briars and brambles twining around its broken supports in hopeless confusion. A dank smell of decay and rotting vegetation permeated the whole atmosphere, enhancing the general air of desolation which hung like a miasma over the place. The house itself, silent and brooding, stood beyond the remains of the garden; a low-roofed building of stone, its staring windows, like watchful eyes, alert for any attempt to disturb its sinister tranquillity.

Mr. Budd, practical and phlegmatic man though he was, felt a little cold shiver run through him. He had visited many old and deserted buildings in his time, but never before had he experienced quite the same sensations as now. There was something indescribably evil about this empty house. Its emanations saturated the air with a palpable and potent force that filled him with a sudden and quite inexplicable terror. He had an almost overpowering desire to flee blindly back to the boat and leave this unhallowed place unmolested.

He shook off this childish feeling with an effort, and advanced slowly and ponderously towards the house. Utter and complete silence reigned everywhere. The wind had dropped and there was a hush as though nature were holding her breath in expectancy.

Cautiously the stout superintendent and the lean sergeant crossed the overgrown lawn, their progress marked by the downtrodden grass. Nobody had come this way before them. Their tracks would have been clearly visible if they had. The person responsible for the light they had seen, if he had come from the house, must have reached the belt of trees by another route. But there was no sign of anybody. Whoever had been there had either gone or was hiding.

They reached the great oak door of the house just as the moon vanished behind another bank of cloud and plunged them into complete darkness.

Mr. Budd muttered an oath and lugged out his torch. The light danced uneasily over the door, revealing a great iron handle, red with rust. Gripping it the big man pushed, expecting to find that the door was locked; but to his surprise it opened slowly. Hesitating for a second, he crossed the threshold and flashed his light about an enormous cavernous hall. Dimly he caught a glimpse of a great staircase disappearing into darkness and a few articles of furniture, grey with dust, and then, with a sudden catch of his breath, he saw footprints — and his flesh crept.

'Look at that!' he whispered hoarsely, and pointed.

Sergeant Leek peered down at the marks in the thick film of dust that covered the floor.

'There must've bin an animal 'ere,' he began in a puzzled voice. Then suddenly realising: 'My God! They're *cloven hoofs!*'

'The House of the Goat,' muttered Mr. Budd, and uttered a startled exclamation as something came sailing through the air and fell with a soft 'plop' at his feet.

'What was that?' gasped Leek, with an involuntary jump backwards.

The big man turned his light on the

object and, stooping, picked it up. It was a shabby, battered hat of soft felt, shapeless and weather-stained.

'Where did that come from?' muttered the wondering Leek, peering uneasily into the shadows that surrounded them.

'All the way from Park Lane!' grunted Mr. Budd, turning the hat about in his podgy fingers. 'I'll bet a month's pay that this once belonged ter the dead man.'

4

Marooned!

The lean sergeant pushed back his hat from his damp forehead and passed an unsteady hand over his face.

'Let's get out o' here,' he whispered uneasily, glancing fearfully into the shadows. 'It ain't healthy.'

'Healthy or not, we're stayin',' snapped Mr. Budd, his big face setting stubbornly. 'There's somebody in this place playin' monkey tricks, an' I'm goin' ter find out who it is — an' why.' Resolutely he went over to the foot of the huge staircase and sent his light flashing up into the gloom.

'Anyone there?' he called sharply.

His voice went echoing and re-echoing through the house, but nobody answered.

'You stop 'ere,' he said to the sergeant. 'I'm goin' ter have a look upstairs.'

Slowly and cautiously, his eyes fixed on the black void above, he began to mount the stairway. The aged wood creaked under his weight, but no sound came from above. And yet the hat had been thrown from the direction of the staircase. There must be somebody there, lurking in the deep shadows which the feeble glimmer of his torch failed to dissipate. But when he reached the landing it was, except for himself, quite deserted. He turned his light on to the floor. Here, as in the hall beneath, the ancient carpet was thick with dust, and he experienced once again that chilling of the spine as he saw more tracks of the cloven hoofs. They led nowhere in particular, but covered the floor in a confused jumble.

Mr. Budd said afterwards that the next hour was the most nerve-racking he had ever spent in his life. He was unarmed, and the evil influence of the house was affecting him powerfully. Added to this, he was convinced that there was someone watching his every movement — someone who, if he was right about the original ownership of the hat which he had stuffed into his pocket, was probably a murderer. And, yet, in spite of this, he forced himself to make a tour of the entire building. From room to room he went, inspecting each carefully, but he found no trace of any human presence. The hoof-marks were everywhere, but nothing else.

The old house had obviously once been richly furnished, but now everything was in a state of dilapidation and decay. The handsome furniture, the carpets, the hangings, were mouldering into ruin, due to neglect and damp, and most of the rooms were festooned with cobwebs, relics of a dynasty of spiders. The whole place was like a slowly decomposing corpse.

Hot and dusty, he rejoined the melancholy Leek, with a sigh of relief.

'There's not a sign of anybody,' he said in reply to the sergeant's question. 'Those hoof-prints are all over the place, though — '

'They weren't made by anythin' 'uman!' declared Leek with conviction. 'If yer ask me — '

'I'm not askin' you!' snarled Mr. Budd. 'You'd be the last person I should ask anythin'! I've got me own ideas about them marks, an' the Devil doesn't come into 'em! There was nothin' supernatural about the way that feller died in Park Lane, an' there's nothin' supernatural about this 'ouse, so get that fixed in yer head! It's queer, but maybe some queer things 'ave happened here at times. A buildin' absorbs atmosphere, an' gives out what it takes in. This house 'as seen some pretty evil things in its time, I'll bet, an' it's goin' ter see some more. If I'm any judge, but there'll be an 'uman agency at the bottom of 'em. When *I* come up against the Devil in person, I'll resign an' leave it ter the old-school-tie brigade from 'Endon to deal with him!'

'Well, what are we goin' ter do now?' asked Leek, considering that it was better not to comment on this unusually long speech. 'It don't seem much good stoppin' 'ere, does it?'

To his surprise and delight Mr. Budd agreed with him.

'No,' he said. 'We'll get back an' see if they can put us up at that pub for the night. We can come back tomorrow an' have a good look round in daylight.'

The sergeant's long face brightened. He was hungry and cold, and the prospect of food and warmth was cheering. He opened the door with alacrity, and they made their way back across the lawn to the place where they had left the boat. But here a shock awaited them, for the dinghy was no longer there!

'Are yer sure this is the place?' asked the sergeant, and Mr. Budd nodded. 'Then you couldn't 'ave tied it up secure — '

'I did,' broke in the big man grimly, and focused the light of his torch on the tree. 'Look there!'

Leek looked, saw the cut rope hanging from the trunk, and his face changed.

'Somebody's pinched it!' he exclaimed in dismay.

'You don't say so!' grunted his superior, peering out across the dark water. 'How you make these remarkable deductions is a constant source o' wonder ter me.'

'But what are we goin' ter do?'

demanded the sergeant agitatedly. 'It means we're stranded 'ere.'

'It certainly looks very much like it,' agreed Mr. Budd calmly. 'Unless you'd like ter swim across an' find another boat.'

'P'rap's there's another boat 'ere, somewhere?' said Leek, receiving the suggestion without enthusiasm.

Mr. Budd dipped a finger and thumb into his waistcoat pocket and pulled out a cigar.

'There's no 'arm in lookin',' he said. 'Let's see.'

They made a complete circuit of the island, but there was no sign of a boat of any description.

'Well, that's that!' grunted the big man when they got back to the place where they had started from. 'Here we are, an' here we've got ter stop!'

'But we can't stop 'ere all night!' expostulated Leek. 'What are we goin' ter do fer grub?'

'If you're 'ungry you'll have to eat thistles!' snarled Mr. Budd irritably. 'I never knew such a feller fer grumblin'!

There's no way of leavin' this place, so we've got ter make the best of it. Let's go back ter the house an' make ourselves as comfortable as we can.'

He turned and walked away, and after one longing glance across the dismal stretch of water the miserable Leek followed.

'After all, it might be worse,' remarked Mr. Budd. 'The place is furnished, after a fashion, an' maybe, if we make up a fire, it won't be *so* bad.'

'I'd like ter know who pinched that boat,' muttered the sergeant dejectedly.

'I'd like ter know a lot o' things!' growled the stout man. 'I'd like ter know what connection there is between this 'ouse and the feller who was killed in Park Lane. An' I'd like ter know what the murderer pinched 'is hat for. Maybe I'll get an answer to some o' these questions before we leave this place.'

His words were prophetic. The night was to bring an answer to most of his questions, and, in doing so, was to provide him with one of the worst experiences of his life.

The first of the series of incidents which were to culminate so tragically on that lonely island in the middle of the desolate broad occurred when they reached the house. Mr. Budd thrust at the door, expecting it to open as it had done previously, but it refused to move. Thinking that it had merely become jammed, he flung his weight against it, but it remained a solid barrier.

'Bolted on the inside,' he said laconically, rubbing a bruised shoulder and eyeing the unyielding door malevolently. 'There's still somebody about here. We'll 'ave ter try another way of gettin' in.'

He moved slowly along the front of the house, and presently stopped by a narrow window, the glass of which was broken.

'It's too small for me,' he said, putting in his hand and fumbling with the catch, 'but you can climb through, an' go round an' unfasten the door.'

Sergeant Leek appeared anything but eager.

'S'posin' there's somebody lurkin' about inside?' he objected dubiously.

'Then they'll get you first!' retorted his

superior. 'That's the advantage o' bein' a sup'intendent!'

He pulled open the casement, and Leek reluctantly scrambled over the sill. As he dropped gingerly into the darkness beyond, an agonising scream broke the silence of the house.

'My Gawd!' whispered the sergeant, his white face appearing against the block oblong of the window. 'What was that?'

'How should I know!' snapped Mr. Budd. 'Get that door open as quick at yer can!'

He hurried back to the great oak door and waited. After what seemed an age he heard stumbling steps, the rasp of bolts, and the massive portal was opened.

'Put on yer light,' breathed Leek hoarsely, 'there's bin murder done 'ere!'

The big man switched on his torch and stepped quickly inside.

'Shut the door,' he ordered sharply; and when the other had obeyed: 'Now, then, what did yer mean?'

'Over there!' muttered Leek, pointing into the gloom of the great hall. 'I nearly fell over it.'

Mr. Budd jerked his light in the direction he indicated and the breath whistled through his teeth. A man lay sprawled unnaturally on the floor, his face upturned to the roof, and the grey dust beneath him was slowly turning a dull red.

5

Strange Company

The stout superintendent went quickly over and peered down at the dead man. One look he gave at the twisted face, and uttered a startled exclamation.

'It's Benny Linkman!' he grunted in amazement.

'Benny Linkman!' echoed Leek, coming to his side. 'So it is. What can 'e have been doin' here?'

Mr. Budd shook his head and dropped heavily on to one knee.

'Goodness knows,' he muttered. 'Benny was never more than a little sneak-thief, poor feller. I s'pose 'e must have got mixed up in this business somehow.' He undid the coat and waistcoat, looked at the gaping wound in the thin chest, and touched one of the lifeless hands.

'Stabbed, like the other feller,' he murmured. 'That scream must've been 'is

46

death cry. He's still warm. Poor feller! Well, he's got his, though why anyone should've killed Benny beats me.'

'P'raps 'e knew somethin',' said Leek.

''E knew somethin' all right,' agreed the big man, getting up with difficulty. 'But what did 'e know? How did 'e come inter this — just a stupid little tea-leaf without brains enough ter know when to come in outer the rain.'

'Maybe 'e was workin' for the people behind this business?' suggested the sergeant.

'An' learnt more than 'e ought to've done?' Mr. Budd nodded several times. 'Yes, that's about it.' He wrinkled his forehead and pulled thoughtfully at his big nose. 'What is the business, that's the question. Who was this bald feller, an' why was 'e killed? Why was 'e so anxious ter see Lancourt, an' why was his hat so important that the murderer took it away with him? An' how did it get 'ere — ?'

'You don't know it *did* get 'ere,' interrupted Leek. 'You're only just guessin' that — '

'I'll bet it's a good guess, all the same,'

grunted the fat man. 'Well, it's no good talkin' an' theorisin'. Let's get this feller away from here. There's a couch in that room.' He jerked his head towards a door on the right of the hall. 'Help me carry 'im in there.'

They picked up the body between them and carried it into the big, musty-smelling room, and laid it on a dusty settee. Mr. Budd made a search of the pockets, but he found nothing to help him. There was some money, not very much, and the return half of a railway ticket from London, dated that day, but nothing that threw any light on the reason for his presence in the old house or offered the smallest suggestion of a motive for his murder.

The big man covered him with an old tablecloth and joined Leek in the hall.

'We'd better set about makin' ourselves comfortable fer the night, I s'pose,' he said, glancing round him disparagingly.

Leek sniffed disgustedly.

'Comfortable!' he muttered lugubriously. 'There's a fat chance o' that, ain't there? Do you realise that the feller who killed Benny is still wanderin' round somewhere?'

'I do,' answered Mr. Budd. 'An' we'll let him wander fer the time bein'. It's no good attemptin' ter try an' find him. I've been all over this buildin' once, an' it's like a warren. Besides, we're unarmed. A dozen people could dodge yer upstairs, if they wanted to.'

'As long as 'e keeps upstairs I shan't complain,' grunted the sergeant, with an uneasy glance towards the big staircase. 'It's the chance that 'e may come wanderin' down stairs that gives me the creeps!'

'You're a fine policeman, you are!' snapped Mr. Budd scathingly. 'Don't be a coward!'

'I'd rather be a live coward than a dead 'ero!' retorted Leek. 'Where d'yer suggest we spend the night — out 'ere?'

The stout man shook his head.

'No,' he replied, 'there's a room over there that'll do us. It's only got one window, an' that's shuttered. If we sit facin' the door, we won't get taken by surprise. There's a couple of easy-chairs, an' we can find wood an' make up a fire — '

'Let's get busy, then, for the Lord's sake!' broke in the lean sergeant. 'I shall feel 'appier when we get in there with the door locked!'

Wood was not difficult to find. They discovered an out-house containing a pile of it, and also some coal — relics evidently of the last tenants. In a very short time they had a cheerful fire blazing up the old chimney, and had settled down in the two easy-chairs which, although mildewed and dusty, were surprisingly comfortable.

The fire offered both warmth and light, and Mr. Budd, with a cigar between his teeth, leaned back wearily and closed his eyes.

'This ain't so bad,' he murmured sleepily.

'It's a pity we couldn't lock that door,' muttered Leek. 'If there 'ad been a handle I could've jammed a chair under it.' He stared apprehensively at the ragged gap where the lock had been. The wood was rotten, and it had apparently dropped out at some period in the house's history.

The wind had risen and was blowing in increasingly powerful gusts round the old house, whistling mournfully in the eaves and tearing through the trees with a sound like the rush of many waters. Mr Budd, with his fat hands loosely clasped over his capacious stomach, appeared to have gone to sleep. Only the intermittent glow from the cigar between his lips showed that he was still awake.

Presently Leek began to nod. The exertions of the day had tired him, and the comfort of the chair and the warmth from the fire were soporifics that lulled his senses. A long and unmusical snore went wavering through the room, and Mr. Budd's heavy eyelids lifted. He rolled his cigar from one side of his mouth to the other, and a long cylinder of ash fell unheeded on to his waistcoat. Raising an arm he looked at the watch on his wrist. Ten minutes past eleven. He was surprised to find that it was no later. Such a lot seemed to have happened.

The night wore on.

The noise of the wind outside increased

in violence, and presently was added to by the splatter of rain against the wooden shutter of the window. A nasty night, thought the fat man drowsily. Even the doubtful hospitality of the old house was a comfort. He shifted to an easier position and, staring through half-closed eyes at the fire, listened to the turmoil without, which was punctuated at irregular intervals by a snore from the sleeping sergeant.

The house, too, began to emit queer and unidentified noises. He became aware of them as his ears grew accustomed to the storm — eerie little creaks and cracks like the soft passage of stealthy feet over loose floorboards. Once he was so convinced that there was somebody moving in the hall outside, that he slid silently out of his chair, and going over to the door peered out. But the light of his torch revealed nothing. The great hall was empty.

Returning to his chair, the big man took the shabby hat from his overcoat pocket and examined it carefully in the light of the fire. It was very old, and showed signs of a great deal of wear. The leather band inside was stained and torn, but there was nothing to suggest why the killer of the bald man had taken it away with him. There was, of course, a possibility that it was not the dead man's hat, though Mr. Budd had very little doubt about this.

He put it away after an exhaustive scrutiny, made up the fire, and sat back once more in his chair. Without exception this was one of the most curious jobs he had ever been connected with. There was nothing on which to base even the beginning of a theory. The murdered man was unknown; his occupation, friends, where he had come from, everything about him that might have been of assistance in solving the riddle of his death. The only tangible clue was the slip of paper with the pencilled scrawl, which had been found in the lining of his coat; and following up that had led to this desolate and ill-omened house in the middle of the broad, and a second dead man.

Mr. Budd thought of Benny Linkman lying in the room across the hall and frowned. Why had he been killed? What was the link between his death and the death of the bald man? That they had both been killed by the same hand seemed evident from the method, but what had been the motive? Who was the unknown, lurking in the silence and the shadows of this deserted mansion, and what was his object? What, above all, was the secret of this ancient building?

The big man yawned wearily. It was all very puzzling and perplexing. When he had left London that morning, he had never imagined the turn events would take.

He was just dropping into a doze, when a sound brought him to startled alertness. It was a soft thud, and it seemed to come from somewhere below.

Instantly wide awake he listened, but the noise was not repeated. All he could hear now was the fury of the wind and the hissing of the falling rain. Perhaps that other sound had been imagination? There came a surge of rain against the shutter, driven before a gust of wind that shook the house. Something fell with a loud and prolonged clatter, and Leek woke up with a start.

'What's that?' he demanded huskily, blinking sleepily. 'What's all that row?'

'The ruddy 'ouse is fallin' down!' grunted Mr. Budd, and the relieved sergeant gave a prodigious yawn.

'Oh, is that all?' he said. 'I must 'ave dropped off ter sleep.'

'If it wasn't for the strange noises you make when yer asleep, nobody'd ever know the difference,' remarked the big man rudely.

'Did I snore?' asked the sergeant. 'I was dreamin' I remember thinkin' I was bein' chased by a lot o' goats — '

'An' I s'pose the row you was kickin' up was the matin call?' said Mr. Budd. 'I've often wondered what you reminded me of — '

'What was that?' interrupted Leek suddenly, and the stout superintendent listened.

'I can't 'ear anythin',' he said after a pause.

'I can't now,' muttered the sergeant. 'But while you was talkin', I thought I 'eard footsteps.'

'It's the house,' said Mr. Budd reassuringly. 'I've heard all sorts o' queer noises — '

'There you are — listen!' exclaimed Leek, jumping to his feet. 'That's not the house! There's someone out there in the 'all — '

'I was fooled like that,' began his superior, and got no further, for the door was suddenly flung open and the tall figure of a man loomed on the threshold.

'You look so comfortable, gentlemen,' he said quietly, 'that it seems a pity to disturb you. Put up your hands and keep still!'

6

Mr. Budd Hears Nothing
to his Advantage

The stout superintendent made a movement to get up.

'I said keep still!' snapped the newcomer curtly, and the firelight glinted on the automatic he held in his hand.

'I 'eard you,' retorted Mr. Budd. 'You can put that thing away. I'm nervous of firearms.'

'You'll have cause to be, if you try any tricks,' said the man in the doorway grimly. 'How many more of you are there?'

'About twenty thousand!' answered the big man calmly. 'Maybe I'm estimatin' a bit low, but that's somewhere near it.'

For an instant the other was taken aback, and then his face darkened.

'Don't try and be funny!' he said angrily.

'I never felt less 'umorous in me life!'

declared Mr. Budd truthfully. 'That's roughly the number constitutin' the Metropol'tan Police Force.'

'Are you trying to pretend that you're a detective?' demanded the man, and Mr. Budd nodded.

'I've been tryin' ter pretend that most o' me life!' he answered. 'So 'as my sergeant.'

'Is that so?' The man with the automatic eyed him sardonically. 'Well, you won't bluff me. I wasn't born yesterday.'

'You'd be a remarkable baby if yer 'ad been,' said Mr. Budd, eyeing the stalwart form of the newcomer. 'How long are yer goin' to stand there wagglin' that gun about? There's no need. We've got nothin' more dangerous between us than a toothpick.'

'That's a likely story,' sneered the other. 'I suppose you think I don't know who you are and what you've come here for? Have another think, my fat friend!'

He took a pace forward, and the stout superintendent got a clearer view of his face as he emerged from the shadows. He was a youngish-looking man with a firm, square jaw — not by any means an unpleasant-looking man if his face had not been so grimly set.

'I suppose you found out about this place when you killed Grunsbacher?' he snapped. 'Well, you're a fast worker, I'll say that.'

Mr. Budd looked at him quickly. Was this really a case of cross-purposes? Had this man really mistaken him for someone else, or was he merely trying to put up a bluff?'

'Was Grunsbacher the feller who was killed in Park Lane?' he asked.

The young man made an impatient gesture.

'What's this?' he said. 'Another little game of 'let's pretend'? Of course he was! You know that very well — '

'Now, look here!' interrupted the big man seriously. 'Let's get this straight. I don't know who you think I am, but whoever it is you're wrong! I'm Sup'intendent Budd, of the Criminal Investigation Department, New Scotland Yard — '

'An' I'm a fairy!' snarled the other. 'It's no good trying to pull that stuff on me, I tell you — '

'I can show you me warrant-card,' said Mr. Budd, and raised his hand towards his breast-pocket.

'Keep your hands still!' snapped the man sharply. 'It's a good idea, if it comes off, but it isn't coming off! If you put your hands near your pockets, this gun of mine is going to do a lot of very serious damage.'

Mr. Budd sighed wearily.

'Well, if you won't let me prove what I say is true, I can't help it,' he said. 'Grunsbacher? It sounds like a German name.'

'You didn't know he was a German, of course?' said the young man sarcastically.

'I don't know anythin' about him at all, except that he was murdered,' answered Mr. Budd. 'I didn't even know 'is name until you told me.'

'I see,' retorted the other. 'I suppose it was sheer accident that you killed him — '

'I didn't kill him!' snarled the big man

60

angrily. 'I wish you'd get some sense inter yer head — '

'You mean you wish I'd be fool enough to believe the cock-and-bull story you're trying to put over?' broke in the young man. 'If you didn't kill Grunsbacher yourself, it was one of your bunch, so what's the good of arguing?'

'It doesn't seem much good,' grunted Mr. Budd. 'Was Benny Linkman one o' my bunch, as you call it?'

'Benny Linkman?' The other frowned questioningly. 'Who's Benny Linkman?'

'He isn't anybody now,' replied the fat man. 'He's dead! He was killed in this house, not so very long ago, an' his body's lyin' on the settee in the big room across the 'all.'

Although his eyelids were drooping so that he had the appearance of being half-asleep, he was watching the other narrowly. The young man started. Unless he was a particularly good actor, the murder of Linkman had come as a complete surprise. He stared at Mr. Budd and his jaw hardened.

'Another of your victims, I suppose?' he

said harshly. 'Well, I can assure you that you won't get what you're after — '

'I'm not after anythin', except the truth,' interrupted the fat detective. 'I wish I could convince you of that.'

'I dare say you do,' sneered the man with the gun. 'You'd like to convince me of a lot of things, wouldn't you? Unfortunately, I know too much. The best thing you can do, my friend, is to clear out, and do it quickly.'

'It ain't a particularly pleasant night ter wander about this island,' murmured Mr. Budd. 'I'd rather — '

'I'm not suggesting that you wander about this island,' broke in the other impatiently. 'I'm suggesting that you clear off altogether.'

'That's not possible,' replied the big man, with a yawn. 'I'm not much of a swimmer, so I couldn't very well go, even if I wanted to.'

'You can go as you came!' snapped the stranger. 'Come on, I'll see you on your way.'

'We came in a boat,' said Mr. Budd, 'but we can't leave in it, because it ain't there. Somebody pinched it.'

'More lies!' came the contemptuous retort. 'Who could have pinched it? There's nobody here, except us.'

'There was somebody 'ere,' declared Mr. Budd. 'Benny Linkman was 'ere, an' the person what killed him — the same person what brought your friend Grunsbacher's hat here — '

'Grunsbacher's hat!' exclaimed the man quickly. 'Is that here? Have you got it?'

The stout superintendent nodded, and the other held out his hand.

'Give it to me!' he ordered.

Mr. Budd reached a podgy hand towards his overcoat which hung across the back of the chair in which Leek had been sitting.

''Ere yer are,' he said wearily, and pulling the hat out of the pocket extended his arm in the other's direction. Warily the man with the gun stepped forward, but he was not quite wary enough. The big man's left hand shot out, as he took the hat, and fastened on his pistol-wrist with a grip like a vice. The unknown's finger

63

tightened on the trigger, and the weapon spat flame and smoke. The explosions were deafening, but the bullets thudded harmlessly into the ceiling as Mr. Budd twisted the other's arm upward.

'Grab 'is ankles!' panted the fat detective, and Leek launched himself at the struggling man's legs and brought him with a crash to the ground.

Mr. Budd wrenched the hot automatic from his hand and straightened up, breathing hard.

'That's better,' he remarked, looking down at the other's rage-distorted face. 'Now, p'raps, we can talk more sensibly. Don't get up!' he added sharply as the man made an attempt to struggle to his feet. 'You're safer an' more comfortable where you are.'

He sat down slowly in his chair, keeping the man on the floor covered.

'You've wasted quite a bit of ammunition,' he went on conversationally, 'but there's still a few cartridges in the clip, an' they'll come in handy if you start any trouble. I don't want to 'urt you, but I'm jest warnin' yer, see?'

The younger man eyed him steadily, and his face was set, but he made no reply.

'There's quite a lot I'd like ter know,' continued Mr. Budd in his rather ponderous way, 'an' I think, maybe, if we have a little, quiet conversation together, a lot o' things'll straighten out. Now, first of all, who are yer?'

A shrug of the shoulders was his only answer.

'Goin' ter take that line, eh?' murmured the big man gently. 'You was talkertive enough a little while ago, but I s'pose that was dif'rent. Well, we shan't get very far, at this rate, shall we?' He screwed up his nose and frowned. 'It's silly, really, because I've got an idea that we could help each other a lot.'

The man on the floor gave a short laugh.

'I've no doubt I could help you,' he said, 'but I've no intention of doing so.'

'That's because you're labourin' under the delusion that I'm somebody else, ain't it?' remarked Mr. Budd.

'I don't know who you are,' was the

reply, 'but I know why you're here, and you won't get any help from me.'

Mr. Budd sighed.

'You're the most obstinate feller I've ever come across,' he said. 'You get an idea in yer head, an' nothin'll shift it. When I told yer I was from Scotland Yard, I was speakin' the truth.' He thrust his hand into his breast pocket, took out his wallet, and with difficulty, for he had only one free hand, produced his warrant card. 'Take a look at that,' he said, and held it out.

The other took it and glanced at it. An expression of doubt crossed his face, and then once again it hardened.

'How do I know that this is genuine?' he demanded. 'I've never seen one before. For all I . . . '

'Listen!' broke in Leek suddenly. 'There's somebody else in the 'ouse!'

Mr. Budd, who was watching the man on the floor, saw him stiffen. Deep lines puckered his forehead and his eyes became alert. The sound which Leek had heard was now audible to all of them — the soft swish of feet from the hall outside. Mr. Budd came silently out of his chair, and as he did so the stranger opened his mouth.

'Look out!' he shouted. 'Run for your life!' The footsteps stopped suddenly, and the big man made a leap for the door.

'Watch him!' he grunted to Leek, and was out in the hall in the same breath. He caught sight of a shadowy figure in the glow from the open door behind him, standing near the foot of the great staircase. It turned as he appeared, with the evident intention of bolting, but Mr. Budd was grimly determined to find out who this second inhabitant of the house might be.

'Stop where yer are!' he cried. 'If yer don't I shall shoot!'

The fleeing figure hesitated at the threat, and lumbering across the hall, the big man caught it by the arm.

'Now,' he muttered, dragging his resisting captive back towards the fire-lit room. 'Who are yer?'

A whiff of perfume came to his nostrils, and the bent head was raised. Mr. Budd uttered an exclamation, and nearly let go the arm he held in his surprise, for he was looking into the face of the girl he had met at Lord Lancourt's house earlier that evening!

7

The Beginning of the Siege

The astonishment was mutual. Into the girl's wide frightened eyes came a look of amazement, and she ceased to struggle.

'So it's you, young lady, is it?' asked Mr. Budd, softly. 'How do you come into this business?'

'Let me go,' she muttered, but he shook his head.

'I can't do that,' he said. 'There's a lot of explainin' ter be done, an' the quicker you do it, the better it'll be fer all of us. Now, what are you doin' here at this time o' night?'

'Don't answer, Sybil!' called the voice of the unknown man. 'We've as much right to be here as he has, and it' not his business, anyway.'

'You're still goin' ter be troublesome, are yer?' murmured the big man, and gently pulling the unresisting girl into the room, he closed the door. 'You're bein' very foolish — yer know — very foolish indeed.'

The man on the floor ignored him altogether.

'I tried to warn you,' he said to the girl. 'When I got here, I found these thugs already in possession — '

'They're detectives!' she broke in quickly. 'They called to see Uncle this evening about — about — ' She stammered, and stopped.

The young man looked disconcerted.

'Are you sure?' he muttered, frowning. 'This fat chap told me that, but I wouldn't believe him — '

'Scepticism is the curse of the age,' said Mr. Budd sententiously. 'Now, p'raps, you'll talk!'

'I don't think I shall!' retorted the other coolly. 'What do you say, Sybil?'

The girl shook her head. Her large eyes were watchful, shooting little darting glances from one to the other.

'There you are!' said the young man, scrambling to his feet. 'Nothing doing in the talking line.'

Mr. Budd made a weary gesture.

'I s'pose you both realise that this is a serious business,' he said reprovingly. 'Two men 'ave already been killed, an' — '

'Two?' whispered the girl questioningly.

'There was a feller called Benny Linkman, stabbed to death in this 'ouse ternight,' answered the big man gravely, and her face went white.

'Stabbed — here?' she said huskily. 'We know nothing about that, or — or the other — '

'Nothin'?' Mr. Budd raised his eyebrows. 'Come now, miss, that's not quite right, is it? I've got an idea that you both know a great deal. I'm not saying that either of you 'ad an 'and in these murders, but you know a great deal about 'em.'

'We're saying nothing,' said the young man quickly, with a warning look at the girl. 'I made a mistake about you; I thought you were somebody else — '

'Who?' demanded Mr. Budd ungrammatically.

'That's neither here nor there,' snapped

the other shortly. 'It makes no difference. I've said all I'm going to say.'

'Stop playin' the fool!' snarled Mr. Budd crossly, his patience exhausted. 'Murder ain't a game, an' there's been murder done twice! Unless you're sensible it may be done again. If you didn't kill Linkman, there's somebody else in this house, d'yer realise that?'

The girl uttered a low gasp, and her eyes filled with dread. The man, too, was obviously startled. 'By Jove!' he muttered, 'I never thought of that — '

'There's so many things that you don't seem to've thought of,' snapped the stout superintendent, 'that it's not much good discussin' 'em! The best thin' you can do is ter come clean.'

There was a moment's hesitation on the part of the young man, and then he shook his head.

'It isn't possible,' he declared crisply. 'If it was, I'd tell you everything. You can count on this, though, you've nothing to fear from us.'

'I'm not altogether shiverin' in me shoes!' said Mr. Budd, sarcastically, and the other flushed.

'I mean,' he explained, 'that in the event of trouble we'll stand together — '

'What trouble are yer expectin'?' asked the big man softly.

Again the young man hesitated. 'I think there's going to be pretty big trouble before the night's over,' he said. 'I thought so directly you mentioned this other person in the house.'

'Oh!' The girl looked at him with sudden understanding. 'You mean — '

'I mean they're here already,' he interrupted. 'They must have found what they wanted when they killed Grunsbacher, and they've acted quickly.'

'Who d'yer mean by 'they'?' snapped Mr. Budd. 'Can't you drop all this stupid secrecy?'

'The people I'm talking about are crooks,' said the man. 'I can't tell you more than that.'

Mr. Budd scratched one fat cheek irritably. All this evasion was getting on his nerves. He hated mysteries and here there seemed to be nothing else. What had brought these two to this old house on such a night? Who was the man still lurking somewhere on the premises, and what was the apparent feud between them? Questions — nothing but questions, he thought disgustedly, questions to which no one would supply the answers.

'Is Lord Lancourt in this?' he asked, suddenly, and the girl shook her head.

'No, my uncle knows nothing about it,' she declared without hesitation.

The big man pursed his lips, and frowned. He was puzzled. The girl's voice held a ring of truth, and yet, if Lancourt knew nothing, what had been the reason for the bald man's inquiry to the constable? It was a hopeless mix-up, and he had to admit that he could make neither head nor tail of it. These two looked trustworthy. Mr. Budd considered that he was a good judge of character, and he was favourably impressed, in spite of appearances. The young man's attitude had changed since he had become convinced of their identity. It was quite natural that he should have mistaken them for the unknown enemies from whom he evidently expected trouble.

The big man would have given a lot to know who these enemies were, and what they were after, but it seemed useless to waste time in questions. The young man had said they were crooks, and the fact that Benny Linkman had been mixed up with them seemed to bear this out. The stout superintendent sighed.

'Well, it looks very much as though I should 'ave ter find things out fer meself,' he murmured, with a shrug of his massive shoulders. 'It ain't no good expectin' any help from either o' you, evidently.'

'No, I'm afraid you'll get no help from us,' said the young man coolly. 'In fact, I may as well be candid with you, we shall do everything we can to hinder you finding out too much!'

Mr. Budd made a wry grimace.

'We know where we are, anyway,' he said. 'I think you're both actin' very foolishly, because there'll come a time when you'll 'ave ter speak. You can't pick an' choose what yer'll say in a court o' law, particularly in a murder case.'

'We'll risk that!' was the reply. 'A far more urgent consideration at the moment is: what are we going to do?'

He addressed the girl, but it was Mr. Budd who replied.

'What were yer goin' ter do?' he asked. 'I mean before yer found us 'ere?'

'We were going to finish a job, and clear out,' answered the other evasively.

'Which reminds me,' murmured the fat detective thoughtfully. ''Ow did yer get 'ere? You didn't come by water, or we should've seen the boat. Don't tell me there's a secret passage, or somethin'. If yer do, I'll begin ter think I'm dreamin'. Secret passages don't belong ter straightforward detective work, at least, not in real life. I'll begin ter think I've walked inter the pages o' one o' these books that are so pop'lar, if you tell me there's a secret passage.'

The young man smiled, and looked at the girl.

'As a matter of fact, there is,' he said after a momentary hesitation. 'It passes under the broad to the mainland.'

'Would you believe it, now!' said Mr. Budd. 'I bet I'll be the first real detective what's ever seen such a thing! So that's how yer got 'ere, is it? I thought there must 'ave been somethin' o' the sort. Do these other people know about it?'

An expression of alarm flashed to the face of the young man before him.

'Good lord, I hope not!' he exclaimed anxiously. 'I just don't see how they could — '

'Where's the entrance from this end?' demanded Mr. Budd. 'If there's goin' ter be any trouble, it 'ud be just as well ter see that it's secure. Judging from what you said some time back, it seems that there might be a number o' these people attackin' us, an' we don't want ter give 'em the opportunity o' takin' us by surprise.'

'The entrance is down in the cellars,' said the girl, after a slight pause. 'It's a stone slab in the floor, and there are steps that lead down to a passage. Dick left it open for me — '

'Is it open now?' asked the fat man quickly, and she nodded.

'Then we'd better go an' shut it,' snapped Mr. Budd, moving towards the door. 'Come an' show me, will yer?'

The man she had called 'Dick' stepped to his side.

'You'd better come with us, Sybil,' he said. 'In case there's any real trouble, you ought to go home.'

She made a grimace of protest.

'I'd rather stay — ' she began.

'I think yer friend *is* right, miss,' interrupted the big man. 'I don't know what kind o' trouble there's likely ter be — you both know more about that than me — but from what I do know, these people seem pretty dangerous, an' we'd all feel more comfortable if you was out of it.'

She continued to protest, but he was adamant, and in the end she gave way.

'You stay 'ere,' said Mr. Budd to the lean sergeant, 'an' if yer see, or 'ear anythin' that looks like trouble, shout!'

The lugubrious Leek gave an unenthusiastic nod.

'I think it 'ud be better if we all went,' he said. 'There ain't no sense in stoppin' 'ere, that I can see — '

'You wouldn't reco'nise sense if it jumped out an' bit yer!' snarled his superior. 'Jest you do as yer told fer once, and don't argue!'

He left the melancholy sergeant, and followed the man called Dick and the girl across the gloomy hall, lighting their way with his torch. They led him beyond the great staircase to the kitchen quarters, and came to a halt in front of an open door in the bare scullery. A narrow flight of wooden stairs led down, and descending these they found themselves in a series of large vaults that appeared to extend under the entire house. Masses of thick cobwebs hung from the arched roof, and the place was redolent with the smell of damp and decay. The floor was thick with debris, and the walls were grey with some fungoid growth that glistened when the light caught it. A number of rotting barrels stood on trestles against the walls, exhaling a sour odour from the lees of the wine which had once been stored in them.

A square, gaping hole near one wall marked the entrance to the passage. A huge flagstone was reared up on end, and the top of a worn flight of stone steps was visible in the light of Mr. Budd's torch.

'The slab works on a counterpoise system,' explained the young man, 'but it's a bit stiff. Those bolts shoot into the bed, and fasten it from this side.'

'I see,' said Mr. Budd, peering into the black void. 'Well, I think we only got here just in time.'

'What do you mean?' asked the man called Dick sharply.

'Listen!' answered the fat detective, and beckoned them closer. Eerily out of the blackness of the passage entrance floated the sound of whispering voices.

8

The Siege

Mr. Budd drew back.

'Help me shut this trap,' he muttered, and the other two came quickly to his assistance.

The heavy slab of stone moved under the pressure of their shoulders, swung downwards, and dropped into its bed with a gentle thud. The young man wrestled with the rusty bolts and, after an effort, succeeded in shooting them home.

'They won't get past that!' he panted, struggling to his feet. 'It was a lucky thing that we came down here when we did.'

'A very lucky thing,' agreed Mr. Budd gravely.

'I wonder how they could have found out about the passage?' said the girl, wrinkling her forehead.

'Maybe they followed you,' replied the big man absently. 'It doesn't matter very much. The point is, that they 'ave found out. What we've got ter do is ter be ready for the next move.'

The man called Dick looked at him inquiringly.

'What do you mean?' he asked.

'Well,' said the stout superintendent, suppressing a yawn. 'They ain't likely ter give up because they find one way barred to 'em. When they find they can't get in here by the passage, they'll try another way.'

'There's only one other way,' said the girl quickly.

'An' that's by water.' Mr. Budd finished the sentence for her, and nodded. 'Yes, an' that's the way they'll come, it looks as if we was goin' ter 'ave a very busy night.'

'It shouldn't be difficult to keep them at bay, if they try that,' said the young man.

Mr. Budd rubbed a huge hand over his face, yawned again, and looked at the other sleepily.

'Shouldn't it?' he murmured. 'I'm not so sure about that. From the little I know about these people, they seem ter be pretty desperate, an' they're sure to be armed. We've only got one pistol between us, an' four out o' the ten shots it holds are in the ceilin' o' that room upstairs. I'm thinkin' that it may be mighty difficult.'

A muffled sound from below the trap coincided with the end of his remark. The intruders were apparently exerting all their efforts to open it. The sounds continued for some time, while the three in the vault above listened in silence, and then they ceased.

'Given it up,' grunted the big man. 'They may try an' bust it, though. Somebody ought ter keep an eye on it.'

'*I* don't think they'll be able to make much impression,' said the young man, shaking his head. 'It would take a dose of dynamite to shift that trap, now it's bolted.'

'There's another way,' broke in Mr. Budd quietly. 'You've fergotten the feller who killed Linkman. 'E's still somewhere about, an' if he could sneak down 'ere, 'e could open it for 'is friends — if they are 'is friends,' he added.

'I'd forgotten that danger,' admitted the other. 'I'll stop here, if you like — '

'Is there only one way down to this place?' asked the fat detective, and the man nodded.

'Yes,' he answered. 'The way we came.'

'Then that's where the watch had better be kept,' said Mr. Budd instantly. 'You could 'ear from there if they tried ter bust the trap, an' you could also stop anyone reachin' it from this side.' He swept his light round the gloomy cellar. 'We'd better make certain there ain't nobody lurkin' about 'ere already, before we go back upstairs,' he added.

He made a thorough search of the vaults, and although he found no one concealed there, he did make a minor discovery. On the top of a stack of barrels he found four queer-looking objects made of leather and iron. They were not unlike ice-skates, except that in each case in place of the blade was a block of iron that had been fashioned into the semblance of a cloven hoof.

'Now I know the meanin' o' the phrase 'playin' the goat',' he remarked, turning to the other two, who had watched him in silence. 'I s'pose you wore these thin's when yer came to the 'ouse, so's to mystify anyone who might chance ter visit the place?'

'Yes,' admitted the young man, 'I found 'em in the passage when I first explored it. They're very old — I should think that they dated back to the period when the house was built.'

'An' they was probably used then fer the same purpose as they've been used now,' murmured the big man. 'I've 'eard o' such things, an' I rather guessed that that was 'ow those 'oofprints was made, when I first saw 'em.' He put the skate-like objects back where he had found them. 'We may as well go,' he said. 'There's nothin' more to do 'ere.'

When they reached the scullery, the young man was left to guard the door to the cellars, and Mr. Budd and the girl went back to the big hall. They found Leek standing in the doorway of the room which they had adopted as their headquarters, peering out into the gloom.

'I've got a job for you,' said Mr. Budd curtly. 'You can go out an' patrol this island. Keep a sharp look-out for any one attemptin' ter land.'

'It's blowin' a gale an' rainin' cats an' dogs!' complained the sergeant, his thin face lengthening. 'Must — '

'I don't care if it's rainin' all the animals in the zoo,' snarled Mr. Budd. 'Jest you do as yer told!'

He went over to the front door and opened it. A great gust of wind came swirling in, raising clouds of dust as it swept through the hall, and making the girl shiver and draw her coat closer round her.

'You'd better take this,' said the big man, thrusting the automatic into the sergeant's hand, 'but don't go wastin' shots. There's only six left, an' we may need 'em before the night's over. An' don't go fallin' asleep anywhere,' he added. 'If yer do you may wake up ter find yerself dead!'

'You've never found me failin' in me duty,' said Leek, without commenting on this paradoxical statement. 'When I does a thing, I does it prop'ly. There ain't a more reliable man at the Yard than me.'

'The rest ought ter sue yer for libel!' said his superior. 'Now get along — ' He stopped suddenly, and stared with narrowed eyes towards a break in the belt of trees at the edge of the island. The expression on his fat face made the sergeant swing round uneasily.

'What's the matter?' he mumbled, peering into the darkness.

'I thought I saw a light — over on the mainland,' muttered Mr. Budd. 'Maybe me eyes was playin' tricks — No, look there!'

A light gleamed momentarily across the broad, and the fat man's jaw set. The unknown foe was watching, and in force. The party which had tried the passage entrance could not yet have had time to get back and round to this side of the island. There must be others, stationed among the rushes. Perhaps the plan was to attack from both places at once. Well, thought Mr. Budd grimly, that idea had been scotched, anyhow.

A gust of wind, even fiercer than the

last, nearly tore the door from his grasp, and the lean sergeant had to clutch hold of a pillar to save himself from being swept off his feet.

'I'll 'ave ter shut this door,' gasped the big man. 'Off yer go, an' fer goodness' sake keep a sharp look-out.'

He closed the heavy door, and the sergeant stumbled away across the neglected garden.

'I always get the rotten jobs,' he grumbled under his breath. 'Fancy 'avin' ter walk round an' round this perishin' place. 'Nough ter give a feller 'is death.'

He ploughed his way through the weeds, soaking his boots and the legs of his trousers, and eventually reached the water's edge. It was very dark and dismal. He could just see the mainland, an uncertain smudge, across the ruffled water. It was also very cold, and the wind seemed to find its way to his bones, with a penetrating chill.

'If I come outer this without a cold, I shall be lucky,' he thought miserably, and began his pilgrimage. He made a complete circuit of the island, keeping a sharp lookout for anything or anybody, but he saw nothing. The sky was heavy with scudding clouds that obscured the moon, and the wind howled and roared through the trees with such violence that at times he had to stop for shelter behind a friendly trunk until it had abated. The mainland showed no signs of life at all. During the frequent lulls, he listened, but he could hear no suspicious sound that might warn him of the presence of the people for whom he was watching. He came back to the place from where he had started, and stood staring over the water at the spot where the light had gleamed, but now all was dark.

Perhaps the light had been nothing after all, he thought. Somebody passing that way and stopping to light a pipe or a cigarette. The place was supposed to be shunned by the people in the district, but that couldn't apply to every one. No doubt there were quite a number who weren't superstitious at all. He turned his back to the wind that came whistling over the broad, and saw the flicker of a light from the dark bulk of the old house. It came from one of the top windows, flashed, shone steadily for a moment, and flashed again.

The lean sergeant swung round. In answer to the signal, a light flashed from the opposite shore.

Leek drew in his breath quickly. The unknown man lurking in the house was signalling to his friends on the mainland.

The sergeant marked the window from which the light had come, and after a short hesitation, set off as quickly as he could for the house. Mr. Budd ought to be informed at once. Now that it was possible to locate the intruder's exact position, he could be captured and one danger eliminated.

He reached the front door, breathless, and in answer to his knock it was opened by the stout superintendent himself.

'What is it?' he demanded sharply, and the panting Leek told him.

'All right,' snapped the big man. 'You go back an' keep watch outside. We'll deal with this feller. Signallin', was he? We'll soon put a stop ter that little game!'

He sent the sergeant back to his patrol

and went in search of the young man who was guarding the cellar door.

'If we take off our boots,' he said when he had explained, 'we ought ter be able ter take this feller by surprise. I know the room 'e's in an' if we're lucky we ought ter get 'im without any trouble.'

The other agreed, and after telling the girl what they were going to do, they crept up the stairs in their stockinged feet. Except for the unavoidable creaking of the old wood their progress was practically noiseless. Up and up they went, moving shadows in the darkness that draped the landings and stairways, until Mr. Budd paused on the top floor.

'That's the room,' he whispered, speaking with his lips close to his companion's ear. 'Come on, we'll take 'im by surprise.'

He tiptoed over to the closed door, and bending down, listened. There was no sound from within. Cautiously he tried the handle. It turned under his twisting fingers, and the door opened an inch.

'Now!' snapped the big man, and flinging the door wide, rushed into the room. He had expected to hear some sound that would locate the position of the man lurking there, but there was neither sound nor movement. Utter silence greeted him. Suspecting a trap, he held his torch sideways at arm's length and pressed the button. The white ray lit up the room, but there was nobody in it. The room was empty!

'Are you sure this was the right room?' asked the young man at his elbow, and received a dramatic reply to his question.

The door was slammed shut, and as they turned in alarm they heard the key grind in the lock.

9

The Attack

In spite of his bulk Mr. Budd was the first to reach the door. Gripping the handle, he pulled, but as he had expected, the door remained firm. Flashing his light over it, he eyed it dubiously. The damp and general decay were more pronounced in the lower part of the house. This door was a solid affair of seasoned oak that would take a battering-ram to break down.

'It looks as if we've been had,' he muttered. 'He must have known we was comin' and planned this little surprise.'

'Can't we smash it open?' said the man called Dick anxiously. 'Let me try.'

He flung himself against the door, but he made no impression. It shook, but that was all.

'You won't do any good,' grunted Mr. Budd. 'It's like buttin' at a rock.'

'But we've got to do something,' cried the other impatiently. 'There's Sybil — all alone — '

He broke off as a faint cry reached them, and his face went white.

'Did you hear that?' he whispered huskily, as though all the moisture in his throat had suddenly dried up. 'That was Sybil! My God! What are we going to do? He's found her!'

'Pull yerself together!' said Mr. Budd sharply. 'You'll do no good by givin' way ter panic.'

'Well, suggest something!' snarled his companion. 'We've got to get out of here, somehow. That brute may be killing her — '

He stopped suddenly and strode over to the window. Flinging it open, he leaned out.

'Give me your torch,' he called. 'There may be a way down.'

Mr. Budd complied, and the other shone the light down the side of the house. A drainpipe, added at some later period than that in which the house had been originally built, ran down the wall from the overhanging eaves. It was more than a yard away from the casement, but close above the window ran the gutter to which it was attached.

The young man made up his mind.

'If I can reach that pipe,' he said, 'I think I can climb down. I'm going to risk it, anyway.'

He thrust the lighted torch into Mr. Budd's hand and, reaching up, gripped the gutter. Hauling himself out of the window, he hung for a moment suspended by his hands, and then began to work his way cautiously towards the pipe.

The big man watched him anxiously expecting every second that the guttering would give way under his weight. Slowly, inch by inch and hand over hand he moved along towards the pipe. The wind buffeted the house and flapped his coat about him, but he hung on grimly. And then, when he was within a foot of the pipe, that which the big man had been dreading happened. With a ripping sound the ancient guttering tore away.

An involuntary cry escaped the fat detective's lips as he saw the hanging man drop. He expected to see him go crashing down into the tangled garden below, but the swing of the falling gutter took him towards the drainpipe, and with a wild clutch he managed to grip it. He slid down for six or seven feet at an appalling speed before he was able to check himself, and Mr. Budd guessed that the friction must have skinned his hands. But the greater danger had been averted. He was swarming down the pipe now, comparatively easily, and the big man was breathing a little more freely, when he saw a man come out of the door of the house and look up.

He switched out his light instantly, but he was too late. The man had seen what was taking place, and a flash, followed by the crack of a shot, told the watching detective what action he was taking. Another and another followed, the flashes streaking the darkness, and at any moment Mr. Budd expected to hear the thud of a falling body as one of those flying bullets found a home in the climbing man.

And then the shooter uttered a startled

oath and the firing suddenly ceased. There was a scraping, scuffling sound and — silence.

The puzzled Mr. Budd was just on the point of risking switching on his light again to see what had happened when the plaintive voice of Leek floated up to him.

'Are yer up there?' said the sergeant mournfully. 'I've settled this bird fer the time bein'.'

Mr. Budd sent a ray of light cutting through the darkness and picked out the lean figure of his subordinate.

'What have yer done to 'im?' he demanded.

''It 'im on the 'ead with the branch of a tree,' answered Leek. ''E won't give us no trouble fer a bit.'

The stout man gave a grunt of satisfaction.

'Take his gun an' come an' let me out,' he said. 'Is that other feller all right?'

'I'm all right,' called the young man. 'Some of those shots came pretty close, though. I'm going to see what has happened to Sybil.'

He joined Leek and they both moved

away. Mr. Budd drew in his head and waited. Presently he heard a sound outside the door, the key grated in the lock, and the sergeant appeared.

'That's the best bit o' work you've done fer a long time,' said his superior. 'What happened to the young lady?'

'She ain't very badly 'urt,' answered the sergeant. 'He give her a bump on the 'ead an' tied her up. 'Is nibs is lookin' after her.'

'How did you manage ter pop up at the right moment?' asked the big man as they went down the stairs.

'I saw your light from the window an' came ter see what was 'appenin',' replied the sergeant. 'I was jest in time ter see this feller come out o' the 'ouse an' start the fireworks. I grabbed a tree branch what was lyin' near an' jumped on 'im. He put up a bit of a struggle, but I got in a couple o' good whacks an' that finished 'im.'

'You did very well,' murmured Mr. Budd approvingly. 'We'll go an' see that 'e doesn't do any more damage. Unless I'm mistaken, he's the feller what killed Benny Linkman and Grunsbacher.'

The girl was seated in one of the easy chairs before the fire when they came downstairs. Her face was pale and she had a large bruise on her forehead, but she seemed little the worse for her experience.

'I thought it was one of you when he came downstairs,' she explained, 'and then when I saw it was a stranger I cried out. He hit me with something, and that's all I remember, until I found myself tied up in this chair.'

'You're lucky it was no worse, miss,' commented Mr. Budd. 'Come on. Let's go an' make sure o' this feller before he comes round.'

'He won't come round yet!' said Leek with great satisfaction, and followed the big man out into the night.

They found the man still sprawling limply on the ground, and when Mr. Budd saw the contused lump on his head he was quite prepared to believe the sergeant's assertion.

'You'd better go an' continue yer watch,' said Mr. Budd. 'We don't want a surprise visit while we're not lookin'. The other chap can 'elp me get this beauty inside.' Rather reluctantly Leek obeyed, after handing over the pistol which he had taken from the unconscious unknown. When he had gone the stout superintendent bent down and made a quick search of the man's pockets. He found, to his satisfaction, a spare clip of cartridges and a letter. The letter interested him immensely. It was addressed to 'Richard Huber' and its contents made clear a great deal that had been obscure. Mr. Budd put it carefully away in his wallet, and his face was very thoughtful. There was nothing else of interest in the man's pockets, and he called for assistance to carry him into the house.

The young man came instantly.

'So this is the brute, is it?' he said, glowering down at the man on the ground. 'It's a pity your sergeant didn't kill him.'

'Let the hangman do his own job,' grunted Mr. Budd. 'Take 'is feet, will yer?'

They picked up the limp form between them and carried it into the house.

'Put 'im down here, Mr. Huber,' said the big man, stopping in the hall, and the other gave him a startled glance.

'How do you know my name?' he asked quickly.

Mr. Budd eyed him sleepily.

'I'm a detective,' he said, 'an' detectives know everythin'.'

'But — ' began Huber, and the fat man interrupted him.

'If yer hold his feet up like that,' he murmured reprovingly, 'the blood 'ull run to 'is head an' he may 'ave a fit.'

The other dropped the unconscious man's feet with a thud.

'But I don't understand,' he began. 'How — '

'There was a lot I didn't understand,' broke in Mr. Budd mildly, 'but nobody 'ud take the trouble ter explain. Now I'm not goin ter do any explain', either.'

He looked down at the man at his feet.

'Not a very nice-lookin' feller, is he?' he remarked, rubbing his shins.

The man was not a prepossessing specimen. His face was thin and swarthy and his hair was very black and oily. His clothes were over-smart and his shoes long and pointed.

Huber looked at him with an uneasy frown, and it was clear to Mr. Budd that he was not very much interested in the man's appearance. That his name was known to the detective had very obviously given him a shock.

'We'll find some rope an' tie this feller up,' he said. 'I should think the rope 'e used ter tie up the young lady 'ud do.'

He ambled away across the hall, and Dick Huber watched him with a curious expression. How much did he know? he wondered.

The big man came back with several lengths of old rope and expertly bound the unconscious man's wrists and ankles.

'There's no need ter gag 'im,' he said, rising a little breathless from his task. 'Unless 'is language, when he comes to, is unfit fer the ears o' the lady, which wouldn't surprise me.' He took out his handkerchief and wiped his face. 'You'd better go back ter your place by the cellar door, 'adn't yer?' he went on. 'We haven't finished with this business yet, yer know. There's more of 'em beside this feller, an' they ought ter be gettin' busy soon. I don't think there's much danger of 'em breakin' a way in through that stone trap, but we can't afford ter take any chances.'

'I agree with you,' answered Huber. His lips parted as though he intended to say something more, but he apparently thought better of it and, turning, walked away.

Mr. Budd stood in the gloomy hall, gently pulling his right ear, his lips pursed in uncertain speculation. He knew quite a lot more than he had. But there was still a lot that he wanted to know. A queer business, he thought. A business that might have some very far-reaching results when it became public. The letter in his pocket would act like a match to gunpowder in certain quarters.

A movement at his feet snapped the thread of his thoughts and he looked down. The dark-faced man was recovering. He opened his eyes and groaned, moving his head restlessly from side to side.

'The best thin' you can do is keep still,' advised Mr. Budd. 'What do they call you when yer at home?'

The man muttered something unintelligible and groaned again, and at that moment from outside came a single shot, followed almost at once by several others in rapid succession. The long-expected attack had begun.

10

The Flood

Mr. Budd woke to life with surprising quickness. He shouted to Huber to stay where he was, muttered a reassuring word to the girl, and was at the front door in well under ten seconds. As he passed out into the night another fusillade of shots sounded from the waterfront.

Dragging the automatic which had belonged to the prisoner from his pocket, the fat man stumbled across the rank grass and plunged into the belt of trees. He heard a shout close at hand and dimly discerned the lean figure of Leek, half-concealed behind a tree.

'They're coming!' whispered the sergeant excitedly as his superior joined him. 'In a boat. I was round the other side of the island when they started. You can just see 'em — out there on the water.'

Mr. Budd peered into the darkness. At

first he could see nothing, and then he made out a vague blot moving slowly on the surface of the broad. Almost at the same time as he distinguished it there was a pencil of flame, a sharp crack, and a bullet hummed viciously through the trees.

He raised the automatic and fired two answering shots, stepping quickly aside as soon as he had done so, to avoid the flashes giving his position away.

A succession of shots came from the boat, and the bullets spattered on the tree trunks near them like hail. The attackers were still some distance away and Mr. Budd thought rapidly. It was useless trying to prevent them landing on the island. Leek's weapon must be nearly empty, and they had only one spare clip of cartridges between them. Against the apparently well-armed men in the boat that would be useless. There was only one thing to do which offered a chance, and that was to take refuge in the house.

'Come on,' he whispered, gripping Leek by the arm. 'It's no good stoppin' 'ere.'

With the sergeant at his heels, he hurried back to the old mansion and stumbled, panting, into the hall.

'Shut the door!' he gasped breathlessly, and called to Huber. That young man came hastily, his face troubled.

'There's a boatload o' men on the way over,' explained the fat detective jerkily. 'We can't stop 'em landin', but we may be able ter stop 'em gettin' what they've come for. Where's the stuff hidden?'

Huber gave a gasp, and his jaw dropped.

'What do you mean?' He recovered himself quickly and tried to assume a blank expression.

'Don't waste time pretendin',' snapped Mr. Budd angrily. 'If yer don't want it to fall into these fellers' hands, you'd better tell me quick.'

'I don't know how you found out,' muttered Huber, 'but it's underneath the hearthstone — in the room on the right of the landing upstairs.'

'Fetch it!' said the big man curtly. 'An' be quick!' he added as the other still hesitated. 'We haven't all the time in the world!'

For a moment Huber seemed uncertain what to do, and then, making up his mind, he hurried up the stairway. Mr. Budd went out into the hall, leaving the girl alone with Leek, and the shivering sergeant took the opportunity to warm his frozen hands at the dying fire.

'Will you come an' hold the torch, miss?' called the big man, and, as she turned to obey, the lean sergeant saw her take something from the pocket of her coat and furtively thrust it deep down among the tattered cushions of one of the old armchairs. The action had been carried out so swiftly that, if Leek had not chanced to turn his head at the sound of his superior's voice, he would never have seen it. Wondering what it was the girl had concealed so hastily, he went over to the chair as soon as she had gone and rummaged among the cushions. His hand closed on a small packet, and at that moment Mr. Budd's voice hailed him from the hall.

''Ave yer gone ter sleep?' he snapped

irritably. 'Come an' give me a hand with this feller, will yer?'

The sergeant thrust the package into his pocket and hastened to obey.

'Take this feller's feet,' said Mr. Budd curtly.

'What are you going to do with me?' demanded the prisoner.

'Hang on ter you like grim death!' retorted the fat man. 'You're goin' ter be 'Exhibit A' in this case, an' I wouldn't lose yer for worlds!'

The man broke into a flow of bad language, which Mr. Budd stopped by calmly stuffing his handkerchief into the man's mouth.

'We can do without the runnin' commentary!' he grunted.

He signed to the sergeant, and they picked up the man and carried him out into the scullery, while the girl lighted the way. Here they were joined by Huber, carrying a flat metal box under his arm. Mr. Budd removed the key from the outside of the cellar door, lifted the prisoner, with Leek's assistance, and carried him down the broken stairs.

'Now,' he panted, when the others had followed him, 'we can make everythin' snug.'

He went back up the steps, shut and locked the door, and with the help of Huber and the sergeant erected a barricade of old barrels, held in position with a great log, taken from a pile in one corner, which fitted between the stone-work of the arch supporting the roof.

'That'll hold 'em back for a bit!' gasped Mr. Budd, wiping his streaming face. He took a cigar from his waist coat pocket and lit it with a grunt of satisfaction. 'Now,' he said, blowing out a cloud of smoke, 'let's have a look at them diamonds.'

The girl gave a gasp, and Huber stared at him open-mouthed.

'How did you know?' he muttered foolishly.

'I keep tellin' yer I'm a detective,' replied Mr. Budd impatiently. 'I know nearly everythin'. Come on, open that box an' let's see 'em!'

The young man seemed about to refuse, and then with a shrug of his

110

shoulders he complied. The next moment he uttered a startled exclamation.

'It's empty!' he cried. 'There's nothing here but bits of coal! The diamonds have gone!'

'Gone?' echoed the girl incredulously, but Huber scarcely heard her. He had swung round furiously on the astonished Mr. Budd.

'What have you done with them?' he demanded, white with anger. 'You took them — '

'Don't be a fool!' snapped the fat man. 'If I'd taken them, d'yer think I'd 've asked yer to open the box? I don't know nothin' about 'em.'

'Nobody else knew about them — ' began Huber. The big man snorted.

'That's why all these people are puttin' up such an effort ter get 'em, I s'pose?' he grunted sarcastically. 'Nobody knows about 'em, an' we've got a regiment o' crooks besiegin' the place! Don't talk silly!'

As he finished speaking there came muffled sounds from the house above, and he looked up.

'They're 'ere,' he said. 'This is where we take to the passage.'

Going over to the prisoner he untied his ankles.

'Get up!' he ordered, and hauled the man to his feet. 'An' remember that I've got a gun two inches from yer spine, an' it'll go off if yer don't do as yer told!'

'Are you going to risk the passage?' asked Huber. 'They're sure to have left a guard at the other end.'

'I'm choosin' the lesser of two evils,' answered the fat detective. 'That door won't keep 'em out of 'ere for long, an' I'm countin' on the fact that there won't be so many at the other end. Open the trap, will yer?'

Huber still looked dubious, but he obeyed.

'I'll go first with this feller,' said Mr. Budd, 'an' the rest of yer can follow on behind.'

He prodded the prisoner in the back with the muzzle of his automatic and propelled him reluctantly down the stone steps. They ended in a square chamber of slimy brick, from one side of which the entrance to a low, arched passage opened. The air was cold and stale, and there was a smell of dampness and decay.

'Did you close the trap?' asked the big man, when the others joined him, and Huber nodded.

'Yes,' he answered. 'You can't fasten it, though, from this side.'

'We'll have ter move quick, then,' muttered Mr. Budd.

He pushed the unwilling captive towards the mouth of the passage, which was pitch-black and the most uninviting-looking place he had ever seen. It proved to be even less prepossessing than it looked. It was of great age and in a very bad state of repair. The brickwork had fallen away in many places and lay in heaps in the muddy ooze that covered the floor. Moisture hung in great drops from the low roof, and there were patches of a curious kind of liver-coloured fungus that grew everywhere.

After running straight for about a dozen yards the tunnel turned sharply to the right and began to dip in a steep declivity. The floor became more soggy, and in a little while they were splashing through shallow pools of stagnant water that had evidently trickled through from the broad above. Presently the downward trend of the passage changed. It ran flat again for a few yards and then began to rise. They had just started to negotiate this ascent when Leek, bringing up the rear, breathed his warning.

'I can 'ear 'em be'ind us!' he whispered excitedly.

Mr. Budd compressed his lips.

'Hurry!' he muttered, increasing his pace. 'Maybe we can reach the outlet before they catch up with us.'

There came a shout from behind, followed by a shot. A bullet went singing angrily past his head and a shower of brick-dust covered his face. The noise of the explosion was deafening in that confined space and rumbled along the tunnel like thunder. Another shot came hard on the heels of the first, and then a straggling volley. Leek uttered an exclamation as his hat was whisked from his head. He stooped to recover it, and as he did so there was a loud, reverberating

114

crash, mingled with cries of alarm.

'What the devil was that?' grunted Huber, and Mr. Budd's face set grimly as the answer flashed to his mind.

'The tunnel's fallen in!' he snapped. 'The vibration o' that shootin' must 'ave loosened the old bricks.'

The words had barely left his lips when there came another sound — a low, continuous murmur that swelled rapidly to a roar, and as the big man realised what it meant the colour ebbed from his florid cheeks.

'Run!' he cried sharply, with a note of real horror in his voice. 'The water's pourin' in where the roof gave way!'

They needed no second bidding. Stumbling over the uneven ground they raced madly for the exit in an attempt to beat the flood, but it was on them before they had gone more than a few feet. It came, a rushing wall of liquid death that swept them off their feet and carried them along with it, tossing them hither and thither like corks in a mill-stream.

Mr. Budd, gasping and spluttering, was whirled along on the breast of the torrent, his head a few inches from the curving roof of the runnel. He caught a momentary glimpse of Huber and the girl, and then the torch, which he had clung on to, went out. He bumped against the roof as the water rose higher, and was driven under. Something collided with him, and his hand touched a face, and then a violent pain shot through his head, and the roar of the chaotic waters faded to a great silence.

11

The Story of the Diamonds

Mr. Budd opened his eyes and blinked painfully. He was cold and wet, and his body felt stiff and sore. There was a dull pain in his head and his mind was cloudy. Dimly he was aware that a light was flickering unsteadily from somewhere, but when he tried to sit up to find from where it came, he discovered that it was impossible to move. Presently his semi-dazed condition wore off, and he remembered.

Somehow or other, then, he had managed to get out of that flooded tunnel alive. But where was he now — and what had happened to the others?

He raised his head with difficulty and saw that he was lying on the floor in a bare, unfurnished room, containing an old packing-case on which a solitary candle guttered in the draught. At first he thought that he was back in the old house on the broad, and then he saw that this room was different to any in that ill-omened building. The ceiling was lower and heavily beamed; the walls were of unpainted stone; the floor composed of large square tiles. This, he thought, must be the place where the tunnel ended.

In spite of his throbbing head he looked about him. The others were lying near him, and even in that feeble light he could see that they had been bound hand and foot, like himself.

'Hallo!' he called feebly. 'Everybody all right?'

Huber, who was nearest to him, looked up.

'How are you feeling?' he asked.

'Pretty rotten!' grunted Mr. Budd. 'What happened after I hit me 'ead?'

'Miss Fordyce and I managed to pull you out of the water onto the steps leading up to the exit,' answered the young man, 'and then we fell into the hands of two men who were waiting, and they collared us.'

'I'll be lucky if I don't catch me death

o' cold after this!' whispered the plaintive voice of Leek huskily.

'You're lucky ter be alive, so don't grumble!' said his superior unsympathetically. 'How are you feelin', miss?'

'I've been more comfortable,' replied the girl dryly.

'I expect you 'ave, miss,' murmured the stout superintendent. 'I s'pose those fellers who came after us was drowned?'

'They couldn't have stood a chance where they were,' said Huber. 'If we hadn't been near the exit, we'd never have got out, either. I don't know what happened to the man you brought along — he's still down there — somewhere.'

'That'll save the hangman a job,' muttered Mr. Budd. 'Where are these fellers who tied us up like this?'

'They're around somewhere,' replied Huber grimly. 'They made a good job of it. I've been trying to get free, but I can't shift these cords at all.'

'Neither can I,' put in Leek mournfully. 'They've tied 'em so tight, they cut inter yer.'

Mr. Budd tested his own bonds, and

quickly discovered that there was not very much hope of loosening them.

'We'll just 'ave ter grin an' bear it, I s'pose,' he remarked philosophically. 'I wonder what they're goin' ter do with us?'

'Leave us here helpless while they make off with the diamonds,' said Huber savagely. 'It must have been one of 'em who took the stones — '

'Talkin' o' diamonds,' interrupted the fat detective thoughtfully, 's'pose you come across with the truth, eh? I know most of it, but there's one or two bits that I'd like cleared up. What about it?'

'How much do you know?' asked the young man quickly.

'Pretty nearly everythin',' answered Mr. Budd sleepily. 'Those diamonds belonged to your father, an' he smuggled 'em out o' Germany. That's right, ain't it?'

'How the devil did you know?' exclaimed the dumbfounded Huber. 'I don't — '

'So it is right,' broke in the big man gently. 'Good! We're gettin' on! Now, what was the idea?'

'It was a safeguard.' muttered Huber.

'For a long time my father has been uneasy at the trend of affairs in Europe. He's got a fairly prosperous business in Berlin, but he was afraid that in the event of a war his capital would be taken by the Nazis.'

'I see,' said Mr. Budd. 'so he converted it into diamonds an' smuggled 'em over to England. I thought it was somethin' like that.'

'You can't bring or send money out of Germany these days without the consent of the Government,' said Huber, 'and such consent is practically impossible to get. Even if he'd sold his business and came to England, he wouldn't have been allowed to bring any money with him.'

'I understand all that,' said the fat man, 'but what was the idea of hidin' 'em in that old house? Why couldn't you have lodged 'em in a bank?'

'Because I'm a German,' explained the young man. 'If there should be a war between Germany and England they would be confiscated.'

'I suggested the House of the Goat as a hiding-place,' put in the girl quietly, 'when Dick told me about the scheme. We'd found the entrance to the passage one day when we were sheltering here from the rain.'

'What is this place, miss?' asked Mr. Budd.

'It's an old cottage near the edge of the broad,' she replied, 'and it's the same age as the house. It's only been empty a little while. There's a panel in the sitting-room. We found it by accident.'

'H'm!' commented the stout superintendent. 'An' these diamonds was smuggled over from Germany, an' you hid 'em in the House of the Goat? That's all clear. Now, how does what's-his-name — Grunsbacher — an' these other fellers come inter it?'

'Grunsbacher was an old servant of my father's,' said Huber. 'He and a man named Al Collins brought the diamonds over between them. I found Collins. He was used to drug smuggling and knew all the tricks and he was willing to take on this job. I never trusted him, though. I always felt that he was waiting to double-cross me, and when I saw him at

East Repton Station this evening with a bunch of unpleasant-looking men, I guessed that he had discovered the hiding place of the diamonds and was out to steal them. That's what brought me to the house. I mistook you for one of the gang.'

'Al Collins, eh?' said Mr. Budd musingly. 'H'm! That accounts fer Benny Linkman. He was mixed up with the Collins bunch.'

'Do you know Collins?' asked Huber quickly.

'Very well, an' nothin' to 'is credit,' answered the big man. 'He's done a bit o' everythin' from thievin' ter peddlin' dope. I think it's all pretty clear ter me now, except one little bit. Why was this poor feller, Grunsbacher, lookin' fer Harvey Bradshaw?'

'I had arranged that any communication from my father should be delivered at Miss Fordyce's address in Park Lane, care of Harvey Bradshaw,' said the young man. 'It was then forwarded to me. It was a precaution to prevent Collins getting to know too much. Grunsbacher used to bring letters from my father in his hat

— it had a double felt crown.'

'I know,' said Mr. Budd. 'He was carryin' a letter that last evenin'.' He hesitated a moment and then he continued: 'I am afraid it was bad news, Mr. Huber. Your father wrote ter tell you that the Gestapo had found out what 'e'd been doin'. He just managed ter get the letter to Grunsbacher before they came ter take 'im. I'm sorry to 'ave ter tell yer this.'

'How do you know?' asked Huber, and his voice was a little hoarse.

'I've got the letter in me pocket,' replied the big man simply. 'I took it off that feller who killed Linkman. I don't s'pose it's very readable now, after gettin' soaked.'

'So that's how you knew so much?' muttered the young man.

'That's how I knew,' admitted Mr. Budd gravely. 'An' what I'd like to know now is what happened to those diamonds — '

'To hell with the diamonds!' cried Huber impatiently. 'I don't care about them. I'm thinking about my father. What will they do to him? It's terrible! The Gestapo are devils — '

He broke off as the door opened suddenly and a man came in. He was a little, wiry man, undersized and wizened, with a pallid face and small, restless eyes that were set too close to his thin nose. A cigarette hung from his drooping lower lip, and he breathed heavily and noisily through his half-open mouth as though he suffered from adenoids.

'Hallo, Sniffy!' greeted Mr. Budd. 'What are you doin' in this racket? I thought you was still in 'bird'.'

The little man's lips curled back in a snarl that showed his broken yellow teeth.

'Did yer?' he snapped. 'Well, I ain't, see!'

'You soon will be,' murmured the stout superintendent. 'What was the last stretch I got yer? Three years, wasn't it, fer robbery with violence? You'll get a 'seven' fer this night's work.'

'Will I?' snarled the other viciously. 'Who'll get it me? Not you, yer perisher! Your number's up, an' a good job, too.'

'Thinkin' of goin' in fer murder in yer

old age, Yates?' said Mr. Budd, and his lips twisted contemptuously. 'You 'aven't got the guts! They 'ang yer for that!'

Sniffy Yates spat out the remains of his cigarette and glared down into the calm face of the fat detective.

'It won't be me what'll do yer in,' he said. 'I'm only actin' under orders.'

'Al Collins', I s'pose,' said Mr. Budd, and the little man was obviously taken aback. 'It don't matter, the result'll be the same. An' accessory ter murder gets the same sentence as the feller what does the killin', don't ferget that. They'll be comin' for yer, Sniffy, at eight one mornin', an' they'll dress yer in your own clothes, except for yer collar — they take that away so's it shan't interfere with the rope — '

'Stop it, d'yer hear!' screamed Sniffy Yates, his face convulsed with mingled fear and fury. 'They'll never get me, they won't.'

'They will, Sniffy,' said the big man calmly. 'Nothin's more certain than that. An' they'll 'ang yer — unless you act sensibly. Set us free, an' I'll do what I can ter get you a light sentence — '

'Oh, stow it!' snarled Yates. 'You're booked fer the 'appy land, so you'd best make yer mind up!'

'I've told you where you're booked for!' snapped Mr. Budd. 'An' if yer brain was bigger than a flea's, you'd take the chance I'm offerin'.'

Sniffy Yates shrugged his thin shoulders, and pulling out a packet of cheap cigarettes stuck one in his mouth. Going over to the candle, he thrust the end of the cigarette in the flame and turned.

'I wouldn't stir a finger ter 'elp yer, you perishin' 'busy', if you offered me a 'undred quid!' he said, and his voice was so venomously vindictive that Mr. Budd realised the real seriousness of their position. These men were safe just so long as there was nobody to give evidence as to what had happened on the island that night. The place was lonely and shunned by the inhabitants of the surrounding villages. Nobody would ever know what had taken place if he, and the others with him, were silenced. The secret passage was unlikely to be discovered, and the men who had died in the flood might lie there for years, their presence unsuspected.

There was a sound outside and a second man came in. He was bigger and more muscular than his companion, with a rugged, weather-beaten face that gave him the appearance of an ex-boxer, which, indeed, he was.

''Ow much longer have we got to wait?' he growled. 'I'm gettin' fed up.'

'If it isn't Mike Leamey,' murmured Mr. Budd. 'Well, well. Al Collins seems ter have collected all the scum o' crookdom for this job!'

The newcomer uttered an oath.

'You shut yer trap!' he grunted threateningly, 'or I'll give yer a bashin'.'

'Bashin' bein' your speciality,' said the big man. 'They call yer 'Basher' Leamey, don't they? You've done time fer bashin' women an' sneakin' their handbags.'

'I'll make you sorry fer that,' snarled Leamey, lurching over to where the big man lay. He raised his foot for a vicious kick, but a voice from the doorway stopped him.

'Stop that!' it said sharply, and Leamey swung round. A tall man in a thick overcoat stood in the shadows near the threshold. The brim of his soft hat concealed his face, but Mr. Budd recognised him.

'We've been expecting you, Collins,' he said pleasantly.

The tall man advanced and peered down at him.

'Oh, it's you, is it?' he muttered. 'I'm rather glad of that. I've got an old score to settle with you.' He turned to Leamey. 'Have you got the diamonds?' he asked.

The man shook his head.

'No,' he replied. 'We searched this lot, but they 'adn't got 'em.'

Al Collins uttered an exclamation of annoyance.

'They must be back at the house,' he said. 'Unless they've hidden them some-where. What have you done with them, eh?'

He glowered down at Mr. Budd.

'I 'aven't done anythin' with 'em,' answered the fat detective truthfully. 'I've never seen 'em. Maybe they're in the middle of that tunnel with the rest of your crowd.'

'That's what you'd like me to believe, wouldn't you?' snarled Collins. 'Well, you're unlucky! They didn't even know what they were after, so they couldn't have got 'em. You'd better come across. Where are the diamonds?'

'We should like to know that ourselves!' said Huber. 'One of your gang has double-crossed you, in the same way that you tried to double-cross me.'

'Stop bluffing!' snapped Collins angrily. 'It won't do you any good. If you didn't bring those diamonds with you, they're back at the house, and I'll make you tell me where!'

'You're talkin' nonsense, Collins,' said Mr. Budd. 'We can't tell yer what we don't know.'

'We'll see about that!' retorted Collins. 'There are ways of making you talk, and I'm not squeamish! What's the good of being stubborn? I'll find those stones, if I have to pull that house down brick by brick — '

'You won't do that!' interrupted a soft

voice gently. 'Will you three men raise your hands, please, and keep quite still? Otherwise I shall shoot, and I'm rather a good shot!'

Mr. Budd gave a gasp of astonishment. Sybil Fordyce had risen noiselessly to her feet and stood coolly facing the three startled men, a tiny automatic gripped firmly in her hand.

12

The Last Surprise

Her sudden intervention came as a complete surprise to all of them. Sniffy Yates gaped stupidly at her with dropped jaw, his thin face ludicrous in its astonishment. The thick-set Leamey scowled and shifted his feet uneasily. Al Collins glared at her with an expression that was murderous in its malignancy.

'How did you get free?' he muttered.

'I was tied very badly,' she answered calmly. 'Perhaps, because I was a woman, they took less care over it. I managed to get my hands free, and the rest was easy.'

'Well done, Sybil!' cried Huber delightedly. 'There's a penknife in my pocket. Come and cut these cords and we'll soon tackle the brutes — '

'I can manage them quite well on my own!' she interrupted, to his surprise. 'If there is any trouble I shall shoot, and, as I said just now, I am a very good shot.'

She stepped quickly over to Al Collins, and, before he realised her intention, pressed the muzzle of her little weapon into his back.

'Tell your friends to take the pistols out of their pockets and throw them in the corner,' she ordered crisply, and at the same time dipped her left hand into the right-hand pocket of his overcoat and whipped out the revolver he carried.

'It will be more useful than mine,' she said. 'After being in the water, I don't suppose mine would really be any good. I wonder you didn't think of that!'

Al Collins began to swear loudly, but she stopped him.

'Do as I tell you!' she snapped. 'A bullet in the spine can be very painful!'

He hesitated for a second, and then shrugged his shoulders.

'Do what she says,' he grunted briefly, but neither Yates nor Leamey seemed anxious to obey.

'What's goin' to 'appen — ' began the thick-set man.

'Do as I tell you, you fool!' burst out

Collins angrily. 'D'you think I want a bullet in my back? She's got the drop on us.'

'You're a sensible man!' said the girl approvingly, and he growled something unprintable.

Reluctantly the other two pulled out a pair of automatics and threw them into a corner of the room. The girl backed away from Collins until she reached the spot where the weapons had fallen, and, without taking her eyes off the three men, stooped quickly and picked them up.

'Now,' she said, slipping them into her pocket, 'I can deal with you more easily. Walk into the next room, and remember that I shall be behind you with this.' She made a gesture with the pistol in her hand.

'What d'you want us to go into the next room for?' demanded Al Collins.

'I've got to do something with you,' she retorted, 'and the passage will make a very good temporary prison. The panel is very thick, and I can easily jam the mechanism from this side — '

'But the place is full of water!' cried

Sniffy Yates. 'Yer can't put us — '

'Not full,' corrected the girl. 'You may find it rather wet, but you'll have to put up with that.'

They argued and cursed, but she forced them to go, under the menace of the pistol. Dick Huber looked anxiously at the door as she disappeared.

'I wish she'd waited to free me,' he muttered. 'Those brutes may take her by surprise. If she'd set us free, we could have helped her.'

Mr. Budd grunted non-committedly. He was a little puzzled. Why hadn't the girl produced her automatic at the House of the Goat? She must have had it with her then — strapped to her leg, probably, since those searchers had failed to find it. It was queer, too, that she hadn't attempted to release them. It was the natural thing she would have done, in the circumstances —

A shot sounded from the next room, and Huber uttered an exclamation.

'What do you think's happening?' he said anxiously, but before the big man could reply there was another shot.

'Something's gone wrong!' cried the young man apprehensively. 'Why on earth did she try to tackle those brutes by herself?'

'I think quite a lot's gone wrong,' murmured Mr. Budd softly, 'but I'm not at all sure that it's the way you think. I'm rather under the impression that you're goin' ter get a shock, young feller.'

'What do you mean?' asked Huber, and at that moment the girl came back. She no longer held the pistol; her hands were thrust into the pockets of her coat. As she came in Huber gave a sigh of relief.

'Thank the lord you've come back!' he said fervently. 'I was wondering what was happening. What was that firing?'

'I put the spring that works the panel out of action,' she answered. 'It can't be opened now without smashing it in.' She walked to the centre of the room and looked at them for a second in silence. 'The question is what am I going to do with you?' she muttered, almost to herself.

Huber stared at her in astonishment.

'Do with us?' he repeated in bewilderment. 'I don't understand — '

'I don't think you do,' she interrupted, and her voice was hard and brittle. 'I'm afraid you're going to get rather a surprise.'

'I told you so!' murmured Mr. Budd.

Dick Huber looked from one to the other helplessly.

'I don't — ' he began.

'You don't understand. I know. You've said that once already.' Again she interrupted him a trifle impatiently. 'It's really very simple. Ever since you told me about your father's plan and the diamonds, I made up my mind to have them. I took them tonight, thinking that if they were missed you would believe they had been taken by these men. It was my intention to go back to the House of the Goat and pick them up from where I'd hidden them, when the excitement was over and nobody would have been any the wiser. But things went wrong. I had to act quickly when those men talked about searching the house. Otherwise I shouldn't have given myself away,

137

and you'd never have known.'

She stopped abruptly, and Huber stared at her in wonder and shocked surprise.

'But — but why, Sybil?' he stammered. 'Why?'

'Because I wanted money,' she said quickly. 'Do you realise what it's like to be a 'poor relation'? To live amongst money and have none of your own? I saw my chance to get money and be independent, and I decided to take it. There was no risk. There is none now. I doubt if you can do anything. You'd have to say how you came by those diamonds, and you won't.' She moved over to the door. 'I think I'll leave you now,' she said. 'You'll be able to get free somehow, I expect, but by that time I shall be a long way away. Good-bye.'

She turned hurriedly and was gone. The door slammed to and the key rasped in the lock. For a moment there was complete silence. And then the silence was broken by a queer noise. For the first time in history the lugubrious Leek chuckled.

'What are you sniggering at?' demanded Mr. Budd crossly.

'I was jest thinkin' what a shock that gal's goin' ter get when she finds them diamonds ain't where she put 'em!' broke in the sergeant.

'Ain't where she put 'em?' echoed Mr. Budd. 'Have you gone light-'eaded?'

'No,' answered Leek. 'Yer see, I saw 'er 'ide somethin' in a chair, when she thought nobody was lookin', an' I collared it. It was a little package, tied up in a scarf, an' I put it in me pocket. In the general excitement I fergot all about it — '

'Where is it now?' demanded the big man.

'In a corner of them steps be'ind the panel,' said Leek. 'I thought maybe them fellers might find it, so I managed to stick it there before we was collared.'

Mr. Budd looked at him expressively.

'That's the first sensible thin' I've known you do in years!' he said.

★ ★ ★

'It was one o' the queerest jobs I've ever tackled, sir,' murmured Mr. Budd, in an interview with the Assistant Commissioner on the following day. 'Unsatisfactory in some ways, yer might say.'

'You did very well, I think, in the circumstances,' grunted Colonel Blair, who had been listening attentively for the past hour. 'It seems to me to have ended in the best way. The less publicity about it, at the present time, the better. What happened to the girl?'

Mr. Budd shook his large head slowly.

'She disappeared altogether after she left the cottage, sir,' he said, 'an' I didn't see much point in tryin' ter find 'er. We got Collins an' the other fellers, an' Torrini, the man who killed Linkman an' Grunsbacher, was drowned in the flooded passage.'

'How did Linkman come into it?' asked the Assistant Commissioner.

''E heard the others talkin',' answered the big man, 'an' thought 'e'd go after the diamonds himself. He pinched the dead man's hat from Torrini, an' found the letter which referred to the House of the

Goat. Torrini, guessin' what he was up to, went after 'im, an' there was a row. It's the first time Benny tried anythin' big an' it'll be the last. I got it all out o' Collins this mornin'.'

'The value of those diamonds is nearly a hundred thousand pounds,' said Colonel Blair thoughtfully. 'The Home Secretary will have to decide what's to be done with them. Probably they'll be handed over to Richard Huber, after he's paid the duty. That was a smart piece of work on the part of Sergeant Leek.'

'Poor feller,' said Mr. Budd sorrowfully, and the Assistant Commissioner looked astonished.

'Why?' he demanded. 'What's the matter with him?'

''Is worst fears 'ave been realised,' replied the big man. 'He's in bed with a cold in 'is 'ead!'

THE SEAL OF
SOLOMON

1

The Murder at Pyramid House

Among the many qualities which had raised Mr. Budd from a humble policeman walking a beat to the position of a superintendent in the C.I.D. was an astonishingly good memory.

Everything that passed within the vision of his sleepy-looking eyes, or came within the hearing of his exceedingly sharp ears, was filed away in the recesses of his mind for possible future reference, and here, the remark made by one, Lew Creech, was to stand him in good stead although a year was to pass before he was able to make use of it.

Lew was an undersized individual with a prodigious strength of muscle, both of which physical characteristics were necessary to his profession, for he gained a precarious livelihood by robbing the houses of the rich while they were innocently dining, gaining access thereto by means of a convenient stackpipe or balcony.

He was gingerly descending an unstable water-pipe, after a visit to Lady Clingfordham's house in Dorchester Square, with most of her ladyship's jewellery in his pocket when he, metaphorically, fell into the arms of Police-Constable Hallows.

'It's a fair cop,' said Mr. Creech philosophically, and allowed himself to be marched to the station house without resistance.

Mr. Budd, the butt of a cigar in the corner of his mouth, was talking to the divisional-superintendent when he was brought into the charge-room, and greeted him as an old friend.

'Hallo, Lew!' he said sympathetically. 'You in trouble again? Well, well, you are a careless feller!'

'Jest bad luck,' said Lew Creech resignedly, shrugging his shoulders. 'It's a bit beneath me dignity to 'ave bin caught by a common flatty, though.'

He said nothing further until after he

had been charged and was being taken to the cells, and then he made the remark which Mr. Budd was to remember when the time came.

'You ever 'eard of a bloke called Solomon?' he asked.

'I've heard of a good many,' answered the big man. 'Which partic'lar Solomon d'yer mean?'

'This feller lived in Jerus'lem 'undreds o' years ago.'

'Oh, you mean *King* Solomon,' interrupted the stout superintendent. 'The feller with a thousand wives! Everybody's 'eard of him.'

'You're goin' ter 'ear more of 'im!' said Lew Creech cryptically. 'That feller's goin' ter give you a devil of a lot of trouble soon!'

'What did he mean by that?' asked the astonished desk-sergeant, as Mr. Creech was led away. ''Ow can a feller what's been dead for centuries start any trouble, anyway?'

It was almost a year to the day before Mr. Budd discovered the answer, and by that time the shadow of war had darkened the world.

The fat detective had the reputation of being the laziest man in Scotland Yard. Although he had a trim little house at Streatham, it was only by a great effort that he could ever summon up sufficient energy to go home at the end of his day's work. It was a habit of his to sit in the padded chair behind his desk until far into the night, a cigar between his lips, his hands clasped loosely over his capacious stomach, ruminating with closed eyes. What he thought about during these long periods of meditation, nobody knew but himself.

He was indulging in his usual practice one rainy night and trying to reconcile himself to the exertion of going home, when the house telephone-bell rang. Rousing from his reverie with an effort, he yawned and picked up the receiver.

'Hallo!' he called sleepily, and then, as the voice at the other end of the wire chattered rapidly he pulled a pencil towards him and began to scrawl notes on a pad at his elbow.

'I've got all that,' he grunted presently, and asked one or two quick questions.

'All right. I'll go at once. If Sergeant Leek's in the buildin', send him in ter me, will yer?'

He put the receiver back on its rack and read through the notes he had made, his forehead puckered in a frown. He was scribbling some additions when the lugubrious Leek came in.

'I was just goin' home,' he said mournfully. 'What's up?'

'We look like bein' — all night!' said Mr. Budd. 'Get yer hat an' coat. We're goin' to Staines.'

'Why?' demanded the sergeant. 'In this 'ere black-out — '

'Never mind the black-out. There's been a murder!' snapped his superior impatiently, struggling out of his chair with difficulty. 'Professor Penruddock Slythe, the Egyptologist, was killed at his 'ouse an hour ago. Don't waste time askin' silly questions, go an' rustle up the fingerprint people and the photographers, an' tell 'em to meet me at the entrance in three minutes.'

Leek departed with an expression of profound gloom on his long face, and Mr.

Budd picked up the telephone and called an extension number.

When he reached the entrance, he found the police-cars he had ordered waiting. The fingerprint experts and the photographers were already in the second car, and the big man climbed laboriously into the first, followed by the lean sergeant.

It was raining when they left London, but the rain had ceased, and a bleary moon was shining fitfully by the time they reached Staines.

Pyramid House, the queerly named residence of the dead man, lay close to the river, and was approached by a gloomy drive formed by a tunnel of huge chestnut trees that shut out every stray ray of light and terminated abruptly within a few yards of the house itself.

This, so far as Mr. Budd could judge in the brief glimpse he caught of it as he got heavily out on to the wet gravel, was an ivy-covered building, low-roofed and rambling, with many windows and a curious air of neglect that may have been attributable to the unkempt condition of its surroundings.

A constable was on duty in the porch, and he escorted the fat detective through a large and overcrowded hall to a huge room partly study and partly museum, and the most incredibly untidy apartment that Mr. Budd had ever seen. There were thousands of books, both old and new, which had overflowed the shelves provided for them, and rioted in hopeless confusion across chairs and tables, and were stacked knee-deep in the corners. Amid these were scattered a collection of queer odds-and-ends that ranged from a full-size sarcophagus to a number of little gaily painted wooden tomb figures. Near a great flat-topped writing-table littered with books and papers stood several ordinary packing-cases, the floor around them strewn with shavings, and beside them sprawled the figure of a man.

So much the stout superintendent had taken in when a sharp-featured, dapper man came toward him and introduced himself.

'I'm Divisional-Inspector Selkerk,' he

151

announced. 'Glad you've got here, Superintendent. This is an extraordinary business.'

'Is it?' murmured Mr. Budd, eyeing him sleepily. 'Well, maybe you're right. I don't know much about it yet. Tell me.'

The divisional-inspector cleared his throat and proceeded to do so. His story was brief and not very illuminating. The discovery of the murder had been made by the dead man's housekeeper, who was, apparently, at that moment recovering from an attack of hysterics in her room. She had telephoned to the police station an incoherent account of what had happened, and Selkerk had immediately come up to the house to investigate.

'I found the old gentleman as you see him now,' he said, nodding towards the figure by the packing-cases. 'He was quite dead, and according to the doctor had been dead for two or three hours. The murderer came through the window — I found it partly open, and there are prints on the gravel path outside. That's practically all there is to tell you.'

Mr. Budd rubbed his fat chin, pursed

his lips and walked over to the body.

Professor Penruddock Slythe had met his death horribly. The grey of his hair was mottled with red, and a large case-opener that was lying near him, among the shavings, bore traces of the same colour. There was little doubt that it had been the weapon which had battered out his life.

The big man peered into a long case that the dead man had, apparently, been unpacking. But it was empty.

'What was in this?' he asked, and Selkerk shook his head.

'I don't know,' he replied. 'Something the old man had brought back from Egypt, I suppose. He only returned two days ago from an expedition, so his housekeeper says.'

Mr. Budd looked slowly round. The contents of the empty case might be among the litter of objects that filled the room. It was impossible to tell, in all the confusion.

'Have yer checked up to find out if there's anythin' missin'?' he murmured thoughtfully.

'Not yet,' answered the divisional-inspector. 'I was waiting for the old gentleman's secretary to come back. It was hopeless trying to get any sense out of the housekeeper.'

'The secretary's out, is he?' said the fat man, his eyes still roving about restlessly.

'Been out since early this afternoon, so I'm told,' said Selkerk. 'There's a girl, too — a niece — but she's out as well.'

'Did the servants 'ear anything?' inquired Mr. Budd, poking about gingerly among the contents of the strange room.

'Not a thing!' declared the divisional-inspector.

'There's only two — Mrs. Borridge, the housekeeper, and a girl named Minnie Hand — and neither of 'em heard a sound. Queer, isn't it?'

'It's *very* queer,' said Mr. Budd, wrinkling his large nose and delicately scratching the extreme tip of it with a podgy forefinger. 'It's very queer indeed. Where was they?'

'The girl was in the kitchen,' answered Selkerk. 'The other woman was upstairs in her room. They ought to have heard something, if there was anything to hear — '

'There must 'ave been somethin' to hear,' broke in Mr. Budd softly. 'Nobody could 'ave come in through that winder without the old gentleman knowin', an' he'd have given the alarm. Unless,' he added thoughtfully, 'it was someone 'e knew an' was expectin'.'

Selkerk had opened his mouth to reply, when there came the sound of voices from the hall — the voices of a girl and a man raised excitedly.

'That'll be the secret'ry an' the niece,' muttered Mr. Budd, moving ponderously to the door. 'They've come back together, apparently.'

He stepped out into the hall and discovered a tall, dark man and a pretty, fair-haired girl arguing with Leek and the constable.

They both ceased speaking and swung round on the appearance of Mr. Budd.

'Look here!' said the dark man curtly. 'What's all this about — '

'Are you Professor Slythe's secret'ry,

sir?' asked the big man, and the other nodded.

'Yes. What — ' he began, but Mr. Budd again interrupted him.

'Will you tell me your name, sir, please?' he said.

'Richard Challis,' answered the dark man curtly. 'What are the police doing here? Has there been a burglary?'

'I'll do all the questionin', sir, if you don't mind,' said Mr. Budd smoothly, and turned his sleepy eyes towards the girl. 'What's your name, miss?'

'June Bennett,' she replied in a low voice. 'What has happened?'

'Somethin' rather serious, miss, I'm afraid,' answered the fat man. 'Would you come in here a moment, sir?'

The secretary followed him to the door of the big room, and Mr. Budd opened it, signing to him to go in. Challis entered, looked quickly about, and drew in his breath with a sharp hiss as he saw the body.

'Good God!' he breathed, the colour ebbing from his face. 'How did this happen?'

'Professor Slythe was murdered by somebody who came through that winder,' murmured Mr. Budd, at his elbow. ''E was killed just after he'd unpacked that crate. Can you tell me what was in it, sir?'

A queer expression flitted across the secretary's face — an expression that was composed of three mingled emotions — horror, incredulity, and fear. He went quickly over the empty packing-case, peered into it, and then glanced sharply round the untidy room.

'The mummy!' he exclaimed, and there was a curious high-pitched note to his voice. 'The mummy's gone!'

'What mummy?' asked Mr. Budd quickly.

'The mummy which Slythe brought back from his expedition,' answered Challis. 'The mummy of Solomon, the ancient ruler of Israel and Judah!'

2

Khynan Hani, the Egyptian

Mr. Budd was the first to break the silence which followed the secretary's statement.

'The mummy of King Solomon, eh?' he murmured thoughtfully. 'H'm! Interestin' an' perculiar. I s'pose there's no doubt that it was in this crate?'

'None whatever,' declared Challis, shaking his head. 'I was here when Slythe unpacked it. He had planned to unwrap it, alone, this evening.'

'Would it be valuable, sir?' asked Selkerk with interest.

'Intrinsically — no,' replied the secretary, shaking his head. 'As a unique specimen — priceless.'

'Not the sort o' thin' that an ordinary thief 'ud bother with,' grunted Mr. Budd, pinching his lower lip and frowning. 'It 'ud be practic'lly impossible ter get rid of it. This is a queer business.'

A small cell in his memory had opened, and the words of little Lew Creech were filtering through. He had known something. He had said that there was going to be trouble connected with Solomon, and now, a year later, his prophecy was coming true.

'Interestin' an' perculiar,' muttered the big man again, and made a mental note to find Lew and question him concerning the source of his information.

A thought occurred to him, and he put it into words.

'My history's a bit rusty, sir,' he said, 'but I always understood that Solomon was a Jew?'

'Quite right, he was,' agreed Dick Challis.

'Then how comes it,' went on Mr. Budd in a puzzled tone, 'that this mummy that's missin' could have been 'is? Ain't that sort o' thin' confined to Egyptians?'

'Solomon married Pharaoh's daughter,' answered the secretary, 'and it was a theory of Professor Slythe's that she had her husband's body embalmed according to the burial rites of the Egyptians. For many years he had been trying to discover the tomb. Eventually he found a papyrus which provided him with a clue to its whereabouts, and this expedition, from which we've just come back, was for the purpose of excavating the tomb. We were entirely successful.'

'It looks very much as if this was a crime of jealousy to me,' said the divisional-inspector. 'Do you know of anybody who was envious of the dead man's discoveries?'

Challis gave a rather mirthless smile.

'Most of his fellow Egyptologists were,' he replied. 'But I don't think any of them would have carried their envy to the point of murder.'

'I don't know,' said Selkerk. 'Some of these fellers are a bit queer in the head. No sane man would pinch a mummy, anyhow.'

'It all depends what it was pinched for,' murmured Mr. Budd. 'Some o' these things have got a lot o' jewels on 'em, ain't they? Was there anythin' of the kind about this one?'

The secretary shook his head.

'No,' he answered. 'For a king, the actual mummy was unusually plain. The sarcophagus was of gold, encrusted with precious stones, and the tomb was extremely elaborate, but the mummy was so ordinary that I remember Professor Slythe was surprised.'

'H'm!' grunted the fat man, rubbing his chin. 'Well, we'd better let the photographers an' the fingerprint fellers in. I don't expect they'll find anythin' helpful, but I s'pose we must stick ter routine.'

He lumbered over to the door and called to Leek.

'What about June — Miss Bennett?' whispered Dick Challis. 'She was Slythe's niece, and she's going to be very upset. Shall I break the news to her?'

'Yes, I think you'd better,' agreed Mr. Budd after a moment's thought, and the secretary went over to the girl and led her away, talking rapidly in a low voice.

While the fingerprint men and the photographers were busy in the big room, Mr. Budd interviewed the housekeeper and the maid, but he learned nothing. They had heard no sound, and it was not until Mrs. Borridge had gone to see if the dead man required anything that they had known there was anything wrong.

Neither was there much to be gathered from an examination of the ground outside the window. There were traces of jumbled footprints, but they became lost in the churned-up gravel of the drive.

'The murderer must 'ave come in a car,' said Mr. Budd, as he returned to the house after this futile task with Leek and Selkerk. 'He couldn't have taken that mummy away without somethin' o' the sort. You'd better circulate an inquiry. Maybe it was seen, though I should think that was unlikely in the black-out.'

The divisional-inspector went in search of the telephone, and Mr. Budd, pausing on the top step, stared thoughtfully down the dark tunnel of the drive.

He thought he had heard the faint hum of an approaching car, and presently, as he watched, a dimmed headlight came into view round the bend. The fat man glanced at his watch. It was nearly twelve.

Who could this late visitor be?

The car stopped behind the others, and a man got out. He was a tall man, wearing a heavy coat that reached almost to his heels, and he walked with a curious kind of arrogant grace. As he saw Mr. Budd standing in the porch he stopped, and, after a moment, spoke.

'I wish to see Professor Penruddock Slythe,' he said in a deep musical voice that bore the merest trace of an accent. 'My name is Khynan Hani.'

'I'm afraid you can't see Professor Slythe, sir,' answered Mr. Budd. 'He's — '

'I have an appointment,' interrupted the newcomer brusquely.

'If yer had fifty appointments you couldn't see him!' retorted the big man a little resentfully, for the other's tone had annoyed him. 'Professor Slythe was murdered earlier this evenin'.'

The visitor stared at him for a second, and then his breath was expelled from between his teeth with a gentle hiss.

'So!' he said softly. 'It is the vengeance of Sakhmet!'

Mr. Budd pricked up his ears.

'Who's this feller you're talkin' about?' he demanded, and the other laughed scornfully.

'Sakhmet is the Egyptian goddess of vengeance,' he said. 'She is the One who protects the good and annihilates the wicked.'

'Oh!' grunted Mr. Budd disparagingly. 'I thought you was talkin' about a real person.'

'The gods of Ancient Egypt are very real,' said Khynan Hani. 'The power of Sakhmet, and of Set, the Destroyer, is as potent today as it was in the time of my forefathers.'

'Are you an Egyptian?' asked the fat detective, suddenly very interested indeed.

The man before him drew himself up haughtily.

'I come from a dynasty of kings,' he said. 'The blood of the Pharaohs runs in my veins.'

Mr. Budd's heavy lids drooped until his eyes were mere slits. Here was someone who might have had a motive in stealing the mummy of Solomon — a self-confessed descendent of the Pharaohs,

164

the daughter of one of whom Solomon had married. It was a queer motive, but then the whole business was queer.

'I think you'd better come inside,' he murmured, and Khynan Hani inclined his head. When they were in the hall Mr. Budd closed the door.

'I'm a police officer,' he said abruptly, 'an' I'm investigatin' this murder. What was your business with the dead man?'

The Egyptian surveyed him calmly.

'I came to talk with him,' he answered. 'Recently he had violated the tomb of the great Suleyman — a sacrilegious act that was inexcusable, the far-reaching results of which he could have had no knowledge. I came to warn him!'

'Of what?' asked Mr. Budd.

'Of the forces which in his ignorance he was releasing,' replied Khynan Hani. 'The tomb of Suleyman was hidden for a purpose, and for that purpose its whereabouts have remained hidden throughout the centuries. There was a secret buried there of such danger and power that he who dared to unveil it did so, not only at the risk of his life, but at the risk of a world upheaval. I am, it appears, too late to warn the man who was responsible, and by that very fact my warning should take on an additional significance. But I would pass on what I came to say to him, to those who come after him. It is this: Return the mummy of Suleyman to the tomb from whence it came.'

'That 'ud be a difficult' job,' murmured Mr. Budd. 'The mummy's been stolen.'

Into the brown eyes of the Egyptian crept an indescribable expression of horror, and the lines of his face slowly changed until it was hard and tense.

'Stolen?' he whispered. 'The mummy of Suleyman has been stolen?'

'Well, it's gone,' said the fat detective phlegmatically, 'an' we can only conclude that the murderer took it away with 'im.'

'Then be warned!' cried the man who called himself Khynan Hani, and his voice was vibrant with the intensity of his emotion. 'The Power is once more active! A potent force for evil has been unleashed upon the world!'

3

The Beginning of the Unknown Voice

Before Mr. Budd had time to comment on the Egyptian's remarkable outburst Richard Challis came hurriedly down the stairs and called to him.

'Stay here, will yer?' said the big man curtly. 'I'd like to have a word with you later.'

Khynan Hani bowed. The colour of his face had deepened to normal, and only a trace remained of the terror in his eyes.

'Keep an eye on that feller,' muttered Mr. Budd below his breath as he passed the wondering Leek, and the sergeant nodded.

'Will you come up to my room?' muttered the secretary under his breath. 'I've got something I'd like to show you.'

The stout superintendent followed him in silence up the stairs to the first floor,

167

and he led the way into a medium-sized room at the end of a corridor that was furnished as an office.

'This came this afternoon,' said Challis, pointing to a square box on the large writing-table. 'It was addressed to Professor Slythe, but when Mrs. Borridge took it in to him he was busy and told her to put it in my room. I've just opened it. Look!'

Mr. Budd looked. The box had contained a quantity of cotton-wool, which lay strewn about the table, and in which had evidently been packed the four cardboard cylinders that stood in its midst. There was no need to ask what they were.

'Dictaphone cylinders,' muttered Mr. Budd wonderingly.

'Yes,' said the secretary, 'and all numbered consecutively. I've no idea what they can be or where they can have come from.'

Mr. Budd took up one of the canisters, opened it and slid the wax record out on to his fat fingers. The surface was covered with the fine lines of speech.

'Was Professor Slythe writin' a book?' he asked.

'He was,' said Challis, 'but he writes by hand.'

'Wasn't there any letter or anythin' in with these thin's?' said the fat man, and the secretary shook his head.

'Nothing at all,' he declared. 'Just those four cylinders.'

Mr. Budd rubbed his chin in perplexity.

'Well, I s'pose the best way to find out what they're about is ter put 'em on a machine,' he remarked after a pause. ''Ave yer got one?'

'There's one downstairs in the study,' answered Challis. 'Professor Slythe bought one some time ago, but he couldn't get on with it.'

'I'll 'ave it sent up,' said the fat man. 'Wait there, will yer?'

'It's in the right-hand corner by the window,' said the secretary, 'near the statue of Anubis.'

Mr. Budd made his way to the head of the stairs and called down to Leek.

'Ask one of them fellers to fetch up the

dictaphone machine that's in that big room,' he said, and added Challis' directions for finding it.

'Now we'll see what these thin's are all about,' he remarked when he returned to the secretary's room. 'Maybe they've got nothin' ter do with this business at all. Do you know a feller — an Egyptian — called Khynan Hani?'

He boggled over the pronunciation of the name, and Challis shook his head.

'No, why?' he inquired.

'He's downstairs,' answered Mr. Budd, jerking his head towards the door, 'shootin' out a lot o' nonsense about the disappearance o' Solomon's mummy 'avin' let loose evil on the world.'

'Did he say that?' asked the secretary quickly.

'That an' a lot o' other bunk,' grunted the big man disgustedly. 'He said he had the blood of Pharaohs in his veins. In my opinion 'e's crazy.'

Richard Challis helped himself to a cigarette from a box on the writing-table, and lit it with a hand that shook slightly.

'Why did he come here?' he asked.

'He said he had an appointment with Professor Slythe,' said Mr. Budd doubtfully. 'Though twelve o'clock at night in these black-out times strikes me as a queer time fer an appointment. He wanted ter warn 'im — '

'He said that?' asked Challis sharply.

'Ain't I just told yer he said it?' snapped Mr. Budd irritably.

The secretary inhaled deeply and let the smoke trickle out slowly through his nostrils.

'I wonder?' he muttered to himself. 'I wonder — '

'What d'yer wonder?' asked the stout superintendent.

'Who this man is, and if he's quite as crazy as you think,' answered Challis. 'I warned Slythe that he was dabbling in dangerous things, but he wouldn't listen to me.'

'Look 'ere,' said Mr. Budd in a tone of annoyance. 'I'm gettin' sick of all this mysterious stuff! I'm a police officer, an' I'm investigatin' a murder. A man has been killed by 'aving his head smashed in with a steel crow bar. If you know anythin' that's likely to help me find the murderer it's yer duty to tell me.'

Challis looked at him, and his face was worried and anxious.

'It's not quite as easy as that,' he said after a pause. 'I don't know anything definite — '

'Well, if you suspect anyone,' interrupted Mr. Budd.

'I don't suspect anyone, but — ' The secretary stopped abruptly.

'Oh, there's a 'but,' is there?' grunted the fat detective. 'Well, what is it? Come on, out with it!'

Richard Challis stubbed out his half-smoked cigarette in the ashtray, and there was a long pause before he answered. And then his answer took the form of a question.

'Have you ever heard of Solomon's Seal?' he asked in a low voice.

Mr. Budd stared at him doubtfully.

'Yes,' he replied, 'it's a plant — somethin' like a lily — '

'No, no. I don't mean that!' broke in Challis impatiently. 'I mean the Seal of Power which Solomon wore as an emblem of his kingship over the Jews.'

Mr. Budd shook his head.

'Can't say that I have,' he admitted. 'What was it?'

Challis lighted another cigarette nervously.

'It was generally supposed to take the form of a ring which Solomon wore on the middle finger of his right hand,' he answered slowly. 'There is no actual proof that it ever existed, but the legend has come down through the centuries that it was buried with him.'

'That's all very interestin', no doubt,' said Mr. Budd. 'But are you tryin' ter tell me that Professor Slythe was murdered, an' this mummy pinched, because someone was after this ring?'

Challis shook his head.

'No,' he answered. 'I'm merely suggesting it is a possibility. I couldn't be more definite, because I don't know that the ring was there. Slythe thought it was. It was his opinion that the ring would be found on the finger of the mummy, but it's quite likely he was wrong. It was only a theory, anyway.'

The stout man rubbed the back of his fleshy neck irritably. He was feeling a little out of his depths. All this talk of legends and rings meant nothing to his practical mind.

'You naturally put a value on these thin's,' he said. 'You look on 'em from a different angle to what the ordin'ry person would. An' maybe from your point o' view you're right. But you won't convince me that anyone 'ud risk committin' murder for the sake o' somethin' they didn't know was there, an' which wouldn't be worth more'n a few pounds, anyhow.'

Challis looked at him queerly.

'It's not the value of the ring that would make it worthwhile someone committing murder to gain possession of it,' he said slowly, after a pause. 'It's the power it would give its possessor. Don't you realise what it represents? The power of Solomon — the emblem of an ancient king ship — '

'What use would that be in the present day?' interrupted Mr. Budd.

'Who controls practically the entire

finances of the world?' asked the secretary seriously. 'The Jews! Behind every big banking organisation, behind every business of any size, behind even Governments you will find — if you go into the matter far enough — a Jew in control. The man who held the Seal of Solomon would wield a power over these people of a scattered and persecuted race that would be greater than that of any dictator. He would be a veritable king — a king of the Jews. Wouldn't that be a sufficient motive for murder?'

As he ceased speaking Mr. Budd began to see dimly the tremendous possibilities of his suggestion. If the Seal did carry with it such a power, then the person who held it would be a force to be reckoned with — such a force for good or evil as the world had never seen. He could command a practically unlimited supply of money and the allegiance of millions. Certainly there was motive enough here for murder — motive enough and to spare.

The stout superintendent experienced

a sudden and curious sense of insignificance. It was as though he were trying to batter down a rock with a toffee-hammer. Here was a criminal who was concerned with so vast a project that his means were almost forgotten in the contemplation of the magnitude of his ends. It was only for a moment that this queer feeling of inferiority possessed him, and then he was his normal phlegmatic self once more.

'I understand somethin' of what that Egyptian feller was talkin' about now,' he muttered softly. 'Though what he's got ter do with it is more'n I can — '

'The fact that he is an Egyptian explains that,' broke in Richard Challis. 'The old hatred of the Egyptians and the Israelites has once more reared its head. Any movement that might result in restoring the lost glory of the Jewish race and setting them back again in the country of their origin would be sufficient to make an Egyptian use every endeavour to prevent it. That is evidently the reason why this man Khynan Hani wanted to try to persuade Slythe to return the mummy of Solomon, unwrapped, to its tomb.'

The big man screwed up his face and pulled gently at his thick nose.

'If this isn't all bunk,' he said thoughtfully, 'this business looks as if it was goin' ter develop into somethin' pretty big — somethin' very big.'

There was a noise in the corridor outside, and two men came in carrying the dictaphone with Inspector Selkerk following them. On his instructions they set the machine down near the desk and withdrew.

'Maybe these cylinders 'ull tell us somethin',' remarked Mr. Budd, picking up the cable attached to the instrument and looking about. 'Is there a plug anywhere?'

Challis pointed out one in the wainscoting, and the fat man stooped with difficulty and inserted the plug.

'Now then,' he said a little breathlessly, 'let's see what these thin's have got ter say.'

He picked up the cylinder marked 'one', and the wax record out of the case, and slipped it onto the mandrel. Raising the vulcanite mouthpiece from its rest, which automatically started the motor, he waited expectantly. The cylinder revolved, and for a moment there was nothing but a gentle scratching sound. Then suddenly and abruptly a whispering voice began to speak:

'I send these records in the earnest hope that you will listen to the story they tell, and heed its warning,' it said clearly. 'Follow closely what I have to say, and do not treat it lightly, for you stand upon the very threshold of death!'

There was a brief interval of silence, and then the queer, whispering voice resumed in a dramatic recitative that in the stillness of the room came loud and clear to the two attentive listeners.

4

The Strange Ending of the Unknown Voice

'Forty-five years ago, on the outskirts of Babylon, there lived a man and his wife. They were humble and poor these Jewish people; so poor that they were hard put to it to find sufficient food to eat and fuel to burn, and this was a source of great worry to them, the more so, since the woman had conceived and was within but a short distance of her time.

'By dint of much pinching and care and hard work on the part of the man, this difficult period was overcome, and the child was born. To their great delight it was a boy, and even at that early stage, possessed remarkable physical beauty.

'There was only one blemish to mar the baby's perfection, and that was a peculiar birthmark on his chest which took the form of two interlaced triangles in scarlet, and was so clear that it might have been tattooed. This strange mark was a source of wonder to the parents, for they could not imagine any reason to account for it, but as the time went on and the child grew older they came to accept its presence as a queer product of nature, and more or less forgot that it existed.

'The boy grew into a youth; a dark-skinned, dark-eyed, handsome youth who quickly began to show an intelligence markedly superior to any of his fellows. He possessed, too, a magnetic quality that was both attractive and repellent, and an air of haughtiness that was looked at askance by the people among whom he lived as being above his station.

'At the age of eighteen he was a proud, reserved, studious youth, older in looks and habits than his years, which is the way with most of the Eastern races, and had secured for himself a situation as assistant-librarian at the public library in Kut-el-Amara. Here he read deeply, and here he met the man who, unconsciously, was to exercise such a strange influence on his life.

'There came to Kut-el-Amara an English professor of history who was writing a book on the origin and history of the Jewish race. This man was astonished at the knowledge of the subject displayed by the young librarian, and a friendship sprang up between them that had for its roots a common interest. The English professor learned of his friend's lowly birth, and was the more amazed at his remarkable erudition and almost regal bearing. Instead of being the son of a humble artisan, he might have been the descendant of a line of kings.

'The English professor was interested, for as well as being a student of history he was a believer in the theory of reincarnation, and here, under his hand, seemed to be a subject that did much to uphold the truth of that theory. He studied the young Jew with the same close attention that a zoologist would give to a rare animal. He encouraged him to talk about his aspirations, his dreams, his theories of life, and he very quickly discovered that he had a brilliant and original mind.

'It was not unnatural that his chief

interest should centre on his own race, and concerning this he held an idea that amounted almost to an obsession that one day the Jewish people would once again possess a country of their own and become a great nation.

' 'There will, sooner or later,' he said, 'arise a man who will lead them, a modern Solomon whose power will be unlimited and who will bring together the scattered remnants of a great race into an organised unity. The wonder and the glory of Ancient Israel will be restored, and a new king will once more rule over his people.'

'The English professor was sceptical. He could understand his young friend's enthusiasm, but he could not see any prospect of what he visualised ever coming to pass. There was no possibility of any man acquiring the power necessary to wield so complete a control over a race whose eight millions were scattered to the four corners of the earth.

' 'There is one way by which a man could acquire that power,' answered his friend. 'If he held the emblem of that great king who once ruled over the Jewish people — if he became possessed of the Seal of Solomon.'

'The English professor pointed out that such a thing was very unlikely. There was no authentic record to show that the Seal had ever existed, and if it had, it had been lost after the overthrow of the mighty kingdom whose ruler, according to legend, had worn it.

''It is lost, but it will be found,' cried the young Jew with conviction. 'When the time is ripe it will be found, and once again become the concrete emblem before which the entire Jewish people will bow their heads. I know it! I feel it! And I believe that I am the destined saviour of my race, for not only was I given the name of Solomon at my birth, but I bear upon my breast a mark which I believe to be a reproduction of that ancient seal of power.'

'He tore open his shirt — he was dining with his friends at the latter's hotel — and revealed the crimson markings on his chest.

''One day the ring will come to light,'

he said, 'and I shall acquire it and wear it on the third finger of my right hand as did the mighty Solomon centuries ago. I know not how or when this shall come to pass, but it will be so.'

'The English professor was startled at the sight of the birthmark, for without any doubt it represented the device which legend attributed to the Seal of Solomon. Was this, he wondered, an authentic instance of reincarnation? Was this handsome youth the re-born Solomon, destined to lead his race to greatness? His lowly birth, his extraordinary magnetic personality, his remarkable good looks, and his almost phenomenal intelligence seemed to suggest that such a theory was by no means wild and improbable. There was, too, something just a little uncanny about him — a queer sort of aura of power that was almost palpable.

'For the remainder of the time that he spent in Kut-el-Amara, he and the youthful Solomon had many talks upon the subject, and it was obvious that the young man was also imbued with the conviction that he was the reincarnated ego of the great king.

'At last the time came for the English professor to take his departure.

' 'I shall hope to hear of you, though we may never meet again,' he said, when he called to say goodbye. The young Jew looked at him steadily with his luminous and inscrutable eyes.

' 'You will hear of me,' he answered. 'You will hear much more of me, and one day we shall meet again.'

'During the years that followed the English professor did hear more of him, and each piece of news that reached him told of his progress. He left Kut-el-Amara and travelled extensively, growing richer and greater as the time went by. Eventually he reached England, and by this time his name was almost a household word. From a poor shack on the fringe of Babylon, he had travelled to — '

There came a sharp report and the tinkling crash of breaking glass. The whispering voice from the dictaphone stopped abruptly as the slowly turning cylinder splintered into a spatter of broken wax. A second and a third shot followed rapidly on the first, and the other cylinders, which Mr. Budd had placed ready to hand, flew to pieces and scattered the floor with black chips.

Challis gave a cry of alarm, and the big man swung round toward the window. The lower pane was shattered, and through the jagged aperture protruded a gloved hand gripping the butt of an ugly-looking automatic. Even as they looked the hand and the pistol were jerked out of sight and they heard a scrambling, scraping sound.

'The balcony!' cried the secretary. 'He's on the balcony! I forgot to draw the curtains!'

But he spoke to an empty room. With remarkable speed for so fat a man, Mr. Budd had reached the door and was lumbering toward the staircase. Challis went after him, and heard him shouting to Leek in the hall below:

'There's a man with a gun — out in the garden!' panted the stout superintendent. 'Goin' after 'im. Get hold of the others an' foller!'

He ran across the hall, jerked open the front door, and had disappeared into the darkness before the astonished sergeant could articulate the questions which flooded to his lips.

The moon was shining palely, and in the meagre light that it gave, the grounds of Pyramid House showed up as a tangled mass of weeds and undergrowth.

'Which way?' gasped the fat detective as Challis caught up with him.

'Round to your right,' answered the secretary, and swore as his foot became entangled with a trailing briar and he fell sprawling into a bed of weeds.

Without pausing to see what had happened to his companion, Mr. Budd continued on his way. He swung round an angle of the house and saw a pillared loggia running the entire length of that side of the building. It supported a balcony, and a gleam of light from above told him that this must be the balcony which Challis' room overlooked. He stopped for a second to listen. There was no sound at all except the dripping of moisture from the trees, and he stared this way and that in the hope of catching sight of the man who had fired the shots.

He could see no sign of anything moving and was trying to make up his mind which way he should go when he heard the sharp crack of a breaking branch. It came from a narrow belt of trees skirting a ragged lawn, and the next second he was plunging across the rank grass towards them.

He heard the swish of hurried feet from the darkness of the copse, and the rustle of leaves as though someone were forcing his way through wet bushes. Another sharp crack reached his ears, and then, as he entered the shelter of the trees, he made out a dim figure skulking from trunk to trunk.

Breathing heavily, the perspiration streaming down his fat cheeks from this unusual exertion, Mr. Budd went in pursuit. The fleeing figure dodged from tree to tree, plunged through a hedge of straggling laurels, and began to run jerkily along a path that led back to the drive.

The big man followed, but he was losing ground. Physical exertion of any kind was not one of his strong points, and his effort had left him nearly spent.

And then he heard a shout and saw the lean form of Leek racing across a strip of grass in the pale moonlight and heading the fugitive off. The man he was chasing saw him, too; stopped, hesitated, and doubled back on his tracks.

Mr. Budd uttered a queer little grunt of satisfaction. He couldn't escape now unless he used his automatic and shot his way to safety, and he seemed to have no intention of doing that.

He made a dart for the cover of the trees, and the big man swerved and crashed his way heavily through the laurel hedge and drew level with him.

'I want you!' he panted, and his huge hand grasped the man's thin shoulder.

The fugitive capitulated instantly, rather to his surprise.

'All right,' he grunted, with a shrug. 'It's a fair cop.'

Mr. Budd recognised the formula of the habitual crook and twisted his captive round so that the light of the moon shone on his face.

It was Lew Creech!

5

Lew Creech Spills the Beans

''Ave yer got 'im?' Leek came running breathlessly up, followed by Selkerk.

'I've got him all right,' said Mr. Budd grimly, and the little man wriggled.

'You don't know yer own strength,' he grunted protestingly. 'Lay off a bit, will yer? You're crushin' me shoulder.'

'Who is it?' demanded the divisional-inspector curiously.

'A feller called Creech,' answered the big man. ''Ow he got here, though, beats me. If everybody 'ad their rights, 'e ought ter be in prison.'

'I bin out fer a week,' put in the prisoner. 'They let me off the rest o' me sentence because I'm an 'ero! There was a bit of a fire, an' I climbed up where no one else could an' saved the life o' the doctor.'

'That's a pity,' remarked Mr. Budd,

'because it looks very like as if you was goin' back again — with a few more months tacked on.'

'What for?' demanded Mr. Creech indignantly. 'What 'ave I done? Nothin'! I come along ter see me old friend Professor Slythe, an' suddenly there's a lot o' shootin' an' I get chased by 'alf the busies in the world! What's the idea, that's what I'd like ter know?'

'That's what I'm goin' ter know!' snapped Mr. Budd. 'Now, stop thinkin' up any fairy tales an' let's 'ave the truth! Why did you smash them cylinders?'

'Smash what cylinders?' asked Mr. Creech in astonishment. 'Whatcher talkin' about?'

'You know very well what I'm talkin' about!' snarled the stout superintendent crossly. 'You was on that balcony with a pistol, an' you shot them cylinders to smithereens.'

'Nuts!' remarked Mr. Creech to the world at large. 'Batty! Potty! You must be! I ain't got a pistol, an' I've never been near no balcony!'

Mr. Budd glowered at him.

'Do you mean ter tell me,' he said sceptically, 'that you weren't up on that balcony a little while ago, an' that you didn't fire four shots through the winder an' smash four dictaphone records?'

'I am tellin' yer, ain't I?' said Lew Creech. 'Blimey! I didn't 'ave a chance ter get near the blinkin' 'ouse, let alone a balcony!'

'Fan him!' ordered Mr. Budd briefly.

The lean sergeant ran his hands expertly over the little man and mournfully shook his head.

'He ain't carryin' a gun,' he announced.

''Ave I ever carried a gun, I ask yer?' demanded Mr. Creech in an injured voice. 'Anybody 'ud think I was a blinkin' amachoor!'

'He may 'ave thrown it away while 'e was bein' chased,' suggested Leek.

'I tell yer — ' began Creech.

'Get someone to make a search,' said Mr. Budd, breaking in in the middle of his protestations. 'Come on, yer comin' back ter the house. There's quite a lot I want ter talk to yer about.'

Mr. Creech shrugged his thin shoulders resignedly.

'What's the good o' talkin'?' he said. 'If I tell yer the truth yer won't believe me.'

'Give me the chance!' snapped the big man.

On the way back they met Richard Challis. His clothes were covered in mud and there was a streak of blood across his face.

'I tripped and fell into a damned flowerbed,' he said crossly, when Mr. Budd asked what had happened to him. 'There was a brick or something among the weeds — and I found it. So you've got him, eh?'

'We've got this feller,' answered the fat detective. 'But whether 'e fired them shots or not, I'm not certain.'

The secretary looked surprised.

'Do you mean there were two of them?' he asked.

'Maybe,' said Mr. Budd. 'Hallo! Where's that feller's car?'

They had reached the space in front of the house, and the big saloon which had brought Khyan Hani was no longer there.

'It must've gone,' muttered the sergeant, staring.

'Gone? Of course it's gone!' snarled Mr. Budd irritably. 'Any blithering fool can see the thin's gone! An' that Egyptian feller's gone with it!'

He mounted the step and pushed open the front door, which was ajar. The photographers and the fingerprint men were packing up, watched by an uneasy-looking constable.

'Why did you let that man go?' demanded Mr. Budd, and the policeman shifted his feet unhappily.

'I couldn't help it, sir,' he muttered apologetically. 'To tell yer the truth, I didn't know 'e 'ad gone until I suddenly saw 'e weren't no longer there, if yer understand me — '

'I don't!' snapped the big man. 'What are you tryin' ter tell me? That this feller did a vanishin' trick?'

'I don't know exactly what 'appened, sir,' replied the man. 'One minute 'e was 'ere an' the next 'e was gone. I'd only taken me eyes off 'im fer a second — ' He met Mr. Budd's withering glance, and his voice trailed away into an embarrassed silence.

'You're a fine policeman, you are!' grunted the stout superintendent.

'Fancy lettin' a feller walk out on yer under yer nose an' never seein' 'im go! Oh, well, it can't be helped, I s'pose. Did yer find anythin'?' He turned wearily to the Scotland Yard men.

They shook their heads. There were a considerable number of fingerprints in the study, as was only to be expected, but the majority had been made by the dead man. There were no prints at all on the case-opener.

'I didn't expect there would be,' muttered Mr. Budd. 'You'd better check up on the people in the 'ouse. Maybe you'll find that all the dabs belong to one or other of 'em.' He gave a prodigious yawn and transferred his attention to Mr. Creech. 'Now you an' me 'ull 'ave a heart-to-heart talk,' he said. 'An' you'd better get ready ter break the 'abit of a lifetime an' tell the truth, otherwise there's goin' ter be trouble, an' it'll be all yours! Where can I have a word with this

195

feller in private?'

'You'd better go into the smoking-room,' said Challis, and jerked his head towards a door on the other side of the hall.

Mr. Budd led his unwilling captive over to it and pushed him inside.

'I shall want ter see you again in a moment or two, Mr. Challis,' he called back over his broad shoulder. 'Don't go inter that room o' yours upstairs until I come with yer. Now,' he went on, switching on the light and shutting the door, 'sit down, Lew, an' let's 'ear from yer.'

Lew Creech perched himself uneasily on the arm of a big chair and pulled a packet of cheap cigarettes out of his pocket.

'What's bin 'appening here?' he asked in a low voice.

'Murder!' answered the fat man briefly. 'Penruddock Slythe was bashed to death in 'is study this evenin'.'

Mr. Creech's wizened face paled, and he fumbled clumsily with the cigarette packet.

'Blimey!' he whispered huskily. 'Murder, eh?'

'Listen, Lew,' said Mr. Budd, producing one of his thin black cigars and slowly stripping off the band. 'A year ago I was in the charge-room o' Carlborough Street Police Station when you was brought in after bein' copped comin' away from Lady Clingfordham's 'ouse. Remember?'

Lew Creech succeeded in extracting a cigarette at last, stuck it between his lips and nodded.

'You said somethin' then,' went on the big man, 'about Solomon givin' me a hell of a lot o' trouble. What did yer mean?'

The little burglar snapped open a cheap lighter and dipped the end of his cigarette in the flame.

'I didn't mean nothin',' he muttered.

'Cut it!' snarled Mr. Budd roughly. 'I told yer to tell the truth, an' you'd better! What did yer mean?'

Lew Creech trickled smoke through his thin nostrils and then expelled a cloud from his lips.

'I 'eard somethin',' he answered reluctantly. 'It came over the grapevine — '

197

'What did yer 'ear?' demanded the fat detective as he hesitated. 'Go on, spill it, Lew.'

'It was somethin' about this feller Solomon an' a Seal,' replied Lew Creech sullenly. 'I don't know what it was all about. Somebody was goin' ter get 'old o' this Seal which 'ud make 'em all-powerful — the biggest crook organisation in the world.'

'Who was this somebody?' asked Mr. Budd quickly.

Creech shook his narrow head.

'I don't know,' he answered, but there was something in his eyes that gave him away.

'Stop lyin', will yer?' snapped the big man angrily. 'Who was this feller?'

'I ain't no squealer,' muttered Lew Creech.

Mr. Budd eyed him sternly.

He had handled men like Lew Creech too many times not to know the best way of going about the job.

'See here,' he said, and there was an edge to his usually placid and rather fruity voice. 'A man has been killed over this business, an' he wasn't killed nicely. You know somethin' an' you're in it up ter your neck. Unless you want ter go to the trap as an accessory you'd better come clean. Understand?'

Apparently Mr. Creech understood only too well, for his pasty face went the colour of dirty putty.

'You've got nothin' on me,' he declared in alarm. 'An' yer can't 'ang nothin' on me!'

'A man was murdered 'ere this evenin',' said Mr. Budd meaningfully, 'an' you was found lurkin' about the garden. Don't talk like a kid o' three. Nothin' on you! I could 'ave yer arrested right away if I wanted to, an' you know it!'

'I had nothin' ter do with the murder,' cried the frightened man. 'I didn't even know the old man was dead until you told me.'

'What was you doin' here, then?' asked the stout superintendent sharply.

'I came ter see 'im. I was goin' ter warn 'im,' answered Lew Creech. 'There weren't no 'arm in that, was there?'

Mr. Budd scratched the side of his

heavy face and wrinkled his broad nose. Everybody seemed to have tried to warn Slythe. It was one of the queerest points about this queer business.

'If you came 'ere to warn him you must have 'ad a reason,' he said thoughtfully. 'What was it?'

'I've told yer,' replied Creech. 'I 'eard that somebody was after this Seal thing, an' — '

''Ow did yer know Slythe had this Seal, anyway?' snapped Mr. Budd.

'Blimey! I can read, can't I?' retorted Lew Creech. 'It was in all the papers that he'd found this 'ere mummy and thought that Solomon's Seal was on its fingers — '

'You knew more than that,' broke in the fat man. 'That wouldn't have been enough ter have brought yer here. You knew who it was who was after the Seal, an' you knew that they was prepared to go ter the length o' murder ter get it. Who was this feller? Was it a man called Solomon?'

It was a shot in the dark, based on the story he had heard from the dictaphone, and rather to his surprise, it produced no startled reaction from Lew Creech.

'Solomon?' said the little crook in evident surprise. 'No, it wasn't Solomon.'

'If you know it wasn't Solomon, you must know who it was,' snapped Mr. Budd instantly. 'You've given yerself away, Lew. Now let's 'ave the rest of it.'

Creech bit his lip. He realised that it was no longer any use denying that he knew anything.

'Look 'ere,' he said. 'If I tell yer what I know, will yer promise not ter let on where yer got yer information from? If it got round that I'd put up a squeal — '

'Make yer mind easy, Lew,' broke in Mr. Budd. 'You ought ter know better'n to worry over that.'

Lew Creech took a deep breath of smoke and slowly exhaled it.

'You know Guldheimer?' he asked, and the big man's sleepy eyes opened very wide.

'You mean Isaac Guldheimer?' he snapped.

'That's the feller,' answered Lew Creech, nodding. 'Well, he's at the bottom o' this.'

Mr. Budd's thick lips pursed into a silent whistle. Isaac Guldheimer was the head of a business in the City of London that dealt in general merchandise. And although nothing had ever been proved against him, the police had always had a suspicion that all was not open and above-board with his business enterprises. He had appeared suddenly from nowhere and purchased the business, which was then more of a liability than an asset. Under his guidance, however, it had rapidly developed into a prosperous concern. For a long time Scotland Yard had been of the opinion that the wily Mr. Guldheimer augmented his income with a considerable amount of judicious fencing.

'Guldheimer, eh?' murmured the fat man softly. 'Now that's very interestin'. So he was the feller who was after Solomon's Seal? He does a bit o' fencin' in his spare time, don't he?'

'I'm not sayin' nothin' more,' declared Lew Creech loudly. 'I've said too much already. This is the first time in me life that I've ever squealed, an' it'll be the last.'

'What brought you ter see Slythe tonight?' said Mr. Budd gently. 'Only ter warn 'im that somebody was after the Seal?'

'Ain't that reason enough?' retorted the little man. 'I know these people 'ud stick at nothin' ter get it, an' I thought 'e ought ter be warned — '

'Very right an' proper of yer, too,' interrupted Mr. Budd. 'An' I s'pose you thought that he might be so grateful fer your trouble that 'e'd drop, eh?'

'Well,' began Mr. Creech, 'times is 'ard — '

'An' you'd just come out o' 'bird.' The big man nodded sympathetically. 'Did you see anybody else in the garden while you was hangin' about?'

'I didn't get a chance,' said Lew. 'I'd only just arrived when I 'eard them shots — ' He broke off and stubbed out the end of his cigarette in a tray on the table near him. 'Can I go now?'

Mr. Budd shook his head sadly.

'No, Lew,' he replied. 'I'm afraid you can't.'

'Why? Whatcher mean?' cried the little

crook in sudden alarm. "'Ave you bin stringin' me?'

'No,' answered the fat detective. 'But I'm detainin' you — until after I've had a word with Mr. Isaac Guldheimer.'

6

Mr. Guldheimer Receives a Shock

Some men are born fat, some acquire fatness, and some have fatness thrust upon them. In which category Mr. Isaac Guldheimer should be placed, it is impossible to state, since there is no existent record of his birth available.

His fatness, however, was indisputable. His waistline was a vague memory, and there was no visible boundary to show where his neck left off and his chin began. With this abnormal supply of blubbery tissue went a smooth sleekness that began at the top of his glistening bald head and ended, so far as could be seen, at the tips of his plump, well-manicured fingers.

Seated behind the kindly screen of his massive desk, he was a not altogether unimpressive figure, but this illusion was instantly dispelled when he stood up, for nature had been very unkind to Mr.

Guldheimer in that she had supplied him with a pair of totally inadequate legs for the size of his body, and the effect was to give him a curiously top-heavy appearance.

Mr. Guldheimer was very sensitive about this, and took the greatest possible care to remain seated as often as he conveniently could.

Unfortunately for his not inconsiderable vanity, there was no kindly desk behind which he could hide the shortcomings of nature in this bare, vault-like chamber in which he stood, but the heavy overcoat which he was wearing did much to conceal the discrepancy of his limbs from vulgar gaze.

Not that there was anyone to see, for Mr. Guldheimer was quite alone. He paced up and down the concrete floor, pausing every now and again to glance at his watch in the light from the single dirt-encrusted bulb that dimly illumined the place. It was not a very pleasant place for anyone to choose to be at that hour of the night — for it was nearing twelve — but Mr. Guldheimer had business to attend to, and was, therefore, prepared to suffer any inconvenience in so sacred a cause.

This cellar-like room was part of a warehouse that belonged to him, and which he often used when the business to be transacted was better for being done in secret and under cover of darkness.

The business which had brought him here tonight, however, was different from that of any previous occasion. For Mr. Guldheimer was very different from what he outwardly appeared in more ways than one. Those people who knew him intimately and were under the impression that he was a Jew would have been both surprised and shocked if they had known that there was not a drop of Jewish blood in his veins and that his name, like everything else about him, was a fake.

Nobody knew this, however, except a small group in the Third Reich who were directly responsible for his arrival in England some five years previously and whose scheme it had been to install him in the position he now held to act as a secret agent for the Nazi Government.

Mr. Guldheimer had been provided with a name, money and a nationality, and in this last lay genius, for who would suspect a Jew of being a secret agent for the Nazis?

He was acting on instructions when he had concerned himself with the Seal of Solomon. That emblem of power in the hands of a man nominated by, and under the control of, the Nazi Government meant an incalculable advantage to them. It meant almost complete control of the finances of more than half the world.

From the time that Professor Penruddock Slythe had left England on his quest for Solomon's tomb to the time when he returned from his successful expedition he had been under the watchful eye of a spy in the employ of Mr Guldheimer, who had faithfully reported every detail connected with the discovery of the mummy.

Mr. Guldheimer had wisely decided that an attempt to steal it during its transit to England was unnecessary. He had made himself acquainted with Slythe's house at Staines: its occupants, the old man's habits, and everything connected with the establishment. It would be easy to take the mummy from that lonely house — as easy as robbing a bird's nest.

That Mr. Guldheimer had delegated this task to others was merely characteristic. He had all his life made a strict habit of never appearing personally in any transaction that held the slightest element of danger. He employed others for that. None of these various people whom he picked from all walks of life, however, knew him for what he really was, and he was clever enough to choose only those over whom he had some hold, so that if they attempted to double-cross him they would inevitably meet with a greater disaster than he. In this way he obtained service with safety, and the comfortable assurance that whatever happened to his servitors they would think several times before incriminating him.

Mr. Guldheimer was a great lover of his own sallow skin.

It was half-past twelve when he heard the sound of a car outside, and after a short interval, a knock on the heavy door of the room in which he waited.

Going over, he unlocked it. A thick-set man came in quickly.

'Well?' said Mr. Guldheimer, his throaty voice shaking a little in his excitement. 'Did you get it?'

The newcomer nodded.

'Yes,' he replied. 'It's outside in the car — with Brandt.'

'Bring it in, bring it in!' said Mr. Guldheimer, rubbing his plump hands together. 'You've done well, Obermann, very well. Did you have any trouble?'

'I wouldn't go through it again for a fortune,' declared Obermann, wiping his damp face on a not over-clean handkerchief. 'Not for a couple of fortunes!'

Mr. Guldheimer looked at him sharply.

'Why, what happened?' he demanded quickly.

'Let's get the thing inside, and then I'll tell you,' replied Obermann. 'It's dangerous out there in the car. If the police come nosing round we're sunk.'

'The police?' Mr. Guldheimer's flabby face went a shade lighter. 'What — '

'I'll tell you when you've got that mummy safely inside,' broke in Obermann curtly.

He turned on his heel and went out of the door. Mr. Guldheimer heard him call to his companion, and presently he reappeared accompanied by another man. They carried between them a long object roughly wrapped in brown paper, which they set down on the floor.

Mr. Guldheimer waddled over to it and gazed down with over-bright eyes.

'It's wonderful!' he breathed thickly. 'Wonderful. The mummy of Solomon.'

'You wouldn't have thought it was wonderful if you'd been there,' grunted Obermann. 'I'll never get the sight of that old man out of my mind.'

'What old man — what are you talking about?' Mr. Guldheimer swung round quickly.

'Slythe, that's what he's talking about,' put in Brandt. 'Slythe, lying there with his head bashed to pulp.'

'You — you had to kill him?' whispered Mr. Guldheimer so hoarsely that his voice was almost a croak.

'No, we didn't touch him,' snapped Obermann. 'He was like that when we got there.'

'Do you mean that he had been murdered?' said Mr. Guldheimer, still in the same husky whisper.

'Well, he couldn't have done it himself, and he was certainly dead,' replied Brandt roughly. 'Somebody must have outed him just before we arrived.'

'Tell me all about it,' said Mr. Guldheimer, thrusting a fat hand into his breastpocket and withdrawing a gold-mounted cigar-case.

'There isn't much to tell,' grunted Obermann. 'We got to the house round about nine, and leaving the car parked in a field nearby, we went to have a look round. We'd no intention of starting anything until later, after everybody had gone to bed, but we thought we'd 'feel' the place. We found a window open, one of those French windows, and looking through a small slit in the curtains we saw that it was the room we were after — the study. The lights were on and it looked to be empty. There were a lot of packing cases near the window, and among them the one containing the mummy. That had been opened, and we could see the thing lying in it. It seemed to be too good an opportunity to miss — the room was empty, and there was the thing we'd come for waiting to be taken.' He paused to clear his throat, and Brandt took up the story.

'We nipped in,' he said, 'and then we found that the room wasn't empty. Near the packing-cases lay Slythe. He was dead as mutton, with his head just a mess, and the blood soaking into the shavings that had come from the case — ' He shivered. 'It was one of the worst sights I've ever seen.'

Mr. Guldheimer produced a gold lighter, flicked it into flame, and lit his cigar.

'Who could have killed him?' he muttered.

'Does it matter?' snarled Obermann. 'I know who everyone'll think killed him, and that's the person who pinched the mummy.'

Mr. Guldheimer took the cigar from

between his lips with a hand that was not quite steady.

'Did anybody see you?' he asked anxiously.

'Not as far as we know,' answered Brandt. 'We nearly left the mummy where it was, but it seemed a pity to go empty-handed — '

'You did right, quite right,' said his employer, nodding approvingly. 'After all, there is no reason why either of you should be suspected. You were not seen — you didn't kill the old man. Perhaps the police will find the real killer, and then it will be a blessing in disguise. He will get the blame for stealing the mummy and no one will be any the wiser.'

He turned and contemplated the mummy in its brown paper covering. He had succeeded. The Third Reich would be pleased with him.

'Had he started unwrapping it?' he inquired. Obermann shook his head.

'As far as I could tell, it hadn't been touched,' he replied. 'It looked as though he'd been struck down just after he'd opened the case and removed the shavings.'

'Give us the money you promised us and we'll go,' said Brandt sullenly. 'I've had enough for one night, and I want a drink.'

Mr. Guldheimer took a bulky wallet from his pocket, withdrew a thick wad of notes and held them out.

'There you are,' he said. 'Split those between you. There's a thousand quid there.'

Obermann looked at the packet of notes in Brandt's hand greedily, and then transferred his gaze to the fat face of Mr. Guldheimer.

'It's a queer idea — paying a thousand quid for a mummy,' he said curiously. 'What's at the back of it?'

'That's my business!' snapped Mr. Guldheimer harshly. 'You did a job and you've been paid for it — that's all that need concern you.'

'I was only curious,' said Obermann.

'Well, don't be!' retorted his employer curtly. 'Curiosity doesn't pay with me. Here,' he added suspiciously as a thought struck him, 'if it was nine when you took the mummy, how is it that you've been such a hell of a time getting here?'

'We had a breakdown in the black-out,' grunted Brandt. 'Come on, Obermann, let's go.'

Mr. Guldheimer made no effort to detain them. They had served their purpose and he was only too anxious to get rid of them. Neither of them knew for which purpose he wanted the mummy or that he was other than he seemed.

When they had gone he threw away his half-smoked cigar, removed the heavy coat he wore, and laying it across a pile of boxes, took off his jacket and rolled up his shirtsleeves. The moment of success was at hand. The scheme which had originated in the distorted brain of the leader of the Third Reich had been carried out. Here, actually in his possession, was the mummy of Solomon, and on that mummy's right hand should be the ancient talisman that would unlock the coffers of the Jewish people and pour their gold into the laps of the Nazis.

And then, quite suddenly, in the midst

of his triumph, Mr. Guldheimer became seized with a great fear. Some thing, he knew not what, seemed to be filling that gloomy place with a tangible presence.

A voice, toneless, soulless, boomed through his brain in thunderous denunciation:

'Hermann Guiding, one of a race who has shamelessly and brutally ill-treated and persecuted my people, who has countenanced such horrors as only a degenerate mind could conceive, dare you carry out the infamy which you contemplate?'

The sweat rolled down Hermann Guiding's, alias Mr. Guldheimer's, fat and flabby face, and his spindle-legs began to shake. That voice, rolling back through the centuries of time, seemed so real that he could almost imagine someone had actually spoken.

He licked his thick lips and glanced fearfully round him. The shadows in the corners hung thickly like veils; there was a stillness that brought an unpleasant smile to his mind. And in the silence came a feeling that he was no longer alone. Some other presence had crept stealthily into the warehouse-room.

Mr. Guldheimer gulped and turned quickly towards the door which he had forgotten to lock.

A man was standing just within, silently watching him!

7

Mr. Budd is Not Satisfied

Mr. Budd sat in the small smoke-room off the hall at Pyramid House with Leek and Selkerk, eating sandwiches and drinking the steaming coffee which a yawning and sleepy-eyed servant had just brought in.

The fingerprint men and the photographers had gone, and the protesting Mr. Creech had been escorted to the local police station in the charge of a stolid constable, with strict orders from the divisional-inspector that he was to be detained there until such time as Mr. Budd should order his release.

'This is a very queer business,' remarked the stout superintendent, putting down his empty cup and wiping his lips with a large, gaily-coloured handkerchief.

'It don't seem so queer now,' said Leek.

'So far as I can see, it's just a question o' whether it was this feller Guldheimer, or the other chap, Solomon What's-'is-name, who killed the old man an' pinched that mummy.'

'Is it?' grunted Mr. Budd, pursing his lips and pinching a fold of his chin between a finger and thumb. 'I'm not so sure o' that. There's somethin' I don't understand, an' that somethin' ain't explained by either o' those fellers killin' the old chap.'

'Who is this Solomon, anyway?' asked Selkerk, frowning. 'And why did the person who sent those dictaphone cylinders have to choose that way to tell his story? It'd have been far easier to write it, surely?'

'It depends on the circumstances,' answered the big man, lying back in his chair and staring at the ceiling. 'Maybe there was some reason why he couldn't write it. The thing that puzzles me is why that story was sent ter Slythe at all.'

'As a warnin',' said Leek. 'You said — that's what it started with — '

'I know,' interrupted Budd, a little

impatiently. 'I know that's what it was s'posed ter be, but if you was goin' ter warn a man who you thought was in danger, would you go ter all that trouble? Of course you wouldn't,' he went on, before either Selkerk or the sergeant had time to reply. 'You'd send a letter or a wire, or you'd telephone, an' you'd just say somethin' like: 'So-an'-so's plannin' ter steal your mummy. Look out.' That's what you'd do, or rather, that's what any sensible person 'ud do. Unless, of course — '

He paused suddenly, and Selkerk shot him a quick glance.

'Unless what?' he asked.

'Unless,' said Mr. Budd slowly, 'there was some reason why you couldn't choose any other way.'

'What reason could there be?' demanded the divisional-inspector.

'Well, not very many, I'll admit,' answered the stout superintendent, 'but here's one. S'posin' this feller wasn't in a position to send his warnin' in any other way. S'posin' 'e couldn't write, or wire, or telephone, because all these thin's was out of his reach — '

'No man could be in such a position,' declared Selkerk.

'Oh, yes, he could,' corrected Mr. Budd. ''E could be ill an' unable ter use 'is hands. That'd stop 'im bein' able ter write, wouldn't it?'

'It wouldn't stop 'im gettin' somebody else ter do it for 'im,' broke in Leek.

'It would if 'e didn't want anybody else ter know what 'e was doin',' retorted his superior. 'But 'e could dictate the stuff into a dictaphone without anyone bein' the wiser. Somethin' of the sort must be the reason fer adoptin' that method, unless he's just eccentric. The thing I can't understand is why 'e 'ad to make such a song about it. There was no need for all that long rigmarole. He could 'ave said all 'e wanted ter say on one cylinder.'

'Maybe 'e is eccentric,' suggested the sergeant.

'The most important thing to my mind,' said Selkerk, 'is who was the person who sent those cylinders, and who is the 'Solomon' he referred to?'

'That's important, certainly,' agreed

Mr. Budd, 'but it ain't the most important thin' by a long way.'

'What would you call the most important thing, then?' asked the divisional-inspector, rather coldly.

'The most important thin',' replied the big man slowly, is — '

He broke off as the door opened and Challis came in.

'Is there anything more you'd like?' asked the secretary. 'More coffee or sandwiches?'

'Not fer me,' said Mr. Budd, shaking his head, and the others shook theirs, too. 'We'll be goin' in a minute or two.'

'I can't say I shall be sorry,' remarked Challis, with a tired smile. 'There's not much more of the night, but I'd like to get a little sleep.'

'I expect you would,' said the stout man sympathetically. 'You've 'ad rather a tirin' day, ain't you. I meant to ask you before — where did you go this afternoon?'

Challis seemed rather surprised at the question, but he answered without hesitation.

'I went to the pictures,' he said.

'With Miss Bennett?' queried Mr. Budd, getting ponderously to his feet and brushing the ash and crumbs off his capacious waistcoat.

The secretary shook his head.

'No,' he answered. 'What made you think that? Oh, I see — because we came back together? That was quite an accident. I met her at the station.'

'You'd been to London?' asked the fat man, and when Challis again replied with a nod: 'Where had Miss Bennett been — to London, too?'

'Yes, I think so,' said Challis rather brusquely. 'What is the idea of all these questions?'

'Nothin', nothin' at all,' broke in Mr. Budd hastily, and a trifle apologetically. 'More or less a matter o' routine, Mr. Challis, that's all — more or less a matter o' routine.'

He yawned and stretched himself, pulled a cigar out of his pocket and looked at it thoughtfully.

'Well, I think we might as well be goin',' he remarked. 'There don't seem anythin' more ter be done here tonight.' He put the cigar to his nose and sniffed at it. 'You smoke cigars, Mr. Challis?'

'Very seldom,' replied the secretary with a smile. 'I prefer cigarettes or a pipe.'

'It's a matter o' taste, I s'pose,' said the big man conversationally. 'I've never bin able ter get on with either.' He sighed. 'I often wish I could get the 'abit, or take ter chewin' gum or suckin' acid-drops. It'ud be cheaper. Well, we won't keep yer up any longer. Come on, Leek.'

He ambled out into the hall, turned slowly and eyed the door of the study thoughtfully.

'Jest somethin' I've forgotten,' he murmured. 'I won't be a minute.'

He stepped across, opened the door, and disappeared from view. He was gone for less than a minute, and when he came back he was smiling gently.

'Good night, Mr. Challis,' he said. 'You comin' along, Inspector?'

Selkerk nodded, and the three of them passed out into darkness.

'What did you go into the study for?' asked Selkerk curiously, when the front door had closed behind them.

'I just thought o' somethin', an' I went ter see if I was right,' replied Mr. Budd absently.

'And were you?' said the divisional-inspector.

'Yes,' answered the stout man. 'Yes, I was right.' He stopped by the side of the police-car which had brought them from London. 'There's two ways o' bein' successful in any undertakin',' he remarked suddenly and surprisingly. 'One way is ter make circumstances suit yer plans, the other way is ter suit yer plans ter circumstances.'

'Meaning — what?' asked Selkerk, raising his eyebrows in astonishment.

'Meanin' just that,' retorted the big man. 'I'll be down some time durin' tomorrow. We oughter be able to clear the whole thin' up then.'

'What's that?' demanded the divisional-inspector, in blank amazement. 'Clear it up — tomorrow?'

'That's what I said,' replied Mr. Budd calmly. 'Clear it up nice an' tidy like.'

'Do you mean — you know — ' began

the bewildered Selkerk.

'Nearly everythin',' interrupted the fat detective complacently. 'If you want ter hide a pebble, there's no better place than droppin' it on the beach!'

This final and completely cryptic remark reduced Selkerk to speechlessness, and by the time he had recovered, Mr. Budd had climbed into the car and it was moving off.

'Why did you tell 'im ter go ter Golders Green?' asked Leek lugubriously, as his superior sank, chuckling throatily, into a corner. 'Ain't we goin' ter get any rest ternight?'

'We're goin' ter Golders Green because Guldheimer lives there,' answered Mr. Budd, who had given that direction to the driver. 'An' as for rest, they say a change is as good as a rest, so you oughtn't ter worry.'

The allusion was too subtle for the weary Leek, although he tried hard to think what his superior had been driving at throughout the rest of the journey.

8

The Man Called Solomon

The sight of that silent figure standing motionless in the shadows brought a husky scream from Mr. Guldheimer's throat. For an instant he was filled with a superstitious fear, and then he saw that the visitant was at least of flesh and blood, and his fear died.

'Who are you? What do you want?' he demanded hoarsely.

The man by the door came forward into the light. He was tall and slender, but with a slenderness that gave the impression of great physical strength. Under the fur-lined coat, which was open, the staring Guldheimer caught a glimpse of evening dress, but the notable feature of the newcomer was his face. The opera hat which he wore enhanced rather than concealed the almost inhuman beauty of the man. The features were clean-cut and

228

flawless, the eyes large and queerly luminous; the head perfectly shaped, and carried on the slim shoulders with an arrogance that was regal.

'You!' muttered Mr. Guldheimer, staring foolishly. 'You!'

'I must apologise for this, I cannot say unwarranted, intrusion, Guldheimer,' said the newcomer in a quiet, melodious voice that held just the trace of an elusive accent. 'I'm afraid my appearance startled you.'

Mr. Guldheimer licked his lips, and swallowed to try to remove the dryness of his throat.

'Why have you come here?' he asked in a whisper. 'What do you want?'

'Do you need to ask that?' inquired the other. 'I am here to prevent you carrying out a certain action for which your life has rendered you unfitted.'

'What has it do with you?' muttered Mr. Guldheimer. 'By what right do you interfere?'

'Knowing who I am, you surely do not require an answer to that question,' replied the tall man. 'You were about to commit an act for which there could have been only one punishment. My presence here has saved your life, Guldheimer.'

The flabby face of the man before him paled. He opened his lips to say something, but no sound came forth.

'You seek the Seal for an unworthy purpose,' went on the tall man in his low, musical voice. 'You seek it to prey upon your own race — for lust of power and personal gain. I have been aware of your ambition for a long time. I tell you, quite candidly, that if you had attained that ambition, if you had found the Seal, your life would not have been worth — that!'

He snapped his immaculately gloved fingers.

'You mean — you mean that you — ' Mr. Guldheimer's husky voice trailed to a quavering silence.

'I should have been compelled to have taken steps,' said the other quietly. 'However, I am in time. No harm has been done, and therefore we need not continue the discussion of an unpleasant possibility.'

He pursed his lips and uttered a low,

peculiar whistle. Instantly, in obedience to the signal, two men came in and stood differentially waiting.

'Take that to the car,' ordered the tall man, extending a hand and pointing to the recumbent mummy. 'Handle it reverently, for it contains the remains of a great and wise man.'

In silence the two men stepped forward, stooped and with infinite care picked up the mummy between them and began to carry it towards the door. Mr. Guldheimer saw the collapse of his cherished plans, and recovered something of his courage.

'Stop!' he snarled, and his hand flew to his pocket. 'You have no more right to that than I have — '

'I should advise you not to be foolhardy, Guldheimer,' broke in the other, and the musical voice suddenly developed a steely ring. 'Keep still, and don't try to draw that weapon you are searching for!'

Mr. Guldheimer stopped still, so suddenly that he might have been turned to stone. In the gloved hand of the tall man had appeared, as though by magic, a small and deadly-looking automatic pistol which covered him unwaveringly. The two men carrying the mummy had not even paused on their way to the door at this outburst.

'You say,' went on the man with the pistol in his normally soft voice, 'that I have no more right to the mummy of King Solomon than you. In some respects you are right — in others, wrong. I have the right of belief that I am he who has been destined to carry on that line of kings. I have the right because I am not actuated by love of power or desire for personal gain, but by a genuine wish to restore the lost glories of a great and noble people — a people whose forefathers saw the building of the Great Pyramid — a people who were civilised when most of the world was inhabited by savages — a people who were great, and can be great again. I have the right because I am a Jew whose one desire is that his race shall once more claim an honoured place in the history of the world.'

'I, also, am a Jew,' muttered Guldheimer untruthfully. He wondered if the man suspected that it was a lie. Did he know?

'You are a Jew who has forgotten the honour of his race,' was the retort, and Mr. Guldheimer was relieved. 'It is Jews like you who have brought ridicule and discredit on the name that was once respected. I have sworn that that name shall once again be restored to its ancient glory. I have already accomplished much toward that end, but only with the aid of the Seal can I hope to attain complete success. That emblem of an ancient kingship is still as powerful as it was centuries ago, and the man who wears it — the man who dares to wear it — will automatically take his place among the monarchs of the world, sovereign over eight million subjects.'

'It's all very well to talk this highfalutin nonsense,' sneered Mr. Guldheimer, regaining his command over himself, 'but what it all boils down to is that you want the Seal for the same reason that I wanted it — because it confers unlimited power.'

'Granted,' replied the tall man, without hesitation. 'The difference lies in the use to which that power would be put. You would have used it to further your own ends, and to have brought further disgrace upon my unhappy race. I know something about you, Guldheimer. You built up your present business on theft and swindling. Can you truthfully say that during the whole of your life there is to be found one completely honest action?'

'And how did you attain your present position?' snapped Mr. Guldheimer, who had no intention of truthfully saying anything. 'The third richest man in the world! Did you acquire that wealth entirely by honest dealing?'

'I acquired it by application and hard work,' was the curt reply.

'Yet you are not above stealing the mummy for the sake of the Seal,' said Mr. Guldheimer.

'That can scarcely be regarded as stealing,' answered the other quietly. 'The mummy of King Solomon belongs to my race by right. If anybody can be said to have stolen it, it was Professor Penruddock Slythe.'

'And does your argument justify murder, too?' said Guldheimer sarcastically. 'Slythe was killed tonight — '

'I am aware of that,' said the tall man gravely, 'but I had no hand in it. He was killed before my emissaries arrived at Pyramid House.' He drew a thin platinum watch from his pocket and glanced at it. 'I'm afraid I must go,' he said. 'Forget this interview tonight, and forget, also, that you had a certain ambition.' With a swift, though apparently unhurried movement, he reached the door and turned.

'It would be as well, too, if you changed your habits, Guldheimer,' he said quietly. 'Remember that there is someone to whom, in future, you will be answerable. Tonight is historic. A new Solomon has arisen to rule over the Jews.'

The next moment he was gone.

For some time Mr. Guldheimer stood staring at the closed door, and then he turned and began to pace up and down the cellar-like room. His plans, which had been so near to fruition, had crumbled in ruins about his ears at the very moment of their realisation. It was very galling. The only thing to be thankful for was that his secret was still unsuspected. Even the man who had just gone thought him to be a Jew. That was a relief, and a big relief. The man was dangerous, though.

Those words of his had been quietly spoken, but they had contained a warning that it would be well to heed. Mr. Guldheimer's small eyes glittered angrily. If he could only discover some way of getting back on the man who had robbed him of his triumph — some safe way —

He drove back to his house in Golders Green with his mind completely occupied with schemes that were discarded as soon as they were born. It would be next to impossible to fight a man wielding the power of a king.

He went to bed and fell into a troubled sleep, to be awakened almost immediately, so it seemed, by his butler. Sitting up and blinking resentfully at the man, he demanded to know what the devil he meant by disturbing him?

'The police are downstairs, sir,' answered

the butler, who was only partially dressed, 'and wish to see you.'

'The police!' Mr. Guldheimer was suddenly very wide awake. 'What do they want?'

'I don't know, sir,' replied the butler, marking his master's evident agitation with inward satisfaction — all the servants hated Mr. Guldheimer. 'They merely desire to see you immediately.'

'All right,' growled Mr. Guldheimer, throwing back the bedclothes. 'Go and tell 'em I'll come down.'

The servant withdrew, and Mr. Guldheimer got out of bed. What was wrong, he thought as he thrust his feet into his slippers and pulled on a heavy silk dressing-gown. Had the police connected him with the theft of the mummy from Slythe's house? Or had they discovered something that would be even worse?

His heart was beating at more than its usual speed as he made his way down the stairs. In the big hall stood two men. One was a mountain of a man, with a heavy, bovine face, and sleepy-looking eyes, the other, thin and weedy, with a long face that was the picture of gloom.

'You wish to see me?' inquired Mr. Guldheimer as calmly as he could, and the big man nodded.

'Surely this is rather an extraordinary time to come?' snapped Mr. Guldheimer irritably. 'Couldn't you have left it until later?'

'I'm afraid the matter's urgent,' answered Mr. Budd. 'Is there somewhere where we can go an' talk?'

'Come in here.' Guldheimer led the way into the dining-room. 'Now, then, what is it?' he demanded, closing the door.

'Durin' yesterday evenin',' said Mr. Budd, 'a certain object was stolen from Professor Penruddock Slythe's house at Staines. I'm given to understand that you may be in a position to supply some information.'

So that was what they'd come about, thought Mr. Guldheimer with a sudden coldness at his heart. Was that all? He achieved a passable expression of astonished surprise.

'What should I know about it?' he asked.

'I'm askin' you that,' said the fat detective.

'Well, I know nothing about it,' declared Mr. Guldheimer indignantly. 'This is outrageous — '

'Don't get all hot an' bothered,' broke in Mr. Budd calmly, suppressing a yawn. 'The information I've got is that yer know quite a lot about it. Were you in Staines yesterday evenin'?'

'Certainly not!' snapped Mr. Guldheimer. 'You'll get into serious trouble for this, my man, I can assure you — '

'I'll take the risk,' interrupted the stout superintendent wearily. 'If you weren't in Staines, where was you?'

'I refuse to answer any question at all!' snarled Guldheimer furiously. 'I'll have your coat off your back for this.'

'Not only was somethin' stolen,' said Mr. Budd, completely ignoring the threat, 'but a man was killed as well. Professor Slythe was murdered — '

'Are you accusing me of that, too?' cried the angry Guldheimer. 'Do you think I smashed his head in — '

He stopped abruptly, realising, as he

saw the heavy face of the man before him change, what he had said.

'That's very interestin',' murmured Mr. Budd. 'Very interestin' an' perculiar. Who said anythin' about his head 'avin' been smashed in?'

'I — I don't know. I suppose I must have guessed that — that — ' Mr. Guldheimer's voice faded into incoherence.

'You're a remarkably good guesser,' said the fat man. 'Now then, Guldheimer — ' His voice changed from its slow, ponderous drawl and became sharp and incisive. ' — what do yer know about this business?'

Mr. Guldheimer tried to put up a further bluff, but his nerve had deserted him. Under Mr. Budd's inexorable questions he finally broke down and made a clean breast of his share in the happenings at Pyramid House.

'So this man who's got the mummy now is Solomon Armeid, eh?' remarked the stout superintendent. 'H'm, that's the well-known banker, ain't it? H'm, get yer clothes on.'

'What for?' mumbled the thoroughly scared Guldheimer.

'I'm arrestin' yer, that's what for,' snapped Mr. Budd. 'I'm chargin' you with the theft o' this mummy, at the moment. When we've executed a search warrant an' searched that warehouse o' yours, an' this house, there'll prob'ly be other charges! Now get a move on, I'm in a hurry.'

Mr. Guldheimer, his flabby face the colour of a November sky, stumbled to the door, accompanied by the lugubrious Leek. Other charges? There certainly would! There was enough evidence in that house to send him to the Tower! What had Solomon said in the warehouse room earlier that night? Something about it being historic. It was — for him!

9

News from Pyramid House

With the unhappy Mr. Guldheimer safely locked up in a cell, the superintendent decided that a few minutes could be spared for breakfast before proceeding with the rest of his programme.

Accordingly he piloted the willing Leek to a nearby tea shop and ordered large quantities of eggs and bacon.

'You came pretty near ter breakin' the regulations over that feller,' remarked the lean sergeant, while they waited for a sleepy waitress to bring the order. Mr. Budd slumped back in his chair and yawned. 'Near ter breakin' 'em!' he echoed. 'I smashed 'em ter little bits! If Guldheimer 'ad bin innocent, there'd 'ave bin some kicks flyin' about, I can tell yer. But he wasn't,' he added complacently.

'D'yer think 'e was tellin' the truth?' asked the sergeant. 'About knowin' nothin' about the murder, I mean.'

'Yes,' answered Mr. Budd. 'I'm willin' ter bet that 'e spilled all 'e knew about that. A nasty bit o' work, that feller! I should think by the time all the charges 'ave bin proved against 'im he'd go down for about ten years.'

He underestimated Mr. Guldheimer's eventual sentence, but then he had no idea of the principal charge against him.

'Well, if 'e didn't kill the old man, who did?' asked Leek, frowning. 'This Solomon What's-'is-name?'

'I've got me own idea about that murder,' murmured the big man thoughtfully. 'It's the queerest part o' the whole queer business, an' nobody seems ter have noticed the really queer thin' about it.' He caressed his fat chin lovingly.

'Was that what you meant when you was talkin' about 'pebbles an' beaches' ter Selkerk?' asked the sergeant curiously.

'No, that 'adn't anythin' ter do with the queer part,' said Mr. Budd slowly. 'Jest you think it over while you eats yer breakfast. There's something that sticks out a mile. I wonder what made that feller

Khynan Hani scoot like 'e did?'

'You don't think 'e killed the old chap, do yer?' asked Leek.

'I don't think anybody killed 'im,' replied the fat man, and the sergeant stared at him in blank astonishment.

'But it couldn't 'ave bin suicide!' he protested. 'He couldn't 'ave hit himself on the 'ead.'

'I never suggested it was suicide,' snapped Mr. Budd. 'Here comes our food, an' I'm just about ready for it. There's nothin' like bein' up all night ter give you an appetite for yer breakfast.'

He set to work with gusto on the plate of eggs and bacon which the waitress set before him, refusing point blank to answer any questions or to discuss the case any further for the moment.

When he had finished he pushed aside his plate, lit a cigar and poured himself out another cup of tea.

'We'll give ourselves another twenty minutes an' then we'll get along,' he said, looking at his watch.

'Where are we goin'?' inquired Leek

over his cup. 'To see this Solomon feller?'

The big man shook his head.

'Not yet,' he replied. 'We're goin' ter the Yard first. There's one or two inquiries I want ter make.'

Leek looked surprised.

'I can't understand what yer gettin' at,' he said, shaking his narrow head. 'Ain't you afraid that this feller 'ull get away?'

'Not a bit,' retorted Mr. Budd. 'If he tried ter get away, 'e wouldn't get very far. Solomon Armeid is as well-known as the King. It's queer, when yer come to think of it, that a feller like that should have got 'imself mixed up in a nasty business like this.'

'Was 'e the feller what was mentioned in them records?' asked the sergeant, and the fat man nodded.

'Yes, that was him,' he said.

Leek gulped the remainder of his tea noisily.

'I wonder who sent them things?' he muttered.

'I know who sent 'em,' said Mr. Budd surprisingly. 'An' I know why they was sent. I know nearly everythin' except — '

'Except what?' asked the sergeant, as he stopped.

'You're as full o' questions as a politician!' snapped the big man. 'Try thinkin' yourself, for a change. An' what a change it 'ud be!' he added.

It was half-past nine when they reached Scotland Yard, and the first thing they learned was that Selkerk had been on the telephone and wanted Mr. Budd to ring him as soon as he came in.

'What's up now, I wonder?' muttered the stout superintendent, picking up the receiver of his telephone. 'Put me through to the police station at Staines, will yer?'

But Selkerk wasn't there. The desk-sergeant who answered said that he was to be found at Pyramid House.

There was a vague look of trouble on Mr. Budd's heavy face as he searched for the number of Slythe's residence.

'What can've happened?' he muttered uneasily, while he waited for the connection. 'Hallo! Is that Staines 67891? Sup'ntendent Budd of New Scotland Yard speakin'. I want Divisional-Inspector — Oh, is that you, Selkerk? What's the trouble — What!' The listening Leek heard a note of sheer horror in his voice, and was startled. 'I'll come along now. Yes, at once.'

Mr. Budd rang off, and his heavy face was white and set.

'That girl's disappeared!' he said harshly. 'I was a fool! I ought to have foreseen that somethin' like that might 'appen!'

'Good lor'!' gasped the sergeant. 'You don't mean that she — '

'Don't you start askin' questions!' snarled his superior, dropping heavily into the chair behind his desk and scribbling rapidly on a pad of paper. He tore off the sheet, read through what he had written, and thrust it into an envelope.

'Take that along to Inspector Chapman,' he ordered. 'Tell 'im to wire me the result to Pyramid House. Get a move on an' meet me down below.'

The bewildered Leek hurried away, and Mr. Budd went ponderously down to the courtyard.

When the sergeant joined him he was already ensconced in the back of a police

247

car, puffing jerkily at one of his eternal black cigars, and frowning.

The sergeant got in beside him and the car sped away.

They were halfway to their destination before the big man opened his mouth.

'I don't like it,' he muttered uneasily. 'I don't like it at all. I oughtn't to've 'eld me 'and. But what could I do? I wasn't ready.'

The curious Leek ventured a question.

'What d'yer mean by the girl disappearing?' he said 'Do yer mean she's run away?'

Mr. Budd nodded several times.

'That's what it looks like,' he said. 'Bed not slept in, small suitcase gone — no girl. Yes, that's what it looks like.'

'But why should she run away?' asked the sergeant, wrinkling his forehead.

'Ah, why should she?' murmured Mr. Budd, passing a huge hand wearily over his face. 'That's the question, why should she? We've got ter find an answer to that, an' we've got ter find it quick.'

Leek watched him in astonishment. Never before had he seen the stout superintendent so perturbed and worried. There must be something very seriously troubling him to have jerked him out of his habitual lethargic calm.

For the rest of the journey Mr. Budd kept twisting and turning restlessly in his corner, drumming with his fingers on his broad knee, or pulling irritably at his large nose.

At last, as the car swung into the drive of Pyramid House, he gave a grunt of satisfaction.

Selkerk met them in the hall, and with him was the anxious-faced Challis.

'This is an unexpected development,' greeted the divisional-inspector. 'I'm glad you've come — '

'Tell me exactly what happened,' cut in Mr. Budd curtly. 'When was it discovered that Miss Bennett had gone?'

'This morning,' answered the secretary, 'when the maid took her tea. June's room was empty, and the bed hadn't been disturbed. We searched the house and the grounds, but there was no sign of her anywhere. Then we discovered that a suitcase had gone from her room and several things from her dressing-table — '

'Who saw her last?' interrupted the big man.

'I did,' said Challis. 'It was just after you'd all gone. I saw her for a second — to say goodnight.'

'Where?' said Mr. Budd.

'In the passage — outside her room.'

'Has any inquiry been made at the railway station?' The fat detective turned to Selkerk, and he nodded.

'Yes,' he answered. 'I've sent a man down there.'

Mr. Budd fingered his chin.

'Take me up to her room,' he said after a pause.

In silence Challis led the way up the stairs. On the landing he turned into a corridor and stopped at the door of a room near the end.

'That's the room,' he said in a husky voice. 'I hope that you can find out what's happened to her. I'm worried to death!'

'Why?' Mr. Budd paused with his hand on the door knob and looked at him.

'Well, it seems so queer that she should go off like this — without a word to anybody,' answered the secretary, looking rather surprised at the sudden question. 'Why did she go? Where can she have gone?'

Mr. Budd gave a little grunt and entered the large, airy bedroom. It was plainly furnished and very neat. The bed was as smooth as when it had been made, but the fat man took the precaution of turning down the sheet and peering underneath. The bed had obviously not been slept in. It was as smooth inside as outside.

He gave a quick glance round and then made a rapid search of the entire room.

'There's nothin' 'ere to tell us anythin',' he muttered when he had finished, and rubbed his chin. 'She said nothin' ter make you think that she might be leavin'?'

Challis shook his head, his face white and troubled.

'Nothing!' he declared.

'Well, it's certainly very queer,' remarked Mr. Budd, and at that moment the telephone-bell shrilled out from below. Challis ran down to answer it, and after a moment called up to Selkerk.

'Will you come down?' he said. 'It's your man on the line. Perhaps he has news.'

Selkerk hurried to join him, and to Leek's surprise, as soon as they were alone, Mr. Budd caught him by the arm.

'Go down an' find the 'ousekeeper,' he whispered quickly. 'Ask her who was up first this mornin'. If it was the maid, ask 'er if everythin' was locked up, or whether there was a winder or anythin' open.'

'She'd 'ave gone by the door, wouldn't she?' began the sergeant, and Mr. Budd interrupted him impatiently.

'I'm not thinkin' about anybody goin' out,' he snapped. 'Do as I tell yer, will yer?'

Leek obeyed, and when Selkerk and the secretary came back Mr. Budd was standing by the window, gloomily looking out.

'There's been no sign of Miss Bennett at the station,' said the divisional-inspector. 'They know her quite well there, but they've seen nothing of her today.'

'I don't see how they can be so sure,'

put in Challis. 'There's usually a pretty fair crowd early. She might have slipped through without being recognised.'

'One woman looks much the same as another these days,' grunted Mr. Budd. 'I didn't expect you'd get anythin' from the station. If she wanted to avoid bein' seen she'd go by bus, or somethin'.'

'Why should she want to avoid being seen?' demanded the secretary angrily. 'June isn't a criminal — '

'You can't say why she wanted to avoid bein' seen,' interrupted the big man, 'until yer know why she disappeared so suddenly.'

He turned away from the window and lumbered heavily over to the door.

'We may as well go down,' he began, and at that moment a loud knocking rang through the silent house.

'Who can that be?' muttered Challis, wrinkling his forehead. Footsteps sounded in the hall beneath, and the front door was opened. There was a murmur of voices, and as they reached the head of the stair they met Mrs. Borridge. The housekeeper carried a card in her hand.

'Will you see this gentleman, sir?' she said, and handed the card to Challis. He looked at it, frowning, and Mr. Budd saw his face change. Peering over the secretary's shoulder, the fat man read the inscription: 'Solomon Armeid.'

10

The Sarcophagus

'Solomon Armeid, eh?' murmured Mr. Budd softly. 'I'm rather anxious to see that feller.'

'What's he want?' muttered Challis, twisting the card in his fingers.

'Maybe he'll tell yer if yer see him!' suggested the big man. 'Let's go down.'

The tall man standing in the hall, hat in hand, turned as they reached the foot of the staircase, and something in his bearing struck a familiar chord in Mr. Budd's memory.

'The last time *I* met you you called yerself Khynan Hani,' he said.

Solomon Armeid bowed courteously, and there was the ghost of a smile on his handsome face.

'I'm afraid I must plead guilty to that slight deception, superintendent,' he replied. 'It was unpardonable but necessary. I wished to learn what had happened here without disclosing my real identity, and by dint of a slight stain applied to my face, I succeeded. I must apologise also for having talked a great deal of nonsense which, I fear, was a trifle melodramatic. But it served its purpose. Had Professor Slythe been alive it would not have been necessary.'

'You said you had an appointment with him,' said the fat detective. 'Was that true?'

'Perfectly true,' answered Solomon Armeid, and such was the power of his personality that Mr. Budd never even thought of questioning his veracity.

'Did you know Professor Slythe?' he asked, and Armeid nodded.

'I did — many years ago,' he replied. 'It is some time since we last met. We corresponded recently.'

'You knew him in Kut-el-Amara, I s'pose?' said Mr. Budd, and again Solomon Armeid nodded.

'I see,' murmured the big man. 'You came to see 'im about this Seal, I s'pose?'

Solomon Armeid inclined his head.

'That and other things,' he answered. 'I had a slight acquaintance with Professor Slythe's niece. It was partly to offer her my condolences that I am here this morning.'

'I'm afraid you won't be able to offer 'em,' grunted Mr. Budd. 'Miss Bennett isn't here — she's disappeared.'

'Disappeared!' The musical voice of the man before him was sharp with alarm. Across the dark, handsome face swept a sudden expression of grave and urgent concern. 'How — when? Tell me!'

It was Challis who told him, quickly and jerkily, speaking in rapid rushes of words interspersed with short intervals of silence.

Solomon Armeid listened attentively to the short recital, his large, luminous eyes disturbed and troubled.

'This is terrible,' he murmured, when the secretary had finished, 'terrible!'

'Why? What do you think 'as happened to her?' asked Mr. Budd sharply.

'Do you remember what I said last night?' answered Armeid in a low voice. 'About Sakhmet?'

Mr. Budd met his eyes and nodded.

'I think,' said Solomon Armeid seriously, 'that Sakhmet returned in the early hours of this morning.'

He was speaking allegorically, but the big man understood.

'I've been thinkin' the same,' he said gravely.

'Who is Sakhmet?' began Selkerk, and was interrupted by the appearance of Leek.

'Well?' asked Mr. Budd.

'The door was chained an' bolted,' said the sergeant, 'but one o' the winders in the dinin' room was open.'

'Then that's the way she went,' said Selkerk, frowning.

'Or that's the way someone came in,' muttered Mr. Budd.

Challis uttered an exclamation.

'You're not suggesting that June — that she didn't go of her own accord?' he cried in alarm. 'You don't mean that anything can have happened to her?'

'I think somethin' very serious 'as happened to her,' replied the fat detective in a worried voice.

'But why?' exclaimed Challis in bewilderment. 'Why should anybody want to harm June?'

'I don't think anybody did want to,' answered Mr. Budd slowly. 'I think it was forced on 'em. I think they had to.'

The large eyes of Solomon Armeid flashed him a look of understanding.

'You are a wise man,' he said softly.

'But — ' Challis' voice was husky and there was a growing fear in his eyes as he glanced quickly from one to the other. ' — but if she didn't go, where is she? What — '

'Yes, that's the question — where is she?' broke in Mr. Budd, his heavy face drawn with anxiety. 'You say you looked through the house when it was first discovered she was missin'. Did you search the place?'

'Heavens!' cried the secretary. 'She can't be still here. You can't mean that. We looked in every room!'

'You looked in every room,' repeated Mr. Budd.

'What were you lookin' for?'

A pallor spread over Challis' face until

it was a ghastly shade of grey.

'June,' he muttered hoarsely.

'Alive!' snapped the big man. 'Which means that you didn't really search at all! You didn't look in the cupboards an' other places where a body could be hidden.'

'No,' groaned Challis. 'We never thought — Oh, heavens, we never thought of that!'

'I thought of it,' said Mr. Budd. 'I've been thinkin' about it ever since I got 'ere.' He gave his massive shoulders a twitch. 'I 'ope I'm wrong — in a way, I'll be responsible if I'm not. Let's make sure. Maybe — there's just a chance — that we'll find nothin'.'

Long afterwards the stout superintendent remembered that nightmare search of the old house. From room to room they went, entering with a fearful expectancy, and leaving, when they found nothing, with an overwhelming sense of relief. And there was nothing — no sign at all of the girl they were searching for, dead or alive.

At last they reached the only room left

to explore — the study.

'There's not likely to be anything there,' said Selkerk, as they paused outside the door. 'I went back and locked it up after you'd gone. The key has been in my possession all the time and still is.'

'We'll 'ave a look, all the same,' grunted the stout superintendent. His fat face had relaxed a little of its gravity and strain. He was beginning to think, and hope, that perhaps after all he had been mistaken.

With a shrug of his shoulders, Selkerk took the key from his pocket, stooped and fitted it in the lock.

The big room was the same as they left it. The books lay scattered everywhere, the various objects which Professor Slythe had collected during his various expeditions were still strewn about in hopeless confusion. The only difference was that the sprawling figure of the owner no longer lay among the reddened shavings beside the open packing-case.

The divisional-inspector went over to the window and examined the hasp.

'You can save time looking here,' he said. 'The window hasn't been touched.

Nobody's been in.'

Mr. Budd glanced swiftly about the room without replying. There certainly did not seem to be any likelihood of finding anything here. There were no cupboards, and although the room was untidy, there was nothing that offered much in the way of a hiding place — except —

The big man went ponderously over to the large wooden sarcophagus that stood facing the fireplace. Solomon Armeid seemed to have had a similar idea, for Mr. Budd found himself facing him over the carved top.

'What's inside this?' he asked, looking across at Challis.

'Nothing,' answered the secretary. 'It's empty.'

Mr. Budd gripped the edge of the lid and tried to raise it, but it resisted his efforts. Neither did it move when Armeid added his strength.

'Pretty heavy, ain't it?' grunted Mr. Budd. 'Come an' lend a hand here, Leek.'

'It has been screwed down,' remarked

Solomon Armeid quietly. 'See here — and here.'

'Not such a long time ago, neither,' muttered the fat man, peering at the places where he pointed. 'The screws are new, an' you can see the bits o' wood dust.' He looked up, and his face was a shade paler than usual. 'I think we've come ter the end of our search.'

'You mean — June's in there?' muttered Challis, staring at the sarcophagus with horrified eyes.

'Yes,' snapped Mr. Budd hoarsely. 'Leek, go an' get a screwdriver from the car.'

The sergeant went at a run, and for a moment there was silence in the room. It was broken by Selkerk.

'How in the world did anyone get in here?' he said. 'I had the key — '

'More than one key will fit a lock,' grunted Mr. Budd He began to drum impatiently with his fingers on the lid of the sarcophagus, suddenly remembered what might be inside, and stopped abruptly. Another silence descended on the room, and then Leek came back with the screwdriver.

There were only two screws, and it did not take long to remove them.

'Now let's see,' murmured Mr. Budd, and once more, with the help of Armeid, attempted to shift the lid. It was heavy, but it moved.

'Slide it!' gasped the fat detective. 'It'll be easier.'

Slowly, inch by inch, the lid with its carved recumbent figure slid towards one end of the sarcophagus as they tugged. Selkerk, his breath coming in quick little jerks, peered into the dark interior as it was revealed.

'She's there!' he cried suddenly. 'She's there!'

A hoarse sound that was half a gasp, half a groan, escaped from Challis.

The lid was right off now, and they let it drop with a thud to the floor. In the deep compartment which it had covered lay the huddled body of June Bennett, and beside her a strapped suitcase. She was dressed as they had last seen her, and her ankles and wrists were tightly tied. A gag had been thrust into her mouth, and her eyes were closed. There was no sign of breathing, and her face looked curiously congested.

'Help me get 'er out,' snapped Mr. Budd. 'There's just a chance she may be alive.'

He stooped into the sarcophagus, and with the assistance of the sergeant lifted the girl out. They laid her on the floor, and Armeid tore the gag away and held his cigarette-case before her lips.

One glance and he looked quickly up.

'She's alive, but I think it's touch and go,' he said. 'Better get a doctor to her at once.'

'I'll go and phone,' cried Challis, and moved to the door.

'You won't!' snapped Mr. Budd. 'You'll stop where you are, Challis!'

'But — ' began the secretary.

'But nothing,' snarled the big man. 'I want you, Challis! You're under arrest for the murder of Professor Slythe, an' the attempted murder of this girl!'

Challis' face went livid.

'You're mad!' he cried violently. 'Stark raving mad! I — '

'Am I?' grunted the fat man. 'We'll see

what a jury 'as ter say. You get on to the doctor, Selkerk, will yer?'

'Of course you're mad!' said Challis, as the astonished Selkerk nodded and went out. 'How could I have killed Slythe when I wasn't here? There's the man who killed Slythe, if you want to know.' He pointed at Solomon Armeid who was calmly cutting through the cords which bound the girl. 'Wasn't Slythe warned against him in those dictaphone records? Wasn't — '

'You made them records yourself,' interrupted Mr. Budd calmly. 'You made 'em an' posted 'em to Slythe with the object o' turnin' suspicion away from yerself. You knew they'd be found after Slythe's death an' you thought anyone 'ud believe that 'e'd been killed because o' the Seal. Slythe didn't open 'em, but that didn't matter. He sent 'em to you to open because 'e was busy, an' that was the same thin'. The great thin' was that the police should 'ear that little story you'd prepared. I bet you was disappointed when we didn't hear it all.'

'I'm afraid a friend of mine who came

266

down with me was to blame,' said Armeid. 'He heard enough to know that the story concerned me, and thought it might be better if the rest was silenced. A very good friend — and a very good shot!'

'It's lies! Lies!' shouted Challis. 'I had nothing to do with those records.'

'You used the cylinders belongin' to Slythe's machine,' said Mr. Budd slowly and ponderously. 'Remember me comin' in here because I'd forgotten somethin'? There's a case over there for six dictaphone cylinders. There's only two left, an' although the dust is pretty thick round where the others stood, there's no dust on the space where they stood.' He sighed. 'It's little thin's like that that 'ang a man.'

Challis was silent.

'You took advantage o' circumstances, didn't yer,' went on Mr. Budd conversationally. 'You knew all about Mr. Armeid here, an' the fact that 'e was after the Seal, from his correspondence with Slythe. You knew there was others after it too. The best place ter 'ide a pebble is on the beach. I told Selkerk that, an' 'e didn't know what I was gettin' at. The best time ter kill a man is when there are plenty o' others who might've done it. You was lucky. All these people poppin' about, an' all this fuss over the Seal o' Solomon very nearly hid you up. But there was one thin' that you overlooked, an' that everybody else overlooked, too, except me. It was that what made me suspicious o' you from the beginnin'. The person who killed Slythe 'ad come by the winder. Can you see Slythe openin' it to a stranger in the black-out, with a lot o' valuable stuff about, or to anyone that wasn't very well-known to 'im? But 'e wouldn't think nothin' of doin' so for 'is own secretary. An' nobody 'eard a sound. He'd 'ave given the alarm if 'e 'adn't known who it was. Why did yer kill him?'

'I tell you — ' began Challis, and Mr. Budd uttered an impatient exclamation.

'What's the good?' he said wearily. 'She's goin' ter be all the evidence we'll need.' He jerked his head towards the girl.

'I'd taken a lot of money,' muttered Challis, licking his lips and staring straight in front of him as though they were no longer there. 'I had charge of the funds for the expedition, and I was up to my eyes in debt. I took three thousand pounds. There was going to be an audit next week — '

'I see,' murmured Mr. Budd, nodding. 'What did she know?'

'She knew I'd come back from London earlier than I was supposed to have done,' said the secretary. 'She saw me. She knew I didn't come on the train she was on, as I'd told her, and when you'd gone she taxed me with it. She was suspicious. I had to do what I did.'

'You had another key to this room, I s'pose,' said the big man, and Challis nodded. He looked apathetic and tired.

'There were two. Slythe had one, I had the other,' he answered.

Selkerk came hurriedly in.

'The doctor's on his way,' he announced.

'Good!' said Mr. Budd. 'You'd better take charge o' that feller, Selkerk. Look after 'im. 'E's dangerous.'

11

The Wisdom of Solomon

Challis was taken away and charged, and the doctor came and examined June Bennett, whom they had carried upstairs and lain on her bed.

'She'll recover,' he said, 'but it was lucky you found her when you did. Another half-hour and it would have been too late. She would have died from suffocation.'

'D'you think he was goin' ter leave 'er there, in that thing?' asked Leek, when the doctor had gone and he and Mr. Budd were left alone with Solomon Armeid.

The big man nodded.

'For the time bein',' he answered. 'The idea was ter make everybody think that she'd gone away. That's why he took the suitcase. Afterwards, when she was dead an' the police 'ad left the 'ouse, he'd 've

270

found an opportunity of disposin' of the body. The river's not far away.' He looked across the smoking-room in which they sat towards Solomon Armeid. 'Strictly speakin', I s'pose I ought ter arrest you,' he said.

Armeid raised his level brows.

'On what charge?' he inquired.

'Receivin' stolen property,' retorted Mr. Budd. 'I pulled in Guldheimer this morning', and he told me what had 'appened durin' the night at that warehouse of 'is.'

'An unpleasant — er — gentleman, Guldheimer,' murmured Solomon Armeid. 'By rights he should have been arrested long ago, but he possessed a certain amount of low cunning which enabled him to avoid that catastrophe. I'm afraid you have no case against me, Superintendent. When I told you I came here this morning to offer my condolences to Miss Bennett, I said, if you remember, that that was partly my reason. The other was to return the mummy, which is at present in my car outside.'

Mr. Budd felt — and looked — astonished.

'You've brought it back?' he said.

Solomon Armeid inclined his head.

'I have brought it back,' he replied.

'Did you find the Seal?' asked the fat detective.

The other looked at him steadily.

'There is no ring on the finger of the mummy,' he answered, and consulted his watch. 'I'm afraid I shall have to be returning to London,' he said, rising to his feet. 'I have a very important appointment. I will have the mummy sent in to you.'

He bowed both to Mr. Budd and to Leek, picked up his hat, and was gone.

The lean sergeant looked at the door and then at his superior.

'I'll bet that ring *was* on the mummy's finger,' he said.

'I'll bet it was, too,' grunted Mr. Budd. 'But what can you do? Nobody could swear it was there — nobody knew it was there.'

'Except 'is nibs,' muttered Leek. ''E was wearing a ring — on the third finger of 'is right 'and. Did you see it? An old ring it was, too, with some sort of a green stone, all queerly carved.'

Mr. Budd nodded. 'I saw it,' he said, yawning wearily. 'Well, come on, let's go. We'll see that mummy locked up in the study, an' then we've finished here. I shan't be sorry ter get some sleep, meself.'

'Nor me!' declared Leek fervently. 'I could sleep fer a week!'

'You prob'ly will!' grunted Mr. Budd unkindly. 'That wouldn't surprise me. The only thin' that'd surprise me 'ud be if yer ever woke up!'

*　*　*

The Prime Minister looked across the big table at his visitor.

'Your offer is an exceedingly generous one, Mr. Armeid,' he said. 'In pursuing this struggle against the forces of aggression it will be of incalculable value.' He sighed, and a shadow crossed his tired face. 'God knows we did not want war,' he went on, 'but it has come, in spite of all my efforts to prevent it, and we shall fight it to a finish, confident that ours is a just cause. We shall fling all our vast resources into the struggle, because until the Nazi Government has been wiped out there can be no permanent peace in Europe. That we shall win, I have no doubt, but the making of war is expensive, and that you should come forward and offer to place at the disposal of His Majesty's Government such vast resources as you have shown me that you control, is an action our appreciation of which no words of mine can adequately express. On behalf of His Majesty's Government I accept your offer, Mr. Armeid, and with it my most heartfelt thanks.'

Solomon Armeid rose to his feet.

'We are facing a period in the history of the world,' he said solemnly, 'when all those who abhor force and brutality should stand together against a common foe. You can count, through me, on every one of my race to the uttermost limit of their resources.'

The Prime Minister held out his hand.

'I can only say 'thank you' once again,' he said simply.

As they shook hands a shaft of sunlight, streaming through the window from Downing Street, struck fire from the ancient ring which Solomon Armeid wore on the third finger of his right hand.

★ ★ ★

On a cold, rainy morning a shivering man was marched out between a guard of soldiers on to the parade ground at the Tower of London.

It was barely dawn, and the City lay swathed in mist and semi-darkness.

The prisoner had to be supported while his eyes were bandaged, for his thin spindle-legs seemed too frail to bear his gross, flabby body. While the formalities were being complied with he kept up a running fire of entreaties, groans and blasphemous oaths, but the stolid soldiers received his pleadings and his oaths in silence.

He was marched to a grey stone wall, and the firing-party raised their rifles.

'Fire!' rapped the officer in charge, and the volley echoed and re-echoed from

275

ancient wall to ancient wall.

The fat, flabby body of Herman Guiding, alias Isaac Guldheimer, secret agent of the Third Reich, slowly collapsed and sprawled at the foot of the wall, an unpleasant twitching heap . . .

THE END

We do hope that you have enjoyed reading this large print book.

Did you know that all of our titles are available for purchase?

We publish a wide range of high quality large print books including:
Romances, Mysteries, Classics
General Fiction
Non Fiction and Westerns

Special interest titles available in large print are:
The Little Oxford Dictionary
Music Book, Song Book
Hymn Book, Service Book

Also available from us courtesy of Oxford University Press:
Young Readers' Dictionary
(large print edition)
Young Readers' Thesaurus
(large print edition)

For further information or a free brochure, please contact us at:
Ulverscroft Large Print Books Ltd.,
The Green, Bradgate Road, Anstey,
Leicester, LE7 7FU, England.
Tel: (00 44) 0116 236 4325
Fax: (00 44) 0116 234 0205

THE CHAINED MAN
AND OTHER STORIES

Gerald Verner

When a band of stranded Christmas travellers is forced to spend the night in an isolated local pub called the Chained Man, the last thing they expect is murder in their midst . . . Lattimer Shrive puts his amazing powers of detection and deduction to work to solve three seemingly inexplicable cases . . . And a real murder on national radio proves surprisingly tricky to solve. These five detective stories by Gerald Verner will baffle and entertain in equal measure.

THE DARCKMOOR DEMON AND OTHER ENIGMAS

John Light

Who or what is responsible for the eerie howling from the night-darkened fells that disturbs the inhabitants of Darckmoor? Is there malice at work in the world of small presses? Why is there an eight-foot-high toadstool on the back of a truck speeding along a remote byway? When a new statue by a reclusive artist is displayed in a small gallery in London's East End, is it the beginning of something bigger? And what is the cause of the sorrowful single-mindedness of the long-term resident of an old-fashioned hotel?

FIRE IN THE BLOOD

Rena George

Gennie Durham buys into the Flying Fox country pub, and finds herself in the middle of a Yorkshire murder mystery — with Oliver Hammond, the man she is becoming increasingly attracted to, as the prime suspect. But there's worse to come . . . An arsonist is on the loose in Fenwick cum Marton. The historic St Stephen's Church has already been burned to the ground. Is Gennie's pub next on the fire-raiser's list?

Epidemiology of Cancer

Wende Levy

Epidemiology is the study of the distribution and determinants of disease in a population. Cancer is not considered an epidemic disease, but the principles of epidemiology are used to study cancer. Epidemiology is used in cancer care to improve the definition and classification of cancers. This approach also assists in the identification of factors leading to the development of cancer.

Cancer is the second leading cause of death in the United States. Twelve million new cases have been diagnosed since 1990. The American Cancer Society has stated that more than 1500 people are expected to die each day from cancer (Landis, Murray, Bolden, & Wingo, 1998). In 1996, cancer contributed to 23.3% of all deaths in the United States, yet overall 5-year survival rates have improved for most cancers, except for lung and bronchus (Figs. 2-1 and 2-2). In the next decade, our nation and healthcare systems will be challenged by the demand for resources to further reduce the incidence and mortality rates of this disease.

Prevention

The goal of epidemiologic studies and research is to prevent disease. Prevention comes from understanding the reasons for disease and the measures that can be taken to prevent them. Maintaining health is a prime focus of epidemiology of prevention and early detection of are currently three levels of prever secondary, and tertiary (Johnson, 1

Primary prevention is the ability to avoid or eliminate the causative agent. Secondary prevention is strongly tied to early detection and treatment, such as in breast cancer. Tertiary treatment involves treatment of the cancer and symptom management. The focus of epidemiology studies in recent years has been on primary prevention. Many examples of these findings are seen every day. One example is the multiplicity of medicinal, marketing, and behavioral strategies being developed to assist people to avoid cigarettes and nicotine. Another is the education of the population regarding the outcomes from prolonged exposure to the sun and sunburns at an early age. Understanding the causes of cancer allows physicians and health care providers to screen individuals for cancer, educate them about the causes of cancer, and prevent certain cancers by early intervention. I general, early intervention in cancer treatm decrease both the morbidity and mort are de cer, but this is not always the cas ping can Prevention

Studies on the epidemic target individ- signed to assess indivi the education and cer and identify p between the cancer strategies ut at example, the American uals ar oping smokers have a ten-fold e (American loping lung cancer compared cancer.org/statistics/cff99, 1999).

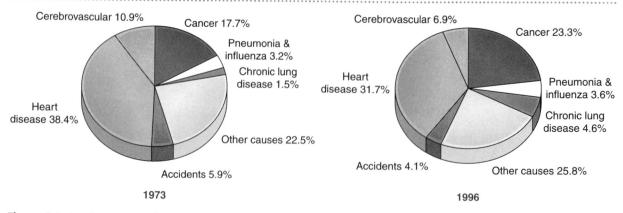

Figure 2-1 Leading causes of death in the U.S.: Percent of all causes of death, 1973 vs. 1996.

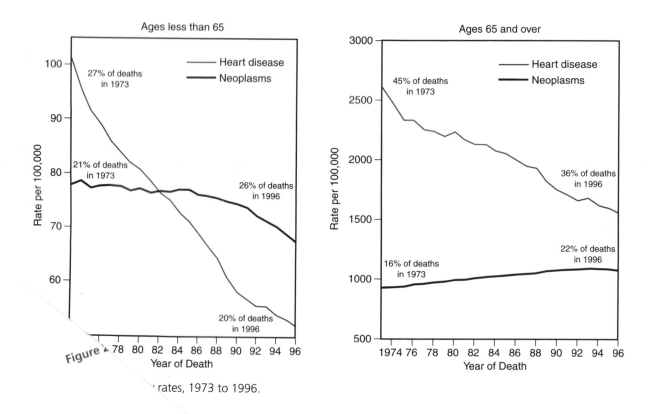

Figure 2- 78 80 82 84 86 88 90 92 94 96   rates, 1973 to 1996.

Epidemiology Terms

The impact of cancer in a population is measured and described by exploring four elements: incidence rates, prevalence, mortality rates, and survival rates.

Incidence

Incidence is defined as he number of new cases per year per 100,000 persons. The total population defines incidence as the number of persons developing a specific condition, in this case cancer, in a specific time frame divided by the total population (Goldman, 1997). In recent years, incidence has been used in breast cancer education and marketing campaigns. The incidence of breast cancer for a woman is 1 in 9 over her lifetime. Incidence rates are used to compare disease processes in different cultures and in persons living in different geographic locations.

In men, the most common cancers are those of the prostate, lung and bronchus, and colon and rectum. Fifty-four percent of all new cancer cases in men will be found in these three sites. Prostate cancer is the leading new diagnosis of cancer in men.

In women, breast, lung and bronchus, and colon and rectum are the most common sites. These three cancers will make up 54% of all new cancer cases in women, with breast cancer accounting for the largest part of that figure.

Prevalence

Prevalence is a critical component of health care planning and is defined as the number of cases of a specific disease, in this case cancer, at a given point divided by the total population. It measures the proportion of the population who have cancer at a specified point or during an interval of time. This measure reflects both the incidences of cancer and survival. The number of cases both newly diagnosed as well as the number of ongoing cases at a specific point in time are included in the prevalence rate (Goldman, 1997).

Mortality and Survival

Other terms that must be defined in order to understand the study of epidemiology are *mortality* and *survival* (Goldman, 1997). We all recognize mortality as the number of deaths, but in this definition it is important to understand that it is the number of persons dying in a specific time period divided by the total population at that time. Every country in the world keeps mortality data. Death rates can be compared worldwide. The shortcoming of this measure is in the reporting mechanism. Certificates of death usually list only the immediate cause of death; in many cases the real cause of death is not identified and is thus not included in mortality figure. Mortality figures do allow us to see trends over time.

Survival is the link between incidence and mortality data (Goldman, 1997). Survival data are the measurements over time of persons with cancer and the probability of dying over a specific time period. Survival data can be useful, but they do not answer the patient's basic question, "If I live for 5 years without a recurrence will I be OK?". In aggressive cancers the length of survival may be shorter; in others, the second 5 years may be a more accurate predictor.

All four of these epidemiologic terms are used to help identify the trends of cancer. Information on trends is the basis for epidemiologic research and study. The National Cancer Institute (NCI) established and funds the Surveillance, Epidemiology, and End-Results Program (SEER) to gather information on cancer incidence, mortality, and survival (Goldman, 1997).

Table 2-1 addresses the estimated prevalence of cancer in the United States by race and sex. Table 2-2 describes the incidence and differentiates new cancer cases and deaths in men and women. Tables 2-3 and 2-4 identify the mortality and survival rates of all primary cancer sites.

The field of epidemiology utilizes three types of studies. The first type is a *descriptive* study that identifies an etiologic hypothesis (Goldman, 1997). A descriptive study looks at the frequency of a cancer. Incidence, prevalence, and mortality are all part of the frequency definition. The disease itself is broken down into the site of the disease, the grade of the tumor or stage of the disease, and the morphologic classification (Goldman, 1997). The second component is the individual. Many factors are included here, including age, gender, race, marital status, nutritional status, socioeconomic status, cultural factors, and susceptibility factors. The factor of geography looks at the phys-

TABLE 2-1

ESTIMATED UNITED STATES CANCER PREVALENCE, 1999: ALL RACES, BY SEX

Primary Site	Estimated Prevalence		
	Total	Males	Females
All Sites	8,368,000	3,465,000	4,903,000
Brain and other nervous system	91,000	49,000	42,000
Breast	2,057,000	13,000	2,044,000
Cervix uteri	211,000	0	211,000
Colon	877,000	408,000	469,000
Corpus uteri	550,000	0	550,000
Hodgkin's disease	158,000	84,000	74,000
Kidney and renal pelvis	204,000	123,000	81,000
Larynx	132,000	106,000	26,000
Leukemias	144,000	80,000	64,000
Lung and bronchus	397,000	212,000	185,000
Melanomas of skin	484,000	234,000	250,000
Non-Hodgkin's lymphoma	300,000	150,000	150,000
Oral cavity and pharynx	214,000	134,000	80,000
Ovary	191,000	0	191,000
Pancreas	25,000	12,000	13,000
Prostate	1,017,000	1,017,000	0
Rectum	379,000	202,000	177,000
Stomach	77,000	42,000	35,000
Testis	130,000	130,000	0
Thyroid	214,000	53,000	161,000
Urinary bladder	601,000	443,000	158,000
Childhood (0–14 yrs)	154,000	78,000	76,000

U.S. 1999 cancer prevalence rates are based on 1994 cancer prevalence rates from the Connecticut registry of the SEER program and 1999 population estimates from the U.S. Bureau of the Census. Connecticut prevalence rates are based on 1940–1993 cancer incidence and survival rates.

ical environment, the biologic environment, and geographic location. Time as a factor is used in descriptive studies to look at frequency patterns over specific time frames.

The next type is the *analytic* study, which tests the hypothesis (Goldman, 1997). There are two types of analytic studies. A prospective study, also known as a cohort study, looks at a specific cause and then follows individuals over time to ascertain the relationship between the cause and the disease. The other, a retrospective or case control study, uses individuals who have an identified outcome and tries to determine the factor that may have been the cause (Goldman, 1997).

The third is the *experimental* study, which is better known as a clinical trial (Goldman, 1997). In this study, a specific action or modification is made and results are obtained to measure the effectiveness of the action.

In epidemiology the cause of cancer is an important key to disease control, prevention, and early detection. Cause is defined as something

TABLE 2-2

ESTIMATED NEW CANCER CASES AND DEATHS FOR 1999: ALL RACES, BY SEX

Primary Site	Estimated New Cases			Estimated Deaths		
	Total	Males	Females	Total	Males	Females
All sites	1,221,800	623,800	598,000	563,100	291,100	272,000
Oral cavity and pharynx	29,800	20,000	9,800	8,100	5,400	2,700
Tongue	6,600	4,300	2,300	1,800	1,200	600
Mouth	10,800	6,400	4,400	2,300	1,300	1,000
Pharynx	8,300	6,100	2,200	2,100	1,500	600
Other oral cavity	4,100	3,200	900	1,900	1,400	500
Digestive system	226,300	117,200	109,100	131,000	69,900	61,100
Esophagus	12,500	9,400	3,100	12,200	9,400	2,800
Stomach	21,900	13,700	8,200	13,500	7,900	5,600
Small intestine	4,800	2,500	2,300	1,200	600	600
Colon	94,700	43.000	51,700	47,900	23,000	24,900
Rectum	34,700	19,400	15,300	8,700	4,800	3,900
Anus, anal canal, and anorectum	3,300	1,400	1,900	500	200	300
Liver and intrahepatic bile duct	14,500	9,600	4,900	13,600	8,400	5,200
Gallbladder and other biliary	7,200	3,000	4,200	3,600	1,300	2,300
Pancreas	28,600	14,000	14,600	28,600	13,900	14,700
Other digestive	4,100	1,200	2,900	1,200	400	800
Respiratory system	187,600	106,800	80,800	164,200	94,900	69,300
Larynx	10,600	8,600	2,000	4,200	3,300	900
Lung and bronchus	171,600	94,000	77,600	158,900	90,900	68,000
Other respiratory	5,400	4,200	1,200	1,100	700	400
Bones and joints	2,600	1,400	1,200	1,400	800	600
Soft tissues	7,800	4,200	3,600	4,400	2,100	2,300
Skin (excluding basal and sqamous)	54,000	33,400	20,600	9,200	5,800	3,400
Melanomas of skin	44,200	25,800	18,400	7,300	4,600	2,700
Other non-epithelial skin	9,800	7,600	2,200	1,900	1,200	700
Breast	176,300	1,300	175,000	43,700	400	43,300
Genital organs	269,100	188,100	81,000	64,700	37,500	27,200
Cervix (uterus)	12,800		12,800	4,800		4,800
Endometrium (uterus)	37,400		37,400	6,400		6,400
Ovary	25,200		25,200	14,500		14,500
Vulva	3,300		3,300	900		900
Vagina and other genital organs, female	2,300		2,300	600		600
Prostate	179,300	179,300		37,000	37,000	
Testis	7,400	7,400		300	300	
Penis and other genital organs, male	1,400	1,400		200	200	
Urinary system	86,500	58,400	28,100	24,500	15,600	8,900
Urinary bladder	54,200	39,100	15,100	12,100	8,100	4,000
Kidney and renal pelvis	30,000	17,800	12,200	11,900	7,200	4,700
Ureter and other urinary organs	2,300	1,500	800	500	300	200
Eye and orbit	2,200	1,200	1,000	200	100	100
Brain and other nervous system	16,800	9,500	7,300	13,100	7,200	5,900
Endocrine system	19,800	5,400	14,400	2,000	900	1,100
Thyroid	18,100	4,600	13,500	1,200	500	700
Other endocrine	1,700	800	900	800	400	400
Lymphoma	64,000	36,400	27,600	27,000	14,100	12,900
Hodgkin's disease	7,200	3,800	3,400	1,300	700	600
Non-Hodgkin's lymphoma	56,800	32,600	24,200	25,700	13,400	12,300
Multiple myeloma	13,700	7,300	6,400	11,400	5,800	5,600
Leukemia	30,200	16,800	13,400	22,100	12,400	9,700
Lymphocytic leukemias	10,900	6,300	4,600	6,500	3,800	2,700
Myeloid leukemias	14,600	7,600	7,000	9,200	5,000	4,200
Other leukemia	4,700	2,900	1,800	6,400	3,600	2,800
All other sites	35,100	16,400	18,700	36,100	18,200	17,900

Excludes basal and squamous cell skin and in situ carcinomas except urinary bladder. Incidence projections are based on rates from the NCI Seer Program 1979–1995. (American Cancer Society Cancer facts and figures—1999. Atlanta; ACS.)

TABLE 2-3

SUMMARY OF CHANGES IN CANCER INCIDENCE AND MORTALITY, 1950–1996 AND 5-YEAR RELATIVE SURVIVAL RATES, 1950–1995: MALES AND FEMALES BY PRIMARY CANCER SITE

	All Races		Whites					
			Percent Change 1950–96[‡]					
	Estimated Cancer Cases in 1996*	Actual Cancer Deaths in 1996[†]	Incidence[§]		U.S. Mortality[‖]		5-Year Relative Survival Rates (Percent)[#]	
Primary Site			Total	EAPC	Total	EAPC	1950–54	1989–95
Oral cavity and pharynx	29,490	7,853	−38.2	−0.7	−37.3	−0.9	46	55.5
Esophagus	12,300	11,231	−8.2	0.2	21.7	0.4	4	13.3
Stomach	22,800	13,335	−77.9	−2.7	−80.1	−3.6	12	19.3
Colon and rectum	133,500	56,754	−2.9	−0.1	−35.4	−0.9	37	61.8
Colon	94,500	48,587	11.5	0.2	−21.3	−0.4	41	62.4
Rectum	39,000	8,167	−26.7	−0.7	−67.1	−2.8	40	60.2
Liver and intrahepatic	19,900	11,584	139.9	1.7	33.6	0.5	1	6.0
Pancreas	26,300	27,256	9.4	0.0	15.9	0.2	1	4.1
Larynx	11,600	3,918	37.6	0.4	−14.4	−0.3	52	66.1
Lung and bronchus	177,000	151,902	249.1	2.4	259.0	3.0	6	14.2
Males	98,900	91,554	178.3	1.6	196.9	2.4	5	12.7
Females	78,100	60,348	577.9	4.5	611.9	5.3	9	16.4
Melanomas of skin	38,300	7,279	453.0	4.1	160.6	2.2	49	87.9
Breast (females)	184,300	43,090	55.1	1.3	−7.5	0.0	60	86.0
Cervix uteri	15,700	4,540	−78.9	−3.0	−75.7	−3.6	59	71.4
Corpus and uterus, NOS	34,000	6,310	−0.3	−0.6	−67.4	−2.3	72	85.5
Ovary	26,700	13,161	3.2	0.2	−2.3	−0.2	30	49.9
Prostate	317,100	34,122	190.1	3.2	10.0	0.3	43	93.1
Testis	7,400	345	105.8	2.0	−72.7	−3.2	57	95.7
Urinary bladder	52,900	11,451	51.1	1.0	−35.3	−1.1	53	81.8
Kidney and renal pelvis	30,600	11,095	125.9	2.0	37.4	0.6	34	61.1
Brain and other nervous	17,900	12,375	68.2	1.2	44.9	0.7	21	29.6
Thyroid	15,600	1,181	141.8	1.7	−48.2	−1.9	80	95.1
Hodgkin's disease	7,500	1,408	16.3	0.2	−73.3	−3.4	30	82.9
Non-Hodgkin's lymphomas	52,700	22,834	195.5	2.9	137.6	1.6	33	51.9
Multiple myeloma	14,400	10,178	197.3	1.8	206.2	2.2	6	28.0
Leukemias	27,600	20,494	9.5	0.2	−3.7	−0.3	10	44.4
Childhood (0–14 yrs)	8,300	1,539	15.7	0.8	−67.2	−2.8	20	75.5
All sites excluding lung and bronchus	1,182,150	387,606	40.5	0.8	−17.7	−0.4	38	68.1
All sites	1,359,150	539,508	53.6	1.0	6.5	0.2	35	60.9

*The EAPC is the estimated annual percent change over the time interval (Wingo, PA., Tong, T., Bolden, S. [1995]. Cancer statistics 1995. *CA: A Cancer Journal for Clinicians, 45;* 8–30.) Excludes basal and squamous cell skin and in situ carcinomas except urinary bladder. Incidence projections are based on rates from the NCI SEER Program 1989–91.

[†]NCHS public use tape.

[‡]All sites, All sites excluding lung and bronchus, liver and intrahepatic, brain and other nervous and childhood cancers are for all races as opposed to whites.

[§]Data prior to 1973 are from Devesa, Silverman, Young, et al. (1987) Cancer incidence and mortality trends among whites in the United States, 1947–84. *JNCI, 79;* 701–770, with the exception of All Sites, All sites excluding lung and bronchus, Liver and intrahepatic, Brain and other nervous and Childhood cancers, which come from historical Connecticut data. Data for 1973–95 are from the same areas used in Devesa or the Connecticut registry of the SEER Program.

[‖]NCHS public use tape. Due to coding changes throughout the years; Colon excludes other digestive tract; Rectum includes anal canal; Liver and intrahepatic includes gallbladder and biliary tract, NOS; Lung and bronchus includes trachea and pleura; Ovary includes fallopian tube; Urinary bladder includes other urinary organs; Kidney and renal pelvis includes ureter; NHL and Multiple myeloma each include a small number of leukemias; NHL includes a small number of ill-defined sites.

[#]Rates for 1950–54 are from NCI Survival Report 5 with the exception of All Sites, All sites excluding Lung and bronchus, Oral cavity and pharynx, Colon and rectum, Non-Hodgkin's lymphomas, and Childhood cancers, which come from historical Connecticut data. Rates for 1989–95 are from the SEER Program with the exception of the sites just listed, which come from the Connecticut registry of the SEER Program.

TABLE 2-4

AGE-ADJUSTED SEER INCIDENCE AND U.S. MORTALITY RATES AND 5-YEAR RELATIVE SURVIVAL RATES BY PRIMARY CANCER SITE, SEX, AND TIME PERIOD: ALL RACES

Site	Incidence* (1992–96)			US Mortality† (1992–96)			Survivals* (1989–95)		
	Total	Males	Females	Total	Males	Females	Total	Males	Females
All sites	404.8	489.1	345.8	170.1	213.1	140.9	59.4	57.5	61.4
Oral cavity and Pharynx	10.3	15.5	6.0	2.7	4.2	1.5	53.3	50.0	60.2
Lip	1.1	2.1	0.3	0.0	0.1	0.0	94.3	93.6	97.9
Tongue	2.2	3.2	1.4	0.6	0.9	0.4	49.9	45.7	58.0
Salivary gland	1.0	1.3	0.8	0.2	0.3	0.1	72.8	66.4	80.3
Floor of mouth	0.9	1.4	0.5	0.1	0.1	0.1	52.3	48.7	60.7
Gum and other oral cavity	1.8	2.3	1.3	0.4	0.6	0.3	48.3	39.1	63.4
Nasopharynx	0.6	0.9	0.4	0.2	0.4	0.1	53.3	52.9	54.4
Tonsil	1.1	1.7	0.5	0.2	0.3	0.1	48.1	47.7	48.8
Oropharynx	0.3	0.5	0.1	0.2	0.3	0.1	29.5	27.3	35.9
Hypopharynx	0.9	1.6	0.4	0.2	0.3	0.1	29.5	28.1	34.2
Other oral cavity and pharynx	0.3	0.6	0.2	0.5	0.9	0.3	24.8	24.5	25.2
Digestive system	73.2	91.4	59.0	39.1	50.5	30.4	43.1	41.3	45.0
Esophagus	3.9	6.5	1.7	3.6	6.3	1.5	12.3	12.1	13.1
Stomach	7.0	10.4	4.4	4.2	6.1	2.8	21.1	18.6	25.2
Small intestine	1.3	1.6	1.1	0.3	0.4	0.3	49.0	47.5	50.8
Colon and rectum	44.3	53.0	37.6	17.5	21.5	14.6	61.0	61.2	60.8
Colon	31.9	36.9	28.1	—	—	—	61.6	62.2	61.0
Rectum	12.4	16.2	9.5	—	—	—	59.5	59.1	60.1
Anus, anal canal and anorectum	1.0	0.9	1.0	0.1	0.1	0.1	59.6	54.0	63.5
Liver and intrahepatic	3.7	5.7	2.1	3.4	4.9	2.2	5.3	4.3	7.2
Liver	3.1	4.9	1.6	2.8	4.2	1.7	5.7	4.4	8.5
Intrahepatic bile duct	0.6	0.8	0.5	0.6	0.8	0.5	2.8	2.8	2.6
Gallbladder	1.0	0.7	1.2	0.6	0.4	0.8	13.7	10.7	14.9
Other biliary	1.1	1.3	0.9	0.5	0.6	0.4	17.0	18.4	15.8
Pancreas	8.9	10.2	7.8	8.4	9.8	7.3	4.1	3.7	4.4
Retroperitoneum	0.4	0.4	0.4	0.1	0.1	0.1	47.0	49.7	44.0
Peritoneum, omentum and mesentery	0.4	0.2	0.5	0.1	0.1	0.1	28.3	19.2	32.8
Other digestive	0.3	0.3	0.2	0.1	0.2	0.1	2.6	2.3	3.8
Respiratory system	62.6	85.7	45.1	51.3	73.8	34.5	17.7	17.5	18.1
Nose, nasal cavity and middle ear	0.6	0.8	0.4	0.2	0.2	0.1	52.3	52.5	51.8
Larynx	4.0	7.1	1.5	1.3	2.4	0.5	64.6	66.2	58.6
Lung and bronchus	57.0	75.9	42.8	49.5	70.8	33.8	13.9	12.4	16.1
Pleura	0.8	1.5	0.3	0.1	0.3	0.1	6.0	3.3	17.4
Trachea and other respiratory organs	0.2	0.3	0.1	0.1	0.1	0.1	46.2	46.5	43.8
Bones and joints	0.9	1.1	0.7	0.4	0.5	0.3	66.4	64.0	69.7
Soft tissue (including heart)	2.4	2.8	2.0	1.3	1.3	1.2	65.2	64.7	65.8
Skin (excluding basal and squamous):	16.6	22.2	11.9	2.9	4.3	1.8	68.7	56.6	90.6
Melanomas of skin	13.0	16.0	10.8	2.2	3.2	1.5	87.7	85.1	90.8
Other non-epithelial skin	3.6	6.2	1.2	0.7	1.1	0.3	25.0	17.5	88.3
Breast	60.2	0.9	110.6	14.2	0.3	25.4	84.7	81.8	84.7

Note: Incidence and mortality rates are per 100,000 and are age-adjusted to the 1970 U.S. standard population. Survival rates are expressed as percents.
*SEER Program
†NCHS public use tape
— Statistic could not be calculated

TABLE 2-5

ENVIRONMENTAL CAUSES OF HUMAN CANCER

Agent	Type of Exposure	Site of Cancer
Aflatoxin	Contaminated foodstuffs	Liver
Alcohol	Drinking	Mouth, pharynx, esophagus, larynx, liver
Alkylating agents	Medication	Leukemia
Androgen-anabolic steroids	Medication	Liver
Aromatic amines	Manufacturing of dyes and chemicals	Bladder
Arsenic	Mining and smelting of certain ores, pesticides, medication, drinking water	Lung, skin, liver
Asbestos	Manufacturing and use	Lung, pluera, peritoneum
Benzene	Leather, petroleum, and other industries	Leukemia
Ether	Manufacturing	Lung (small cell)
Chloronaphazine	Medication	Bladder
Chromium compounds	Manufacturing	Lung
Estrogens	Medication	
Synthetic		Vaginal, cervix
Conjugated		Endometrium
Steroid contraceptives		Liver, cervix
Immunosuppressants	Medication	NHL, skin, soft tissue tumors
Ionizing radiation	Atomic bomb explosions, treatment and diagnosis, radium dial painting, uranium and metal mining	Most sites
Isopropyl alcohol production	Manufacturing by a strong acid production	Nasal sinuses
Leather industry	Manufacturing and repair	Nasal sinuses, bladder
Mustard gas	Manufacturing	Lung, larynx, nasal sinuses
Nickel dust	Refining	Lung, nasal sinuses
Parasites	Infection	
Schistosoma haematobium		Bladder
Clonorchis sinensis		Liver
Pesticides	Application	NHL, lung
Phenacetin-containing analgesics	Medication	Renal pelvis
Polycyclic hydrocarbons	Coal carbonization	Lung, skin
Tobacco chews	Snuff dipping and chewing of tobacco	Mouth
Tobacco smoke	Smoking	Lung, larynx, mouth, pharynx, esophagus, bladder, pancreas, kidney
Ultraviolet radiation	Sunlight	Skin, lip
Viruses	Infection	
Epstein-Barr		Burkitt's lymphoma, esophageal carcinoma
Hepatitis B and C		Hepatocellular carcinoma
HIV		Kaposi's sarcoma, NHL
Human T-cell lymphoma		T-cell leukemia
Vinyl chloride	Manufacturing of polyvinyl chloride	Liver
Wood dust	Furniture manufacturing	Nasal sinuses

NHL = Non-Hodgkin's lymphoma
(Fraumeni, J.F. et al [1993]. Epidemology of cancer. In V.T. DeVita, S. Hellman, & S.A. Rosenberg [Eds.], *Cancer: Principles and practice of oncology* [4th ed.]. Philadelphia: Lippincott.)

that produces the effect (Goldman, 1997). Table 2-5, for example, lists environmental causes of cancer.

Cancer is a disease that has many factors and multiple causative agents and components. All of these together increase the occurrence of cancer. The identification of the causative agents of cancer is the key to controlling cancer. Only when agents are identified can we limit exposure and decrease cancer risk. Education concerning these agents and their role in cancer prevention is an integral part of a nurse's role in health education.

REFERENCES

American Cancer Society, *http://www.cancer.org/stsatistics/cff99*, 1999.

Goldman, K. (1997). Epidemology. In S. Otto, *Oncology nursing* (3rd ed.). St. Louis: Mosby.

Johnson, B. (1994). Prevention and early detection. In J. Gross & B. Johnson (Eds.), *Handbook of oncology nursing* (2nd ed.). Sudbury, MA: Jones and Bartlett.

Landis, S. H., Murray, T., Bolden, S., & Wingo, P.A. (1998). Cancer statistics, 1998. *CA: A Cancer Journal for Clinicians, 489*(1), 6–29.

Oleske, D. & Groenwald, S. (1990). Epidemiology of cancer. In S. Groenwald, M. H. Frogge, M. Goodman, & C. H. Yarbro. (Eds.), *Cancer nursing: Principles and practice* (2nd ed.). Boston: Jones and Bartlett.

Cancer Biology

Constance Visovsky
M. Linda Workman

Cancer, also called a malignancy, is a type of common disorder involving the uncontrolled growth of cells. Approximately 1.2 million people in the United States are newly diagnosed with cancer each year (American Cancer Society, 1998). Without appropriate treatment, cancer usually leads to death. With appropriate treatment, however, about 50% of cancers can now be cured. When the cause is known, some types of cancer can be prevented. When a cause is not known or cannot be avoided, the best chance for cure or long-term survival is early diagnosis and treatment.

Cancers, actually cancer cells, do not invade the body like an infection but, rather, arise from normal cells that are changed (transformed) by contact with a carcinogen (substance that damages cellular DNA and alters cell growth). Many human body cells continue to "grow" by cell division (mitosis) long after adult development and maturation are complete. Mitosis is the process by which one cell splits and becomes two cells that are identical to each other and to the cell that began the split. Cells that usually undergo mitosis are located in body areas where constant damage or wear is likely. The cells replace themselves when other cells die. Cells of the skin, hair, mucous membranes, bone marrow, linings of glandular organs (lungs, stomach, intestines, bladder, uterus), and support cells of the brain (glial cells), among others, can undergo mitosis throughout the life span. Cell growth is usually well controlled, only replacing cells as needed.

Some cells are unable to divide after development is complete, but the tissue or organ can get larger as each individual cell increases in size (*hypertrophy*). For example, skeletal muscle cells no longer divide in the adult. The size of the skeletal muscles increases when an adult exercises because each of the cells gets larger, but the number of muscle cells does not increase. Thus, the muscles get larger by hypertrophy.

Hyperplasia occurs when adult tissues or organs increase in size by increasing the number of cells, such as when the skin gets larger to accommodate weight gain (Figure 3-1).

Cell division (mitosis) not needed for normal development or replacement of dead cells is called *neoplasia* and is always considered abnormal. Therefore, cancer cells are a type of neoplasia. Again, cancer cells were once normal cells, but transformed and no longer look, grow, or function normally. The control mechanisms for normal growth and function have been lost or suppressed. Cancer cells are different from normals cells in many ways. Identification of these differences assists in the diagnosis and prognosis of many types of cancer.

Normal Cellular Biology and Characteristics

Features of Normal Cells

HAVE WELL-REGULATED GROWTH. Normal cells only divide (undergo mitosis) to either develop normal tissue or replace lost or damaged tissue. Normal cells capable of mitosis do not divide un-

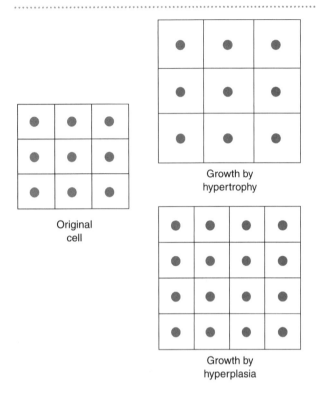

Figure 3-1 Comparison of growth by hypertrophy and by hyperplasia.

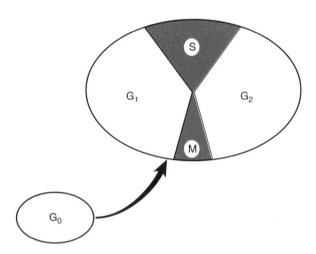

Figure 3-2 The cell cycle. G_0 = reproductive resting state; G_1 = beginning of cell cycle with synthesis of membrane, cytoplasm, increased uptake of nutrients; S = doubling of DNA content; G_2 = protein synthesis and production of intracellular organelles; M = mitosis, actual splitting of one cell into two daughter cells.

less there is a need for more cells, with adequate space and sufficient nutrients to support cell division. Cell division, occurring in a well-recognized pattern, is described by the cell cycle (Figure 3-2).

HAVE DESIGNATED APPEARANCE. Each type of normal cell has a distinct and recognizable appearance. For example, all normal heart muscle cells look alike and look different from skeletal muscle cells, liver cells, or skin cells.

SHOW A SMALL NUCLEUS-TO-CYTOPLASM RATIO. The space that the nucleus occupies inside a normal cell is small compared with the size of the cell. Therefore, the nucleus is a relatively small part of the cell.

HAVE SPECIFIC DIFFERENTIATED FUNCTIONS. Each normal cell has at least one special job or function. For example, skeletal muscle cells contract for movement, thyroid cells secrete thyroid hormones, and red blood cells make hemoglobin to carry oxygen.

ARE JOINED TIGHTLY TOGETHER. Normal cells bind closely together because they secrete cell-surface proteins that make cells of one type stick to each other.

DO NOT MIGRATE. Because normal cells are tightly bound together, they do not wander from one tissue to the next (with the exception of erythrocytes and leukocytes).

SHOW CONTACT INHIBITION. Cell division only occurs if space is adequate for the presence of new cells. Once a normal cell is in direct contact on all surface areas with other cells, it no longer undergoes mitosis. So, normal cell division is *contact inhibited.*

Abnormal Cellular Biology and Characteristics

Abnormal cells are the result of personal and environmental changes that alter cell growth and function. Some abnormal cells are considered *benign* even though they can form a tumor. Essentially, a benign tumor is composed of cells that retain normal cell features or characteristics but are growing at the wrong rate or in the wrong place. Table 3-1 compares characteristics of normal, benign tumor, and cancer cells.

TABLE 3-1
COMPARISON OF NORMAL AND ABNORMAL CELL FEATURES

Characteristic	Normal Cells	Benign Cells	Cancer Cells
Mitosis	Well-regulated	Inappropriate	Continuous
Appearance	Designated size and shape	Designated size and shape	Anaplastic
Size of nucleus	Small	Small	Large
Specific functions	Maintain specific functions	Maintain specific functions	Lose most or all specific functions
Adhesion	Strong/tight	Strong/tight	Loose/poor
Migration	Do not migrate	Do not migrate	Migrate/invade
Mitotic index	Low	Low	Low–high
Chromosome number	Euploid	Euploid	Aneuploid

Features of Benign Cells

Examples of benign tissues or tumors include moles, nerve ganglia, cysts, uterine fibroid tumors, endometriosis, and rectal polyps.

HAVE INAPPROPRIATE CELL GROWTH. Benign tumors are tissues unnecessary for normal function and often represent overgrowth of normal cells, or hyperplastic expansion. However, benign tumor cells follow normal cell growth patterns even though their growth is not needed.

HAVE DESIGNATED APPEARANCE. Benign tumors strongly resemble their parent tissues, retaining the size and shape (morphology) of the tissue from which it arose.

SHOW A SMALL NUCLEUS-TO-CYTOPLASM RATIO. As with normal cells, benign tumor cells have a small nucleus compared with the rest of the cell.

HAVE SPECIFIC DIFFERENTIATED FUNCTIONS. Benign tumors do not simply look like their parent tissues, they also perform the same differentiated functions. For example, moles, one type of benign skin tumor, have cells that make keratin and other skin products. They simply overgrow in an area where excess skin cells are not needed.

ARE JOINED TIGHTLY TOGETHER. Because benign tumor cells make and secrete the same cell-surface proteins as normal cells, they also bind tightly to one another. Often, benign tissues are "encapsulated," surrounded with fibrous connective tissue, helping to keep the benign tissue together.

DO NOT MIGRATE. Benign tissues remain tightly bound together and do not invade other body tissues.

Features of Cancer (Malignant) Cells

Cancer (malignant) cells have no useful function, are harmful to normal body tissues, and are always abnormal. The following features and characteristics are common in malignant tumors.

HAVE CONTINUOUS CELL DIVISION AND POORLY CONTROLLED GROWTH. Some cancer cells divide rapidly, perhaps in as little as 2 to 4 hours; other cancer cells may take even longer to divide than the average normal cell. It is a myth that cancer cells always divide faster than do normal cells. Usually, cancer cells have a dividing time similar to that of the tissue from which they arose. For example, bone marrow cells divide rapidly. As expected, cancerous bone marrow cells (leukemia) also divide very rapidly.

A characteristic of cancer cells is that cancer cells divide nearly continuously. Almost as soon as one round of mitosis is complete, the next begins. Cancer cells extend and invade into other tissues (close by and more distant from the original tumor) by a process called *metastasis*. Persistent growth and metastasis make cancer more difficult to treat and more likely to lead to death.

LOSE DESIGNATED APPEARANCE. Cancer cells lose the specific appearance (size and shape) of the cells from which they arose. As a cancer cell becomes even more malignant, it becomes smaller and rounder, an appearance termed *anaplastic*. This anaplastic appearance makes many types of cancer cells look alike and can make identification of the primary site more difficult.

SHOW A LARGE NUCLEUS-TO-CYTOPLASM RATIO. A cancer cell has a large nucleus compared to the size of the actual cancer cell. The nucleus takes up much of the space within the cancer cell, making a large nucleus-to-cytoplasm ratio.

LOSE SOME OR ALL DIFFERENTIATED FUNCTIONS. Along with changing the original appearance, cancer cells lose some of the specific jobs or functions they once had as normal cells. Cancer cells have no useful purpose.

ARE JOINED LOOSELY TOGETHER. Cancer cells do not make the same cell-surface proteins as normal cells. As a result, they do not stick together well, and they break away from the tumor with only slight pressure.

DO MIGRATE. Cancer cells are able to slip through blood vessels and tissues and spread from the original tumor site to many other body sites because they do not bind tightly together. In addition, many cancer cells have enzymes on their surfaces that allow them to "eat through" blood vessels and other tissues. This characteristic helps cancer cells to spread (metastasize).

DO NOT SHOW CONTACT INHIBITION. Cancer cells continue to divide even when contacted on all surface areas by other cells; thus, their growth is not contact inhibited. The persistence of cancer cell division, even under adverse conditions, is one factor making the disease so difficult to control.

Carcinogenesis/Oncogenesis

Carcinogenesis and *oncogenesis* are synonyms for cancer development, also known as malignant transformation. Malignant transformation results when a cell with a normal appearance and function changes into a cell with malignant characteristics. To become transformed, cells must go through a series of processes consisting of *initiation, promotion, progression,* and *metastasis* (Caudell, Cuaron, & Gallucci, 1996).

Initiation

Initiation begins as a normal cell's proto-onco-genes are turned back on any time after fetal life. Proto-oncogenes are genes that regulate the early, rapid cellular growth of embryonic life. Any event or exposure that can damage the DNA may dam-age the genes of a normal cell, turning on genes that should remain repressed (silent) and turning off normal genes (Cooper, 1995). Carcinogens are substances that can change the activity of a cell's genes so the cell acquires malignant characteristics. Carcinogens may be chemicals, physical agents, or viruses. Table 3-2 lists some known common carcinogens and the types of cancers they are thought to cause.

Some types of carcinogens start changes (mutations) in a cell's genes. Because they start the changes, these types of carcinogens are called *initiators*. Once a cell has been initiated by a carcinogen, it can become a cancer cell if it undergoes a process known as *promotion*. One cancer cell is not problematic unless it can divide. Cancer cells capable of dividing and growing lead to tumor formation. *Under the right conditions, widespread cancer can result from just one cancer cell.*

Promotion

Initiation of a normal cell gives that cell cancer cell characteristics. However, it usually takes some time before that one cancer cell grows sufficiently to form a discernible tumor. The time between when a normal cell is initiated to a cancer cell and when an actual tumor develops is called the *latency period*. The latency period is different for each cancer type and can last indefinitely, from months to years. One factor in the latency process is *promotion*. *Promoters* are substances that shorten the latency period by promoting or en-

TABLE 3-2
LIST OF KNOWN COMMON CARCINOGENS

Agent	Common Cancer Sites
Tobacco	Lung, oral cavity, bladder, uterine cervix, stomach, pancreas, liver, colon, rectum
Ultraviolet light	Skin, eye
Alcohol	Liver, oral cavity, breast, colon, rectum
Hair dyes	Bladder, skin
Radiation	Bone marrow, skin, lymph system, bone, any organ in radiation pathway
Benzene	Leukemia
Polychlorinated biphenyls	Skin, liver

hancing initiated cell growth (Weinberg, 1996). Some examples of promoters are hormones, drugs, and many industrial chemicals.

Progression

Eventually, cancer cells grow enough to form a detectable tumor. This growth requires many rounds of cell division. A 1-cm tumor consists of at least 1 billion cells. To threaten the health of a person, the tumor must establish its own blood supply. In the early stages, the center cells of the tumor are well nourished by diffusion from the surrounding fluids. However, after the tumor reaches 1 cm, diffusion becomes less efficient and cells in the center of the tumor lose their oxygen supply and begin to die. To counteract this process, the tumor makes *tumor angiogenesis factor* (TAF). TAF causes capillaries and other blood vessels in the area to grow new branches into the tumor, thus providing a continuing source of nourishment.

As the tumor grows with many cells dividing, the new cells experience even more change from the original initiated cancer cell. Colonies or subpopulations within the tumor begin to appear. These subpopulations differ from the original cancer cell in some special ways that provide them with "selection advantages" that allow the new cells to grow and thrive in spite of less than ideal environmental conditions. Changes that a tumor undergoes at this time allow it to become more malignant, having fewer and fewer normal cell characteristics.

The original tumor formed from transformed normal cells is called the *primary* tumor. The tissue from which they arose (parent tissue) identifies the primary tumor, such as in breast cancer or lung cancer. Primary tumors located in vital organs, such as the brain or lungs, can grow large enough to cause lethal damage or "crowd out" normal organ tissue, thus interfering with the organ's ability to function. Sometimes, the primary tumor is located in soft tissue that can expand without damage as the tumor grows. For example, the breast is not a vital organ; therefore, a large primary tumor would not cause the patient's death. As a tumor spreads from the original site into vital sites, essential life functions can be disrupted.

Metastasis

Metastasis occurs when cancer cells move from the primary site to more remote sites by breaking off from the original tumor. The cancer cells can then roam the body and establish additional tumor sites. These additional tumors are called *metastatic* or *secondary tumors*. Although the tumor is now in another organ, it is still a cancer from the original primary site. For example, when lung cancer spreads to the brain, it is lung cancer in the brain, not a primary brain tumor. Metastasis occurs through several progressive steps, as shown in Figure 3-3.

TUMOR EXTENSION

Tumors secrete enzymes that allow cancer cells to invade areas of surrounding tissue. In addition, pressure is created as the tumor increases in size, forcing tumor cells into surrounding areas.

TUMOR PENETRATION

Tumor-secreted enzymes also make large pores in the patient's blood vessels, allowing tumor cells to enter blood vessels and travel to distant sites.

TUMOR CELL RELEASE

Because tumor cells are loosely held together, portions of cells break off the primary tumor. These detached cells can enter blood vessels for transport to distant sites or may migrate into local tissue areas.

TISSUE INVASION

Having broken away from the primary tumor, cancer cells frequently circulate through the blood and enter tissues at distant sites. When conditions at the distant site are right, the cells stop circulating (arrest) and invade the new site, creating metastatic or secondary tumors. Table 3-3 lists the usual metastatic sites for common types of malignant tumors. The circulatory system, or bloodborne route, is the major route of metastasis for cancer cells; however, two additional routes also are responsible for some degree of metastasis, local seeding and lymphatic spread.

BLOODBORNE METASTASIS. Tumor cell release into the blood is the most common means of cancer

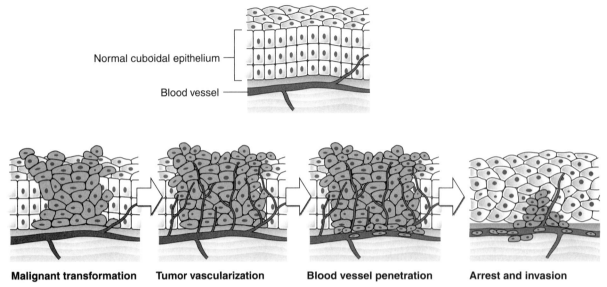

Normal cuboidal epithelium —

Blood vessel —

Malignant transformation

Some normal cuboidal cells have undergone malignant transformation and have divided enough times to form a tumorous area within the cuboidal epithelium.

Tumor vascularization

Cancer cells secrete tumor angiogenesis factor (TAF), stimulating the blood vessels to bud and form new channels growing into the tumor.

Blood vessel penetration

Cancer cells have broken off from the main tumor. Enzymes on the surface of the tumor cells make holes in the blood vessels, allowing cancer cells to enter blood vessels and travel around the body.

Arrest and invasion

Cancer cells clump up in blood vessel walls and invade new tissue areas. If the new tissue areas have the right conditions to support continued growth of cancer cells, new tumors (metastatic tumors) will form at this site.

Figure 3-3 The metastatic process. (Redrawn from Ignatavicius, D., Workman, M., & Mishler, M. [1995]. *Medical surgical nursing: A nursing process approach* [2nd ed.]. Philadelphia: W.B. Saunders.)

spread. Cancer cells, broken away from the primary tumor and carried through the bloodstream, determine the area of metastases. Groups of tumor cells can become trapped in capillaries, damage the capillary wall, and invade the surrounding tissue. However, the blood is not always a friendly environment for tumor cells. Tumor cells can be destroyed through damage incurred while circulating by the immune system or by unfavorable conditions at the secondary site.

LOCAL SEEDING. In local seeding, cancer cells from the primary tumor are shed in the local area surrounding the tumor. For example, ovarian cancer cells often spill from the ovarian tumor into other areas of the peritoneal cavity.

LYMPHATIC SPREAD. Primary tumors residing close to lymph nodes and lymphatic vessels are more susceptible to early metastatic spread than are tumors in areas with few lymphatics. Lymphatic spread is determined by the number, structure, and location of lymph nodes and vessels.

Classification of Cancer

Cancer arises from various tissues and organs. Generally, cancers are categorized as either solid tumors or hematologic malignancies. Solid tumors refer to the organs from which they develop, for

TABLE 3-3
SITES OF METASTASIS FOR COMMON TUMORS

Cancer	Sites of Metastasis
Lung cancer	Lymph nodes, brain, bone, liver, pancreas
Colorectal cancer	Adjacent lymph nodes, liver
Breast cancer	Bone, brain, lung, liver
Leukemia	Visceral organs, brain
Prostate cancer	Bone, adjacent lymph nodes, lung

example, colon cancer and breast cancer. Although cells from solid tumors can break off the tumor and travel in the blood, they will reform into a solid tumor at the metastatic site. Hematologic malignancies are cancers such as leukemia and lymphoma that originate from blood cell-forming tissues, such as the bone marrow. At first, hematologic malignancies remain in a liquid suspension rather than forming a palpable tumor.

Cancer can arise in any organ or tissue, although some organs and tissues develop cancer more frequently than others. More than 100 different types of cancer have been identified. Table 3-4 lists the five most common malignancies for men and for women. Terms that describe neoplasia by tissue origin and classify the tumor as benign or malignant are listed in Table 3-5. Other terms describe the tumor's biologic behavior, anatomic site, and degree of differentiation.

Cancer Grading and Staging

A classification system for the grading and staging of tumors was created as a means of standardizing criteria for cancer diagnosis, prognosis, and treatment. When a tumor is *graded,* it is examined for its cellular characteristics. Staging of a tumor classifies the cancer according to its clinical presentation.

GRADING

Grading compares the cancer cell with the normal parent tissue from which it arose on the basis of both cell appearance and cell activity (Caudell,

Cuaron & Gallucci, 1996). By classifying cancer cells' cellular characteristics, predictions can be made regarding the aggressiveness of the cancer and how it may respond to treatment. This classification system rates tumor cells, with a "low grade" given to those tumors that most closely resemble normal cells. Cancer cells that are very aggressive and metastasize rapidly are considered a "high-grade tumor." High-grade tumors barely resemble the parent tissue. An example of a standard grading system is presented in Table 3-6. In addition to providing standardization, grading of tumor cells allows health care professionals to evaluate the results of management and be able to compare local, regional, and international statistics.

CHROMOSOMAL FEATURES

A biologic feature useful in describing cancer cells is *ploidy status.* Ploidy status refers to the number of complete chromosome sets within the nucleus of a cell. Normal human cells have 46 chromosomes (23 pairs), considered the normal diploid number. Cells that contain the normal diploid number are referred to as *euploid.* Malignant transformation can cause changes in the genes and chromosomes. Tumor cells can gain or lose whole chromosomes, or have structural abnormalities of the chromosomes. When a tumor cell has more or less than the normal diploid number, it is said to be *aneuploid.* As malignant transformation progresses, the amount of aneuploidy also increases.

TABLE 3-4

INCIDENCE AND DEATHS FOR THE FIVE MOST COMMON CANCER TYPES FOR MEN AND WOMEN

Cancer Incidence		Cancer Deaths	
Men	*Women*	*Men*	*Women*
Prostate	Breast	Lung	Lung
Lung	Lung	Prostate	Breast
Colorectal	Colorectal	Colorectal	Colorectal
Bladder	Uterus	Pancreas	Pancreas
Non-Hodgkin's lymphoma	Ovary	Non-Hodgkin's lymphoma	Ovary

(Data from American Cancer Society. [1998]. *Cancer facts & figures–1998.* Atlanta: American Cancer Society.)

TABLE 3-5

NOMENCLATURE OF SELECTED NEOPLASTIC TISSUES

Parent Tissues	Benign Tumors	Malignant Tumors
Epithelial (Glandular)		
Breast (ductal	Adenoma	Adenocarcinoma
Liver	Hepatoma	Hepatocarcinoma
Colon	Polyps	Adenocarcinoma
Uterine cervix	Cervical dysplasia	Cervical carcinoma
Connective (Fibrous)		
Skin	Papilloma	Papillosarcoma
Bone	Osteoma	Osteosarcoma
Adipose	Lipoma	Liposarcoma
Uterine muscle	Myoma	Myosarcoma
Blood vessel	Hemangioma	Hemangiosarcoma
Hematologic/Lymphatic		
Leukocytes	—	Leukemia
Lymphoid tissue	—	Lymphoma
		Myeloma

TABLE 3-6

CANCER GRADING SYSTEM

Grade Level	Cellular Features
I	Low-grade malignancy
	Cells are similar to normal parent tissue and have a slow growth rate
	Well-differentiated in appearance and function
II	Low- to moderate-grade malignancy
	Cells have some normal and some malignant cell features
	The tissue of origin is apparent
III	Moderate- to high-grade malignancy
	Cells have more malignant features than normal cell features
	Tissue of origin may not be obvious but can be determined
IV	High-grade malignancy
	Cells have no normal cell features in appearance or function
	Tissue of origin may be unknown

STAGING

Staging allows the clinician to pinpoint the exact location and degree of metastatic spread of a given tumor. Tumor stage at the time of diagnosis also influences the selection of therapy. Usually, the smaller the tumor is at diagnosis and the less it has spread, the better the prognosis. Three different types of staging are usually performed:

1. *Clinical Staging.* In clinical staging, the patient's clinical manifestations are assessed. Also, clinical signs are evaluated for the tumor size and degree of metastasis. Clinical tests, such as computed tomography (CT) scans, are used to assist in clinical staging. Tumor cells are also obtained for biopsy.
2. *Surgical Staging.* During inspection at surgery, tumor size, number, sites, and degree of metastasis are determined.
3. *Pathologic Staging.* The most definitive type of staging is pathologic staging. Here, tumor size, number, sites, and degree of metastasis are determined by pathologic examination of tissues obtained at surgery.

The Dukes' staging of colon and rectal cancer and the Clark's levels method of staging skin cancer are two examples of site-specific staging systems. The TNM (tumor, node, metastasis) system was developed to describe the anatomic extent of cancers. TNM staging systems are specific to each solid tumor site. This staging system is not useful for cancers arising from the bone marrow or lymphoid tissues. The TNM staging system is based on the fact that similar cancers share similar patterns of growth and extension. Table 3-7 lists basic definitions for the TNM staging system.

In staging, tumor growth is discussed in terms of doubling time (the amount of time it takes for a tumor to double in size) and mitotic index (the percentage of actively dividing cells within a tumor). A 1-cm tumor likely to be detected by a physical examination or diagnostic test contains 1 billion cells. A tumor would need to undergo at least 30 doublings to reach this size. A mitotic index of less than 10% indicates a rather slow-growing tumor, whereas a mitotic index of 85% indicates a tumor that is growing quickly. Tumors vary widely in their growth rates. Fast-growing tumors, such as small cell lung cancer, may double

TABLE 3-7

STAGING OF LUNG CANCER: TNM CLASSIFICATION

Stage	Tumor	Node	Metastasis	
I	T_1	N_0	M_0	
	T_1	N_1	M_0	
	T_2	N_0	M_0	
II	T_2	N_1	M_0	
III	T_3	N_{0-2}	M_{0-1}	
	T_{1-3}	N_2	M_{0-1}	
	T_{1-3}	N_{0-2}	M_{0-1}	

Key: T T_1 = tumor size < 3.0 cm; T_2 = tumor > 3.0 cm or shows invasion of visceral pleura; T_3 = tumor any size with direct extension to adjacent tissue

N N_0 = no metastasis to the lymph nodes; N_1 = cancer present in lung lymph nodes; N_2 = cancer present in mediastinal lymph nodes

M M_0 = no known metastasis to any distant site
M_1 = known metastasis to any distant site

(Modified from Beahrs, O., Henson, D., Hutter, R., & Myers, M. [eds.] [1988]. *Manual for staging of cancer* [3rd ed., p. 7]. Philadelphia: Lippincott-Raven.)

in 3 to 4 weeks; an adenocarcinoma of the colon may double in 30 to 40 weeks.

Causes of Cancer Development

Cancer development through the processes of carcinogenesis/ oncogenesis can take years and depends on both tumor and patient factors. Three interacting primary factors influence the development of cancer: (1) environmental exposure to carcinogens, (2) genetic predisposition to a cancer, and (3) immune system status. These factors account for variation in cancer development from one person to another, even if each is exposed to the same hazards.

For some cancers, specific causes have been identified. In some cases, people considered at risk for cancer development can avoid contact with specific agents associated with the development of a particular cancer. This is called *primary prevention* of cancer. For many types of cancer, absolute causes remain unknown or exposure cannot be

avoided, making primary prevention impossible. For most people, early detection, or *secondary prevention,* can be helpful. Secondary prevention focuses on diagnosis of small tumors that have not metastasized, making the outcome of treatment more favorable.

Activation of Oncogenes

The activation of proto-oncogenes into oncogenes is the main mechanism of carcinogenesis. Normal cells exposed to any carcinogen (initiator) can damage or mutate the normal cell's DNA. The resulting mutations can cause the early embryonic genes (proto-oncogenes), which should be repressed forever, to be turned on or activated again. The proto-oncogenes become oncogenes, causing the mutated cell to change and become malignant (Cooper, 1995).

Approximately 50 different proto-oncogenes that can be activated into oncogenes have been identified. Scientists estimate that at least 50 more proto-oncogenes exist (Cooper, 1995; Weinberg, 1994). *Proto-oncogenes are not abnormal genes,* but a normal part of every cell's makeup, and are important in early embryonic development. Oncogenes lead to cancer development only if they are activated after development is complete, as a result of exposure to carcinogenic agents or events. The activation of certain oncogenes is directly associated with the development of specific cancers. Conditions both internal and external to the person are thought to be able to activate oncogenes and cause cancer.

Internal Conditions That Promote Cancer Development

Some conditions or factors unique to the individual influence a person's chances of developing cancer. Such conditions include age, immune system status, and genetic heritage.

AGE

Aging is the greatest risk factor associated with cancer development. Fifty percent of all cancers occur in people older than 65 years (American Cancer Society, 1998). Cancer occurs least commonly in people between the ages of 18 and 40 years. Three theories have been proposed to account for the higher cancer incidence in older adults.

The first theory suggests that older people have had more opportunity for greater exposure to environmental carcinogens that mutate DNA and can cause malignant transformation. Some of these exposures may have been to relatively mild carcinogens, but the chronicity of the exposure may have led to cumulative DNA damage, eventually resulting in oncogene activation. Thus, cancer in older people may reflect life-long carcinogenic events.

A second theory proposes that, as cells age, they are less able to repair the damage inflicted even by mild carcinogens (in much the same ways that older cells and tissues take on the appearance of aging because the cellular repair processes slow down.)

Finally, immune function in older people gradually decreases. Because immune function, particularly cell-mediated immunity, is critical in the early identification and elimination of cancer cells, age-related immune deficiency reduces the likelihood that an early-stage cancer could be successfully destroyed by the body's own defenses. Thus, malignant transformation may not occur any more frequently in older adults than in younger adults, but the transformation is more successful in older adults than in younger adults.

IMMUNE SYSTEM STATUS

A well-functioning immune system protects the body from foreign invaders and growth of unhealthy body cells, including cancer cells. The immune system can recognize when normal cells have undergone malignant transformation and take steps to eliminate the transformed cells before they can form tumors. Thus, the immune system plays a continuing role in surveillance and cancer protection. The specific immune function responsible for cancer protection is cell-mediated immunity.

People whose immune systems are chronically functioning at less than optimum levels have a greater incidence of cancer development. Such groups include children younger than 2 and adults older than 60, organ transplant recipients taking immunosuppressive drugs to reduce the risk of organ rejection, and people with acquired immunodeficiency syndrome (AIDS).

GENETIC HERITAGE

Oncogenes are considered internal conditions associated with cancer development. Proto-oncogenes, precursors of oncogenes, are passed on from generation to generation. However, cancer development requires more than just the presence of these genes. The proto-oncogene needs to be damaged or altered to allow activation to oncogene status. The location of specific proto-oncogenes is different in some people and allows the proto-oncogenes to be activated more easily (Cooper, 1995). In other people, the position of the oncogene may be normal, but the gene controlling the oncogene's activity, the *suppressor gene,* may be inactive or out of place. One example of this situation is women who have a mutation of the BRCA-1 gene. If only one of the pair of these genes is abnormal, the woman has a 50% risk for developing breast cancer. If both genes of the pair are abnormal, the risk for developing breast cancer may exceed 90%.

Some variations in gene location or degree of activity are inheritable. Thus, some people are more at risk for certain types of cancers than is the general population. Usually, inherited types of cancer occur at an earlier age than noninherited cancers of the same type. In addition, the incidence of cancer development is higher within a family that has alterations or mutations of either oncogenes or suppressor genes. Detailed family histories can help to identify people at high risk. Once such individuals are identified, secondary prevention with frequent screening is important for long-term survival.

Some families have a higher incidence of all types of cancer, rather than of just one type. This situation probably represents the effects of more than one gene and does increase the risk for all members of the family; however, the risk for any one family member is less predictable than when the cancer is associated with a known single gene mutation. In addition, some families may have higher incidences of inherited health problems that have a high association with cancer development, such as Down syndrome, Turner's syndrome, Klinefelter's syndrome, and Fanconi's anemia.

The incidence of cancer varies among races, also suggesting a link between genetic heritage and susceptibility to cancer development. American Cancer Society (1998) data show that African Americans have a higher incidence of cancer than Caucasians do, and the death rate from cancer also is higher for African Americans. The incidence of prostate cancer and uterine cancer is higher among African Americans than among Caucasians. The incidence of breast cancer is highest among Caucasian women and lowest among Asian women.

External Conditions That Promote Cancer Development

Up to 80% of cancer in the United States may be the result of environmental, or external, conditions (Trichopoulos, Li & Hunter, 1996). Many environmental carcinogens have been identified as causative of human cancer. Such carcinogens include physical, chemical, and viral agents.

PHYSICAL CARCINOGENS

Physical agents or events can induce DNA damage and stimulate cancer development. Two types of physical agents with the potential to cause cancer are radiation and chronic irritation.

RADIATION. Even small doses of radiation can enter cells and damage the DNA. Some damages are temporary and can be repaired if the person is healthy, immunocompetent, and not yet suffering the cellular consequences of aging. Other damage is irreversible and either may be lethal to the damaged cell or may initiate malignant transformation as the damaged cell tries unsuccessfully to repair itself. Both ionizing radiation and ultraviolet radiation can cause cancer, depending on the type of exposure and the dose of radiation received. Ionizing radiation occurs naturally in such minerals as radon, uranium, and radium, but the most common sources of ionizing radiation exposure in this country are diagnostic x-rays, radiation therapy, and industrial accidents. Common sources of ultraviolet (UV) rays are solar radiation (sunlight), tanning beds, and germicidal lights. UV rays are most commonly associated with skin cancers because this type of radiation does not penetrate deeply into body tissues.

Both ionizing and ultraviolet radiation induce gene mutations and can transform cells. Radiation exposure induces cancers more frequently among cells that can divide, although it can also cause cancer among nondividing cells.

CHRONIC IRRITATION. Chronic irritation, particularly tissue trauma, appears to be a predisposing condition to cancer development. Support for this theory includes the fact that the incidence of skin cancer is higher in people with burn scars and other tissues that have sustained severe injury. Chronically irritated tissues, such as the intestinal lining in people with Crohn's disease, undergo frequent mitosis and, thus, are at an increased risk for spontaneous DNA mutations leading to cancer development.

CHEMICAL CARCINOGENS

Many chemicals, drugs, and other products used in everyday life are known to be carcinogenic, and hundreds more are suspected of causing cancer. Some of these chemical carcinogens are so dangerous and powerful that they can both initiate and promote cancer. Others are capable of inducing only initiation or only promotion. Certain chemicals, such as tobacco and alcohol, are only mildly carcinogenic. As a result, chronic exposures to large amounts of these chemicals are required before a cancer develops. However, these two substances can act synergistically as co-carcinogens. Thus, when a person is exposed to both substances over a lifetime, they enhance the carcinogenic activity of each other and other carcinogens.

Cells are not equally susceptible to damage and transformation by chemical carcinogens. The cells at greatest risk for malignant transformation are those that retain the ability to divide even after physical development is complete. Thus, cancers develop most frequently in skin, the lining of the gastrointestinal tract, the ductal cells of the breast, the lining of the lungs, and in the bone marrow. All of these cells normally divide (undergo mitosis) throughout the life span. Cancers are much more rare in tissues that do not normally undergo cell division in adults, such as cardiac tissue, nerves, and skeletal muscle.

Although tobacco is considered to be a relatively mild carcinogen in that chronic exposure is required for cancer development, tobacco use contributes to at least 30% of cancers diagnosed in the United States (American Cancer Society, 1998). Tobacco contains many different agents that can initiate and/or promote malignant transformation over time. Thus, elimination of tobacco use has the potential to prevent hundreds of thousands of needless illnesses and deaths by cancer every year.

Cancer risk with tobacco use is greatest for tissues that have direct contact with tobacco smoke. Cigarette smoking and tobacco use also are associated with cancer development even in tissues that do not come into direct contact with tobacco smoke, such as the uterine cervix.

VIRAL CARCINOGENESIS

Thus far, only a few viruses have been proved to cause cancer in humans, although many are suspected to be directly or indirectly involved in the carcinogenesis process. Viruses are intracellular parasites and must infect a living cell in order to reproduce. When viruses infect human body cells, they break the human DNA chain and insert their own genetic material into the human DNA chain. The insertion of viral genetic material into human DNA and breaking the human DNA can mutate the infected cell's DNA and initiate the malignant transformation process. Viruses known to cause human cancers are called *oncoviruses*.

Diet and Cancer Development

Some epidemiologic studies implicate high-fat and/or low-fiber diets as contributing to development of certain types of cancer. Because the evidence is not clear cut, diet is not currently considered an actual cause of cancer; however, diet may interact with other personal (internal) and external conditions to have an impact on the process of carcinogenesis. Food additives (dyes, flavorings, and sweeteners), preservatives, contaminants, and processing methods (such as smoking) may increase the carcinogenic potential of some foods.

Role of the Immune System

The immune system plays a pivotal role in protecting a person from developing cancer through a process called *immunosurveillance*. Humans are exposed to carcinogens daily. It is likely that at least a few cells undergo malignant transformation every day; however, malignancies usually fail to develop from these transformations because of the protection provided by the cell-mediated portion of immune function. Therefore, maintaining immunologic health is critical in cancer prevention.

Cell-mediated immunity (CMI) or cellular immunity provides protection from cellular antigens. These antigens can be invading microorganisms or body cells that are no longer completely healthy. Cells that have undergone malignant transformation are considered unhealthy body cells by the immune system. The white blood cells (leukocytes) composing cell-mediated immunity are able to recognize a transformed cell on contact as being unhealthy and, therefore, undesirable. The specialized leukocytes of the cell-mediated branch of the immune system take action to destroy or eliminate the unhealthy body cell. If the transformed cell is either eliminated from the body or destroyed, it cannot develop into a malignant tumor capable of metastasis.

Many different leukocyte types compose cell-mediated immunity. The types thought to be most important in protecting the body from cancer development are three lymphocytes: helper/inducer T-lymphocytes, cytotoxic T-lymphocytes, and natural killer (NK) cells. These three cell types start out in the bone marrow as undifferentiated cells and undergo partial maturation into prelymphocytes. These prelymphocytes leave the bone marrow and complete maturation under the influence of hormones from the thymus gland (hence the designation T-lymphocytes).

Helper/Inducer T-Lymphocytes

The helper/inducer cells express the T_4 membrane protein and are known as T_4 cells, CD_4 cells, or "helper T-cells." Their role in cancer prevention is important but indirect. These cells are efficient in the recognition of unhealthy body cells but do not take direct defensive actions against them. Instead, the helper T-cell secretes proteins that improve the efficiency of all immune system cells, making them better defenders and fighters. In effect, the helper T-cells act as "generals" in organizing various squads of fighter lymphocytes to defend the body from cancer cells.

Cytotoxic T-Lymphocytes

Cytotoxic T-lymphocytes are also called CD_8 cells and T_8 cells because they express the T_8 protein on their cell surfaces. Cytotoxic T-cells function by breaking open unhealthy body cells that have been infected by parasitic organisms, such as viruses.

This action is direct when the cytotoxic T-cell recognizes a virally infected cell to which it has been previously exposed. The cytotoxic T-cell binds to the virally infected cell (which may have undergone malignant transformation as a result of the viral infection) and delivers a "lethal hit" of enzymes to the infected cell, causing it to lyse and die.

Natural Killer Cells

Natural killer (NK) cells may be the most important cell contributing to cancer protection. NK cells direct cell-killing effects on any body cell that appears unhealthy, including cancer cells. NK cells conduct "seek and destroy" missions in the body to eliminate invaders and unhealthy self cells.

Summary

Cancer is a common health problem in the United States, accounting for great personal suffering and significant expenditure of health care dollars. Not all people are at equal risk for cancer development. Conditions both internal to the person and external to the person influence if or when cancer will develop. Some cancers can be prevented through lifestyle modifications and avoidance of known carcinogens (primary prevention of cancer). Other cancers do not yet appear to be preventable because an exact cause is not known. Because most cancer types are more likely to be cured when they are diagnosed at an early stage with small tumors that have not spread to other body areas, screening practices for early detection (secondary prevention) can make a difference in cancer survival rates.

REFERENCES

American Cancer Society. (1998). *Cancer facts & figures–1998* (98—300M—No. 5008.98). Atlanta: American Cancer Society.

American Cancer Society. (1991). *Proceedings of the national workshop on cancer control and the older person* (91—3M—No. 3043). Atlanta: American Cancer Society.

Ames, B., Gold, L., & Willett, W.C. (1995). The causes and prevention of cancer. *Proceedings of the National Academy of Sciences, 92*(12), 5258–5265.

Baron, R., & Borgen, P. (1997). Genetic susceptibility for breast cancer: Testing and primary prevention options. *Oncology Nursing Forum, 24*(3), 461–468.

Bishop, J. (1995). Cancer: The rise of the genetic paradigm. *Genes and Development, 9*(11), 1309–1315.

Caudell, K., Cuaron, L., & Gallucci, B. (1996). Cancer biology: Molecular and cellular aspects. In R. McCorkle, M. Grant, M. Frank-Stromborg, & S. Baird (Eds.), *Cancer nursing: A comprehensive textbook* (2nd ed., pp. 150–170). Philadelphia: W. B. Saunders.

Cooper, G. (1995). *Oncogenes* (2nd ed.). Boston: Jones & Bartlett.

Fidler, I., & Hart, I. (1982). Biologic diversity in metastatic neoplasia: Origins and implications. *Science, 217*(4564), 1998.

Frank-Stromborg, M., Heusinkveld, K., & Rohan, K. (1996). Evaluating cancer risks and preventive oncology. In R. McCorkle, M. Grant, M. Fran-Stromborg, & S. Baird (Eds.), *Cancer nursing: A comprehensive textbook* (2nd ed., pp. 213–264). Philadelphia: W. B. Saunders.

Liotta, L. (1992). Cancer cell invasion and metastasis. *Scientific American, 266*(2), 54–62.

Mettlin, C., & Michalek, A. (1996). The causes of cancer. In R. McCorkle, M. Grant, M. Frank-Stromborg, & S. Baird (Eds.), *Cancer nursing: A comprehensive textbook* (2nd ed., pp. 138–149). Philadelphia: W. B. Saunders.

Mitelman, F. (1994). Chromosomes, genes, and cancer. *CA: A Cancer Journal for Clinicians, 44*(3), 133–135.

Olsen, S., & Frank-Stromborg, M. (1996). Cancer screening and early detection. In R. McCorkle, M. Grant, M. Frank-Stromborg, & S. Baird (Eds.), *Cancer nursing: A comprehensive textbook* (2nd ed., pp. 265–297). Philadelphia: W. B. Saunders.

Pitot, H. (1986). *Fundamentals of oncology* (2nd ed.). New York: Marcel Dekker.

Ruoslahti, E. (1996). How cancer spreads. *Scientific American, 275*(3), 72–77.

Trichopoulos, D., Li, F., & Hunter, D. (1996). What causes cancer? *Scientific American, 275*(3), 80–87.

Weinberg, R. (1996). How cancer arises. *Scientific American, 275*(3), 62–70.

Weinberg, R. (1994). Oncogenes and tumor suppressor genes. *CA: A Cancer Journal for Clinicians, 44*(3), 160–170.

Wingo, P., Bolden, S., Tong, T., Parker, S., Martin, L., & Heath, C. (1996). Cancer statistics for African Americans, 1996. *CA: A Cancer Journal for Clinicians, 46*(2), 113–125.

CHAPTER 4

Lung Cancer

Ryan Iwamoto

Lung cancer remains a major health problem, causing more deaths in the United States than any other cancer. In spite of aggressive therapies used to treat lung cancer, there has been no improvement in long-term survival. Nursing care is aimed at improving quality of life by controlling symptoms associated with the disease and treatment and providing education and support to patients and families.

Incidence and Risk Factors

It is estimated that 171,600 new cases of lung cancer will be diagnosed in 1999 (Landis, Murray, Bolden & Wingo, 1999). In addition, an estimated 158,900 deaths from lung cancer (90,900 men and 68,000 women) will occur during the year (Landis et al., 1999). Figures 4-1 and 4-2 graph the age-adjusted lung cancer death rates in the United States between 1930 and 1994. Although the incidence of lung cancer is decreasing in middle-aged men (87/100,000 in 1984 to 80/100,000 in 1991), it is increasing in women (37.7/100,000 in 1987 to 42/100,000 in 1991). This increase in the incidence of lung cancer in women is attributed to the increase in the numbers of women who are smoking. In 1987, lung cancer surpassed breast cancer as the leading cause of cancer death in women. Lung cancer now accounts for 25% of the cancer deaths in women (Landis et al., 1999). African Americans experience poorer survival rates for lung cancers than white Americans. The 5-year survival is 11% for African Americans and 13% for white Americans.

Several epidemiologic studies have proved a causal link between lung cancer and smoking (Novello, Davis & Giovino, 1991; Samet, 1993; Zang & Wynder, 1996). It is estimated that 80% to 90% of lung cancers can be prevented if people do not smoke. The relative risk of lung cancer increases with the number of cigarettes smoked per day and the number of years of smoking history. People who start smoking before age 15 have a significantly greater risk of lung cancer than those who start after age 25. In patients with similar pack-years of consumption, the duration of smoking appears to be more important than the number of cigarettes smoked per day. However, the exact mechanisms by which smoking causes lung cancer are unknown.

Second-hand smoke or passive smoking is the involuntary exposure of nonsmokers to tobacco smoke. Second-hand smoke occurs within families when one member smokes in the presence of others, as well as in the workplace and in public areas, such as drinking establishments that usually do not restrict smoking. Although second-hand smoke is qualitatively similar to smoke inhaled by the smoker, fewer lung cancers are attributable to passive than active smoking.

The incidence of lung cancer is higher in urban than rural areas. This difference may be ascribed to more air pollution in urban areas. Pollution in the air can contain elements such as polycyclic hydrocarbons, metals, radionuclides, diesel exhaust, and asbestos fibers. However, it is un-

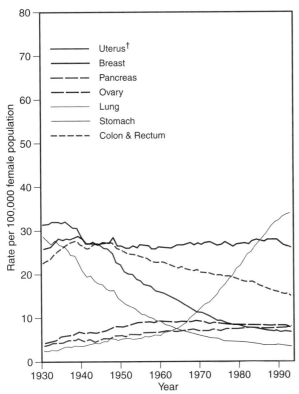

Note: Due to changes in the ICD coding, numerator information has changed over time. Rates for cancer of the uterus, ovary, lung, and colon & rectum are affected by these coding changes.

*Rates are per 100,000 population and are age-adjusted to the 1970 US standard population.

†Uterine cancer death rates are for cervix (uterus) and endometrium (uterus) combined.

Data source: Vital Statistics of the United States, 1997

Figure 4-1 Age-adjusted cancer death rates for females in the United States, 1930–1994. (Reprinted by permission from Landis, S.H., Murray T., Bolden S., & Wingo P.A. [1998]. Cancer statistics, 1998. *CA: A Cancer Journal for Clinicians, 48,* 6–29.)

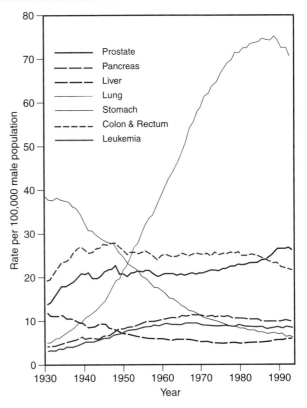

Note: Due to changes in the ICD coding, numerator information has changed over time. Rates for cancer of the liver, lung, and colon & rectum are affected by these coding changes.

*Rates are per 100,000 population and are age-adjusted to the 1970 US standard population.

Data source: Vital Statistics of the United States, 1997

Figure 4-2 Age-adjusted cancer death rates for males in the United States, 1930–1994. (Reprinted by permission from Landis, S.H., Murray T., Bolden S., & Wingo P.A. [1998]. Cancer statistics, 1998. *CA: A Cancer Journal for Clinicians, 48,* 6–29.)

clear whether air pollution functions as a promoter or as a carcinogen in the development of lung cancer.

Chronic occupational exposures to arsenic, asbestos, chloromethyl ethers, and nickel account for 12% of lung cancer deaths. Industrial workers such as shipyard workers, miners, and pipe fitters are commonly exposed to asbestos and petroleum products. Asbestos exposure is a known risk for lung cancer. Limiting occupational and other types of exposure to asbestos will help minimize risks for lung cancer. Uranium miners experience a higher incidence of small-cell lung cancers; this in-

crease may be due to their exposure to radon. In addition, smoking compounds the risk for lung cancer in people who are chronically exposed to industrial carcinogens.

Occupational health measures such as on-site smoking cessation programs, premarket testing of new chemical compounds, use of industrial hygiene techniques, legal and regulatory approaches, and epidemiologic surveillance can all reduce the occupational risk for lung cancer.

Radon is a naturally occurring gas that results from the decay of uranium and is emitted from soil and rocks. Radon is colorless, tasteless, and odorless and can enter homes through cracks in the foundations as well as drains or wells. Radon is estimated to cause 9,000 to 13,000 cancer deaths per year. Home monitoring kits are available. The Environmental Protection Agency recommends that steps be taken to clear and stop the emission of radon when levels exceed 4 pCi/L.

There is little evidence to suggest a genetic link for lung cancer. Evidence does point to a link between both chronic obstructive pulmonary disease and progressive systemic sclerosis and lung cancer. Lung scars from tuberculosis or pulmonary inflammatory processes and parenchymal fibrosis can become sites of lung cancer, which are usually adenocarcinomas.

Prevention

Eliminating tobacco use can control lung cancer. Although per capita cigarette consumption has declined in the last 20 years, cigarette use among adolescents and African Americans remains relatively high. Programs are needed to prevent initiating smoking and to help smokers to quit. Both behavioral and pharmacologic efforts are needed for smoking cessation to be effective (Tsoh et al., 1997). One of three people in smoking cessation programs remains abstinent for 1 year after attempting to quit. Success at quitting increases with the number of attempts made because it usually takes several attempts before a smoker quits for good.

The Agency for Health Care Policy and Research has published guidelines for smoking cessation (Fiore et al., 1996). Table 4-1 lists clinical practice recommendations for smoking cessation. These guidelines are cost-effective by including intensive counseling and using adjuvant pharmacologic therapy such as the nicotine patch (Cromwell, Bartosch, Fiore, Hasselblad & Baker, 1997).

A variety of pharmacologic interventions are available (Cinciripini & McClure, 1998; Sarna, 1998; Tsoh et al., 1997). Nicotine replacement products help to control symptoms of nicotine withdrawal during smoking cessation and improve cessation rates and reduce relapse of smoking. Nicotine replacement is available in several forms. Nicotine gum is chewed every 1 to 2 hours for 30 minutes and may be used for up to 3 months. Nicotine patches are worn daily for approximately

---

T A B L E 4 - 1

SMOKING CESSATION: RECOMMENDATION FOR CLINICAL PRACTICE

Nicotine replacement therapy, clinician-delivered social support, and skills training are the three most effective components of smoking cessation treatment. The four "A"s of smoking cessation are listed below.

Ask about smoking:

  Ask and record tobacco use status of every patient at each office visit.

Advise to stop smoking.

Assist to quit:

1. Offer smoking cessation treatment at each office visit for patients who smoke.
2. Help patient set a "quit date."
3. Assess and target motivations to quit.
4. Stress importance of total abstinence from tobacco.
5. Review past quit attempts and why they failed.
6. Anticipate any challenges or barriers to success and help patient devise plans to deal with challenges.
7. Ensure that smoking cessation program is sufficiently extensive using a variety of clinical specialists and program formats such as support groups.
8. Offer nicotine replacement therapy.

Arrange follow-up contact:

  Congratulate successful attempt and help patient to learn from failed attempts.

(From Fiore M.C., Bailey W.C., Cohen S.J., et al. [1996]. *Smoking cessation. Clinical Practice Guideline No. 18.* Rockville, MD: Department of Health and Human Services, Public Health Service, Agency for Health Care Policy and Research. Publ. 96-0692; and Sarna, L. & Brown, J. [1995]. Tobacco prevention and cessation in oncology nursing practice, education and research. *Oncology Nursing Forum, 22,* 256–257.)

8 weeks. Patients are instructed to stop smoking at the time the patches are started. Buprion is an antidepressant and the first non-nicotine replacement therapy. Combined with counseling sessions, these pharmacologic measures can help increase smoking cessation rates.

For heavy smokers who have had previous attempts at cessation, formal smoking cessation programs may be necessary. To be effective, these programs need to be at least 2 weeks in length with four to seven sessions, with each session lasting at least 30 minutes. The American Cancer Society, the American Lung Association, and the National Cancer Institute provide educational tools and self-help quit kits for smokers. The annual Great American Smokeout sponsored by the American Cancer Society encourages smokers to try quitting for 1 day.

Those who smoke need to be told that smoking cessation is associated with a gradual decrease in the risk of lung cancer. Estimates are that in people who abstain from smoking for 10 years, the risk of lung cancer approaches the level of those who have never smoked (Samet, 1992).

Government initiatives to control tobacco use are also important in the effort to control smoking-related diseases. Regulatory activities such as cigarette taxes, community education programs, warning labels on cigarette packaging, restriction of advertising, and limiting smoking in public places can all decrease smoking rates for the general public.

Diets that are high in fruits and vegetables may be protective against lung cancer, whereas diets deficient in vitamin A appear to be associated with the disease. However, chemoprevention trials with vitamin A have shown no benefit in preventing lung cancer (Alpha-Tocopherol, Beta Carotene Cancer Prevention Study Group, 1994).

Clinical Presentation

Cough is the most frequent presenting symptom (Emami & Perez, 1992). Although lung cancers usually grow for years before clinical presentation, they are rarely diagnosed in a localized stage. In addition, because a chronic "cigarette cough" is common in smokers, it may not seem significant until more advanced symptoms such as blood-tinged sputum occur (Held, 1995). Recurrent respiratory infections may also signal the presence of lung cancer.

The only screening tests available for asymptomatic lung cancers are chest x-ray and sputum cytology. These tests are usually used together in screening; however, their cost limits their use in mass screening efforts. Chest x-rays are able to detect peripherally located tumors, and sputum cytologies are helpful in detecting centrally located lung tumors. Sputum cytologies are used to detect malignant cells in the sputum. The patient produces three early-morning specimens of sputum for microscopic evaluation. Earlier detection seems to lengthen the interval between diagnosis and death without increasing total life span.

The presenting symptoms depend on the location and type of tumor. Local symptoms include cough, chest pain because of invasion of the pleura or chest wall by the tumor, hemoptysis, dyspnea, and wheezing as well as frequent respiratory infections. Systemic complaints may include anorexia, weight loss, fever, and fatigue.

Paraneoplastic syndromes are more common with lung cancer than with any other type of cancer. These syndromes cause various systemic symptoms. Paraneoplastic syndromes are more commonly seen with small-cell lung cancer (SCLC) than non–small-cell lung cancers (NSCLC). The symptoms of paraneoplastic syndrome with lung cancer include clubbing of fingers, ectopic hormone production (adrenocorticotropic hormone, calcitonin, human chorionic gonadotropin, antidiuretic hormone, parathormone), and a variety of neuromuscular syndromes.

Hypercalcemia (calcium > 11 mg/dL; normal: .5–10.5 mg/dL) and parathormone syndrome are frequently seen with squamous cell carcinomas. The symptoms of hypercalcemia may be subtle and mimic those of advanced cancer (Schmitt, 1993). These symptoms include nausea, vomiting, anorexia, constipation, lethargy, drowsiness, fatigue, polyuria, and polydipsia. Late symptoms include confusion, coma, bradycardia, and hypertension. Paraneoplastic hypercalcemia is relieved with treatment of the primary tumor. Other measures include minimizing immobilization, rehydration with loop diuretics, and the use of biphosphonates such as pamidronate.

Lung cancers can also occur in the apices of the lung and progress to include chest wall invasion with destruction of adjacent ribs or vertebrae. The patient experiences shoulder pain, dysesthesias, and Horner's syndrome; this is called Pancoast's syndrome.

When there are right-sided lung tumors or large mediastinal lymph nodes, obstruction of the superior vena cava can occur. Patients report dyspnea as well as swelling of the face, neck, and arms. Upon examination, thoracic vein and neck vein distention and evidence of collateral circulation over the anterior chest may be seen.

Diagnostic Workup

The chest radiograph is generally the first and most valuable diagnostic tool for lung cancer (Feld, Ginsberg, Payne & Shepherd, 1995). The diagnostic workup for lung cancer includes a thorough history and physical examination. Radiologic studies include a chest radiograph and may also include computed tomography (CT) scanning. The CT scan is used to determine the extent of tumor and lymph node involvement and determine if the patient is a surgical candidate. A CT scan of the abdomen may also be obtained to determine the presence of hepatic and adrenal metastases. If brain metastases are suspected in high-risk patients with SCLC, adenocarcinomas, and large-cell carcinomas, a CT scan of the brain is performed. The presence, duration, and severity of pulmonary and extrapulmonary symptoms are evaluated. Risk factors are reviewed as well as other systemic symptoms such as weight loss.

Centrally located tumors may yield positive sputum cytology and may be accessible for bronchogenic visualization, washing, brushing, and biopsy. Cells from peripheral tumors frequently can only be obtained by fluoroscopy- or CT-guided percutaneous needle biopsy. Seventy percent of all patients with lung cancer have regional lymph node involvement at the time of diagnosis. CT scanning, transbronchial needle aspiration, bronchoscopy, and mediastinoscopy evaluate lymph node involvement. Those with mediastinal node metastases are usually considered surgically unresectable. Bone scans and subsequent radio-

graphs of suspicious areas are performed to determine bone metastases. Laboratory studies, such as a complete blood count, serum calcium, alkaline phosphatase, and liver function tests, are done to evaluate spread of the disease. A bone marrow biopsy may be performed to determine whether the patient with SCLC has limited or extensive disease.

Classification and Staging

The classification and staging of lung cancer are important because of the differences in presentation, natural history, and response to therapy. Over 90% of all primary lung tumors arise from the bronchial epithelium. The two major histologic classes of bronchogenic cancer are non–small-cell lung cancer (NSCLC) and small-cell lung cancer (SCLC). NSCLC constitutes approximately 80% of all lung cancers, and SCLC constitutes approximately 20% of lung cancers. There are three types of NSCLC—adenocarcinomas, squamous cell carcinomas, and large-cell carcinomas.

Adenocarcinomas are the most common lung cancers, constituting 30% to 50% of all lung cancers, and are thought to arise from chronic irritation, scarring, and fibrosis of lung tissue. Adenocarcinomas are frequently found in women, nonsmokers, and young people. These cancers are usually found on the lung periphery, and hematogenous spread is common, especially to the brain, bone, liver, and kidney.

Squamous cell carcinomas are strongly associated with cigarette smoking and constitute approximately 30% of all lung cancers. These cancers tend to be located near the main stem bronchi and cause obstruction leading to atelectasis and pneumonia. Squamous cell carcinomas generally remain localized and can be resected. For this reason, patients with squamous cell carcinomas of the lung experience a relatively longer survival than patients with other types of lung cancers.

Large-cell carcinomas account for 10% to 15% of lung cancers and are histologically undifferentiated. Survival is poor. Large-cell carcinomas are more often peripheral to the bronchi and tend to metastasize to the brain, adrenal glands, and bones.

Small-cell lung cancers are strongly associated with smoking. These cancers usually arise in the central region of the lung and, as a result of their high growth rate, involve both sides of the chest, metastasize early and widely by way of hematogenous and lymphatic spread, and generally confer a poor prognosis. Patients usually have distant metastasis to the lymph nodes, liver, adrenal glands, bones, and central nervous system at the time of diagnosis (Glover & Miaskowski, 1994).

Metastases of lung cancer occur by invasion through the walls of the lung and along the inside of the bronchial lumens. The tumors can cause bronchial occlusion, which results in dyspnea and cough. Widespread metastases of lung cancer frequently occur and are due to the invasion of the pulmonary vascular system. At diagnosis, most patients have advanced disease that has widely metastasized. Although multimodality treatment can prolong survival, the 5-year survival rate is only 11%.

The most widely used staging system for NSCLC is the American Joint Committee for Cancer Staging TNM Staging System (Table 4-2). SCLC are staged either as limited or extensive. Limited SCLC is disease confined to one side of the chest and its corresponding lymph nodes. If the cancer has spread beyond these margins or if a pleural effusion contains malignant cells, it is considered extensive SCLC. The anatomic extent of disease is a crucial determinant of treatment and ultimate survival.

TABLE 4-2
1997 TNM STAGING FOR LUNG CANCER

Stage		T	N	M
Stage	I	T_{1-2}	N_0	M_0
Stage	IIA	T_1	N_1	M_0
	IIB	T_2	N_1	M_0
		T_3	N_0	M_0
Stage	IIIA	T_{1-3}	N_2	M_0
		T_3	N_1	M_0
	IIIB	T_4	Any N	M_0
		Any T	N_3	M_0
Stage	IV	Any T	Any N	M_1

T_1 Tumor 3 cm or less in greatest dimension, surrounded by lung or visceral pleura, without bronchoscopic evidence of invasion more proximal than the lobar bronchus.

T_2 Tumor with any of the following features of size or extent: More than 3 cm in greatest dimension; involves main bronchus, 2 cm or more distal to the carina; invades the visceral pleura; associated with atelectasis or obstructive pneumonitis that extends to the hilar region but does not involve the entire lung.

T_3 Tumor of any size that directly invades any of the following: Chest wall (including superior sulcus tumors), diaphragm, mediastinal pleura, parietal pericardium; or tumor in the main bronchus less than 2 cm distal to the carina, but without involvement of the carina; or associated atelectasis or obstructive pneumonitis of the entire lung.

T_4 Tumor of any size that invades any of the following: Mediastinum, heart, great vessels, trachea, esophagus, vertebral body, carina; or separate tumor nodules in the same lobe; or tumor with a malignant pleural effusion.

N_0 No regional lymph node metastasis.

N_1 Metastasis to ipsilateral peribronchial and/or ipsilateral hilar lymph nodes, and intrapulmonary nodes including involvement by direct extension of the primary tumor.

N_2 Metastasis to ipsilateral mediastinal and/or subcarinal lymph node(s).

N_3 Metastasis to contralateral mediastinal, contralateral hilar, ipsilateral or contralateral scalene, or supraclavicular lymph node(s).

M_0 No distant metastasis.

M_1 Distant metastasis present.

(Fleming, I.D., Cooper, J.S., Henson, D.E., et al. [1997]. *American Joint Committee for Cancer Staging manual* [5th ed]. Philadelphia: Lippincott-Raven.)

Treatment

Treatment decisions are based on histology, tumor extent, and physical condition of the patient. Careful patient assessments, including an inquiry into patient preferences, are required in the decision-making process.

Non–Small-Cell Lung Cancer

SURGERY. Complete surgical resection of the tumor offers the best chance for cure of lung cancer. However, only 20% to 25% of patients are eligible for surgical resection at the time of diagnosis. Many lung cancer patients are chronic smokers and poor surgical candidates (Ruckdeschel, 1995). Patients with localized stage I and II disease, and occasionally some patients with localized stage IIIA squamous cell carcinomas, may be considered for surgery. For patients with stage I disease, localization of the tumor must be achieved before surgery. Traditional bronchoscopy or laser photo-irradiation may be used. Surgical resections may include wedge resection, segmentectomy (also called sleeve resection), lobectomy, and pneumonectomy to excise all existing disease and provide maximum conservation of normal lung tissue. Anatomic location and extent of tumor are critical factors in selection of surgical approaches (Figure 4-3). For patients with stage II disease, surgery is usually the treatment of choice, with cure being the therapeutic goal. Although local radiation and systemic chemotherapy have been used both before and after surgery, they have not significantly affected survival rates. For patients with stage III disease, in which the primary tumor and local metastases can be completely resected, surgical resection in combination with radiation therapy, chemotherapy, or both can be beneficial. Postoperative radiation therapy or chemotherapy, or both, may provide a modest prolongation of life in completely resected patients.

RADIATION THERAPY. Radiation therapy is used for patients who are not surgical candidates because of limited pulmonary function or because the tumor is surgically unresectable. Doses of radiation range from 6000 to 6600 cGy. Poor general overall condition, large tumor size, distant metastases, inadequate pulmonary reserve, and malignant pleural effusions are contraindications for primary radiation therapy. With radiation therapy, there is a 30% relapse rate and 5% to 10% increases in long-term survival (Bezjak & Payne, 1993). Most NSCLCs have poor radiosensitivity.

Radiation therapy may be used to sterilize tumors before surgery and to treat regional lymph nodes after surgery. However, neither has been shown to affect survival. Most studies fail to demonstrate that preoperative radiation therapy is beneficial for either the operability or survival of patients (Damstrup & Skovgaard-Poulssen, 1994). Preoperative radiation therapy is also used for surgically resectable Pancoast tumors. Radiation can shrink the tumor if the tumor is located near vital organs (Payne, 1994). However, preoperative radiation therapy can predispose the patient to more postoperative complications.

Postoperative radiation therapy is used after complete resection of NSCLC with positive lymph nodes to decrease local recurrence. However, no increase in overall survival is seen (Lung Cancer Study Group, 1986; Payne, 1994).

Palliative radiation therapy is used to treat the tumor or its metastases and improve symptoms by reducing tumor size and impingement on adjacent structures. Radiation therapy can decrease hemoptysis, cough, dyspnea, obstruction of airways, chest pain, and hoarseness. Metastatic bone lesions from lung cancer can be effectively treated with radiation therapy to reduce pain, prevent pathologic fractures, and maintain activity level and function. Brain metastases, which cause neurologic changes, are also treated with radiation therapy. Spinal cord compression as a result of a metastatic lesion on the spinal column can be treated with radiation therapy to prevent paralysis. Superior vena cava obstruction (SVCO) occurs in 5% of patients with both NSCLC and SCLC. SVCO occurs by external compression by a right main stem bronchial lesion, surrounding lymph nodes, or, rarely, intraluminal thrombus. Patients complain of shortness of breath (50%–70% of the time) and facial swelling (39%–43%). Thoracic vein distention and neck vein distention are common. Radiation therapy is

Tumor

Suture

Lung reaction

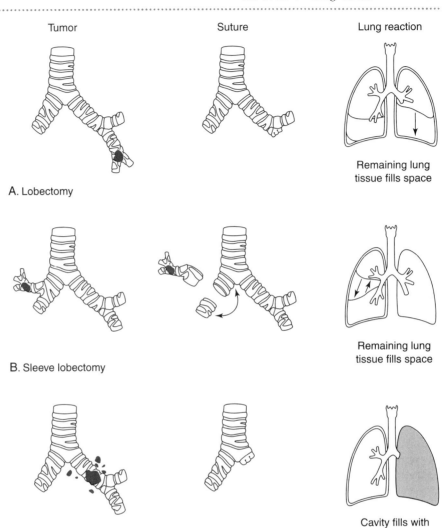

A. Lobectomy

Remaining lung tissue fills space

B. Sleeve lobectomy

Remaining lung tissue fills space

C. Pneumonectomy

Cavity fills with fluid and tissue

Figure 4-3 Surgical procedures for lung cancer. (*A*) Lobectomy: removal of lobe of lung; lower morbidity and mortality than pneumonectomy for small tumors. (*B*) Sleeve lobectomy: a segment of the main bronchus is removed with the lobe followed with an end-to-end anastamosis. (*C*) Pneumonectomy: removal of one lung; higher incidence of perfusion and ventilation problems, circulatory overload, and pulmonary hypertension. (Reprinted by permission from Elpern, E.H. [1993]. Lung cancer. In S.L. Groenwald, M.H. Frogge, M. Goodman & C.H. Yarbro [Eds.], *Cancer nursing: Principles and practice* [3rd ed.] [pp. 1174–1199]. Boston: Jones and Bartlett.)

the primary treatment modality. Chemotherapy is used for SVCO occurring in patients with SCLC. Eighty-five to 90% of patients will have relief of symptoms within 3 weeks of starting radiation therapy. Palliative radiation therapy is usually delivered in a short period of time, resulting in few side effects.

Prophylactic brain irradiation is used for patients at high risk for brain metastasis, such as those with adenocarcinoma of the lung. Brachytherapy with iridium 192 (^{192}Ir) may be used as an adjuvant therapy to lung surgery, as a boost component of initial radiotherapy, or for palliation of

hemoptysis, dyspnea, and cough at the time of recurrent endobronchial disease (Aygun & Blum, 1995).

Patients with pleural mesotheliomas frequently experience dyspnea and nonpleuritic chest wall pain. Treatment may include radioactive colloids such as phosphorus 32 (^{32}P) instilled into the pleural cavity combined with external beam radiation therapy.

CHEMOTHERAPY. Chemotherapy for localized NSCLC has not improved prognosis. Chemotherapy is used for stage IIIA and IIIB tumors. Chemotherapy may be also be used before radiation therapy or combined with radiation therapy as a radiosensitizer (Salazar, Van Houtte & Rubin, 1993). Cisplatin is often selected for combination therapy. Table 4-3 lists commonly used chemotherapeutic agents for NSCLC.

Small-Cell Lung Cancer

The prognostic indicators for SCLC are extent of disease, performance status, weight loss, and response to treatment. Because of the high incidence of distant metastases, SCLC is not surgically treated. Because SCLC is considered a systemic disease at the time of diagnosis, the mainstay of treatment is combination chemotherapy with or without radiation therapy. Multiple chemotherapeutic agents that are administered simultaneously are preferable to single-agent therapy. Drug regimens frequently used to treat SCLC are listed in Table 4-3. Although higher doses of chemotherapy produce better responses, more toxicity is experienced. Most responders to chemotherapy relapse within a short time and frequently at the initial intrathoracic disease site. Tumor drug resistance also occurs, which necessitates alternating regimens. Less than 20% of patients survive more than 2 years after diagnosis. Median survivals are 14 months for limited disease and 7 to 9 months for extensive disease. Radiation therapy for SCLC

for consolidation after chemotherapy can reduce the frequency of tumor recurrence in the chest. An increased 2-year survival has been reported from combined modality therapy in patients with limited disease (Arriagada, Pignon, & Le Chevalier, 1995). Although many patients with SCLC develop brain metastases, the value of prophylactic brain irradiation for long-term survival is still unclear (Gregor, 1998). Side effects of cranial irradiation include impaired mentation, ataxic gait, and urinary incontinence, all of which can occur approximately 6 to 18 months after radiation therapy (Abner, 1993). Patients who quit smoking before or at the time of diagnosis have longer survival times than those who continue to smoke. Continuing smokers with SCLC also have a greater risk of developing NSCLC. The YAG laser is used palliatively to shrink an obstructing tumor and make it amenable to removal by forceps. Bleeding is a potential complication of laser therapy.

Complications of Disease and Treatment

Surgery

Preparing a patient for surgery involves careful assessment of respiratory status as well as provision of patient and family education about perioperative procedures and activities. Preoperative education must include instruction about postoperative activities such as frequent coughing and deep breathing, use of an incentive spirometer, and splinting the wound to make coughing easier (Held, 1995). Instructions should also include leg exercises, the use of elastic stockings to prevent deep vein thrombosis, and arm and shoulder exercises to prevent stiffness and improve mobility. Because smoking is contraindicated, smoking cessation and the use of nicotine replacement to prevent withdrawal symptoms need to be discussed with the patient who smokes.

Postoperative care focuses on maintaining respiratory function, assessing the airway, suctioning secretions, and promoting ventilation. Oxygen may be prescribed after surgery. Pain control is usually accomplished with a patient-controlled analgesia device. With adequate pain

---

TABLE 4-3

CHEMOTHERAPY FOR LUNG CANCER

Non-Small-Cell Lung Cancer	Small-Cell Lung Cancer
Carboplatin/cisplatin	Cyclophosphamide
Paclitaxel/docetaxel	Carboplatin/cisplatin
Vinorelbine	Doxorubicin
	Etoposide
	Paclitaxel
	Vincristine

(Data from Babni, C. [1998]. Paclitaxel/carboplatin in the treatment of non-small-cell lung cancer. *Oncology*, Suppl. 2, 74–79.; Choy, H., Akerley, W. & Devore, R. [1998]. Paclitaxel, carboplatin, and radiation therapy for non-small-cell lung cancer. *Oncology*, Suppl. 2, 80–86.; Ettinger, D.S. [1998]. The role of carboplatin in the treatment of small-cell lung cancer. *Oncology*, Suppl. 2, 36–43.; Postmus, P.E. & Smit, E.F. [1998]. Small-cell lung cancer: Is there a standard therapy? *Oncology*, Suppl. 2, 25–30.)

control, the patient will then be able to perform deep breathing and coughing exercises. Chest tubes, if present, are frequently monitored and checked for patency and function, and the character and amount of drainage are documented. All wound sites are assessed, and dressings are changed as prescribed.

Discharge planning includes preparing the patient and family to manage wound care, respiratory rehabilitation, and nutritional care. In some instances, home care assistance is necessary for continued rehabilitation.

Radiation Therapy

The acute side effects of radiation therapy include cough, pharyngitis, esophagitis, anorexia, weight loss, fatigue, and skin reaction. These side effects occur during the course of radiation therapy and generally resolve within a month of completion of therapy. Delayed side effects include pneumonitis and lung fibrosis. The effects on pulmonary function include a progressive decline in lung volumes and a decrease in lung compliance and diffusing capacity. Pneumonitis occurs 1 to 3 months after radiation therapy and resolves in 2 to 3 months. It can be severe, with cough, dyspnea, fever, and tachycardia. Pneumonitis is treated symptomatically with corticosteroids for 2 to 3 weeks. Bronchodilators and sedatives may be used to help coughing.

Pulmonary fibrosis occurs 6 to 24 months after radiation therapy. Arteriolar and interstitial fibrosis occurs. The symptoms of pulmonary fibrosis are related to the lung parenchyma involved and the patient's pulmonary reserves. Dyspnea, cough, and decreased exercise tolerance are assessed. In addition, chest radiograph and pulmonary function tests are conducted to monitor pulmonary insufficiency. The chest radiograph will reveal linear streaking from the area of previous pneumonitis, regional contraction, thickening of the pleura, and tenting of the diaphragm (McDonald, Missaillidou, & Rubin, 1995). Interventions for pulmonary fibrosis are aimed at supportive care. Oxygen and bronchodilators are used for symptomatic relief.

Central nervous system symptoms, including memory loss, tremor, slurred speech, and somnolence, may be seen in patients who have received prophylactic cranial irradiation. These late effects are due to arteriocapillary fibrosis and microvascular injury.

Chemotherapy

The side effects of chemotherapy depend on the specific agent used. Before chemotherapy is administered, blood counts need to be checked. Cisplatin is nephrotoxic, and blood urea nitrogen and creatinine should be checked (Held, 1995). Measures to decrease nephrotoxicity of cisplatin include maintaining hydration and forcing fluids. Intravenous fluids are administered to assist with the excretion of the medication. In addition, the patient is instructed to drink an additional 2 L of fluids once returning home. Patients are advised to call if urine output decreases, new breathing problems occur, swelling of ankles and feet occurs, or nausea and vomiting continues and prevents consumption of the required amounts of fluids. Cisplatin also causes significant nausea and vomiting, requiring an aggressive antiemetic regimen. Because myelosuppression can occur with many of the chemotherapeutic agents, careful monitoring of blood counts is required after chemotherapy. Patients are instructed on neutropenia and thrombocytopenia precautions. In addition, symptoms of anemia are monitored. Aggressive, multiagent chemotherapy can cause preleukemic and leukemic states in patients. Several drugs cause lung injury, especially when chemotherapy is given concurrently with radiation therapy. Risks of pulmonary toxicities for cytotoxic drugs may increase with cumulative drug dose, age, radiation therapy to the chest, and concurrent oxygen therapy.

Symptom Management

COUGH

Coughing can interfere with rest and appetite and may increase fatigue and dyspnea. Lung tumor growth can result in dry or productive coughs (Cowcher & Hanks, 1990). Irritation of the throat and nonproductive coughs can be managed with cough suppressants. Productive coughs resulting from hypersecretion of mucus require consistent use of therapeutic deep breathing and coughing to clear secretions. Assess the frequency, intensity, duration, and precipitating factors for coughs. Monitor the amount, type, and color of sputum as well as frank hemoptysis. A chronic, nonproductive cough in a patient with underlying chronic obstructive lung disease may respond to inhaled bronchodilators. Increasing hydration by encouraging fluid intake, increasing humidification, and using cough suppressants and expectorants can be helpful to relieve cough (Cowcher & Hanks, 1990). Low doses of opioids, such as morphine and codeine, are effective cough suppressants. However, if the patient is already on an opioid for pain management, the addition of another opioid to control cough will probably not be of any benefit. Advise the patient to avoid lung irritants such as tobacco smoke and perfumes. Hemoptysis, or expectoration of blood, is common with bronchogenic lung cancer. Assess the patient's use of medications, such as nonsteroidal antiinflammatory medications, that can cause bleeding. Minor hemoptysis is treated conservatively; more significant hemoptysis can be treated with palliative radiation therapy (Cowcher & Hanks, 1990).

PHARYNGITIS/ESOPHAGITIS

Pharyngitis and esophagitis frequently occur approximately 2 to 3 weeks after starting radiation therapy. The severity of these symptoms varies from a mild sore throat to severe pain that limits all intakes of solid foods. It is important to monitor the patient's weight because these effects can lead to weight loss. Modifying the diet to include soft, nonirritating foods and nonacidic and noncarbonated fluids will be beneficial. Nutritional supplementation with commercially available products or enriched milkshakes should be used. The patient should be encouraged to consume small, frequent meals. Gargling with warm saline can be soothing. Antacids or topical anesthetics may be used before meals to provide short-term relief of pharyngitis. However, for more severe pain, systemic analgesics are required. Patients should avoid consuming tobacco and alcohol because these will increase the pharyngitis and esophagitis. An acute onset of esophagitis may signal esophageal candidiasis.

NAUSEA AND VOMITING

Many factors cause nausea and vomiting in the patient with lung cancer (Held, 1995; Schmitt, 1993) (Table 4-4). The patient's risk for nausea and vomiting is assessed. Nausea and vomiting associated with chemotherapy may be delayed and may require a prolonged course of antiemetics. Relaxation techniques can be used in addition to antiemetics to control nausea and vomiting. Constipation as a result of narcotic use can also exacerbate nausea. Antiemetics are administered around the clock when a patient receives highly emetogenic chemotherapy such as cisplatin and are continued for 3 to 4 days as necessary. Dietary modifications such as serving foods that are cool or at room temperature and foods that are not spicy or do not have a strong aroma will be better tolerated.

MUCOSITIS

Mucositis can occur with several chemotherapeutic agents. This inflammatory reaction can occur within 2 weeks of chemotherapy administration and can take up to 2 weeks to resolve. When painful ulcers occur, the patient is unable to maintain nutritional intake. Oral care with frequent saline mouth rinses and brushing and flossing the teeth as tolerated is necessary to prevent mouth infections. Medicated anesthetic oral solutions are also available to promote mouth comfort and are used before meals and at bedtime. With severe mucositis, systemic analgesics are required.

TABLE 4-4

CAUSES OF NAUSEA AND VOMITING IN PATIENTS WITH LUNG CANCER

Gastrointestinal disturbances
    Obstruction
    Liver metastasis
Central nervous system involvement
    Increased intracranial pressure
Medications
    Narcotics
    Chemotherapy
Metabolic
    Hypercalcemia

HEARING LOSS

Hearing loss can occur with cisplatin and carboplatin. This loss may be permanent. Before starting chemotherapy, hearing acuity tests are conducted to serve as a baseline measure. Follow-up hearing acuity tests may be obtained as the patient experiences changes in hearing acuity.

PAIN

Chest pain from bronchogenic tumors is usually a dull ache that is poorly localized. Pain may increase in intensity and duration with advancing metastatic disease and cancer treatment. If standard cancer therapies fail to relieve or control pain, pharmacologic agents are usually required. Patients are asked to rate the level of intensity of pain. An analog scale numbered from 0 to 10, with "0"= no pain at all, to "10" = the worst pain imaginable, can be used. The location, frequency, duration, precipitating factors, and effectiveness of pain relief measures are assessed. Nonpharmacologic measures to control pain, such as relaxation exercises and distraction, can be helpful. Because narcotic medications can be constipating, the patient requires a bowel program including high-fiber diet, stool softeners, and laxatives that will maintain bowel function and prevent constipation.

DYSPNEA

Dyspnea involves several physiologic and psychological processes (Ripamonti & Bruera, 1997; Wickham, 1998) and can be a result of the lung cancer, its treatment, or both. *Dyspnea* is defined as a subjective sensation of difficult or uncomfortable breathing (Gift, 1990). As with pain management, the patient is the only one who is able to determine the level of dyspnea experienced. The patient may complain of shortness of breath, difficulty breathing, or fatigue. The patient may also have copious secretions, cough, and chest pain (Wickham, 1998). Fifteen to 40% of patients with lung cancer report dyspnea (Coy & Kennely, 1980). Complications such as infections and anemia will increase the dyspnea.

Treatment for dyspnea is determined by the results of a thorough history of symptoms, including alleviating and exacerbating factors, physical examination, and diagnostic studies. These diagnostic studies may include chest radiograph, digital oximetry, complete blood count, and arterial blood gases.

Dyspnea is usually inadequately assessed and, as a result, poorly managed (Brown, 1997; Foote, Sexton & Pawlik, 1986; Roberts, Thorne & Pearson, 1993). The patient's self-report of dyspnea and its impact on his or her activities is crucial (Ripamonti & Bruera, 1997). Several tools are available to assess dyspnea (Brown, 1997) (Table 4-5). Physical examination includes assessing the rate, depth, and pattern of respiration, as well as the patient's use of accessory muscles for breathing. Lung sounds are assessed for wheezes, crackles, rales, and absent breath sounds. An assessment of cardiac function is also performed.

Pharmacologic and nonpharmacologic interventions are used for dyspnea. Interventions are aimed at treating the underlying causes of dyspnea with consideration of the patient's life expectancy and the potential adverse effects of the interventions. Morphine sulfate is effective in alleviating the symptoms of dyspnea. Opiates can help alter the perception of breathlessness and, in so doing, decrease anxiety. Opiates can decrease the ventilatory response to hypoxia and hypercapnea, decrease oxygen consumption at rest and

TABLE 4-5
TOOLS FOR ASSESSING DYSPNEA

Visual Analog Scale

Patients are asked to rate the level of dyspnea on a scale of 0 to 10:

No Breathlessness   Worst Possible Breathlessness

0--10

From Aitken, 1969; Ripamonti & Bruera, 1997.

Verbal Descriptors Scale

Patients are asked to select the word that best describes their level of dyspnea:

Absent------Mild------Moderate------Severe------Excruciating

(Ventafridda, V., DeConno, F., Ripamonti, C., Gamba, A., & Tamburini, M. [1990]. Quality of life assessment during a palliative care programme. *Annals of Oncology, 1,* 415–420.)

with exercise, and increase exercise tolerance (Wickham, 1998). Opiates decrease the respiratory drive and rate and produce antitussive benefits to relieve cough (Cowcher & Hanks, 1990). Many health care providers oppose the use of opiates for dyspnea (Johanson, 1990). Their opposition stems from lack of knowledge of the effectiveness of opioids for dyspnea, lack of clinical experience using opioids to treat dyspnea, and a reflexive avoidance of any drug that potentially depresses respiration. Many believe that dyspnea is uncommon and of low priority for patient management and fear that opioids will actually hasten death. Table 4-6 lists the principles for morphine use for dyspnea (Wickham, 1998). Morphine is most conveniently delivered by mouth. However, parenteral injection, infusions, rectal suppository, and nebulized morphine are also used (Wickham, 1998). Nebulized, preservative-free morphine exerts a local effect on the lungs to palliate dyspnea.

Other medications are used to symptomatically treat dyspnea. Corticosteroid medications can decrease exercise-induced shortness of breath, shortness of breath due to airway obstruction, lymphangetic carcinomatosis, superior vena cava obstruction, chronic obstructive pulmonary disease, and radiation pneumonitis (Wickham, 1998). Bronchodilators and expectorants are also used to treat "asthma-like" symptoms and to increase the patient's ability to expectorate tenacious sputum. Anxiolytic agents such as benzodiazepines can be used to treat anxiety, which exacerbates dyspnea.

Nonpharmacologic interventions for dyspnea include blowing cool air over the cheek/face to stimulate the trigeminal nerve as well as the temperature and mechanical receptors of the cheek and nasopharynx to alter the perception of breathlessness (Cowcher & Hanks, 1990; Rousseau, 1996). Controlling other environmental factors, such as dust and pollen in the air and crowded environments, can help to minimize dyspnea.

Body positioning can also help decrease dyspnea. Instruct the patient to lean forward at the edge of the chair or bed when breathing, leaning over a pillow or using a table to support the arms. Using pursed lip breathing can also help to decrease dyspnea. Sometimes a change of position, such as lying down, or moving slowly will decrease dyspnea. Because anxiety increases dyspnea, provide measures such as relaxation techniques/exercises, meditation, and prayer to minimize anxiety. In addition, encourage the patient to use resources for chores and activities of daily living to maintain energy levels. Oxygen therapy may help relieve dyspnea when a patient has partial pressure oxygen levels of < 55 mm Hg or oxygen saturation of < 89% (Wickham, 1998).

TABLE 4-6

PRINCIPLES OF MORPHINE USE FOR DYSPNEA

Explain to patient and caregivers that morphine:
- Will decrease sensations of drowning, suffocation, or other manifestations of air hunger
- Will help them to rest and sleep, and is not "dangerous" or "addictive", but will not change the underlying problem.
- There is no "standard" dose that will relieve shortness of breath in all patients.
- If the patient already takes an opioid for pain, increase disage by 25% to 50% to treat dyspnea; the usual three-to-one oral-to-parenteral ratio is used to convert doses.
- Titrate dose 30% to 50% daily or more frequently until dyspnea improves or sedation becomes a problem.
- If a patient becomes overly sedated, reduce dose by 50% (patients will usually awaken and request that dose be restored to former level).
- Do not administer naloxone, even to opioid-naive patients who are sedated but whose respiratory rate is > 8 to 10/min.
- Sedation may occur secondary to exhaustion from dyspnea, rather than as an adverse reaction to morphine; sleep, therefore, may be a therapeutic response.
- Reassess frequently and intervene aggressively; dyspnea affects quality of life in individuals with a limited life expectancy.
- Administer prophylactic laxative plus stool softener (eg, senna plus docusate) to prevent constipation due to morphine.

(Reprinted with permission from Wickham, R. [1998]. Managing dyspnea in cancer patients. *Developments in Supportive Care, 2,* 33–40.)

HEMOPTYSIS

Hemoptysis may be caused by bronchial irritation from coughing or tumor erosion into the pulmonary blood vessels. Assess the source, amount, and duration of hemoptysis. Mild hemoptysis is usually treated conservatively in the outpatient setting. Patients with significant bleeding should be positioned so the bleeding lung is dependent. These patients should be monitored for increased blood loss, changes in blood pressure and pulse, and respiratory distress. Measures to control massive bleeding include angiographic embolization of the source of the bleed and emergency surgery.

WHEEZING

Wheezing is usually caused by a tumor that partially obstructs an airway. Positioning may be helpful in alleviating the wheezing. Diffuse wheezing may represent underlying chronic airway obstruction.

FATIGUE

Fatigue can be caused by several factors in the person with lung cancer. Dyspnea, anemia, pain, medications, malnutrition and weight loss, chemotherapy, surgery, and radiation therapy all contribute to fatigue. Assessment of fatigue is important to provide appropriate interventions in a timely manner. Included in the assessment are the pattern, duration, and intensity of fatigue as well as activities that increase fatigue and those that alleviate it. Controlling symptoms that contribute to fatigue and increasing nutritional intake will help lessen the fatigue. Patients need to pace their activities and plan frequent rest periods throughout the day. Utilization of resources to assist with activities of daily living can help to minimize energy expenditure.

ANOREXIA

Anorexia can result from the dyspnea and fatigue as well as the side effects of treatments for lung cancer. More than 50% of persons with lung cancer will have weight loss during the 6 months before diagnosis (DeWys et al., 1980). Minimal weight loss, good performance status, and minimal symptom distress were variables predictive of treatment response and survival in persons with lung cancer (Sarna, Lindsey, Dean, Brecht & McCorkle, 1993). Assess the amount of food consumed. Weight should be monitored weekly. Interventions for anorexia include managing other symptoms that contribute to anorexia, such as nausea, vomiting, constipation, pain, pharyngitis, esophagitis, and fatigue. Mouth care should be performed before and after each meal to refresh the mouth. Frequent small meals and nutrient-dense foods, such as commercially prepared nutritional supplements, should be offered. Megestrol acetate (800 mg/day) can also help to increase appetite and improve food intake (Tchekmedyian et al., 1992).

Psychosocial Issues

Quality of life is defined as the impact of physical symptoms and side effects of treatment on the patient's functioning and well-being (Fergusson & Cull, 1991). The intent of treatment for lung cancer is more often palliation than cure. Because the primary goal of palliative treatment is to improve quality of life, the emphasis is placed on assessing the individual's subjective experience (Bernhard & Ganz, 1995; Fergusson & Cull, 1991; King et al., 1997; Schmitt, 1993).

The physical symptoms of lung cancer can include dyspnea, fatigue, and weight loss. As a result, patients may socially restrict and isolate themselves as a way of coping with these distressing symptoms. If they still smoke, they may isolate themselves to avoid criticism. This isolation further compromises their quality of life. Coping with a poor prognosis requires support from nurses to provide education as needed and allowing patients and families to discuss their fears and concerns. In some instances, family disruptions occur because the disease progression may be especially rapid, and major shifts in family roles and dynamics may occur in a short period of time. These changes can strain the family's coping resources. By anticipating problems and discussing potential solutions with the patient and family, the nurse is able to provide support and help the family avert crises (Knopp, 1997). In addition, early referrals to appropriate community resources and personnel will

Case Study

77-year-old man with lung cancer

MM is a 77-year-old man diagnosed with inoperable, locally advanced, poorly differentiated large cell carcinoma of the right lower lobe of lung with extensive mediastinal adenopathy (stage IIIA). He initially presented with a 6-week history of productive cough with recent blood streaking in sputum. In addition, he had had a 2-week history of dysphagia. Chest radiograph and subsequent chest CT scan revealed mediastinal adenopathy and a confluent mass in the subcarinal region with smaller nodes in the pretracheal space. Bone scan and head CT scan were negative for metastasis.

His medical history was significant for a 50-year smoking history of two packs of cigarettes per day and poor pulmonary function due to COPD. Combined chemotherapy plus radiation therapy was recommended with weekly cisplatin (30 mg/m^2) and 6600 cGy of radiation to the tumor volume.

Before the start of therapy, MM was fatigued, mildly anorexic, and experienced dysphagia. He had a productive cough that increased during the day. His weight at the start of therapy was 200 lb. His first week of therapy was uneventful, with fatigue being his most significant symptom.

A blood test obtained before his third chemotherapy revealed neutropenia (WBC: 1.3, ANC: 61%, Hct: 35, Plt: 74). MM was more fatigued, and he experienced pharyngitis, cough, and anorexia with a 10-lb weight loss. Although daily radiation therapy continued, chemotherapy was not resumed. MM was counseled on nutritional care, including a soft diet with the use of commercial nutritional supplements. MM also began taking 800 mg of megestrol acetate solution once a day for anorexia.

A week later, MM was evaluated to potentially resume chemotherapy. However, he remained neutropenic (WBC: 2.2, ANC: 56%, Hct: 35, Plt: 79) and, although radiation therapy continued, chemotherapy was withheld for another week. He continued to be fatigued,

and his pharyngitis had increased with mild odynophagia. An oral solution consisting of an antacid, diphenhydramine, and viscous xylocaine was prescribed for use before meals and at bedtime. In addition, oxycodone with acetaminophen was prescribed for more severe pain.

The following week, MM's blood counts were stable (WBC: 2.9, ANC: 78%, Hct: 34, Plt: 136) so chemotherapy was resumed. MM's major symptoms were pharyngitis, esophagitis (rated pain level "8" when most severe on scale of 0 to 10), anorexia, and weight loss (a total of 16 lb in the past month). Fentanyl patches, 25 µg/h, were prescribed to be used in addition to the oral solution and oxycodone/acetaminophen for breakthrough pain. MM was counseled to increase his intake of nutritional supplements. He continued on megestrol acetate solution. MM reported good pain control within 24 hours.

The following week, MM's blood counts remained stable (WBC: 2.7, ANC: 82%, Hct: 33, Plt: 145), and the fourth course of chemotherapy was given. MM experienced more pharyngitis, and the fentanyl dose was increased from 25 µg/h to 50 µg/h. MM reported less anorexia but lost an additional 4 lb.

The following week, MM was more neutropenic (WBC: 1.2, ANC: 68%, Hct: 29, Plt: 60), and chemotherapy was discontinued. Pain was well controlled with fentanyl 50 µg/h. He reported his appetite to be improving, and his weight had stabilized.

MM was able to complete his course of radiation therapy without further increase in symptoms. As a matter of fact, toward the end of therapy, although his fatigue was unchanged, MM's appetite improved and his cough lessened. One month after completing combined therapy, MM's blood counts began returning to normal levels (WBC: 4.2, ANC: 72%, Hct: 29, Plt: 100). Restaging at that time revealed no evidence of disease.

foster continuity of care throughout the illness trajectory. For instance, hospice referrals can be especially helpful to patients and families during the terminal phase of illness.

Smoking and the Person With Lung Cancer

The person with lung cancer who continues to smoke can benefit from smoking cessation (Table 4-7). The person will experience a decrease in the symptoms associated with the disease and treatment and, as a result, will enjoy an improved quality of life (Sarna, 1998). Smoking during radiation therapy can increase mucosal irritation (Knopp, 1997). In addition, cough, esophagitis, and dysphagia all worsen with smoking. Patients with early-stage lung cancer who continue to smoke increase their risks of disease recurrence and secondary tobacco-related cancers such as head and neck, stomach, pancreatic, kidney, and bladder cancers (Gritz, 1991; Richardson et al., 1993; Sarna, 1998; Tucker et al., 1997).

Other benefits of smoking cessation include improved ventilation, appetite, and taste, all of which can increase quality of life in advanced stages of the disease (Knopp, 1997). Patients who desire to stop smoking need support in their efforts. Smoking cessation techniques as described earlier in the chapter may be applied to the patient with lung cancer and family.

Conclusions

Nursing care involves patient education, symptom management, and emotional support to patients with lung cancer and their families as they face significant physical and emotional challenges. Because a variety of treatment modalities may be employed, this care can only be provided with knowledge of the different facets of the disease and its treatments combined with skills to foster coping with a frequently incurable illness. Therefore, nursing interventions are prescribed to provide support with the goals of ensuring continuity of care and improving quality of life.

TABLE 4-7

WHY SMOKERS WITH LUNG CANCER SHOULD QUIT

Decrease shortness of breath and cough
Decrease risk of recurrence
Decrease risk of secondary tobacco-related malignancies
Decrease risk/worsening of other tobacco-related diseases: heart disease, chronic obstructive pulmonary disease, stroke
Decrease risk of treatment side effects
Decrease risk of weight loss: improve food tastes and smells
Increase feelings of well-being and being in control
Decrease risk of lung cancer and heart disease from second-hand smoke for other members in the household
Be a role model for family and friends

(Reprinted with permission from Sarna L. [1998]. Smoking cessation after the diagnosis of lung cancer. *Developments in Supportive Care, 2,* 45–49.)

REFERENCES

Abner, A. (1993). Prophylactic cranial radiation in the treatment of small cell carcinoma of the lung. *Chest, 103,* 445S–448S.

Aitken, R. C. (1969). Measurement of feelings using visual analogue scales. *Proceedings of the Royal Society of Medicine, 62,* 989–993.

Alpha-Tocopherol, Beta Carotene Cancer Prevention Study Group. (1994). The effect of vitamin E and beta carotene on the incidence of lung cancer and other cancers in male smokers. *New England Journal of Medicine, 330,* 1029–1035.

Arriagada, R., Pignon, J. P., & Le Chevalier, T. (1995). The role of chest radiation in small cell lung cancer. *Cancer Treatment and Research, 72,* 255–271.

Aygun, M. D., & Blum J. E. (1995). Treatment of unresectable lung cancer with brachytherapy. *World Journal of Surgery, 19,* 823–827.

Belani, C. (1998). Paclitaxel/carboplatin in the treatment of non-small-cell lung cancer. *Oncology, 12,* Suppl. 2, 74–79.

Bernhard, J., & Ganz, P. A. (1995). Psychosocial issues in lung cancer patients. *Cancer Treatment and Research, 72,* 363–390.

Bezjak, A., & Payne, D. (1993). Radiotherapy in the management of non-small cell lung cancer. *World Journal of Surgery, 17,* 741–750.

Brown, M. L. (1997). Measuring dyspnea. In M. Frank-Stromborg & S. J. Olsen (Eds.), *Instruments for clinical health-care research* (2nd ed.). Boston: Jones and Bartlett.

Choy, H., Akerley, W., & Devore, R. (1998). Paclitaxel, carboplatin, and radiation therapy for non-small-cell lung cancer. *Oncology, 12,* Suppl. 2, 80–86.

Ciniripini, P. M., & McClure, J. B. (1998). Smoking cessation: Recent developments in behavioral and pharmacologic interventions. *Oncology, 12,* 249–256, 259.

Cowcher, K., & Hanks, G. W. (1990). Long-term management of respiratory symptoms in advanced cancer. *Journal of Pain and Symptom Management, 5,* 320–330.

Coy, P., & Kennely, G. M. (1980). The role of curative radiotherapy in the treatment of lung cancer. *Cancer, 45,* 678–702.

Cromwell, J., Bartosch, W. J., Fiore, M. C., Hasselblad, V., & Baker, T. (1997). Cost-effectiveness of the clinical practice recommendations in the AHCPR guidelines for smoking cessation. Agency for Health Care Policy and Research. *Journal of the American Medical Association, 278,* 1759–1766.

Damstrup, L., & Skovgaard-Poulssen, H. (1994). Review of the curative role of radiotherapy in the treatment of non-small cell lung cancer. *Lung Cancer, 11,* 153–178.

DeWys, W. D., Begg, C., Lavin, P. T., Band, P. R., Bennett, J. M., Bertino, J. R., Cohen, M. H., Douglass, H. O. Jr., Engstrom, P. F., Ezdinli, E. P., Horton, J., Johnson, G. J., Moertel, C. G., Oken, M. M., Perlia, C., Rosenbaum, C., Silverstein, M. N., Skeel, R. T., Sponzo, R. W., & Tormey, D. C. (1980). Prognostic effect of weight loss prior to chemotherapy in cancer patients. *American Journal of Medicine, 69,* 491–497.

Elpern, E. H. (1993). Lung cancer. In S. L. Groenwald, M. H. Frogge, M. Goodman, & C. H. Yarbro (Eds.), *Cancer nursing, principles and practice* (3rd ed., pp. 1174–1199). Boston: Jones and Bartlett.

Emami, B., & Perez, C. (1992). Carcinoma of the lung. In C. Perez & L. Brady (Eds.). *Principles and practice of radiation oncology* (2nd ed.). Philadelphia: J. B. Lippincott.

Ettinger, D. S. (1998). The role of carboplatin in the treatment of small-cell lung cancer. *Oncology, 12,* Suppl. 2, 36–43.

Feld, R., Ginsberg, R. J., Payne, D. G., & Shepherd, F. A. (1995). Lung. In M. D. Abeloff et al. (Eds.), *Clinical oncology* (pp. 1083–1152). New York: Churchill Livingstone.

Fergusson, R. J., & Cull, A. (1991). Quality of life measurements for patients undergoing treatment for lung cancer. *Thorax, 46,* 671–675.

Fiore, M. C., Bailey, W. C., Cohen, S. J., Dorfman, S. F., Goldstein, M. G., Gritz, E. R., Heyman, R. B., Holbrook, J., Jaen, C. R., Kottke, T. E., Lando, H. A., Mecklenburg, R., Mullen, P. D., Nett, L. M., Robinson, L., Stitzer, M. L., Tommasello, A. C., Villejo, L., & Wewers, M. E. (1996). *Smoking cessation. Clinical Practice Guideline No. 18.* Rockville, MD: Department of Health and Human Services, Public Health Service, Agency for Health Care Policy and Research. Publ. 96-0692.

Fleming, I. D., Cooper, J. S., Henson, D. E., Hutter, R. V. P., Kennedy, B. J., Murphy, G. P., O'Sullivan, B., Sobin, L. H., & Yarbro, J. W. (1997). *American Joint Committee for Cancer Staging manual* (5th ed.). Philadelphia: Lippincott-Raven.

Foote, M., Sexton, D., & Pawlik, L. (1986). Dyspnea: A distressing sensation in lung cancer. *Oncology Nursing Forum, 13,* 25–33.

Gift, A. (1990). Dyspnea. *Nursing Clinics of North America, 25,* 955–965.

Glover, J., & Miaskowski, C. (1994). Small-cell lung cancer: Pathophysiologic mechanisms and nursing implications. *Oncology Nursing Forum, 21,* 87–97.

Gregor, A. (1998). Prophylactic cranial irradiation in small-cell lung cancer: Is it ever indicated? *Oncology, 12,* Suppl. 2, 19–24.

Gritz, E. R. (1991). Smoking and smoking cessation in cancer patients. *British Journal of Addiction, 86,* 549–554.

Held, J. L. (1995). Caring for a patient with lung cancer. *Nursing 95, 25,* 34–43.

Johanson, G. A. (1990). Should opioids or sedatives be used for dyspnea in end-stage disease? *American Journal of Hospice and Palliative Care, 7,* 12–13.

King, C. R., Haberman, M., Berry, D. L., Bush, N., Butler, L., Dow, K. H., Ferrell, B., Grant, M., Gue, D., Hinds, P., Kreuer, J., Padilla, G., & Underwood, S. (1997). Quality of life and the cancer experience: The state-of-the-knowledge. *Oncology Nursing Forum, 24,* 27–41.

Knopp, J. M. (1997). Lung cancer. In K. H. Dow et al. (Eds.), *Nursing care in radiation oncology* (2nd ed., pp. 293–315). Philadelphia: W. B. Saunders.

Landis, S. H., Murray, T., Bolden, S., & Wingo, P. A. (1999). Cancer statistics, 1999. *CA: A Cancer Journal for Clinicians, 49,* 8–31.

Lung Cancer Study Group. (1986). Effects of postoperative mediastinal radiation on completely resected stage II and stage III epidermoid cancer of the lung. *New England Journal of Medicine, 315,* 1377–1381.

McDonald, S., Missaillidou, D., & Rubin, P. (1995). Pulmonary complications. In M. D. Abeloff et al. (Eds.). *Clinical oncology* (pp. 789–807). New York: Churchill Livingstone.

Novello, A. C., Davis, R. M., & Giovino, G. A. (1991). The slowing of lung cancer epidemic and the need for continued vigilance (editorial). *CA: A Cancer Journal for Clinicians, 41,* 133–135.

Payne, D. G. (1994). Is preoperative or postoperative radiation therapy indicated in non-small cell cancer of the lung? *Lung Cancer, 10,* 5202–5212.

Postmus, P. E., & Smit, E. F. (1998). Small-cell lung cancer: Is there a standard therapy? *Oncology, 12,* Suppl. 2, 25–30.

Richardson, G. E., Tucker, M. A., Venzon, D. J., Linnoila, R. I., Phelps, R., Phares, J. C., Edison, M., Ihde, D. C., & Johnson, B. E. (1993). Smoking cessation after successful treatment of small-cell lung cancer is associated with few smoking-related primaries. *Annals of Internal Medicine, 119,* 383–390.

Ripamonti, C., & Bruera, E. (1997). Dyspnea: Pathophysiology and assessment. *Journal of Pain and Symptom Management, 13,* 220–232.

Roberts, D. K., Thorne, S. E., & Pearson, C. (1993). The experience of dyspnea in late-stage cancer patients' and nurses' perspectives. *Cancer Nursing, 16,* 310–320.

Rousseau, P. (1996). Non-pain symptom management in terminal care. *Clinical Geriatric Medicine, 12,* 313–327.

Ruckdeschel, J. C. (1995). Carcinoma of the lung. In R. E. Ravel (Ed.), *Conn's current therapy* (pp. 156–162). Philadelphia: W. B. Saunders.

Salazar, O. M., Van Houtte, P., & Rubin, P. (1993). Lung cancer. In P. Rubin (Ed.), *Clinical oncology: A multidisciplinary approach for physicians and students* (7th ed.). Philadelphia: W. B. Saunders.

Samet, J. M. (1993). The epidemiology of lung cancer. *Chest, 103,* 20S–29S.

Samet, J. M. (1992). The health benefits of smoking cessation. *Medical Clinics of North America, 76,* 399–414.

Sarna, L. (1998). Smoking cessation after the diagnosis of lung cancer. *Developments in Supportive Care, 2,* 45–49.

Sarna, L., & Brown, J. (1995). Tobacco prevention and cessation in oncology nursing practice, education and research. *Oncology Nursing Forum, 22,* 256–257.

Sarna, L., Lindsey, A. M., Dean, H., Brecht, M. L., & McCorkle, R. (1993). Nutritional intake, weight change, symptom distress, and functional status over time in adults with lung cancer. *Oncology Nursing Forum, 20,* 481–489.

Schmitt, R. (1993). Quality of life issues in lung cancer. *Chest, 103,* 51S–55S.

Tchekmedyian, N. S., Hickman, M., Siau, J., Greco, F. A., Keller, J., Brewder, H., & Aisner, J. (1992). Megestrol acetate in cancer anorexia and weight loss. *Cancer, 69,* 1268–1274.

Tsoh, J. Y., McClure, J. B., Skaar, K. L., Wetter, D. W., Cinciripini, P. M., Prokhorov, A. V., Friedman, K., & Gritz, E. (1997). Smoking cessation 2: Components of effective intervention. *Behavioral Medicine, 23,* 15–27.

Tucker, M. A., Murray, N., Shaw, E. G., Ettinger, D. S., Mabry, M., Huber, M. H., Feld, R., Shepherd, F. A., Johnson, D. H., Grant, S. C., Aisner, J., & Johnson, B. E. (1997). Second primary cancers related to smoking and treatment of small-cell lung cancer. *Journal of the National Cancer Institute, 89,* 1782–1788.

Ventafridda, V., DeConno, F., Ripamonti, C., Gamba, A., & Tamburini, M. (1990). Quality of life assessment during a palliative care programme. *Annals of Oncology, 1,* 415–420.

Wickham, R. (1998). Managing dyspnea in cancer patients. *Developments in Supportive Care, 2,* 33–40.

Zang, E. A., & Wynder, E. L. (1996). Differences in lung cancer risk between men and women: Examination of the evidence. *Journal of the National Cancer Institute, 88,* 183–192.

Breast Cancer

Cindi Bedell

Breast cancer is one of the most feared illnesses for women. The majority of women believe that their risk for breast cancer is greater than their risk for any other type of illness, including heart disease. Breast cancer does account for 30% of all cancers in women, with approximately 178,700 new cases being diagnosed in 1998. It is the most common cancer in women but is second to lung cancer in the cause of cancer deaths. In the United States, five women die from breast cancer every hour—over 43,000 women in 1998 (Landis, Murray, Bolder & Wingo, 1998).

The good news is that that there is a downward trend in the number of deaths from breast cancer for the first time, decreasing 1.8% per year between 1990 and 1994. The 5-year survival rates have increased for white women to 86% in 1986. Survival for African-American women (70%) has also improved; however, it still lags behind that for white women. African-American women are more likely to be diagnosed at a later stage, and the 5-year survival rates are lower even when accounting for extent of disease. The United States has one of the highest age-adjusted mortality rates in the world at 21.1 per 100,000 people. Ireland and Denmark have the highest rates (27.4 and 27.2, respectively) and Albania, China, and Japan have the lowest (4.9, 5.0, and 6.8, respectively) (Landis, Murray, Bolder & Wingo, 1998).

Risk Factors

Breast cancer is every woman's risk. The two most common risk factors for breast cancer are gender and aging. Less than 1% of breast cancer occurs in men. Despite a common misconception among older women, the risk of breast cancer increases every year a woman ages. The lifetime risk for women to develop breast cancer is 1 in 8; however, a woman in her twenties has less than a 1 in 200 chance, and a woman in her sixties has a 1 in 15 chance (Table 5-1) (Feuer et al., 1993; Landis, Murray, Bolder & Wingo, 1998).

Genetic Risk

Over two thirds of women diagnosed with breast cancer each year have no known risk factors other than gender. Although family history has been emphasized for many years, only 5% to 10% of all breast cancers are believed to be genetically linked. This gene has been labeled the BRCA gene; BR for breast and CA for cancer. As new genetic mutations have been discovered, they have been numbered BRCA1, BRCA2, and BRCA3.

The gene mutation for breast cancer can be inherited from either the father or the mother, so a careful history needs to explore both family pedigrees. The risk for carrying the mutated gene is greater in women who have a first-degree relative with breast cancer at a young age, have several rel-

TABLE 5-1

BREAST CANCER RATES AT CERTAIN AGES

Age	Rate	Percentage
Birth to 39 years	1 in 227	0.44
40 to 59 years	1 in 25	3.94
60 to 79 years	1 in 15	6.89
Birth to death	1 in 8	12.52

(Landis, S., Murray, T., Bolder, S., & Wingo, P. [1998]. Cancer statistics. *CA: Cancer Journal for Clinicians, 48,* 6–29.)

atives with breast and/or ovarian cancer, or are of Ashkenazi Jewish heritage.

If a woman inherits the BRCA gene mutation, her actual risk is uncertain. Early studies predicted an 80% to 85% lifetime risk; however, more recent studies suggest that the risk may actually be much lower.

Any woman wishing to be tested for the BRCA gene mutation should undergo genetic counseling first for confirmation of the increased risk and for education and psychological support. Counseling needs to be available both before and after the testing. Positive test results can be emotionally devastating. Learning that there is a high probability for cancer to develop without a foolproof method of prevention creates a myriad of emotions. Positive results can also lead to work and insurance discrimination. Negative test results can lead to a false sense of security that there is no risk for breast cancer. However, these women still need regular screening and medical care because over 90% of breast cancers are not genetically linked. For all women who are tested, a personal health plan needs to be developed that includes a schedule for screening, possible lifestyle changes, and/or other prevention strategies that may lower the risk.

Commercial testing for the presence of the genetic mutation is available for women. Testing centers may charge as much as $2500 for the test, and many are not doing any follow-up research on the women being tested. For some laboratories, the only education and follow-up provided include the consent form and a list of genetic counselors available in a woman's geographic region. However, these laboratories have made testing available to many more women, and test results are available in a timely fashion. University centers provide free testing as part of ongoing research. However, it may take months to get tested and even longer to obtain the results.

In a family with a pedigree indicating a high risk for the BRCA gene mutation, family members with known breast cancer should be tested first. If test results are negative for the gene mutation, then the women in the family without breast cancer should also be negative (Bilimoria & Morrow, 1995; Hoskins et al., 1995; Marcus et al., 1996).

Other Risk Factors

Other risk factors for breast cancer are specific characteristics in a woman's life that are associated with a higher rate of breast cancer. These have not been proved as cause-and-effect factors but rather have a relationship with a higher incidence of breast cancer. They are useful in identifying women at increased risk for breast cancer and those who need closer surveillance or more thorough evaluation when a problem presents (Table 5-2).

Prevention

There is no definite way to prevent breast cancer. Recent studies suggest that lifestyle changes may lower a woman's risk for breast cancer, although more definitive research is still needed.

Diet

Epidemiologic studies have indicated that countries with a diet low in fat; high in fruits, vegetables, and grains; and low in animal proteins have lower rates of breast cancer. A very low-fat diet has been shown to reduce circulating estrogen levels, which may translate into lower breast cancer rates. Also, animal studies have shown that rats fed high-fat diets developed more breast cancers. Other studies have suggested that phytoestrogens (natural plant estrogens) such as soy protein

TABLE 5-2

FACTORS ASSOCIATED WITH INCREASED RISK OF BREAST CANCER

Personal history	• Benign biopsy with atypia or LCIS • Previous history of breast cancer or DCIS
Gynecologic history	• Early menarche (before age 12) • Late menopause (after age 55) • Late first pregnancy (after age 30) • No pregnancies • Abortion?
Family history	• Two or more first-degree relatives (mother, sisters); especially if diagnosis before menopause • Family pedigree that indicates genetic risk
Lifestyle history	• Obesity • Radiation exposure, especially during teen and early adult years • Long-term estrogen replacement therapy • Diet high in fats • Moderate alcohol intake • Sedentary lifestyle
Environmental	• Pesticides • Hormone-fed animal products

lower the risk of breast cancer. More research is needed in this area, but nurses can inform the public about the importance of a good diet for healthy living. All people should limit fat to less than 30% of total calories, increase fruits and vegetables to five servings a day, increase intake of whole grains, limit the amount of animal proteins, and minimize use of pure fats such as salad dressings, butter, and mayonnaise (Bagga et al., 1995).

Exercise

Research is beginning to show that women who exercise and maintain an ideal body weight have a lower risk of breast cancer. Body fat is a source of circulating estrogen, especially after menopause. One study found that 3 hours of aerobic activity a week lowered a women's risk for breast cancer by 30% to 40%. Another study found rates for breast cancer lower among women who were physically active in their employment compared with those with sedentary jobs. Public education should emphasize the importance of an active lifestyle, including a regular exercise program (Bernstein, Hen-

derson, Hanisch, Sullivan-Halley & Ross, 1994; Friedenreich et al., 1998; Bernstein et al., 1998).

Tamoxifen

Tamoxifen is a hormone therapy that has been used for years to prevent and treat metastases in women who have a diagnosis of breast cancer. Tamoxifen significantly reduces the risk of breast cancer in high-risk women. The Gail Model Risk Assessment Tool provides women with a numerical risk factor, with any woman scoring greater than 1.67 considered at high risk for breast cancer. A new clinical trial is under way in which 22,000 post-menopausal high-risk women will be randomized between tamoxifen and raloxifene to determine the best agent with the least toxicity (STAR trial—the Study of Tamoxifen and Raloxifene). More information about this National Surgical Adjuvant Breast and Bowel Project can be obtained by calling the Cancer Information Service at 1-800-4CANCER. Other chemoprevention agents under trial include dimethyl sulfoxide (DMSO) and differentiating agents such as retinoids.

Mastectomy

The last possible way to prevent breast cancer is to remove the breasts. In the past, a subcutaneous mastectomy was performed that removed all breast tissue but left the nipple aerolar complex intact. Subcutaneous mastectomies leave as much as 10% to 15% of breast tissue, which may still be at risk for breast cancer.

A simple mastectomy removes all of the breast tissue on the chest, including the nipple. However, this also leaves behind remnant breast tissue high in the axilla and inferior to the clavicle. There has been no large registry or randomized trial to determine the rate of breast cancer in women who undergo prophylactic mastectomies, but there are scattered anecdotal reports of cases. A woman considering prophylactic mastectomy should undergo genetic counseling to confirm perceived risk and psychological counseling to help prepare for the loss of breasts. Because this is never a medical emergency, a woman should also seek a second opinion on the benefits of mastectomies and types of reconstruction available (Bilimoria & Morrow, 1995; Loescher, 1993).

Early Detection

Susan, age 48, was never really concerned about breast cancer. She had no family history, had 2 children ages 17 and 25, ate a fairly healthy diet, and ran 3 miles at least four times a week. She was surprised when her gynecologist recommended that she have her mammograms annually, and, with her busy lifestyle, she put it off another 6 months after her doctor's visit.

The most important tool for early detection is mammography. It is estimated that a mammogram can detect a breast cancer 2 years before it can be felt. During the 1970s, great technological advances were made to allow for the routine use of mammograms with minimal radiation exposure to women. In the 1990s the standards for mammograms were developed, and now any facility performing a mammogram is required by the FDA to be certified, ensuring that the woman is receiving the lowest possible radiation exposure, that films are clear of artifacts so a cancer can be found, and that personnel have special training and expertise to take the pictures and interpret them.

Every woman should begin having yearly mammograms at the age of 40 unless she has a family history, in which case she should begin to have mammograms 10 years before the age of diagnosis of the relative (Table 5-3). It has been shown that regular mammograms do save lives in both pre- and postmenopausal women. A women should continue this schedule for the rest of her life unless she develops a life-threatening illness and is not expected to live more than 5 years.

Although mammograms are the best tool for early detection, they are not 100% accurate, especially in women who have very dense breast tissue. Therefore, every woman should also have a breast examination performed by a health professional every 1 to 3 years between ages 20 and 40 and every year beginning at the age of 40.

Breast self-examination is the third early detection method (Box 5-1). Most palpable lumps are found by the woman herself. Although there has never been any research to prove that breast self-examination has an impact on survival, there is a movement to teach women to be comfortable touching and getting to know their breasts. A woman should report immediately to a health care provider any changes she finds in her breast.

Susan finally had her screening mammogram. She didn't realize how nervous she was until she was sitting, waiting for her turn to be called. She just felt so vulnerable.

Clinical Presentation

The most common presentation of breast cancer is a painless lump. Other signs to watch for include:

- Retraction or dimpling of the skin over the breast
- New onset of nipple inversion
- New thickening in the breast that is not present in the mirror image of the other breast
- Spontaneous, unilateral nipple discharge or bloody nipple discharge
- Generalized inflammation or edema with dimpling (peau d'orange)

Any changes in the breast should be further evaluated with mammograms or ultrasound. Any suspicious areas may need to be biopsied.

Diagnosis

Breast cancers can be seen on a mammogram as a starlike density, asymmetry, or calcification. The radiologist examines the film for obvious abnormalities, compares the right breast with the left while looking for asymmetry, and compares this year with previous years, looking for changes.

TABLE 5-3	
AMERICAN CANCER SOCIETY GUIDELINES FOR EARLY DETECTION	
Mammography	Age 40 and over—every year
Clinical breast examination	Age 20 to 40—every 1 to 3 years
	Age 40 and over—every year
Breast self-examination	All women—monthly

BOX 5-1

Breast Self-Examination

1. Breast self-examination should be done the same time each month—if you are having periods, about 5 to 7 days after the first day of your period. Whatever method you use, be consistent so you can get to know the patterns of your breast.

2. Take off all of your clothes from the waist up.

3. In front of a well-lit mirror, examine your breast with arms at your side, over your head, hands on hip pressing down and leaning over at the waist. You are looking for any changes in breast size, color, shape and for any dimpling of the skin or new retraction of skin or nipple.

4. Lie down on the bed with a small towel or pillow under the shoulder of the breast you will examine first.

5. Use the pads of your middle three fingers on your opposite hand to feel your breast.

6. Press into the breast using dime-size circles, pressing down lightly, then a medium pressure, and then deeply into the breast tissue.

7. Move your fingers in a pattern on the breast so you do not miss any breast tissue. The strip method is the best for covering all tissue, moving up and down in rows until the whole breast has been examined.

8. Repeat, examining the other breast.

Other imaging procedures may be needed to help define the abnormality in the breast (Table 5-4).

> *The day after her screening mammogram, there was a message on her answering machine. "The radiologist wants more films of your breast, but don't worry, this is very routine and often turns out to be nothing but just movement or artifacts on the films. Please call the office first thing tomorrow."*

> *The next day, Susan's mammogram revealed an asymmetry in her right breast. Magnified mammogram demonstrated an actual starlike mass, and biopsy was recommended.*

Once an abnormality is found in a woman's breast, a biopsy is needed to determine if it is benign or malignant. Fortunately, 70% to 80% of all biopsies are benign. Not only do biopsies cause an incredible amount of emotional distress, they also

TABLE 5-4

DIAGNOSTIC TOOLS FOR BREAST CANCER

Ultrasound	High-frequency sound waves useful in defining changes in the breast (ie, to see if a mass is fluid filled or a cyst).	No special preparation. Painless procedure.
Galactogram (ductogram)	Radiopaque dye is injected into the ducts that have abnormal discharge, and mammographic pictures are taken.	May be uncomfortable while the duct is being cannulated with a blunt needle and the woman may feel pressure sensation during injection of the dye.
Magnetic resonance imaging (MRI)	FDA approved only for detected leaks in silicone implants. Research is being conducted on the use of MRI to differentiate benign from malignant lesions.	Must lie prone on a special pillow that suspends and separates the breasts. Some women will need sedation if prone to claustrophobia.
Nuclear medicine dye studies (Sesta-MIBI)	Experimental procedures to search for occult malignancies or to differentiate benign from malignant lesions.	Need injection of radiopaque dye and to wait for the dye to be taken up in the breast. Painless except for venipuncture.

can lead to scarring in the breast, which causes difficulty in interpreting future mammograms. Therefore, less invasive procedures (Table 5-5) now are being used to obtain tissue from the abnormality to make a diagnosis. The goal is to minimize the number of women who have to go to the operating room for an open biopsy. In breast centers of excellence, the malignant rate for open biopsies is greater than 60%.

Susan's surgeon was fairly certain that the mass was a cancer. She was scheduled for a stereotactic core biopsy to obtain tissue for a diagnosis. Susan's emotions wavered be-

tween panic and denial—"Couldn't we put this off until after I finish this big project at work?"

Understanding the Pathology Report

The diagnosis of breast cancer represents a range of malignant abnormalities from in situ to invasive, slow growing to fast growing, and a variety of different histologic types. The nurse should be able to understand the basics of the pathology re-

TABLE 5-5
BIOPSY PROCEDURES

	Procedure	Advantages	Disadvantages
Fine-needle aspiration	Small-gauge needle is inserted into the mass and fluid is aspirated. If no fluid obtained, the needle is manipulated around in the mass to loosen some cells, and these are then aspirated. Cells are fixed to slide and sent to pathology for cytologic review.	Well-tolerated outpatient procedure performed by palpation or under ultrasound	Low yield of cells without normal surrounding structure. Need experienced cytopathologist.
Core-needle biopsy	A large-bore needle is placed into the area of suspicion and a core of tissue is removed. Usually several core biosies are taken of the area to ensure adequate sampling of the abnormality. This may be done with palpation, under stereotactic mammography, or ultrasound guidance.	Higher yield of tissue so less chance of false readings. Tissue is removed with normal structure and architecture intact, which enables more accurate interpreation.	Greater risk for bleeding, bruising, or infection. Slightly more uncomfortable.
Incisional biopsy	A small amount of the abnormality is removed through an open incision; usually used when the probability of cancer is high.	High yield of tissue makes diagnosis easier. Does not remove large amounts of tissue for benign lesions.	Does not remove all of the cancer and, therefore, another procedure is necessary.
Excisional biopsy	The entire abnormality is removed through an open incision.	High yield of tissue and often the entire abnormality removed during one procedure.	May remove large amounts of tissue that are benign.
Wire localization	When an abnormality is seen but not palpable, the surgeon needs guidance on where to remove breast tissue. A wire is placed by the radiologist under mammogram or ultrasound guidance.	If placed correctly, the surgeon can remove the smallest amount of tissue either to sample or completely remove the abnormality with exact precision.	Procedure may be uncomfortable and is not 100% accurate.

port in order to be able to answer questions and anticipate future treatments.

In Situ

Carcinoma in situ is a premalignant lesion. The definition of malignant is the ability to metastasize. In situ literally means inside. The in situ cells have actually undergone malignant transformation, but they have not invaded or broken through the membrane of the duct (ductal carcinoma in situ—DCIS) or lobe (lobular carcinoma in situ—LCIS) in which they are contained. Therefore, they do not have the capacity to metastasize.

LCIS is usually bilateral and is considered a high-risk marker, indicating a six to ten times greater risk of developing breast cancer in either breast. Because LCIS is a marker and not an actual malignancy, it can be treated with close medical surveillance alone. The only acceptable surgical procedure should be bilateral mastectomy because LCIS is usually multifocal (in more than one area of the breast) and bilateral.

DCIS is considered a premalignant lesion that, if left alone, has a high probability of progressing to an invasive cancer. The natural progression of the disease, such as how long it takes to break through the duct and what causes it to become invasive, is not well understood. Although the exact treatment of DCIS remains under considerable debate, it is agreed that all evidence of DCIS should be removed surgically. DCIS can be further classified into subcategories, comedo and noncomedo, with varying degrees of aggressiveness. If the cell type appears aggressive, radiation therapy will also be used to prevent local recurrence because 50% of DCIS that recurs is invasive.

Histologic Types

Invasive breast cancer is most commonly an adenocarcinoma that originates in the distal end of the breast ducts. Infiltrating ductal carcinoma accounts for two thirds of all histologic types of breast cancer and is often referred to as the "garden variety" breast cancer. It is aggressive, with a high rate of spread to the lymph nodes and distant sites. Infiltrating lobular carcinoma is the second most common type and is usually less aggressive. However, there is a variant of lobular carcinoma that acts just like a ductal carcinoma. Other less

common subtypes include medullary, mucinous, and tubular, which are all less aggressive.

Inflammatory breast cancer is a rare form of breast cancer that involves the lymphatics of the breast skin. The clinical presentation is inflammation and/or a large mass or hardening of the breast that appears to arise almost overnight. It is often misdiagnosed as mastitis and treated initially with antibiotics. This is a very aggressive type of breast cancer, requiring chemotherapy before any surgery, and the 5-year survival is very low.

Paget's disease is carcinoma involving the nipple. It is not an invasive lesion; however, often it is an indicator of a subclinical cancer elsewhere in the breast.

Grade

Breast cancers are given a grade that provides more information about the cancer's aggressiveness. The pathologist uses a standardized nine-point scale called SBR (Scarff-Bloom-Richardson) to grade the tumor on three factors—tubule formation, nuclear grade, and number of mitotic figures (Table 5-6).

Prognostic Factors

The two most important prognostic factors are size and node involvement. The larger a tumor is, the greater the likelihood that there has been either lymphatic or vascular invasion and, therefore, distant spread. Any lymph node involvement indicates the propensity of the tumor to travel; multiple positive nodes are a strong indication for distant spread.

Estrogen and progesterone receptors are the next most important prognostic factors. Breast

TABLE 5-6

BREAST CANCER GRADING

Grade	Differentiation	SBR Score	
I	Well differentiated	3–5	Least aggressive
II	Moderately differentiated	5–7	
III	Poorly differentiated	8–9	Most aggressive

cancer cells may have hormonal receptors on the cell surface that promote cell growth and function. Breast cancers that are estrogen and/or progesterone receptor positive have a better prognosis.

There are many other prognostic tests that are done to try and predict the odds of recurrence of the breast cancer. To date, we are unable to predict with any degree of accuracy. Women with very small tumors and negative nodes can develop metastases, whereas those with very large tumors and positive nodes can live disease free for many years. Additional tests are used to help predict who needs further treatment and what type of additional treatment is necessary.

No single prognostic test can predict the chance of recurrence. However, the following tests can provide additional information on the potential of the cancer to metastasize and to respond to therapy:

- S phase—The percentage of cells in the tumor that are in the division phase of the cell cycle. A high percentage indicates a rapidly growing breast cancer.
- DNA content—Analysis of the amount and configuration of DNA in the cancer cells. Diploid indicates a more normal population and less aggressive cancer, whereas aneuploid and tetraploid are abnormal and more aggressive.

The following, when present, indicate a more aggressive cancer and are considered poor prognostic factors:

- Cathepsin-D—A protein secreted by the cancer cells
- Her2/neu—An oncogene that indicates a possible resistance to CMF (cyclophosphamide, methotrexate, 5-fluorouracil) chemotherapy and potential sensitivity to Herceptin, a monoclonal antibody
- p53—An oncogene that may initiate cancer growth
- EGFR—Epidermal growth factor receptor, which stimulates growth

Staging

A staging workup is usually done to determine the presence of metastases before primary surgery. This may consist of a chest radiograph, bone scan, and abdominal CT scan or ultrasound. Breast cancer is staged using the TNM staging system (Table 5-7).

- Stage I breast cancer is a small tumor localized to the breast, and prognosis is over 85%.
- Stage II breast cancer can be a 2- to 5-cm tumor with no lymph node involvement or a small tumor with anywhere from 1 to over 20 nodes involvement. Prognosis is 60% to 85%.
- Stage III breast cancer is a large tumor over 5 cm with positive nodes or tumor that invades the skin or chest or fixed and matted lymph nodes. Prognosis is under 50%.
- Stage IV is any distant spread of cancer, and prognosis is less than 20%.

Tumor Markers

Tumor markers are tumor antigens or proteins that can be measured in the blood. Markers that are often elevated in breast cancer are CA15-3, CA 27.29, and CEA. These blood tests are controversial when used in screening women for metastatic disease because they may be elevated months before any clinical evidence of disease. These markers are very helpful in evaluating response to treatment in that a downward trend in the value suggests clinical response to treatment and an upward trend suggests disease progression.

Susan's biopsy revealed an infiltrating ductal carcinoma with ductal carcinoma in situ. Like most premenopausal women, her tumor was

---

TABLE 5-7

TNM CLASSIFICATION STAGING SYSTEM

- 0: in situ breast cancer.
- Stage I breast cancer is a small tumor localized to the breast, and prognosis is over 85%.
- Stage II breast cancer can be a 2- to 5-cm tumor with no lymph node involvement or a small tumor with anywhere from 1 to over 20 nodes involvement, and prognosis is 60% to 85%.
- Stage III breast cancer is a large tumor over 5 cm with positive nodes or tumor, which invades the skin or chest or fixed and matted lymph nodes, and prognosis is under 50%.
- Stage IV is any distant spread of cancer, and prognosis is less than 20%.

estrogen and progesterone receptor negative. The other prognostic factors were also worrisome with the DNA content aneuploid, the S phase high (rapidly dividing), and Her2/neu positive. Susan could not even grasp the implications of having cancer because she was in the middle of trying to decide what surgery she wanted, who was going to fill in for her at work, and how were they going to manage their busy home schedule without her active participation.

Before any treatment decisions, Susan underwent staging that included a chest radiograph, bone scan, and ultrasound of her abdomen, which were all negative for metastases.

Breast Cancer Management

Breast cancer can spread through local invasion or through the lymphatics or blood vessels. Regional spread is to the axillary nodes or to the nodes under the mediastinum. The most common sites of distant spread are lung, bone, and liver. Breast cancer can also spread to the brain, ovaries, and adrenal glands and to distant skin. There are two theories about the spread of cancer. The Halstedian theory proposes that breast cancer spreads mainly by direct extension, out to the lymph nodes and then to the rest of the body. This led to the old radical surgeries, in the belief that if all local tissue was removed, there was no risk of recurrence. It took over 70 years of radical surgery to prove this theory wrong, which led to the development of the Fisher theory. The Fisher theory holds that by the time a cancer is detected in the breast, there has already been microscopic spread through the blood and lymphatic vessels in the breast. Therefore, radical surgery is not necessary and systemic therapy is required for long-term survival.

Surgical Treatment

The primary treatment of breast cancer remains the surgical removal of all gross evidence of cancer. This can be achieved by lumpectomy, quadrantectomy, or mastectomy.

Lumpectomy is the removal of all the tumor and a rim of healthy tissue around it (clear margins). If the cancer is invasive, this must be followed with radiation therapy to the breast and chest wall to minimize the risk of local recurrence. A *quadrantectomy*, or removal of a whole quarter of the breast, may need to be performed when the tumor is large to ensure clear margins around the tumor. A simple *mastectomy* is the removal of the entire breast, including the nipple, but sparing the pectoralis muscle. Modified radical mastectomy is the removal of the entire breast and the axillary nodes. Radical mastectomy is rarely necessary and removes the breast, the nodes, and the pectoralis muscles.

It has been found that women who make their own decision about which type of surgery to undergo are more satisfied with the results and have fewer issues related to body image. Factors that determine whether a woman should consider a mastectomy include:

- Tumor size—Tumors over 5 cm or a large tumor in a small breast are at greater risk for local recurrence and for poor cosmetic results with lumpectomy
- Clear margins—Residual disease at the margin increases risk for recurrence
- Connective tissue disease—Increases radiation toxicity
- Nipple involvement—Not an absolute contraindication, but some women may not want radiation therapy if they have to lose their nipple anyhow
- Fear of recurrence
- Fear of radiation therapy
- Extensive ductal carcinoma in situ—Only if unable to obtain clear margins
- Prior radiation therapy to the chest
- Very large, pendulous breasts
- Convenient radiation therapy centers—It may be impractical for a woman who has to travel 2 to 3 hours to a radiation therapy center for daily treatments
- Personal choice

RECONSTRUCTION

Once the decision to undergo a mastectomy is made, the woman then must decide whether to undergo reconstruction. Reconstruction may be immediate or delayed. Immediate reconstruction allows for the woman to wake up without a completely flat chest. It also reduces the number of times a woman must undergo lengthy general anesthesia. Delayed reconstruction allows a woman to have more time to learn about and choose between the different types of reconstruction. Whether a woman undergoes immediate or delayed reconstruction, she will still experience a loss of her own breast and needs to be allowed time to grieve this loss.

Reconstruction can be done with a woman's own tissue or with a device implanted in the chest. Implants are silicone shells, which may be filled with saline, silicone, or many new substances under research such as peanut oil. They are placed under the pectoralis muscle to provide a thicker covering over the implant, produce a better cosmetic result, and allow examination of the overlying skin and residual breast tissue for signs of recurrence. Implants are relatively simple surgical procedures, requiring little additional recovery over the basic mastectomy. Often, a tissue expander is placed initially to stretch the skin and muscle. This partially filled silicone sac is slowly expanded over several weeks with saline to provide space for the permanent implant. The expander may be overinflated so the smaller permanent implant will rest in the stretched tissue with a more natural droop.

The most common complication of implants is a fibrous contracture or scar tissue that forms around the implant. This can lead to implant displacement and disfigurement, hardness and immobility of the implant, and pain. Other potential complications include implant rupture or leakage, erosion through the chest muscle, and infection.

Autologous tissue reconstruction uses a woman's own tissue to build a new breast. Tissue may be tunneled to the breast from the site of origin while maintaining the original blood supply (myocutaneous flap), or it may be completely removed with the blood supply reanastomosed in the breast (free flap). Tissue can be taken from the region around the latissimus dorsi muscle (the back muscle that moves the shoulder), from the rectus abdominus muscle (large vertical abdominal muscle—TRAM flap), or from the gluteal muscle. The autologous reconstructed breast appears and feels more natural and will naturally fluctuate in size as a woman's weight changes.

Autologous tissue reconstruction is a much larger surgery requiring longer time in surgery and a longer recovery period. Potential complications include flap necrosis, infection, abdominal wall hernia, and functional deficits of the donor muscle site (decrease in shoulder motion or abdominal weakness).

The finishing touches of reconstruction include surgery to the opposite breast and nipple reconstruction. The reconstructed nipple has no innervation to allow for sensation or physical changes to stimulation by temperature or touch. The nipple is made using the skin on the breast, skin from the donor site, the groin, behind the ear, or from the opposite breast areola. Once the reconstructed nipple has healed, it may be tattooed to match the color of the opposite nipple. To achieve symmetry of the breasts, the opposite breast may need to be lifted (mastoplexy), reduced, or augmented. Some states mandate that reconstructive surgery be paid for not only on the removed breast but also to achieve symmetry to the chest.

AXILLARY NODE DISSECTION

Axillary node dissection is performed on the majority of women who have an invasive breast cancer. It is not done for in situ disease because the risk of regional spread is minimal due to the lack of local invasion. There is continued debate about the value of axillary node dissection for women with invasive disease. Lymph node status is very important in understanding the patient's prognosis and planning for additional therapy. In the past, a very radical surgery was performed, removing all of the lymph nodes, cutting through muscles, and risking cutting through nerves. With less radical surgeries being performed today, most surgeons do a limited sampling, removing level 1 and 2 axillary nodes. The goal is to remove at least 10 nodes to have an adequate sampling to determine the extent of spread. Skip metastasis, in which the lower nodes are negative and the upper nodes are positive, is rare. Research is being done to minimize the extent of axillary surgery by searching for and removing the sentinel node. The sentinel node is felt to be the first node receiving drainage from the area around the tumor. Dye and/or radioactive material is injected into the tumor bed of the breast. After time for the dye or radioactive material to travel to the axilla, the node that has taken up most of the injected material is removed. If this node is positive, a full sampling is performed. However, if the node is negative, the woman is spared this further surgery. Complications of axillary node dissection include a frozen shoulder, numbness in the arm and/or axilla, arm weakness, and lymphedema.

> *Susan was given almost all of the options available. She could choose between lumpectomy or mastectomy, and all types of reconstruction were available to her. After much discussion, she decided to undergo mastectomy with immediate reconstruction using her abdominal tissue (TRAM flap). She also wanted to try the sentinel node surgery so she could possibly be spared a full axillary node sampling.*
>
> *Susan's final pathology revealed a 2.9-cm infiltrating ductal carcinoma with extensive ductal carcinoma in situ. The sentinel node was positive, and Susan had to return to surgery once more for an axillary node sampling. Two of twelve nodes sampled tested positive for metastases. Her final stage was IIB, T2, N1, M0.*

Radiation Therapy

Radiation therapy is necessary when the breast is conserved and at times with mastectomy to prevent local recurrence and possibly improve long-term survival. Before treatment is begun, there is a 1- to 2-hour session of planning called simulation. At the end of this session, the radiation field is marked with permanent ink and/or tattoos to ensure proper positioning over the several weeks of treatment. Treatments are given daily for 5 to 6 weeks or a total of 5000 to 6000 cGy. The daily treatment takes less than 10 to 15 minutes but involves travel to and from the center, disrobing, and positioning. Some women who have cancer close to the surgical margins may require a boost or higher dose of radiation to the tumor bed. This is often done with radioactive implants or an electron beam.

Side effects during the treatments are minimal and consist mainly of fatigue and skin changes, which can range from a mild tanning and drying to moist desquamation, especially in skin folds. Many centers use an aloe vera–type lotion to minimize the toxicity. If the skin burn is severe, treatment will be interrupted to allow for healing. Long-term complications include changes to the texture, size, and appearance of the breast; pneumonitis; increased potential for lung cancer in smokers; and sarcoma of the chest.

> *It was decided that Susan should also undergo radiation therapy even after her mastectomy because of the new evidence of a survival advantage for young women who undergo chest radiation therapy. This was scheduled to begin in the middle of chemotherapy.*
>
> *Susan tolerated the radiation therapy well except for the profound fatigue. She found that she could not get through the afternoon without a short nap. She did find that on the days she went out for a brisk 2-mile walk, she had more energy. She experienced only mild tenderness on her skin from the skin burn and was able to complete her treatments without interruption.*

Palliative radiation therapy may be necessary for the treatment of bone or brain metastases. These treatments are usually well tolerated and often welcomed because of the symptomatic relief they provide.

Systemic Adjuvant Therapy

Adjuvant therapy is the use of medicine after surgery to treat any microscopic residual disease. Adjuvant therapy for breast cancer arose out of Fisher's theory that breast cancer is a systemic disease at the time of diagnosis. Systemic adjuvant therapy is the use of hormonal therapy and/or chemotherapy to prevent the spread and growth of breast cancer anywhere else in the body.

The decision to use adjuvant therapy is not always black and white. Adjuvant therapy reduces the risk for systemic recurrence by approximately 30%. This risk reduction has to be applied to a woman's risk so that a 60% risk of recurrence is reduced to 40% and a 10% risk is reduced to 7%. For every ten premenopausal women with stage IIA breast cancer, three will recur and only one of the three will benefit from adjuvant therapy. All ten will be offered treatment because those who will recur and those who will benefit cannot be identified.

Usually, chemotherapy is given as a combination of drugs to maximize the tumor effects while minimizing the side effects. The most common combination of chemotherapy is CMF (cyclophosphamide, methotrexate, and 5-fluorouracil). The type, dose, and duration of chemotherapy are dependent on a woman's stage, number of positive lymph nodes, age, and menopausal status (Table 5-8). The majority of premenopausal women with tumors over 1 cm will be offered some form of chemotherapy. Postmenopausal women also can benefit from chemotherapy, especially if their tumor appears aggressive, is greater than 2 cm, or there are positive nodes.

The more aggressive the cancer appears, the more aggressive the adjuvant therapy required. Women with more than 10 nodes positive or with inflammatory breast cancer may benefit from the most intensive therapy, high-dose chemotherapy with stem cell rescue. To overcome the dose-limiting toxicity, bone marrow suppression, of large doses of chemotherapy, the woman's stem cells are harvested and cryopreserved (frozen). Stem cells, precursors from all three blood cell lines, are harvested from the bone marrow (usually the iliac crest) or the blood by plasmapheresis. After the high-dose chemotherapy is completed, the stem cells are thawed and reinfused as a transfusion. With the development of growth factors (G-CSF, GM-CSF, Epogen) that promote bone marrow recovery, this procedure is much safer with rare fatal complications. Some centers are completing the majority of the treatment and aftercare in the ambulatory setting.

The oncologist was concerned about Susan's prognosis because of several factors. She had a T2 tumor (over 2 cm) with two nodes positive, which put her at moderate risk for systemic spread. She also was Her2/neu positive, which indicated a possible resistance to CMF alone. It was recommended that she undergo fairly aggressive chemotherapy with four cycles of AC followed by four cycles of Taxol.

Susan was devastated at the thought of 6 months of chemotherapy; however, she did not believe she could compromise her chances by taking less aggressive treatment. Her nurse told her to purchase a wig before starting treatment so she would be prepared for her hair loss, but he did not tell her how difficult it

TABLE 5-8

ADJUVANT CHEMOTHERAPY REGIMENS

	Regimen	Most Common Side Effects	Nursing Care
CMF	Cyclophosphamide–methotrexate–5-Fluorouracil given in 3- or 4-week cycles for 6 months	• Hair thinning • Mild to moderate nausea • Weight gain • Stomatitis	• 50% women do not require wig but need to know resources • Antiemetics as needed • Instruct on possibility for weight gain. Watch types of caloric intake. Mild aerobic activity helps minimize • Instruct on mouth care
FAC	5-Fluorouracil–doxorubicin (Adriamycin)–cytoxan given all IV in 3- or 4-week cycles for 6 months	• Complete alopecia • Moderate nausea • Cardiomyopathy	• Provide resources for hair loss • Antiemetics on regular schedule for 48 hours after treatment • May need baseline evaluation of heart such as MUGA or echocardiogram
AC	Doxorubicin–cyclophosphamide given in higher doses every 3 weeks for 3 months (four cycles)	• Complete alopecia • Moderate nausea • Possible cardiomyopathy • Moderate to severe neutropenia • Increased risk for leukemia	• Same as FAC • Monitor CBC weekly • Instruct on neutropenia precautions if WBC low • May need prophylactic antibiotics and/or growth factors
A-CMF	Doxorubicin (Adriamycin) as a single agent for four cycles (3 months); then standard CMF for 6 months	• Complete alopecia • Mild to moderate nausea • Possible cardiomyopathy	• Same as FAC
AC—paclitaxel	Doxorubicin and cyclophosphamide for four cycles (3 months), followed by four cycles of paclitaxel (3 months)	• Same as AC • Possible allergic reactions • Severe myalgias, usually 48–72 hours after treatment • Peripheral neuropathy	

would be to find a wig to match her salt-and-pepper hair. With the new nausea medication, Susan had very little problem with nausea and actually gained 9 lb, to her dismay. She did experience some mouth sores and nail changes. Worst of all was the fatigue, which never went away. She felt like each leg weighed 100 lb, and even doing simple tasks exhausted her.

Hormonal therapy is also used to prevent breast cancer from returning and to prevent a new breast cancer from developing in the opposite breast. The most common form of hormonal therapy is tamoxifen, which is usually given to postmenopausal women who are estrogen or progesterone receptor positive. Premenopausal women may also be given tamoxifen or may undergo oophorectomy to remove the major source of estrogen.

Tamoxifen is a weak estrogen and an antiestrogen, which binds with the estrogen receptors, thereby blocking the body's estrogen from entering the cancer cell. It is believed to be a chemostatic agent rather than a chemotoxic agent, meaning that it does not cause cell death (apoptosis) but puts the cell to rest so it is not actively dividing. This pill is taken 10 mg twice a day or 20 mg once a day for 5 years. The major side effects include hot flashes, vaginal discharge, vaginal dryness, decreased libido, increased difficulty in achieving orgasm, depression, short-term memory loss, and increased potential for blood clots. Long-term use increases a woman's risk for uterine cancer (from 1 to 3 in 1000) and cataracts. However, some benefits of tamoxifen include lowering blood cholesterol and reducing the rate of osteoporosis in postmenopausal women. Research is looking for new, effective hormonal agents with fewer side effects.

Susan's cancer was hormone receptor negative so she did not require any hormonal therapy.

Treatment for Advanced Disease

The 5-year survival rate for women with breast cancer is less than 20%. It is generally believed that once breast cancer has metastasized it cannot be cured. Therefore, palliative treatment is offered, which is aimed at prolonging life while balancing the disease symptoms with treatment side effects. The choice of treatments depends on the extent of disease, sites of metastases, hormonal status of the tumor, menopausal status, age, and medical condition of the woman.

Chemotherapy is usually given first for premenopausal women, women with rapidly advancing disease, or those who are hormone receptor negative. The type of chemotherapy chosen depends on what, if any, drugs were used in adjuvant therapy. An anthracycline-based regimen is usually given first if Adriamycin has not already been used. The taxenes (paclitaxel [Taxol] and docetaxel [Taxotere]) are also very effective agents against breast cancer. The response rate and length of response decrease with each new regimen that is given. Research is always looking for new agents or combinations of agents that will provide a response after the cancer has become resistant to standard therapy (Table 5-9).

Hormonal therapy is often the first line of treatment for postmenopausal women who are hormone receptor positive. The response rate for first-line hormonal therapy is 30% to 80% with a median duration of response of 1 to 2 years and some women responding for several years. Even after failing the first type of hormonal therapy, 20% of women will respond to a second hormonal agent with a median response of 18 to 24 months (Table 5-10).

Oncologic Emergencies

Treatment may also be needed for the complications of advanced disease. Women with bone metastases are at risk for hypercalcemia, spinal cord compression, and pathologic fractures. Serum calcium levels need to be monitored carefully for hypercalcemia (over 13 mg/dL), and the woman must be assessed for signs of nausea, vomiting, constipation, polyuria, polydipsia, lethargy, and confusion. Cord compression can present as unrelenting back pain, leg or arm weakness or numbness, or incontinence. Pathologic fractures can occur when the bone metastases cause lytic lesions or holes in the bones. Simply rolling over in bed or coughing can cause the bone to fracture through an area of weakness. The main treatment for these complications is chemotherapy or hormonal therapy for the breast cancer. Radiation therapy may be used for focal areas of bone metastases to relieve pain and prevent fractures. A new drug,

TABLE 5-9
CHEMOTHERAPY FOR ADVANCED BREAST CANCER

Drug	Major Side Effects	Nursing Care
Adriamycin	• Complete alopecia • Possible cardiomyopathy	• Resources for wigs and hair coverings • Assess for signs of congestive heart failure • Use Zinecard, which is a cardioprotective agent
Taxol	• Possible allergic reactions • Severe myalgias usually 48–72 hours after treatment • Peripheral neuropathy	• Premedicate with steroids • Antihistamines, steroids, or pain medications if needed for pain • May use Amifostine as a chemoprotective agent
Taxotere	• Capillary leak syndrome • Neutropenia	• Premedicate and continue steroids for minimum 4 days after treatment • Monitor weight for fluid retention • Monitor WBC and use prophylactic antibiotics and/or growth factors as needed
Capecitabine	• Diarrhea • Stomatitis • Palmar plantar erythema	• Imodium as needed • Instruct on mouth care • Same as above • Oral agent that needs to be discontinued if symptoms moderately severe
Navelbine	• Fatigue • Neutropenia	• Encourage hydration drinking at least 2 quarts a day • Monitor WBC and treat as needed
Mitomycin/Velban	• Vesicant • Possible renal toxicity	• Should be given through central line • Monitor creatinine and BUN
Doxil (in clinical trials)	• Palmar plantar erythema	• Vitamin B_6 150 mg/day • Bag balm to hands and feet • Ice packs or cool compresses for pain

TABLE 5-10
HORMONAL AGENTS FOR ADVANCED BREAST CANCER

Class of Drugs	Drug Name	Most Common or Unique Side Effects
Anti-estrogen	tamoxifen (Nolvadex)	• Hot flashes • Vaginal dryness or discharge • Aggravation of cataracts • Increased risk for uterine cancer and blood clots
Progestin	megestrol acetate (Megace)	• Weight gain • Increased risk for blood clots
Aromatase inhibitor	anastrozole (Arimidex) letrozole (Femara) aminoglutethimide	• Nausea, hot flashes • Nausea, myalgias • Skin rash and sleepiness that improves over time
Gonadotrophin	goserelin (Zoladex)	• Often used with tamoxifen for premenopausal women • Menopausal symptoms
Androgen	fluoxymesterone (Halotestin)	• Masculinization with deepening of voice, increased facial hair • Increased libido
Estrogen	diethylstilbestrol (DES)	• Increased risk for blood clots • Weight gain • Nausea

(Adapted from Weiss, M., & Weiss, E. [1997]. *Living beyond breast cancer* [p. 335]. New York: Times Books.)

pamidronate disodium (Aredia), prevents the complications of bone metastases by inhibiting bone resorption. Aredia is given IV every 3 to 4 weeks and is well tolerated with few side effects. Some women complain of an increase in their bone pain 48 to 72 hours after treatment.

Survivorship Issues

Emotional Recovery

The journey to emotional recovery from breast cancer is an individual journey and, for the majority, is most intense during the first 1 to 2 years. The beginning of the journey is often traveled in a fog, with the woman going through the motions but not experiencing the emotions. She may need to rely on family and friends to help with information gathering and treatment decisions.

The next part of the journey is surviving from day to day. Tremendous energy and emotional reserves are needed to get through the surgery, chemotherapy, and/or radiation therapy. During this time, all focus is on finishing and surviving the side effects of treatment. Once acute treatment is completed (3–9 months), there is time for reflection and some of the most intense emotions surface. Often, women experience mixed emotions about the end of treatment—relief that it is finally over, along with fear that they are no longer actively fighting the cancer. Women find they miss the security of the frequent office visits and become anxious waiting for the next checkup. Many

women describe the journey as being on an emotional roller coaster in which the highs and lows are very extreme.

During the initial phase of the emotional recovery, peer counseling such as The American Cancer Society's Reach to Recovery program is very useful in coaching a woman through the emotional impact of a cancer diagnosis and loss of body integrity. The volunteer is a role model, a confidant, and a source of everyday hints that make treatment and recovery easier. Support groups, either general or specific for breast cancer, can promote emotional healing for the woman and often family members as well. Many national and local organizations provide printed educational material, peer volunteers, support groups, and/or political activism. The Internet is also a useful resource, but one should take care when searching for information to use reputable sites and verify all information obtained from anecdotal sites (Table 5-11).

Medical Follow-Up

After a diagnosis of breast cancer, women need close medical follow-up to watch for signs of recurrence and/or complications of therapy. Traditionally, she was seen by her medical and/or radiation oncologist and her surgeon at regular intervals. With managed care, much of the follow-up is now done by the primary care physician after the acute complications of treatment have resolved.

The schedule for follow-up usually consists of clinical examinations every 3 months for 2 years, every 6 months for 3 years, and then annually;

TABLE 5-11

NATIONAL ORGANIZATIONS FOR BREAST CANCER RESOURCES AND SUPPORT

Organization	Internet Address	Phone Number
American Cancer Society	www.cancer.org	1–800–ACS–2345
Association of Cancer Online Resources	www.acor.org	
BreastCancer.Net	www.breastcancer.net	
Look Good Feel Better	www.lookgoodfeelbetter.org	1–800–395–LOOK
National Alliance of Breast Cancer Organizations	www.nabco.org	1–800–719–9154
National Cancer Institute—Cancer Information Service	www.nci.nih.gov	1–800–4–CANCER
National Breast Cancer Coalition	www.natlbec.org	1–202–296–7477
National Coalition for Cancer Survivorship	www.cansearch.org	1–877–NCCS–YES
National Lymphedema Network	www.lymphnet.org	1–800–541–3259
The Susan G. Komen Breast Cancer Foundation	www.breastcancerinfo.com	1–800–IM AWARE
Y-ME	www.y-me.org	1–800–221–2141

mammogram and chest x-ray yearly; and, for some high-risk women, an annual bone scan. Breast cancer tumor markers, CEA, CA27.29 or CA 15-3, may be followed on a regular basis. However, this is controversial for at least two reasons. First, markers may become elevated months before any signs of disease, and treatment is usually not initiated for markers alone. The time between an elevated marker and clinical signs of disease is extremely distressing for women who feel like they are waiting for their "death sentence." Second, there has been no research to support that early detection of recurrence by tumor markers improves survival.

Return to Work

Many women continue to work throughout their treatment, whereas others return to work only after all therapy is over. Women have reported job discrimination, including being passed over for promotion, after a cancer diagnosis. They may be forced to stay in their jobs for fear of losing their health insurance. New insurance plans may require a waiting period before coverage, may exclude coverage of preexisting conditions, or may require changing physicians if their new employer belongs to a different managed care plan. Any woman with concerns about work discrimination or insurance problems can get more information from the National Coalition of Cancer Survivors at 1-301-560-8868.

Fertility and Pregnancy

Between one third and one fourth of all women diagnosed with breast cancer are of child-bearing age. Even if a woman maintains fertility after chemotherapy, many oncologists discourage preg-

---

BOX 5-2

Eighteen Steps to Prevention of Lymphedema

1. Never ignore any swelling in the arm, hand, fingers, or chest wall, and call your doctor immediately.

2. Never allow an injection or blood draw in affected arm.

3. Never have blood pressure checked in affected arm.

4. Keep the swollen arm clean at all times. Use lotion after bathing, and dry gently and thoroughly.

5. Avoid vigorous, repetitive motions with affected arm.

6. Avoid heavy lifting with affected arm. Never carry heavy handbags on affected arm.

7. Do not wear tight jewelry or elastic bands on affected arm.

8. Avoid extreme temperature changes such as sauna or hottub. Avoid sunburns.

9. Avoid any trauma to arm like cuts, scratches, burns.

10. Wear gloves when doing housework or gardening.

11. Avoid cutting your cuticles.

12. Exercise such as walking, swimming, biking, and aerobics is helpful. Avoid lifting weights over 15 lb.

13. When traveling by air, if swelling already present use compression sleeve.

14. Wear a well-fitting bra and a well-fitting prosthesis that does not cause strain on chest or back.

15. Use electric razor to shave under arms.

16. If swelling is present, wear compression sleeve during the day. Have sleeve fitted every 4 to 6 months.

17. Watch for any signs of infection such as rash, redness, fever, pain, blistering, and report to MD immediately.

18. Maintain your weight with adequate fiber, vegetables, and protein. Avoid smoking and alcohol.

(Adapted with permission from the National Lymphedema Network, 1997.)

nancy after a diagnosis of breast cancer for fear that the high levels of hormones will promote metastases. Research has not shown a survival difference in women who became pregnant after breast cancer. However, a 2-year wait after treatment, to fully recover from the physical and emotional aspects of treatment, is advised.

Lymphedema

Lymphedema, blockage of lymphatic drainage due to scarring of the lymph channels, is a major fear of women who undergo axillary node dissection. Lymphedema can occur anytime after the surgery, sometimes years later. There is no means to predict who will develop lymphedema and no scientific studies to prove that preventive measures actually work. However, we do know that it is often triggered by an event that causes fluid backup in the arm, such as an infection or constrictive clothing. Therefore, prevention consists of common-sense practices to avoid infection, constriction, or overuse of the affected arm (Box 5-2).

Once lymphedema develops, it is very difficult to correct. The goal of therapy is to control the swelling and prevent infection in the arm. Methods to control the swelling include:

- Compression sleeve and/or glove that prevents swelling during the day
- Electrical gradient pumps that force the fluid back into circulation
- "Bandaging" that combines compression with motion to help move fluid out of the arm
- Manual lymphatic drainage, which is a light touch massage that helps move the fluid back into circulation

An excellent resource is the National Lymphedema Foundation, which provides education and treatment for people with lymphedema. To obtain printed educational material or to find a treatment center, call 1-800-541-3259.

Early Menopause

Chemotherapy and/or hormonal therapy may cause a woman to enter an early menopause. Generally, the closer a woman is to her natural menopause (mid to late 40s), the greater the prob-

ability that she will permanently stop menstruating. Younger women may develop menstrual irregularities and/or temporarily stop menstruating for several months after treatment. All women who were menstruating at the start of treatment should use some form of birth control for at least 1 year, even if they are no longer menstruating, to prevent pregnancy.

Women who enter menopause report a wide range of symptoms from none at all to life-changing problems. Most physicians are reluctant to use estrogen replacement after a breast cancer diagnosis for fear that the estrogen may promote metastasis. Increasingly, studies are being conducted to determine if there is an actual risk for women who take estrogen after breast cancer. Some women find that their menopausal symptoms are so severe that the benefits of estrogen outweigh the risk. Other women are able to manage their symptoms with the help of nonhormonal therapy (Table 5-12).

TABLE 5-12	
NONHORMONAL TREATMENT OF MENOPAUSAL SYMPTOMS	
Hot flashes	• Avoid triggers such as alcohol, caffeine, spicy foods
	• Layer clothing, carry a hand-held fan
	• Vitamin E 800 to 1600 IU/d
	• Vitamin C 1000 mg/d
	• Bellergal 1 per day
	• Effexor 12.5–37.5 mg qd–bid
	• Clonidine 0.1 mg/d
Vaginal dryness	• Regular use of water-based vaginal lubrication (M-W-F)—Replens
	• May need extra lubrication with intercourse—Astroglide, KY Jelly,
	• Add flaxseed oil or flaxseed meal to diet
Urinary incontinence	• Kegel (pelvic squeezing) exercises
Mood swings/ insomnia	• Vitamin B$_6$ 150–250 mg
	• Exercise
	• Serotonin-based antidepressants (Zoloft, Paxil)
Decreased libido	• Exercise
	• Allow time for increased romance or schedule time for intimacy during high-energy periods
	• May need low-dose testosterone
Skin dryness	• Add flaxseed oil or flaxseed meal to diet
	• Frequent skin moisturizers

Nursing Care

Nursing Diagnosis	Nursing Care
Knowledge deficit R/T: diagnostic procedures, staging procedures, understanding the pathology report, understanding treatment options.	• *Education is a challenge with limited contact due to shortened hospital stays and more procedures done in ambulatory settings. Use varied media and provide information repeatedly throughout the breast cancer journey.* • *Knowledge level should be assessed frequently and prior to any new procedure or a change in procedures.* • *Use community resources (see Box 5-3) for both volunteer support and printed information.*
Pain R/T: diagnostic procedures, surgical procedures, complications of radiation or chemotherapy, metastases	• *Assess for pain and plan treatment appropriately.* • *Most biopsy procedures are managed with non-narcotic analgesics.* • *Post-surgical pain depends on the type of surgery: simple mastectomy often requires only Tylenol or Vicodin, whereas reconstruction may require narcotics with PCA pump.* • *Avoid non-steroidal analgesics for any procedure-related pain since they may increase bleeding and/or bruising.* • *Women may have phantom sensations in the removed breast. Some women report long-term pain and/or numbness along the surgical incision.* • *Use around-the-clock analgesics for chronic pain.* • *Teach and incorporate non-pharmacological pain-relief methods for individuals with chronic pain.*
Anxiety R/T: diagnosis, the unknown, prognosis, potential side effects	• *Provide information as needed to minimize the unknown and unexpected.* • *Listen.* • *Teach relaxation techniques: breathing exercises, guided imagery, "stop talk."* • *Refer to community resources, e.g., Reach to Recovery, Y-Me, ACS, for peer support and support groups.* • *Refer to a clinical nurse specialist, social worker, or therapist for more intense support.*
Altered tissue perfusion R/T: actual or potential lymphedema	• *No B/P, IVs, or venipunctures in affected arm after axillary node dissection.* • *While drain is in place, avoid abduction of the arm and keep the arm elevated on pillows above the level of the heart to facilitate drainage.* • *Instruct on steps to prevent lymphedema.* • *Provide early treatment and/or referral to lymphedema center if any swelling develops.*

Nursing Diagnosis	*Nursing Care*
Risk for infection R/T: biopsies, drains, surgical procedures, neutropenia from chemotherapy	• *Instruct the woman on signs and symptoms of infection.* • *Instruct the woman on the importance of good handwashing, especially before wound or drain care and if neutropenic.* • *Instruct the woman to take her temperature if not feeling well and to report any fever over 100.5°F.*
Impaired physical mobility R/T: pain, drains, arm weakness, scar tissue	• *Keep the woman as comfortable as possible to facilitate free movement.* • *Encourage the woman to be active with her own care (brushing hair, eating), using the affected arm immediately after surgery.* • *Teach isometric (squeezing ball) and gentle flexing exercises to do while the drain is in place.* • *Demonstrate range-of-motion exercises to be started as soon as the drain is removed.* • *Refer women who have not achieved full range of motion in 4 to 8 weeks to physical therapy for more intense exercises.* • *Some women may need to stretch arms every day for life to maintain flexibility.*
Body image disturbance R/T: breast changes from surgery and/or radiation therapy, mastectomy, alopecia, weight gain, skin and nail changes	• *Prepare woman for potential physical changes and give tips for adjustment.* • *For women who undergo mastectomy without reconstruction, provide resources and information about a prosthesis. The American Cancer Society Reach to Recovery program will provide a temporary prosthesis that a woman can use while the chest is healing.* • *Provide support for all women, regardless of the type of breast surgery, to grieve over the changes in her breast or the loss of a breast. Even women who undergo breast conservation or reconstruction experience a sense of loss due to the physical or tactile changes in the breast.* • *Women who undergo breast conservation or reconstruction may also need referral for a partial breast prosthesis*
Risk for altered family process R/T: hospitalizations, work disability, change in roles related to side effects of treatments and/or progressive disease	• *Promote sharing of open, honest information with all family members since the fear of the unknown is greater than dealing with reality.* • *Provide a list of community resources that may be available to help with chores to free family for quality time.* • *Encourage the woman to enlist help from her social network (church, friends, classmates) for meal preparation and child care during treatment phase.*

Nursing Diagnosis	*Nursing Care*
	• *Provide resources for a significant other and/or children to receive emotional support. Some communities have support groups for family members. The school guidance counselor may provide support and resources for children.*
Sexual dysfunction R/T: altered body image, pain, premature menopause	• *Encourage open, honest communication between partners.* • *Provide support and resources for improving body image.* • *Women with pain may need tips about positioning or use of pillows to support and/or cushion the chest during sexual activities.* • *Inform the woman that vaginal dryness, pain with intercourse, and/or libido changes are potential treatment-related side effects. Encourage the woman to discuss concerns or problems she may be experiencing.*

Women who go through menopause at a younger age may be at greater risk for heart disease and/or osteoporosis. A healthy lifestyle with a diet low in fat; calcium supplementation; maintaining weight; exercising; and monitoring bone density, serum cholesterol, and blood pressure are important.

Susan began to feel almost normal about 3 months after her last chemotherapy. She returned to teaching first graders that fall and found that she was very emotional over the smallest things. It took about 6 months before she felt that her energy level was 95% normal. She wore her wig for teaching for al-

---

BOX 5-3

Books Recommended for Women with Breast Cancer

Baker, N. (1991). *Relative risk: Living with a family history of breast cancer.* New York: Viking Penguin Books.

Benedet, R., & Rounsaville, M. (1996). *Healing: A woman's guide to lumpectomy and radiation therapy.* San Francisco, CA: Benedet.

Benedet, R., & Rounsaville, M. (1996). *Healing: A woman's guide to recovery after mastectomy.* San Francisco, CA: Benedet.

Berger, K., & Bostwick, J. (1994). *A woman's decision: Breast care, treatment and reconstruction* (2nd ed.). St. Louis: Quality Medical Publishing.

Kaye, R. (1991) *Spinning straw into gold.* New York: Simon & Schuster.

King, S. (1997). *Treading the maze: An artist's journey through breast cancer.* New York: Chronicle Books.

Kelly, P. (1991). *Understanding breast cancer risk.* Philadelphia: Temple University Press.

Love, S. (1995). *Dr. Susan Love's breast book* (2nd ed.). Reading, MA: Addison-Wesley.

Weiss, M., & Weiss, E. (1997). *Living beyond breast cancer.* New York: Times Books.

Wittman, J. (1993). *Breast cancer journal.* Golden, CO: Fulcrum.

most 6 months after the chemotherapy. Even then, it was a drastic change from her long, straight wig to her new, short, curly mop of hair.

Susan quit menstruating just about the time she completed the Adriamycin portion of her chemotherapy. She really had a rough time with hot flashes, but the worst was not being able to think clearly and just feeling sad much of the time.

Vitamins E and C seemed to help the hot flashes a little, but vitamin B$_6$ was not enough for the depression. She really started to feel better after she was started on Paxil and found that it helped her memory and thinking also.

Susan missed seeing her doctors and nurses every 3 weeks. Those visits made her feel safe. At first, it seemed she called the nurse for little things every other week just to keep in touch. Now, she is more comfortable with the every 3-month schedule, but becomes very anxious about 3 weeks before her next visit, worrying about whether the cancer has returned.

Overall, life has returned to normal—almost too much so. During chemotherapy, she thought she would change everything that she didn't like in her life before cancer. But things aren't so bad after all. Susan is planning on returning to school for a graduate degree next year, and she and her husband promise to have a date night once a month. Life does go on.

BIBLIOGRAPHY

Bagga, D., Ashley, J., Geffrey, S., Wang, H., Barnard, R., Korenman, S., & Heber, D. (1995). Effects of a very low fat, high fiber diet on serum hormones and menstrual function. Implications for breast cancer prevention. *Cancer, 76,* 2491.

Bernstein, L., Henderson, B., Hanisch, R., Sullivan-Halley, J., & Ross, R. (1994). Physical exercise activity and reduced risk of breast cancer in young women. *Journal of the National Cancer Institute, 86,* 1403.

Bernstein, L., et al. (1998). Physical activity and breast cancer risk in a cohort of young women. *Journal of the National Cancer Institute, 90* (24), 1907–1909.

Bilimoria, M., & Morrow, M. (1995). The woman at increased risk for breast cancer: Evaluation and management strategies. *CA: Cancer Journal for Clinicians, 45,* 263–278.

Bonadonna, G., Zambetti, M., & Valagussa, P. (1995). Sequential or alternating doxorubicin and CMF regimens in breast cancer with more than three positive nodes. *Journal of the American Medical Association, 273,* 542–547.

Cox, A., Yeatman, T., Smith, D., et al. (1995). Lymphatic mapping and sentinel node biopsy in the breast cancer patient. *Proceedings From the Annual Meeting of the American Society of Clinical Oncology, 14,* A99.

Dow, K. (1992). The experience of surviving breast cancer and having children after treatment [Abstract]. *Oncology Nursing Society Congress.*

Feuer, E., Lap-Ming, W., Boring, C., et al. (1993). The lifetime risk of developing breast cancer. *Journal of the National Cancer Institute, 85,* 892–897.

Friedenreich, C., et al. (1998). Epidemiologic issues related to the association between physical activity and breast cancer. *Cancer, 83,* 600–610.

Gelber, R. (1993). Adjuvant therapy for breast cancer: Understanding the overview. *Journal of Clinical Oncology, 11,* 580–585.

Hjelmstad, L. T. (1993). *Fine black lines.* Englewood, CO: Mulberry Press.

Hoskins, K., Stopfer, J., Calzone, K., et al. (1995). Assessment and counseling for women with a family history of breast cancer. *Journal of the American Medical Association, 273,* 577–585.

Landis, S., Murray, T., Bolder, S., & Wingo, P. (1998). Cancer statistics. *CA: Cancer Journal for Clinicians, 48,* 6–29.

Loescher, L. (1993). Strategies for preventing breast cancer. *Innovations in Oncology Nursing, 9,* 2–6.

Love, S., McGuigan, K., & Chap, L. (1996). The Revlon/UCLA Breast Center practice guidelines for the treatment of breast disease. *The Cancer Journal, 2,* 2–14.

Maccabee, H. (1994). Ten revolutions in breast cancer. *Mammography Today,* 43–45.

Marcus, J., Watson, P., Page, D., et al. (1996). Hereditary breast cancer. *Cancer, 77,* 697–709.

Winchester, D., & Cox, J. (1998). Standards for diagnosis and management of invasive breast carcinoma. *CA: Cancer Journal for Clinicians, 48,* 83–107.

Winchester, D., & Strom, E. (1998). Standards for diagnosis and management of ductal carcinoma in situ (DCIS) of the breast. *CA: Cancer Journal for Clinicians, 48,* 108–128.

Colon Cancer

Susan Weiss Behrend

Epidemiology

Individuals experiencing a diagnosis of colorectal carcinoma are profoundly affected. Colorectal cancer is identified as one of the most common cancers worldwide with approximately 1 million diagnoses made annually. Within the United States, an estimated 129,400 cases will be identified in 1999 (American Cancer Society, 1999; Landis, Murray, Bolden, & Wingo, 1998). Colorectal cancer affects men and women equally. In 1999, colorectal cancer was identified as the third leading cause of new cancer cases among both men (10%) and women (11%). Additionally, colorectal cancer accounted for 9% of male cancer-related deaths and 11% of female cancer-related deaths in 1999. Incidence rates have declined recently, from 53 per 100,000 in 1985 to 44 per 100,000 in 1994. This decline had been noted primarily for the white population in the United States; however, a declining trend has begun to be noted among African Americans (American Cancer Society, 1999). This recent decline may be attributed to more accessible and extensive screening programs coupled with advanced diagnostic procedures, which enable prompt detection of benign and potentially malignant processes.

Colorectal cancer-related mortality has been estimated at 56,600 in 1999 (47,700 from colon cancer, 8,800 from rectal cancer). These figures account for approximately 10% of cancer deaths. Mortality rates for colorectal cancer have fallen 25% for women and 13% for men during the past 2 decades, which presents hopeful data reflecting decreasing incidence rates and increasing survival rates (American Cancer Society, 1999).

As with many cancers, the probability of developing colorectal cancer increases with age. In 1994, the United States reported deaths from colorectal cancer according to age ranging from 221 for ages 15 through 21 to 11,972 for men over 75. Similar age-related findings were reported for women, with 2,115 deaths for ages 35 through 54 and 16,074 for women over 75 (Landis et al., 1998). Men between the ages of 60 and 79 years have a 4.0% chance (1 in 23) of being diagnosed with colorectal cancer. Women between 60 and 79 years of age have a slightly lower risk of diagnosis, 3% (1 in 30) (Parker, Tong, Bolden & Wingo, 1996).

The statistics that constitute the epidemiologic data on colorectal cancer are important to know. The disease can cause tremendous suffering and requires the clinical support of numerous components of the health care team. Knowledge of the incidence, prevalence, and morbidity and mortality profiles will enable nurses to understand the intricacies of patient care and find creative ways to identify specific interventions.

Etiology

Many risk factors have been associated with the development of colorectal cancer, including age, ethnicity, genetic predisposition, preexisting bowel disease, history of other cancers, diet, and degree of physical activity (Table 6-1). These factors evolve slowly over time and are associated with a high

T A B L E 6 - 1	
WHO IS AT RISK FOR DEVELOPING COLORECTAL CANCER?	
Age	Older age—Most important risk factor
Familial Factors	Inherited susceptibility syndrome (FAP or HNPCC)
Personal Factors	History of colon cancer Intestinal adenomatous polyps Inflammatory bowel disease
Diet and Lifestyle	Animal fats (red meat) Obesity/sedentary

FAP, familial adenomatous polyposis; HNPCC, heriditary nonpyposis colorectal cancer

risk for developing colorectal cancer. Most people who develop colorectal cancer are not in this high-risk group, and, therefore, screening asymptomatic people is advocated (Ferrante, 1996).

Age

The incidence for developing colorectal cancer increases slightly at 40 years, increases dramatically at age 50, and doubles each subsequent decade (Parker et al., 1996). Age has contrasting effects on the diagnosis of colorectal cancer. Patients younger than 40 years old have a worse outcome than those who are middle-aged. People greater than 70 years of age present with an earlier stage of disease. It is theorized that the poor outcome of younger patients may be because they frequently present with more advanced disease or disease with a worse histologic grade (Jessup, Menck, Fremgen, & Winchester, 1997).

Ethnicity

Advanced colorectal cancer may be associated with ethnicity among African Americans. Epidemiologic tracking has found that inner-city African-American males are diagnosed with colorectal carcinoma at an earlier age than white people (Thomas, Gale & Evans, 1990). Additionally, a trend has been documented that reports the frequency of localized cancer at diagnosis to be lower in African Americans, which may be attributed to limited health care access (Boring, Squires &

Heath, 1992). An effort to increase early diagnosis should be the focus within African and American minority populations.

Genetic Factors

Genetic factors associated with the development of colorectal cancers include a variety of clinical situations. A family history of colorectal cancer (two or more first-degree relatives) predisposes a person to the development of familial adenomatous polyposis, which is a precursor for colorectal cancer. A variety of genetic syndromes that are lacking genetic material (absence of chromosome 5) and are known as the polyposis syndrome category include diseases such as Gardner's syndrome, Turcot syndrome, Peutz-Jeghers syndrome, and juvenile polyposis. The nonpolyposis category has a defect of chromosome 2. People with nonpolyposis syndrome are middle-aged and have a 50% risk of developing colon cancer. Families exhibiting a high incidence of colorectal cancer may have an inherited trait known as familial adenocarcinomatosis. These families are found to have histories of other adenocarcinoma sites. This syndrome is also known as family cancer syndrome (Hoebler, 1997; McMillan, 1996).

Colonic Polyps

Inflammatory bowel disease can be a precursor for the development of colorectal cancer. Villous adenomas are colorectal polyps that are classified as either neoplastic (adenomatous polyps) or non-neoplastic. All adenomatous polyps have malignant potential; however, the majority are benign when detected. Adenomatous polyps, or adenomas, are attached to the bowel wall by a stalk or by a broad, flat base. It is recognized that all colorectal cancers originate from a precursor adenoma (Markowitz & Winawer, 1997). The National Polyp Study indicates that colonoscopic removal of adenomatous polyps significantly reduces the risk of developing colorectal cancer (Markowitz & Winawer, 1997; Winawer et al., 1993).

Preexisting Bowel Disease

Ulcerative colitis is a chronic condition characterized by an inflammatory bowel, intermittent constipation and diarrhea, abdominal cramping, and inflammatory changes of the intestinal mucosa on colonoscopic examination. The longer the duration of this condition, coupled with the amount of involved bowel, the greater is the risk for dysplastic changes and, ultimately, malignancy. Crohn's disease, an inflammatory condition of the intestinal mucosa, also is associated with the potential for malignant transformation (Levin, 1992; Nugent, Haggitt, & Gilpin, 1991). The cumulative incidence of colorectal cancer in inflammatory bowel disease is estimated to be 5% to 10% at 20 years and 12% to 20% at 30 years (Levin, 1992). Therefore, it is vital that people with inflammatory bowel disease be methodically monitored to ensure early diagnosis of neoplastic conditions.

Diet and Life Style

Environment is thought to be responsible for the wide geographic variance in the prevalence of colorectal cancer. Incidence rates of colorectal cancer are low in Japan. These rates rise within one generation when Japanese immigrants adopt a new country of origin (Kim & Lance, 1997). Differences in rates between countries have prompted the suggestion that up to 90% of colorectal cancer in the United States can be attributed to environmental factors and could be prevented by dietary changes (Kim & Lance, 1997).

High fat intake has been associated with an increased risk for colorectal cancer. Fat stimulates mucosal-cell proliferation of the bowel as well as bile-acid production and excretion. Bile acids have toxic, tumor-promoting effects. Animal fat increases the numbers of anaerobes that activate carcinogens and transform bile acids and cholesterol into carcinogens.

Reducing beef-fat intake decreases this enzyme activity (Giovannucci, Stampfer, Colditz, Rimm & Willett, 1992; Hansen, 1995; Howe et al., 1992). People who consume low-fat poultry (without the skin) or fish instead of red meat have a lower incidence of colorectal cancer. Processed and smoked meats contain nitrosamines, which are known carcinogens (Hansen, 1995).

Scientific evidence shows that a diet containing fibrous foods decreases the risk of colorectal cancer. High fiber intake has the ability to accelerate intestinal transit time and therefore reduces the length of time that the colon mucosa is in contact with potential carcinogens. Fiber increases stool bulk and dilutes and absorbs carcinogens. Additionally, fiber enhances the growth of beneficial microbial flora and enzyme activity, which increases the numbers of bacteria capable of utilizing and inactivating ammonia and other nitrogen-containing compounds and potential carcinogens. Fiber increases short-chain fatty acid production, which promotes normal-cell maintenance and differentiation and inhibits tumor growth (Hansen, 1995).

Several different types of dietary fiber exist, and attempts to identify the most beneficial have been controversial. Fruit fiber containing pectin—a water-soluble fermentable fiber—may have a protective effect by stimulating beneficial intestinal microbes. Cruciferous vegetables may also promote degradation of carcinogens.

MICRONUTRIENTS

Micronutrients such as vitamin A and other retinoids, vitamin C, and vitamin E are antioxidants that prevent damage to cell membranes and DNA. They stabilize cellular membrane structure, regulate DNA synthesis, and enhance cell differentiation and reduce cell proliferation (Hansen, 1995).

Dietary modification is a vital factor in the prevention of colorectal cancer. The National Cancer Institute has issued dietary recommendations that promote the protective effects of certain food groups and nutrients.

ALCOHOL

Alcohol consumption increases the risk of colorectal cancer. Specifically, wine, whiskey, and beer increase the risk for colorectal cancer. Colon cancer incidence is affected when alcohol contributes more than 15% of daily calories. This may be due to the displacement of cancer inhibitors (Hansen, 1995).

TOBACCO

Cigarette smoking may have a significant effect on the development of colorectal adenomas and carcinomas, with the relative risk related to both the amount (the number of pack-years) and the length of time since the initiation of smoking (Giovannucci et al., 1994a).

Prevention/Detection and Screening

Prevention

Epidemiologic studies and etiologic factors associated with colorectal cancer appear to indicate that alterations in diet and lifestyle may encourage prevention of this disease (Table 6-2). Currently, clinical practice focused at diminishing disease incidence involves the detection and removal of premalignant polyps/lesions coupled with the earliest possible detection of malignant tumors.

Recent studies have suggested that specific pharmaceutical agents may have properties that protect against the development of colorectal cancer. These include estrogen replacement agents and nonsteroidal anti-inflammatory drugs such as aspirin (American Cancer Society, 1998; Morgan, 1997). Regular aspirin use, at doses recommended for the prevention of cardiovascular disease, has been found to substantially reduce the risk of colorectal cancer. This benefit may only be noted after long-term use (greater than a decade; Giovannucci et al., 1999S; 1994b). The exact mechanism for the chemopreventive effect of aspirin is not known. It is theorized that aspirin has the ability to regulate cell growth by acetylating proteins and catalyzing the synthesis of prostaglandins

(Marcus, 1995). The clinical recommendation of aspirin use has been made and suggests that people at risk for colorectal cancer ingest a single aspirin tablet (325 mg) every other day (barring a contraindication to aspirin). Those with a family history of colorectal cancer should consider this regimen as well (Marcus, 1995; Morgan, 1997).

The World Health Organization prioritized the prevention of colorectal cancer and updated its guidelines in 1995 (Winawer et al., 1995). The WHO primary prevention guidelines include:

- Primary prevention of colorectal cancer
- Screening for average-risk people
- Screening for relatives of people with colorectal cancer
- Surveillance of people with colorectal polyps
- Surveillance of people with chronic ulcerative colitis

Detection and Screening

Current early detection guidelines according to the American Cancer Society are as follows (Table 6-3): Beginning at age 50, men and women should have one of the following: a yearly fecal occult blood test plus flexible sigmoidoscopy every 5 years, or colonoscopy every 10 years, or double-contrast barium enema every 5 to 10 years. A digital rectal examination should be done at the same time as sigmoidoscopy, colonoscopy, or double-contrast barium enema. These tests provide an op-

TABLE 6-2

PROTECTIVE MECHANISMS THAT GUARD AGAINST THE DEVELOPMENT OF COLORECTAL CANCER

Diet	Micronutrients Vitamin A Vitamin C Vitamin E Calcium Selenium Fruit, cereal and vegetable fibers
Physical Activity	Regular physical activity
Hormone Replacement Therapy	May decrease risk in post-menopausal women
Aspirin Use	Use of nonsteroidal anti-inflammatory drugs

TABLE 6-3

AMERICAN CANCER SOCIETY COLORECTAL CANCER EARLY DETECTION GUIDE

- Men and women at average risk begin screening at age 50.
- Fecal occult blood test and flexible sigmoidoscopy. If normal, repeat annually, and flexible sigmoidoscopy every 5 years.
- Colonoscopy. If normal, repeat every 10 years.
- Double-contrast barium enema. If normal, repeat double-contrast barium enema every 5 to 10 years.
- Begin screening at younger age if risk category is high.

(American Cancer Society. [1999]. *Cancer facts and figures.* Atlanta, GA: American Cancer Society.)

portunity to detect colorectal cancer at an early stage and to prevent some cancers by detection and removal of polyps. People should begin colorectal cancer screening earlier and/or undergo screening more frequently if they have a personal history of colorectal cancer or adenomatous polyps, a strong family history of colorectal cancer or polyps, a personal history of chronic inflammatory bowel disease, or if they are a member of a family with hereditary colorectal cancer syndromes (American Cancer Society, 1998).

The tests recommended to screen asymptomatic persons are the digital rectal examination, fecal occult blood test, and flexible sigmoidoscopy. Colonoscopy and barium enemas are recommended for high-risk populations.

FECAL OCCULT BLOOD TEST

Fecal occult blood (FOB) testing is a widely recommended component of colorectal cancer screening. The objective is to assess bleeding lesions at an early stage. A variety of FOB testing kits are available and are inexpensive. The guaiac on the test strip turns blue in the presence of hemoglobin. Rectal bleeding can be intermittent; for this reason, two samples are obtained on three consecutive days for a total of six samples. A positive test occurs when one or more slides are positive (Mahon, 1995).

Controversy has surrounded the FOB since studies have indicated poor sensitivity and nonspecificity. Positive test results may indicate colorectal bleeding but may also be attributed to dietary factors (Lush, 1994). Two types of FOB testing exist: nonrehydrated testing and rehydrated. A large cancer control study using the rehydrated method reported a 33% decrease in colorectal cancer mortality (Mandel et al., 1993). This study has been criticized due to the high rate of positive results attributed to the testing method. Critics claimed that a large proportion of the cancers found may have been chance discoveries (Toribara & Sleisenger, 1995). Clinically, until better testing methods evolve, it has been suggested that FOB testing be used by clinicians who must weigh the ethics of early cancer discovery with the costs of invasive diagnostic interventions if the result is ultimately a false positive (Mandel et al., 1993).

DIGITAL RECTAL EXAMINATION

The digital rectal examination has not been studied in a controlled or randomized trial (Ferrante, 1996). It is considered to have limited value as a screening test because fewer than 10% of cancers are within the reach of the examiner's finger (Eddy, 1990). This screening method is simple, low cost, and has a relatively low risk.

SIGMOIDOSCOPY

A 60-cm flexible sigmoidoscope can visualize the descending colon and detect two to three times more neoplasms than the rigid sigmoidoscope (Toribara & Sleisenger, 1995). Flexible sigmoidoscopy has been estimated to detect 68% of all colorectal cancers (DeCosse, Tsioulias & Jacobson, 1994). Flexible sigmoidoscopy has been found to be superior to the rigid scope because patients report it to be more comfortable, it creates less anxiety and embarrassment, and it may have a lower complication profile (Ferrante, 1996). The cost of sigmoidoscopic examination is comparatively low because it is performed without sedation. The high sensitivity and specificity of this test, coupled with its safety profile and ease of performance, suggest that flexible sigmoidoscopy be an integral part of a multimodal approach to colorectal cancer screening (Toribara & Sleisenger, 1995). Sigmoidoscopy screening can be successfully performed by professionally trained nurses (Maule, 1994), according to a study that documented the outcome of nurse endoscopists screening approximately 1800 patients in a large urban medical center. Utilizing the expertise of advanced practice nurses to screen for colorectal cancer can have tremendous impact on prevention and early detection efforts in a cost-effective and efficient manner (Gruber, 1996; Porrett, 1996; Spiegel, 1995).

COLONOSCOPY

Colonoscopy is the clinical standard used to visualize, biopsy, and remove colon neoplasms. Colonoscopy has the advantages of high sensitivity and specificity. The majority of asymptomatic people with polyps in the colon found on routine examination do not develop malignancy in their lifetime (Ferrante, 1996; Toribara & Sleisenger, 1995). No evidence exists for the effectiveness of screening asymptomatic patients with colonoscopy. Low patient compliance, high cost, and advanced technical skill make colonoscopy an impractical way of screening asymptomatic, average-risk patients. Colonoscopy should be reserved for people in a high-risk category. Additionally, this procedure has a higher complication rate, notably bleeding and perforation (Ferrante, 1996).

BARIUM ENEMA

The use of the double-contrast barium enema has declined due to the popularity of colonoscopy. The barium enema (BE) is less sensitive than colonoscopy in finding polyps smaller than 1 cm. A high-quality BE coupled with a flexible sigmoidoscopy can provide an adequate substitute for colonoscopy. If, however, attention to small pathologic changes is the clinical goal, the BE is not an acceptable alternative. The BE is more cost-containing than colonoscopy; however, it does expose clinical staff to radiation (Toribara & Sleisenger, 1995).

Screening for Colorectal Cancer: Controversial Issues

Public policy–making organizations have different recommendations regarding screening for colorectal cancer despite the significant morbidity and mortality and the improved survival rates obtained with treatment of early-stage cancers. Several reasons are attributed to the controversial platform regarding colorectal cancer screening. The need to balance the benefits against the risks of screening must be ascertained. The sensitivity and specificity of the screening procedures are important. False-positive results lead to unnecessary tests, increased costs, complications, and anxiety and discomfort (Ferrante, 1996). Compliance of the study population undergoing mass screening is key to the success of the screening initiative. Compliance rates in uncontrolled trials of fecal occult blood testing have been historically low. Additionally, lower rates of compliance for screening sigmoidoscopy have been linked to patient cost and fear of discomfort during the examination (Ferrante, 1996). Physicians have been found to be noncompliant

regarding the American Cancer Society guidelines for colorectal cancer. A survey conducted over a decade ago found that, of 1000 primary care physicians, 88% agreed with the American Cancer Society guidelines for testing FOB and 64% agreed with the American Cancer Society guidelines for proctoscopic examinations; however, only 56% and 23%, respectively, actually followed the guidelines as stated (American Cancer Society, 1990).

The screening protocol must be feasible to be accomplished. Family physicians trained to use the flexible sigmoidoscope must be able to commit the time to initially screen patient populations and to provide follow-up surveillance regularly. This may be too cumbersome a task. If an average practice has 3000 patients, five sigmoidoscopies would have to be done for screening purposes, and two surveillance scopes daily (Ferrante, 1996).

Cost is a pivotal factor to consider when establishing a massive screening program. The costs of screening can be substantial. Screening methods have a proven ability to discover premalignant lesions, detect colorectal cancer earlier, and thus decrease mortality. Society must decide whether the benefits are worth the cost. Cost–benefit analysis can be exceedingly complex. Routine FOB for Americans over the age of 50 would cost more than $1 billion annually (Clayman, 1989). The approximate cost of diagnosing a single person with colorectal cancer is $8800. These figures would have to be compared with the costs of saving almost 3 lives per 1000 from colorectal cancer (Ferrante, 1996). Current expense projections and data suggest that it will ultimately be less expensive to diagnose bowel cancers before they cause symptoms. Managed care organizations are proceeding with screening programs throughout the United States. These groups have studied individual members of HMOs diagnosed with cancer compared with controls diagnosed within a fee-for-service setting. Data show that the elderly within the HMOs are diagnosed at earlier stages of disease for breast and colorectal cancer (Jessup et al., 1997). This information is vital as managed care increasingly penetrates the market. The effect on early disease prevention/detection program development will be closely scrutinized.

The optimal age to begin screening remains controversial. Age has been identified as a risk factor for the development of colorectal cancer. The benefits of screening at older ages can be difficult due to other underlying illnesses contributing to morbidity and mortality (Ferrante, 1996). Overall screening at the age of 40 may yield only a few cases of malignancy and may contribute to the creation of a tremendous expense profile with little benefit.

Screening of asymptomatic patients of average risk for colorectal cancer may be inappropriate. Significant costs, increases in clinician training, improved health care access, coupled with enhancing public and physician compliance, may lead to tremendous expense with disproportionate overall benefit. Accordingly, it may be inappropriate to embark on a crusade to screen low-risk/asymptomatic people at this time. Primary prevention strategies should be refined, including the promotion of healthy lifestyles. Research regarding the viability and ethics of genetic testing coupled with examining those at high risk should be supported. On an individual basis, if screening is desired, full informed consent should precede any investigation (Ferrante, 1996).

Genetic Implications

Several genes have been discovered in relationship to specific cancers. The following genes have been associated with the development of colorectal cancer.

The *K-ras protooncogene* is named for the rat sarcoma virus in which it was first found. The ras family of oncogenes is believed to play a role in colorectal cancer development by permitting a continuous exposure to tumor growth factor (Ahnen, 1991). The *adenomatous polyposis coli mutated gene* has been found in the germline of people with familial adenomatous polyposis (FAP). This is an autosomal dominant condition characterized by the development of hundreds of adenomatous polyps throughout the large intestine. Some of these polyps will become malignant (Ahnen, 1991). The *DCC anti-oncogene* is related to colorectal cancer. This anti-oncogene is absent in colorectal cancer patients who have a poorer prognosis. It may play a role in FAP (Bodmer, 1994). *Hereditary nonpolyposis colorectal cancer gene (hMLH-1)* is a common genetic disease; it affects about 1 in 200 people. This gene causes spontaneous mutations in DNA. People with this gene experience a high rate of right-sided bowel tumors (Bodmer, 1994).

New genetic knowledge may carry implications for early diagnosis. Ras mutations have been found in the DNA extracted from the stools of people with colorectal cancer. This is the beginning of the discovery of important scientific evidence that could lead to accurate, prompt diagnosis of colorectal cancer. Cancer-prone families, such as those with FAP, can benefit from genetic findings so their potential susceptibilities can be determined. Public concern and interest in genetic testing for colon cancer have been found to be significant for those with a perceived risk for colon cancer (McMillan, 1996). Genetic screening will be a key component of future detection efforts and treatment protocols. In the future, people may express a strong desire to know their genetic templates to make personal decisions regarding self-care and future life plans. As they evolve, these decisions will be more complex and will require a well-orchestrated health care team founded on the ethics of medical science and coupled with the highest regard for human behavior.

Clinical Features (Characteristics)

Anatomy

The colon extends from the terminal ileum to the anal canal. It consists of four parts: the ascending/right colon, the transverse/middle colon, the descending/left colon, and the sigmoid colon (Figure 6-1). The rectum is continuous with the sigmoid colon, terminates at the distal anal canal, and is covered with peritoneum. The rectum has an anatomic transitional zone between keratinized and nonkeratinized stratified squamous epithelium at the anal verge. The epithelium of the anus is differentiated by the anatomic landmarks of the anorectal ring, pectinate line, and anal verge (Chang & Bland, 1997).

Venous drainage from the colon and upper to middle third of the rectum enters the portal system to the liver. The lower third of the rectum drains to the portal system and to the inferior vena cava. The colon, rectum, and anus are located near the

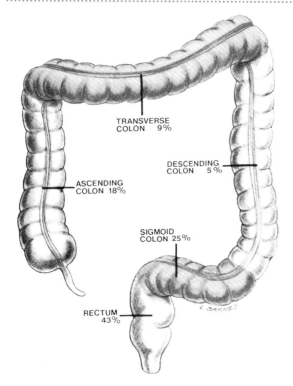

TRANSVERSE
COLON   9%

DESCENDING
COLON   5%

ASCENDING
COLON 18%

SIGMOID
COLON 25%

RECTUM
43%

L. BARNES

Figure 6-1 Distribution of colon and rectal cancer.

vagina in females and near the bladder, seminal vesicles, prostate, and urethra in males.

Pathophysiology

The colon's several functions include the processing and movement of ileal contents through the bowel, the storage of feces, and regulation of defecation. The colon receives up to 1000 mL of ileal contents daily. The absorption of water and electrolytes occurs in the proximal/right colon. Feces in the right has a greater fluid content than in the sigmoid colon. The movement of ileal contents through the bowel occurs in response to innervation of the signals. Submucosal structures control secretion, blood flow, and sensory perception. A combination of circular constrictions and longitudinal contractions moves ileal contents through the colon (Chang & Bland, 1997).

Feces is exposed to the bowel wall for absorption of nutritional elements and then pushed into the rectum by bowel peristalsis. Fecal matter is stored in the left colon until defecation occurs. During defecation, the rectal wall becomes dis-

tended by feces, then peristalsis occurs as the anal sphincter relaxes and defecation occurs. Anal sphincter impulses respond to conscious control; if the signal is ignored, the defecation reflex can subside (Chang & Bland, 1997).

Clinical Presentation

Changes in stool consistency and color, or the inability to move stool through the bowel (painful cramps and abdominal distention/obstruction), may indicate a diagnosis of colorectal cancer. Presentation of symptoms are often associated with the location of the tumor: rectal lesions, blood in stool; left colon lesions, obstruction; right colon, anemia and right, lower quadrant pain. A recent trend has demonstrated more frequent colon cancers within the ascending colon (Coia & Moylan, 1994).

Presenting symptoms are related to the anatomic location of the tumor. Left-sided tumors cause colicky abdominal pain more often than right-sided tumors. Cecal carcinomas are associated with anemia due to chronic/gradual gastrointestinal blood loss, not gross rectal bleeding or obstruction. Abdominal pain may accompany a cecal lesion, not colicky pain (Pazdur, 1994).

Rectal carcinoma may cause rectal bleeding, constipation, rectal fullness, and tenesmus due to involvement of pelvic peripheral nerves. Meenic stools may indicate right-sided tumors or obstructing lesions. Benign conditions, such as rectal fissures and hemorrhoids, can cause rectal bleeding. Rectal bleeding should not be considered benign unless a barium enema and sigmoidoscopy/colonoscopy have been performed to rule out malignancy (Pazdur, 1994). Rectal bleeding is more commonly associated with rectal (50%) than colon (14%) cancer. Rectal bleeding may be associated with early lesions, which are more vascularized and may have a better prognosis (Jessup et al., 1997).

Additional presenting symptoms and signs of colorectal carcinoma are rectal bleeding (gross in the stool, or positive guaiac on digital rectal examination), abdominal pain, a change in bowel habits, (pencil-thin stools, stools containing mucus, alternating constipation with diarrhea), vomiting, anorexia, weight loss (greater than 5 kg). Physical examination may show abdominal distention and the presence of enlarged abdominal veins due to portal obstruction. Additionally, auscultation of abnormal bowel sounds and the palpation of inguinal and supraclavicular nodes may be present. Colon obstruction and perforation are additional signs of colorectal cancer. Obstruction must be classified as complete (without flatus and/or bowel movements for 24 hours). Perforations must also be detailed as free into the peritoneal cavity or contained, occurring through the cancer or proximal to a complete obstruction. Location of the cancer affects the probability of developing a complete obstruction. Obstructions are common at the splenic flexure and less likely at other sites and at the rectum. Obstruction is a predictor of poor outcome (obstructed patients had a 31% 5-year survival compared with a 72% survival for patients who did not obstruct; Jessup et al., 1997). Perforation occurs less often than obstruction. Most perforations occur through the tumor and extend either into the abdominal cavity or into an abscess cavity. Perforations are associated with local disease recurrence due to spread of malignant cells at the site of an infection (Jessup et al., 1997). Perforation increases mortality significantly and changes the pattern of pain.

Prognosis

Presenting clinical signs of colorectal cancer are associated with survival rates. Asymptomatic people with colorectal cancer have better survival rates than symptomatic ones (Pazdur, 1994). Hemorrhage as a presenting sign is correlated with good survival because early interventions are often sought. Iron deficiency anemia due to microscopic bleeding typically from a right-sided colon lesion may indicate a poor prognosis, especially if accompanied by weight loss and fatigue. This symptom is associated with significant risk of metastatic disease (Cappell & Goldberg, 1992).

Survival rates are generally lower in patients with rectal cancer than with colon cancer. If presentation involves obstruction, perforation, fistulas, or tumor adherence to adjacent organs, prognosis is compromised. The size of the colorectal tumor does not correlate with survival (as with other tumor diagnoses; Pazdur, 1994). The baseline carcinoembryonic antigen (CEA) level may correlate with survival and should be serially tracked to assess patient response to the treatment plan.

Younger patients may have lower survival rates because people less than 40 commonly have poorly differentiated carcinoma that is associated with advanced stages. Patients between 75 and 80 years of age may more commonly have cancers of a lower grade, which have a more favorable prognosis. Sepsis and surgical complications may occur more frequently in the elderly population; however, 5-year survival rates of older patients have been shown to be equal to those of younger patients (Hobler, 1986; Payne, Chapuis, & Pheils, 1986; Wise Jr. et al., 1991).

Presenting signs and symptoms such as rectal bleeding, complete or partial bowel obstruction, and a change in constitutional physical signs such as fatigue, weight loss, anorexia, anemia, and pain must be assessed and stabilized clinically. Additionally, these clinical indicators can be associated with prognostic factors that ultimately guide the selection of options to treat colorectal cancer.

Pattern of Spread

Colorectal cancer does not typically demonstrate extensive microscopic longitudinal spread. Radial spread is common and depends on the tumor location. Over 25% of colon cancers extend through the bowel wall. Rectosigmoid cancers spread through the bowel wall in 50% to 70% of cases with a 50% to 60% spread to lymph nodes. Colon and rectal cancers have different natural histories. Therefore, it has been suggested that these disease sites be considered distinct when developing treatment strategies (Coia & Moylan, 1994).

Local extension of colorectal cancers occurs through the penetration of layers of bowel. The bowel wall comprises four layers: the mucosa, submucosa, muscularis, and serosa (Chang & Bland, 1997). The deeper the penetration of the tumor, the increased channel for spread. Tumors that extend into and beyond the submucosa have access to lymphatic and vascular drainage, which enhances metastatic potential to adjacent structures. Distant metastatic spread occurs to the liver and lungs most commonly and less frequently to the adrenal glands, bone, and brain (Chang & Bland, 1997). Anal cancers exhibit local extension to the anal sphincter muscles, prostate, urethra, and bladder in males and vagina in females. Potential sites of distant metastases can be the lungs and liver. The variance in natural histories and the pattern of spread of colon and rectal cancers indicate that treatment strategies should be specifically tailored (Coia & Moylan, 1994).

Pathology

Most colorectal cancers are pathologically diagnosed as moderately well-differentiated adenocarcinomas. Mucinous adenocarcinoma is seen in 10% to 15% of cases and is associated with a less favorable prognosis (Coia & Moylan, 1994).

Staging

The purpose of staging people with colorectal cancer is to determine which groups might require postoperative adjuvant therapy. Pathologic staging serves to identify people at high risk of relapse. Prognosis after colorectal surgery depends on the pathologic stage of the tumor (Vaughn & Haller, 1997a). The first staging system, known as the Dukes System, was described 60 years ago. Since that time, other systems have been developed that more sensitively describe tumors and associated prognoses (Vaughn & Haller, 1997a).

Two systems are presently used: the Modified Astler-Coller (MAC) version of the Dukes system and the TNM (tumor-node-metastasis) system, which is based on the classification of the 1988 American Joint Committee on Cancer (AJCC). Staging of colorectal cancer predicts risk of recurrence and delineates treatment options. Clinicians must understand and utilize staging recommendations when managing patients with colorectal cancer (Tables 6-4, 6-5, and 6-6).

The majority of patients with early-stage colon cancer (A and B1; stage I) are cured by surgery alone. Once a tumor invades through bowel wall (B2-3; stage II), 5-year survival decreases to 70%. If pericolonic lymph nodes are involved (stage C1-3; stage III), 5-year survival falls to 25% to 60% (with shorter survivals if more lymph nodes are involved; Vaughn & Haller, 1997a).

Diagnostic Workup

If a person is suspected of having colorectal cancer, a full diagnostic workup must commence and include the following: history and physical, including

TABLE 6-4

MODIFIED ASTLER-COLLER STAGING SYSTEM (MAC)

A	Tumor involving only mucosa; nodes negative
B_1	Tumor within bowel wall; nodes negative
B_2	Tumor through bowel wall; nodes negative
B_3	Tumor adherent to or invading adjacent structures; nodes negative
C_1	Tumor within bowel wall; nodes positive
C_2	Tumor through bowel wall; nodes positive
C_3	Tumor adherent to or invading adjacent structures; nodes positive

TABLE 6-5

1997 AJCC STAGING SYSTEM: TNM STAGING CRITERIA

Primary Tumor (T)

TX	Primary tumor cannot be assessed
T_0	No evidence of primary tumor
TIS	Carcinoma in situ
T_1	Tumor invades submucosa
T_2	Tumor invades muscularis propria
T_3	Tumor invades through muscularis propria into subserosa or into nonperitonealized pericolic or perirectal tissues
T_4	Tumor perforates visceral peritoneum, or directly invades other organs or structures

Lymph nodes (N)

NX	Regional lymph nodes cannot be assessed
N_0	No regional lymph node metastases
N_1	Metastases in one to three pericolic or perirectal lymph nodes
N_2	Metastases in four or more pericolic or perirectal lymph nodes
N_3	Metastases in any lymph node along course of a major named vascular trunk

Distant Metastasis (M)

MX	Presence of distant metastases cannot be assessed
M_0	No distant metastases
M_1	Distant metastases

Stage Grouping

Stage 0	TIS, N_0, M_0
Stage 1	T_1, N_0, M_0; T_2, N_0, M_0
Stage II	T_3, N_0, M_0; T_4, N_0, M_0
Stage III	Any T, N_1, M_0
	Any T, N_2, M_0
	Any T, N_3, M_0
Stage IV	Any T, any N, M_1

(Fleming et al. [1997]. *AJCC cancer staging manual* [5th ed.]. Philadelphia: Lippincott-Raven.)

TABLE 6-6

CORRELATION OF MODIFIED ASTLER-COLLER AND TNM SYSTEMS

Mac	TNM
A	T_1N_0
B_1	T_2N_0
B_2	T_3N_0
B_3	T_4N_0
C_1	T_2N_1; T_2N_2; T_2N_3
C_2	T_3N_1; T_3N_2; T_3N_3
C_3	T_4N_1; T_4N_2; T_4N_3

a digital rectal examination, stool sampling to detect occult blood, colonoscopy, barium enema with air-contrast, chest x-ray, and urinalysis (Table 6-7). Laboratory tests include a hemogram to assess anemia (found with right-sided colon lesions), renal and liver function studies, and a baseline carcinoembryonic antigen (CEA), which is then used to monitor response to therapy and follow-up care. Patients with stage II and III tumors whose preoperative CEA is less than 5 ng/mL have statistically improved survival compared with those who have preoperative CEA values of greater than 5 ng/mL (Pazdur, 1994). Serial CEA monitoring to detect recurrence has been studied after effective curative treatment for primary colorectal cancer and was found to have a minimal survival advantage of less than 5% (Wolf & Cohen, 1997). These data indicate the lack of benefit for attempting curative re-resection based on CEA levels of asymptomatic patients. CEA levels may occasionally be normal even when cancer is present.

Evaluation of the liver, kidney, and ureters for metastases should be done with a computed tomography (CT) scan of the abdomen and pelvis. If radiation therapy is proposed as part of the treatment plan, an additional CT scan may be obtained to assist with treatment planning (Coia & Moylan, 1994), as well as a transrectal ultrasound (Eckhauser & Knol, 1997).

Colonoscopy is the most common diagnostic procedure providing entire colorectal visualization and biopsy. Due to the need for preprocedure bowel preparation, associated discomfort with scope insertion and manipulation, the need for sedatives before and during the procedure, and institutional requirements for people to be accompa-

nied, many forgo the test. An experimental procedure currently being studied is known as virtual colonoscopy and may save lives by increasing the number of consenting people. This technique is less expensive, more expedient, and more comfortable than the usual examination. Virtual colonoscopy involves the insertion of a tiny probe 4 cm into the rectum, enabling visualization of the entire colon in a relatively painless manner (Macari & Megibow, 1998).

Treatment Options

Surgery

Surgery is the intervention of choice for colon cancer arising from the ascending, transverse, and descending regions. The history of bowel surgery has been traced to the writings of Hippocrates (460 BC), who described the repair of small bowel fistulas. Contemporary colon surgery is based on the work of 19th-century surgeons and is founded on the following four basic tenets: maintenance of an adequate blood supply to the remaining resected colon; absence of infection; absence of inflammation; and absence of tension on the anastomosis. Following these principles minimizes the risk of surgical complications (Eckhauser & Knol, 1997).

Advances in surgical techniques included the use of the circular enteric end-anastomosis device, which is a bowel stapling device that revolutionized the construction of low rectal anastomosis and extended the safe distal margin of rectal resection close to the dentate line (Eckhauser & Knol, 1997). Additional advances in the refinement of perioperative care, including the use of broad-spectrum antibiotics and nutritional support, have contributed to overall mortality of elective cases at 5% (Eckhauser & Knol, 1997) (Figure 6-2). Scrupulous surgical technique and expert nursing interventions are vital facets of safe surgery.

Preoperative evaluation must focus on minimizing complications and assessing the extent of disease. In addition to preoperative tumor staging, thorough evaluation of the candidate for comorbidities must take place. A preoperative history and physical must assess for cardiopulmonary risk factors such as congestive heart disease, history of myocardial infarction, symptomatic aortic stenosis,

TABLE 6-7

DIAGNOSTIC STRATEGIES FOR DETECTING COLORECTAL CANCER

Procedure/Rationale	Time Required	Possible Sensations	Potential Side Effects/Complications	Self-Care
Digital Rectal Examination (DRE) Health care professional inserts lubricated, gloved finger into rectum to assess for irregular or abnormal areas limited to only rectum. Should be done before other studies.	2–5 min	Pressure on rectal area; sensation to defecate	Mild bleeding	Hygiene—wipe rectum
Fecal Occult Blood Test (FOBT)	Preparation: 48–72 h		*False-positive results:* Results from meat in diet, hemorrhoids, fissures, gastritis from aspirin *False-negative results:* Failure to use high-residue, high-fiber diet 72 h before test. Vitamin C in diet. Delay between collection and examination. Failure to prepare slides properly. Lesion not bleeding at time of examination.	No red meat 72 h before test Withhold iron and aspirin Collect three specimens
Barium Enema Enema of barium sulfate through the rectum to partially fill and open the colon. Colon partially inflated with air to expand colon. Increase contrast and quality of radiographs.	30–45 min	Fullness, abdominal discomfort/cramping, urge to defecate	Bowel obstruction, perforation	Preparation includes liquid diet day before, and low residue diet 1–3 d before test. Bowel preparation; laxatives before and after examination.
Sigmoidoscopy Placement of slender, flexible, hollow, lighted tube into the rectum to view the inside of the rectum and *lower* colon. If polyp or mass found, recommended for biopsy.	15–30 min	Abdominal pressure, discomfort	Possible bleeding, if tissue removed	Clear liquid diet 24 h before; laxative—evening before
Colonoscopy Tube similar to sigmoidoscope but longer. Inserted into rectum to view *entire* colon. Connected to video camera and display to view entire colon. Wire loop inserted through colonoscope, cuts polyps for pathologic sampling.	15–30 min	Abdominal pressure, discomfort, intravenous infusion with sedation. Left-sided positioning, sensation to defecate	If tissue removed, bleeding. Possible adverse effects from sedation.	Clear liquid for 24 h. Overall bowel prep. Laxative, evening before. Cleansing enemas NPO p MN flatus after examination
Laboratory Studies Hemoglobin and hematocrit levels to evaluate anemia found with right-sided lesions, carcinoembryonic antigen (CEA) for monitoring response to therapy and follow-up care.	Minutes	Feelings associated with venipuncture	Possible hematoma	Elevate arm, apply pressure
Computed Tomography (CT) Scan	50–60 min	Feelings of confinement, systemic warmth if dye used	Hypersensitivity to contrast material	May be required to maintain NPO before test

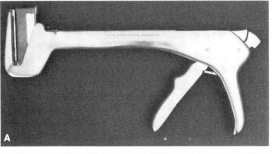

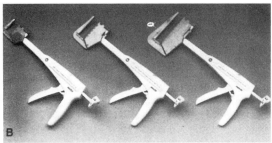

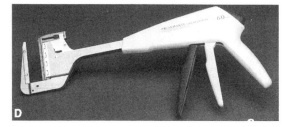

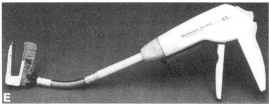

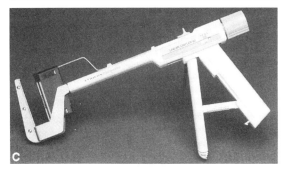

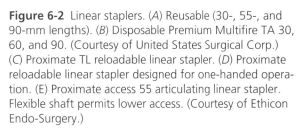

Figure 6-2 Linear staplers. (*A*) Reusable (30-, 55-, and 90-mm lengths). (*B*) Disposable Premium Multifire TA 30, 60, and 90. (Courtesy of United States Surgical Corp.) (*C*) Proximate TL reloadable linear stapler. (*D*) Proximate reloadable linear stapler designed for one-handed operation. (E) Proximate access 55 articulating linear stapler. Flexible shaft permits lower access. (Courtesy of Ethicon Endo-Surgery.)

premature ventricular contractions, hypertension, bleeding disorders, and compromised performance status. Identifying people with these preexisting risks can enhance surgical outcome as specific medical management needs are identified prospectively.

Preoperative mechanical bowel preparation has been identified as the most effective way to prepare a colon vacant of stool. Oral antibiotics are suggested to minimize the incidence of postoperative wound infection. An example of a bowel preparation is shown in Table 6-8. The objective of this preparation is to decrease the bacterial count within the colon. Prophylactic antibiotics that cover gram-negative bacilli and anaerobes are given before the start of surgery. Timing of antibiotic administration is crucial for full benefit to occur. Following these precautions can diminish the incidence of postoperative wound infection to under 10% (Eckhauser & Knol, 1997).

The goals of surgical resection for colorectal

cancer should include complete removal of the tumor, the accomplishment of adequate surgical margins, dissection of the surrounding lymph nodes, a patent anastomosis, and preservation of anorectal function (Eckhauser & Knol, 1997). Surgical laparotomy provides abdominal exploration and identifies the macroscopic extent of disease. The proximity of the tumor to the lymphatics and adjacent organs is delineated, and the liver is

TABLE 6-8	
PREOPERATIVE BOWEL PREPARATION	
Day before surgery	Light lunch; then clear liquids until midnight; then NPO
Afternoon before surgery	4 L of polyethylene glycol (PEG) in salt solution given orally
Day before surgery	Erythromycin and neomycin, 1 g each at 1 PM, 2 PM, and 11 PM

manually palpated for metastatic disease. The extent of resection depends on the tumor location, blood supply, draining lymphatics, and extension into adjacent organs. A safe anastomosis is accomplished when well-vascularized bowel margins are joined without tension (Eckhauser & Knol, 1997).

Resection of colorectal cancer includes the removal of the tumor's blood supply. The various types of colon surgery follow the anatomy of the large bowel. Right hemicolectomy is the routine procedure for tumors involving the cecum, ascending colon, and hepatic flexure. This surgery involves removal of the bowel from 4 to 6 cm proximal to the ileocecal valve to the portion of the transverse colon. Anastomosis is performed between the terminal ileum and the transverse colon (Eckhauser & Knol, 1997).

The extended right hemicolectomy involves division of the right and middle colic vessels at their ori-

gin, with removal of the right and transverse colon supplied by these vessels. The anastomosis is between the terminal ileum and the proximal left colon. This anastomosis is well vascularized; it is the procedure of choice for many transverse colon lesions (Eckhauser & Knol, 1997) (Figures 6-3 and 6-4).

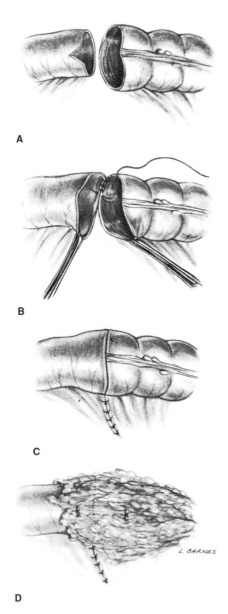

A

B

C

D

Figure 6-4 Right hemicolectomy. (*A*) Any disparity between the luminal ends can be corrected by dividing the smaller segment of bowel along its antimesenteric border. (*B*) The anastomosis is accomplished using a single layer of interrupted sutures. (*C*) Note the single mattress suture used to effect final closure. The rent in the mesentery is closed. (*D*) Omentum is placed around the anastomosis.

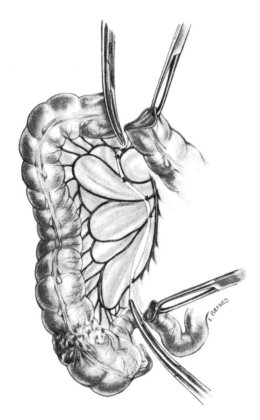

Figure 6-3 Right hemicolectomy. After ligation of the vascular supply and mobilization of the bowel, crushing clamps are applied to the ileum and transverse colon, and the bowel is divided with a scalpel, leaving the ends open for anastomosis.

The transverse colectomy is rarely performed because it requires an anastomosis between the ascending and left colon, which results in a compromised blood supply and unsatisfactory organ tension (Figure 6-5).

The subtotal colectomy, which is also known as a total colectomy, involves the removal of the bowel from the cecum to the peritoneal reflexion with an ileorectal anastomosis (Figure 6-6). This procedure results in a high postoperative stool frequency due to the loss of absorptive capacity of the bowel. Patients less than age 55 adapt to this procedure with the ability of small bowel mucosa to absorb excess water and eventually yield up to three stools daily. Older patients exhibit a higher morbidity due to chronic diarrhea. This procedure is done for multiple primary tumors and for those with hereditary nonpolyposis colon cancer (Eckhauser & Knol, 1997).

Colorectal carcinoma is commonly associated with large bowel obstructions. Approximately 15% to 20% of patients with colorectal lesions present with obstructions (McGregor & O'Dwyer, 1993). Obstruction correlates with elderly patients and with left-sided tumors. For right-sided and transverse tumors, right colectomy or extended right colectomy with primary anastomosis is the surgical treatment of choice. The management of left-sided tumors is controversial; therefore, several treatment options are practiced. These techniques include proximal fecal diversion followed by reanastomosis and delayed colostomy takedown; resection with colostomy and distal mucous fistula, then colostomy takedown; immediate resection with reanastomosis without bowel preparation or combined with on-table antegrade lavage; immediate subtotal/total colectomy with reanastomosis; and laser recanalization of colon lumen followed by elective resection (used only for partial obstruction) (Eckhauser & Knol, 1997) (Figure 6-7).

Perforation of colorectal tumors requires surgical resection at the initial operation to avoid the spread of cancer cells through the bowel wall and to minimize infection from contamination of the peritoneal cavity. Containing infection is the primary objective when surgically managing a perforated colorectal tumor. Therefore, the abdominal cavity should be thoroughly irrigated with physiologic saline, which assists in decreasing bacterial presence. Once the perforation is surgically removed, reanastomosis may be probable with the formation of a protective proximal stoma and drainage of the contaminated surgical area. Sometimes, surgical slips are placed where the perforation occurred if adjuvant postoperative radiation therapy is planned (Eckhauser & Knol, 1997).

Laparoscopic colorectal surgery (LCR) is a suggested alternative to open laparotomy and has been used in the United States since the early 1990s. Advantages of LCR include less postoperative pain, fewer postoperative complications, quicker recovery and return to activities of daily life, reduced utilization of acute-care resources, and improved cosmesis. LCR surgery outcome data must be provided by clinicians and include overall and disease-free survival, quality of life, and cost-effective profiles (Eckhauser & Knol, 1997).

The evolution for intestinal laparoscopic surgery was linked to the success of laparoscopic cholecystectomies. Intestinal laparoscopic surgery was pioneered at the Cleveland Clinical Foundation, with benign intestinal diseases such as Crohn's, familial polyposis, diverticulitis, incontinence, and rectal prolapse (Hammerhofer-Jereb,

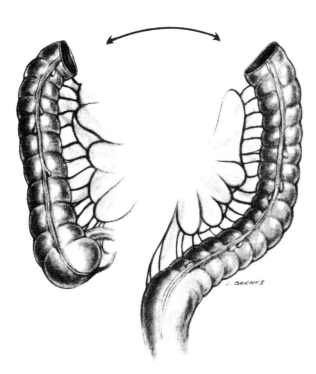

Figure 6-5 Transverse colon resection. Anastomosis may not be feasible because of tension.

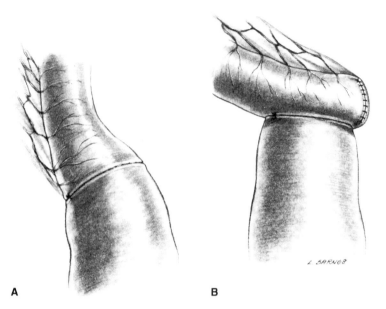

Figure 6-6 Ileorectal anastomosis can usually be accomplished (*A*) end-to-end, with or without a Cheatle cut of the ileum, or (*B*) as a side-to-end anastomosis.

A   B

1996). A clinical trial was conducted to compare the outcomes of people who undergo bowel resection laparoscopically with those who have conventional abdominal surgery. Study participants were

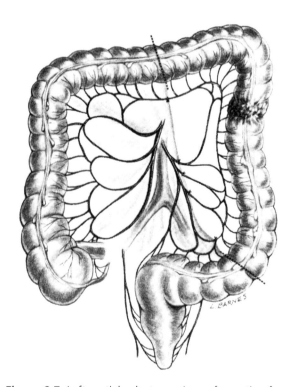

Figure 6-7 Left partial colectomy. Area of resection for lesion of descending colon, with preservation of sigmoid and rectal vessels.

required to have a successful diagnostic laparoscopy to ensure that laparoscopic resection was feasible. Exclusionary factors occurred if the patient had fatty mesentery, previous abdominal or pelvic scar tissue, tumors deep in the pelvis, or tumors that had invaded other parts of the body. The findings of this study were favorable and included 53 patients: 27 had laparoscopic surgery and 26 conventional surgery. Those in the study group recovered faster, returning to work within 3 weeks of surgery. Postoperative nursing care was the same for both groups; however, the study group had their nasogastric tubes removed 24 hours after surgery and did not require daily dressing changes. Use of pain medications was less for the study group, and the study group had less deviation on their baseline pulmonary status (Hammerhofer-Jereb, 1996). Open bowel resection remains the standard of care for colorectal cancer; however, laparoscopic resection has the potential to increase clinical use in particular situations.

The major limitation with LCR is the preservation of oncologic surgical techniques. The adequacy of resection margins and lymph node retrieval have demonstrated similar results to open techniques. Incisional recurrence rates have been reported but may be due to disseminated incurable systemic disease rather than an issue of tumor implantation. If patients present with liver metastases that are resectable, this would obviate LCR. Additionally, the tumor location and stage need to be strategically accessible to the laparoscope; those in the distal sigmoid colon or proximal rectum may be too low for the reach of the laparoscopic stapler. For this reason, intraoperative colonoscopy has been used to localize tumors for LCR (McGregor & O'Dwyer, 1993).

DIFFERENCE IN THE PROCEDURES OF CONVENTIONAL BOWEL RESECTION AND INTESTINAL LAPAROSCOPIC SURGERY

CONVENTIONAL RESECTION. The surgeon makes a midline incision, 7 to 10 inches in length, across the patient's abdominal wall to expose the contents. The cancer is identified; a large area of tissue around the cancer is removed, including the mesentery and lymph nodes; and the main mesenteric vessels are tied off close to their origins. The size of the tumor determines the extent of the surgery. When the excision of the tumor is complete, the anastomosis is created.

LAPAROSCOPIC RESECTION. Five to six small incisions are created, which range in length from 5 to 12 mm. A laparoscope, which has a small camera attached, is then inserted into one of the incisions. The camera projects magnified images of the abdominal region to an external video monitor, which the surgeon watches during the procedure. The surgeon maneuvers various instruments through cannulas placed in the incisions and is able to cut out and remove the cancerous segment. An impermeable bag is placed around the specimen before tissue removal to prevent cancer cells from spreading to surrounding tissue. The bag with the tumor specimen is drawn out through an enlarged cannula. The bowel anastomosis is constructed by creating a small incision in the abdominal wall, and the ends of the bowel are brought to the exterior for either hand-sewn or stapled anastomosis (Hammerhofer-Jereb, 1996). The use of LCR for colorectal cancer remains controversial even though some data suggest that LCR is similar to open resection because the longitudinal margins and the number of lymph nodes resected are the same. Concerns remain regarding staging adequacy, recurrence patterns, and 5-year survival rates. The surgical oncology profession is awaiting the results of a large, prospective, randomized trial comparing LCR with conventional open colectomy (Bertagnolli, Mahmoud & Daly, 1997) (Figure 6-8).

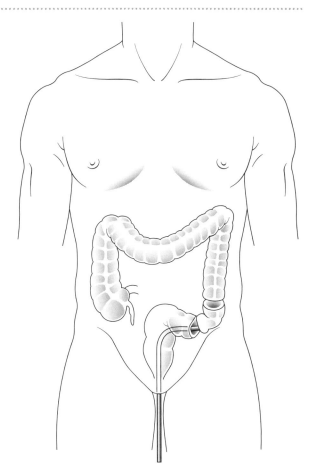

Figure 6-8 Laparoscopic colectomy. Bowel is retrieved through the open end of the rectal stump using colonoscope.

SURGICAL OPTIONS FOR RECTAL CANCER

Historically, rectal cancers have been treated with abdominoperineal resection (the Miles procedure). This procedure is the standard operation for cancers arising in the distal rectum. It involves the entire removal of the rectum, the mesorectum, portions of the levator animusculature, and the anus. Effective treatment is provided by this procedure; however, a permanent colostomy is required, and significant sexual and bladder dysfunctions may result. An abdominoperineal resection is indicated when the tumor involves the anal sphincter, when it penetrates into the rectovaginal septum, and in patients in whom sphincter-preserving surgery is not possible owing to unfavorable body image due to the formation of a colostomy, poor preoperative sphincter control, and diminished ability to perform activities of daily living (Bertagnolli et al., 1997) (Figure 6-9).

SPHINCTER-SPARING PROCEDURES

Other surgical alternatives have been developed, which include restorative resection with sphincter preservation and local excision. When appropriate, these procedures are used frequently due to the improved quality of life associated with them. The Miles abdominoperineal resection is the standard treatment of distal rectal cancers. Patients with limited local disease may be adequately treated with sphincter-sparing procedures. Preservation of continence is a most important quality-of-life indicator and requires the preservation of the anal sphincters, an accomplishment that expert surgical technique has made a reality. Outcome assessment has been difficult to document due to lack of prospective randomized trials comparing sphincter-sparing surgery with abdominoperineal resection.

Several factors have assisted in the development of sphincter-sparing rectal resections, including improved knowledge of pathologic recurrence

patterns of rectal cancer, the development of surgical stapling instruments that facilitate resections that would have been difficult to perform by hand suturing, and refined multimodality treatment regimens including the adjuvant use of chemotherapy and radiotherapy (Coia & Moylan, 1994; Eckhauser & Knol, 1997). The rectum is divided into upper, middle, and lower thirds. Cancers within the upper and middle thirds of the rectum can be treated with restorative anterior resection. These cancers are between 5 and 15 cm proximal to the dentate line. Cancers in the distal third of the rectum are more difficult to treat with restorative resection and need to be carefully considered. The distance between the lower edge of the tumor and the dentate and the dentate line is the most important factor when selecting a surgical option (Eckhauser & Knol, 1997). Original research suggested that a surgical margin of at least 5 cm was necessary for successful low anterior resection. This requirement would preclude the majority of patients with lower-third rectal cancers from having restorative resections. Recent data have suggested that a distal margin of 1 to 2 cm is adequate clear-

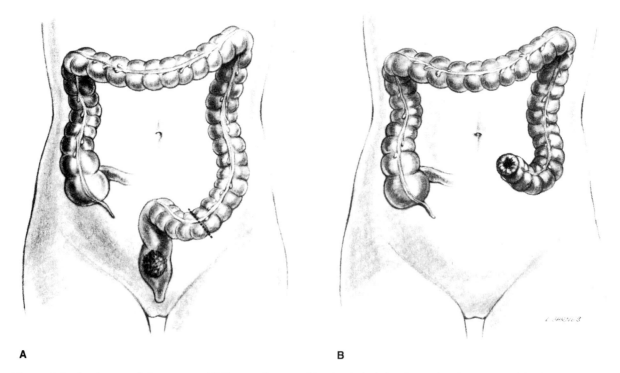

A   **B**

Figure 6-9 Carcinoma of the rectum. (*A*) Extent of removal in classical abdominoperineal resection. (*B*) The sigmoid colostomy is created in the left iliac fossa.

ance for carcinomas of the rectum, and this justifies restorative resection for the cancers located more than 3 cm proximal to the dentate line (Marcus, 1995) (Figure 6-10).

Restorative resections of the rectal and rectosigmoid cancers include the removal of the tumor as well as the lymphovascular pedicle. Surgical stapling instruments are used in sphincter-sparing and restorative resection of rectal cancer to complete the anastomosis. The risk of pelvic recurrence is lessened by the excision of the mesorectum with clearance beyond the distal line of bowel resection. Patients with advanced disease and low-lying tumors commonly demonstrate mesenteric and lymph node involvement. The spread of rectal cancer to pelvic and lymph nodes is associated with a poor prognosis. Surgical removal of the involved nodes is associated with a significant risk of bladder and sexual dysfunction; therefore, adjuvant chemoradiation may provide a treatment alternative that may improve survival and provide a more tolerable side-effect profile (Eckhauser & Knol, 1997).

COLOANAL ANASTOMOSIS

This procedure involves transabdominal removal of the proximal rectum to the level of the levator ani muscles, followed by transperineal excision of

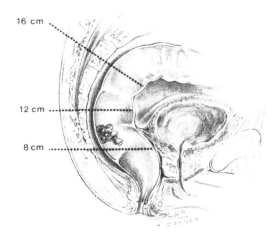

Figure 6-10 Rectal cancer. Tumors of the upper one third (23 to 16 cm) are amenable to anterior resection. Tumors of the lower one third (0 to 8 cm) usually require an abdominoperineal resection. It is the middle one third tumor that most often represents the management problem.

the most distal portion of the rectum. The integrity of the anal sphincter is preserved by the dissection of the anal mucosa. Anastomosis is created between the sigmoid colon and the anal verge either by hand-sutured or stapled technique. Survival rates are 64% to 88% at 3 to 5 years after surgery. Deaths are due to metastatic disease. Fecal continence is preserved in 80% to 90% of patients. Functional results improve over time while the neorectum is increasing its capacity to store feces (Enker & Paty, 1993). Coloanal anastomosis with neorectal construction is indicated for patients with a good performance status, low rectal tumors, good preoperative sphincter function, and no sphincter tumor involvement (Bertagnolli et al., 1997) (Figure 6-11).

LOCAL EXCISION

Local excision for rectal cancer involves the removal of the primary tumor by a full-thickness excision followed by restoration of the bowel lumen in the rectal canal. This surgical procedure does not provide a complete staging because only a partial lymph node dissection is included (Bertagnolli et al., 1997). This procedure should be used when the risk of local recurrence is low. Local excision should be reserved for T1 or T2 lesions that are limited to the submucosa and muscularis propria; are within 6 cm of the anal verge; are well or moderately differentiated and have no vascular or lymphatic invasion; are mobile on examination; and are less than one third of the circumference of the rectum (Jessup et al., 1997). Lack of nodal disease should be clinically documented by preoperative CT scan and transrectal ultrasound. Local excisions are used for palliation of advanced cancers and for people who are compromised candidates for more extensive surgery. Local excisions can be performed using a transanal, trans-sacral, or transsphincteric approach (Bertagnolli et al., 1997).

SURGICAL TREATMENT OF RECURRENT RECTAL CANCER

The risk of local recurrence after rectal cancer surgery is a significant clinical problem. The majority of rectal cancer recurs within 2 or 3 years after surgery and is either locally extensive or widely disseminated. The risk of local recurrence is attributed to a combination of factors, which may in-

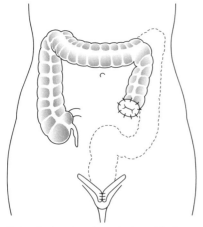

Abdominal perineal proctosigmoidectomy with permanent end colostomy

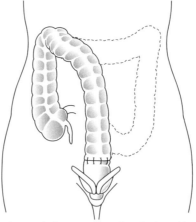

Low anterior resection of rectosigmoid with colorectal anastomosis

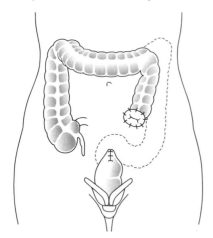

Hartmann resection

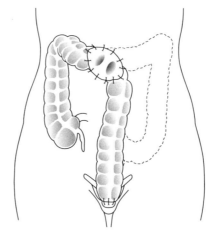

Low anterior resection of rectosigmoid with coloanal anastomosis and protecting loop-transverse colostomy

Figure 6-11 Options in the surgical management of rectal cancer.

clude the type of surgery; the extent of resection; prior history of splenectomy; history of blood transfusion; size/location of tumor; stage and grade of tumor; and evidence of lymphovascular permeation. Combination postoperative radiation with chemotherapy is used to prevent local recurrence in patients with transmural extension or regional lymph node involvement.

A challenging clinical issue is the inability to accurately stage recurrent rectal disease. Conventional CT and MRI studies are unable to detect re-

currences less than 2 cm in size. Transanal and transvaginal ultrasound can assist in finding recurrent disease; however, they are limited in the ability to differentiate inflammatory from metastatic lymph nodes.

Few treatment options are available for locally recurrent rectal cancer. Radical surgery is a consideration only in a very select patient population. This surgery may involve resections of the entire sacrum and bony pelvis and adjoining organs and should only be done if the ability to remove all gross tumor is feasible. If the recurrent disease demonstrates extensive pelvic involvement, reoperation is not an option. This clinical situation could be managed palliatively with a combination of external beam radiation and systemic chemotherapy. New radiation planning procedures have increased the tolerance of surrounding pelvic organs, and the use of intraoperative radiation has resulted in longer improvement in local control and survival data (Eckhauser & Knol, 1997).

SURGERY AS A TREATMENT MODALITY FOR METASTATIC COLORECTAL CANCER

Approximately 50% of patients with colorectal cancer develop local-regional or distant metastases. Metastatic disease can present as disseminated systemic disease or as small nodules that are confined to a specific organ. Surgical removal of these nodules has been shown to yield 5-year survival rates of 25% to 40%. Colorectal metastases to the liver and the lung are common and can sometimes be successfully removed surgically (Eckhauser & Knol, 1997).

Patients who undergo colorectal surgery with curative intent must be thoroughly assessed preoperatively for the potential evidence of microscopic or gross metastatic disease. Consideration of pursuing surgery for metastatic disease should only occur according to the following criteria: complete removal of the primary tumor; no presence of residual colorectal disease; metastatic disease should be resectable; patient should have adequate performance status; and risk-to-benefit ratio should favor surgery (Bertagnolli et al., 1997).

Patients with colorectal liver metastases commonly die of liver failure. A correlation exists between the extent of liver disease and length of survival. Patients with colorectal metastases to the lungs often die from diffuse metastatic disease. Early detection of metastatic disease provides the best chance for successful surgical resection. Imaging studies, including CT of the abdomen and pelvis and chest x-ray, and CEA results are used to determine potential metastatic nodules. If a clinical question regarding the findings arises, sometimes a biopsy is recommended before surgery is offered to confirm findings.

Additional Treatment Options for Metastatic Colorectal Cancer

CRYOSURGERY

Cryosurgery involves tissue destruction through the application of freezing and thawing techniques. It is used as a treatment modality with possible curative properties in select patients with colorectal metastases to the liver. With the assistance of ultrasound guidance, small probes are placed through the liver tissue into the tumor. The lesions are identified, and then the cryosurgery system controls the flow of liquid nitrogen through the cryoprobes to achieve a probe tip temperature between −190°C and −180°C. Freezing progresses over 15 minutes. At the completion of the freezing process, the frozen lesions are allowed to thaw for approximately 10 minutes. Patients experience only one freeze cycle, which has been found to reduce the propensity of the liver parenchyma to crack. Cryosurgery can be done laparoscopically for accessible lesions; however, an open surgical procedure is most common. Cryosurgery is used as an adjunct to surgical resection for both primary and metastatic liver cancer, when standard resection would require too much removal of liver parenchyma (Brandt, DeAntonio, Dezort, & Eyman, 1996).

Lesions near the hilum of the liver are not amenable to cryosurgery due to the risk of bile duct damage. Large lesions (greater than 6 to 7 cm) are generally not treated because they are beyond the size of the technology. Associated complications include bleeding thrombocytopenia, diffuse intravascular coagulation, pleural effusions, and bile duct injuries. Controlled randomized studies are necessary to determine the long-term survival benefit of cryosurgery for metastatic liver disease. The majority of recurrences after cryosurgery are associated with liver micrometastases as well as distant sites of disease. Therefore, the use of adjuvant chemotherapy for this patient population may be appropriate. Knowledgeable nursing and medical support are required to manage people receiving this type of surgical treatment (Brandt et al., 1996).

ALCOHOL INJECTION

Limited clinical experience exists with the technique of injecting 95% ethanol into colorectal liver metastases. This procedure is performed percutaneously, does not require general anesthesia, and can be repeated. It is reserved for small lesions (less than 3 cm), and no data exist to support this intervention (Eckhauser & Knol, 1997).

LASER HYPERTHERMIA

Laser hyperthermia is a technique using photocoagulation to treat colorectal liver metastases. This technique uses low-power laser energy, which is transmitted into the metastatic nodule through a laser fiber under ultrasound guidance. This is done percutaneously or laparoscopically. Laser hyperthermia has been compared with alcohol injection and found to be superior. Clinical utility of this intervention has not been identified (Amin, Bown & Lees, 1993; Eckhauser & Knol, 1997).

A high failure rate exists in response to regional therapies for colorectal liver metastases; therefore, it has been suggested that this patient population might benefit from the use of adjuvant regional chemotherapy. The documented advantages of the use of hepatic infusion of floxuridine or 5-fluorouracil (5-FU) may indicate the appropriateness of this type of treatment alone or in combination with surgery (Eckhauser & Knol, 1997).

SURGICAL RESECTION OF COLORECTAL LUNG METASTASES

As with hepatic metastases, the assessment of patients for resection of metastatic lung nodules from colorectal cancer must rule out local recurrence as well as distant metastases. A CT of the chest is a standard diagnostic tool used for preoperative staging to determine the location and size of the pulmonary nodules. Patient performance status must be acceptable, and lack of evidence of unresectable extrapulmonary metastases is required for surgical clearance. No data exist to indicate that extensive pulmonary colorectal metastases can be successfully resected. The median survival after pulmonary resection of colorectal metastases is approximately 24 months (Eckhauser & Knol, 1997; Goya et al., 1989).

Complications of Colorectal Surgery

Morbidity associated with colorectal surgery ranges from 8% to 15% with a mortality of 1% to 2% (Brown, Walsh, Abraham, & Sykes, 1991).

Major complications include anastomotic leakage, obstruction, and infection. Postoperative anastomotic dehiscence or leakage ranges between 5% and 8% (Enker & Paty, 1993). Obstruction can occur and is repaired by a side-to-side bowel anastomosis. Rates for wound infection are 3% for most abdominal procedures. If an intra-abdominal abscess forms, it requires percutaneous drainage and systemic antibiotics (Bertagnolli et al., 1997).

Complications associated with rectal surgery are distinct and occur in response to extensive pelvic dissection with the concomitant disruption of autonomic nerves. This can cause urinary retention and loss of sexual function. Permanent impotence after rectal cancer surgery varies from 14% to 76% and is age dependent (Enker & Paty, 1993). Dissection near the anal sphincters is associated with incontinence and less integrity of overall sphincter function. The most serious complication of rectal surgery is the risk of locoregional recurrence because methods for reoperation do not exist. Patients who are receiving sphincter-sparing surgery must be informed of this possibility (Bertagnolli et al., 1997).

Postoperative Follow-Up Schedule

Once patients have received surgical intervention for colorectal cancer, establishing a surveillance plan is pivotal for monitoring both acute and delayed surgical complications as well as promoting the early detection of potential disease recurrence. Approximately 50% of patients having had curative surgery for primary colorectal cancer develop local, regional, or distant recurrence (Steele, 1991). A surveillance plan should be based on the biology of colon cancer metastases, patterns of tumor recurrence, risk factors for recurrence, and the potential benefit of additional therapy. Most recurrences develop within 5 years of the initial surgery, and up to 8% are detected within 2 years (Steele, 1991). The prognosis associated with the primary tumor should guide the follow-up course. All patients, regardless of primary tumor pathology, are at equal risk of developing additional bowel lesions. Surveillance colonoscopy is performed to diagnose and treat recurrent lesions or second primary bowel tumors.

Follow-up schedules vary and have not been supported by randomized controlled clinical trials to discern if rigorous follow-up improves overall survival. Patients may derive little survival benefit even with a combined follow-up approach including serum tumor markers and radiologic and endoscopic methods. The use of serum tumor markers, commonly CEA, has created an interest in second-look operations if an elevated trend is detected. This may be questionable because the specificity and sensitivity of CEA values vary, yielding a high number of false-negative rates (Eckhauser & Knol, 1997).

It is important to survey people who have had a surgically excised colorectal cancer. Considering the controversy regarding the impact of surveillance on survival, an aggressive schedule including history and physical examination, stool Hemoccult, CEA every 3 months, and colonoscopy or double-contrast barium enema annually for 2 years and every 2 years thereafter should only be followed within a multi-institutional study of adjuvant or experimental protocols (Eckhauser & Knol, 1997). A conservative and acceptable follow-up course should include colonoscopy every 2 to 3 years to detect secondary colon lesions and serial CEA measurements every 3 to 6 months for 5 years. The results of the initial screening and the presence of secondary polyps should dictate the frequency of colonoscopy. While the patient is being followed, it is important that a rising trend in CEA warrant an additional clinical investigation.

Adjuvant Radiation Therapy as a Treatment Modality for Colorectal Cancer

Radiation therapy is used as a locally effective treatment modality for colorectal cancer. Adjuvant radiation therapy should be used only when there is a high risk of local disease recurrence. It is of the utmost importance that a safe and effective course of radiation be administered to the site at high risk of disease recurrence.

The Role of Radiation Therapy in Colon Cancer

The natural history of colon cancer is different than that of rectal cancer, and for this reason the use of radiation therapy for colon cancer is not as well delineated. Common disease recurrence sites of colon cancer are not local but are found within the abdominal cavity and at distant sites. Additionally, most local failures of colon cancer are extrapelvic and are characterized by less associated clinical pain than rectal cancer recurrence (Minsky, 1997).

The standard treatment for node-positive (T1–4 N1–2 M0) or high-risk (T3 N0 M0) colon cancer is postoperative adjuvant treatment with 5-FU based chemotherapy and leucovorin or levamisole. A large retrospective trial studying the role of local/regional radiation for colon cancer initially showed some promising results. Over 200 patients at risk for local/regional recurrence received 45 Gy to the site of recurrence and then a shrinking field to 50.4 to 55 Gy; 173 were treated adjuvantly, 30 were treated after subtotal resection, and 63 received a bolus of 5-FU on varying schedules (Willett, Fung, Kaufman et al., 1993). These study results were compared with a large control group of 395 patients who received only surgery. The results indicate clinical benefit for several patient groupings: patients with T4 N0 M0 or T4 N1–2 M0 disease demonstrated a significant improvement in local control and disease-free survival. Patients with T4 N0 disease with a bowel perforation or fistula had improved local control and disease-free survival. Additionally, radiation therapy was able to salvage some patients with residual disease after surgery. These encouraging data have led to additional phase III trials that combine postoperative adjuvant radiation therapy with varied cycles of chemotherapy to continue to enhance local-regional control of colon cancer (Coia & Moylan, 1994; Minsky, 1997).

The effectiveness of administering adjuvant radiation to the whole abdomen postoperatively due to the potential for a high incidence of abdominal failure has been investigated. The ability to treat the whole abdomen with radiation is limited due to the potential for the development of toxic side effects. To achieve a potential cure and to arrest microscopic disease, the whole abdomen should be dosed to receive 45 Gy. Only limited portions of the abdomen can tolerate this dose because the limit of tolerance to the whole abdomen is 30 Gy (Minsky, 1997).

Study results continue to be promising for treating patients at high risk of recurrence with whole abdominal radiation combined with chemotherapy after surgery. Delivery of radiation therapy to the whole abdomen must be monitored due to the risk of serious toxicity. Adding 5-FU based chemotherapy enhances the effect but increases the risk of additional dose-limiting toxicity (such as diarrhea). Therefore, limiting the radiation dose to a maximum of 30 Gy and closely monitoring side-effect profiles are essential to safe patient management.

Rectal Cancer

Local recurrence is more common than distant metastases with rectal cancer; therefore, the role of adjuvant radiation as an effective local treatment modality is indicated. Two components of adjuvant rectal cancer treatment include pelvic irradiation and 5-FU based chemotherapy. Radiation treatment has the ability to decrease local recurrence and increase the possibility of sphincter preservation in patients with resectable disease. Chemotherapy potentiates radiation by acting as a radiosensitizer and improves survival by diminishing the risk of distant metastasis.

POSTOPERATIVE RADIATION THERAPY FOR RECTAL CANCER

Radiation therapy used to treat rectal cancer has been studied in both pre- and postoperative settings. Each sequence has distinct clinical advantages and limitations. The standard approach to sequencing treatment has been after surgery. Several advantages exist in using adjuvant radiation treatment after surgery. It allows for the identification of areas at higher risk for local recurrence by the placement of surgical clips that mark the areas of tumor adherence and hence more accurately define the tumor bed for radiation planning. Disadvantages of postoperative adjuvant radiation therapy include the potential for an increased amount of small bowel in the radiation field; a potentially hypoxic postoperative radiation field and, if an abdominoperineal resection is done, inferior extension of the radiation field to include the perineal scar must be planned; and diminished sphincter function, resulting in increased bowel movements, occasional inconti-

nence, and urgency (Coia & Moylan, 1994; Minsky, 1997).

Adjuvant radiation therapy can be given alone or in combination with chemotherapy after surgical resection. Patients with stage II or III rectal cancer receiving postoperative radiation alone showed a local recurrence rate of 4% to 31% and 8% to 53%, respectively (Willett, Tepper, Kaufman et al., 1992). Local recurrence is severely debilitating, and the ability to successfully salvage has been limited; therefore, the goal of diminishing the risk of recurrent disease is vital. Although postoperative adjuvant radiation does not improve survival, the ability of radiation therapy to decrease the possibility of local recurrence is a significant option for patient management (Coia & Moylan, 1994; Minsky, 1997).

Patients who are stage III or N1–2 disease are candidates for combined modality therapy involving chemotherapy and radiation therapy. Two classic randomized studies have demonstrated that the adjuvant use of chemotherapy given at the same time as radiation therapy results in a significant improvement in local recurrence, disease-free survival, and overall survival (Table 6-9). The Gastrointestinal Tumor Study Group (GITSG) study randomized patients with stage B2 and C rectal adenocarcinomas after surgery to four treatment

TABLE 6-9

LOCAL RECURRENCE AND SURVIVAL IN PUBLISHED RANDOMIZED POSTOPERATIVE ADJUVANT TRIALS IN RECTAL CANCER

Trial	Number of Patients	Local Recurrence (%)	5-Year Survival (%)
GITSG	202		
Sx alone	58	24	47
XRT	50	20	58
CT	48	27	56
XRT + CT	46	11	72
NCCTG	204		
XRT	101	25	49
XRT + CT	103	13	55

Sx = surgery; XRT = radiation; CT = chemotherapy.

arms: no adjuvant therapy, radiation therapy alone, chemotherapy (5-FU, methyl CCNU), and combined radiation therapy and chemotherapy (5-FU, methyl CCNU). Survival comparisons at 10 years show a twofold improvement in survival for combined therapy versus the control. A postoperative combined modality compared with radiation alone decreases local recurrence by half and decreases systemic failure by one third (GITSG, 1985). Acute toxicity of the combined modality arm was more intense than the others, but late toxicity did not increase. The Mayo/North Central Cancer Treatment Group conducted a two-arm trial comparing postoperative radiation alone versus combined chemo/radiation. After surgery in the chemo/radiation arm, 5-FU and methyl CCNU were given as the initial treatment with radiation and concurrent 5-FU (deferred for 8 weeks), followed by a final cycle of 5-FU and methyl CCNU. As with the GITSG study, a significant reduction in local recurrence was seen in the combined modality arm versus surgery alone (O'Connell et al., 1996).

Long-term toxicity profiles and proven lack of benefit in one randomized trial suggest that methyl CCNU does not contribute to the improved results seen in combined modality trials (O'Connell et al., 1994). Therefore, methyl CCNU is no longer used in the adjuvant treatment of rectal cancer. A recent trial indicated superiority of protracted venous infusion of 5-FU over bolus 5-FU when given concurrently with radiation. Although continuous-infusion 5-FU shows a significant decrease in the overall rate of tumor relapse, distant metastasis, and improvement in survival compared with bolus, the toxicity profiles of continuous infusion and bolus 5-FU are different (Coia & Moylan, 1994; Minsky, 1997). Patients receiving combined modality treatment and continuous infusion of 5-FU reported a significant increase in grade 3+ diarrhea; however, leukopenia was reported as a 3+ decrease compared with bolus 5-FU. If 5-FU is used as a single agent with radiation therapy, the data suggest that it is more effective administered continuously than by bolus (Minsky, 1997). Current trials are investigating issues addressing the optimal mode of combining 5-FU and radiation, the effects of biochemical modulation of 5-FU by leucovorin, and the use of 5-FU, levamisole, and leucovorin with radiation (Coia & Moylan, 1994).

PREOPERATIVE RADIATION THERAPY FOR RECTAL CANCER MANAGEMENT

The advantages of administering radiation therapy preoperatively for patients with rectal cancer include the following: a decreased chance of tumor seeding at the time of surgery; increased cell sensitivity to radiation due to improved oxygenation; lack of small bowel adherence in the pelvis; the ability to change the operation from an abdomino-perineal resection to a sphincter-sparing low anterior resection (LAR) or coloanal anastomosis; and an increase in the resectability rate (Minsky, 1997). A major disadvantage may be the possibility of overtreatment. This rare occurrence may be avoided by the use of advanced diagnostic procedures that identify precise tumor location and avoid the possibility of excessive intervention. Randomized trials of preoperative radiation for rectal cancer treatment showed improved local control but not improved survival. These trials did not use adequate radiation doses, and the time interval between completion of radiation and surgery was too short; no attempt was made to minimize the amount of small bowel in the treatment field; and the radiation techniques were suboptimal and, hence, responsible for an increase in complications (Minsky, 1997). Although the randomized trials had inadequacies, the overall results indicated a significant decrease in local recurrence with the use of preoperative radiation therapy.

For patients with operable rectal cancer, the rationale for preoperative radiation therapy has been to provide sphincter preservation. Preoperative radiation therapy provides sphincter preservation in approximately 80% of patients who were prospectively examined and declared to need an abdominoperineal resection. Of those 80%, approximately 75% to 80% have good to excellent sphincter function. Additional data are needed regarding the long-term efficacy and functional results of this treatment sequence (Minsky, 1997).

Preoperative combined modality treatment including radiation therapy and chemotherapy is increasingly used for patients with both resectable and locally advanced/unresectable disease. Patients with recurrent, unresectable, and locally advanced disease have a poorer prognosis. Therefore, it is important to attempt to provide long-term local control if possible. The advantages of chemoradiation combined preoperatively rather than chemotherapy alone include the potential to make an unresectable lesion resectable; sphincter preservation; prompt administration of systemic treatment; and the ability to tolerate higher doses of radiation with less toxicity (Minsky, 1997). Patients with locally advanced or unresectable rectal cancer are currently treated preoperatively with radiation with or without chemotherapy.

If local excision and radiation therapy can be done, an improved quality of life can be provided. Sphincter-preserving surgery is a more desirable procedure for long-term function than abdominoperineal resection. Local excision can be performed alone for T1 tumors or in combination with radiation and chemotherapy for T2 and above tumors. Clinical research continues to evolve regarding conservative therapy for low-lying rectal lesions. Preoperative chemoradiation followed by a sphincter-sparing procedure such as resection and coloanal anastomosis remains under investigation. This intervention may be useful for tumors that are too advanced for local excision and/or radiation (Coia & Moylan, 1994).

Radiation is only moderately effective in palliating obstructive symptoms associated with colorectal cancer. High radiation doses are required for palliation (greater than 50 Gy). Pain is decreased in 80% of patients irradiated, although only 20% report relief. Bleeding is controlled in greater than 70% of all patients. Surgical resection and/or diversion, with formation of colostomy to divert feces are, therefore, the most effective means of palliating obstructive symptoms. Recurrent rectal cancers can be controlled palliatively in about 15% of patients treated with radiation with a median survival of less than 2 years. Additionally, laser treatment may be effective in controlling rectal bleeding and reducing pain. If patients have mobile, less advanced pelvic recurrences, surgical resection may be superior to radiation for palliation (Coia & Moylan, 1994).

The standard dose of radiation for rectal cancer is 50 Gy to 54 Gy. A three- or four-field treatment technique is used, and, after achieving 45 Gy to 50 Gy, a cone down (specific tumor targeting with the radiation beams) is used. It is clinically possible to use a higher dose of radiation up to 60 Gy for patients with unresectable or locally ad-

vanced disease. The radiation treatment field for rectal cancer includes the tumor and surrounding local and regional lymph nodes. The planning is often done with the use of a CT scan simulator, which enhances the view of the rectum and adjacent structures. Contrast may be inserted through a catheter into the rectum to further assist with visualizing key structures. It is imperative that the dose of radiation to the small bowel be minimized by utilizing a prone position for patient placement during treatment and treating patients with full bladders. Diminishing the amount of radiation received by the small bowel well lessens the toxicity profile associated with rectal radiation (Kelvin, 1997).

Chemotherapy as a Treatment Modality for Colorectal Cancer

The fluoropyrimidine antimetabolite 5-fluorouracil (5-FU) is the chemotherapeutic agent that provides the foundation for treatment of colorectal cancer. This agent was first synthesized in 1957 and continues to be effectively used to treat a variety of solid tumors. 5-FU is activated by intracellular metabolism and is similar to the analog agent fluoropyrimidine fluorodeoxyruidine (FUDR). When used to treat colorectal cancer, 5-FU is administered systemically and FUDR is delivered by an implantable pump to treat liver metastases (Fulton, 1994).

The biochemical actions of the fluoropyrimidines function to block synthesis of cellular DNA. This results in the continued production of RNA protein until an imbalance in cell growth occurs with resultant cellular death. Fluoropyrimidines are cell-cycle specific agents known as antimetabolites. They demonstrate their pharmacologic effect on the progression of cells through the cell cycle with activity centered during the S phase. Analogs of 5-FU have been found to become incorporated into DNA, which makes it more sensitive to the effects of radiation. For this reason, 5-FU is considered to be a radiation sensitizer and is often given during or before radiation treatment (Fulton, 1994).

The administration of additional drugs together with 5-FU may affect the metabolic function of this agent. These other drugs include methotrexate (and sodium methotrexate), leucovorin (known as calcium folinate or folinic acid), levamisole (an isomer of tetratramisole), and N-(phophonacetyl)-L-Aspartate disodium (PALA, also PALA disodium). Methotrexate administered immediately before 5-FU promotes the conversion of 5-FU to active drug. Timing of this event is critical because the effect only occurs if the sequence is maintained. Research data do not provide evidence that methotrexate with 5-FU is better than 5-FU alone, and studies are ongoing (Fulton, 1994).

Leucovorin provides intracellular reduced folates, which biomodulate 5-FU and enhance its activity. Studies have shown that both high and low doses of leucovorin combined with 5-FU are associated with longer survival time than 5-FU alone. 5-FU plus leucovorin is the most widely used chemotherapy combination in the United States for adjuvant treatment of metastatic colorectal cancer and has been and continues to be intensively studied (Fulton, 1994; Saltz & Kelsen, 1997). A review of various studies of 5-FU plus leucovorin in patients with metastatic colorectal cancer demonstrated the following clinical trends: response rates ranging from 7% to 58% were shown in patients who had not received prior chemotherapy; survival advantages; mild and transient hematologic toxicity associated with leucovorin plus 5-FU; and gastrointestinal toxicities were most common and resolved within a few days. This review found that leucovorin plus 5-FU provides a favorable treatment regimen for people with metastatic colorectal cancer. Response rates may be affected by altering the dose and schedule of both of these agents. It has been suggested that continued study of leucovorin plus 5-FU take place to determine optimal dosing regimens (Machover, 1997).

Another drug combination of 5-FU and levamisole has improved disease-free survival time. Levamisole is a synthetic anthelminthic agent (anti-worm) primarily used in veterinary medicine to treat intestinal parasites. In the early 1980s, the combination of 5-FU and levamisole was used as an effective postoperative adjuvant regimen. The exact mechanism of levamisole is unknown; however, it is thought to enhance 5-FU's antitumor activity against human colon cancer in a dose-dependent manner. This agent may inhibit tyrosine phosphatases in tumor cells (Diaz-Canton & Pazdur, 1997). Levamisole given alone is ineffective

and, therefore, must be used in combination with 5-FU to achieve antitumor effect.

A tolerable and resolvable toxicity profile is associated with postoperative 5-FU plus levamisole. Side effects associated with levamisole alone include altered taste, arthralgias, and associated myalgias. Side effects associated with the combination of agents include diarrhea, stomatitis, nausea, vomiting, dermatitis, leukopenia, hepatic toxicity (abnormal elevation of liver function tests or fatty infiltration of the liver), and neurotoxicity (Vaughn & Haller, 1997b).

Research has compared 5-FU plus leucovorin with 5-FU plus levamisole in an attempt to document the differences between the regimens and to identify the superior one. In a large trial comparing these regimens, no significant difference was found for disease-free survival for patients with B or C stage colon cancer (Wolmark, Rockette, Mamounas et al., 1996). Research remains ongoing in an attempt to identify the most appropriate dosing schedules, while limiting the toxicity profiles.

Adjuvant therapy is the use of treatment with no evidence of measurable disease. Adjuvant chemotherapy is used after primary surgical treatment to treat micrometastases. Micrometastatic tumors are sensitive to chemotherapy because they have a rich vascular supply, a high growth fraction, and are less drug-resistant (Fulton, 1994). Colorectal cancers that extend through the bowel wall or involve local lymph nodes tend to recur with distant metastases. Early attempts to improve surgical cure rates by adding adjuvant chemotherapy postoperatively failed to demonstrate any significant advantage for adjuvant therapy compared with control patients who were treated with surgery alone. Recent research including 5-FU with other chemotherapy agents has still not shown a therapeutic benefit. The one area of clinical promise is the use of 5-FU with biochemical modulators such as leucovorin and levamisole. Adjuvant therapy for patients with Dukes B and C colorectal cancer has been designated as beneficial although still controversial. To demonstrate the significance of this, the National Cancer Institute does not sanction clinical trials with observation-only arms; an adjuvant treatment option is a mandatory requirement for all submitted studies (Fulton, 1994).

Local Regional Treatment Strategies

Portal Vein Infusion of Chemotherapy

Adjuvant portal vein infusion of chemotherapy using 5-FU is based on the rationale that, at surgery, tumor cells have the propensity to embolize the portal venous system and may seed the liver. The liver is the most common and often the only site of colon metastases. Direct infusion of chemotherapy into the liver may be advantageous because higher dose intensity for known metastases and for micrometastases can be achieved. The liver may be the only site of recurrence in 25% of patients who develop metastatic colorectal carcinoma. The delivery of chemotherapeutic agents directly into the portal vein may impede the development of micrometastatic disease. A recent analysis of ten randomized trials of adjuvant portal vein infusion therapy involving more than 4000 patients confirmed a significantly lower mortality for those treated with portal vein infusion with 5-FU (Gray, 1997).

Intraperitoneal Chemotherapy Administration

An additional local-regional treatment strategy involves the administration of 5-FU directly into the peritoneal cavity. The peritoneal cavity is drained by a chain of lymphatics directly into the portal veins. Intraperitoneal (IP) chemotherapy should deliver high concentrations of drug through the portal vein to directly treat early hepatic metastases and potential peritoneal metastases. This administration route has been used to treat ovarian cancer patients postoperatively for remaining small-volume residual disease. IP-administered drugs are cleared from the peritoneal region by the portal vein, and this results in lower systemic concentrations and less toxicity. IP administration provides a significantly higher (up to ten times) drug concentration than the systemic route, as well as prolonged (up to 8 hours) tumoricidal drug dose in the abdominal cavity (Saltz & Kelsen, 1997). Clinical experience using IP chemotherapy remains limited. Studies have demonstrated ease of patient tolerance and a low toxicity profile; however, emphasis should be placed on documenting a significant decline in the development of hepatic metastases, and only preliminary data exist from small studies to support this finding. IP 5-FU chemotherapy administration must be continued to be studied using longer time frames and large controlled trials (Casillas, Pelley, & Milsom, 1997; Fulton, 1994; Saltz & Kelsen, 1997).

Immunotherapy as Adjuvant Treatment for Colorectal Cancer

Immune-mediated adjuvant treatment approaches to treat colorectal cancer have been investigated. These approaches include the administration of monoclonal antibodies to attack tumor cells and attempts to stimulate antibody production through the use of vaccines. Targeting small micrometastases that arise after primary surgical intervention may facilitate the ability of monoclonal antibodies and antitumor vaccines to penetrate the tumor. Preclinical trials have shown a potential mechanism of interaction between 5-FU and recombinant interferon alfa-2a. Studies incorporating 5-FU plus leucovorin with or without rINF alfa-2a are pending (Casillas et al., 1997). Toxicity profiles were extreme, including severe mucositis and diarrhea. Colorectal cancer cells may have the potential to be targeted with antibodies during the early postoperative phase; continued research is indicated.

The use of an autologous tumor vaccine Bacillus Calmette-Guerin (BCG) as an adjuvant regimen for colon cancer treatment has been studied in recent trials. Patients receiving an autologous vaccine postoperatively demonstrated improved survival compared with those treated with surgery alone. These studies have been small with faulty designs; a large, well-designed, prospective study of the effect of BCG vaccine plus 5-FU plus levamisole is ongoing (Casillas et al., 1997).

Immunotherapy as a treatment approach for advanced colorectal cancer holds tremendous promise due to enhanced understanding of tumor proliferation and the importance of prompt adjuvant treatment in the postoperative setting.

Chemotherapy for Recurrent Disease

The desire to improve the therapeutic response profile of 5-FU so that overall survival is enhanced includes modification of route, dose, and schedule.

Continuous intravenous infusion of 5-FU has been enabled with the use of refined central venous access devices and ambulatory infusion pumps. Infusion schedules may vary from days to months and will allow higher total doses with fewer side effects. A variety of clinical trials are attempting to validate the most therapeutic regimen for 5-FU and modulating agents. Some schedules offer 5-FU daily for 5 days by peripheral or central intravenous access, repeating the course every 5 weeks; some schedules combine a modulating agent such as varying doses of intravenous leucovorin.

Drug doses vary, ranging from 5-FU 200 to 2600 mg/m^2/day (2600 mg/m^2/day is a one-time dose that is not repeated for a few weeks due to toxicity issues) and leucovorin ranging from 20 to 500 mg/m^2/day. Randomized clinical trials aim at identifying the most therapeutic dose. Patients receiving adjuvant treatment or those with recurrent disease benefit by clinical trial data that identify the most effective schedule, dose, and route.

Hepatic metastases are usually refractory to treatment. Hepatic artery infusion is most effective if surgical resection of the lesions is possible. FUDR is the agent given through a surgically implanted infusion pump. The catheter of the pump is surgically threaded into the gastroduodenal artery, and the pump is placed in a subcutaneous abdominal wall pocket. Chemical hepatitis and biliary stenosis can occur as the major hepatic effects. Both are reversible once the FUDR is discontinued. Biliary stenosis precludes continued therapy; however, FUDR can be continued in an attenuated dose once the hepatitis has resolved (Fulton, 1994).

In an attempt to improve the efficacy of 5-FU, prolonged venous infusion (PVI) is used as an alternative to biochemical modulation. In advanced colorectal cancer, phase III trials have shown improved response rates for PVI compared with bolus administration of 5-FU. PVI 5-FU treatment may demonstrate similar response rates to 5-FU plus leucovorin. Studies of PVI versus bolus dosing are ongoing in an attempt to identify the most clinically effective approach (Vaughn & Haller, 1997b).

New Agents

The fluoropyrimidine family of drugs has been used to treat colorectal cancer for over 40 years. When 5-FU was first used, it was given as a single, rapidly administered intravenous injection. Over-all results with this agent have been marginal, producing low response rates of brief duration with little impact on survival. 5-FU continues to be widely used but with alteration of dosing schedules, varied routes of administration, and in combination with biochemical modulators and other chemotherapeutic agents. The development of new agents has focused on stronger inhibitors of thymidylate synthase (TS), which may have the capacity to show encouraging results (Isacoff & Borud, 1997).

Tomudex (ZD1694) is a quinazoline that is a potent inhibitor of TS. Trials have demonstrated that this agent has significant single-agent activity in metastatic colorectal cancer, comparable to results seen with 5-FU plus leucovorin (Vaughn & Haller, 1997b). Tomudex converts into polyglutamate form, which is a cellular component that is 100 times more potent as an inhibitor of TS. Dose-limiting toxicities are diarrhea and myelosuppression. Comparison between tomudex and standard 5-FU plus leucovorin showed similar safety and efficacy (Isacoff & Borud, 1997).

Trimetrexate is categorized as a nonclassic folate antagonist. This agent is similar to methotrexate; however, the differences are distinct: trimetrexate enters the cell differently than methotrexate; it is completely active as the parent compound; it may have activity against cancers resistant to methotrexate; and it has a different spectrum of pharmacologic activity than methotrexate (Isacoff & Borud, 1997). During phase II testing, trimetrexate was administered by a brief intravenous infusion daily for 5 days. Myelosuppression was the most common side effect, and nonhematologic toxicity was minimal. Preclinically, trimetrexate has been shown to enhance the cytotoxicity of 5-FU plus leucovorin. This agent will be tested in phase III trials as sequential trimetrexate, 5-FU, and leucovorin against 5-FU and leucovorin (Isacoff & Borud, 1997).

Irinotecan hydrochloride, also known as CPT-11 or camptothecin (camptosar), was the first new drug to treat metastatic colorectal cancer refractory to 5-FU to be approved by the FDA in 40 years. Irinotecan is a semisynthetic topoisomerase I inhibitor, which is a new class of chemotherapeutic agents. Topoisomerase I is a nuclear enzyme responsible for controlling and modifying DNA during replication and translation of genetic materials. Topoisomerase I enables the DNA to unravel or uncoil, which causes breaks that relieve the tension along the replicating DNA helix. The topoisomerase I inhibitor compounds stabilize the DNA breakage and interfere with the resealing process. This results in permanent breakage of the replicating DNA and eventual cell death (Berg, 1998).

Irinotecan shows consistent clinical activity in advanced refractory colorectal cancer. The starting dose is 125 mg/m^2 as a weekly infusion for 4 weeks, followed by a 2-week rest. Most common side effects are diarrhea, neutropenia, and nausea and vomiting as well as alopecia and fatigue. The side effects are reversible and manageable with dose attenuation. Many phase II studies using CPT-11 in patients with advanced colorectal carcinoma have reported response rates that range from 14% to 32% (Isacoff & Borud, 1997). Additionally, CPT-11 has activity in previously untreated patients. Irinotecan is being studied as combination regimens with 5-FU to determine future application in the adjuvant setting (Vaughn & Haller, 1997b).

UFT is a new agent that is a combination of tegafur, a 5-FU prodrug, and ruacil, an agent that inhibits the degradation of 5-FU. Phase II studies of UFT plus oral leucovorin showed activity in advanced colon carcinoma similar to that with 5-FU plus leucovorin. The oral regimen of UFT is associated with less mucositis and neutropenia and less morbidity related to side effects of the intravenous 5-FU regimen.

Additional new agents, such as capecitabine, UFT, and tomudex, which are classified as 5-FU prodrugs, are being studied in phase III trials in metastatic colorectal cancer comparing these agents with intravenous 5-FU plus leucovorin regimens. These agents may be incorporated into future adjuvant therapy trials.

Combination Chemotherapy

Combination chemotherapy regimens have been successfully administered to treat a variety of malignancies. Several combined regimens have been used to treat colorectal cancer. The first regimens incorporated 5-FU, methyl-CCNU, and vincristine (MOF). When this regimen was compared with 5-FU alone, it was found that MOF had a higher response rate, however, of shorter duration and without an impact on median survival (Isacoff & Borud, 1997).

Many trials have combined several alkylating-type drugs to bolus 5-FU and were unable to identify a single combination that had a survival advantage compared with 5-FU alone. Cisplatin has recently been added to 5-FU because cisplatin has shown in vitro synergy with 5-FU. Despite this synergy, little advantage was demonstrated with 5-FU and cisplatin compared with 5-FU alone. Cisplatin was therefore abandoned as a potential effective agent for colorectal cancer.

Oxaliplatin is a new drug with a different spectrum of activity than that of cisplatin and has shown increased activity against colorectal cancer. Although oxaliplatin is a platinum-based compound, it does not have the typical toxicity profile associated with platinum-based compounds. Oxaliplatin can be combined with 5-FU and leucovorin given by circadian infusion and has demonstrated an unusually high rate of objective response (58%) with 3-year survival at 17%. Oxaliplatin has been approved in France and is currently undergoing registration procedures at the European and American agencies (Levi, Zidani, & Misset, 1997).

Chemotherapeutic Treatment of Rectal Cancer

The rectum is the portion of the large bowel below the peritoneal reflexion. Tumors at or below the peritoneal reflexion are treated as rectal tumors. Several randomized trials have demonstrated that patients with either full-thickness tumor involvement of the rectal wall (B2) and/or node-positive disease (C) have improved local control and survival rates when treated with adjuvant chemotherapy plus pelvic radiotherapy. Active trials are planning to clarify the appropriate chemotherapy agents and radiation schedules for adjuvant treatment of rectal cancer. Trials compare different combinations of agents, different methods of administration and varied dosing schedules. Preoperative radiation and chemotherapy as neoadjuvant treatment for locally advanced rectal cancer have recently gained clinical utility. Similar agents used for colon cancer are invoked for rectal cancer treatment. Side-effect profiles and patient management issues are similar (Saltz & Kelsen, 1997).

The major treatment approaches for colorectal cancer include surgery, radiation therapy, and chemotherapy. These modalities have evolved in recent decades to a higher degree of sophistication, which has enabled improved methods of treatment delivery systems to enhance patient outcomes. The observation in the early 1990s that postsurgical adjuvant 5-FU plus levamisole lessened tumor recurrence and increased overall survival in stage III colon cancer realized the potential for adjuvant treatment. Continued queries surrounding agent dosing, schedules, and mode of administration are vital to improve disease control and ultimately effect survival. Combined modality postoperative pelvic irradiation and chemotherapy for stage II and III rectal cancer has been shown to reduce both local and systemic recurrences and to prolong survival compared with patients treated with only local surgery and radiation. Rectal cancer surgery continues to be refined, and the ability to preserve sphincter control has borne this out. New agents with proven efficacy in refractory disease are now approved and are being used. Continued research of the biochemical modulation of 5-FU as well as the use of immunotherapy to treat colorectal cancer brings the promise of sound scientific research to the bedside. The goal of improving overall survival while maintaining minimal toxicity profiles must continue to be prioritized. Clinical research will continue to examine the impact of this disease on quality of life, pharmacoeconomics, and genetic correlates.

Nursing Management of Patients With Colorectal Cancer

The interventions required to care for the patient with a diagnosis of colorectal cancer are varied and complex. The treatment course of these people involves many levels of care, and associated decision-making processes can be difficult for patients and caregivers who may have little prior experience with health care issues. It is essential that the nursing team caring for these patients be committed to the integration of patient involvement. Nursing interventions must begin at the prediagnosis stage and continue throughout the disease trajectory. Nursing interventions must be carefully crafted to include prevention and early detection strategies; minimizing the incidence and severity of side effects associated with treatment options; monitoring complications related to the diagnosis and treatment course; developing a practical and clinically sound follow-up regimen; promoting self-care skills for patients and caregivers; and establishing educational guidelines about colorectal cancer. Additionally, an evaluation plan for all nursing interventions must be created to document and, hence, validate professional nursing practice outcomes.

Prediagnosis Stage Interventions

Prevention and early detection programs are integral to the identification of populations at risk for developing colorectal cancer. Nursing interventions should include instructing people about familial risks associated with colorectal cancer; recommending screening guidelines for high-risk populations; suggesting lifestyle modifications to minimize risk; and recognizing early signs and symptoms of colorectal cancer. Professional nursing interventions related to prevention and detection of colorectal cancer can be performed at health fair screenings, during community programs, and in both ambulatory and acute care settings. It is vital that nursing's voice be heard at the prediagnosis phase so colorectal cancer is detected at earlier, less virulent stages and that, ultimately, consensus forms regarding the value of prevention and early detection methods for the public.

Interventions to Minimize the Incidence and Severity of Treatment-Related Side Effects

Treatment for colorectal cancer often requires a multimodality approach, and, therefore, nursing interventions must focus on each component of the treatment plan. Interventions should be supported by effective rationale and comprehensive educational support mechanisms.

Nursing Interventions for the Surgical Patient

Surgical preparation for patients having bowel resections requires nursing intervention at three phases: preoperative, immediately postoperative, and long-term postoperative. Preoperative teaching must focus on preparing the bowel for surgery, and instructions usually involve ingestion of a low-residue, liquid diet; antibiotic prophylaxis; and administration of cleansing enemas. Scrupulous bowel preparation is indicated to clear the bowel of fecal material, which lowers the risk of infection and provides as clean a bowel as possible for surgery. Preoperative teaching must also include highlighting the surgical routine and hospital environment to minimize fear and anxiety of the unknown. Patients should be given information that supports the informed consent process given by the surgical team. This information should include care in an acute care setting and possibly in an intensive care unit. Preoperative teaching should be aimed at prevention of postoperative complications such as: *pulmonary*—the need to use incentive spirometry, and requirement to cough, turn, and deep-breathe; *thrombus*—use of compression boot, and subcutaneous heparin; *bowel*—NG drainage, diet progression; *fluid balance*—Foley catheter, IV hydration; *transfusion*—potential need for support of blood products (Spencer-Cisek, 1996). Additionally, patients should be prepared preoperatively for the type, size, and location of surgical incision so both abdominal and perineal wounds are explained. Patients and family members should be told the estimated length of the surgical procedure, when they can communicate with the surgical team, and the expected hospital stay.

An important aspect of preoperative teaching for colorectal surgery must focus on the formation of a colostomy if one is planned. Patients must first know whether the colostomy will be permanent or temporary. A temporary colostomy may have a single stoma and will look differently than a double-barrel stoma. The location of the stoma will determine the type of output. Ileostomy produces liquid output; transverse stoma produces semisolid output; and a descending stoma produces solid output. Stoma location is identified preoperatively to decrease the incidence of skin reactions. The stoma site should be marked approximately 2 inches below the waist and away from leg creases, bony prominences, deep skinfolds, scars, fistulas, and pendulous breasts. A minimum of 2 inches of smooth skin should surround the stoma to provide appliance adherence. The stoma

site should be marked while the client is in a variety of positions, including lying flat, sitting, standing, and bending. This facilitates daily management while dressing, when emptying the appliance, and during equipment changes. The stoma site should be marked within the borders of the rectus muscles to minimize the risk of herniation and prolapse.

Appliance selection for the stoma depends on the character of the stool, the contour of the surrounding skin, the ability of the patient to manage equipment, and the associated costs. Typical stoma care involves:

- Weekly appliance changes
- Applying skin barrier paste and powder (such as Stomahesive and Karaya powder)
- Avoiding the use of irritating or ill-fitting skin products or appliances
- Routine assessment of stoma and surrounding skin for irritation such as erythema, edema, erosion, bleeding stoma protrusion, retraction, herniation, or narrowing (Strohl, 1998)

Common problems associated with ostomy management include the control of odorous gas due to offensive food. It is recommended to avoid ingestion of gaseous foods and to utilize charcoal and odor-absorbing appliance pouches.

An enterostomal therapy nurse is an integral part of the team managing the patient with colorectal cancer. This nurse specialist provides preoperative and postoperative support and education. The enterostomal nurse will assess the patient's preoperative physical and emotional needs. This individual will measure the patient for stoma placement and will begin to educate the patient regarding appliance choice and use. Patients facing ostomy procedures must be supported psychosocially and assessed for coping skills and the potential for anticipatory grieving associated with alteration of body image. Patients and families must be given information regarding support groups where they can gain confidence by establishing a "buddy" system. Patient and family skills in ostomy management must be continuously assessed during the postoperative recovery phase and within the home environment. The cost of supplies can be unaffordable to the majority of patients, especially if they do not have health care reimbursement plans. Medicare reimburses for supplies on a quota basis; therefore, proper use must be encouraged to avoid unnecessary waste and a potential shortage.

Postoperative nursing interventions for patients having colorectal surgery should include the monitoring of postoperative complications.

- Obstruction or paralytic ileus: typical signs are pain, constipation, diarrhea, nausea, vomiting, or abdominal distention
- Bleeding: monitor pulse rate, respiratory rate, blood pressure, amount and color of wound and/or stoma drainage
- Infection: fever, pain, redness at incision site, edema, or changes in amount or color of wound drainage
- Ostomy complications: retraction, protrusion onto the abdomen, narrowing of opening, herniation, drainage from fistulous tracts around stoma, discoloration of the stoma
- Change in sexual function: males may experience retrograde ejaculation and erectile failure due to nerve severing. Females are more difficult to assess but may experience dyspareunia, foreshortened vaginal length, pain during sexual intercourse, fear of stool leakage, or vaginal dryness requiring lubricants and estrogen creams.

In the postoperative phase, patients must be monitored for return of bowel function by assessing bowel sounds, flatus, and stool production. Ability to tolerate oral intake is an indication of degree of bowel function (Strohl, 1998).

Postoperative colostomy management involves assessing the stoma for color and position. The stoma should be pink and moist, and the position should be without associated retraction, prolapse, narrowing, or hernia formation. Care of the peristomal skin must focus on providing an appropriately fitting appliance and utilizing effective skin barriers. Stoma size changes in the postoperative setting and shrinkage due to postoperative edema must be accounted for when adjusting appliance fit. Patient support is integral to adaptation in the postoperative phase. It is vital that the patient is given ample opportunity to discuss feelings and to evolve through a period of adjustment. The clinical goal is to provide ample demonstration and

written material so the patient's physical needs are met. Additionally, encouraging the promotion of self-care techniques with the assistance of a caregiver will provide invaluable support and acceptance during the crucial postoperative phase. Occasionally, nursing interventions require additional members of the health care team to help with patient participation and adaptation. It is important that appropriate referrals are made promptly to facilitate postoperative recovery.

Nursing Interventions for Patients Receiving Radiation Therapy to the Colon or Rectum

The side effects of radiation therapy to the pelvis include tenesmus, diarrhea, and dysuria. If chemotherapy is used during the course of radiation treatment, these toxicities can be enhanced. Patients receiving radiation therapy to the gastrointestinal tract must be closely monitored for the development of inflammation of the bowel or bladder, nausea, blood in the stool or urine, ulceration of the gastrointestinal mucosa with associated pain, necrosis, or changes in sexual activity due to inflammation of the perineal skin.

Nursing interventions during radiation therapy for colorectal cancer are aimed at controlling diarrhea, minimizing nausea, managing skin reactions, and creating adaptive skills to manage radiation-induced fatigue. Diarrhea can be controlled by providing antidiarrheal medications; promoting adequate hydration; and avoiding foods that may promote loose stool such as caffeine, milk, spicy or fried food, fresh fruits and fibrous vegetables. The nurse can suggest a diet that has foods that bind the gastrointestinal tract such as rice, potatoes, apple juice, and tea. Patients experiencing nausea should eat lightly before receiving treatment; ingest dry, bland food at frequent intervals; be provided antinausea medications (antiemetics); and be encouraged to use relaxation techniques.

The management of radiation-induced skin reactions in the treatment field causes tremendous discomfort. This typically occurs if the radiation field includes the perineum after A-P resections. The anatomic area of greatest sensitivity is the perianal region. Patients should be advised to use hydrophilic lubricants (Eucerin, Aquaphor, or Lubriderm) a few times daily; barrier ointments such as vitamin A and D or zinc oxide should be applied to protect the anal area if diarrhea begins; the perineal area should be cleansed with warm water and mild soap after each bowel movement; perfumed bath gels and foams should be avoided; and cotton underpants should be worn because they wick moisture and provide ventilation for damaged skin. Patients must be advised not to apply ointments before treatment. Ointments and creams can enhance the radiation rays and further excoriate the skin.

The exact mechanism of radiation-induced fatigue is unknown. It has been theorized that an increase in basal metabolic rate occurs during radiation treatment to eliminate toxic tumor by-products. Energy is required to repair damaged tissues and cells. The patient's energy reserves are often weakened from utilization for other physiologic and psychological needs. It has also been theorized that a relationship exists between radiation dose, field size, and degree of fatigue. For example, a patient who receives treatment to a deeply seated tumor with a large field at a high dose such as colorectal tumors is more susceptible to fatigue than a patient who receives smaller doses to a surface tumor with a smaller field (Behrend & Slivjak, 1996). Nursing interventions to manage fatigue related to radiation treatments involve thorough assessment of the duration and intensity of the fatigue; factors that enhance or diminish fatigue; patient's nutritional and emotional state; laboratory studies; the effect of fatigue on daily activities; and assessment of the patient's usual rest and sleep patterns. The information gleaned from this nursing assessment can provide invaluable material for the creation of interventions that balance rest and modified activity (Behrend & Slivjak, 1996).

It is important that patients are assured that the side effects associated with radiation therapy are reversible and occur usually within 10 days of beginning treatment and resolve within a few weeks of treatment cessation. The severity of radiation-related reactions is cumulative and dose dependent. It is important that patients be closely monitored throughout the treatment course and encouraged to report symptoms and seek support promptly.

Complications of radiation therapy may include proctitis, intestinal obstruction, stricture, and fistula. These may occur as late side effects 6 to 12 months after radiation. Conservative management with diphenoxylate, dipentim, and steroid or Rowasa enemas allows healing; laser treatment or colostomy may be required (Coia & Moylan, 1994). About 3% to 5% of all patients who receive radiation to the pelvis develop complications requiring hospitalization and operative treatment (DeCosse & Cennerazzo, 1997). Small bowel damage related to radiation treatment, which leads to obstruction or perforation, is seen in less than 5% of patients receiving 50-Gy pelvic irradiation. Patients who have had prior surgery or pelvic infection with large radiation doses or volumes are at greater risk. Refined surgical techniques excluding bowel from the pelvis, coupled with CT-simulated customized radiation treatment planning, decrease morbidity associated with radiation to the pelvis (Coia & Moylan, 1994).

Nursing Interventions for the Patient Receiving Adjuvant Chemotherapy for Colorectal Cancer

The patient receiving chemotherapy for colorectal cancer will receive a combination of chemotherapeutic agents that have proven benefit profiles that outweigh the risks. The major drugs used are 5-fluorouracil (5-FU), levamisole, leucovorin, interferon, cisplatin, vincristine, and methotrexate. Antineoplastic agents may be associated with anemia, neutropenia, diarrhea, nausea, altered taste, vomiting, and anorexia. Delay of chemotherapy may adversely affect survival, so agents such as erythropoietin and filgrastim are used when anemia or leukopenia occurs. Erythropoietin stimulates red blood cell production, and filgrastim is a granulocyte colony-stimulating factor that helps to decrease infection (DeCosse & Cennerazzo, 1997). The mild nausea and vomiting associated with 5-FU can be controlled by antiemetics.

If patients are receiving continuous-infusion 5-FU, stomatitis and mucositis can be a dose-limiting side effect that requires oral agents to control the buccal lesions. Frequent salt water saline mouthwash and topical anesthetics are used to promote cleanliness and facilitate swallowing. Occasional dose attenuation must occur to avoid superimposed infections.

Diarrhea associated with 5-FU administration can be mild to severe and is often worse if the patient is receiving combined radiation therapy. It is essential that the patient's metabolic state be closely monitored for potential imbalance. Antidiarrheals should be provided, and the treatment course should be modified if necessary.

Additional gastrointestinal symptoms associated with 5-FU and FUDR include mild nausea and vomiting controlled with antiemetics, epigastric burning, abdominal pain, cramping, and anorexia. These side effects can be effectively managed with agents such as Maalox or Mylanta, mild analgesics, antispasmodics, and appetite inducers. Peripheral neuropathies associated with vincristine are irreversible and dose limiting. Nephrotoxicity and ototoxicity associated with cisplatin must be closely monitored through laboratory studies and adequate hydration protocols during administration.

Nursing interventions for the patient receiving adjuvant chemotherapy must include the following: monitoring hematologic status; changing dietary habits to minimize the risk of diarrhea coupled with providing antidiarrheals; providing antiemetics as needed to control nausea and vomiting; and developing a thorough mouth care assessment regimen to avoid untoward side effects.

Nursing Interventions for the Patient With Persistent or Recurrent Colorectal Cancer

The patient with advanced colorectal cancer provides a special situation for nursing care to make a significant difference in the quality of life. Patients with advanced disease are fearful, angry, and depressed. Multiple issues must be addressed when interventions must be crafted with the goal of palliation is the primary focus.

Surgical palliation in advanced colorectal cancer must consider the patient's performance status, the goal of surgical resection, associated chronic illnesses, and risk–benefit ratio of survival or development of complications. Some patients require palliative surgery of the colon or upper rectum to control anemia associated with gastrointestinal blood loss or to prevent large bowel obstruction from a tumor expanding into the bowel lumen.

Radiation therapy to palliatively treat a bleeding rectal tumor will avoid an abdominoperineal resection and creation of a colostomy and will achieve cessation of bleeding. Partial hepatectomy or lung resection for metastasis can provide potential long-term survival (DeCosse & Cennerazzo, 1997). These surgical procedures must be carefully presented to the patients and families. An opportunity for discussion surrounding quality of life, survival, and benefit must be provided. Nurses can provide nonjudgmental environments and assist patients with decision making regarding surgical palliation for advanced colorectal disease.

Palliative radiation therapy is the treatment of choice for localized, symptomatic, recurrent colorectal cancer. If patients develop symptomatic metastases in the bone, brain, or presacral space, radiation therapy should be given. Radiation can effectively control the debilitating side effects associated with these metastases such as pain and bleeding. Palliative radiation is usually given as a short course over a brief time period and has little associated side effects.

Control of pain in the palliative setting of advanced colorectal cancer is vital to the patient's quality of life. In addition to radiation, which is the primary treatment for symptomatic pelvic and bone recurrence, orthopedic stabilization of pending fractures as well as analgesics also provide pain relief (DeCosse & Cennerazzo, 1997). Chronic malignant pain control should involve standard administration of morphine. Steroids and antidepressants may be added for additional effect. Stepwise increments are prescribed without an upper limit until pain is controlled. A morphine supplement may be provided for breakthrough pain. Nonsteroidal anti-inflammatory drugs used in conjunction with morphine provide an opioid dose-sparing effect. Ninety percent of patients can have pain control without the use of invasive procedures if these interventions are provided (DeCosse & Cennerazzo, 1997). Included in nursing interventions to manage pain must be a regimen to manage concomitant constipation. Opioids inhibit gastrointestinal motility, causing constipation. This side effect can be very painful and must be managed with the simultaneous administration of stimulant laxatives and stool softeners (DeCosse & Cennerazzo, 1997).

The patient with metastatic or recurrent colorectal cancer requires a nursing intervention plan that is highly individualized and addresses the patient's physical and psychological needs. The professional nurse should be responsible for coordinating the efforts of the entire health care team so that anticancer treatment can be provided and symptoms ameliorated.

Care Requirements Across the Continuum

The patient with a diagnosis of colorectal cancer requires the establishment of strong professional and personal support systems. These networks will enable the patient and family to navigate the health care system with the assurance that they will be receiving the best health care package offered. Comprehensive programs include the point at which the patient enters the health care setting, through the diagnostic and treatment phase, and ultimately to follow-up. It is a difficult and challenging task even for the most knowledgeable individual to enter an unknown system such as the hospital environment and proceed to access the appropriate resources. Patients and families must receive educational information about the planned treatment course and all of the concomitant available options. Education regarding the development of self-care measures will reduce the complications of the disease and its treatment.

Currently, a patient with a major diagnosis of colorectal cancer may enter the health care system and proceed through a diagnostic, therapeutic, and interventional course within a rapid time frame. Cost containment and conversion to managed health care systems are the reasons for shortened hospital stays, clinical pathway templates, and emphasis on ambulatory, home care, and hospice care. Because the patient with colorectal cancer usually requires a multimodality treatment approach, it is essential that professional nurses create the plans to provide these patients and their families with comprehensive knowledge regarding surgical management, chemotherapy regimens, and radiation treatment. Patient care must be coordinated across disciplines so that these people are referred to the appropriate groups of subspecialists in a timely fashion.

Patients and families must be aware of the personal demands that are required to successfully proceed with treatment. Additionally, a follow-up plan must be established at the time of entry into the health care setting so patients can plan ahead for future requirements associated with long-term treatment regimens and surveillance schedules. Patients should be given information about available resources that provide supportive literature for those with colorectal cancer:

- National Cancer Institute publications
- American Cancer Society, 1599 Clifton Road NE, Atlanta, GA 30329
- Support and education groups: I Can Cope, CanSurmount, Ostomy Clubs
- United Ostomy Association, 36 Executive Park, Suite 120, Irvine, CA 92714

Integral to a plan of care for patients with colorectal cancer is the ability to demonstrate patient competence in achieving self-care measures as well as patient satisfaction with the health care system and professionals providing their care. Nursing must focus on documenting the fine points of caring for this complicated patient population by creating comprehensive documentation systems, which will validate the care given and ultimately effect patient outcomes.

Summary

Colorectal cancer has been identified as the third leading cause of new cancer cases in 1999. Recent declines in incidence rates indicate tremendous progress in areas of prevention and early detection. The identified risk factors associated with the development of colorectal cancer, such as age, ethnicity, genetics, history of preexisting bowel disease, and diet, are being studied by researchers in an effort to continue to minimize human vulnerability for developing this serious disease.

Refined diagnostic techniques are enabling practitioners to identify the disease at earlier stages, which provides a broader opportunity for achieving cure and improved control. Additionally, treatment options have been refined and modified. Surgical techniques vary and focus on minimizing complications, using detailed preoperative tumor staging, performing fewer ostomies when possible, and providing sphincter-sparing procedures. Radiation therapy techniques have been customized to spare surrounding vital organs from receiving treatment while focusing on the site of tumor involvement, hence minimizing toxic side effects and maximizing tumor target volumes. The use of adjuvant chemotherapy has been researched, and various administration routes coupled with combination regimens have created new standards for treating colorectal cancer.

Indeed, all of these advances are creating a clinical milieu that demonstrates progress in the management of colorectal cancer. The ability to achieve long-term, durable cure has been demonstrated, along with the success of local disease control in clinical settings. It is vital that these patients be given every opportunity to choose treatment options that will afford them the best chance of cure or control. It is important that each case be individually evaluated and that nurses provide the impetus for medical science to continue to nurture its curiosity about this disease process so that research continues to be refined and translated into clinical practice for patient benefit.

REFERENCES

Ahnen, D. J. (1991). Genetics of colon cancer. *Western Journal of Medicine, 154,* 700–705.

American Cancer Society. (1999). *Cancer facts and figures— 1999.* Atlanta, GA: American Cancer Society.

American Cancer Society. (1990). 1989 survey of physicians' attitudes and practices in early cancer detection. *CA—A Cancer Journal for Clinicians, 40,* 77–101.

Amin, Z., Bown, S. G., & Lees, W. R. (1993). Local treatment of colorectal liver metastases: A comparison of interstitial laser photocoagulation (ILP) and percutaneous alcohol injection (PAI). *Clinical Radiology, 48,* 166.

Behrend, S., & Slivjak, A. (1996). Radiation therapy. In M. C. Liebman & D. Camp-Sorrell (Eds.), *Multimodal therapy in oncology nursing* (pp. 44–58). St. Louis: Mosby–Year Book.

Berg, D. (1998). Irinotecan hydrochloride: Drug profile and nursing implications of a topoisomerase I inhibitor in patients with advanced colorectal cancer. *Oncology Nursing Forum, 25*(3), 535–543.

Bertagnolli, M. M., Mahmoud, N. N., & Daly, J. M. (1997). Surgical aspects of colorectal carcinoma. *Hematology/Oncology Clinics of North America, 11*(4), 655–677.

Bodmer, W. F. (1994). Cancer genetics. *British Medical Bulletin, 50,* 517–526.

Boring, C. C., Squires, T. S., & Heath, C. W., Jr. (1992). Cancer statistics for African Americans. *CA—A Cancer Journal for Clinicians, 42,* 7–17.

Brandt, B. T., DeAntonio, P., Dezort, M. A., & Eyman, L. M. (1996). Hepatic cryosurgery for metastatic colorectal carcinoma. *Oncology Nursing Forum, 23*(1), 29–36.

Brown, S. C. W., Walsh, S., Abraham, J. S., & Sykes, P. A. (1991). Risk factors and operative mortality in surgery for

colorectal cancer. *Annals of the Royal College of Surgeons in England, 73,* 269–272.

Cappell, M. S., & Goldberg, E. S. (1992). The relationship between the clinical presentation and spread of colon cancer in 315 consecutive patients: A significant trend of earlier cancer detection from 1982 through 1988 at a university hospital. *Journal of Clinical Gastroenterology, 14*(3), 227–235.

Casillas, S., Pelley, R. J., & Milsom, J. W. (1997). Adjuvant therapy for colorectal cancer: Present and future perspectives. *Diseases of the Colon and Rectum, 40*(8), 977–992.

Chang, H. R., & Bland, K. I. (1997). Tumors of the colon. In M. J. Zinner (Ed.), *Maingot's abdominal operations* (Vol. II, pp. 1281–1308). Stamford, CT: Appleton & Lange.

Clayman, C. B. (1989). Mass screening for colorectal cancer: Are we ready? *Journal of the American Medical Association, 261,* 609.

Coia, L. R., & Moylan, D. J. (1994). *Introduction to clinical radiation oncology* (2nd ed.). Madison, WI: Medical Physics Publishing.

DeCosse, J. J., & Cennerazzo, W. J. (1997). Quality-of-life management of patients with colorectal cancer. *CA—A Cancer Journal for Clinicians, 47*(4), 198–206.

DeCosse, J. J., Tsioulias, G. J., & Jacobson, J. S. (1994). Colorectal cancer: Detection, treatment, and rehabilitation. *CA—A Cancer Journal for Clinicians, 44,* 27–42.

Diaz-Canton, E. A., & Pazdur, R. (1997). Adjuvant medical therapy for colorectal cancer. *Surgical Clinics of North America, 77*(1), 211–225.

Eckhauser, F. E., & Knol, J. A. (1997). Surgery for primary and metastatic colorectal cancer. *Gastroenterology Clinics of North America, 26*(1), 103–127.

Eddy, D. M. (1990). Screening for colorectal cancer. *Annals of Internal Medicine, 113,* 373–384.

Enker, W. E., & Paty, P. B. (1993). Advances in rectal cancer surgery: The combined goals of curing cancer and reducing morbidity. In D. K. Andersen (Ed.), *Advances in Colorectal Carcinoma Surgery* (p. 33). New York: World Medical Press.

Ferrante, J. M. (1996). Colorectal cancer screening. *Medical Clinics of North America, 80*(1), 27–43.

Fulton, J. S. (1994). Chemotherapeutic treatment of colorectal cancer: Rationale, trends, and nursing care. *Journal of the Wound, Ostomy and Continence Nurses Society, 21*(1), 12–21.

Gastrointestinal Tumor Study Group (GITSG). (1985). Prolongation of the disease-free interval in surgically resected rectal cancer. *New England Journal of Medicine, 315,* 1294–1295.

Giovannucci, E., Egan, K. M., Hunter, D. J., Stampfer, M. J., Colditz, G. A., Willett, W. C., & Speizer, F. E. (1995). Aspirin and the risk of colorectal cancer in women. *New England Journal of Medicine, 333*(10), 609–614.

Giovannucci, E., Rimm, E. B., Stampfer, M. J., Colditz, G. A., Ascherio, A., Kearney, J., & Willett, W. C. (1994a). A prospective study of cigarette smoking and risk of colorectal adenoma and colorectal cancer in U.S. men. *Journal of the National Cancer Institute, 86,* 183–191.

Giovannucci, E., Rimm, E. B., Stampfer, M. J., Colditz, G. A., Ascherio, A., & Willett, W. C. (1994b). Aspirin use and the risk for colorectal cancer and adenoma in male health professionals. *Annals of Internal Medicine, 121*(4), 241–246.

Giovannucci, E., Stampfer, M. J., Colditz, G., Rimm, E. B., & Willett, W. C. (1992). Relationship of diet to risk of colorectal adenoma in men. *Journal of the National Cancer Institute, 84,* 91–98.

Goya, T., Miyazawa, N., Kondo, H., Tsuchiya, R., Naruke, T., & Suemasu, K. (1989). Surgical resection of pulmonary metastases from colorectal cancer: 10-year follow-up. *Cancer, 64,* 1418.

Gray, R. (1997). Portal vein in chemotherapy for colorectal cancer: A meta-analysis of 4000 patients in 10 studies. *Journal of the National Cancer Institute, 89*(7), 497–505.

Gruber, M. (1996). Performance of flexible sigmoidoscopy by a clinical nurse specialist. *Gastroenterology Nursing, 19*(3), 105–108.

Hammerhofer-Jereb, K. (1996, March). Laparoscopic bowel resection? *RN,* 22–25.

Hansen, C. (1995, January). Colorectal cancer: A preventable disease. *Physician Assistant,* 15–28.

Hobler, K. E. (1986). Colon surgery for cancer in the very elderly: Cost and 3-year survival. *Annals of Surgery, 203,* 129–131.

Hoebler, L. (1997). Colon and rectal cancer. In S. L. Groenwald, M. H. Frogge, M. Goodman, & C. H. Yarbro (Eds.), *Cancer nursing: Principles and practice* (4th ed., pp. 1036–1054). Boston: Jones & Bartlett.

Howe, G. R., Benito, E., Castelleto, R., Cornee, J., Esteve, J., Gallagher, R. P., Iscovich, J. M., Deng-ao, J., Kaaks, R., Kune, R. A., et al. (1992). Dietary make of fiber and decreased risk of cancers of the colon and rectum: Evidence from the combined analysis of 13 case-control studies. *Journal of the National Cancer Institute, 84*(24), 1887–1896.

Isacoff, W. H., & Borud, K. (1997). Chemotherapy for the treatment of patients with metastatic colorectal cancer: An overview. *World Journal of Surgery, 21,* 748–762.

Jessup, J. M., Menck, H. R., Fremgen, A., & Winchester, D. P. (1997). Diagnosing colorectal carcinoma: Clinical and molecular approaches. *CA—A Cancer Journal for Clinicians, 47*(2), 70–92.

Kelvin, J. F. (1997). Gastrointestinal cancers. In K. H. Dow, J. D. Bucholtz, R. Iwamoto, V. Fieler, & L. J. Hilderley (Eds.), *Nursing care in radiation oncology* (2nd ed., pp. 152–183). Philadelphia: W. B. Saunders.

Kim, E. C., & Lance, P. (1997). Colorectal polyps and their relationship to cancer. *Gastroenterology Clinics of North America, 26*(1), 1–17.

Landis, S. H., Murray, T., Bolden, S., & Wingo, P. A. (1998). Cancer statistics, 1998. *CA—A Cancer Journal for Clinicians, 48*(1), 6–29.

Levi, F., Zidani, R., & Misset, J.-L. (1997). Randomised multicentre trial of chronotherapy with oxaliplatin, fluorouracil, and folinic acid in metastatic colorectal cancer. *The Lancet, 350,* 681–686.

Levin, B. (1992). Ulcerative colitis and colon cancer: Biology and surveillance. *Journal of Cell Biochemistry* (Suppl. 16G), 47–50.

Lush, D. T. (1994). Screening for colorectal cancer. *Postgraduate Medicine, 96*(1), 99–106.

Macari, M., & Megibow, A. (1998, May 10). Virtual colonoscopy. *Philadelphia Inquirer.*

Machover, D. (1997). A comprehensive review of 5-fluorouracil and leucovorin in patients with metastatic colorectal carcinoma. *Cancer, 80*(7), 1179–1187.

Mahon, S. M. (1995). The impact of mailing fecal occult blood test kits on return rate in a community cancer screening center. *Oncology Nursing Forum, 22*(8), 1259–1263.

Mandel, J. S., Bond, J. H., Church, T. R., Snover, D. C., Bradley, G. M., Schuman, L. M., & Ederer, F. (1993). Reducing mortality from colorectal cancer by screening for fecal occult blood. *New England Journal of Medicine, 328*(19), 1365–1371.

Marcus, A. J. (1995). Aspirin as prophylaxis against colorectal cancer. *New England Journal of Medicine, 333*(10), 656–658.

Markowitz, A. J., & Winawer, S. J. (1997). Management of colorectal polyps. *CA—A Cancer Journal for Clinicians, 47*(2), 93–112.

Maule, W. F. (1994). Screening for colorectal cancer by nurse endoscopists. *New England Journal of Medicine, 330*(3), 183–187.

McGregor, J. R., & O'Dwyer, P. J. (1993). The surgical management of obstruction and perforation of the left colon. *Surgery Gynecology and Obstetrics, 177*(2), 203–208.

McMillan, S. C. (1996). Genetically linked cancers: Prevention, detection, and treatment. *Journal of Intravenous Nursing, 19*(6), 321–328.

Minsky, B. D. (1997). The role of adjuvant radiation therapy in the treatment of colorectal cancer. *Hematology/Oncology Clinics of North America, 11*(4), 679–697.

Morgan, G. (1997). Non-steroidal anti-inflammatory drugs in the treatment of colorectal cancer. *European Journal of Cancer, 33*(8), 1335–1336.

Nugent, F. W., Haggitt, R. C., & Gilpin, P. A. (1991). Cancer surveillance in ulcerative colitis. *Gastroenterology, 100,* 1241–1248.

O'Connell, M. J., Laurie, J. A., Shepherd, L., Kahn, M. J., Pazdur, R., Fitzgibbons, R. J., Erlichman, C., & Wieand, H. S. (1996). *A prospective evaluation of chemotherapy duration and regimen as surgical adjuvant treatment for high risk colon cancer: A Cancer Institute of Canada Clinical Trials Group.* Paper presented at the ASCO, Philadelphia.

O'Connell, M. J., Martenson, J. A., Weiand, H. S., Krook, J. E., Macdonald, J. S., Haller, D. G., Mayer, R. J., Gunderson, L. L., & Rich, T. A. (1994). Improving adjuvant therapy for rectal curative surgery. *New England Journal of Medicine, 331,* 502.

Parker, S. L., Tong, T., Bolden, S., & Wingo, P. A. (1996). Cancer statistics, 1996. *CA—A Cancer Journal for Clinicians, 46*(1), 5–27.

Payne, J. E., Chapuis, P. H., & Pheils, M. T. (1986). Surgery for large bowel cancer in people aged 75 years and older. *Diseases of the Colon and Rectum, 29*(11), 733–737.

Pazdur, R. (1994, April). Pitfalls, controversies and strategies. *Consultant,* 561–576.

Porrett, T. (1996). Extending the role of the stoma care nurse. *Nursing Standard, 10*(27), 35–37.

Saltz, L. B., & Kelsen, D. P. (1997). Adjuvant treatment of colorectal cancer. *Annual Review of Medicine, 48,* 191–202.

Spencer-Cisek, P. A. (1996). Lower gastrointestinal cancers. In M. C. Liebman & D. Camp-Sorrell (Eds.), *Multimodal ther-*

apy in oncology nursing (pp. 152–171). St. Louis: Mosby–Year Book.

Spiegel, T. (1995). Flexible sigmoidoscopy training for nurses. *Gastroenterology Nursing, 18*(6), 206–209.

Steele, G., Jr. (1991). Follow-up plans after treatment of primary colon and rectal cancer. *World Journal of Surgery, 15,* 583.

Strohl, R. A. (1998). Nursing care of the client with cancer of the gastrointestinal tract. In J. itano & K. Kaoka (Eds.), *A core curriculum for oncology nursing* (3rd ed., pp. 459–483). Philadelphia: W. B. Saunders.

Thomas, C. R., Jr., Gale, M., & Evans, N. (1990). *Racial differences in the incidence of colon and rectal cancer in patients under the age of forty.* Paper presented at the Third International Conference on Anticancer Research.

Toribara, N. W., & Sleisenger, M. H. (1995). Screening for colorectal cancer. *New England Journal of Medicine, 332*(13), 861–867.

Vaughn, D. J., & Haller, D. G. (1997a). Adjuvant therapy for colorectal cancer: Past accomplishments, future directions. *Cancer Investigation, 15*(5), 435–447.

Vaughn, D. J., & Haller, D. G. (1997b). The role of adjuvant chemotherapy in the treatment of colorectal cancer. *Hematology/Oncology Clinics of North America, 11*(4), 699–717.

Willett, C. G., Fung, C. Y., Kaufman, D. S., et al. (1993). Postoperative radiation therapy for high-risk colon cancer. *Journal of Clinical Oncology, 11,* 1112.

Willett, C. G., Tepper, J. E., Kaufman, D. S., et al. (1992). Adjuvant postoperative radiation therapy for rectal adenocarcinoma. *American Journal of Clinical Oncologists, 15,* 371.

Winawer, S. J., St. John, D. J., Bond, J. H., Rozen, P., Burt, R. W., Waye, J. D., Kronborg, O., O'Brien, M. J., Bishop, D. T., Kurtz, R. C., et al. (1995). Prevention of colorectal cancer: Guidelines based on new data. *Bulletin of the World Health Organization, 73*(1), 7–10.

Winawer, S. J., Zauber, A. G., Ho, M. N., O'Brien, M. J., Gottlieb, L. S., Sternberg, S. S., Waye, J. D., Schapiro, M., Bond, J. H., Panish, J. F., et al. (1993). Prevention of colorectal cancer by colonoscopic polypectomy. The National Polyp Study Workgroup. *New England Journal of Medicine, 329*(27), 1977–1981.

Wise Jr., W. E., Padmanabhan, A., Meesig, D. M., Arnold, M. W., Aguilar, P. S., & Stewart, W. R. (1991). Abdominal colon and rectal operations in the elderly. *Diseases of the Colon and Rectum, 34*(11), 959–963.

Wolf, R. F., & Cohen, A. M. (1997). The miniscule benefit of serial carcinoembryonic antigen monitoring after effective curative treatment for primary colorectal cancer. *Journal of the American College of Surgeons, 185,* 60–64.

Wolmark, N., Rockette, H., Mamounas, E., et al. (1996). The relative efficacy of 5-FU + Leucovorin (FU-LV), 5-FU + levamisole (FU-LEV), and 5-FU + leucovorin + levamisole (FU-LV-LEV) in patients with Dukes' B and C carcinoma of the colon. First report of NSABP C-04. *Proceedings of the American Society of Clinical Oncologists, 15,* 205.

Prostate Cancer

Gabriele Snyder

CHAPTER 7

Cancer of the prostate is the most common cancer diagnosed in men, excluding skin cancer, and the second leading cause of cancer death, exceeded only by lung cancer (Landis, Murray, Bolden & Wingo, 1998). The incidence of prostate cancer increases sharply after 60 years of age, so this cancer appears to be a function of aging. The age factor will be of particular significance in the next several decades as the population boom from the middle of the 20th century begins to approach its golden years. In 1998, an estimated 334,500 men will be diagnosed with prostate cancer and approximately 42,000 will die of the disease (Pienta, Sandler, & Wilson, 1998). Yet there is no universally agreed-upon strategic plan for its diagnosis and management. One factor that lends to the confusion is the slow growth of most prostate cancers, which leaves the majority of these men dying not of prostate cancer but rather with it. This, in the context of often devastating treatment-related side effects, makes the choice between exercising watchful waiting or treating a difficult one. What is known, though, is that if the disease is to be cured, it must be detected before it spreads outside the prostate gland. Unfortunately, less than half of men diagnosed with prostate cancer fall into this category.

The prostate gland is a small, firm, walnut-sized organ made up of glandular tissue and musculature, enclosed in a paper-thin fibrous capsule, through which the urethral tube passes as it exits the bladder. The gland is divided into three zones: the transition and central zones, which are closest to the urethra, and the peripheral or outermost zone, which is the area examined during digital rectal examination. The prostate is made up of two types of tissue: epithelial cells, which are glandular tissue, and the stromal cells, which are muscular connective tissue. The epithelial cells produce the prostate-specific antigen (PSA) detected in the PSA blood test. Epithelial cells are also responsible for secreting the chemicals that make up the prostate's contribution to the seminal fluid. Stromal cells are the connective tissue that gives structure to the epithelial cells. The stromal tissue also serves to contract and expel the glandular secretions. Figure 7-1 illustrates the anatomic relationships of the prostate.

Types of Prostate Cancer

Adenocarcinoma is, by far, the most common type of prostate cancer and arises from the epithelial cells (glandular) of the prostate. It accounts for approximately 95% of all prostate cancer cases (Davis, 1991; Figlin & deKernion, 1995). Although rare, other types of prostate cancer may arise from supporting or connective tissues within or surrounding the prostate, whereas others still develop in the ducts within the prostate. Over half of prostate cancers develop in the peripheral or outer part of the gland that lies closest to the rectum, just beneath the prostatic capsule. For this reason, rectal examination is important to detect the tumor. Cancers can also spread to the prostate

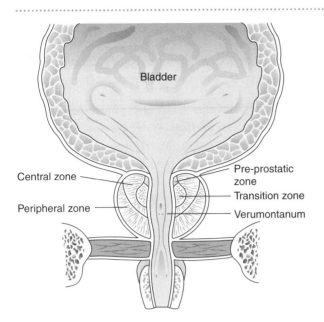

Figure 7-1 The zones of the prostate, cross-section forward view.

Central zone

Bladder

Peripheral zone

Pre-prostatic zone

Transition zone

Verumontanum

from other locations such as the bladder or adrenal gland (Zinner, 1991).

Risk Factors and Incidence

The exact cause of prostate cancer is not known, but there is strong evidence that age, hormones, and infectious agents play a role in its development. Age is the most prominent variable, with a peak incidence age of 70 years (Miller et al., 1993). Autopsy series indicate approximately 30% of men over 50 years old have incidental evidence of prostate cancer, and this incidence increases with age (Kassabian & Graham, 1995; Sheldon, Williams & Fraley, 1980). Based on these findings, it is estimated that 60% of men develop prostate cancer over time (Kantoff & McConnell, 1996). Although the hormonal role is not well understood, a definite relationship exists, evidenced by the successful manipulation of prostate cancer with testosterone-inhibiting hormonal agents. Literature also suggests that men who have had orchiectomies (testicles removed) before adolescence, so that male hormone testosterone was never produced, seldom develop prostate cancer. There are also findings that suggest workers in certain indus-

tries with infectious agents are at increased risk of developing and dying from prostate cancer, including those exposed to cadmium, tire and rubber manufacturing, farmers, mechanics, and sheet metal workers (Carter, 1989; LaVecchia, 1992).

Genetic factors are also suspected in the development of prostate cancer. A family history of a first-degree relative who has the disease, meaning a father or brother, increases the risk of prostate cancer twofold. Men with two first-degree relatives have a ninefold risk of developing the disease (Steinberg et al., 1998). Furthermore, patients with relatives who also have prostate cancer are up to three times more likely to die of the disease than those patients who do not have relatives with prostate cancer (Kantoff & McConnell, 1996). African-American men are at considerably higher risk of developing prostate cancer than non-black men, whereas Asian men have the lowest incidence (Landis et al., 1998).

Other linked risk factors for the development of prostate cancer are dietary fat, vasectomy, and a history of sexually transmitted diseases. Some studies have suggested that a diet high in fat, as with other types of cancer, may correlate with a higher risk of prostate cancer, although there is no definitive proof of this (LaVecchia, 1992). Other research suggests a relative increase in risk of 1.85% in men who have had a vasectomy. Again, this association is unproven. The association between sexually transmitted disease and its impact on risk of prostate cancer development needs to be studied further (Pienta, Sandler, & Wilson, 1998).

What remains to be studied is the environmental/behavioral impact on the development of prostate cancers and so many other neoplasms. The United States has one of the highest rates of prostate cancer incidence and prostate cancer death when compared with other countries. Although the literature is conflicting about whether prostate cancer rates are higher in rural or urban areas, the common denominator seems to be that of poverty and its associated behaviors and limitations, including lack of medical attention. Interestingly, research indicates that when men move from areas of low prostate cancer incidence (Japan, Africa) to areas of high incidence (USA), their rate of cancer occurrence increases to that of their new area. This finding points strongly to a cultural/behavioral correlation.

Most certain about prostate cancer development is what does not cause it. There is no conclusive evidence that prostate cancer is caused by excessive sexual activity, masturbation, prostatic stones, infection of the prostate, or benign prostatic hyperplasia (BPH). No relationship has been shown between prostate cancer and smoking, use of alcohol, disease patterns, circumcision, weight, height, blood group, hair distribution, sexual activity, or benign prostatic hyperplasia. Also, there are no known ways to protect against the development of prostatic cancer, so the best that can be accomplished is early detection through yearly screening.

Clinical Presentation

Symptoms are seldom present in the early stages of prostate cancer development, when it is the most curable. Symptoms, when they do occur, can be local or generalized. Local symptoms include painful or frequent urination, a sudden decrease in the size and force of the urinary stream, and/or blood in the urine. These are similar to the signs and symptoms of benign prostatic hyperplasia. Generalized symptoms relate to those resulting from prostate tumor spread such as to pelvic lymph nodes or bone. Prostate cancer is seldom curable once symptoms develop, and this fact serves as the best argument for early detection through preventive screening.

The diagnosis of prostate cancer is described in terms of its progression or stage of disease. The tumor stage refers to the size of and degree of spread of the tumor. The three broad stages include early stage, locally advanced stage, or advanced stage. Early stage prostate cancer means the cancer is completely confined to the prostate organ—that is, within the prostate capsule—and the patient is asymptomatic. These are diagnosed incidentally, following transurethral resection surgery for men with benign prostatic hypertrophy. These men have no other signs that distinguish these symptoms of BPH from early-stage, microscopic prostate cancer.

Locally advanced stage prostate cancer means the cancer has invaded a larger part of the prostate gland and possibly some surrounding tissue. Depending on the degree of spread and tumor encroachment, these men may present with bladder outlet obstruction. Some may exhibit hematuria, urinary tract infections, and irritative voiding symptoms.

Advanced-stage prostate cancer means the cancer has spread (metastasized) to distant body parts. These men may present with bulky lymph node invasion of cancer and/or spread of the cancer to bones. Lower extremity edema, although rare, may be present with pelvic lymph node invasion. Some men may present with lower extremity weakness or paralysis secondary to spinal cord compression by tumor spread. Bony metastases present with bone pain in the affected region. Common sites for bone metastasis include the back, hips, thighs, ribs, and shoulders. There may also be weight loss and fatigue as tumor growth progresses.

Spread of Prostate Cancer

The spread of prostate cancer occurs by way of the lymphatic system to pelvic lymph nodes and through the bloodstream to bones and other tissues. The earliest spread is often detected in the lymph nodes in the pelvis, near the prostate. Other areas of spread include lymph nodes surrounding the arteries and veins leading to the legs and pelvic organs, periaortic nodes, and occasionally even supraclavicular nodes. Bone spread is by way of the hematopoietic system to bones in the spine, legs, arms, ribs, and hips. It can ultimately reach almost any organ in the body, although spread to the lungs and liver is rare. The tumor may also spread directly throughout the prostate to surrounding tissues or may grow inward, obstructing the flow of urine.

Although the natural history of prostate cancer is disputed, data reveal that 75% of those with localized diagnosis will have local extension within 10 years, and 65% of these will die from cancer. Of those diagnosed with metastatic disease, 50% will die of the cancer within 3 years (Pienta, Sandler, & Wilson, 1998). If prostate cancer can be detected early, treatment can be effective with minimizing morbidity.

Diagnostic Workup

Prostate-Specific Antigen and Other Blood Tests

PSA testing has revolutionized prostate cancer screening. PSA is a serine protease produced exclusively by the prostatic epithelial cells and secreted in the seminal fluid in large quantities. Prostatic disease alters the cellular barriers that normally keep PSA within the ductal system of the prostate and, therefore, alters serum levels. The PSA may be increased in inflammation of the prostate (prostatitis), benign prostatic hypertrophy, prostatic calculus (stones), prostate cancer, and prostate manipulation. In general, digital rectal examination does not increase the PSA, although, if serial PSA levels are done, they should be collected before the digital rectal examination.

Measurement of PSA in tandem with digital rectal examination has greatly influenced early detection of prostate cancer, which may be one explanation for the dramatic increase in incidence rates over the last decade. Historically, when digital rectal examination was the only screening modality, 40% had metastatic disease at the initial time of diagnosis (Miller et al., 1993). In addition, when digital rectal examination alone was employed, approximately 30% of stage B (early) prostate cancers were pathologically upstaged to locally advanced (Kantoff & McConnell, 1996). PSA is interpreted in relation to age. It is known that as men age and the prostate enlarges, the PSA increases. Therefore, a slightly elevated PSA in a man over 70 years old is quite different from that in a man 50 years old.

What remains to be answered is whether early detection translates into better long-term outcomes and survival. Multicenter clinical trials are addressing just that question. Are increasing numbers of men receiving drastic treatments for disease that may be less than life threatening or, conversely, inevitably incurable? Also being studied is age-adjusted PSA. Current recommendations for screening are that annual DRE and PSA blood testing should begin in men at 50 years of age, and for those who are at high risk (black men, first-degree family history) at 40 years of age. The normal value for PSA is <4 ng/mL.

Digital Rectal Examination

A digital rectal examination (DRE) is a diagnostic procedure in which a practitioner palpates the prostate using a gloved finger inserted into the rectum (Figure 7-2). Digital rectal examination allows the palpation and examination by touch of the surface and texture of the prostate gland. The main finding during DRE is a lump, firmness, or irregularity in the prostate, which can be felt with the examining finger. The prostate may seem enlarged but can also be normal sized. Lending most to the index of suspicion is inconsistent contour and texture of the prostate during examination. In early cancer, it may feel like a nonraised, firm lesion that may have a sharp margin or edge (Lind & Irwin, 1991; Pasacreta & McCorkle, 1996). Other descriptions may include a cobblestone, rippled, or lumpy surface. Most easily detected are those lesions found in the posterior aspect of the prostate. Later stage prostate cancer may present as uniform firmness or an immobile prostate on palpation. In addition to a digital rectal examination, a complete history and physical examination should be performed to evaluate both the overall health status and any signs and symptoms of metastatic disease. If either PSA or DRE (or both) is abnormal, a transrectal ultrasound should be performed for further evaluation of the prostate.

Biopsy and Other Endoscopy

A transrectal needle biopsy is the removal of a small piece of the tumor for examination by a pathologist. Ultrasound is used to help guide the needle for accuracy of tumor location and needle placement for tissue biopsy. A spring-loaded biopsy gun with a cored needle is used for tissue sampling. When the spring-loaded biopsy gun is discharged, the needle pierces the tumor, packs a sample of tissue into the core of the needle, and automatically retracts back out of the tumor. Needle core biopsies are taken of any suspicious areas of lumpiness, hardening, or palpable nodules. Core biopsies are obtained from both lobes whether both or just one has a palpable abnormality. The same is true if the PSA is suspiciously elevated in the absence of visible or palpable disease. This biopsy procedure seldom requires anesthesia, although many men describe it as somewhat un-

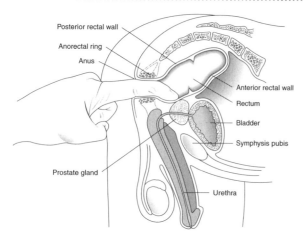

Posterior rectal wall

Anorectal ring

Anus

Anterior rectal wall

Rectum

Bladder

Symphysis pubis

Prostate gland

Urethra

Figure 7-2 Technique for palpation of the prostate gland.

comfortable. Symptoms of hematuria and hematospermia may persist for several days to weeks following a needle core biopsy.

A cystoscopy may be performed to provide a different view of the prostate anatomy because it allows movement and visualization of the prostate while it is being examined and manipulated with a finger in the rectum. In this way, the lump can be visualized from a number of angles. Furthermore, there is visualization of whether the lump has attached to adjacent tissues. Biopsies may also be obtained through the cystoscope.

Flow cytometry and nuclear shape analysis are tests used to evaluate the unique characteristics of the prostate cells removed by biopsy. Cancer cells tend to be less uniform than normal cells.

Imaging Studies

Transrectal ultrasound is performed to view the prostate by way of an internal transrectal probe. Ultrasonic sound waves are passed into the tissue and transformed into a visual image. Varying tissue density varies the wave pattern and thus the image. Ultrasound allows visualization of the size and contour of the prostate gland as well as tumor location. It can identify spread beyond the prostate capsule into surrounding structures and the integrity of the capsular surface. This procedure is used to guide transrectal prostate needle biopsy because the ultrasound image can identify the

exact location parameters for the tumor. If the tissue proves positive for cancer, further staging studies take place to determine the spread of the disease.

Magnetic resonance imaging (MRI) of the prostate may be considered when looking for tumor extension beyond the prostate. Many believe this is a more sensitive imaging technique than ultrasound for visualizing local spread of the disease. Using an endorectal coil, it is possible to visualize both the bone and soft tissue that surround the prostate gland.

Computer-enhanced tomography (CT) scanning is another imaging tool that is useful in identifying nonbony tissue disease in structures surrounding the prostate. It provides fairly detailed horizontal slice images of the body and produces much clearer images of soft tissue than do standard x-rays. A CT of the pelvis can be useful in identifying lymph node involvement, whereas a CT of the chest and abdomen looks for systemic soft tissue metastasis such as in the lungs or liver.

Bone scans are a routine part of the staging workup for prostate cancer, particularly in the presence of an elevated PSA level, because of the high risk of bone metastasis with prostate cancer. Approximately one third of men at the time of diagnosis have bone metastasis (Kantoff & Mc-Connell, 1996). A bone scan locates areas of unusual metabolic activity. The procedure involves intravenous administration of a radioisotope marker, which is then absorbed by living bone tissue that is in the process of repair. The scanner detects radioactive emissions from the absorbed marker isotope and forms an image. The image is more enhanced in areas of concentrated uptake such as at the site of bone metastasis. Enhanced uptake can also occur at sites of trauma and arthritis. Given a history of prostate cancer and/or elevated PSA, it is highly suspect that bone metastasis is possible.

Radiographs of the abdomen, pelvis, kidneys, and bladder may be obtained to demonstrate whether the tumor has spread within those structures. An intravenous pyelogram (IVP) proves useful to visualize the urinary system, including the kidneys, ureters, and bladder. A chest radiograph and CT scan or MRI of the abdomen and pelvis are obtained to demonstrate other potential metastasis.

Staging and Grading

Staging and grading of a tumor are done to define the extent of the disease and the aggressive potential. Stages of prostate cancer are divided into A, B, C, and D according to the degree of spread. They are further defined by substages 1 and 2, which more precisely define spread of the disease within the given stage.

A—The gland feels normal. Cancer is present microscopically, meaning the individual is asymptomatic. This stage represents an incidental finding.

B1—Tumor invasion is confined to one lobe of the prostate. Stage B tumors range between 1 and 2 cm.

B2—Tumor is present in both lobes of the prostate, but still contained within the prostate capsule. The patient usually is still asymptomatic with stage B1 or B2.

C1—Tumor is invading tissues just outside the prostate capsule.

C2—Tumor invasion is more extensive to tissues just outside prostate capsule, including seminal vesicles, bladder neck, and/or lateral pelvic wall.

D1—Tumor has spread beyond the prostate to the pelvic lymph nodes.

D2—Tumor has spread beyond the prostate to distant sites. This is most commonly bone and can occasionally involve liver and/or lung.

Stage A and B tumors seldom have elevated PSA levels and are asymptomatic. Stage C tumors may or may not have mildly elevated PSA levels and only occasionally cause some urinary symptoms. Stage D tumors tend to demonstrate elevated PSA levels and are symptomatic depending on where metastasis has developed. Patients might have hydronephrosis from ureteral obstruction, peripheral edema from pelvic lymph node invasion, and pain from bone metastasis (Pienta, Sandler, & Wilson, 1998).

The pathologic grading of tumor cells looks at the cellular disorganization of the tumor that helps identify the aggressive potential of that type cancer cell. They are described as well-differentiated, moderately differentiated, or poorly differentiated cancer. One such system for measuring pathologic cell aggressiveness is the Gleason grading system that categorizes prostate cell growth and behavior on a 1 to 10 scale. This score represents a total score of two parts. One part is given to the predominant cell type, and the second part is given to the most aggressive cell type. These two scores are added to become the Gleason rating and offer some gauge about the anticipated aggressiveness of the tumor. Tumors given a Gleason rating of 2 to 4 are generally slow growing and are less likely to be life threatening because slower growing cancer cells take longer to spread. Tumors that receive a Gleason rating of 8 to 10 are the more dangerous ones because their aggressive potential predictably leads to metastatic disease (Table 7-1).

Treatment

Perhaps the most difficult aspect of prostate cancer is deciding which cancers are clinically important and necessary to treat immediately and which are amenable to watchful waiting. Pathologic disease, which means cancer that is seen microscopically during examination of a biopsy, does not mean the same as clinical prostate cancer, which is what the clinician sees on examining the person. Pathologic prostate cancer can exist asymptomatically for years and never be detected clinically. Definitive treatment, then, depends on a number of factors that weigh the pros and cons of intervention, such as stage, size, and volume of disease; degree of spread to other sites; grade or degree of aggressiveness; and PSA level. The higher the PSA, the likelier the cancer is outside the prostate gland, making it less amenable to being cured. These factors must be weighed against the side effects and benefits of treatment. For example, if the cancer has spread, it can be treated but not cured.

Tumors that are low grade are less likely to have spread than those that are high grade. Finally, the person's baseline health and personal preference must factor into determining definitive treatment. For curative treatment in early prostate cancer, surgery and radiation are the treatments of choice. In early stage disease, these treatment measures show equivalent results in long-term survival, although the residual effects differ to some extent with surgery versus radiation (Hank, 1992; Walsh

TABLE 7-1

RISK OF METASTATIC DISEASE, ACCORDING TO GLEASON SCORE,[a] IN MEN WITH LOCALIZED PROSTATE CANCER

Gleason Score	Risk of Developing Metastatic Disease (%)
2–4	20
5–7	40
8–10	75

Gleason Grade	Description
1	Single, separate, uniform glands in close-packed masses with definite rounded limiting edges
2	Single, separate, slightly less uniform glands, loosely packed; definable but less sharp edge
3A	Single, separate, very variable glands; may be closely packed but usually are widely separated with ragged, poorly defined tumor edge
3B	Like 3A but tiny glands or small cell clusters
3C	Sharply and smoothly circumscribed, often rounded masses of papillary or loose cribriform tumor
4A	Ragged infiltrating "fused-glandular" tumor
4B	Like 4A but large pale cells ("hypernephroid")
5A	Sharply, smoothly circumscribed, rounded masses of almost solid cribriform tumor, usually with some central necrosis ("comedocarcinoma")
5B	Ragged masses of anaplastic carcinoma with only enough gland formation or vacuoles to ensure that it is an adenocarcinoma

[a]The Gleason system is based on the architectural pattern of the tumor and derives a score for each cancer based on the sum of the grade assigned to the most predominant and secondary architectural patterns.
(Pazdur, R., Coia, L., Hoskins, W., & Wagman, L. [Eds.] [1998]. *Cancer management: A multidisciplinary approach* [2nd ed.]. Huntington, NY: PRR.)

& Partin, 1994; Pienta, Sandler, & Wilson, 1998). These decisions about treatment depend on the patient's age, medical condition, and personal desires. For advanced disease, treatment options include therapy with hormones, removal of the testicles (orchiectomy), and chemotherapy. Although these measures may relieve symptoms and thereby improve quality of life, they will not produce a cure.

Surgical Intervention

A radical prostatectomy is surgical removal of the entire prostate and surrounding structures, including the seminal vesicles and a portion of the bladder neck. Radical prostatectomy is the only certain way to remove the entire cancerous gland. This will lead to a cure if the cancer is confined to the prostate. The procedure can be done with or without pelvic lymph node dissection. There are two different surgical approaches to radical prostatectomy: retropubic and perineal.

A retropubic prostatectomy is the most common approach. The surgeon makes an incision in the lower abdomen and removes pelvic lymph nodes and the prostate through the abdominal opening. The remaining urethra is reattached to the bladder, minus the prostate gland that used to encircle it. In the perineal approach, the incision is made in the perineum through which the prostate is removed. Pelvic lymph nodes are sampled and removed through a separate abdominal incision. Lymph nodes may also be removed laparoscopically. With this technique, surgery is performed with instruments passed through small incisions in the lower abdomen. Visualization of the internal structures is accomplished with the use of a fiberoptic device (laparoscope) and the manipulation of long, slender, chopstick type instruments. Biopsy forceps and cautery for hemostasis can be passed through these little incisions. Both the suprapubic and perineal prostatectomy approaches can be accomplished with either general anesthesia or epidural anesthesia with intravenous sedation.

Radical prostatectomy is indicated for men with early stage disease (stage A and B), particularly in younger men who are without metastatic findings and have a normal PSA level. General practice includes verifying tumor status in the pelvic lymph nodes through frozen section, before proceeding onto radical prostatectomy. If the lymph node status is negative for carcinoma, the radical prostatectomy is performed. If the frozen section is positive for carcinoma, there is no need to go forward with the surgery. The treatment of choice in the case of metastatic disease is hormonal therapy and/or orchiectomy (Rous, 1994; Kantoff & McConnell, 1996; Pienta, Sandler, & Wilson, 1998).

Transurethral resection surgery (TUR) may be performed for palliation, meaning to reduce symptoms in advanced-stage prostate cancer. This procedure removes prostate tissue with electric cautery through the opening of a cystoscope that is inserted into the bladder. Tissue is shaved in small sections through the cystoscope, thereby opening the urethral diameter. This procedure is not for curative purposes but rather palliative, to reduce urinary obstruction in advanced stages of the disease.

Radiation Therapy

Radiation therapy for prostatic ablation in early stage prostate cancer has been demonstrated to have long-term survival results comparable with surgical resection (Howard, 1997; Kantoff & McConnell, 1996; Pienta, Sandler, & Wilson, 1998). It can be accomplished using either external beam radiation or radiation seed implants. Radiation is generally the first-line approach for men over 70 years of age or otherwise at poor surgical risk. Again, the aim is one of cure; thus, the treatment is indicated for those with early disease (stage A and B) without metastasis findings and a negative PSA. External beam radiation is given with deep penetrating, high-energy x-rays while the patient lies on the table. The duration of external beam radiation for early stage prostate cancer is approximately 6 weeks, or about 30 treatments.

Brachytherapy or radiation implants for prostate cancer is by way of small radioactive seeds that are inserted into the prostate. This places the radiation source close to the cancerous cells. These seed implants produce particle radiation that does not penetrate into tissue as deeply as external beam radiation. The seeds emit radiation for weeks until all of the radiation is decayed. The seed implants are inserted through the skin of the perineum by CT or ultrasound guidance. The potential benefit is that the radiation load is more directly aimed at the tumor and affects surrounding tissues less than with external beam radiation.

Adjunct radiation may be attempted after surgery for stage C disease in which cancer has invaded surrounding structures outside the capsule. Radiation after surgical treatment for stage C has been shown to decrease the rate of local recurrence of cancer.

Prophylactic radiation of the regional lymph nodes may be used in patients at significant risk of residual tumor cells in regional lymph nodes. This may be external beam or irradiated seed implants. Impotence is decreased with radiation therapy over surgical intervention, with seed implants resulting in the best preservation of sexual function. The side effects of radiation therapy are proctitis, diarrhea, urinary frequency and irritation, cystitis, and dermatitis from external beam radiation.

PSA testing is performed regularly after either surgical prostatectomy or radiation ablation of the prostate. Postsurgical PSA levels should be nondetectable because all of the prostatic epithelial cells have been removed. If the PSA remains detectable, it is certain that malignant cells remain, although they may not necessarily have spread to distant sites. Positive surgical margins may harbor residual disease. Residual cells may also be present at the reanastomosis site of the urethra to the bladder. This site may be biopsied or a radionuclide scan may be performed, which radiographically tags prostate cells and provides an image of where residual disease remains. Persistent elevated PSA levels after surgery mean further therapy is indicated. More important even than an actual level of detectable PSA is a rising trend of PSA after surgery. Restaging should take place with testing and imaging studies.

PSA levels after radiation ablation produce a much more gradual drop in PSA level than after surgery, because the prostate epithelial cells die over time with repeated treatments. With postradiation PSA testing, the trend should be one of gradual and certain decline. If the decline in PSA levels after radiation therapy plateaus or PSA levels begin to rise again, there is cause for concern of persistent disease and further testing is warranted. A rising PSA within months of definitive treatment speaks to a higher aggressive potential (rate of tumor growth) of the cancer than a PSA that rises years later.

Strontium-89 (Metastron) is a radioactive isotope that is readily absorbed in areas of new bone formation. Metastatic areas are sites of active bone formation, so strontium-89 has an affinity for these sites, delivering a higher dose of radiation from the pharmacologic isotope. Strontium-89 has been available for years and has shown its greatest impact on reducing bone pain from metastasis. A slight increase in pain may occur when initiating this medication, but then it improves. Strontium-89 is given as an injection every 3 months and is repeated for as long as it is tolerated, with myelo-suppression being its greatest limiting factor. Education must include careful handling of urine when receiving strontium-89 and proper disposal, observing biohazard precautions (Pienta, Sandler, & Wilson, 1998).

External beam radiation may be used to treat bony metastasis, especially in the case of spinal cord compression. Bones may also be stabilized with surgically placed rods and plates for treatment or prevention of fractures at bony metastatic sites. As much as possible, the person's mobility is preserved and encouraged because it is important for bone strength.

Hormonal Therapy

When the patient is not a candidate for surgery or radiation or the prostate cancer can no longer be cured, hormonal therapy is used to slow the growth of the tumor and reduce symptoms. It is not a cure, but results can be very good. The idea behind this treatment is that the principal male androgen hormone, testosterone, helps prostate tumor cells thrive. If hormone therapy can disrupt testosterone production or utilization, it effectively shuts off androgen supply to the prostate. Depriving the prostate tumor cells of this hormone, as such, theoretically helps arrest tumor growth.

Suppression of testosterone can be accomplished in a number of ways: surgical removal of the testicles (bilateral orchiectomy), hormone suppressants, or hormone blocking agents. None of these methods is the first-line treatment of choice in early prostate cancer; rather, they are most often used to help delay disease progression or control the symptoms of more advanced disease. Hormonal therapy may also be used as adjuvant therapy after definitive surgical or radiation intervention has taken place but PSA levels remain detectable or elevated (Kantoff & McConnell, 1996).

Malignant cells usually do not reproduce well without the presence of androgens. Some malignant cells are more dependent on androgens than others; these are said to be mitogenic. The proportion of androgen-dependent cells in the metastasis is the key factor in the effectiveness of hormone treatment. There are two ways to accomplish a total reduction in testosterone level: surgical orchiectomy and pharmacologic ablation.

Luteinizing hormone-releasing hormone (LHRH) suppresses the pituitary gland, which suppresses testosterone production by the testes. Given every 1 to 3 months as a deep intramuscular injection or as a pellet inserted beneath the skin, it decreases the serum androgen level. Two main types of LHRH are available, leuprolide (Lupron) and gosereline (Zoladex). Surgical orchiectomy results are equivalent to those of leuprolide because both achieve a total reduction in testosterone level. These are the most likely to cause remission, evidenced by decreased PSA, decreased pain, and improvement of metastatic bone disease. Response is highly variable, but the average is around 2 years. LHRH may be continued until there is relapse of disease or remission.

Antiandrogens are agents that do not suppress testosterone production but rather interfere with testosterone's effect on prostate tissue at a cellular level. These antiandrogenic agents are often prescribed in conjunction with LHRH or orchiectomy to prolong remission. This treatment is often also used with watchful waiting, when other treatments are not feasible or desired. Two common types of antiandrogen agents are flutamide (Eulexin) and bicalutamide (Casodex). Common side effects of this treatment include decreased libido and diarrhea. Changes in liver function may occur, so regular monitoring of liver function levels in the blood serum is recommended.

Nonsurgical androgen suppression includes Diethylstilbestrol (DES). This is an older form of therapy, and others have shown more favorable results. The exception to agents that block or reduce the effect of hormones is estrogen, a female hormone. Diethylstilbestrol 1- to 3-mg oral tablets are taken once daily. If hormonal intervention fails in metastatic cancer, strontium-89 may be used.

Cryosurgical Ablation

With the advent of rectal ultrasound and improvement in liquid nitrogen techniques, cryosurgery is thought by some to be a viable option for treating localized early-stage prostate cancer. In this treatment a probe is inserted into the rectum in much the same manner as for a biopsy; the probe contains supercold liquid nitrogen, which is inserted directly into the tumor. The extreme cold freezes and kills the tumor cells. Because the entire gland and surrounding tissues cannot be frozen because of damage to the urethra and bowel, the chance for recurrence is higher, as residual cancer cells may remain untreated (Kantoff & McConnell, 1996). As with prostatectomy, the most common side effects with cryosurgical ablation are impotence and incontinence.

Future Experimental Treatments

Research is looking at newer forms of radiopharmaceutical interventions, which include rhenium-186 and samarium-153 (Pienta, Sandler, & Wilson, 1998). Selective testosterone receptor modifiers are also the subject of a great deal of clinical research. These are potency-sparing hormone treatments that interfere with attachment of male hormone to receptors on prostate cells. Finasteride (Proscar) inhibits an enzyme that prostate cells need to convert testosterone to dihydrotestosterone, which is the more potent stimulator of prostate cancer cell growth.

Intermittent hormonal treatment is based on the theory that prostate cancer cells have varying degrees of dependence on male androgen. Eradicating sensitive clones through uninterrupted hormone treatment might actually permit uncontrolled growth of hormone-insensitive prostate cancer cells. Periodic LHRH interruption may decrease the proportion of uncontrollable cancer cells in the tumor (Pienta, Sandler, & Wilson, 1998). This approach is still unproven. Finally, researchers are looking at vaccines that decrease luteinizing hormone production in the pituitary gland.

Chemotherapy

Chemotherapy has a limited role in the treatment of prostate cancer; however, it is a reasonable option when trying to delay growth of advanced distant bulky cancer that has been unresponsive to hormonal therapy. Chemotherapy is not intended to cure the disease but may instead control its growth to some extent. Both single-agent and combination therapies have been tried, but the results remain marginal. Significant advances have however been made in identifying newer active regimens for hormone-refractory prostate cancer. Suramin is an agent that binds with the growth factors that stimulate growth and motility, and so interferes with the growth and function of cancer cells. Estamustine (Emcyt) has been used in combination with etoposide, and with vinblastine to interrupt cellular replication of cancer cells. Mitoxantrone and prednisone have been approved for use in patients with metastatic pain (Pienta, Sandler, & Wilson, 1998).

Watchful Waiting

Watchful waiting, although controversial, is a treatment option for men with early-stage disease that involves no intervention per se, except regular monitoring of the individual for cancer spread. Many practitioners believe this to be a reasonable approach for men older than 70 to 75 years of age, many of whom may likely die of other age-related causes before distant metastases develop. Because it is not possible to determine for certain whose disease will progress rapidly and whose will not, this is not a widely accepted recommendation for younger or otherwise healthy men.

Complications of Disease and Treatment

Prostate cancer is somewhat unique in that the majority of men who have been diagnosed with it were asymptomatic. Of concern is the projection that countless others are living with it unwittingly. The complications of prostate cancer are broken down into two main categories: treatment-related side effects and long-term complications of disease progression. Most notable are the treatment-related side effects of impotence, urinary incontinence, and gastrointestinal distress, as they can affect most aspects of the patient's sense of self and well-being, the core of masculinity and dignity. The second order of side effects are the complications seen with disease progression, including outlet obstructive disorder, spinal cord compression, myelosuppressive disorders, and pain secondary to metastasis.

Impotence

Impotence, or the inability to attain or maintain an erection, is most often due to the nerve damage related to treatment. Erection of the penis results when innervation of the nerve bundles around the prostate causes increased blood flow to fill two fibrous cylindrical tubes that lie side by side along the centerline of the upper penis. These tubes are called corpora cavernosa or cavernous bodies. When the cavernous bodies swell with blood, the flaccid penis lifts into an erect position. Interrupting the nerves that control blood flow to the corpora cavernosa, such as by severing them during surgery or damaging them with radiation treatments, affects the ability to achieve or maintain erection. The incidence of surgically induced impotence has been greatly reduced with the nerve-sparing retropubic approach for prostatectomy (Kantoff & McConnell, 1996; Pienta, Sandler, & Wilson, 1998). Erections may be achieved through a number of means other than the normal nerve impulse mechanism.

Several options are available to men for treatment of impotence (erectile dysfunction), including surgically inserted penile implants, vacuum pump devices, and medications. In the absence of physical etiology, psychotherapy is often useful in sexual dysfunction. Penile implants come in a variety of styles. One option of implant is a set of two semirigid, malleable rods that are implanted into the corpora cavernosa, from the base of the penis to the tip. Because it is flexible, the penis can be bent down along the inner thigh except during sexual activity, when it can be raised into an erect position. Although this type of implant can be discreetly concealed, not all men feel comfortable with a permanent semierection. A more elaborate implant is the saline-filled reservoir-and-pump system. Again, a pair of tubes are implanted into the upper part of the penis with an attached saline-filled reservoir unit implanted into the scrotum. When an erection is desired, the pump is activated, usually by squeezing the reservoir, which fills the tubes and effectively causes erection. After sexual activity, the pump empties the fluid from the implanted tubes back into the reservoir.

Vacuum pumps work on the principle of negative pressure and are a mechanical means of filling the penis with blood. The flaccid penis is inserted into a clear, plastic cylinder that is held tight against the pubis, creating a seal. Attached to the end of the cylinder is a hollow tube with a one-way valve and a hand mechanism that evacuates air from inside the cylinder through a hand-grasp maneuver. As air is removed from the interior of the cylinder, a negative pressure is produced, forcing the tissue of the penis to stretch to the point where blood vessels in the corpora cavernosa open and fill with blood. Once the penis is sufficiently engorged, a specialized rubber band is rolled off the base of the cylinder onto the base of the penis. This band serves to constrict the blood flow in the penis while sexual activity takes place. When erection is no longer desired, the rubber band is removed by rolling it down and off the penis.

Medications can also be used to induce erection. These are given as a subcutaneous injection into the tissue at the base of the penis. Although the idea may initially be an unappealing one, the needles are tiny and men quickly adapt and find it far less uncomfortable to perform than it sounds. The injected medicine is a prostaglandin that stimulates blood flow into the penis corpora cavernosa. The most commonly prescribed medication for this is papaverine and regitine.

Although orgasm can be successfully achieved using any of the above methods, the ability to ejaculate is almost always lost after radical prostatectomy. A common concern to men is whether they will remain capable of producing sperm after treatment. Sperm is produced in the testicles, which are not affected. Although the mechanical process is altered after surgery, sperm is still produced. Men are capable of fertilizing an ovum after treatment using special artificial insemination techniques, but not through sexual intercourse.

Incontinence

Stress incontinence is seen in approximately 10% to 30% of men after prostatectomy. As with post-treatment impotence, incontinence is an adverse outcome related to the surgical or radiologic treatment of prostate cancer. The external urethral sphincter is disrupted by the severing of the urethra at the base of the bladder and reattachment of the bladder neck to the urethral stump. After the bladder catheter is out, men seldom have control of urinary function, and the muscles need to be retrained to control urine with the new type of urethra. Kegel exercises help to improve the tone of voluntary muscles that are required to control and stop urine flow. The exercise is performed by contracting the same muscles one would use to stop urine flow during the micturition process.

Gastrointestinal/Urogenital Distress

Diarrhea and abdominal cramping are perhaps the most bothersome problems following a surgical prostatectomy, radiation, or cryotherapy to the prostate. The duration of diarrhea varies with the type of treatment, with radiation-induced diarrhea lasting the longest. Abdominal cramping and bladder spasms are common and may be accompanied by hematuria. Symptom management may include antidiarrheals, antispasmodics, and barrier creams for the perirectal area. Proctitis is more severe with external beam radiation and prostate seed implants. Perineal/rectal skin irritation is caused by external beam radiation and responds well to tepid sitz baths.

Hormonal Therapy Side Effects

The most common side effects of LHRH treatments and surgical orchiectomy are transient episodes of hot flashes, diaphoresis, rebound chills, nausea, and diarrhea. These symptoms are often self limiting and improve in time. Symptomatic support for hot flashes includes agents such as megastrol (Megace), clonidine, and low-dose DES. Antiemetics and antidiarrheals may be used to reduce the discomfort of nausea and diarrhea. Loss of libido (sex drive) is a permanent side effect of orchiectomy. Unlike the mechanical difficulty of impotence, which can be treated, loss of testosterone removes the sexual urge completely.

Pain

The threat of severe and lingering pain is perhaps the most fearful aspect of metastatic prostate cancer for the patient. Pain is generally related to bone metastasis. Chemicals are secreted by the tumor that stimulate both unnatural bone growth (osteoblasts) and bone destruction. The new metastatic bone formation is overly dense and weaker than normal bone. Overproduction of osteoblasts causes pressure within the marrow channels and produces pain. Another destructive bony process is metastatic lytic lesions, in which bones become riddled with little holes that destabilize them, making them susceptible to pathologic fractures. Tumors can also secrete chemicals that cause nerves to transmit pain impulses.

Bone pain is generally referred to as dull and aching and localized to the areas of metastasis. Contributing further to pain is inadequate sleep, anxiety, and depression. Pain needs to be thoroughly evaluated and treated systematically with consistent routine pain assessment to evaluate analgesic effectiveness. A widely accepted template for pain management is the World Health Organization (WHO) analgesic ladder, which addresses pain needs across the spectrum of the pain experience, with a wide variety of treatment modalities.

Pharmacologic pain management can be augmented with a number of other techniques that help reduce pain, anxiety, and depression and may offer an improved sense of well-being. This broad category of relaxation therapy includes guided imagery, music therapy, soft touch and light massage, pet therapy, hypnosis, and biofeedback (Payne, 1993).

Neurologic Impairment

Neurologic impairment can occur as a result of bone metastasis and tissue compression on the nerves of the spinal column causing spinal cord compression (SCC), an oncologic emergency. The common symptoms of SCC are persistent back pain, weakness in the lower extremities, urinary and rectal incontinence, or anuresis and constipation. Spinal cord compression is treated with a combination of steroid therapy and external beam radiation. Occasionally, surgery also needs to be done to stabilize the affected spinal vertebrae with rods. Tumor nerve compression may also impair sensations of heat or cold and/or cause numbness and tingling in the extremities.

Hematopoietic Disorders

Metastatic cancer with profound bone metastasis often leads to myelosuppression and an overall reduction in blood cell production. Because blood cells are formed in the bone marrow, tumor encroachment interferes with hematopoiesis. Reduced blood cell counts can lead to fevers and infections, anemia and sluggishness, and bleeding disorders. Prostate cancer patients are at increased risk for systemic fibrinolysis and disseminated intravascular coagulopathy. Prostate tissue contains plasmin, an enzyme activator of fibrinolysis. Clotting disorders may lead to thrombus formation and pulmonary embolus.

Obstructive Uropathy

Obstructive uropathy is frequently associated with bulky intra-abdominal, retroperitoneal, and pelvic malignancies. Ureteral blockage secondary to pelvic lymph node involvement and tumor compression can occur, leading to obstructive nephropathy, hydronephrosis, renal failure, uremic syndrome, and eventual death. Ureteral bypass stent placement may be considered, although this is not a permanent solution. Without treatment of the underlying tumor or reimplantation of the ureters, obstruction will eventually occur.

Sexuality and Body Image

The emotional impact of the disease and its various treatment modalities is naturally varied from one individual to the other and is influenced by a wide spectrum of variables. Regardless of age, the initial impact of the diagnosis is one of emotional turmoil. As with any diagnosis of cancer, there are periods of anxiety, anger, hopelessness, loneliness, and depression. Prostate cancer and its treatment additionally affect the core of masculinity and sexual identity. Supportive interventions for these men include encouraging open communication with partners, participation in support groups, and information seeking.

REFERENCES

Carter, B. S. (1989). Epidemiologic evidence recording predisposing factors to prostate cancer. *Prostate, 16,* 187–197.

Davis, M. (1991). Genitourinary cancers. In S. Otto (Ed.). *Oncology nursing* (pp. 97–116). St. Louis: Mosby Year Book.

Doherty, K., & Breslin, S. (1996). Prostate cancer: An update on screening and management. *Oncology Updates, 3*(3), 1–13.

Figlin, R. A., & deKernion, J. B. (1995). Urinary tract cancers. In D. A. Casciato & B. B. Lowitz (Eds.). *Manual of clinical oncology* (3rd ed., pp. 237–257). Boston: Little, Brown.

Howard, P. (1997). Prostate cancer support group. *Quality of Life, 5,* 9–14.

Kantoff, P. W., & McConnell, M. (1996). *Prostate cancer: A family consultation.* Boston: Houghton Mifflin.

Kassabian, V. S., & Graham, S. D. (1995). Urologic and male genital cancers. In G. Murphy, W. Lawrence, & R. E. Lenhard (Eds.). *Clinical oncology* (2nd ed., pp. 311–329).

Landis, S., Murray, T., Bolden, S., & Wing, P. A. (1998). Cancer statistics 1998. *CA: A Cancer Journal for Clinicians, 48,* 6–29.

LaVecchia, C. (1992). Cancers associated with high fat diets. *Monograph of National Cancer Institute, 12,* 79–85.

Lind, J., & Irwin, R. (1991). Genitourinary cancers. In S. Baird, R. McCorkle, & M. Grant (Eds.). *Cancer nursing* (pp. 466–484). Philadelphia: W. B. Saunders.

Lind, J., Kravitz, K., & Greig, B. (1993). Urologic and male genital malignancies. In S. Groenwald, M. Frogge, M. Goodman, & C. Yarbro (Eds.). *Cancer nursing principles and practice* (3rd ed., pp. 1258–1313). Boston: Jones & Bartlett.

Miller, B., Ries, L., Hankey, B., Kosary, C., Harras, A., Devesa, S., & Edwards, B. (Eds.). (1993). *SEER cancer statistics review 1973–1990.* NIH Pub. No. 93-2789. Bethesda, MD: National Cancer Institute.

Payne, R. (1993). Pain management in the patient with prostate cancer. *Cancer Supplement, 71,* 1127–1131.

Pienta, K. J., Sandler, H., & Wilson, T. G. (1998). Prostate cancer. In R. Pazdur, L. Coia, W. Hoskins, & L. Wagman (Eds.). *Cancer management: A multidisciplinary approach* (2nd ed.). Huntington, NY: PRR.

Rous, S. N. (1994). *The prostate book.* New York: W. W. Norton.

Sheldon, C. A., Williams, R. D., & Farley, E. E. (1980). Incidental cancer of the prostate: Review of literature and critical reappraisal of classification. *Journal of Urology, 24,* 626–631.

Steinberg, G. D., Carter, B. S., Beaty, T. H., Child, B., & Walsh, P. C. (1990). Family history and risk of prostate cancer. *Prostate, 17,* 337–347.

Talcoot, J. A., Rieker, P., Propert, K. J., Clark, J. A., Wishnow, K. I., Loughlin, K. R., Richie, J. P., & Kantoff, P. W. (1997). Patient-reported impotence and incontinence after nerve-sparing radical prostatectomy. *Journal of the National Cancer Institute, 89,* 1117–1123.

Yarbro, C. H., & Ferrans, C. E. (1998). Quality of life of patients with prostate cancer treated with surgery or radiation therapy. *Oncology Nursing Forum, 25*(4), 685–693.

Zinner, N. R. (1991). Prostate. In M. Dollinger, E. H. Rosenbaum, & G. Cable (Eds.). *Cancer therapy* (pp. 485–495).

CHAPTER

8

The Gynecologic Cancers

Terry Chamarro

The gynecologic malignancies comprise a number of diseases along the female reproductive tract with divergent symptoms, biologic courses, and outcomes. Common to all is the significant challenge to clinician and patient alike. The cause, indication, ages at onset, and treatment of these diseases differ notably. Ovarian cancer, the most demanding of the malignancies, continues to defy early diagnosis and, as such, predicts a long, difficult treatment regimen for its victim. By contrast, endometrial cancer is usually detected early because of apparent symptoms, and it is largely curable with limited treatment. Undue estrogen stimulation appears to play a role in the origin of many endometrial carcinomas and forms the basic profile of the woman at risk for this malignancy. Although less well known, gestational trophoblastic disease uniquely follows normal pregnancy or the strange aberration known as molar pregnancy. Sexually transmitted viral diseases, specifically human papilloma viruses (HPV), have been identified through intense molecular research as the major contributor to the origin of cervical, vaginal, and vulvar cancers.

Women diagnosed with a gynecologic cancer share one common experience—the threat to sexual identity. In some, loss of the ability to bear children may become the prime focus of concern or grief although that option was no longer prominent in future plans. To others, the reproductive organs, even after cessation of functionality, are symbolic of female gender. To a last group, the mere loss of any organ at any age is an unbearable assault on the integrity of body image. These malignancies collectively represent a small minority of cancer diagnoses annually. To nurses who care for women with gynecologic cancer, however, the physiologic and psychological dynamics of the diseases present an intellectual and emotional challenge of no small significance.

A Perspective on Gynecologic Cancers

Although new occurrences of disease within the group of gynecologic cancers predicted in 1998 will total less than half that of breast cancer alone, the mortality rate is expected to be well over half, or about 63%. A 25% rise in incidence of breast cancer over the last 10 years is much more alarming than the 12% increase seen in gynecologic cancer. Comparing mortality statistics of the two entities shows a different perspective, however. Gynecologic mortality increased 17% in the last decade, whereas deaths from breast cancer held to a 1% increase (Landis, Murray, Bolden & Wingo, 1998; Silverberg & Lubera, 1989). Such statistics warrant heightened attention to the gynecologic diseases, and, indeed, concern is surfacing as demonstrated in public awareness and a marked increase in donor contributions for research in gynecologic cancers.

Early Diagnosis of Disease

The rise in gynecologic mortality seems puzzling in view of successful promotion of the Pap test as part of the average woman's health surveillance. Deaths from cervical cancer, indeed, have dropped a dramatic 30% in the decade of 1988 to 1997. Favorable detection by the Pap smear and follow-up diagnostics lead to treatment of early cervical lesions while still in their premalignant state. Sharply rising in incidence, however, is endometrial cancer, a uterine disease predominantly in the peri- and postmenopausal woman and the most common pelvic malignancy. This increase is expected to continue as the population of women over age 50 steadily grows. The Pap test is a poor indicator for an endometrial malignancy because it frequently remains negative despite fully invasive uterine disease. Fortunately, many women are frankly symptomatic with abnormal bleeding, and further workup is indicated. Uterine cancer is highly curable often by surgery alone. Ovarian cancer is most responsible for the unsettling gynecologic statistics. Lacking any real means of surveillance in its early or premalignant state, ovarian cancer advances silently and is not diagnosed until an advanced stage. This limits any successful treatment outcome and accounts for a high mortality from this disease.

The reasons women increasingly experience breast, endometrial, and ovarian cancers are not fully apparent. As information continues to build on the molecular biology of cancer, we expect a significant impact on the diagnosis and management in this set of female cancers. Evidence for a family of genes that may play a role in both breast and ovarian cancers currently offers the promise of focused screening for these diseases, which will perhaps begin the reversal of some of the devastating statistics (Young, 1995).

Origin and Growth

Malignancies in the female pelvis are addressed by site of origin and cell type. The sites are broadly identified as the vulva, vagina, uterine cervix, endometrium, fallopian tube, and ovary. Rarely, some gynecologic cancers originate on other external sites such as the perineal body or internal tissue such as the peritoneum. Each site has a prevalent cell type that occurs in the majority of the cancers from that area, but there are also numerous types with rarer cellular origins. In reality, there are many different cancers in the gynecologic domain. Each will have its own unique biologic characteristics and will require treatment design closely corresponding to the sensitivity of the cell or site of the growth.

When a gynecologic cancer is initially diagnosed, it is staged or classified into one category within its site-specific clinical group. The stage of the disease generally depicts its spread from the original anatomic site. A precancerous epithelial lesion in which abnormal cells exist but remain confined to the intraepithelial layer is referred to as stage 0 or in situ. Other terms are *dysplasia* or *intraepithelial neoplasia*. These lesions are not a true malignancy but carry a high probability of becoming one if allowed to progress without attention. Invasive cancer is indicated when the abnormal cells penetrate below the basement membrane and invade underlying tissues. Now, they are able to gain access to lymphatics and capillaries for transport of cancerous cells to adjacent and distant sites.

The Cancer Committee of the International Federation of Gynecology and Obstetrics (FIGO) devised an anatomic staging system that is periodically upgraded as further understanding of a disease emerges. FIGO groups the gynecologic cancers into four stages designated numerically from I to IV. It is the common classification system used by specialists caring for these patients, although the TNM staging addresses the gynecologic malignancies as well. The stage initially designated on discovery of disease is retained thereafter even if there is disease recurrence some time after successful treatment. Stages may be further divided by the subcategories of *a, b,* and sometimes *c.* As with systems used in other malignancies, staging is a standard that encourages comparison of data among centers in this country and abroad. Most significantly, it helps physicians in planning appropriate treatment as well as prediction of prognosis. The classification system is complex, and a detailed understanding is not required for the nurse to anticipate a treatment approach and assist the patient and family in coping with coming events. The stages categorized in general terms of growth or spread are shown in Table 8-1.

TABLE 8-1
GENERAL OVERVIEW OF GYNECOLOGIC CANCER STAGING

Stage 0	Preinvasive lesions: Dysplasia; Intraepithelial neoplasia; carcinoma in situ (Not included in statistics on gynecologic malignancies)
Stage I	Confined to the organ, limited in dimension
Stage II	Local extension of tumor, larger in dimension
Stage III	Regional extension but not invasive of other organs
Stage IV	Distant metastasis outside pelvis and abdomen; invasion into organs such as bowel and bladder

Cancer Detection in Gynecology

Risk Factors and Screening in Cervical Cancer

About 45 years have elapsed since the Pap test, named after its discoverer, George Papanicolaou, was introduced on a large scale as a cancer-screening tool. The Pap smear is a cytologic test dealing only with the structure and function of the individual cell. It is a true screening test, and final diagnosis of cancer must be made from histologic or pathologic analysis of tissue from the site.

The usefulness of the Pap test was discovered in the 1930s, but it did not become a standard part of gynecologic care until 1960 (Celentano, 1988). Before the 1940s, cervical cancer was the leading cause of cancer deaths among women in the United States. Thirty cases per 100,000 women were discovered annually in 1940 (totaling about 45,000 a year), but it has rapidly declined to the current incidence of around 10 cases per 100,000 (Fowler, 1993).

A five-class system for reporting smear results was originally devised by Papanicolaou. There have been revisions through the decades as better standardization was sought. The latest revision occurred in 1988 when a consensus panel of gynecologists and pathologists under auspices of the National Institutes of Health developed a cervical cytology nomenclature called the Bethesda system. The numerical designation in the early Papanicolaou class system has been replaced with narrative terminology using more precise diagnostic terms.

Now, the results of the smear may be quoted as "within normal limits" or progress through a range of abnormalities from "atypical squamous" or "atypical glandular" to the frankly invasive "squamous cell carcinoma," "adenocarcinoma," or "nonepithelial malignant neoplasm." Also important in the Bethesda system is the reporting of the adequacy of representative cells in the specimen. The new system places the cytology report at the level of significance of a medical consultation and obligates the cytopathologist to guide the clinician for further evaluation when indicated (Rose, 1993).

Cells on the cervix are generally squamous in type, whereas those higher in the endometrium or inner lining of the uterus are glandular and columnar in structure. The most important criterion in evaluation of the cervix is obtaining the correct sampling of cells. Cells must be scraped from the squamocolumnar junction of the cervix, that area in which the glandular cells natural to the endometrial environment separate from the squamous cells typical of the vagina and outer cervix. If a cancer originating from the cervix is found to be glandular (adenocarcinoma) in origin rather than squamous, it will have a different biologic nature and require different treatment considerations. It is often more threatening in outcome as well.

The earliest cell changes that may ultimately result in invasive cervical cancer are thought to begin in the vulnerable years of adolescence to young adulthood when active cell change, called the transformational process, is going on. Some knowledge of the physiology in action at this time in the lower reproductive tract may be helpful in understanding the risk concept of cervical and vaginal cancer. The vagina is lined with glandular cells from birth through young childhood. During the transformation process, metaplasia occurs in which these cells are replaced by squamous cells and there is the appearance of a continual upward recession of glandular cells as the young girl matures. At full maturity, columnar glandular tissue resides solely inside the cervical canal and in the endometrium or uterine lining, and the cervix and vagina are made up of squamous cells. The squamocolumnar junction, therefore, is the focal point of this transformational process called metaplasia. By the time of puberty, the junction exists at the outer portion of the cervix and the onset of menarche brings about many cellular and chromosomal changes. The current belief in cervical cancer is that a carcinogenic agent acts primarily on the squamocolumnar junction, setting off the progression from normal to abnormal cellular structure and finally to fully invasive cancer (Rose, 1993).

The technique used in obtaining the Pap smear is very important because legitimate results rely on an adequate representation of cells from the correct anatomic site. Usually, two samplings are obtained for the Pap test, one using a cervical spatula on the ectocervix (outer cervix) and a second using a brushlike applicator reaching well into the endocervix (the cervical canal). Some clinicians will use a moist cotton-tipped applicator for the second collection. In the woman of advanced years, the squamocolumnar junction exists well inside the cervical canal, possibly denying successful cell collection.

It was recognized 150 years ago that the incidence of cervical cancer was virtually nonexistent in nuns and, if encountered, was likely to have occurred in the woman entering the convent late in life as a widow. The logical association, therefore, revolved around a potential infectious process that was sexually transmitted. At different times in the past, trichomoniasis, gonorrhea, *Chlamydia*, condylomata, and cytomegalovirus have all been thought to play a part in the development of cervical neoplasias. In the 1970s, herpes simplex II was strongly implicated in the etiology, but this has been discounted in more recent studies, although it may be involved in a synergistic relationship with other viruses (Tinkle, 1990). Women who are moderate to heavy smokers (15 or more cigarettes daily) have significantly increased risk for cervical dysplasias and invasive cancer. The mechanism in which tobacco influences cervical abnormalities is unclear, but a recent study suggests that it may cause a local immunologic effect that could facilitate infection with an oncogenic virus (Burger, Hollema, Gouw, Pieters & Quint, 1993).

Since the early 1980s, a great deal of interest has focused on the study of HPV and their relationship to cervical lesions as well as other male and female lower genital tract and anal cancers or precursors. Genital warts or condylomata accuminata is the most commonly diagnosed sexually transmitted viral disease in the United States

today, accounting for about 200,000 first visits to physician offices (Fowler, 1993; Reid, 1987). These common, verrucous-looking condylomata are among the more than 60 HPV types identified today. They are seldom seen in association with malignancies as much as other HPV types, which tend to be flat and less visible. About 15 to 20 HPV types affect the genital or anal areas. Of these, HPV types 16, 18, 33, 35, and 39 were implicated early as potential causative agents, and evidence continues to mount in some newer HPV types. Early sexual activity and multiple partners obviously increase viral exposure, and these two factors place the woman into a high-risk category for cervical cancer.

Detection of Cervical Lesions

When abnormal cytology is reported on the Pap results, the next diagnostic step in cervical cancer involves a histologic (pathologic) evaluation. Here, not only the cells but also their intercellular substances are studied in total. Tissue must be obtained from the precise area of the abnormal cells. This assumes that an area of abnormality will have a distinctly different appearance and that this can be noted somehow on direct visualization. In the case of cancers in the lower genital tract, there is a unique look to the abnormal tissue, but, unfortunately, it cannot be seen without magnification. The change in appearance from that of normal tissue is apparent in minute vascular patterns, and these can be seen using an instrument known as a colposcope. The colposcope is a binocular microscope that can be directed to the vagina and cervix where it magnifies 4 to 8 times (Rose, 1993). The tissue field must be swabbed with acetic acid to clear the cervical mucus and aid visualization. The odd pattern of vessels, which are characterized by a spotted, punctated, or mosaic appearance, provides the site for biopsy. Using an instrument that will punch a small amount of tissue, one or more specimens are taken for pathologic examination. There is little discomfort to the procedure because, unlike other lower genital tract areas, there are relatively few nerve endings on the cervix. The set of evaluative procedures commonly performed in gynecologists' office is shown in Table 8-2.

If the biopsy report confirms that this is an intraepithelial lesion, it should be removed. Several

TABLE 8-2	
OFFICE GYNECOLOGIC EVALUATION	
Observation of the external genitalia	Abnormalities of the vulva • Redness • Swelling • Open draining lesions
Speculum examination	• Rotate speculum to visualize vaginal tube and cervix • Appearance of vaginal walls • Observation of the cervix • Obtain cell specimen(s) for Pap test
Manual examination	• Palpation of vaginal wall and cervix with fingers • Bimanual palpation of areas of ovaries (vaginal route concurrent with external pelvis) • Rectovaginal palpation
Endometrial biopsy	• Based on history or symptoms • Suction aspiration of sample of endometrium
Colposcopy and biopsy	• Cervix/other areas must be swabbed with acetic acid • Squamocolumnar junction is visualized • Evaluation of abnormal vascular patterns (characterized by mosaicism, punctations) • Punch biopsy

treatment techniques can be done in the office without general anesthesia and under colposcopic vision. Cryosurgery is one method in which a probe, cooled with carbon dioxide or nitrous oxide refrigerant, is placed on the cervix until the tissue is frozen. The cervix is thawed and usually re-treated in a few minutes (DiSaia & Creasman, 1993). This procedure is relatively painless and has few or no side effects other than a watery vaginal discharge for a few days. Laser surgery, by which tissue is destroyed by vaporization created by the laser beam, is another treatment method for premalignant cervical lesions. It takes somewhat more time to perform and is a little more painful than cryosurgery. The advantage to laser is that, unlike the cryoprobe, only affected tissue need be removed and normal tissue in surrounding areas is spared. Some bleeding or spotting may occur for a few days after laser surgery. The loop electrosurgical excision procedure (LEEP) can also be done in the office. Here, the transformation zone is excised using a low-voltage diathermy loop. Local anesthesia to the cervix must be used. The advantage to this method is that tissue can be obtained and sent for pathology so both diagnosis and therapy are completed in the single visit (DiSaia & Creasman, 1993).

In approximately 10% of cases, colposcopic visualization is not successful and the woman will need to undergo a cone biopsy. This is done under anesthesia in a surgical setting. As the name implies, a conical piece of tissue is excised from the cervix and sent for histologic analysis.

If the histology (pathology) reports invasive cancer, there must be an adequate biopsy and grading of the tumor in order to understand more of its characteristics before medical management can be planned. Epithelial tumors are graded based on certain cellular configurations. The tumor is described as grade I, well differentiated; grade II, moderately differentiated; and grade III, poorly differentiated. Some cell types are nearly completely undifferentiated or anaplastic. In gynecology, much attention is given to tumor grade as well as stage in determining prognosis—the more poorly differentiated tumor generally has a less optimal outcome.

Detection of Vaginal Cancer

Carcinoma of the vagina is a rare disease usually seen in women between ages 50 and 70. Most frequently, it is squamous cell histology, and adenocarcinoma is uncommon. Melanomas have occurred in the vagina as well as on the vulva. Good visualization of the vaginal walls is the only measure used to screen for potential disease, and this should be part of the routine gynecologic examination. Added attention should be given to vaginal surveillance when the patient has been previously treated for premalignant or invasive cervical or vulvar disease, which increases the chances of a new malignancy at the vaginal site. The concentration of the physician is important during the speculum portion of the examination to ensure that the speculum blades do not obscure any lesion or open ulceration on the vaginal wall. The most common site of vaginal cancer is on the upper third of the posterior wall, an area frequently hidden by the speculum when the cervix is viewed. Appearance of a gross lesion or the suggestion of incriminating symptoms in the verbal history leads the clinician to place special emphasis on examining the vagina more thoroughly. For instance, if vaginal bleeding or discharge without pain is reported, a more careful look is demanded. A history of urinary retention or frequency, bladder spasm, or bleeding upon urination also requires that extra attention be given to the anterior vaginal wall. Rectal symptoms such as blood in the stool, tenesmus, or constipation warrant a focused observation of the posterior wall (Hatch, 1996). In these instances, searching for a submucosal lump or swelling becomes particularly important in the bimanual examination. Magnification with colposcopy may be called for as well in vaginal surveillance. As in the case of cervix cancer, biopsy must be taken to show the depth and special characteristics of the lesion.

Rare Adenocarcinoma of the Vagina

To the young woman exposed to *diethylstilbestrol (DES)* in utero, there is an increased risk of developing the rare clear-cell adenocarcinoma of the vagina. Under physician supervision, DES was used from the 1940s until 1971 by women to preserve a pregnancy after a previous spontaneous abortion(s) or other complicating factors. DES-associated cancer has received much attention from the media. Evidence began emerging that an alarming number of their daughters were presenting with this unusual malignancy, and they differed by occurring more frequently on the anterior wall rather than posterior as in squamous (Veridiano, 1993). The average age of the young patient diagnosed with vaginal adenocarcinoma was about 19, and since this cohort of exposed women has now grown older, the most immediate con-

cerns about this disease have diminished. All women who state that their mother took DES should be given special gynecologic surveillance throughout life, however. Many will show a lifelong pattern of glandular cells on the vaginal walls, unlike nonexposed women, where glandular cells receded in the transformational process described earlier in the chapter. Because these glandular patches are visually evident, it is easier for the physician or nurse practitioner to give them attention. This disease no longer seems so commanding, but uncertainty remains about occurrences in the later decades of life (Hatch, 1996). Knowing that cervical cancer arises at the squamo-columnar junction, one can recognize the potential threat to these women who retain multiple cellular junctions in the vagina throughout adulthood.

Evaluating Vulvar Cancer

No screening measures exist for cancer of the vulva because vulvar lesions are usually apparent in the form of a lump or mass or a raised, fleshy, ulcerated lesion, which can be easily biopsied (Hacker, 1996). Perhaps as many as 20% of cases will have a warty appearance. Many women may describe a history of recurrent pruritus long before the appearance of an overt lesion, and such a history might indicate to the attentive clinician that a more explicit evaluation is required.

Vulvar cancer remains an uncommon malignancy, constituting about 5% of cancers in the female genital tract. Most will be of the squamous cell variety like their counterparts in other areas of the lower genital tract. It is usually found in the older, postmenopausal age group and, like vaginal cancer, can occur in women who had earlier treatment for cervical cancer. Recently, an increased number of cases have been reported in premenopausal patients, which supports the belief that a common pathogen or set of pathogen(s) exists between cervical, vaginal, and vulvar cancers (Brinton, Nasca, Mallin, Baptiste, Wilbanks & Richart, 1990; Chamorro, 1990). HPV is that likely pathogen. The chance of infection will increase as the woman's sexual partners multiply. A history of genital warts is prominent in as many as 60% of patients with invasive vulvar cancer, and HPV DNA has been identified in many of the tumor specimens. Higher tobacco use is also common (Veridiano, 1993). In vulvar cancer, a preinvasive in situ lesion often accompanies the invasive component. In the last 2 decades, vulvar in situ lesions are occurring more extensively, although there is no rise in the rates of invasive cancer (Sturgeon, Brinton, Devesa, & Kurmon, 1992).

Because the vulva is external and subject to easy inspection, self-examination remains the most effective method of discovery. In past decades, when this disease was encountered most exclusively in the elderly age group, patients reported a distinct discomfort with self-examination. Although sometimes aware of symptoms, many allowed disease to progress significantly before seeking medical intervention. This same population group, out of a sense of modesty, was equally reluctant to establish gynecologic visits as part of their routine health care as well. Fortunately, changing norms and increased knowledge have reversed these attitudes.

Uterine Cancer

About 95% of cancers of the uterus arise in the endometrium, or internal lining. The area is inaccessible to visualization or any simple collection of cells for screening cytology. On occasion, abnormal cells from the endometrium will slough and find their way externally where they are coincidentally captured by the applicator during the Pap collection. Further investigation must be undertaken if abnormal glandular cells are found on the Pap results. Usually, it is postmenopausal bleeding that initiates endometrial evaluation, although only about 10% of these cases are caused by cancer. Endometrial atrophy or some form of benign hyperplasia accounts for the overwhelming majority of the postmenopausal symptoms. If encountered, cells or tissue from the internal uterus is obtained using aspiration by means of a small tube inserted through the cervical canal (Chambers & Chambers, 1992). This procedure is done in the gynecologic office, and there is some cramping or discomfort while the cervix is dilated to accommodate the small instrument required for the suction. Periodic endometrial sampling may be required as part of surveillance for any women identified at higher risk for uterine cancer, however.

The high-risk profile for endometrial cancer is formulated on the premise that its origin is related to excess estrogen stimulation. Women who experience unopposed estrogen stimulation without the appropriate balance of the hormone progestin are at risk. This includes those who experience long periods of chronic anovulation from polycystic ovaries, when estrogen is expressed in large quantities without opposition from progestin. Women menstruating later in life (beyond age 52) also are identified to be at higher risk because of prolonged estrogen stimulation. The prime high-risk candidate, however, is the obese woman over 40 years in age. Women with excess adipose tissue are at risk of a higher estrogen load due to an intricate metabolic mechanism related to conversion of circulating androstendione to estrogen in fat cells (Lurain, 1996). After menopause or surgical removal of ovaries, women in whom hormone replacement is prescribed with estrogen alone are also significant in this group. Those on the antiestrogen tamoxifen after breast cancer are also believed to be at risk. Without any of the higher risk contingencies, endometrial evaluation is not undertaken until overt symptoms appear or other factors are present, such as a strong family history.

Even if cytology from the endometrial suctioning is reported as negative in the woman who is symptomatic or at high risk for the disease, it is unwise to accept this outcome without further investigation. The next step toward making an accurate diagnosis involves dilatation and curettage carried out in the surgical suite under anesthesia. Here, the cervix is dilated sufficiently to visualize the uterine wall and obtain a large sample of tissue (Pastner, 1993).

Sarcomas, cancers in the muscle wall of the uterus, are rare, but they are the most malignant group of uterine tumors. No screening technique is available for this disease, and efforts at diagnosis will only be undertaken on complaint of pain, bleeding, or palpable pelvic mass. Diagnosis can not be made definitively except on pathology of the surgical specimen after hysterectomy. Although differing considerably from endometrial cancer in all aspects—diagnosis, clinical behavior, patterns of spread, and management—sarcomas are staged according to the same FIGO staging as endometrial cancer. Not seen in younger women, they generally occur in perimenopausal years or beyond, and it is not unusual to encounter uterine sarcoma up to 20 years after pelvic radiation. Leiomyosarcomas are the one type diagnosed before menopause when a woman is in her early to mid-forties. A higher incidence of this disease occurs in African-American women, and the prognosis is also poorer for some unexplained reason. Sarcomas are not graded like epithelial tumors. In this histology, the number of mitoses per microscopic field seems to be the best indicator of prognosis. Tumors with five mitoses per high-powered field (HPF) tend to behave like benign tumor and have an excellent survival, whereas tumors with greater than 10 mitoses per field are frankly malignant and have only about a 15% survival rate. In the mid range, tumors with 5 to 10 mitoses per field are not very predictable, and many will recur or metastasize after treatment. Studies show about a 45% survival with this histologic indicator (Lurain, 1996).

Gestational Trophoblastic Tumors

Obstetricians encounter a series of rare but curable tumors, collectively called gestational trophoblastic disease (GTD). Among its variants are the hydatidiform mole and choriocarcinoma. All of the diseases arise from fetal tissue and follow a gestational event, whether a full-term pregnancy, a therapeutic or spontaneous abortion, or, more commonly, a molar pregnancy. The incidence of molar pregnancies is an estimate because of varied record-keeping worldwide. It seems to occur between 0.6 and 1.1 times per 1000 pregnancies in Europe and North America but up to three times that incidence in Asia. In this disease, as with other gynecologic malignancies, there is an interest in worldwide patterns to help pinpoint environmental or genetic risk. One risk factor seems to be maternal age, because the ova are thought to be more susceptible to abnormal fertilization after age 40. Another possible association with molar pregnancies is vitamin A deficiency or low dietary intake of carotene. Dietary factors could also explain differences between populations (Soper, Hammond, & Lewis, 1992).

In pregnancy, the chorionic villi naturally establish a connection to the endometrium and give rise to the placenta. If an abnormal process begins,

the villi degenerate, resulting in rapid growth of multiple watery vesicles (hydatid swelling) inside the uterus, hence the name hydatidiform mole. The complete mole is devoid of identifiable embryonic or fetal tissue. The partial mole may contain the hydatidiform swelling of the chorionic vesicles as well as some fetal tissue, which tends to be abnormal in nature. Presenting symptoms are not as conspicuous in partial moles, and diagnosis often occurs after pathologic review of tissue obtained by curettage after incomplete abortion. Fortunately, many women in this country receive early treatment for complete hydatidiform moles because vaginal staining or hyperemesis is a prominent symptom. Sophisticated diagnostic tools such as ultrasound with vaginal probe assist the detection, which is easy, because the mole will display a "honeycomb" pattern on ultrasound images (Berkowitz & Goldstein, 1996).

Moles are evacuated by suction curettage or hysterectomy if infertility is not the issue. However, hysterectomy does not prevent metastasis, and patients will need follow-up in the months afterward due to certain characteristics of moles: their potential for malignant degeneration, their ability to locally invade the uterus or spread distantly, and their frequent persistence after the molar pregnancy has been evacuated. Trophoblastic tissue produces human chorionic gonadotropin (hCG), which can be measured in serum by radioimmunoassay. hCG is always present during the first 100 days of pregnancy, but its continued elevation is troublesome and should be watched (Rivlin, 1994).

The very malignant trophoblastic tumor, choriocarcinoma, is characterized by sheets of anaplastic cells without any chorionic villi. About half of choriocarcinomas develop after molar evacuation, and the other half follow a normal aborted or full-term pregnancy. They have a tendency to disseminate and metastasize widely through vascular invasion. The lung is the most prevalent site of choriocarcinoma metastasis (80%), followed by the vagina, pelvis, liver, and brain. Metastatic sites bleed easily due to the fragile nature of the vessels. The diagnosis of choriocarcinoma is usually a surprise when preceded by a normal pregnancy, unlike the case in which the molar pregnancy is antecedent.

Although gestational trophoblastic diseases express a high level of hCG, screening is not undertaken as part of ordinary antenatal care, and it is the onset of symptoms that drives further diagnostic measures. Because very high levels of the beta subunit of hCG from the trophoblast tissue are measurable in serum, this marker is most important in initial diagnosis. The diagnosis is made if serum hCG plateaus or rises in three serial samplings over a 2-week period. No other diagnostic test is needed. If disease is detected, weekly levels of serum hCG become the definitive tool for continued surveillance through the treatment period.

Ovarian Cancer

The most threatening cancer and the leading cause of death in the gynecologic group is ovarian carcinoma. Upon initial diagnosis, the disease is frequently already in an advanced stage of III or IV because its early, precipitating signs were silent or obscure and sometimes puzzling. Comparing ovarian cancer stage for stage with endometrial cancer indicates that long-term survival is similar but the outcome in endometrial cancer is much better because it is usually detected at a much earlier stage (Young, 1995). Like endometrial malignancy, it is predominantly a postmenopausal disease, with more than 80% of the common epithelial types occurring after age 62 (Berek, Fu & Hacker, 1996).

Complaints of increasing girth attributed to weight gain, vague gastrointestinal discomfort, urinary frequency, or constipation are the most commonly reported symptoms. The Pap test has no role in detecting this disease, and bimanual palpation undertaken during routine gynecologic examination is ineffective unless a mass of larger dimensions is apparent. Historically, physicians believed that if the ovary could be felt on physical examination after menopause, operative diagnosis of such an abnormality was warranted. This was called the postmenopausal palpable ovary syndrome and was based on the understanding that the ovary, now no longer functioning, is atrophied and too small for detection by palpation (Barber & Graber, 1971). The premise is no longer reliable because many examples have been reported in which small foci of cancer were found in ovarian tissue removed surgically for nonmalignant rea-

sons. However, if the ovary can actually be felt in the woman after menopause, further testing measures such as ultrasound are mandated (Teneriello & Park, 1995).

Early detection is rare and usually occurs coincidental to other diagnostic or treatment procedure, such as a gastrointestinal workup. If the malignancy can be found while still confined to the ovary (stage I), 90% of patients will be cured in contrast to the mere 10% survival rate in patients diagnosed in advanced stages (Piver & Hempling, 1993). Although the common ovarian tumors are epithelial in origin, no other organ naturally possesses as many inherent cell types. Therefore, the ovary has the capacity to produce varied and rare tumors in every age group from prepuberty to advanced age. Fallopian tube cancer, although acting much like ovarian cancer, is classified as a separate disease. It occurs usually in ages 50 to 60, and, although there is no official FIGO staging, the disease is usually diagnosed and managed in the same manner as an ovarian malignancy (Berek, Fu, & Hacker, 1996).

It has long been noted that ovarian cancer is predominantly a disease of women in highly industrialized countries such as Sweden, Norway, England, and the United States and is significantly higher in white women. In contrast, Japan, also a highly industrialized country, has a very low incidence of ovarian cancer. However, as Japanese women migrate to the United States, they experience nearly the same rate of ovarian malignancy. Capitalizing on these and other epidemiologic aspects, factors as divergent as diet, infertility, and industrial waste have been considered (Piver & Hempling, 1993).

With the recent knowledge explosion in molecular biology, families of genes that may play a role in both the breast-ovarian syndrome and familial ovarian cancer have been identified. Cellular oncogenes are transforming genes that are able to get into the cell, changing its entire metabolism and forcing it to grow in a malignant fashion (Weinberg, 1994; Cooper, 1990). Studies have shown that women with mutations of the *BRCA1* gene carry about a 50% lifetime risk of ovarian cancer, and it is even higher for breast cancer (Easton, Ford, & Bishop, 1995). The mutation inheritance is particularly high among Ashkenazi Jews (Struewing et al., 1997). Furthermore, patients with breast cancer often experience a diagnosis of ovarian cancer later in life (Hetzel, Olt, Ndlovu & Podczaski, 1998). Screening for *BRCA1* mutation is the major screening component used in various Familial Ovarian Cancer programs established around the country today. Proto-oncogenes, normal cells that may be converted into an oncogene, are also receiving much attention in looking at the clonal origin of ovarian cancer. Using some of these molecular markers, it has been determined that primary peritoneal carcinoma has a similar cellular origin (Chen, Yamada, Fu, Baldwin, & Karlan, 1998). This disease sometimes presents in women whose ovaries and tubes have been removed. For this reason, prophylactic oophorectomy does not bring certainty of a cancer-free survival in women who have an unfortunate family history.

Significant interest is directed to tumor suppressor genes, which are cellular oncogenes whose *loss* of function leads to tumor development. The *p53* gene is a tumor suppressor gene, and, if it becomes defective, it fails to stop normal programmed cell death or control rampant cell growth. Of interest is the fact that a protein of the HPV, which was discussed earlier in connection with cervical cancer, also is found to inactivate the *p53* gene. There is some evidence that the BRCA1 gene is also a tumor suppressor gene because the mutation leads to loss of the suppressor function and uncontrolled cell proliferation (Daly, 1994). Unquestionably, evolving knowledge about the role of damaged genes in carcinogenesis will be used not only in ovarian cancer but also many others to distinguish populations of women at significant genetic risk and, therefore, effectively implement screening measures for specific malignancies (Young, 1995). Furthermore, replacement of damaged genes as a mode of cancer treatment is in the experimental phase. In fact, *p53* gene replacement in combination with chemotherapy has been proposed as treatment in cases of particularly aggressive ovarian cancers (Sood, Dolan & Buller, 1998).

The fact that ovarian cancer appears to occur in a significant number of women with first- or second-degree relatives who have had the disease caught early attention. In 1981, a Familial Ovarian Cancer Registry was formed, which has now become the Gilda Radner Registry in honor of the actress who died of the disease without ever knowing that she had three or four close relatives with

this disease. Analysis of data emerging from the registry indicates that the lifetime risk in women with two or more first-degree relatives with ovarian disease may be as high as 50% compared with a 1.4% risk in the general population of women without the family pedigree. In those with one relative, the lifetime risk appears to be about 6%. The disease also appears to occur at a much earlier age in the inheritance group (Piver & Hempling, 1993; Piver et al., 1996) In addition to the unique breast-ovarian linkage, the Lynch II family syndrome has been identified. Here, families have a high degree of ovarian, endometrial, and breast cancers along with familial colon and other gastrointestinal or genitourinary malignancies (Berek, Fu, & Hacker, 1996).

Screening techniques for ovarian cancer have been sought for some time. At one time, the tumor marker serum CA 125 seemed promising as a screening tool. CA 125 is a cell-surface glycoprotein of unknown function. It is found in increased levels in at least half of all women with stage I ovarian disease and in 90% of those with advanced ovarian cancer. However, it is also present in benign conditions, so lack of specificity rules out its use in screening. It can be an important marker later in the evaluation process and in following the course of diagnosed ovarian malignances during or after treatment (Teneriello & Park, 1995).

Screening techniques using ultrasound are gaining acceptance, but, because of expense and low yield, these measures are usually employed only when indicated by unique aspects in the woman's history. Ultrasound passes easily through body fluids and is reflected by the solid masses of the pelvic organs. Transabdominal ultrasound uses high-frequency sound waves transmitted abdominally through a full bladder to evaluate the uterus, tubes, and ovaries. Transvaginal ultrasound in which the ultrasound probe is placed vaginally is in closer proximity to the ovaries and gives improved resolution and quality images. Transvaginal color-flow Doppler ultrasonography offers the best opportunity to differentiate a malignant process from benign pelvic masses capitalizing on the increased intratumor vascularization and blood flow characteristic of malignancies. Details of these diagnostic procedures are reviewed in Table 8-3. Promising as these tests are, studies have shown that if they were used as screening

TABLE 8-3	
ADVANCED DIAGNOSTIC TECHNIQUES IN PELVIC MALIGNANCIES	
Transabdominal ultrasound	• Uses high frequency sound waves through body fluids via external probe • Simultaneous evaluation of pelvis, abdominal and retroperitoneal structures • Requires patient preparation with full bladder for test • Low specificity between benign and malignant mass
Transvaginal ultrasound	• Uses vaginal probe for closer proximity to structures • Assesses pelvic structures, greater resolution of ovarian architecture • No full bladder required • Findings quantified, provides better assessment of malignancy risk
Color flow Doppler imaging	• Additive information combined with transvaginal ultrasound, improves ovarian cancer detection • Visually assesses impedance to blood flow in vessels proximate to ovary • Uses vaginal probe • In premenopausal women, must do between 3rd and 10th day of cycle to avoid confusion with luteal phase • Neoplasms form abnormal vessels with lower impedance to blood flow
Pelvic and abdominal computed tomography (CT)	• Best used to evaluate response to treatment, diagnoses of recurrent disease, other organ involvement • Limited ability to scan solid lesions <1–2 cm • Requires oral or IV contrast material
Pelvic magnetic resonance imaging (MRI)	• Assesses pelvic and uterine pathology • Detailed images distinguish between various benign ovarian neoplasms
Positron-emission tomography (PET)	• Can diagnose occult, reccurent disease

tools, the estimated cost of actually diagnosing one case of ovarian cancer would be approximately $1 million (Piver & Hempling, 1993). There should be no hesitation to use the full array of tests, including genetic studies, tumor markers, and ultrasonography, when there is a strong family history or symptoms suggestive of ovarian cancer.

Conclusions on Preinvasive Gynecologic Disease

Because of the characteristically long preinvasive period, prevention and early control of the squamous types of cervical, vaginal, and vulvar diseases are possible. With successful cytologic screening, colposcopic evaluation, and directed biopsy, the disease can be effectively treated while still in an intraepithelial stage. This is responsible for the dramatic decrease in cancer statistics of those diseases in recent years. Obvious symptomatology encourages immediate evaluation of the endometrium, and this can lead to early reversal of preinvasive endometrial cancer through simple treatment. Unfortunately, the opportunity for detection of ovarian lesions while still in a preinvasive state is not available. In this disease, there is hope that genetic research will yield simpler surveillance measures and provide a means of reversing the early cellular abnormalities in ovarian tissue.

Nursing Role in Screening and Detection

The important role of the nurse as bearer of information cannot be overemphasized. Although the medical management of women with gynecologic cancer occurs most frequently in specialty centers generally outside the setting of generalist nurses, screening and diagnosis occur elsewhere. Historically, friends and family often turn to a nurse outside the healthcare setting for clarification or advice on gynecologic issues, perhaps because of the intimate nature of the problem or because explanation will be given at a level more easily grasped by the average consumer. Irrespective of the site of employment, nurses are positioned to help any woman understand facts about screening and the reason for each step in the routine gynecologic examination (see Table 8-2). After screening, further tests may be recommended if findings are abnormal or questionable (see Table 8-3). It is always beneficial for the patient to have as much information as possible about an impending test, especially because there is a natural apprehension in taking tests such as CT scan and MRI because of imposing machinery and concerns about radioactivity.

Determining Individual Risk

Armed with knowledge of currently known cancer risk factors, the nurse will be able to advise the woman about specific personal risk related to her family history, lifestyle, physiologic makeup, or other circumstance and suggest an appropriate gynecologic surveillance schedule to match that risk. Known factors associated with the common gynecologic cancers are reviewed in Table 8-4.

Much has been said about the frequency of Pap smear and pelvic evaluation. Even when guidelines are clear, evidence points to the fact that most women fail to follow recommendations for annual examination, and the actual interval between smears varies between 18 and 27 months (Rose, 1993). General guidelines were developed more than 20 years ago, initially based on studies of rural Canadian women. These recommendations called for annual Pap test and pelvic examination for 3 consecutive years. If findings were normal, thereafter the interval could increase to every 3 years at the discretion of the woman's physician. Later, in a controlled study, the risk of cervical cancer was found to increase significantly in women with 3-year screening intervals over the risk in women with annual screening. For women with a known history of early intercourse and any sexually transmitted disease, particularly genital HPV, some authorities are recommending that screening be undertaken at 6-month intervals. Screening in the elderly population is particularly underutilized, and cervical cancer is found at a more advanced stage in these older age groups who undergo Pap smears at infrequent intervals. If it can be diagnosed while in situ, survival can be virtually ensured, unlike the dismal mortality statistics reflected in advanced disease (White, Begg, Fishman, Guthrie & Fagan, 1993). The older pop-

---

TABLE 8-4

RISK FACTORS IDENTIFIED IN GYNECOLOGIC MALIGNANCIES

Cervical cancer	• Early sexual intercourse, under 18 years
	• Multiple heterosexual partners or serial monogamy
	• Male partners having multiple sexual partners
	• HPV infections, especially flat varieties
	• Immune suppression (eg, corticosteroid therapy, organ transplantation, diabetes)
	• Possible cofactors:
	  –Smoking
	  –*Chlamydia* or other sexually transmitted infections

Vaginal cancer	• Squamous carcinoma: same factors as cervical cancer • Previous cervical cancer • ? Vaginal trauma • Adenocarcinoma: DES exposure in utero

Vulvar cancer	• ? Same factors as cervical cancer
	• Previous granulomatous venereal diseases (syphilis)
	• Associated with:
	  –Obesity
	  –Hypertension
	  –Diabetes

Endometrial cancer	• Obesity • Hormonal replacement therapy with estrogen alone • Never had children • Late menopause, after age 52 • Chronic annovulation (eg, polycystic ovary disease) • Diabetic or prediabetic • Tamoxifen therapy after breast cancer • Prior pelvic radiation • History of endometrial hyperplasia • Strong family history of other hormonally mediated cancer (possible genetic factor) • Hypertension and hypothyroidism
Ovarian cancer	• Previous diagnosis of breast cancer • Family pedigree linked to breast, ovarian, colon, endometrial malignancies • Nulliparity with uninterrupted ovulation • ? Environmental factors related to industrialization • ? Exposure to talc and asbestos • ? High-fat diet • ? Mumps virus

(Adapted from De Stefano & Bertin-Martin, 1996; Hetzel et al., 1998; Ibbotson & Wyke, 1995; Lurain, 1996; Pastner, 1993; Rose, 1993; and Tinkle, 1990.)

ulation should be watched for vaginal or vulvar cancer as well as cervical cancer because similar HPV origins are suggested.

Less emphasis has been put on vulvar self-examination than other self-examination programs such as breast or testicular. Its importance has been demonstrated, particularly in the older woman. Like breast examination, it can be done in the shower or bath where soap and water serve as sufficient lubricant for the hand to move over all surfaces. Nothing more is demanded than to feel for lumps or masses because they are usually painless and do not otherwise command attention.

Women who fit the profile of familial ovarian cancer express significant fears. Because there is no simple screening, many who carry a significant risk because of multiple first- and second-degree relatives with the disease will seek advice on genetic counseling. Nurses may also be questioned about the advisability of early removal of ovaries and tubes for prophylaxis, just as some women with breast cancer histories choose prophylactic mastectomy. They may have received a recent recommendation to step up childbearing plans (if desired) and then have the oophorectomy. Unfortunately, such drastic measures have not always been preventive because data show that the disease may present later as primary peritoneal cancer. Advice can be given to the at-risk woman about the locations of major centers that focus on genetic testing and diagnostic examinations specific to ovarian cancer. The option of seeking a genetic workup is not to be taken lightly because of the enormous psychological impact on women found to carry the susceptibility gene BRCA1. Much has been written about the psychosocial status of women who are aware of their family risk and their choice of formal genetic risk assessment and workup or not (Lerman, Daly, Masny & Balshem, 1994; Ritvo et al., 1998; Smith & Schwartz, 1995). Any woman entertaining the idea of a medical genealogic study may be referred to the book *How Healthy Is Your Family Tree?: A Complete Guide To Tracing Your Family's Medical And Behavioral Tree* by Carol Krause. The author and her sisters decided to become very well informed before making decisions about prophylactic surgery based on their genetic makeup. The issues faced are complicated and far reaching, both to others in the same generation and to those in the next.

Support Through the Diagnostic Phase

After suspicion of malignancy through earlier screening processes or diagnostic tests, the most difficult time of all may be in those few days before the full scope of the malignancy can be defined. Many women describe this period of uncertainty, however brief, as the most difficult to endure. A number of women have reported to this author that after cancer was confirmed, fears were significant but the ordeal became more bearable because treatment and procedures that lay ahead could now be defined. The future becomes more concrete, plans can be made, and support and coping skills can be mobilized. After the treatment plan is presented, some women will specifically seek out the nurse for support. Patients have stated that they want the closeness of a medical professional who can share past experiences and outcomes to help the woman assemble her armament. According to some, the nurse is easier to converse with than the physician and better able to define the event holistically in relationship to other life factors.

Diagnosis During Pregnancy

Particularly tragic is the circumstance of cancer diagnosis during pregnancy. Here, the woman is suddenly confronted with loss of her unborn child and perhaps ultimate loss of her own life. The diagnosis of a gynecologic cancer in the pregnant female does not always mean loss of the fetus. Each circumstance is unique, and all factors must be weighed—type of cancer, cell type, and natural characteristics for spread, plus sensitivity to the various treatments. Both surgery and chemotherapy have been used variously in the early and the late phases of pregnancy without fetal loss or harm. Radiation, on the other hand, will result in fetal damage or loss. Surgical excision is possible if the tumor is confined. One cancer that may appear during pregnancy is the germ cell tumor, one in a rare group of neoplasms constituting about 5% of ovarian cancers in Western countries but about 15% of ovarian cancers in Asian- and African-American women (Berek, Fu, & Hacker, 1996). It normally occurs in young patients in their teens and potential childbearing years of the twenties. If it is still small, the tumor can usually be surgically removed intact and the pregnancy continued. If disease is more advanced and the pregnancy is into the second or third trimester, full-dose chemotherapy can be given because agents used have no apparent detriment to the fetus (Gershenson & Wharton, 1985).

Because of association with younger age groups, epithelial types of ovarian cancer and cervical cancer are the other gynecologic diseases likely to be found during pregnancy. Treatment is tailored to the cancer stage and gestational age. If in the second or third trimester of pregnancy, a number of women have opted to carry to term or to a gestational age ensuring fetal viability. In these instances, the threat to the mother's life can be significant, but each woman should be maximally supported whatever her decision, as long as the medical professional can be assured that all facts have been disclosed. Generally, the baby is delivered vaginally, but cesarean section is recommended by some clinicians who believe that vaginal delivery in proximity to the cancer may encourage more rapid dissemination of the cancer. The woman should always be assured that the cancer does not affect the fetus, nor is it thought that the pregnancy will affect the cancer by encouraging a more aggressive growth (Barber, 1980).

Treatment of Gynecologic Malignancies

All modalities of cancer treatment are employed in gynecologic cancer. No matter the type or site of the disease, however, surgery is likely to be part of the treatment plan, whether for exploration and staging, primary treatment, or management of critical consequences such as bowel obstruction. The major treatment modalities are listed in Table 8-5 by disease site. These are only guidelines; each case is different, with plans circumscribed by the individual characteristics of the case.

Although obstetrician/gynecologists or general surgeons during other surgical procedures may encounter gynecologic cancers, care of these patients is best in the hands of gynecologic oncologists well schooled in the radical surgery required of the specialty. These specialists may also retain management of the patient through chemotherapy, or this phase may be under guidance of a medical oncologist. Radiation oncologists always manage radiation therapy. In most cases, a team effort is promoted with consultation submitted by all parties.

Surgery

Cervical Cancer

Total abdominal hysterectomy (TAH) is the treatment for early stages of cervical cancer when the disease is small. This includes removal of uterus and the cervix, excision of a small vaginal cuff, and some tissue to the side of the cervix. The procedure called radical hysterectomy is done for larger lesions. Here, tissue that surrounds the ureter adjacent to the cervix and uterine body is removed. The bladder is freed from the vagina and approximately one fourth to one third of the vagina is removed. It is customary to remove pelvic lymph nodes and sample some of the para-aortic nodes higher up as well.

Pelvic exenteration is a very complex surgical procedure reserved for special cases of vaginal or cervical cancer in which the tumor has recurred at a very central location. It is done only with cure in mind, not palliation. This procedure is performed less frequently now than in the past because of improved radiation therapy, which has reduced the incidence of central recurrence. Usually, cervical cancer recurrence happens in the first 1 to 2 years after primary treatment. If the woman is experiencing leg edema, weight loss, and pelvic pain especially radiating down the thigh, chances of exenteration are vastly reduced because this triad implies that tumor has regrown in proportions unsuited to successful surgery. Pelvic exenteration is a very radical surgery that involves removal of bladder and urethra (anterior exenteration), rectum (posterior exenteration), or both (total exenteration), along with uterus, cervix, and vagina. A urinary conduit will be constructed to replace the bladder. New techniques in establishing continent urinary diversions have helped improve physical appearance as well as psychological outlook. On occasion, a colostomy can be avoided if the transverse colon can be pulled into position for reanastomosis to the lower rectum. It is not uncommon to construct a new vagina at the time of surgery employing muscle and skin from the inner thigh (called a myocutaneous flap), which is rotated upward to form a new "vaginal" barrel. Immediate postoperative support requires critical care nursing to properly maintain hemodynamic monitoring and other supportive measures. Recovery can be long as well, requiring a number of months before return of normal activity.

Vaginal Cancer

The close proximity of bowel and bladder to the thin vaginal wall limits the consideration of surgery as primary treatment of vaginal carcinoma. Radiation is the preferred modality, therefore, in all squamous cancers except those of minimal proportions. In small stage I lesions confined to the upper vagina, the radical hysterectomy is done in conjunction with partial vaginectomy. In diseases located in the middle or lower vagina, pelvic exenteration will be needed. Adenocarcinoma is less radiosensitive, and, therefore, surgery is seriously considered in all small lesions of this variety. Because these women are younger in age, the ovaries may be spared. Surgery is not possible in any large stage I and the more advanced vaginal malignancies. Anatomic differences in vaginal lesions require much individualization in the treatment plans for vaginal cancer.

Vulvar Cancer

Surgery is clearly the preferred method of treatment of vulvar cancer, both in early and more advanced disease. If the cancer is small, a hemivulvectomy and groin node dissection on the affected side suffice for treatment. Slightly larger lesions require radical vulvectomy with removal of the vulva and skin over the mons pubis up to the iliac crest along with bilateral groin node dissection. Some surgeons favor separate incisions for these parts, but others remove the tissue in one single block. Surgery becomes more radical as the stage of disease advances and may involve removal of urethra, vagina, or anus. Pelvic exenteration with removal of bladder or rectum or both is indicated in some stage IV disease. Less radical surgery, however, is an option in conjunction with radiation. Proximity to the femoral artery is a major risk of the surgery, and the healing process for vulvar surgery is com-

plicated by frequent wound breakdown because of poor blood supply to the area, moist environment, and infection from contamination.

Endometrial Cancer

Total abdominal hysterectomy is the primary treatment mode in endometrial cancer. Removal of tubes and ovaries, the bilateral salpingo-oophorectomy (BSO), accompanies the hysterectomy, but lymph node removal is usually not indicated. Radiation, delivered in varied ways, may be added both before or after surgery. This addition reduces the need for more radical surgeries. The radical hysterectomy may be required if disease is more extensive, however. A surgical approach to treatment of most gynecologic cancers is favored because there are fewer long-term adverse effects than with other modalities.

Ovarian Cancer

Exploratory laparotomy is needed to diagnose ovarian cancer. After initial evaluation, the surgical goal becomes maximal cytoreduction. This term means that tumor bulk is reduced to the optimum possible, with every effort made to excise microscopic as well as large deposits of malignant tissue from the peritoneal cavity. Survival in ovarian cancer has been shown in numerous studies to relate directly to the amount of disease remaining after surgery. Best prognosis is given to those in which there is no visible disease. If only microscopic disease rather than large tumor mass is left, the chemotherapy that follows will have the best chance of success. The surgical challenge relates to the widespread location of tumor nests. The spread of the ovarian tumor occurs because of shedding of cells from the cancerous ovary, which then disseminate through peritoneal fluid to implant along the peritoneal surfaces of the intestines, the right diaphragm, the liver capsule, and the omentum. The disease seldom invades the intestinal lumen, but it does bind down loops of bowel, leading to functional intestinal obstruction, which require future operative procedures. Ovarian cancer seldom spreads to lymph nodes so lymphadenectomy is not done (Berek, Fu, & Hacker, 1996).

In ovarian cancer, "second-look" surgery is often part of the long-term treatment plan. After a
(text continues on p. 152)

TABLE 8-5
OVERVIEW OF TREATMENT OF GYNECOLOGIC MALIGNANCIES

	Cervical	Vaginal	Vulvar	Uterine	Trophoblastic	Ovarian
Surgery	Radical hysterectomy for stage 1 Pelvic exenteration for selected recurrences	Radical vaginectomy, hysterectomy and pelvic nodes Pelvic exenteration	Vulvectomy	Simple hysterectomy	D&C of mole Hysterectomy in choriocarcinoma Thoracotomy with pulmonary metastases	Exploratory laparotomy, TAH, BSO, extensive tumor debulking Subsequent exploratory laparotomy for evaluation and tumor debulking
Surgery with Radiotherapy	Hysterectomy after radiation in stage I "bulky" disease	Laparoscopic evaluation for lymph node involvement	Postoperative pelvic and groin nodes	Postoperative pelvic in stage I disease		
Radiotherapy External Beam	Pelvic tissues, regional lymph node, and para-aortic nodes	Extended field if upper lesion	Recently used as primary treatment in selected cases Adjuvant use in selected high-risk patients	Adjunct to surgery to prevent recurrence Primary if patient poor surgical candidate Curative in vaginal or pelvic recurrence	Whole brain radiation to 3000 cGy in brain metastasis	Whole abdominal radiation to 2200–3000 cGy Most effective in low-grade and low-stage disease
Radiotherapy Intracavitary	Alone or combined with external beam	High dose to tumor, may combine with external beam				

Radiotherapy Interstitial	Increasingly used for advanced or recurrent disease	Primary or secondary treatment—combined with external beam	Primary or secondary treatment—combined with external beam			
Intracavitary Radioisotopes						^{32}P in early disease, confined to peritoneum
Chemotherapy Intravenous	Advanced/recurrent Iphosfamide Cisplatin Hydroxyurea Bleomycin Mitomycin-C				Primary treatment Methotrexate Actinomycin-D Combination of MTX, Act-D, etoposide, cyclophosphamide, vincristine	Cisplatin and paclitaxel Carboplatin and paclitaxel May dose escalate using G-CSF
Intraperitoneal						Cisplatin in minimal disease
Radiotherapy with IV Chemotherapy	5FU or cisplatin with external beam	Not currently used but trials are warranted	5FU or cisplatin with external beam			
Hormonal Therapy				Progesterone therapy Tamoxifen		Progesterone

(Adapted from Berek, Fu & Hacker, 1996; Berkowitz & Goldstein, 1996; Hacker, 1996; Hatch & Fu, 1996; Lurain, 1996; Young & Thomas, 1996.)

several-month course of chemotherapy, the patient may appear to be cancer free, but this must be proved before any decision is made to discontinue treatment. If an indwelling peritoneal dialysis catheter was placed in the peritoneum during primary surgery, this is used to obtain intraperitoneal washings. In this procedure, saline is flushed into the peritoneal cavity, then drained and sent for cytologic analysis. If tumor cells are found, treatment with chemotherapy continues; if not, the second-look surgery is recommended for a more thorough evaluation before absolutely concluding the chemotherapy regimen. Should tumor be found, optimal resection again becomes the goal. On occasion, the second surgery is done for further tumor debulking in the face of known disease, but this is controversial among clinicians because it adds a great deal of morbidity to the woman's life without appreciably improving long-term survival. The general perspective, however, for many women with ovarian cancer becomes one in which multiple surgeries for tumor debulking or release of bowel obstruction are interspersed with chemotherapy and radiation.

Radiation Therapy

Radiation administered in a variety of ways is a prominent treatment modality in gynecologic cancers. The reader is encouraged to review Chapter 13 for a general understanding of the principles. External beam therapy to the pelvis is the most common mode, and it may be given daily over several weeks. Cervical and endometrial cancers are particularly suited to radiotherapy given externally or internally using a special applicator. Intracavitary radiotherapy, in which the metal applicator is placed against the cervix, can be given over one or two applications. In some treatment centers, interstitial administration using a template to hold numerous small rods or "needles" containing the radioactive source is popular. Greater variance is allowed with the template because placement can be customized to optimally reach tumors that are closer to the pelvic sidewall. The choice of radiation over surgery or the two in combination depends on the clinician preference as well as the woman's disease characteristics. In stages I and II of cervical cancer, ex-ternal beam radiation to the pelvis may be planned. One or two intracavitary or interstitial insertions along with radical hysterectomy may be in order.

In very early stage ovarian cancer, radiation can be given by the intraperitoneal route. Radioactive colloids, specifically ^{32}P, are infused into the peritoneum for a brief period of time. Currently, this mode is less commonly used because improved chemotherapy agents are available. External beam radiation to the whole abdomen also might be used in ovarian treatment at some centers instead of chemotherapy when there is remaining microscopic disease after cytoreductive surgery. Other clinicians avoid the radiation approach because the field is high on the abdomen and initiates the potential for acute or chronic bowel obstruction. Some studies report this in 30% of patients receiving radiation (Hacker, Berek, Burnison, Heintz, Juillard & Lagasse, 1985).

Although radiation therapy is not the recommended primary mode of treatment in certain diseases, it is always considered for first-line treatment when the woman is a poor candidate for surgery. It may be used on vulvar lesions, especially if small, although there is the potential for increased adverse side effects because of anatomic location. Radiation of inguinal lymph nodes instead of surgical resection is sometimes used in this disease.

The scope of surgical procedures in gynecologic malignancies includes palliative measures such as release of bowel obstructions or resection of distant metastasis. Increased years of survival have been demonstrated recently with excision of lung metastasis in cervical or endometrial cancer (Moreno et al., 1998).

Radiation Therapy With Chemotherapy

Several chemotherapy agents have been given concurrently with radiotherapy to "sensitize" the hypoxic tumor cell. This renders the tumor more susceptible to the radiation, but it may also significantly increase adverse effects on the skin because all tissues, not just tumor, are involved. Cisplatin, 5FU, hydroxyurea, and mizonidazole are examples of agents used in this role.

Chemotherapy

Certain lower-risk categories of gestational tropho-blastic disease are dramatically cured with a few courses of single- or multiple-agent chemotherapy. In the higher-risk categories of trophoblastic disease, including choriocarcinoma, combination chemotherapy using anywhere from 3 to 8 drugs offers complete cure in about 80% of cases. Unfortunately, this represents the only gynecologic malignancy in which cure is achieved with chemotherapy alone.

In more advanced gynecologic malignancies, systemic chemotherapy will be an adjunct to surgery, when it follows extensive tumor debulking, or it may be considered for first-line treatment. A number of drugs are active. Agents in use for a number of years include 5FU, Adriamycin, actinomycin-D, and methotrexate. Hexamethylmelamine and etoposide entered the picture about 15 years ago. For nearly 2 decades, cisplatin has played a very strong role in gynecologic cancer treatment, and it remains a pivotal agent in ovarian cancer therapy. Its analogue, carboplatin, is also very effective but has not gained quite the importance of cisplatin. It is a particularly active second-line agent in patients who have responded to prior cisplatin therapy but failed to achieve total tumor eradication. Unfortunately, with few exceptions, no more than 30% of patients usually achieve response from second-line chemotherapy treatment (Berek, Fu, & Hacker, 1996). Despite such poor success, second- and third-line chemotherapy will be offered the patient. Positive results in several gynecologic malignancies, particularly ovarian, have been achieved with the introduction of newer drugs like ifosphamide and paclitaxel.

Alkylating agents, particularly melphalan, were among the earliest drugs used in gynecologic cancers, and, if response was noted, the patient generally stayed on a maintenance dose for months or years. It was alarming when mortality rates suddenly rose in these patients, most of whom had no remaining evidence of cancer. It seems that chronic bone marrow depression resulting from the drug therapy became irreversible and frequently precipitated both aplastic anemia and leukemia. In the last 2 decades, the effort has been made to limit the treatment span and to give drugs in combination so that no one agent will leave lasting adverse effects from excessive toxicity. Now, combination chemotherapy is the norm in gynecologic cancer. The reader is referred to other sources that outline cell kinetics related to drug therapy as well as expected side effects.

Instilling chemotherapy directly into the peritoneal cavity began about a decade ago. Intraperitoneal chemotherapy (IP) was devised on the principle that high concentration of drugs can be administered directly onto surfaces of tumor with good uptake while avoiding toxic effects to the system as a whole. A peritoneal catheter of the type used for peritoneal dialysis (Tenckhoff) or an implantable port-a-cath is placed into the abdomen and kept for several months for the periodic installation. The chemotherapy agent is diluted in dyalisate and warmed to room temperature for administration. Unfortunately, adhesions from surgery often impair the free flow of fluid through the tubing, as does a slow buildup of fibrin at the internal tip of the tubing. Extravasation of drug into skin tissue around the catheter, identical to intravenous therapy, is a rare occurrence. Peritonitis is always of concern with intraperitoneal therapy as well (De Stefano & Bertin-Matson, 1996). Nevertheless, good responses have been achieved by this innovative approach without the unpleasant gastrointestinal symptoms associated with IV chemotherapy.

Hormonal Therapy

Because high estrogen levels appear to play a prominent role in the origin of endometrial cancer, the theory of using its opposing hormone as a therapeutic agent has long been of interest. Oral progestin therapy (Megace) is frequently prescribed after tumor recurrence, and there is good response in a large number of patients. The hormone interferes with estrogen uptake at the receptor site. Tamoxifen is an antiestrogen commonly used in breast cancer, and this drug has also been used effectively alone or in combination with progestin with good effect in recurrent disease (Lurain, 1996). Progestin is also found useful in ovarian cancer, with a 25% response rate in late-stage disease. Both of these drugs have minimal effect in patients with poorly differentiated (grade

III) or anaplastic tumors, but the response is quite significant in patients with the grade I, well-differentiated cell type (Berek, Fu, & Hacker, 1996).

Nursing Issues in the Treatment of Gynecologic Cancers

Throughout the continuum of care, an ever-changing set of issues comes before nurses who encounter the patient with a gynecologic malignancy. A brief overview of some of the concerns as they appear at a particular phase in care is provided in Table 8-6. Few of the issues are unique to the gynecologic patient with the exception of some sexual and reproductive issues. Most problems are the same as those encountered by patients experiencing other types of malignancies. Many care issues are outcomes of the therapy itself, and other texts outline management of their related adverse effects. Some unique problems related to gynecologic cancers are discussed in the sections below. Management of many will require nothing beyond basic nursing skills, the foremost being excellent assessment skills. Awareness of the common issues in the gynecologic patient will help the nurse focus history taking and assessment efficiently so that intervention or prompt reporting can be initiated.

Pain

In the early stages of cancer, pain is negligible or nonexistent from the tumor itself. Until a tumor mass reaches sufficient proportions, there may be little awareness of its presence. Once the mass is larger, its demand for space compresses nerves and interferes with function. One of the unique pain patterns associated with gynecologic cancers is the low pelvic pain that often radiates down the back of the leg (sciatic nerve). This is identified with advanced or recurrent cervical disease. It is characterized by a chronic, deep ache, which is unrelieved by positional change. Round-the-clock analgesic regimens are appropriate here. The woman may experience the same type of pain while undergoing internal radiation by the obturator type of applicator or the template. Continuous narcotic analgesia infusion often accompanies this procedure.

Along with nausea and vomiting, severe cramping may characterize the bowel obstruction associated with ovarian cancer. The loop of bowel expanded by the natural production of gases by bowel flora produces a very uncomfortable situation until decompression by means such as nasogastric (NG) suction. Narcotic analgesia usually offers minimal relief, although it certainly will be provided.

The experience of pain is one of the most feared among patients diagnosed with cancer. When the treatment plan comprises multiple surgeries, as is particularly prevalent in ovarian cancer, pain management with medication tailored to the pain level is the logical approach. Multiple treatises have been published about effective management of acute and chronic pain that will be typically experienced by the gynecologic patient.

Pulmonary Embolism and Deep Vein Thrombosis

Deep vein thrombosis (DVT) and pulmonary emboli are possible sequelae of pelvic surgery. Immobility during the postoperative period increases the threat, especially in patients undergoing vulvectomy or pelvic exenteration in whom bedrest will be enforced for a number of days. Anticoagulation therapy and/or pneumatic calf compression are very important at this time. Non–weight-bearing leg movement is also helpful. Doing frequent assessments with DVT in mind should be routine for the postoperative nurse in acute care. DVTs were also shown in one study to be an adverse outcome in the patient population who had undergone pelvic radiation (Morgan, Iyegar, Schwartz, Mikuta & Rubin, 1998).

Wound Breakdown

Wound care is a major issue for nurses caring for gynecologic patients. Poor vascularization in tissues occurs from radiation as well as the from compromise resulting from surgery. The proximity of the genitourinary and gastrointestinal tract to surgical incisions increases the risk of contamination and infection. Not all surgical wounds can be closed and left to heal by primary intention; many must be left open because of contamination or

---

TABLE 8-6
NURSING CONCERNS IN GYNECOLOGIC CARE

The Nurse in the Community
- Recognize high-risk candidates for a gynecologic malignancy
- Educate patients on anatomic structures and disease
- Encourage routine gynecologic examinations appropriate to woman's risk profile
- Intensive patient education about risk factors and follow-up

The Nurse in the Ambulatory Screening/Diagnostic Setting
- Patient education regarding diagnostic procedures and associated preps
- Support through painful tests
- Precise record-keeping and follow-up on abnormal test results
- Thorough explanation and interpretation of test findings
- Emotional support at time patient is informed of diagnosis
- Establish trust in the medical team, assistance with informed consent
- Prepare for surgical procedures by providing preoperative teaching

The Nurse in the Acute Hospital Setting
- Standard, basic nursing management after radical surgery
- Management of actue perioperative pain
- Protect from infection
- Attentive wound care
- Educate and support patient with new urinary or fecal diversion appliance
- Prepare for protracted treatment course with chemotherapy or radiation
- Solicit assistance of social service, home care, and group support services

The Nurse in the Ambulatory Treatment Setting
- Management of chronic pain
- Nutritional support
- Preparation and support if undergoing radiation therapy
- Administration of intravenous and intraperitoneal chemotherapy
- Physiologic and psychological support with adverse effects of treatment
- Monitor and advise on home infusion
- Guidance on sexual concerns or dysfunction

The Nurse in the Home Care Setting
- Assess home environment for needed aids and equipment
- Alleviate fears of the family in providing nursing care at home
- Help with diet in relationship to anorexia and cachexia
- Observe for late onset of adverse effects from chemotherapy or radiation
- Be alert to signs of disease recurrence
- Provide information for management of death at home
- Contact the family on anniversary dates after patient's death

(Adapted from Chamorro, T. [1985]. Gynecologic malignancies: Medical and nursing management. *NAACOG Update Series, 2,* Lesson II. Princeton: Continuing Professional Education Center, Inc.)

---

compromised vascularity, especially in the obese patient. These must heal by secondary intention and may require a vigorous debridement regimen. Closed system drainage will be used for a few days after most of the big, radical surgeries and will be discontinued when their effluence is significantly reduced. Some wounds may open at the drainage site and require special attention. Wound assessment is critical so that potential complications receive early identification and appropriate treatment. Consultation with an enterostomal therapist will help in the choice of an appropriate dressing or debridement schedule.

Bowel Obstruction

The frequency of bowel obstruction in late-stage ovarian cancer is significant. Nasogastric suction along with intravenous fluids is standard management in all patients with a life expectancy of at least 2 months (Berek, Fu, & Hacker, 1996). It should be avoided, however, in palliative care because of the profound discomfort of the tube. The patient is kept NPO while the tube is in place. In patients who are not undergoing gastric suction, minimal amounts of fluids may be given, although this may provoke vomiting. Likely, a gastrostomy tube will be placed to manage the stomach secretions. The patient remains mildly dehydrated, but this will reduce gastric secretions and the amount of vomiting. Frequent mouth care is an important nursing measure. Bowel obstruction is one of the most unpleasant sequelae of gynecologic or gastrointestinal cancers, and an empathic approach by the nurse is of great benefit.

Fistula

An unfortunate consequence of vaginal or cervical radiation is the vaginal fistula. Tumor growth in proximity to the vagina is also responsible for a number of fistulas, both vesigovaginal (bladder) and rectovaginal (bowel). Surgical closure of the fistula may be required, but this is not always possible until other measures are taken. Sometimes, a permanent or temporary fecal or urinary diversion is done to allow the fistula opportunity to heal spontaneously, with the later goal of taking down the urinary conduit or colostomy when the fistula is closed. Unfortunately, repeat fistulas are often seen in the radiated patient because the vaginal wall tissue is extremely thin and friable. Success with fistula self-repair or surgical closure is not ensured because of compromised vascularity inhibiting the healing process. With the onset of a fistula, the patient must deal not only with the problem of urine and feces control but also with a strong, repulsive odor related to the necrotic process. Patients report that no other circumstance is as distressing and devastating to pride and self-image as this event. The antibiotic metronidazole may reduce odor from necrosis. The nurse can assist the patient in keeping clean with sitz baths and frequent change of pads. Skin protection and dryness to avoid excoriation is a major nursing challenge, as is emotional support.

Ascites and Pleural Effusions

The "seeding" of the serous peritoneal membrane with nests of ovarian tumor is thought to cause the ascites so often seen in ovarian cancer. Although much less common, pleural effusions are also seen when extensive tumor studding is on the diaphragm. Lymphatic and venous obstruction is also thought to play a role in ascites. Para- or pleurocentesis must be done when the fluid reaches larger proportions and respiratory function becomes compromised. Rapid reaccumulation of the fluid is characteristic, so intervals between paracentesis become shorter and shorter. Many physicians discourage fluid evacuation, believing that encourages an acceleration of fluid buildup. The fluid is protein rich, and hypoalbuminemia can result. Use of oral diuretics such as spironolactone has been suggested. Although not actually sclerosing agents, several chemotherapy agents—for example, bleomycin, nitrogen mustard, 5FU, and thiotepa—have been used with minimal success to scar off the serous membrane and reduce the weeping. Paracentesis is momentarily discomforting to the patient when the needle enters the abdomen, but she soon feels relief with her breathing as the fluid is tapped off.

Anorexia and Weight Loss

It is characteristic of many cancers to bring about cachexia. Among the gynecologic malignancies, it is most pronounced in ovarian cancer. The physiologic mechanism is unexplained, but it appears to involve more complex factors than just appetite loss. For instance, with ascites, the protein loss will affect the patient's nutritional status as well as the increased girth, which might bring about early satiation at mealtime. Typically, small, frequent meals should be the nurse's recommendation. Some women have reported that cold foods are more palatable when appetite is nonexistent; in others, the opposite is true, and warm, somewhat salty meals are more appealing. In women with ovarian cancer who are started on Megace, several have reported an upswing in appetite. Corticosteroids and metoclopramide also are appetite stimulants (Pickett & Yancy, 1996).

Cystitis and Proctitis

Radiation-induced cystitis frequently occurs 2 to 3 weeks after radiation therapy is begun. Fluid intake of at least 2 L daily is the most important measure to ameliorate this symptom. Analgesics and antispasmodics will help with the discomfort of bladder contractility. The mucosa of the rectum is also affected by radiation, and diarrhea is an early consequence. The nurse can advise the patient as well as the person who may be preparing meals about a low-residue diet. Antidiarrheal medications should be ordered, but if the first medication is not found effective, a trial should be made of several others because individual response is variable. Return of normal bowel function may require months, and many women have reported that symptoms sometimes improve but there is never a full return to the pretreatment state.

Hydronephrosis

Renal failure is often the actual cause of death in patients with cervical cancer.

Obstructive nephropathy is a common outcome of advanced disease in which tumor encases the ureters and slowly closes them. Insertion of stents into the ureters is frequently done, and oral dexamethasone is given daily for 3 to 5 days to help maintain patency (Lickiss & Wiltshire, 1996). When these measures are no longer effective, a nephrostomy tube is placed. This large, bulky tube can be painful if not held completely immobile. Teaching the patient to manage a nephrostomy tube is a nursing obligation. As renal function diminishes, compromised mentation and double vision are two symptoms for the nurse to assess and report.

Neuropathies

Because cisplatin is perhaps the drug most actively used in gynecologic malignancies, the patient must be assessed frequently for neuropathies. A late onset of "glove and stocking" anesthesia can occur sometime after chemotherapy treatment is discontinued, or it may appear earlier in the midst of treatments. Gait may be affected from loss of proprioception, and the woman is in jeopardy of falling. Nurses can provide patient education to alert the patient to report discomforting symptoms and to take extra precautions for her own safety.

Leg Edema

One consequence of vulvectomy and the inguinal lymphadenectomy is leg edema. This is very distressing to the woman because of appearance and reduced function, but it also invites cellulitis in the feet and lower legs. Venous or lymphatic obstruction because of tumor near the inguinal vessels is another cause of edema, although it is usually not as severe. Providing small doses of diuretics or elevating the extremity(s) and gently massaging toward the trunk may be helpful. Historically, legs were wrapped with elastic bandages or custom support stocking were used, but this practice is discouraged now because it is known to further compromise venous circulation. The nurse should carefully examine legs and feet for cellulitis or infection.

Coping

The emotional aspects associated with the gynecologic cancers vary as the woman progresses from diagnosis through the different treatment phases. Coping abilities may diminish further with protracted treatment, such as that seen in ovarian cancer, until she feels a sense of hopelessness with each new treatment initiated in the fight against persistent disease. Patient education is probably the most effective tool the nurse can offer the woman. Armed with appropriate knowledge, the patient may be able to envision options along each step and control feelings of unbridled despair.

The Family

Cancer has been described as a family disease. The victim is not just the woman with the diagnosis but all those in her close association. The age at which cancer is diagnosed may fall in the early parenting years, as is often the case in some aggressive cervical cancers, and young children are frequently seen at the bedside with their fathers. Nurses are particularly moved by the tragedy about to befall the young family experiencing the death of a wife and mother. A recurring experience of this author surrounds the one person often overlooked in the incident—the aging parent of the cancer victim, who is also in the scenario. So much attention is placed on the husband and children that no one is alerted to the quiet grief experienced by the elderly parent sitting in the corner who is going through an event most never expect—having an adult child precede them in death. The nurse who can take a few minutes to comfort the elderly parent will always be rewarded for the small gesture. Aiding the human experience through death becomes part of the art form of nursing.

REFERENCES

Barber, H. R. K. (1980). Pregnancy and malignancy. In H. R. K. Barber (Ed.), *Manual of gynecologic oncology* (pp. 51–57). Philadelphia: J. B. Lippincott.

Barber, H.K., & Graber, E.A. (1971). The PMPO syndrome (postmenopausal palpable ovary syndrome). *Obstetrics and Gynecology, 38,* 921–923.

Berek, J. S., Fu, Y. S., & Hacker, N. F. (1996). Ovarian cancer. In J. S. Berek, E. Y. Adashi, & P. A. Hillard (Eds.), *Novak's gynecology* (12th ed., pp. 1155–1230). Baltimore: Williams & Wilkins.

Berkowitz, R. S., & Goldstein, D. P. (1996) Gestational trophoblastic disease. In J. S. Berek, E. Y. Adashi, & P. A. Hillard (Eds.), *Novak's gynecology* (12th ed., pp. 1261–1282). Baltimore: Williams & Wilkins.

Brinton, L. A., Nasca, P. C., Mallin, K., Baptiste, M. S., Wilbanks, G. D., & Richart, R. M. (1990). Case control study of cancer of the vulva. *Obstetrics & Gynecology, 75,* 859–866.

Burger, M. P., Hollema, H., Gouw, A. S., Pieters, W. J., & Quint, W. G. (1993). Cigarette smoking and human papillomavirus in patients with reported cervical cytological abnormality. *British Medical Journal, 306,* 749–752.

Celentano, D. (1988). Updated approaches to screening for cervical cancer in older women. *Geriatrics, 43,* 37–48.

Chambers, J. T., & Chambers, S. K. (1992). Endometrial sampling: When? Where? Why? With what? *Clinical Obstetrics and Gynecology, 35,* 28–39.

Chamorro, T. (1990). Cancer of the vulva and vagina. *Seminars in Oncology Nursing, 6,* 198–205.

Chamorro, T. (1985). Gynecologic malignancies: Medical and nursing management. *NAACOG Update Series, 2,* Lesson 11. Princeton: Continuing Professional Education Center, Inc.

Chen, L. M., Yamada, S. D., Fu, Y. S., Baldwin, R. L., & Karlan, B. Y. (1998). Molecular similarity of primary peritoneal and primary ovarian carcinomas. [CD-ROM] *Proceedings of the Society of Gynecologic Oncologists, 208.*

Cooper, G. M. (1990). *Oncogenes.* Boston: Jones and Bartlett.

Daly, M. B. (1994). New perspectives in breast cancer: The genetic revolution. In S. M. Hubbard, P. E. Greene & M. T. Knobf (Eds.), *Oncology nursing* (pp. 1–10). Philadelphia: J. B. Lippincott.

De Stefano, M. S., & Bertin-Matson, K. (1996). Gynecologic cancers. In R. McCorkle, M. Grant, M. Frank-Stromberg & S. B. Baird (Eds.), *Cancer nursing: A comprehensive textbook* (2nd ed., pp. 698–728). Philadelphia: W. B. Saunders.

DiSaia, P. J., & Creasman, W. T. (1993). Preinvasive disease of the cervix. In P. J. DiSaia & W. T. Creasman (Eds.), *Clinical gynecologic oncology* (4th ed., pp. 1–36). St. Louis: C. V. Mosby.

Easton, D.F., Ford, D. & Bishop, D.T. (1995) Breast and ovarian cancer incidence in BRCA1-mutation carriers. Breast Cancer Linkage Consortium. *American Journal of Human Genetics, 56*(1), 265–271.

Fowler, J. (1993). Screening for cervical cancer: Current terminology, classification, and technique. *Postgraduate Medicine, 93,* 57–72.

Gershenson, D. M., & Wharton, J. T. (1985). Malignant germ cell tumors of the ovary. In D. S. Albert & E. A. Surwit (Eds.), *Ovarian cancer* (pp. 227–269). Boston: Martinus Nijhoff.

Hacker, N. F. (1996). Vulvar cancer. In J. S. Berek, E. Y. Adashi & P. A. Hillard (Eds.), *Novak's gynecology* (12th ed., pp. 1231–1257). Baltimore: Williams & Wilkins.

Hacker, N. F., Berek, J. S., Burnison, C. M., Heintz, P. M., Juillard, G. J., & Lagasse, L. D. (1985). Whole abdominal radiation as salvage therapy for epithelial ovarian cancer. *Obstetrics and Gynecology, 65,* 60–66.

Hatch, K. D. (1996). Cervical and vaginal cancer. In J. S. Berek, E. Y. Adashi & P. A. Hillard (Eds.), *Novak's gynecology* (12th ed., pp. 1111–1154). Baltimore: Williams & Wilkins.

Hetzel, D. J, Olt, G. J., Ndlovu, H., Frauenhofer, E., & Podczaski, E. S. (1998). Ovarian epithelial carcinomas in patients with breast cancer. [CD-ROM] *Proceedings of the Society of Gynecologic Oncologists, 85.*

Ibbotson, T., & Wyke, S. (1995). A review of cervical cancer and cervical screening: Implications for nursing practice. *Journal of Advanced Nursing, 22,* 745–752.

Landis, S. H., Murray, T., Bolden, S., & Wingo, P. A. (1998). Cancer statistics, 1998. *CA—A Cancer Journal for Clinicians, 48,* 6–29.

Lerman, C., Daly, M., Masny, A., & Balshem, A. (1994). Attitudes about genetic testing for breast-ovarian cancer susceptibility. *Journal of Clinical Oncology, 12,* 843–850.

Lickiss, J. N., & Wiltshire, J. (1996). Palliative care and pain management. In J. S. Berek, E. Y. Adashi, & P. A. Hillard (Eds.), *Novak's gynecology* (12th ed., pp. 1303–1319). Baltimore: Williams & Wilkins.

Lurain, J. R. (1996). Uterine cancer. In J. S. Berek, E. Y. Adashi, & P. A. Hillard (Eds.), *Novak's gynecology* (12th ed., pp. 1057–1110). Baltimore: Williams & Wilkins.

Moreno, N. Chiva, L. M., Aragoneses, F. G., Fontan, E. G., Leon, P., Pena, E., Orusco, E., Lozano, M. A., Garcia, N. L., Folque, E., & Maranon, H. G. (1998). Salvage surgical treatment of lung metastases from cervical and endometrial carcinoma [CD-ROM]. *Proceedings of the Society of Gynecologic Oncologists, 247.*

Morgan, M. A., Iyegar, T. D., Schwartz, J. S., Mikuta, J. J., & Rubin, S. C. (1998). The clinical course of deep vein thrombosis in patients with gynecologic cancer [CD-ROM] [Abstract #10]. *Proceedings of the Society of Gynecologic Oncologists.*

Pastner, B. (1993). Screening for gynecologic malignancies in primary care: Uterine cancer. *Emergency Medicine, 25,* 157–161.

Pickett, M., & Yancy, D. (1996). Symptoms of the dying. In R. McCorkle, M. Grant, M. Frank-Stromberg & S. B. Baird (Eds.), *Cancer nursing: A comprehensive textbook* (2nd ed., pp. 1157–1182). Philadelphia: W. B. Saunders.

Piver, M. S., Goldberg, J. M., Tsukada, Y., Mettlin, C. J., Jishi, M. F., and Natarajan, N. (1996). Characteristics of familial ovarian cancer: A report of the first 1000 families in the Gilda Radner Familial Ovarian Registry. *European Journal of Gynaecological Oncology, 17,* 169–176.

Piver, M. S., & Hempling, R. E. (1993). Screening for gynecology malignancies in primary care: Ovarian cancer. *Emergency Medicine, 25,* 141–148.

Reid, R. (1987). Human papillomaviral infection: The key to rational triage of cervical neoplasia. *Obstetrics and Gynecology Clinics of North America, 14,* 407–429.

Ritvo, P. G., Robinson, G. E., Irvine, M. J., Brown, L. J., Murphy, K. J., Stewart, D. E., Styra, R. G., Wang, C. C., & Rosen, B. P. (1998). Familial genetic risk assessment for ovarian cancer: Psychosocial status and risk communication. [CD-ROM] [Abstract #37] *Proceedings of the Society of Gynecologic Oncologists.*

Rivlin, M. E. (1994). Gestational trophoblastic disease. In M. E. Rivlin & R. W. Martins (Eds.), *Manual of clinical problems in obstetrics and gynecology* (4th ed., pp. 14–19). Boston: Little, Brown.

Rose, G. R. (1993). Screening for gynecologic malignancies in primary care: Cervical cancer. *Emergency Medicine, 25,* 109–140.

Silverberg, E., & Lubera, J. A. (1989). Cancer statistics, 1989. *CA—A Cancer Journal for Clinicians, 39,* 3–20.

Smith, P. M., & Schwartz, P. E. (1995). New fears in gynecologic cancer. *Cancer, 76,* 2133–2137.

Sood, A. K., Dolan, M., & Buller, R. E. (1998). Distant metastases in ovarian cancer: Why do they occur? [CD-ROM] [Abstract #10] *Proceedings of the Society of Gynecologic Oncologists.*

Soper, J. T., Hammond, C. N., & Lewis, J. L. (1992). Gestational trophoblastic disease. In W. J. Hoskins, C. A. Perez & R. C. Young (Eds.), *Principles and practice of gynecologic oncology* (pp. 795–825). Philadelphia: J. B. Lippincott.

Struewing, J. P., Hartge, P., Wacholder, S., Baker, S. M., Berling, M., McAdams, M., Timmerman, M. M., Brody, L. C., & Tucker, M. A. (1997). The risk of cancer associated with specific mutations of BRCA1 and BRCA2 among Ashkenazi Jews. *New England Journal of Medicine, 336,* 1401–1408.

Sturgeon, S. R., Brinton, L. A., Devesa, S. S., & Kurmon, R. J. (1992). In situ and invasive vulvar cancer incidence trends from 1973–1987. *American Journal of Obstetrics & Gynecology, 166,* 1482–1485.

Teneriello, M. G., & Park, R. C. (1995). Early detection of ovarian cancer. *CA—A Cancer Journal for Clinicians, 45,* 71–87.

Tinkle, M. B. (1990). Genital human papillomavirus: A growing health risk. *Journal of Obstetrical, Gynecologic, and Neonatal Nursing, 19,* 501–507.

Veridiano, N. P. (1993). Screening for gynecologic malignancies in primary care: Vaginal and vulvar cancer. *Emergency Medicine, 25,* 149–154.

Weinberg, R. A. (1994). Oncogenes and tumor suppressor genes. *CA—A Cancer Journal for Clinicians, 44,* 161–170.

White, J. E., Begg, L., Fishman, N. W., Guthrie, B., & Fagan, J. K. (1993). Increasing cervical cancer screening among minority elderly: Education and on-site services increase screening. *Journal of Gerontological Nursing, 5,* 28–34.

Young, R. C. (1995). Ovarian cancer [guest editorial]. *CA—A Cancer Journal for Clinicians, 45,* 69–70.

Hematologic Cancers

Mary Ann Crouch

Malignant lymphoma is a diverse group of neoplasms that originate in the lymphatic system. Included in this system are organs and tissues such as the thymus, lymph nodes, spleen, bone marrow, and lymph. Lymphocytes are the predominant cell present in lymph nodes and are the cellular element involved in malignant lymphoma. As lymphocytes originate in the bone marrow, they mature into different types of lymphocytes. At any state of differentiation, the normal cells may turn malignant. Based on the characteristics of the malignant cells, lymphomas are divided into two major subgroups—Hodgkin's disease (HD) and non-Hodgkin's lymphoma (NHL). These two disease entities have markedly different clinical characteristics. HD commonly occurs as a localized area of lymph node enlargement. HD tends to spread to contiguous lymph node groups, whereas NHL tend to be disseminated at presentation and spread in a discontinuous fashion (Gautier & Cohen, 1997).

Hodgkin's Disease

An estimated 7200 new cases of HD will be diagnosed in the United States in 1999. These will be slightly more prevalent in the male population (3800) versus females (3400). In general, HD occurs more frequently in young adults aged 20 to 30 years. The incidence of HD also is more prevalent in adults greater than 45 years of age. Approximately 1300 cancer deaths in the United States will be caused by HD in 1999. HD represents approximately 15% of all malignant lymphomas and only 1% of all cancers. Since the advent of combination chemotherapy, adult HD has become one of the most curable malignancies. There has been a statistically significant difference in the rate of cure of HD from the years 1974 to 1976 (72%) and in 1986 to 1993 (82%). As in other diseases, the African-American population has an overall lower 5-year survival rate (Landis, Murray, Bolden & Wingo, 1998).

The exact etiology of HD remains unclear. Epidemiologic studies have suggested a viral etiology or disturbance of the immune system. All forms of HD have evidence of Reed/Sternberg cells. These are large, multinucleated cells. There is continued debate regarding the origin of this cell line. There are four subtypes of HD: nodular sclerosing, mixed cellularity, lymphocyte predominant, and lymphocyte depleted (Gautier & Cohen, 1997).

Clinical Presentation

Patients are often asymptomatic and may present with painless lymphadenopathy. This adenopathy (over 70% of people present with palpable lymph node enlargement) is most commonly found in the supraclavicular, cervical, and mediastinal lymph node region. Older patients are more likely to have systemic symptoms and abdominal disease and to have tumor burden greater than 10 cm, often called bulky disease. Other associated symptoms of HD occur in as many as a third of patients. Patients present with fevers, night sweats, and weight loss of over 10% of body weight. Other symptoms include fatigue, weakness, and pruritus (Moore, 1994).

Diagnostic Workup

The Ann Arbor classification is the most commonly used staging system for HD (Table 9-1). Patient therapy depends on stage, and accurate staging is essential. Diagnosis is generally confirmed by lymph node and bone marrow biopsy. Chest radiographs and chest/abdominal-pelvic computed tomography (CT) should also be completed as a component of workup. Various chemistries provide important diagnostic information: CBC, differential, platelets, erythrocyte sedimentation rate, LDH, LFTs, albumin, BUN, and creatinine. In addition, gallium scans are used to examine mediastinal or hilar lymph nodes, and lymphangiograms may be used to evaluate lower extremity lymphatics (Yarbro & McFadden, 1997).

Treatment

Treatment for HD should be approached with a curative intent. Choice of therapy depends on stage of disease. Table 9-2 outlines the guidelines of treatment of HD by stage. In general, localized disease can be treated with radiotherapy. As complexity increases, variations of combination chemotherapy and radiation are employed. Combination chemotherapy has been shown to be ef-

fective in the treatment of HD. Table 9-3 outlines the two most common combination chemotherapy regimens for HD. Of special note is that the ABVD regimen is an improved therapy over the MOPP regimen, with fewer reported toxic effects. The use of high-dose chemotherapy and autologous bone marrow transplant may be considered as an optional treatment for patients with relapse in stage 3 or 4 disease.

Complications of Disease and Treatment

General acute side effects of chemotherapy can be anticipated in the treatment of HD, including nausea and vomiting, myelosuppression, alopecia, and potential mood changes associated with steroid therapies. In addition, vincristine-containing regimens may also lead to neurotoxicity. Complications of radiation therapy may also be exhibited in the treatment of HD. These include skin reactions, myelosuppression, and fatigue. Up to 20% of the patients may experience radiation pneumonitis. In general, the higher-dose therapies and combination therapies lead to more severe side effects. As such, in multimodal therapy, general doses for radiation therapy may be decreased. Long-term effects may include the risk of secondary malignancies, such as acute leukemia. There may also be potential effects on reproductive ability. A younger woman may be at risk for premature menopause. Male patients should consider sperm banking before undergoing chemotherapy treatment for HD (Anderson, 1997).

TABLE 9-1
ANN ARBOR CLASSIFICATION OF HODGKIN'S LYMPHOMAS

Stage I	Involvement of a single lymph node region (I) or a single extralymphatic organ or site.
Stage II	Involvement of two or more lymph node regions on the same side of the diaphragm alone or with localized involvement of an extralymphatic organ or site.
Stage III	Involvement of lymph node regions or structures on both sides of the diaphragm.
Stage IV	Diffuse involvement of one or more extralymphatic organs with or without associated lymph node involvement.

For all stages
  A = No symptoms
  B = Presence of symptoms (fever, night sweats, weight loss of >10% of body weight)

TABLE 9-2

GUIDELINES FOR TREATMENT OF HODGKIN'S DISEASE

Stage	Recommended Therapy	Alternative Therapy
I, II (A or B, negative laparotomy)	Subtotal lymphoid irradiation	Irradiation to involved field with combination chemotherapy
I, II (A or B, with mediastinal mass>1/3)	Combination chemotherapy followed by irradiation to involved field	Subtotal lymphoid irradiation followed by chemotherapy
III A$_1$, (minimal abdominal disease)	Total lymphoid irritation	Combination of chemotherapy with irradiation to involved sites
IIIA$_2$, (extensive abdominal disease)	Combination chemotherapy with irradiation to involved sites	Total lymphoid irradiation or combination chemotherapy alone
III B	Combination chemotherapy	Combination chemotherapy with irradiation to involved sites
IV (A or B)	Combination chemotherapy	Combination chemotherapy with irradiation to involved sites

(From Eyre, H. J., & Farver, M. L. [1991]. Hodgkin's disease and non-Hodgkin's lymphoma. In A. I. Holleb D. J. Fink, & G. P. Murphy [Eds.], *Textbook of clinical oncology*. Atlanta: American Cancer Society.)

TABLE 9-3

THE MOPP AND ABVD REGIMENS FOR HODGKIN'S DISEASE

Drug	Dosage	Schedule
MOPP Regimen		
Nitrogen *mustard*	6 mg/m^2 IV	Days 1 and 8
Vincristine (*Oncovin*)	1.4 mg/m^2 IV	Days 1 and 8
Procarbazine	100 mg/m^2 PO	Days 1 through 14
Prednisone (cycles 1 and 4 only)	40 mg/m^2 PO	Days 1 through 14
ABVD Regimen		
Doxorubicin (*Adriamycin*)	25 mg/m^2 IV	Days 1 and 15
Bleomycin	10 units/m^2 IV	Days 1 and 15
Vinblastine	6 mg/m^2 IV	Days 1 and 15
Dacarbazine	375 mg/m^2 IV	Days 1 and 15

Repeat cycle every 28 days for a minimum of six cycles. Complete remission must be documented before discounting therapy.

(From Yarbro, C. & McFadden, M. [1997]. Malignant lymphomas. In S. Groenwald, M. Frogge, M. Goodman, & C. Yarbro, [Eds.], *Cancer nursing: Principles and practice* [4th ed.]. Boston: Jones and Bartlett.)

Non-Hodgkin's Lymphoma

Overview

Approximately 56,800 new cases of NHL will be diagnosed in 1999. Approximately 25,700 deaths will be related to NHL in 1998. The disease is nearly six times more frequent than HD, and the death rate is also greater. NHL occurs more often in males and the white population. It is now the fifth most common cancer in the United States. The NHLs can be divided into two prognostic groups: the indolent or nodular lymphomas (small lymphocytic, mantle cell, follicular cell) and the aggressive or diffuse lymphomas (large B-cell, lymphoblastic, peripheral T-cell, Burkitt's). Indolent lymphomas have a relatively good prognosis, with a survival as long as 10 years. The aggressive types of NHL have an overall poor survival rate, with approximately 50% to 60% overall survival at 5 years. However, there has been a statistically significant increase in the percentage of patients with a 5-year relative survival rate in 1993 as compared with 1974. NHL occurs more frequently in the elderly; however, there has been an increasing number of aggressive lymphomas reported in the human immunodeficiency virus (HIV) patient population (Landis et al., 1998).

Although there is no clear etiology of NHL, several known factors increase risk. Environmental exposures such as chemicals, pesticides, solvents, and infectious etiologies may contribute to the increased incidence of lymphoma. Immunodeficient states, either acquired, iatrogenic, or genetic, also may predispose patients to NHL (Skarin & Dorfman, 1997).

Table 9-4 outlines one of the three staging classification systems for NHL. In general, low-grade lymphomas frequently present with few symptoms but disseminated disease. Intermediate- and high-grade lymphomas present with localized disease. However, in NHL, the histology of the tumor type seems to be more important to prognosis than the extent of the disease (Gautier & Cohen, 1997).

Clinical Presentation

Low-grade lymphomas, which make up about 20% to 40% of NHL, tend to occur in patients of the median age 50 to 60. The majority of patients have advanced disease, and patients commonly present with localized or generalized lymphadenopathy. They may also present with infiltration of the bone marrow. Patients may describe vague symptoms of back pain or abdominal discomfort, often indicating a potential abdominal mass. They may also exhibit systemic B symptoms, as in HD, including night sweats, fever, and/or weight loss.

One third of patients may have splenomegaly or hepatomegaly. Table 9-5 outlines various systemic alterations in NHL.

TABLE 9-4

RAPPAPORT STAGING CLASSIFICATION

Low Grade	Diffuse, lymphocytic, well-differentiated Nodular, lymphocytic, poorly differentiated Nodular, mixed lymphocytic and histiocytic
Intermediate Grade	Nodular, histiocytic Diffuse, lymphocytic Diffuse, mixed, lymphocytic, and histiocytic
High Grade	Diffuse, histiocytic Diffuse, lymphoblastic Diffuse, undifferentiated

TABLE 9-5

SYSTEMIC ALTERATION IN NON-HODGKINS LYMPHOMA

System	Manifestations
Lymphoid system	Lymphadenopathy—peripheral or central hepatosplenomegaly Thymic (anterior superior mediastinal) mass Waldeyer's ring involvement Bone marrow involvement
Gastrointestinal system	Abdominal or pelvic mass Upper or lower gastrointestinal bleeding Malabsorption Intussusception Perforation Fistula Biliary obstruction Pancreatic mass Ascites Salivary gland swelling
Genitourinary system	Renal mass, ureteric obstruction Testicular mass Ovarian mass Vaginal bleeding
Nervous system	Meningeal involvement Cranial nerve palsies Intracranial mass (extradural or intracerebral) Paraspinal mass Intraorbital, periorbital, or ocular mass Peripheral neuropathy Progressive multifocal leukoencephalopathy
Endocrine system	Thyroid mass Adrenal mass
Other	Bone involvement Paranasal sinus involvement Jaw involvement Skin infiltration Venous or (rarely) arterial obstruction Pericardial effusion Pulmonary infiltration
General	Pyrexia/night sweats Weight loss Lethargy

(From Magrath, I. T., Wilson, W. Horvath, K. et al. [1990]. Clinical features and staging. In I. T. Magrath [Ed.] *The non-Hodgkin's lymphomas.* Baltimore: Williams & Wilkins.)

Diagnostic Workup

The patient's clinical examination should focus on a detailed history and physical examination. The presence or absence of these symptoms should be determined. Box 9-1 outlines the staging evaluation necessary for diagnostic evaluation for NHL.

Treatment

In general, the treatment of NHL depends on the histology, extent of disease, and performance status of the patient. Low-grade lymphomas most commonly occur in older people, where intensive therapy may not be well tolerated. In general, treatment includes radiation, single-agent chemotherapy, or combination chemotherapy. Agents such as cyclophosphamide and chlorambucil have been used alone, with response rates in the 50% to 80% range. Other combination chemotherapy regimens include COP (cyclophosphamide, vincristine, and prednisone) and CHOP (cyclophosphamide, hydroxydaunomycin, vincristine, and prednisone).

The management of patients with intermediate-grade or high-grade lymphomas also incorporates radiation plus combination chemotherapy. Although it has been demonstrated that intermediate-grade lymphoma has improved with combination chemotherapy, many patients do not attain or maintain a complete remission. Table 9-6 outlines other combination chemotherapy regimens used for aggressive intermediate- and high-grade lymphomas. Other approaches being employed to increase rates of remission from NHL are high-dose chemotherapy with bone marrow or stem cell support and the design of new treatment regimens that are evaluating agents such as new chemotherapy agents, as well as applications of biotherapy (Skarin & Dorfman, 1997).

Complications of Disease and Treatment

Again, managing the side effects of radiation and chemotherapy is necessary for the care of the patient with NHL. Patients may remain neutropenic for prolonged periods of time and be vulnerable to infection. Patients with NHL may also experience a large tumor mass that may cause obstruction

---

BOX 9-1

Staging Evaluation of Non-Hodgkin's Lymphomas

Required Studies

Standard blood studies
  Complete blood count, differential blood count, blood smear examination
  LDH and B$_2$-microglobulin levels
  Liver function tests
  Renal function tests
  Serum, electrolyte, calcium, and uric acid levels
Bilateral bone marrow biopsies and aspirates
Radiologic studies
  Chest film (posteroanterior and lateral)
  CT scan of the thorax if chest symptoms are present or chest film is abnormal
  CT scan of the abdomen and pelvis

Gallium-67 scan (in intermediate-grade and high-grade lymphoma)

Additional Studies in Selected Cases

CT or MR imaging of the head and spine for cranial/spinal symptoms
Upper and lower gastrointestinal tract contrast studies or ultrasound for abdominal complaints
Bone imaging or plain bone radiographs for skeletal complaints
MR imaging to detect bone marrow involvement
Spinal fluid analysis for suspected meningeal lymphoma

(From Skarin, A. T., & Dorfman, D. M. [1997]. Non-Hodgkin's lymphomas: Current classification and management. *CA—A Cancer Journal for Clinicians, 47* [6], 362.)

TABLE 9-6

CHEMOTHERAPY REGIMENS IN AGGRESSIVE LYMPHOMAS

Regimen	Drugs
M-BACOD	Methotrexate, bleomcyin, doxorubicin, cyclophosphamide, vincristine, dexamethasone
MACOP-B	Methotrexate, doxorubicin, cyclophosphamide, vincristine, prednisone, bleomycin
ProMACE-CytaBOM	Prednisone, methotrexate, doxorubicin, cyclophosphamide, etoposide, nitrogen mustard, vincristine, procarbazine, cytarabine, bleomycin

(From Skarin, A.T., & Dorfman, D. M. [1997]. Non-Hodgkin's lymphomas: Current classification and management. *CA—A Cancer Journal for Clinicians*, 47 (6), 351–372.)

and pressure, resulting in complications such as spinal cord compression, superior vena cava syndrome, ascites, or gastrointestinal or ureteral obstruction. Permanent sterility is also associated with radiation and doses of cyclophosphamide. In addition, patients have an elevated risk of secondary malignancy.

Leukemia

Overview

Leukemia is a malignant disorder of the blood and blood-forming organs (bone marrow, lymphatics, and spleen). Leukemias result due to a loss of cell division regulation, often resulting in an accumulation of abnormal amounts of dysfunctional, immature cells. These cells infiltrate the bone marrow, peripheral blood, and other organs.

Leukemia is classified into two types, acute and chronic, depending on the onset of symptoms and the differentiation (level of maturity) of the cells involved. Approximately 60% of the leukemias are acute in nature and result from an overproduction of cells in the blast (early nonfunctional) stage of maturation. Forty percent of the leukemias are chronic in nature (Chaney & Jassak, 1997).

Acute and chronic leukemias are further differentiated by the predominant cell affected, which is either lymphocytic or myelocytic. Table 9-7 classifies the various subtypes of acute leukemias.

Risk Factors and Incidence

Tables 9-8 and 9-9 outline projected new leukemia cases and deaths caused by leukemia in 1998 (Landis et al., 1998).

Acute Myeloid Leukemia

The incidence of acute myeloid leukemia (AML) increases steadily with age. The median age is 55 to 60 years. There is evidence that AML is associated with certain congenital chromosomal abnormalities such as Down syndrome, Bloom's syndrome, and Fanconi's anemia. Patients with other acquired diseases such as myelodysplastic syndromes, myeloproliferative disorders, and other preleukemic states also have an increased incidence of AML.

In addition, a variety of environmental factors, both work and treatment related, are known to cause AML. These include exposure to ionizing radiation; chemical exposure to benzene, possibly hydrocarbons, and solvents; and treatment with alkylating agents (e.g., melphalan, cyclophosphamide), and treatment with other drugs (e.g., chloramphenicol). In addition, epidemiologic research is investigating exposure to various viruses

TABLE 9-7

FRENCH-AMERICAN-BRITISH (FAB) CLASSIFICATION OF ACUTE LEUKEMIA

Myeloid		Lymphocytic
MI	Undifferentiated myelocytic	L1, childhood (pre B- and T-cell)
M2	Myelocytic	
M3	Promyelocytic	L2, adult (Pre B- and T-cell)
M4	Myelomonocytic	L3, Burkitt's type (B cell)
M5	Monocytic	
M6	Erythroleukemia	
M7	Megakaryocytic	

(From Wujcik, D. [1997]. Leukemia. In S. Groenwald, M. Frogge, M. Goodman, & C. Yarbro [Eds.], *Cancer nursing: Principles and practice* [4th ed.]. Boston: Jones and Bartlett.)

TABLE 9-8

ESTIMATED NEW CANCER CASES BY SEX, UNITED STATES, 1998

	Total	Male	Female
Leukemia	**28,700**	**16,100**	**12,600**
Acute lymphocytic leukemia	3,100	1,700	1,400
Chronic lymphocytic leukemia	7,300	4,100	3,200
Acute myeloid leukemia	9,400	4,700	4,700
Chronic myeloid leukemia	4,300	2,500	1,800
Other leukemia	4,600	3,100	1,500

(From Landis, S. H., et al. [1998]. Cancer statistics—1998. *CA—A Cancer Journal for Clinicians*, 48 [1], 6–29.)

as a potential precursor to AML (Chaney & Jassak, 1997).

Clinical Presentation

The patient presenting with a potential diagnosis of leukemia may provide some very nonspecific complaints, such as fever, weight loss, and fatigue. In addition, there may be a report of recurrent infections, unexplained bleeding, joint pain, or vague neurologic complaints such as headache,

TABLE 9-9

ESTIMATED CANCER DEATHS BY SEX, UNITED STATES, 1998

	Total	Male	Female
Leukemia	**21,600**	**12,000**	**9,600**
Acute lymphocytic leukemia	1,300	700	600
Chronic lymphocytic leukemia	4,800	2,800	2,000
Acute myeloid leukemia	6,600	3,600	3,000
Chronic myeloid leukemia	2,400	1,400	1,000
Other leukemia	6,500	3,500	3,000

(From Landis, S.H., et al. [1998]. Cancer statistics—1998. *CA—A Cancer Journal for Clinicians*, 48 [1], 6–29.)

vomiting, or visual disturbances. Table 9-10 demonstrates various clinical features as presented in leukemias.

Diagnostic Workup

A thorough workup is imperative. Special emphasis is given to the identification and classification of the predominant cell type involved. Appropriate workup for a patient with AML includes a complete history, including family and medical history, physical examination, and evaluation for potential signs of infection; peripheral blood studies, including CBC and white blood cell differential count; bone marrow biopsy to determine cellularity and appropriate stain smears to determine immunologic phenotyping; and blood chemistries such as serum electrolytes, uric acid, blood urea nitrogen, coagulation profiles, and liver function tests. Patients should also have a chest radiograph as well as a transfusion workup to determine blood type and potential typing for antigen type (human leukocyte antigens; HLA). HLA typing of family members will also be necessary to identify potential marrow donors and/or platelet donors in the treatment course for the patient (Meili, 1994). Table 9-11 outlines physical examination findings, laboratory results, and bone marrow results in patients presenting with either acute lymphoblastic leukemia or acute myeloid leukemia.

Treatment

Treatment of AML requires control of bone marrow and systemic disease and specific treatment of central nervous system (CNS) disease if present. Various combinations of chemotherapy are used for treatment.

The treatment for AML includes two phases: induction (to attain a remission) and postremission, often called consolidation (to maintain remission). Chemotherapy often given as induction therapy for AML includes a combination of a cytarabine with an anthracycline, either daunorubicin or doxorubicin. Other drugs that are being used in combination may include mitoxantrone and idarubicin. Complete remission is defined as the presence of less than 5% blasts in the patient's bone marrow. Peripheral blood counts must also return to normal, and any preexisting adenopathy

TABLE 9-10

CLINICAL FEATURES IN ACUTE LEUKEMIAS

Sytem	Manfestation	Cause
HEENT	Retinal capillary hemorrhage	Infiltration of leukemic cells
	Fundic leukemic infiltration	Infiltration of leukemic cells
	Papilledema	Infiltration of leukemic cells
	Oropharyngeal infections	Secondary to immunocompromise
	Periodontal infections	Secondary to immunocompromise
	Gingival hyptertrophy (AML)	Leukemic infiltration
	Dry mucous membranes	Overall systemic illness
	Dysphagia	Possible leukemic infiltration
	Cervical adenopathy	Leukemic infiltration
	Epistaxis	Thrombocytopenia
	Gingival bleeding	
Cardiovascular/	Possible tachycardia, tachypnea	Anemia or infection
Pulmonary	Conduction defects	Leukemic infiltration of bundle of His, valves,
	Murmurs	pericardium or myocardium (rare)
	Pericarditis	
	Congestive heart failure	
	Abnormal lung sounds	Possible bacterial pneumonia
Abdomen	Splenomegaly (ALL)	Leukemic infiltration
	Enlarged, tender kidneys (more common in pediatric ALL)	Leukemic infiltration
	Hepatomegaly	Leukemic infiltration
	Menorrhagia	Thrombocytopenia
Genitourinary Rectal	Renal failure or anurai	Uric acid nephropathy
Extremities	Perirectal abscesses	Decreased infection-fighting capabilities
	Skin pallor	Anemia
	Leukemic skin infiltrates: small, raised, pinkish nodules	Thrombocytopenia
		Leukemic infiltration
	Swollen joints or tenderness (most common in pediatric ALL)	
Neurologic	Headache, vomiting	Possible infiltration of CNS
	Visual disturbances	Possible CNS hemorrhage
	Cranial nerve VI, VII palsy	Infiltration of nerve sheath
Muskoskeletal	Bone or joint pain	Leukemic infiltration
	Swelling	
	Osteolytic lesions	

(From Moore, J. [1994]. Malignant lymphoma. In S. Otto [Ed.], *Oncology nursing* [2nd ed.]. Boston: Mosby.)

or organomegaly must be absent. In general, a complete response rate of at least 65% can be expected with induction therapy for AML. Consolidation therapy is administered to prevent recurrence of disease. In general, one to two courses of intensive, short therapy are given. In some patients, consolidation therapy is followed by maintenance therapy, which may require months to years of less intensive therapy to prevent further recurrence, or bone marrow transplantation. Allogeneic bone marrow transplantation is the treat-ment of choice for patients who have achieved a complete remission after their first induction therapy for AML. Disease-free survival rates using allogeneic transplantation have ranged from 45% to 60%. This, of course, depends on the patient having an HLA-matched marrow donor. Autologous bone marrow transplantation may also be used in patients with AML with disease-free survival rates between 35% and 50%. Relapse or recurrent disease is a frequent experience for the patient with AML. Patients may undergo second induction

TABLE 9-11

PHYSICAL EXAMINATION FINDING, LABORATORY RESULTS, BONE MARROW, AND CSF EVALUATION IN ALL AND AML PATIENTS

	Acute Lymphoblastic Leukemia	Acute Myeloid Leukemia
History/ Physical Examination		
Infection	Frequently present	30% have serious infections
Bleeding	Mild in 30%	30% have significant bleeding or petechiae
		75% have intracutaneous bleeding
Adenopathy	Minimal to moderate cervical adenopathy	Rare
Splenomegaly	Minimal to moderate	Occurs in 25%
Gingival hypertrophy	Rare	Present with monocytic element
Neurologic	Headaches, visual disturbances	Rare
Laboratory Findings		
WBC	85% normal to high	30% decreased
	25% WBC >50,000/mm^3	30% normal
	15% neutropenic	30% increased
	All patients have blasts	>50,000/mm^3 in 25%
	Two thirds have >50% blasts	10% have no blasts
Platelets	<50,000/mm^3 in 30%	<20,000/mm^3 common
Uric acid	Increased	Increased in 50%
LDH	Increased	Commonly elevated
Bone Marrow		
Cellularity	Hypercellular	Hypercellular
Blasts	50% or greater	50% or greater
Erythroid elements	Decreased	Increased
Morphology	Normal	Bizarre granulation of mature granulocytes
Cerebrospinal Fluid		
Cytology	5%–10% + at presentation	<5% occurrence; greater risk in M$_4$ and M$_5$, greater risk with WBC >100,000

(From Moore, J. [1994]. Malignant lymphoma. In S. Otto [Ed.], *Oncology nursing* [2nd ed.]. Boston: Mosby.)

therapy; in addition, allogeneic bone marrow transplant may be considered (Wujcik, 1997).

Complications of Disease and Treatment

Patients with AML may present with severe myelosuppression. In addition, the therapy rendered produces such effect. Supportive therapy includes red blood cell and platelet transfusions. Empiric broad-spectrum antimicrobial therapy is an absolute necessity for patients who are febrile and profoundly neutropenic. Patients must be closely monitored for potential infectious complications, as well as bleeding. Typical signs and symptoms of infection may be absent in the neutropenic patient, due to an impaired immunologic response. Temperature elevation is frequently the only sign and should be promptly evaluated. Antifungal therapy with agents such as amphotericin B may also be considered if fever continues. Strict care to prevent the occurrence of infection must be maintained, such as maintaining skin integrity and nutrition. Patients should avoid uncooked foods, not allow plants or fresh flowers to be available, and restrict visitors, especially those who are ill. Patients may also experience the standard side effects of chemotherapy such as nausea and vomiting and/or diarrhea. Oral mucositis is a common event for the leukemia patient, often requiring systemic parenteral medications for pain control. Frequent oral care should be provided to reduce the chance of infection. Finally, doses of a cytarabine may induce cerebellar toxicity. This is more prevalent in patients who are older than 50 years of age. Toxicity is irreversible if not detected early. Treatment with anthracyclines will also carry the risk of potential cardiotoxicity. Direct damage to the heart muscle may occur with cumulative doses. Signs and symptoms similar to those seen with congestive heart failure may indicate cardiac toxicity.

Patients cured from therapy for AML may experience many long-term side effects that are outlined in Chapter 1.

Acute Lymphocytic Leukemia

Overview

Acute lymphocytic leukemia (ALL) is a malignant disease of the lymphoid cell line, which arise from the bone marrow, thymus, and lymph nodes, although the exact etiology of ALL is not clear (Wujcik, 1997). Adult ALL accounts for 20% of all acute leukemias seen in patients over the age of 20 (Ong & Larson, 1995). The remission rates for adult ALL are 68% to 91% with a cure rate of approximately 25% to 41% (Hoelzer, 1993).

Risk Factors and Incidence

In 1999, it is estimated that there will be 3100 new cases of ALL diagnosed with 1400 associated mortalities (Landis et al., 1999). It has been noted that there is a slight male predominance in the United States, with Caucasians being affected more than African Americans (Mitus & Rosenthal, 1995).

Although the exact etiology of ALL is unclear, it has been demonstrated that there is an increased risk of ALL in Japanese atomic bomb survivors. Other risk factors for ALL include ataxia telangiectasia, Down syndrome, and Fanconi's anemia (Mitus & Rosenthal, 1995).

Clinical Presentation

Initial presentation of adult ALL is outlined in Box 9-2. Hepatosplenomegaly and lymphadenopathy are frequent presenting factors in all subtypes of ALL, affecting about one half of adults with ALL (Devine & Larson, 1994). Mediastinal masses and bulky abdominal nodes are typical of T-cell and B-cell subtypes, respectively (Mitus & Rosenthal, 1995).

Diagnostic Workup

The first critical step is to differentiate between AML and ALL. The initial assessment is to determine if the ALL is derived from the B-lymphocytes (B-cells) or T-lymphocytes (T-cells) (Ong & Larson, 1995). Although a peripheral smear may be suggestive of ALL, examination of the bone marrow is required for a confident diagnosis (Wujcik, 1997). The white blood count may be low, normal, or elevated, with about 90% of patients having peripheral blasts evident. Routine chemistries may reveal hyperuricemia and increased lactic dehydrogenase (LDH) (Wujcik, 1997).

BOX 9-2

Clinical Presentation of Adult ALL

Abrupt onset of malaise
Fatigue
Bony pain
Bleeding
Bruising
Weight loss

Night sweats
Infection and hemorrhage (presents in one third of patients at presentation)
Headache and cranial nerve palsies (imply CNS infiltration, present in about 10% of patients at initial presentation)

(Adapted from Devine, S., & Larson, R. [1994]. Acute leukemia in adults: Recent developments in diagnosis and treatment. *CA: A Cancer Journal for Clinicians, 44*[6], 326–352; and Mitus, A., & Rosenthal, D. [1995]. The adult leukemias. In G. P. Murphy et al. [Eds.], *American Cancer Society textbook of clinical oncology* [2nd ed.]. Atlanta: ACS.)

Treatment

Treatment for ALL differs from treatment for AML in two distinct aspects: prolonged administration of chemotherapy and CNS prophylaxis (Mitus & Rosenthal, 1995). Treatment for ALL is divided into two types: induction therapy and postremission therapy. In general, induction therapy for ALL is less toxic than that for AML, and a greater number of patients achieve complete remission (Devine & Larson, 1994). Multiple regimens are available to treat ALL for induction therapy; however, it appears that the most active chemotherapeutic agents include anthracyclines, vincristine, prednisone, L-asparaginase, methotrexate, cyclophosphamide, cytosine arabinoside, 6-thioguanine, and 7-mercaptopurine (Mitus & Rosenthal, 1995). The induction therapy of ALL may span 2 years with this drug combination.

Postremission consolidation follows induction therapy with a goal of eliminating minimal residual disease. If treatment does not continue after induction therapy, relapse usually occurs within 2 to 3 months. Prolonged chemotherapy may yield up to a 40% overall cure rate (Wujcik, 1997). In intensification/consolidation therapy, multiple chemotherapeutic agents are used, such as in induction with the addition of an antimetabolite (Ong & Larson, 1995). CNS prophylaxis is also implemented at this time. The CNS is a site for leukemia cells to hide or sequester. Additionally, the drugs used to treat ALL do not cross the blood–brain barrier in sufficient amounts to adequately treat any leukemia infiltration (Wujcik, 1997). CNS prophylaxis typically involves cranial irradiation and/or intrathecal (into the CNS fluid by way of lumbar puncture or Ommaya reservoir) methotrexate, cytarabine, or hydrocortisone with methotrexate (Hoelzer, 1993).

In addition to consolidation therapy, maintenance therapy is part of the postremission treatment phase of ALL therapy. Maintenance therapy is the prolonged treatment phase with low doses of chemotherapy. General treatments include methotrexate, mercaptopurine, vincristine, and prednisone with a length of treatment of 2 to 3 years (Hoelzer, 1993).

Consideration must be given to patients with a poor prognosis. In these patients, bone marrow transplantation (BMT) may be the treatment of choice. Presently, BMT is not recommended for low-risk patients; however, for high-risk patients, BMT is recommended in first complete remission (CR) (Hoelzer, 1993).

Even with intensive treatment, more than half of adult patients with ALL will relapse, most within the first 2 years (Devine & Larson, 1994). About 80% of patients will have a relapse within the bone marrow, with the remainder occurring in the extramedullary sites, usually the CNS. A variety of treatment protocols have been used in the relapse or refractory patients. High-dose cytarabine has been used with an approximately 50% rate of remission. However, the medial survival is short, usually less than 6 months, with only a small percentage of these patients being long-term survivors (Devine & Larson, 1994).

Complications of Disease and Treatment

Left untreated, ALL has a median survival of less than 2 months. The major complication related to ALL is that of low blood counts (cytopenias), with infections being related to low WBC (neutropenia) and bleeding (thrombocytopenia) (Box 9-3) (Gautier & Cohen, 1997).

Supportive care for the patient undergoing treatment for ALL is complex. Patients are primarily at risk for infection. The majority of patients undergoing therapy for ALL require a central line for administering medications and blood products as well as obtaining blood samples. Central lines are prime sites for infection and should be evaluated when a patient presents with a fever. Also, an Ommaya reservoir is considered a potential site for infection. Once a patient presents with a fever, prompt evaluation must ensue. Obvious sources of infection include blood, urine, CNS, and pulmonary.

Effects of chemotherapy are classified into acute and late. The administration of anthracyclines is associated with a risk of cardiac disease, especially congestive heart failure. Vincristine is related to peripheral neuropathies. Chemotherapeutic agents associated with hepatotoxicity are methotrexate, 6-mercaptopurine, cytarabine, and L-asparaginase. Additionally, the patient must be informed of the possibility of infertility related to treatment, with the option of sperm and/or egg

BOX 9-3

Prognostic Factors in ALL

Remission Induction

Age >60 years
White blood cell count >30,000 mL
Non-T-cell phenotype
Lack of mediastinal adenopathy
Poor performance status

Remission Duration/Survival

Age >35 years
White blood cell count >30,000/mL
Non-T-cell phenotype
t(9:22) or BCR/ABL rearrangement
t(4:11)
Burkitt cell (L3) phenotype (Sig +)
t(8:14) and variants
BCR: Breakpoint cluster region

(From Ong, S. & Larson, R. [1995]. Current management of acute lymphoblastic leukemia in adults. *Oncology, 9* [5], 433–442.)

storage being presented. There is a risk of secondary malignancies of which the patient must be informed. The importance of continued follow-up must be stressed (Camp-Sorrell, 1997).

Myelodysplastic Syndromes

Overview

Myelodysplastic syndromes (MDS) are a group of hematologic disorders with an increased risk of transformation into AML (Wujcik, 1997). The majority of these patients are 60 years of age or older. These disorders are thought to be unrelated; however, they are clinically similar and are grouped together. The etiology of MDS is unknown, although it is believed that they are related to a chromosomal abnormality. MDS are termed a clonal disorder because the stem cell maintains the capacity to differentiate into the different cell lines but not mature (Cain, Hood-Barnes & Spangler, 1991).

Risk Factors and Incidence

The overall incidence is estimated to be 3 to 5 in 100,000 per year; however, in people over 70, the incidence may be as high as 15 in 100,000 (Boogaerts, Verhoef, Demuynck, 1996). MDS may be primary, such as an acquired defect intrinsic to

the bone marrow, or secondary to marrow damage (Ho, Gibson, Vincent & Joshua, 1993). Exposure of the bone marrow to chemicals increases the risk of MDS. Of particular interest, previous exposure to chemotherapeutic agents remains the major risk factor for MDS (Gautier & Cohen, 1997).

Of patients diagnosed with MDS, 20% are older than 50 years of age, with a median age of 60. There is a slightly higher ratio of males to females. Approximately one half of all patients with MDS will develop AML (Wujcik, 1997).

Clinical Presentation

MDS may present as anemia, neutropenia, or thrombocytopenia; however, the most frequent presentation is that of trilineage cytopenias (Gautier & Cohen, 1997). Peripheral blood films will demonstrate an abnormal picture. The bone marrow is hypercellular or normocellular; about 10% are hypocellular (Ho et al., 1993). Survival rates range from 9 to 16 months.

Diagnostic Workup

A bone marrow biopsy is necessary for the diagnosis and classification of MDS and the specific subtype. Also, review of a peripheral blood smear is required for determination of the subtype of MDS. The relationship between the number of circulating blast cells and the number of blasts in the bone marrow is the main prognostic factor for disease severity (Cain, Hood-Barnes & Spangler, 1991).

Treatment

Treatment of MDS is problematic. For younger patients with high-grade disease, intensive chemotherapy and bone marrow transplant have yielded good results (Gautier & Cohen, 1997). Therapy based on treatment of AML has demonstrated improvement, although this is often transient and not appropriate for the elderly population.

Because there is no cure for MDS, supportive therapy is often the treatment of choice. The determining factor for implementing therapy is based on the aggressiveness of the disease. Most patients will receive supportive therapy consisting of monitoring hematologic parameters, implementing antibiotic therapy when warranted, and providing blood product transfusion support (Wujcik, 1997).

Corticosteroids, anabolic steroids, and differentiation-inducing agents such as cis-retinoid acid, vitamin D analogues, and interferon alpha or gamma have data to support their activity (Boogaerts et al., 1996). The use of hematopoietic growth factors has been of increasing interest. Erythropoietin in large dosages has improved anemia in about half of those who take it (Gautier & Cohen, 1997). The use of low-dose chemotherapy, usually low-dose cytarabine, has produced a response, with approximately one third of patients having a partial or complete remission.

Complications of Disease and Treatment

As mentioned earlier, there is an increased risk of AML with MDS. It should be noted that 75% of patients with MDS die as a result of the cytopenias rather than transform to AML (Estey, 1995). The nurse must be vigilant to assess for signs of disease progression. The patient and family must have information regarding the conservation of energy in the presence of anemia. Also, with neutropenic manifestations, the patient and family must know the signs and symptoms of infection. With thrombocytopenia, the patient and family must be aware of the potential of bleeding, even with adequate platelets because often the platelets are dysfunc-

tional. Additionally, the frequency of transfusion demands the education of the patient and family regarding the risk of a transfusion reaction.

Further complications are based on the treatment modality initiated. With the use of hormonal therapy, side effects include fluid retention, increased appetite, mood swing, moon face, and fragile skin. The use of differentiation-inducing agents has side effects such as dry skin, dry lips, myalgias, lethargy, and hypercalcemia. The use of interferons or interleukins can induce fever, chills/rigors, and fatigue. The hematopoietic growth factors can induce side effects such as bone pain, chills/rigors, fever, or leukocytosis (Cain, Hood-Barnes & Spangler, 1991).

Chronic Myelogenous Leukemia

Overview

Chronic myelogenous leukemia (CML) is a disorder involving a pluripotent hematopoietic stem cell. This disorder is associated with a chromosomal abnormally called the Philadelphia chromosome. Approximately 90% of patients with CML have the Philadelphia chromosome as a diagnostic marker; however, there are rare cases of Philadelphia chromosome–negative CML (Gautier & Cohen, 1997).

Risk Factors and Incidence

CML occurs in all age groups, although less than 10% of cases occur in patients less than 20 years old (Cortes, Kantarjian, Giralt & Talpaz, 1997). The median age at diagnosis is between 55 and 60 years. It is estimated that in 1998, there will be 4500 new cases of CML diagnosed in the United States with an estimated mortality of 2300. There is a slight predominance of males versus females (Landis et al., 1999). In the United States, there is no difference between races related to the occurrence of CML.

There is an increased risk of developing CML with exposure to ionizing radiation. Increased risk also is associated with chronic exposure to chemicals, such as benzene, and from some chemotherapy exposure. Research continues into whether there is a viral connection; however, there is no direct link between any known virus and the occurrence of CML (Ferrajoli, Fizzotti, Liberati & Grignani, 1996).

Clinical Presentation

CML is characterized by a triphasic course. About 40% of patients are diagnosed in the initial phase, called the chronic or stable phase (Mughal and Goldman, 1995). In the chronic phase, the clinical presentation is mild and often nonspecific. Generally, the diagnosis is made by a routine blood examination. Early symptoms include fatigue, fever, malaise, decreased tolerance to activity, weight loss, and night sweats (Mitus & Rosenthal, 1995). In about half of patients, there are complaints of early satiety, left upper quadrant fullness or pain, and referred left shoulder discomfort, which are secondary to an enlarged spleen. Splenomegaly is the most common physical initial presentation (over 90%). Anemia and thrombocytopenia may contribute to the presenting symptoms (Gautier & Cohen, 1997).

Within 3 to 4 years, the chronic phase will give way to the accelerated phase. Clinical presentation of this phase is heralded by progressive leukocytosis with worsening cytopenia and progressive splenomegaly. In addition, there may be fever, bone pain, and weight loss (Mitus & Rosenthal, 1995). This phase may or may not be observed.

The blast phase has the same clinical presentation as acute leukemia (Gautier & Cohen, 1997). This phase is characterized by the presence of at least 30% blasts in the peripheral blood or bone marrow or the presence of extramedullary blastic disease (Cortes et al., 1997). In this phase, the spleen can enlarge dramatically, leading to progressive pancytopenia, hemorrhage, and/or infection (Mitus & Rosenthal, 1995). Table 9-12 outlines clinical and laboratory features of CML.

Diagnostic Workup

As mentioned before, CML may be recognized by a routine complete blood count. There may be a normal hemoglobin and hematocrit. Examination of the bone marrow usually demonstrates hypercellularity with a shift in myeloid-to-erythroid ratio.

Treatment

CHRONIC PHASE

Until recently, treatment for CML was directed at controlling the white blood cell count and platelet count. Standard therapy consisted of hydroxyurea

TABLE 9-12
CLINICAL AND LABORATORY FEATURES OF CML IN THE THREE PHASES OF DISEASE

	Phase		
	Stable	*Accelerated*	*Blast Crisis*
Symptoms*	None/minimal	Moderate	Multiple
Splenomegaly	Mild	Increased	Pronounced
WBC	Elevated	Erratic	Elevated or decreased
Differential	<1%–2% blast on blood film	Increasing basophils and immaturity	Circulating blasts, often >25%
HCT	Normal	Normal or decreased	Decreased
Platelets	Normal or increased	Erratic	Decreased
Leukocyte alkaline phosphatase (LAP)	Decreased	Normal or increased	Normal
Bone marrow	<10% immature	Increased immaturity	>30% blasts
Cytogenetics	Philadelphia chromosome (Ph)	Ph, additional abnormalities	Ph, additional abnormalities
Median survival	3–4 years	6–24 months	2–4 months

*Symptoms: bone pain, night sweats, fatigue, weight loss.
(Adapted from Mitus, A., & Rosenthal, D. [1995]. The adult leukemias. In G. P. Murphy et al. [Eds.], *American Cancer Society textbook of clinical oncology* [2nd ed.]. Atlanta: ACS; Gautier, M., & Cohen, H. [1997]. Hematologic malignancies. In C. K. Cassell et al. [Eds.], *Geriatric medicine* [3rd ed.]. New York. Springer; and Cortes, J., et al. [1997]. Natural history and staging of chronic myelogenous leukemia. *Balliere's Clinical Hematology, 10*[2], 277–290.)

1 to 3 g/day orally with the goal of maintaining the white blood count from 10,000 to 20,000. Other chemotherapeutic agents used are myeleran and busulfan (Ferrajoli et al., 1996; Mitus & Rosenthal, 1995).

Since 1985, the use of interferon (INF) has improved the survival of patients with CML. INF has been shown to induce remission in 70% to 80% of patients with stable disease (Mitus & Rosenthal, 1995). Additional data suggest that patients treated with INF benefited whether or not they obtained remission, because they experienced a median survival of 1 to 2 years longer than those treated with hydroxyurea (Mughal & Goldman, 1995). Early toxicities of IFN are fever, chills, malaise, myalgias, arthralgias, fatigue, and headache. These toxicities usually resolve in 1 to 2 weeks. However, toxicities associated with prolonged use include elevated transaminases, nausea, diarrhea, proteinuria, hypothyroidism, and transient hair loss (Morrison, 1994).

Allogeneic BMT has offered the only potential for a cure of CML. The 5-year disease-free survival is 50% to 60% for patients who undergo transplantation while in the chronic phase; 30% for patients who undergo transplantation in the accelerated phase; and 10% to 20% for patients who undergo transplantation in the acute phase (Morrison, 1994). Unfortunately, two thirds of patients diagnosed with CML are too old to undergo BMT or do not have an HLA-compatible match (Gautier & Cohen, 1997). The role of autologous or peripheral blood stem cell harvesting and unrelated BMT continues to be controversial. For those patients who are not candidates for BMT, the use of combination IFN and low-dose cytarabine has yielded remission in 55% of patients.

The prognosis for patients in blast phase remains poor, with a median survival of 3 to 6 months. Patients who evolve into a myeloid blast crisis can be treated with standard AML therapy. However, the response is of short duration and median survival is short, ranging from 2 to 12 months. Those patients who evolve into a lymphoid blast crisis are treated with standard therapy for ALL. They have a somewhat better outcome, with a response of 40% to 70%, with remission duration ranging from 6 to 10 months and a median survival of 9 to 12 months (Morrison, 1994).

In patients for whom aggressive therapy is not an option, palliation can be obtained with hydroxyurea, 2 to 4 g/day.

Complications of Disease and Treatment

CML impacts quality of life through its manifestations, such as fatigue, malaise, weight loss, and pain. The patient and family need education for symptom management. Additionally, there is an increased risk of infection and/or bleeding, which requires education for the patient and family.

Side effects of the therapy depend on the modality used. The side effects of chemotherapy include neutropenia, thrombocytopenia, nausea, vomiting, and fatigue. Specific agents, such as busulfan and myeleran have life-threatening toxicities such as pulmonary fibrosis. The nurse should review these side effects with the patient and assess their impact on quality of life.

BMT is successful in 50% to 60% of cases; however, the toxicity is significant. About 20% of patients die within the first 100 days from acute and chronic graft-versus-host disease, interstitial pneumonitis, viral infections, and failure to engraft (Mitus & Rosenthal, 1995).

Chronic Lymphocytic Leukemia

Chronic lymphocytic leukemia (CLL) is a lymphoproliferative disorder. It is the most common form of leukemia in the Western hemisphere, accounting for 30% of all leukemias; however, fewer than 5% occur in the Eastern hemisphere (Morrison, 1994). It is estimated that in 1999 there will be 7800 new cases of CLL, with an associated 5100 deaths attributed to CLL (Landis et al., 1999). CLL is characterized by the proliferation and accumulation of small mature-looking lymphocytes. The majority of the cases are B-cell neoplasms, accounting for 95%, whereas T-cells account for about 5% (Montserrat & Rozman, 1993).

Risk Factors and Incidence

The etiology of CLL remains unclear. It is the only leukemia not associated with radiation or drug exposure or to lack a known retroviral association

(Morrison, 1994). It is known that CLL can arise from an immunodeficiency state, such as ataxia telangiectasia, or immunosuppression after organ transplantation (Mitus & Rosenthal, 1995).

CLL is a disease affecting the elderly, with a median age of 55 (Flinn & Vogelsang, 1998). Patients over the age of 50 account for 90% of all patients with CLL. Of interest, there appears to be no difference in survival between elderly and younger patients. There is a 2:1 male-to-female ratio.

Clinical Presentation

CLL is usually an incidental finding. With increased screening in asymptomatic people, there has been an increase in the number of cases of CLL diagnosed in an early phase (Lima, O'Brien, Lerner, & Keating, 1998). Patients in the early phase may have no symptoms or have mild fatigue. However, in more advanced phases, patients may present with fatigue, shortness of breath, night sweats, and bleeding. The incidence of viral infections, especially herpes zoster, approaches 20%. Autoimmune hemolytic anemia, thrombocytopenia, and viral and/or bacterial infections hallmark the immune deficiencies associated with CLL. Splenomegaly and lymphadenopathy are present in about two thirds of patients at presentation (Mitus & Rosenthal, 1995).

CLL may have an indolent course, with medial survival ranging from over 10 years to a few months after diagnosis (Montserrat & Rozman, 1993). Progressive disease may be heralded by fever, rapid and disproportional growth of one lymph node group, weight loss, pancytopenia, and abdominal pain. CLL transforms into an aggressive form of large-cell lymphoma in 3% to 10% of cases (Mitus & Rosenthal, 1995).

Diagnostic Workup

Initial diagnosis is often made by peripheral blood. The peripheral blood will demonstrate a lymphocytosis with normal or immature lymphocytes. It is not uncommon to have a lymphocyte count greater than 20,000/mm^3 in the early phase and greater than 100,000/mm^3 in the late phase (Wujcik, 1997). The bone marrow aspirate will demonstrate infiltration with lymphocytosis, although the degree will depend on the severity of the CLL

(Wujcik, 1997). A lymph node biopsy can show a pattern of malignant lymphoma. Additional tests that may be obtained include ultrasound of the abdomen, chest radiograph and/or chest CT, quantitation of serum immunoglobulins, serum immunofixation electrophoresis, and Coombs' test.

Treatment

The most challenging issue remains when the initiation of treatment is warranted. In general, the patient is treated when he or she is at high risk or is demonstrating symptoms of CLL related to the tumor burden. Some indications for treatment include symptomatic lymphadenopathy, hepatosplenomegaly, anemia, and thrombocytopenia (Byrd, Rai, Sausville & Grever, 1998).

Treatment for CLL has involved the use of chlorambucil with or without corticosteroids. Fludarabine is being used as an initial or secondary therapy. Patients treated with fludarabine therapy are at high risk of developing *Pneumocystis carinii* pneumonia; therefore, prophylactic antibiotics may be administered (Byrd et al., 1998). Patients have similar response to 2-CDA (2-chlorodeoxyadenosine). Second-line treatment may include CVP (cyclophosphamide, vincristine, prednisone) or CHOP (cyclophosphamide, doxorubicin, vincristine, and prednisone) (Mitus & Rosenthal, 1995).

Table 9-13 outlines several new drugs that are in the investigational phase for treatment of CLL. The use of bone marrow transplantation (allogeneic or autologous) is in clinical trials.

In the palliative setting, therapies such as radiation therapy to the site of bulky disease may be beneficial. Additionally, a splenectomy may offer some patients improved blood counts and regression of autoimmune hemolysis (Flinn & Vogelsang, 1998).

Complications of Disease and Treatment

People diagnosed with CLL are at risk for chronic infections and bleeding. At diagnosis, 35% of patients present with anemia and 25% with thrombocytopenia (Mitus & Rosenthal, 1995).

Because CLL is incurable with an indolent course, education must be a strong component of

TABLE 9-13

CURRENT INVESTIGATIONAL TREATMENTS FOR CLL

Drug	Action
Fludarabine with either chlorambucil or cyclophosphamide	Synergy has been noted between alkylator agents and fludarabine—synergy believed to occur as a consequence of alkylator-induced DNA damage and inhibition of DNA repair by fludarabine
IDEC-C2B8	Monoclonal antibody directed against CD20 (protein on the surface of the majority of CLL cells)
Theophylline with chlorambucil followed by fludarabine	Synergistic cell death (apoptosis)
UCN-01	Interrupts cell proliferation with minimal side effects
Bryostatin	Synergistic effect with drugs, such as fludarabine
Flavopridol	Interrupts cellular replication by inhibiting proteins necessry for proliferation
Campath 1-H	Antibody that binds to an antigen expressed on >95% of B- and T-cells
Melarsoprol	Arsenic moeity against CLL cells: neurotoxicity may be dose-limiting side effect
Gemcitabine	Trials in heavily treated patients are ongoing

(Adapted from Byrd, J., et al. [1998]. Old and new therapies in chronic lymphocytic leukemia: Now is the time for a reassessment of therapeutic goals. *Seminars in Oncology, 25*[1], 65–74.)

this disease process. Each patient and family member must understand the rationale for treatment. The signs and symptoms of infections must be reviewed. Patients may also experience profound fatigue, which requires education and support (Hays & McCartney, 1998).

Hairy Cell Leukemia

Overview

Hairy cell leukemia (HCL) has a chronic course characterized by splenomegaly, pancytopenia, recurrent infection, and hairy cells on a peripheral blood film. HCL accounts for about 1% to 2% of all adult leukemias (Morrison, 1994).

Risk Factors and Incidence

There are no known predisposing toxic or occupational exposures for HCL. HCL is more prevalent in males than females by a ratio of 4:1, with a median age at diagnosis of 50 (Mitus & Rosenthal, 1995).

Clinical Presentation

Initial symptoms at presentation include weakness, fatigue, and splenic pain. Splenomegaly, which may be massive, is present in 70% to 90% of patients. In 50% of patients, pancytopenia is present. Infection occurs in about two thirds of patients and accounts for the majority of deaths (Morrison, 1994).

Diagnostic Workup

A complete blood count may demonstrate anemia, neutropenia, and thrombocytopenia. There may be an elevation of leukocyte alkaline phosphatase level, hypergammaglobulinemia, and elevated liver transaminases (Morrison, 1994).

Treatment

HCL is a chronic disease, and in 10% of patients no treatment will be warranted. Indications to initiate treatment include anemia, neutropenia, thrombocytopenia, leukemia phase, symptomatic splenomegaly, bulky lymphadenopathy, recurrent infections, bone marrow involvement, and autoimmune syndrome (Morrison, 1994).

Splenectomy was the first line of treatment for many years. However, other methods are available at present. Splenectomy has been replaced by the use of alpha interferon, pentostatin, or 2-CDA. Although interferon can offer a complete or partial response in 80% of cases, when sustained for 12 to 18 months 2-CDA has the potential for cure and is becoming increasingly used as first-line therapy (Mitus & Rosenthal, 1995).

Complications of Disease and Treatment

Left untreated, HCL is an indolent disease, with about 10% of patients not requiring therapy (Morrison, 1994). Interferon causes a normalization of peripheral blood counts in most patients; however, fewer than 5% will have a complete bone marrow remission (Morrison, 1994). Deoxycoformycin (pentastatin) may also be administered as treatment three times a month. About 95% of patients exhibit a response, with 60% to 90% of these having complete response. Toxicities include fever and infection (Morrison, 1994). Administration of 2-CDA produces a complete response in 78% to 92% with a prolonged remission. Major toxicities include myalgias, nausea, rash, headache, and weakness (Morrison, 1994).

Multiple Myeloma

Overview

Plasma cell disorders is a broad term used to identify a category of clonal neoplastic disorders that result from overproduction of a monoclonal antibody (Bubley & Schnipper, 1995). The malignant components in this disorder are the plasma cells and plasmacytoid lymphocytes, which are the most mature cells of the B-cell maturation of the B-lymphocyte origin. This process leads to clones of plasma cells, which produce large quantities of monoclonal immunoglobulin (Ig) (Bubley & Schnipper, 1995). Included in this category are multiple myeloma (MM), Waldenström's macroglobulinemia, monoclonal gammopathies, and monoclonal gammopathy of undetermined significance (MGUS).

Normal humoral immunity is regulated by the plasma cell. Normal antibodies consist of four polypeptide chains with two heavy and two light chains. The classes of human immunoglobulins that make up the heavy chains are IgG, IgA, IgM, IgE, and IgD. The light chains consist of two varieties: lambda and kappa. With unregulated production, there is overpopulation of one specific type of antibody, thus leading to the term *monoclonal antibody* (Gautier & Cohen, 1994). The accumulation of monoclonal antibodies is frequently called an M spike or M protein, which can be rep-

resentative of the malignant process of MM (Gautier & Cohen, 1997). MM is the most common malignant plasma cell disorder, which is associated with an overproduction of monoclonal IgG, IgA, and/or light chains. The overproduction of IgM is termed Waldenström's macroglobulinemia (Bubley & Schnipper, 1995).

Risk Factors and Incidence

MM represents 1% of all hematologic malignancies in the United States (Sheridan, 1997). In 1999, it is estimated that 13,700 new cases of MM will be diagnosed with a mortality of 11,400 (Landis et al., 1999). The incidence increases with advancing age, with less than 2% of cases occurring before age 40 (Bubley & Schnipper, 1995). Incidence increases until the 8th decade (Bubley & Schnipper, 1995), with the median age at diagnosis being 69.1 years (Gautier & Cohen, 1994). MM is more common in African-American populations than Caucasian by a ratio of 2:1. African-American males have a higher incidence than African-American females, followed by Caucasian males, then Caucasian females. An increased incidence of MM is associated with occupational exposure to asbestos, wood, textile, rubber, metal, and petroleum products, as well as with certain occupations such as farming (Sheridan, 1997). There is also evidence that exposure to radiation is an associated risk, with examples from atomic bomb survivors and workers exposed to radium (Riedel, 1991).

Clinical Presentation

The major clinical manifestations of MM are a result of the accumulation of the plasma cells and the proteins (antibodies) secreted by them (Gautier & Cohen, 1994).

Skeletal Complications

The most common presentation for a newly diagnosed patient is bone pain, occurring in 60% to 80% of patients (Gautier & Cohen, 1994; Sheridan, 1997). Bone lesions may present as multiple osteolytic lesions or "punched-out" lesions, a single osteolytic lesion, or a generalized osteopenia (bone thinning). Typical diagnosis is by plain films of the skeleton or a "metastatic bone survey." The use of a radionuclide bone scan is not the method of choice to determine the extent of disease related to the lack of significant osteoblastic activity in MM (Gautier & Cohen, 1994). Magnetic resonance imaging (MRI) is the test of choice when there is need to evaluate for spinal cord compression (Sheridan, 1997). Back pain is common and compression fractures of the vertebrae occur frequently, with an accompanying loss in height (Bubley & Schnipper, 1995).

Hypercalcemia

Hypercalcemia is a common sequela of MM, occurring in 30% of presenting patients and increasing in the course of the disease to another 30% of patients (Bubley & Schnipper, 1995). Hypercalcemia is often difficult to detect because the symptoms are subtle and often confused with other etiologies. Symptoms include anorexia, nausea, vomiting, constipation, weakness, pain, confusion, and lethargy (Gautier & Cohen, 1994).

Hematologic Compromise

Anemia is a common presentation of MM, occurring in over 60% of patients at initial diagnosis (Sheridan, 1997). The etiology of anemia is multifactorial. The reticulocyte (young red blood cells) count is usually low, and, with continued increase in tumor burden or with introduction of chemotherapy, this condition will progress (Bubley & Schnipper, 1995).

Infections are common in patients with MM. Between 50% and 70% of patients die as a result of a bacterial infection (Sheridan, 1997). Periods of greatest risk for infection include initiation of therapy, relapse, and the presence of refractory disease (Gautier & Cohen, 1994).

Renal Insufficiency

As many as one half of patients will have renal insufficiency at initial presentation (Gautier & Cohen, 1994). The etiology of renal insufficiency is related to several factors. The most common factors, accounting for over 90% of renal dysfunction, are identified as hypercalcemia and precipitation of light protein chains in the renal tubules (Bence-Jones protein) leading to obstruction and dilation of the tubules, leading, in turn, to nephron atrophy (Gautier & Cohen, 1994). Renal insufficiency often responds to hydration and treatment of MM. Other contributing factors to renal insufficiency include infection, hyperuricemia, and amyloid deposits in the kidney (Sheridan, 1997).

Diagnostic Workup

MM must be considered when a patient presents with pathologic fractures, renal insufficiency, anemia, hypercalcemia, or repeated bacterial infections (Marks & Shulman, 1995). The physical examination may include findings such as bone pain, limited range of motion, inability to bear weight, or signs and symptoms of spinal cord compression

---

BOX 9-4

Diagnostic Work-up for Multiple Myeloma

CBC
Electrolytes
BUN and creatinine
Serum Ca, uric acid
Quantitative immunoglobulins
24-hour urine electrophoresis
Total skeletal radiographs
+/– Bone marrow aspirate and biopsy

Biopsy of single soft tissue mass or lytic bone lesion
Specialized test to stage multiple myeloma
B_2 microglobulin
+/– Plasma cell labeling index
Serum viscosity
Rectal biopsy to evaluate amyloid
MRI for spinal cord evaluation

(Sheridan, 1997). Box 9-4 lists diagnostic tests that assist in evaluation of MM.

Treatment

At the current level of understanding, there is no cure available for MM. Therapy is used to control the disease. Initiation of therapy is based on symptomatic or progressive disease. Initial therapy is often a combination of chemotherapeutic agents melphalan and prednisone (MP). The regimen VAD (vincristine, doxorubicin, and dexamethasone) is considered a primary or secondary treatment (Gautier & Cohen, 1997). Table 9-14 outlines other regimens used to treat MM.

Research continues to explore better treatment. Clinical trials of agents such as interferon alpha, interleukin-6, and high-dose chemotherapy with bone marrow rescue are in progress (Gautier & Cohen, 1994; Marks & Schulman, 1995).

When there is no longer a specific response to therapy or no further reduction in the M spike is noted, this is called the plateau. Presently, there are no data that indicate further therapy is warranted and the patient is followed off therapy until there is an increase in measurable disease.

Complications of Disease and Treatment

Table 9-15 lists nursing considerations for the patient with MM. Along with sequelae related to the disease, one must also consider the treatment-related complications. These include cardiomyopathies related to doxorubicin; peripheral neuropathies related to vincristine; and issues of

---

TABLE 9-14
FREQUENTLY USED REGIMENS FOR MULTIPLE MYELOMA

Regimen	Drugs	Nursing Implication
MP	Melphalan Prednisone	Observe for neutropenia (low WBC); instruct patient regarding signs and symptoms of infection; if patient is diabetic, monitor for hyperglycemia
BCP	BCNU (carmustine) Cyclophosphamide Prednisone	Observe for neutropenia; instruct patient regarding signs and symptoms of infection; instruct patient to contact health care team if hematuria present; monitor for hyperglycemia in diabetic patients
VBMC P (M2)	Vincristine BCNU melphalan cyclophosphamide prednisone	Observe for neutropenia; instruct patient regarding signs and symptoms of infection; instruct patient to contact health care provider if hematuria develops; monitor for hyperglycemia in diabetic patients; monitor for constipation and peripheral neuropathies
VMCP	Vincristine Melphalan Cyclophosphamide Prednisone	As above
VCAP	Vincristine Cyclophosphamide Doxorubicin Prednisone	As above; monitor for signs and symptoms of CHF (related to doxorubicin); instruct pateint of reddish urine after administration of doxorubicin for approximately 24 h
VBAP	Vincristine BCNU Doxorubicin Prednisone	As above
VAD	Vincristine Doxorubicin Dexamethasone	As above: observe site of infusion; recommend only via central line

(From Gautier & Cohen, [1997]. Hematologic malignancies. In C.K. Cassell, H. J. Cohen, E. B. Larsen, D. E. Meren, N. M. Resnick, L. Z. Rubenstein, & L. B. Sorenson [Eds.] *Geriatric medicine* [3rd ed.]. New York: Springer; and Marks, P. & Shulman, L. [1995]. The diagnosis of multiple myelooma. *Comprehensive Therapy, 21* [1], 7–12.)

TABLE 9-15

NURSING CONSIDERATIONS FOR THE PATIENT WITH MULTIPLE MYELOMA

System	Signs and Symptoms	Patient/Family Education
Neuromuscular	Pain (acute and/or chronic)	Pain control measures: narcotic, visualization, biofeedback, distraction
	Hypercalcemia	Signs and symptoms of hypercalcemia
	Hyperviscosity syndrome	Signs and symptoms of increased plasma viscosity
	Spinal cord compression	Signs and symptoms of cord compression; pain control
	Pathologic fractures	Prevention of pathologic fractures; signs of fracture
	Depression	Cognitive strategies; counseling
Protective mechanisms	Anemia	Energy conservation strategies; exercise (as tolerated)
	Neutropenia	Prevention of infection; signs and symptoms of infection
	Thrombocytopenia (low platelets)	Prevention of bleeding
Respiratory	Pneumonia	Prevention of pooling of pulmonary secretions; increase in gas exchange; use of incentive spirometer
Gastrointestinal	Constipation	Preventive measures; change in fluid and dietary intake; exercise
Genitourinary	Renal insufficiency	Increase fluid intake; allopurinol administration as indicated; recognition of signs of urinary tract infection

(From Sheridon, C. [1997]. Multiple myeloma. In S. L. Groenwald, M. Goodman, M. H. Frogge, & C. H. Yarbro [Eds.], *Cancer nursing: Principles and practice* [4th ed.]. Boston: Jones and Bartlett.)

hyperglycemia, which can compound renal insufficiency related to steroids.

MM is a chronic illness, and the nurse must work with the patient and family to achieve the highest level of functioning possible. Nursing care directed at early recognition of complications and management of toxicities will enhance patient and family quality of life.

REFERENCES

Anderson, M. G. (1997). Lymphomas. In C. Varricchio, M. Pierce, C. L. Walker & T. B. Ades (Eds.), *A cancer source book for nurses* (7th ed., pp. 390–400. Atlanta: American Cancer Society.

Boogaerts, M., Verhoef, G., & Demuynck. H. (1996). Treatment and prognostic factors in myelodysplastic syndromes. *Bailliere's Clinical Hematology, 9*(1), 161–178.

Bubley, G., & Schnipper, G. (1995). Multiple myeloma. In G. P. Murphy, W. Lawrence, Jr., & R. E. Lenhard, Jr. (Eds.), *American Cancer Society textbook of clinical oncology* (2nd ed., pp. 470–485). Atlanta: American Cancer Society.

Byrd, J., Rai, K., Sausville, E., & Grever, M. (1998). Old & new therapies in chronic lymphocytic leukemia: Now is the time for a reassessment of therapeutic goals. *Seminars in Oncology, 25*(1), 65–74.

Cain, J., Hood-Barnes, J., & Spangler, J. (1991). Myelodysplastic syndromes: A review for nurses. *Oncology Nursing Forum, 8*(1), 113–117.

Camp-Sorrell, D. (1997). Chemotherapy: Toxicity management. In S. L. Groenwald, M. Goodman, M. H. Frogge, & C. H. Yarbro (Eds.), *Cancer nursing: Principles and practice* (4th ed., pp. 1319–1333). Boston: Jones & Bartlett.

Chaney, C. M., & Jassak, P. (1997). Leukemia. In C. Varricchio, M. Pierce, C. L. Walker, & T. B. Ades (Eds.), *A cancer source book for nurses* (7th ed., pp. 379–389). Atlanta: American Cancer Society.

Cortes, J., Kantarjian, H., Giralt, S., & Talpaz, M. (1997). Natural history and staging of chronic myelogenous leukemia. *Bailliere's Clinical Hematology, 10*(2), 277–290.

Devine, S., & Larson, R. (1994). Acute leukemia in adults: Recent developments in diagnosis and treatment. *CA—A Cancer Journal for Clinicians, 44*(6), 326–352.

Estey, E. (1995). Treatment of acute myelogenous leukemia and myelodysplastic syndromes. *Seminars in Hematology, 32(2), 132–151.*

Ferrajoli, A., Fizzotti, M., Liberati, A., & Grignani, F. (1996). Chronic myelogenous leukemia: An update on the biological finding and therapeutic approaches. *Critical Reviews of Oncology/Hematology, 22*(3), 151–174.

Flinn, F., & Vogelsang, G. (1998). Bone marrow transplantation for chronic lymphocytic leukemia, *Seminars in Oncology, 25*(1), 27–33.

Gautier, M., & Cohen., H. (1997). Hematologic malignancies. In C. K. Cassel, H. J. Cohen, E. B. Larson, D. E. Merer, N. M. Resnick, L. Z. Rubenstein, & L. B. Sorenson (Eds.), *Geriatric medicine* (3rd ed., pp. 337–354). New York: Springer.

Hayes, K., & McCartney, S. (1998). Nursing care of the patient with chronic lymphocytic leukemia. *Seminars in Oncology, 25*(1), 75–79.

Ho, P., Gibson, J., Vincent, P., & Joshua, D. (1993). The myelodysplastic syndromes: Diagnostic criteria and laboratory evaluation. *Pathology, 25*, 297–304.

Hoelzer, D. (1993). Therapy of the newly diagnosed adult with lymphoblastic leukemia. *Hematology/Oncology Clinics of North America, 7*(1), 139–159.

Landis, S. H., Murray, T., Bolden, S., & Wingo, P. A. (1998). Cancer statistics, 1998. *CA—A Cancer Journal for Clinicians, 48*(1), 6–29.

Lima, M., O'Brien, S., Lerner, S., & Keating, M. (1998). Chronic lymphocytic leukemia in the young patient. *Seminars in Oncology, 25*(1), 107–116.

Marks, P., & Schulman, L. (1995). The diagnosis of multiple myeloma. *Comprehensive Therapy, 21*(1), 7–12.

Meili, C. (1994). Leukemia. In S. E. Otto (Ed.), *Oncology nursing* (2nd ed., pp. 278–301). Boston: Mosby.

Mitus, A., & Rosenthal, D. (1995). The adult leukemias. In G. P. Murphy, W. Lawrence, Jr., & R. E. Lenhart, Jr. (Eds.), *American Cancer Society textbook of clinical oncology* (2nd ed., pp. 470–485). Atlanta: American Cancer Society.

Montserrat, E., & Rozman, C. (1993). Chronic lymphocytic leukemia: Prognostic factors and natural history. *Bailliere's Clinical Hematology, 6*(4), 849–864.

Moore, J. G. (1994). Malignant lymphoma. In S. E. Otto (Ed.), *Oncology nursing* (2nd ed., pp. 340–360). Boston: Mosby.

Morrison, V. (1994). Chronic leukemias. *CA—A Cancer Journal for Clinicians, 44*(6), 353–377.

Mughal, T., & Goldman, J. (1995). Chronic myeloid leukaemia: A therapeutic challenge. *Annals of Oncology, 6*(7), 637–644.

Ong, S., & Larson, R. (1995). Current management of acute lymphoblastic leukemia in adults. *Oncology, 9*(5), 433–442.

Riedel, D. (1991). Epidemiology of multiple myeloma. In P. H. Wiernik (Ed.), *Neoplastic diseases of the blood* (pp. 347–372). New York: Churchill Livingston.

Sheridan, C. (1997). Multiple myeloma. In S. L. Groenwald, M. Goodman, M. H. Frogge, & C. H. Yarbro (Eds.), *Cancer nursing: Principles and practice* (4th ed., pp. 1319–1333). Boston: Jones and Bartlett.

Skarin, A. T., & Dorfman, D. M. (1997). Non-Hodgkin's lymphomas: Current classification and management. *CA—A Cancer Journal for Clinicians, 47*(6), 351–372.

Wujcik, D. (1997). Leukemia. In S. Groenwald, M. H. Frogge, M. Goodman & C. H. Yarbro (Eds.), *Cancer nursing: Principles and practice* (4th ed., pp. 1235–1259). Boston: Jones & Bartlett.

Yarbro, C. H., & McFadden, M. E. (1997). Malignant lymphomas. In S. Groenwald, M. H. Frogge, M. Goodman, & C. H. Yarbro (Eds.), *Cancer nursing: Principles and practice* (4th ed., pp. 1291–1318). Boston: Jones & Bartlett.

Skin Cancer

Linda Russell

Skin cancer is emerging as an epidemic, being the most common type of cancer in the Western world and Australia. It affects the Caucasian population far more often than African Americans and Asians, and continues to rise in incidence. (See Box 10-1 for risk factors.)

The three most prevalent types of skin cancer are malignant melanoma, basal cell carcinoma, and squamous cell carcinoma. Basal cell carcinoma (BCC) is the most common cancer in humans and accounts for 75% of all nonmelanoma skin cancers (NMSC). It rarely metastasizes or causes death. Squamous cell carcinoma (SCC) is the second most common skin cancer, with nearly 100,000 new cases diagnosed each year. SCC occasionally metastasizes, causing over 2000 deaths each year. BCC and SCC are considered to be diseases of older people, although BCC is increasing in incidence in the younger population. Malignant melanoma is the least common but most lethal skin cancer, representing 4% to 5% of all skin cancers (American Cancer Society, 1997).

Management of skin cancer is determined by the type, location, and extent of disease at diagnosis. Prevention and early detection continue to be the hallmark of intervention for this disease.

Risk Factors and Incidence

Skin cancers will constitute one third of all cancers diagnosed in 1998 (Marks, 1994; Sondak & Margolin, 1998). The American Cancer Society (ACS) predicted 900,000 cases of BCC or SCC in 1997 and 40,300 cases of melanoma (Sondak & Margolin, 1998). The current risk of developing melanoma is 1 in 100 (Slingluff & Seigler, 1997), and it is estimated that the cumulative lifetime risk for melanoma will be 1 in 75 Americans by the year 2000 (Chuang et al., 1993; Rigel & Friedman, 1991). Mortality rates for 1997 were predicted by the ACS to be 7300 from melanoma and 2190 from other skin cancers (American Cancer Society, 1997). Despite the fact that the incidence of all skin cancers is rising, deaths from melanoma have been relatively constant since 1989 at about 2 per 100,000 (ACS, 1997). The current 5-year survival rate for people with melanoma is 84% as compared with a rate of 60% for the period between 1960 and 1963; this represents a marked improvement in survival. This stabilization in mortality rates and increased survival are attributed to increased public education and awareness.

Gender

There is a male predominance of BCC and SCC; however, the incidence of melanoma by gender is controversial (Fraser, Hartge, & Tucker, 1991; Friedman, Rigel, Nossa, & Dorf, 1995; Slingluff & Seigler, 1997; Sondak & Margolin, 1998; Walton, Keczkes, Bury, & Nicholson, 1994). According to Armstrong and English (1992), melanoma does not differ substantially between the sexes. However, females have a greater survival rate than males.

BOX 10-1

Risk Factors for the Development of Skin Cancer

Fair skin, light eyes, blonde or red hair

Excessive sun exposure

Tendency to sunburn

Family or personal history of skin cancer

Geographic proximity to the equator

Celtic ancestry

Age

Age is a factor in the development of BCC and SCC. These carcinomas are more commonly seen during the sixth and seventh decades of life. BCC, however, is becoming more common in people in their 20s, most likely due to increased exposure to the sun. Melanoma has a propensity to affect a younger population, with 80% of patients presenting between the ages of 25 and 65, with a mean age of 48 at diagnosis (Slingluff & Seigler, 1997). Skin cancers are rarely seen in children and, if they do occur, usually develop after puberty.

Race

Skin cancer is much less common in African Americans, Asians, and Hispanics than in Caucasians, although it does occur in these populations. The risk ratio of whites to African Americans for melanoma is 20 to 1 (Reintgen, McCarty, Cox, & Seigler, 1983). More deeply pigmented skin presumably offers more protective effect against skin cancer risk, particularly as it relates to sun exposure. When melanoma occurs in African Americans or other people with deeply pigmented skin, the location of the primary lesion is usually in nonpigmented sites, such as the palms of the hands, soles of the feet, or subungual areas (beneath the nail). BCC, which is usually nonpigmented in whites, is almost always pigmented in African Americans, and SCC, which occurs on sun-exposed skin surfaces in whites, appears on less sun-exposed surfaces in African Americans. These differences are clearly related to skin pigmentation.

Environmental Factors

Greater than 90% of BCC and SCC result from ultraviolet (UV) ray exposure, with the incidence increasing with each decade of life. UVB radiation (wavelength, 290 to 320 nm) is generally credited with the most carcinogenic properties of sunlight and is responsible for aging of the skin and sunburning. UVA (wavelength, 320 to 400 nm) is more prevalent on earth than UVB (with more of its rays reaching the earth's surface) and, until recently, was believed to be safe. However, UVA has been found to play a far more important role in contributing to the harmful effects of sun exposure than was previously thought (Fraser, Hartge, & Tucker, 1991). Depletion of the ozone layer is believed to be a factor because of its decreased ability to screen out UV radiation. Tanning booths use UVA radiation and are believed to contribute to the development of skin cancers, but this has not been proved.

The relationship of melanoma and sunlight exposure is more complex than for NMSC. Whereas there is a clear-cut association between *cumulative* sun exposure and the development of NMSC, the correlation between melanoma and UV exposure is less well defined. Exposure to intermittent solar radiation, severe sunburn as a child, or chronic childhood sun exposure appears to have a greater effect on the development of melanoma (Marks, 1994). People who migrate to sunnier climates have a higher incidence of melanoma, particularly if migration occurs during childhood. People with a history of BCC or SCC are at higher risk for melanoma, but this may be related to skin type. Conversely, indoor workers have a higher incidence of melanoma than outdoor workers, complicating the picture of sun exposure as the *cause* of melanoma. The mechanism responsible for the carcinogenic effects of sunlight exposure is not completely understood. The most likely explanation is that UV rays cause photochemical alteration of DNA and partial suppression of immunity (Kripke, 1988).

Other environmental factors for BCC and SCC have been identified. Chronic exposure to arsenic has been associated with an increase in these skin cancers. Chemicals found in chimney soot, coal tars, pitch, asphalt, creosotes, anthracenes, paraffin waxes, and lubricating oils have been shown to induce skin cancers in animals. Ionizing radiation has been implicated in the cause of NMSC since 1902 when roentgen x-ray machine workers reported skin cancers. However, greater industrial and occupational controls have limited exposure to this type of radiation.

Genetic Factors

The likelihood of any person developing skin cancer depends on his or her genetic predisposition and subsequent UV ray exposure. People of Celtic ancestry have the highest propensity for skin cancer. Among whites, people with fair skin, light eyes, and blonde or red hair are at greatest risk of developing skin cancer. These people tend to burn rather than tan when exposed to strong sunlight.

The presence of large numbers of moles and freckles, as well as a family or personal history of melanoma, represent important constitutional risk factors.

Geographic Predominance

Proximity to the equator is related to the development of skin cancer, with the greatest correlation seen with the incidence of SCC. There is also marked correlation with BCC and melanoma. The highest rates of skin cancer around the world have been demonstrated in Australia, South Africa, and southern Arizona, followed by Ireland. Ireland has less intense UV rays but a higher population of fair-skinned, white people. The incidence of melanoma decreases with increasing latitude (i.e., the more northern regions are associated with a lower frequency of melanoma).

Immunologic Influence

The incidence of malignancies in patients who are immunosuppressed is greater than in the population at large. Specifically, SCC is found more frequently in organ transplantation recipients who are on chronic immunosuppressive agents and in immunosuppressed patients with lymphoma or leukemia. These people have only a slight increase in BCC. Persons infected with HIV have an increased risk for the development of BCC.

Clinical Presentation

Nonmelanoma Skin Cancer

BCC and SCC are more difficult to differentiate from each other than from melanoma. Whereas melanomas are generally pigmented, BCC and SCC are not. BCC usually has a pearly, translucent appearance with a rolled border and may be associated with superficial telangiectases (Figure 10-1). It is flesh colored or pink and scaly and may be nodular, giving the impression of a psoriatic patch. Occasionally, melanin may be present, giving a pigmented appearance to the lesion. BCC is most often found on the trunk and extremities but may also appear on the head and neck.

SCC is usually dull red in color but may be white, often ulcerated, and arises in sun-damaged skin (Figure 10-2). It may appear as a round or irregularly shaped, plaquelike nodule. The margins are usually distinct, but it is often surrounded by erythema and bleeds easily. When SCC becomes invasive, it may appear as an erythematous, firm, dome-shaped nodule with a corelike center that is ulcerated. It may be smooth or papillomatous and wartlike. Lesions that are fixed to underlying tissue indicate aggressive growth.

Malignant Melanoma

The classic presentation of malignant melanoma consists of a pigmented lesion with irregular borders, color variation or dark black color, large diameter (>6 mm), and rapid growth (elevation) or change in color (Figure 10-3 and Box 10-2). Bleeding, crusting, or itching may be present. A raised area that was previously flat should be considered suspicious for melanoma. Melanoma most often

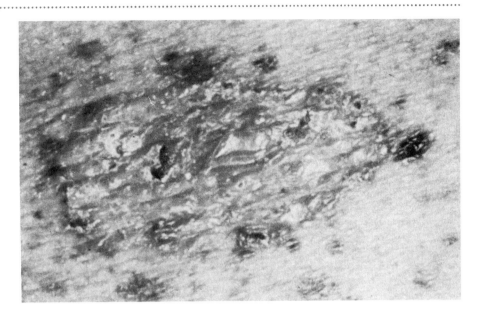

Figure 10-1 Basal cell carcinoma with pearly, translucent appearance.

occurs on the trunk in males and the lower extremity in females. Although melanoma usually presents as a cutaneous lesion, it may also originate in other sites, such as the choroid of the eye, anus, vagina, or other mucous membranes.

There are four basic classifications of melanoma, each of which has individual characteristics that identify it as histologically unique (Box 10-3).

SUPERFICIAL SPREADING MELANOMA (SSM)

This type of melanoma, the most common type, constitutes approximately 70% of all melanomas and is characterized by horizontal or radial extension from the lesion. It usually has an irregular border and ranges in color from black to pink to flesh colored. It is associated with a better prognosis than all the other types except lentigo maligna melanoma.

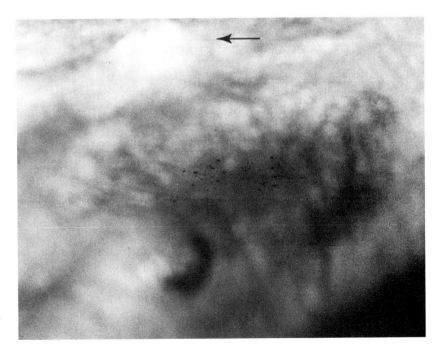

Figure 10-2 Squamous cell carcinoma with an irregularly shaped, white nodule (*arrow*) arising in sun-damaged skin.

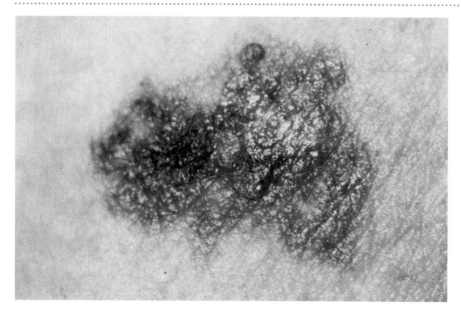

Figure 10-3 Superficial spreading melanoma with an irregular border, asymmetry, and variegated color.

NODULAR MELANOMA

This classification of melanoma constitutes 15% to 30% of melanomas. This lesion is often dark brown or blue-black; grows rapidly in a vertical direction, becoming more invasive; and bleeds. It has the appearance of a tick attached to the skin, with well-circumscribed borders. It may be polypoid and, thus, carry a poor prognosis because of the extreme thickness of the lesion.

LENTIGO MALIGNA MELANOMA (LMM)

One percent to 5% of melanomas will be classified as lentigo maligna melanoma. LMM is most commonly seen on the face of people in their 60s, 70s, or 80s, arising in a Hutchinson's freckle. LMM is a macular brown or tan lesion that has usually been present for decades. It is slow growing and carries little potential for metastasis.

ACRAL LENTIGINOUS MELANOMA (ALM)

Acral lentiginous melanoma is the most common melanoma in African Americans, occurring on the palms and soles or under nail beds. When ALM arises under the nail bed (subungual), it often appears as a hematoma with a black discoloration under the nail. On the sole of the foot, it clinically mimics a plantar wart. For these reasons, diagnosis is often delayed and prognosis is poor.

Diagnostic Workup

There is a relatively low mortality rate associated with non-melanoma skin cancers; therefore, diagnostic workup for BCC and SCC is limited. Clinical diagnosis is rendered based on palpation of the lesion and the regional lymph nodes. Pathologic

---

BOX 10-2

ABCDs of Melanoma

Asymmetry

Border irregularity

Color variation

Diameter >6 mm

BOX 10-3

Classification of Melanomas

Superficial spreading melanoma (SSM)

Nodular melanoma

Lentigo maligna melanoma (LMM)

Acral lentiginous melanoma (ALM)

diagnosis is necessary to confirm the clinical diagnosis; therefore, subsequent biopsy of a suspicious lesion is warranted. This may be performed by shave biopsy or punch biopsy, with confirmation of the diagnosis by dermatopathologic evaluation. No additional diagnostic studies are performed in the absence of physical abnormalities.

Malignant melanoma has the potential to metastasize by lymphogenous or hematogenous routes. Pathologic diagnosis must be rendered by wedge or punch biopsy rather than shave biopsy for the purpose of examining the entire lesion pathologically. Because regional lymph nodes are the most common site for recurrence, clinical diagnosis must include examination of the regional lymph nodes. Lymphoscintigraphy, a diagnostic procedure used to map the lymphatic drainage from a primary melanoma to determine the nodal drainage pattern, may be helpful in high-risk cases.

Additional diagnostic workup consists of a chest radiograph. Melanoma has a propensity to spread to the lungs very silently and can be detected early by chest radiograph. Baseline laboratory values including alkaline phosphatase (alk. phos) and lactic dehydrogenase (LDH) to rule out possible hepatic metastasis. If chest radiograph, alk.phos, or LDH is abnormal, computed tomography (CT) scans are performed regardless of the abnormality. Brain CT or magnetic resonance imaging (MRI) and bone scan should be performed only if symptoms suggestive of metastasis occur.

Treatment

The treatment of NMSC and malignant melanoma differs significantly. Because BCC and SCC have a lower propensity to metastasize, treatment is aimed at complete excision and continued surveillance. Factors that determine the treatment include histologic identification, tumor size, and anatomic location. Other considerations are the need for histologic control, age, and general health of the patient as well as morbidity associated with the surgical procedure. For high-risk or deeply invasive SCC without lymphadenopathy, the treatment may consist of local control alone, but prophylactic lymph node dissection may be recommended for regional control.

The types of treatments for BCC and SCC include curettage and electrodesiccation, excision, cryotherapy, Mohs micrographic surgery, and radiation therapy. *Curettage and electrodesiccation* are the most common method of treatment of BCC and small, <1 cm SCC and are usually performed by dermatologists. A sharp, spoonlike instrument is used to scoop out the tumor cells in a scraping method. The base of the wound is electrodesiccated or burned until normal tissue is reached. A variation of electrodesiccation is the use of the carbon dioxide laser to vaporize the tumor. This procedure is most useful for treating tumors that lie on fixed tissue surfaces, for example, lesions of the ear, temple, postauricular area, trunk, and temple. Electrosurgery is advisable in elderly patients who might not be able to sustain larger surgical procedures. The cure rate for NMSC using this method is quite high, approaching 98%.

Surgical *excision* is recommended for BCC and SCC of the forehead, scalp, and distal extremities measuring greater than 3 cm, because of poor healing of skin over bony prominences. The excision must include a minimum margin of 4 mm of noninvolved skin to completely excise the tumor. Excision allows for excellent wound healing with a linear scar.

Cryotherapy is a noninvasive procedure in which heat is extracted from tumor cells through liquid nitrogen. This is typically referred to as "freezing." It is useful in small BCC and noninvasive SCC, with a 5-year cure rate as high as 96%. Scarring is minimal.

Mohs microsurgery is the treatment of choice for invasive SCC, large BCC (>2 cm) with indistinct margins, and recurrent BCC. This is a more time-consuming procedure, requiring that patients wait at the time of removal for the margins of the tissue to be examined under the microscope. The tumor is debulked, and the margins are submitted for immediate pathologic interpretation. If margins are deemed to be involved with cancer cells, further re-excision is performed until margins return clear by pathologic examination. This procedure is particularly recommended when cosmesis is a factor, such as for removal of large NMSC of the face. Mohs microsurgery allows for maximum conservation of tissue. Dermatologic surgeons often work in concert with plastic surgeons for difficult tumors or when reconstruction is necessary.

Radiation therapy is an excellent option for elderly patients with SCC and for some patients with BCC who do not wish to undergo surgery. Normal tissue and functional integrity are preserved, and reconstructive surgery can be avoided.

Initial treatment of melanoma consists of adequate wide surgical excision for prevention of local recurrence. Mohs microsurgery is inadequate for melanoma. After diagnosis is made by punch biopsy, the extent of the excision is determined by histologic measurements of Clark's levels and Breslow thickness.

Clark's levels are divided in five levels of invasion (Box 10-4).

Breslow thickness measures the entire thickness of the malignancy and is classified as very thin (<1 mm), intermediate thickness (between 1 mm and 3.99 mm) or very thick (4 mm or greater) with local recurrence rate being correlated with greater thickness (Box 10-5). Surgical margins of 5 mm are recommended for melanoma in situ (level 1), and 1-cm margins are recommended for invasive melanomas up to 1 mm thick. Lesions thicker than 1 mm should be excised with 2-cm margins (Slingluff & Seigler, 1997). For subungual lesions of the finger or toe, amputation at the distal interphalangeal joint is recommended. Subungual lesions of the thumb are generally amputated at the interphalangeal joint to maintain opposition and functional integrity.

The issue of prophylactic lymphadenectomy continues to be debated. Elective lymph node dissection (ELND) can be associated with significant morbidity, and prospective, randomized trials have failed to demonstrate increased survival. However, because regional lymph nodes are the most frequent site of metastasis, assessment of these nodes by a technique called intraoperative mapping and sentinel node biopsy is the current trend at many academic institutions. Intraoperative mapping with a vital blue dye is performed under general anesthesia. Once the first node in the nodal basin (sentinel node) is identified

---

B O X   1 0 - 4

Clark's Levels of Tumor Invasion

Level 1: Confined to the epidermis

Level 2: Invades the loose connective tissue of the papillary dermis

Level 3: Invades to the junction of the papillary and reticular dermis

Level 4: Penetrates the reticular dermis

Level 5: Invades into the subcutaneous fat

BOX 10-5

Breslow Thickness of Tumor

<1 mm: Very thin lesion

1 mm–3.99 mm: Intermediate thickness lesion

4 mm or greater: Very thick lesion

with the dye, selective node dissection is performed. This procedure greatly reduces the morbidity associated with radical node dissection.

Immunotherapy after surgery for melanoma is being investigated by many comprehensive cancer centers for its adjunctive effect. The only FDA-approved adjuvant therapy for malignant melanoma is interferon, IFN-a-2b (Intron A). It is self-administered subcutaneously three times weekly for up to 2 years. Side effects are severe and consist of extreme fatigue and flulike symptoms. Desquamation and sterile abscess at the injection site are common. Studies are ongoing to determine the efficacy of IFN-a-2b in the adjuvant setting.

Specific active immunotherapy regimens in the form of tumor cell vaccines are being developed by many investigators. In these studies, the melanoma tumor cell antigen is isolated and irradiated with high doses of radiation to destroy the growth potential. The antigen is then placed in saline for subcutaneous injection to stimulate an immune response in the host to the tumor cell. Side effects of this type of immunotherapy are minimal, with fatigue being the most common complaint. The most recent melanoma antigen to be studied, GM2, is being compared with IFN-a-2b in controlled experiments.

Other treatment modalities under investigation include dendritic cell therapy, gene therapy, and combination therapies. Chemotherapy and radiation therapy are not recommended for patients with resected melanoma who are free of disease. These therapies are reserved for the treatment of metastatic disease, specific to the location and extent of tumor.

Complications of Skin Cancers

Complications from non-melanoma skin cancers are rare and are generally related to surgical excision. SCC can metastasize to regional lymph nodes, requiring further surgery and complications, but is most often considered cured after adequate surgery, although vigilance in follow-up is recommended for invasive SCC.

Melanoma can metastasize to virtually any part of the body. The most common site, other than lymph nodes, is distant skin and lung. This is

TABLE 10-1
SKIN TYPES

Sun Reactivity	Genetic Characteristics
I. Always burns, never tans	Very fair; red or blond hair; freckles
II. Burns easily, tans minimally	Usually fair skin, red or blond hair
III. Sometimes burns, gradually tans	Medium skin, brown hair
IV. Minimum burning, always tans	White with medium pigmentation
V. Very seldom burns, always tans	Medium to heavy pigmentation
VI. Rarely burns, tans darkly	African Americans as well as others with heavy pigmentation

followed in incidence by liver, central nervous system, bone, and gastrointestinal system. Treatment of metastatic melanoma depends on the site and magnitude of the metastases.

Nursing Interventions

Using the nursing process, nurses must first *assess* the person's risk factors for the development of skin cancers according to skin type, genetic background, race, gender, and environmental influence. Skin types, as defined by the American Cancer Society (Table 10-1), are categorized according to skin, eye, and hair coloration, as well as sun reactivity, and can be determined by observation during the interview process.

The person's *knowledge* of his or her risk factors must be ascertained to implement any type of intervention. Once a knowledge deficit has been identified, appropriate educational *intervention* can then be applied. Instruction should be initiated at any available opportunity with people who are at high risk and should be specific to the person's learning capabilities and knowledge deficits. The ABCDs of melanoma is a simple tool for beginning the teaching session (see Box 10-2). Other teaching points should relate to minimizing environmental risks and offering alternative behaviors for skin protection (Box 10-6).

Skin surveillance should be performed by all nurses in all settings, because the identification of suspicious lesions is paramount to early detection. *Referral* to a dermatologist must be made in a timely fashion to avoid unnecessary delay in diagnosis, and patients who have risk factors for skin cancer should be *counseled* about the routine annual examination of their skin by a health care professional.

Campaigns against suntanning should be implemented, and people and communities should be educated about the use of sunscreens to prevent skin cancers. Sunscreens with a sun protection factor (SPF) of 15 or higher should be recommended for all people. Dermatologists agree that the higher the SPF, the greater the protection against photoaging and skin cancer.

Nurses *can* make a difference in the outcome for patients who are at high risk.

BOX 10-6

Guidelines for Skin Protection (The Skin Cancer Foundation)

1. **Minimize sun exposure** during the hours of 10 AM to 2 PM.

2. **Wear a hat,** long-sleeved shirts, and long pants when out in the sun.

3. **Apply a sunscreen** before every exposure to the sun; reapply frequently and after swimming or perspiring heavily.

4. **Use a sunscreen** during high-altitude activities such as mountain climbing and skiing.

5. **Don't forget to use sunscreen** on overcast days.

6. **People at high risk for skin cancer** should apply sunscreen daily.

7. **Photosensitivity** (increased sensitivity to sun exposure) can occur with certain medications (eg, birth control pills, some antibiotics) requiring extra precautions.

8. **If allergic reaction to sunscreen develops,** change sunscreens.

9. **Beware of reflective sufaces!** Sand, snow, concrete, and water can reflect more than half of the sun's rays onto the skin. Shade does not guarantee protection from sunburn.

10. **Avoid tanning parlors.**

11. **Keep young infants out of the sun.**

12. **Teach children sun protection early.** Sun damage accumulates over the course of a lifetime.

REFERENCES

American Cancer Society. (1997). *Cancer facts and figures–1997*. Atlanta: American Cancer Society.

Armstrong, B., & English, D. (1992). Epidemiologic studies. In C. Balch, A. Houghton, G. Milton, A. Sober & S. Soong (Eds.), *Cutaneous melanoma* (pp. 12–22). Philadelphia: J. B. Lippincott.

Chuang, T., Reizner, G., Elpern, D., Stone, J. & Farmer, E. (1993). Keratocanthoma in Kauai, Hawaii: The first documented incidence in a defined population. *Archives of Dermatology, 129*, 317–319.

Davidoff, A., Cirrincione, C., & Seigler, H. (1993). Malignant melanoma in children. *Annals of Surgical Oncology, 1*(4), 272–282.

Fraser, M., Hartge, P., & Tucker, M. (1991). Melanoma and nonmelanoma skin cancer: Epidemiology and risk factors. *Seminars in Oncology Nursing, 7*(1), 2–12.

Friedman, R., Rigel, D., Nossa, R., & Dorf, R. (1995). Basal cell and squamous cell carcinoma of the skin. In G. P. Murphy, W. Lawrence, Jr. & R. E. Lenhard, Jr. (Eds.), *American Cancer Society textbook of clinical oncology* (2nd ed., pp. 330–339). Atlanta: American Cancer Society.

Kripke, M. (1988). Immunoregulation for carcinogenesis: Past, present and future. *Journal of the National Cancer Institute, 80*, 722–727.

Marghoob, A., Slade, J., Salopek, T., Kopf, A., Bart, R., & Rigel, D. (1994). Basal cell and squamous cell carcinomas are important risk factors for cutaneous malignant melanoma: Screening implications. *Cancer Supplement, 75*(2), 707–713.

Marks, R. (1994). An overview of skin cancers: Incidence and causation. *Cancer Supplement, 75*(2), 607–612.

Miller, B., Ries, L., & Hankey, B. (1993). *SEER Cancer Statistics Review 1973–1990*. Department of Health and Human Services publication. Washington, DC: National Cancer Institute.

Reingten, D., McCarty, K., Cox, E., & Seigler, H. (1983). Malignant melanoma in the American black. *Current Surgery, 40*, 215.

Rhodes, A. (1994). Public education and cancer of the skin: What do people need to know about melanoma and nonmelanoma skin cancer? *Cancer Supplement, 75*(2), 613–631.

Rigel, D., & Friedman, R. (1991). Malignant melanoma in the 1990's: Tracking a deadly disease. *Skin Cancer Foundation Journal, 9*(9), 61.

Russell, L., & Murray, J. (1992). Patient education: Recommendations regarding sunscreens, drugs and diet. *Annals of Plastic Surgery, 28*(1), 14–16.

Slingluff, C., & Seigler, H. (1997). Melanoma. In D. Sabiston & H. Lyerly (Eds.), *Textbook of surgery: The biological basis of modern surgical practice* (15th ed., pp. 515–527). Philadelphia: W. B. Saunders.

Sondak, V., & Margolin, K. (1998). Melanoma and other skin cancers. In R. Pazdur, L. Coja, W. Hoskins & L. Wagman (Eds.), *Cancer management: A multidisciplinary approach* (2nd ed., pp. 361–387). Huntington, NY: PRR.

Urist, M., Miller, D., & Maddox, W. (1995). Malignant melanoma. In G. P. Murphy, W. Lawrence, Jr. & R. E. Lenhard, Jr. (Eds.), *American Cancer Society textbook of clinical oncology* (2nd ed., pp. 304–310). Atlanta: American Cancer Society.

Vargo, N. (1991). Basal and squamous cell carcinomas: An overview. *Seminars in Oncology Nursing, 7*(1), 13–25.

Walton, C., Keczkes, K., Bury, H., & Nicholson, C. (1994). The emerging epidemic of skin cancer. *British Journal of Dermatology, 130*, 269–272.

Cancer Surgery

Margaret M. Barclay

Most patients with cancer have some surgical procedure during their experience with cancer. Thus, nurses who work in surgical areas in a hospital or ambulatory care center frequently meet people with a cancer diagnosis. It is the rare organization that has an inpatient unit dedicated to surgical oncology. This chapter is written to provide an overview of the various roles surgery has in the treatment of cancer and of the key considerations when caring for a cancer patient. Types of surgeries are described in the chapters about specific cancers, and detailed information about perioperative care can be found in the general surgical textbooks noted at the end of this chapter.

Surgery is considered the oldest of the cancer treatments. In the earliest days of cancer treatment, the standard was radical removal of visible tumors, often at the expense of a person's body image. With the advent of X-ray, deeper tumors were diagnosable and radical procedures continued to be the standard. The goal of surgical treatment was to cure the cancer by removing the entire tumor, leaving disease-free margins. At times that included affecting adjacent organs. In recent years, nonsurgical approaches have emerged for the primary treatment of some cancers that were previously treated surgically, and the role of surgery has changed. No longer are the radical and disfiguring surgeries of 2 to 3 decades ago seen. Today, multimodality therapy has expanded the role of surgery in the treatment of cancer. Unlike a short decade ago, many cancer surgical procedures are performed in the outpatient setting or using a same-day admission process with short lengths of inpatient stays. These changes in the surgical care delivery process require that nurses provide thorough preoperative preparation efficiently, comprehensive postoperative care and education, and a clearly understood plan for recovery and rehabilitation at home.

Types of Surgical Procedures

There are several reasons to use a surgical intervention for someone with cancer: diagnosis and staging, cure, palliation, reconstruction, and prevention. Most cancer surgeries are not urgent or emergent, but can be planned. However, to a person who is contemplating a diagnosis of cancer, the faster the surgical procedure can be scheduled the better. It is essential that the patient fully understand the aim of the surgery proposed.

Surgical Biopsy

A surgical biopsy may be needed to confirm the diagnosis of cancer, to define the type of tumor cells involved (histologic diagnosis), or to ascertain the presence of metastatic disease. It may also result in the removal of the tumor in its entirety (e.g. colon polyp, breast lump). There are several types of biopsies.

A *needle biopsy,* or aspiration biopsy, is often used for first-line diagnosis of disease or to confirm the presence of recurrent disease. It can be performed in the office or radiology department (if CT, mammography, or ultrasound guidance is indicated) and is usually done under local anesthesia. A needle biopsy is limited in that it can confirm the diagnosis of cancer if tumor cells are present in the sample, but a negative biopsy cannot guarantee that the patient is disease free. The needle biopsy is usually the first step in diagnosis and often leads to further intervention.

An *incisional biopsy* is the sampling of suspicious tissue through a surgical incision. A small part of the mass is taken and sent to pathology. The same sampling error can occur with this type of biopsy as with a needle biopsy, although an error is less likely. An example of an incisional biopsy is a liver biopsy performed in the course of an exploratory laparotomy.

Removal of a small tumor or lymph node through a surgical incision is called an *excisional biopsy*. This method of obtaining a biopsy for diagnosis is preferable as it ensures an adequate amount of tissue for accurate diagnosis and minimizes the risk of dissemination of tumor cells. By removing the entire lump or node through a small incision, the sampling error found with the other types of biopsies is eliminated, and the absence of cancer cells within the biopsy denotes absence of disease. An example of an excisional biopsy is a mediastinoscopic biopsy of mediastinal lymph nodes to stage lung cancer.

An *endoscopic biopsy* may be used for suspected malignancies of the gastrointestinal tract. During an endoscopic evaluation, polyps that are found throughout the gastrointestinal tract can be biopsied or removed in their entirety, depending on the size of the lesion.

Surgical Resection

The selection of a candidate for surgical intervention depends on several factors, including tumor site, tumor stage, and patient condition at the time of diagnosis. Given these factors, a variety of scenarios are possible.

CURATIVE RESECTION

In the absence of metastatic or locally advanced disease, the intervention of choice for solid organ tumors may be curative resection. Preoperative screening including computed tomography (CT) scans, magnetic resonance imaging (MRI), lymph node biopsy, chest x-rays, and other tests help to determine whether a curative resection is possible. During surgery, the tumor is removed in its entirety along with adjacent tissues, which include lymph nodes. Pathologic confirmation of disease-free margins and negative lymph nodes in surrounding tissues confirms a curative resection. The need for adjuvant treatment is then decided on the basis on cell histology, degree of invasion, and suspicion of micrometastasis.

PALLIATIVE RESECTION

When a curative resection is not possible, surgical resection is considered palliative and is undertaken for the prevention of symptoms related to advanced disease. The patient with impending bowel obstruction or a near-obstructing colorectal lesion may have a surgical resection of the tumor or a diverting colostomy to prevent obstruction. A gastrostomy tube may be inserted endoscopically or surgically to treat a small bowel obstruction or to allow the patient with esophageal cancer to be fed. Debulking or diversion (e.g., gastrojejunostomy) can delay the onset of pain or obstruction for the patient with advanced cancer.

PREVENTIVE OR PROPHYLACTIC RESECTION

With greater understanding of the role of genetic screening in cancer care, the case for preventive surgery strengthens. It has long been a standard of care to remove "precancerous" lesions such as colon polyps. Elective total proctocolectomy is standard treatment for cancer prevention in the patient identified with familial polyposis. With the advent of genetic screening, the case is made for prophylactic mastectomy following the identification of genetic markers in the patient with a strong family history of breast cancer. We may expect to see increasing numbers of patients treated surgically to prevent the development of malignant processes.

Other Uses of Surgery

EXCISION OF METASTATIC DISEASE

Only a select group of patients are candidates for excision of metastatic disease. Patients with a single site metastasis, which can be resected with low morbidity and mortality, may be considered for surgical resection. Thorough evaluation to rule out more than one site of metastasis must be performed prior to surgery.

SURGERY FOR STAGING PURPOSES

Surgery may be planned as part of the cancer staging process. A mediastinal or axillary lymph node biopsy may be part of the staging process. An exploratory laparotomy may be necessary for the determination of a treatment strategy in the patient with lymphoma. The staging process is based on knowledge of the natural history of the disease.

SURGERY AS AN ADJUNCT TO OTHER THERAPIES

Prior to the initiation of chemotherapy or radiation therapy, the patient may need surgery to facilitate administration of nonsurgical interventions. Oncologists consult the surgery team for *insertion of intravenous access devices* such as Hickman catheters or Portacaths. These are usually placed in the operating room under local anesthesia, monitored anesthesia care, or general anesthesia depending on patient condition and preference. This assures optimal sterile conditions as well as management of complications during insertion.

In select circumstances, surgery is performed to *debulk* tumors prior to chemotherapy regimens in which efficacy is related to tumor volume. Surgery can also be used to free nonaffected organs from the radiation field to prevent damage to these healthy organs.

It is essential that the multidisciplinary team evaluate the patient to determine the type of surgical intervention most appropriate and to help determine the timing of surgery. The team carefully considers the order in which therapies are administered when multimodality treatments are used. If radiation therapy or chemotherapy is performed prior to surgery, there are implications for the timing of the surgical intervention. The window for post-radiation surgery is relatively small, and careful planning can prevent delays in treatment.

Since adjunctive treatment can impede healing of normal tissues, postoperative treatment is usually timed to allow for a healing interval of several weeks prior to the initiation of treatment. Delayed healing can result in wound infections and complications that must be monitored during treatment.

The Surgical Experience

For any person facing surgery, there are standard operative processes and preparations. Many institutions have developed clinical pathways that guide preoperative and postoperative care. For a person with a diagnosis of cancer, factors that can necessitate modification to a pathway include more complex procedures that can result in temporary or permanent alterations in physiologic functioning, the emotional impact of the cancer diagnosis, and the combination of other therapies at the time of surgery. The benefits of patient and family teaching done before and after surgery are well documented; people do better when they know what to expect. Thus, a key responsibility of the nurse is preparing the patient for the surgical experience.

Preparing the Patient

Informed consent has been the hallmark of medical care for the latter half of the 20th century. It has been demonstrated that patients who are part of the decision-making process have better outcomes. It is the responsibility of the surgical team to ensure that the patient is informed about his or her treatment plan. In addition to a clear explanation about the goal of surgery, as discussed earlier in this chapter, the surgeon should provide information specific to the proposed procedure. The nurse can and should reinforce what has been said because the patient will need to hear the information more than once to understand it. This information is outlined in Box 11-1.

Prior to surgery, the physician may order diagnostic tests to stage the cancer and evaluate whether it has metastasized (see Chapter 3). The physician may also order tests that are helpful in the identification of co-morbidities, which could effect the outcome of the surgery itself. Some of the most frequently ordered tests with a brief description and indications for ordering are outlined in Table 11-1. Although these tests were once part of a "standard" preoperative evaluation, payers now ask the surgeon to give careful consideration to the need for each piece of information before ordering a battery of tests.

BOX 11-1

Informed Consent

The following information should be presented to the patient prior to surgery:
- Detailed description of the surgical procedure, including
  - Type of incision
  - Organ systems involved
  - Duration of the surgery
  - Anesthetic options
  - Changes in function as a result of surgery

- Expected outcome of surgery
- Possible complications/risks
- Likelihood and risks of blood transfusions
- Expected length of hospitalization
- Probable outcome if surgery is not undertaken
- Treatment options other than surgery

Preoperative Teaching

One of the primary roles of the nurse is preoperative teaching. This process includes assessment of the patient's and family's learning needs and their readiness to learn. Under ideal conditions patient teaching should occur prior to the immediate perioperative period. The teaching should be multimodality and should be reinforced throughout the preoperative period.

Studies on patient education indicate that patients hear and absorb only a small amount of the

TABLE 11-1		
COMMON DIAGNOSTIC TESTS		
Name of Test (Abbreviation)	*Description*	*Indication*
Complete blood count (CBC)	WBC, RBC, Hgb, Hc, indices, platelet count	Hgb, Hct for any surgery in which bleeding is expected
		Presence of infection
		Known bone marrow dysfunction
		Hypersplenism
		Recent chemotherapy
		Bleeding disorders
		Confirm suspicion of ETOH abuse
Prothrombin time/partial prothrombin time (PT/PTT)	Coagulation studies	Liver disease, malnourishment, or malabsorption
		History of bleeding
		Currently on anticoagulation medicine
Chemistries (Chem, SMA)	Glucose, potassium, sodium, BUN, creatinine, CO_2, liver enzymes, albumin	Potassium—potassium wasting diuretics, known renal dysfunction, history of serious arrhythmias, patient on digoxin
		Glucose—patients with known diabetes or on systemic steroids
		Liver enzymes—presence of liver disease
Electrocardiogram (EKG)	Demonstrates electrical activity of the myocardium	Patients with history of heart disease or with risk factors for heart disease
Chest x-ray	Looks at lung fields and heart size	Rule out pneumonia
		Rule out cardiomegaly to confirm CHF
		Evaluate for metastic disease
Urinalysis	Analyzes urine for blood, bacteria, nitrites	Patient history indicates a possible urinary tract infection

material that is presented to them at a single sitting. This statistic, combined with the fact that the patient is overwhelmed by a new cancer diagnosis, emphasizes the need to present information in several different formats over a period of time. Preoperative teaching may begin in the outpatient office setting at the time surgery is planned. Written materials, videotapes, or lists of available resources can be sent home with the patient to help reinforce this initial teaching. Publications related to specific diagnoses and treatment options are available from groups such as the American Cancer Society. (See inside covers.)

The first component of preoperative teaching is assessment of the patient's readiness to learn. The ability to hear and understand material presented is determined by several physical, mental, and emotional factors. This assessment should include the patient's past experience with surgery and cancer, emotional state, sensory or learning deficits that may make learning difficult, and physical condition, including fatigue, pain, and nutrition. Spending a few minutes to understand the patient's learning needs and learning style is essential for effective preoperative instruction. It is often helpful to include family members or close friends in the teaching process.

Many patients who are preparing for surgery have already had a long day of tests and appointments. They are often overwhelmed by the information they have received in addition to being fatigued, hungry, or in pain. The proposed surgery may have financial and other considerations about which the patient is concerned. Allowing the patient time to express these concerns and needs and helping him or her find solutions or resources for these concerns is essential to creating a learning environment.

Other determinants of learning readiness are related to the patient's ability to hear and understand instruction. Visual, auditory, and cognitive impairments require alternative approaches to teaching. Patients with language barriers may need an interpreter trained in medical terminology. Information elicited from the patient about learning styles will help in planning the education. Questions about past experiences with surgery elicit information about specific concerns, prevent unnecessary repetition, and provide opportunities for clarification.

Patients are often hesitant to ask to have a family member or friend accompany them into the examination/consultation room. By suggesting to the patient that it is helpful to have more than one person participate in the teaching, the nurse gives permission to have others present. This scenario often provides an advantage to the patient and nurse since another person is able to hear and reinforce information and can ask questions the patient may not think of. Preoperative teaching can only begin when it is determined that the patient is ready to learn. The nurse may determine that the conditions are not optimal for teaching and reschedule at a time more convenient for the patient (when logistically possible). Even under optimal conditions, learning theory tells us that patients hear approximately 25% of verbal explanations; therefore, providing the patient with pamphlets, brochures, articles, pictures, and/or videotaped information reinforces teaching done in the office setting.

The actual preoperative teaching process should include reinforcement of information specific to the diagnosis and proposed surgery, description of the perioperative process, expectations for hospitalization, and the initiation of discharge planning. A brief review of the proposed surgical procedure can be elicited from the patient to assess his or her understanding of what the physician discussed. The nurse can then clarify any points that the patient does not understand and reinforce his or her understanding of the surgery itself. Next, the nurse should outline specific information about preoperative preparation as well as the perioperative process. As increasing numbers of patients come to the hospital on the same day that surgery is scheduled, it is essential that the patient understand preparation that must be done at home such as bowel preparation, skin cleansing, and dietary restrictions. The patient's medications should be reviewed, and he or she should be instructed whether to take or hold doses prior to surgery. Written instructions should accompany these verbal explanations to assure patient compliance.

When presenting the perioperative routine, detailed descriptions of the process help decrease the patients' anxiety by giving them a clear understanding and a feeling of control over a situation in which they can feel out of control. Until patients receive information about the time and place of surgery, they are often unable to hear any more detailed explanations. Step-by-step descriptions of the routine should include any variations they may encounter. At this time the nurse may include an introduction to the members of the perioperative team and their roles and a tour of the physical facility. Specific instructions to family members should include the location of waiting rooms and an estimate of the time the patient will be in the operating room and the post-anesthesia care unit.

Postoperative Care

During the preoperative teaching, discussion of the postoperative period is beneficial. This includes describing the incisions (location, size, type of closure, presence of dressing), the presence of drains and tubes, and the equipment that will be used in caring for the patient. The patient should be given some idea of expected activity limitations and dietary restrictions. The expected length of recovery, whether in an ambulatory setting or in the hospital, can also be estimated prior to surgery; this will help the patient and family make necessary arrangements at home.

Postoperative nursing care is directed at returning the patient to optimal functioning. Clinical pathways serve to guide the postoperative course and outline nursing assessments and interventions. These include monitoring vital signs and the surgical site, maintaining fluid and electrolyte balance, reestablishing nutrition, ensuring an effective pulmonary state, resuming physical activity, and preventing postoperative complications such as venous stasis. Some of the simplest of nursing measures, such as helping a patient to turn or to use incentive spirometry, can prevent the development of major postoperative complications. Prevention and early recognition of infection postoperatively is essential because cancer patients may be at higher risk if they are immunocompromised from the cancer or from treatment they received concomitant with the surgery. Emotional support is also critical, particularly if the diagnosis of cancer is confirmed by the surgical procedure. The nurse needs to offer the patient an opportunity to discuss the meaning of the diagnosis with the nurse or another member of the multidisciplinary team.

One of the most important focuses postoperatively is pain management. Many of the other physiologic functions, such as appetite, rest, and elimination, can be seriously affected if pain is not controlled. Discharge can be delayed if pain is not managed and postoperative recovery does not progress as expected. It is best to discuss pain management strategies prior to surgery. Learning about the patient's past experiences with pain and what his or her personal coping mechanisms are helps the nurse plan for the postoperative period. Many people have misconceptions about pain and the use of narcotics. They may fear addiction and thus hesitate to ask for pain medications.

Effective pain control begins with assessment of the pain. A visual analog scale or other pain scale may be used to help the patient define his pain (Fig. 11-1). The nurse should also assess the patient's comfort level by noting nonverbal responses as well as what the patient says. Continuous infusions of narcotics, intravenously or epidurally, are now common pain-management approaches following surgery. The use of patient-controlled analgesia allows the patient control in augmenting the relief from continuous infusions. The patient should also be given information on nonpharmacologic strategies such as guided imagery, diversion, and relaxation. Chapter 22 provides specific information on the interventions for pain management.

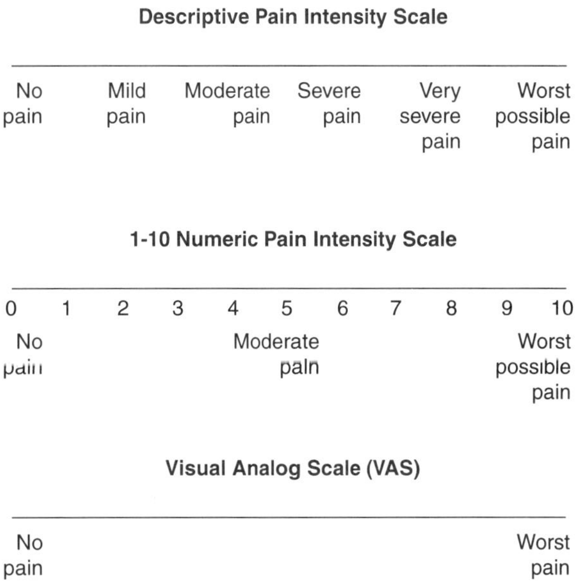

Figure 11-1 Pain assessment scales.

Recovery and Rehabilitation

With shortened lengths of stay and more ambulatory procedures, most of the recovery and rehabilitation from surgery occurs at home. Planning for discharge at the time of preoperative teaching helps the patient to prepare for the first few weeks following surgery. This is a good time to assess the patient's living situation, including physical surroundings, the presence of others in the home, and responsibilities that the patient will continue to have after discharge from the hospital. Family member involvement is important when exploring options that will affect the entire family. Discussion should include functional limitations that may be posed by surgery and problem solving about ways these responsibilities could be met if the patient is unable to do so. Other members of the care team can be consulted at this time to help identify resources available to the patient and family members. Referral to a home health agency may be needed to help the patient regain strength and function. Volunteer groups, such as Reach to Recovery for women with mastectomies, can provide valuable emotional support and practical advice on how to manage from someone who has shared the same experience.

Summary

Surgery is the oldest of the cancer treatments and has undergone extensive change in how it is used. Although it is still most frequently used for localized solid tumors, surgery is now a part of multi-modality therapies. At some time in the course of diagnosis and treatment, a patient is likely to have a surgical procedure. During these procedures, the nurse has an opportunity to make a difference in the patient's ability to cope with a diagnosis of cancer as well as in his or her physical recovery. To achieve the best care of the patient, nurses need to provide thorough preoperative preparation, comprehensive perioperative care, and well-planned rehabilitation.

REFERENCES

Anderson, C. (1990). *Patient teaching and communicating in an information age.* Albany: Delmar Publishers.

Baird, S. B. (1991). *A cancer source book for nurses.* Atlanta: American Cancer Society.

Baird, S. B., McCorkle, R., & Grant, M. (1991). *Cancer nursing: A comprehensive textbook.* Philadelphia: W. B. Saunders.

DeVita, V. T. Jr., Hellman, S., & Rosenberg, S. A. (1997). *Cancer: Principles and practice of oncology* (5th ed.). Philadelphia: J.B. Lippincott.

Ignatavicius, D., Workman, M. L., & Mishler, M. A. (1999). *Medical-surgical nursing across the health care continuum.* Philadelphia: W. B. Saunders.

McKenna, R. J. Sr. & Murphy, G. P. (1994). *Cancer surgery.* Philadelphia: J.B. Lippincott.

Miaskowski, C. & Buchsel, P. (1999). *Oncology nursing: Assessment and clinical care.* St. Louis: Mosby.

Rankin, S. H. & Stallings, K. D. (1990). *Patient education: Issues, principles and practices.* Philadelphia: J.B. Lippincott.

Steele, G. Jr. & Cady, B. (1992). *General surgical oncology.* Philadelphia: W.B. Saunders.

Timby, B. K., Scherer, J. C., & Smith, N. E. (1999). *Introductory medical-surgical nursing* (7th ed.). Philadelphia: Lippincott Williams & Wilkins.

Chemotherapy Administration

Julie Painter

The purpose of this chapter is to provide accurate, current information about the administration, safe handling, management of side effects, and education of the patient and family related to chemotherapy. The information is intended for the non-oncology nurse who provides care to the patient receiving chemotherapy. In the ideal situation, all chemotherapeutic agents would be administered by an oncology nurse with expertise in the area of chemotherapy. Owing to the rapid and vast changes occurring in healthcare today, however, the reality is that an oncology nurse is not always available. Therefore, a networking system must exist to allow access to expert resources in the specialty of oncology. Through such networking, an opportunity then exists to provide quality patient care to all patients who receive chemotherapy regardless of their location. The national Oncology Nursing Society provides such a network through its national and international membership.

Chemotherapy is one modality of treatment for both cancerous and non-cancerous conditions. The term chemotherapy historically was utilized to describe chemicals for cancer treatment and was developed by Paul Erhlich, the "father of chemotherapy." Chemotherapy was a result of the advances Erhlich made in discovering chemicals to treat infections. The belief that treatment could be developed to treat malignant disease was supported by the successes seen with the use of synthetic chemicals and natural products to treat common bacterial infections and tuberculosis (Burchenal, 1977).

The modern era of chemotherapy was initiated by the discovery of effective estrogens to treat prostate and breast cancer (Shimkin, 1977). Alkylating agents were discovered through the work of Chemical Warfare Services and evaluation of the toxic effects of poisonous gases, such as nitrogen mustard. Through exposure to the agent nitrogen mustard, severe bone marrow suppression was noted, leading to speculation about the drug's impact on cancers such as lymphoma.

Today, over 50 chemotherapeutic agents exist, and chemotherapy is believed to be as valuable in cancer treatment as surgery and radiation. The development of paclitaxel (Taxol), docetaxel (Taxotere), and gemcitabine has resulted in improved quality of life as well as significant clinical improvement in the treatment of cancers of the ovary, breast, and pancreas. To date, the research and development efforts in the area of chemotherapy are mainly focused on the comparison of agents in various combinations with one another or with other treatment modalities.

Currently, chemotherapeutic agents are being utilized in the treatment of cancer, HIV/AIDS, sickle cell anemia, lupus, rheumatoid arthritis, and multiple sclerosis, to name a few. The use of chemotherapy agents for some non-cancerous conditions is based on the belief that specific diseases not only originate from the immune system but also may occur due to the failure of the immune system.

The goals of chemotherapy are similar to those of other cancer treatment modalities. Curative treatments are aimed at the total elimination of the cancerous cells, including those that may have spread to other parts of the body. Adjuvant chemotherapy is used in addition to surgery and/or radiation to eliminate systemic microscopic cancerous cells. The purpose of adjuvant therapy is to provide a complete cure or a remission. The intent of palliative chemotherapy is to reduce tumor size, extend life, and improve the overall quality of life (Brown & Hogan, 1991). It is critical that the healthcare provider be aware of the purpose of the chemotherapy regimen or protocol, as some patients may not comprehend the rationale for the use of chemotherapeutic agents in their specific diagnosis.

Regardless of the purpose of the chemotherapy administration, it is critical always to treat the handling and administration of these medications with caution and respect. Chemotherapy agents should be handled appropriately and according to national recommendations, to reduce the risk to patient, employee, and enviroment. As with any medication, the healthcare provider must be familiar with the medication, mode of action, side effects, and appropriate administration and disposal procedures. Chemotherapeutic agents, regardless of purpose, route or dose, hold the possibility of side effects, risks, and benefits.

Cell Cycle

Chemotherapeutic agents are developed to target cells at the cellular development level, meaning that the agents will be targeted and effective at various phases of cellular growth and development. Currently, chemotherapeutic agents are developed to hit cell cycle phases and cannot detect the difference between a normal or malignant cell. Because chemotherapy affects normal cells, the patient experiences side effects. Chemotherapy agents work best on rapidly dividing cells such as those in the hair, skin, mucous membrances, and the bone marrow system. Thus, these systems are the most likely to have effects related to chemotherapy administration.

Chemotherapeutic agents are classified as either cell cycle phase–specific or cell cycle phase–non-specific. Cell cycle phase–specific means that the agent works to kill cells only in a specific part of the cell cycle. Cell cycle phase–non-specific

means that the agent does not depend on the phase of the cycle to be active, but affects cells at all phases.

The cell cycle is a sequence of steps by which normal and malignant cells reproduce. The cell cycle includes five steps: G0, G1, S, G2, and M. The G step represents the gap phases, which are time periods during which cells are either preparing for the active phases of DNA (deoxyribonucleic acid) synthesis and mitosis, or resting. G1 is called the first gap or first growth phase of the cellular cycle. During this phase the cell prepares for DNA synthesis by producing RNA (ribonucleic acid) and protein. G1 also includes a resting phase called G0. Cells in this phase are not within the active cell cycle. While in the G0 phase the cell does not undergo replication. Cells can stay in the G0 for varying lengths of time and divert back into the G1 phase based on the organism's needs (Barton Burke, Wilkes, Berg, Bean, & Ingwerson, 1991).

During the S phase DNA is synthesized. DNA holds the genetic information needed for growth, repair, and replication of the cell. Normal and malignant cells differ in the amount of time they spend in the S phase. Various chemotherapeutic agents are aimed at impacting the cell during S phase, thereby disrupting DNA organization and synthesis, and ultimately can result in cell death.

G2 is the second growth phase or second gap. As the cell prepares for mitosis there is synthesis of RNA and proteins. The cell produces the mitotic spindle apparatus during this phase. The mitotic spindle apparatus is the process by which chromosomes are condensed and prepared for the process of division.

Mitosis is the M phase, where cell division actually occurs. Mitosis has four steps: prophase, metaphase, anaphase, and telophase. As the cell completes the M phase it may either re-enter the cell cycle at G1 or go into G0 to rest and wait for activation.

Chemotherapeutic agents are ordered according to regimens or protocols that are known to be effective in the treatment of a particular disease. Agents that are cell cycle phase–specific and cell cycle phase–non-specific are then ordered in combination with the intent of obtaining greater cell kill and better tumor response.

Classification of Chemotherapeutic Agents

Chemotherapeutic agents can be classified in one of two ways: by the effect the agent has on the cell or by the pharmacologic properties of the agent. The second is the most commonly noted way of classifying these drugs. The classifications are alkylating agents, antimetabolites, antitumor antibiotics, plant alkaloids, hormones, and miscellaneous agents (Brown and Hogan, 1991).

Alkylating Agents

Alkylating agents are considered to be cell cycle phase–non-specific. These agents are effective throughout the cell cycle but are especially effective in rapidly dividing cells. The alkylating agents work to interact with the DNA through a chemical reaction that prevents cellular replication.

Alkylating agents work well in the treatment of lymphomas, breast cancer, multiple myeloma, and others. A potential side effect of high-dose alkylating agents is the later development of a second malignancy, most commonly a bladder cancer, leukemia, or blood dyscrasia. Other noted side effects of the alkylating agents can include alopecia, anorexia, stomatitis, diarrhea, nausea, vomiting, immunosuppression, and in some cases hepatotoxicity.

Among the alkylating agents are the nitrosoureas, such as BCNU, CCNU, and methyl-CCNU. BCNU is an intravenous agent that is reconstituted with alcohol; therefore, it can be irritating to the veins during administration. Administration of BCNU may be too painful via a peripheral line, and a central venous access may be preferable. Since this agent is mixed with alcohol it has the potential to cross the blood–brain barrier. These agents are most commonly utilized to treat primary brain tumors.

CCNU and methyl-CCNU are oral agents that require dietary intake alterations; review of dietary needs should occur before administration. Side effects with these agents can include myelosuppression, nausea, vomiting, pulmonary fibrosis, nephrotoxicity, and hepatotoxicity.

Common Alkylating Agents
- Busulfan (Myleran)
- Carmustine (BiCNU, BCNU)
- Chlorambucil (Leukeran)
- Carboplatin (Paraplatin)
- Cisplatin (Cis-Platinum, CDDP, Platinum, Platinol)
- Cyclophosphamide (Cytoxan, Endoxan, Neosar)
- Dacarbazine (DTIC-Dome, Imidazole, Carboximide)
- Estramustine phosphate (Estracyte, Emcyt)
- Ifosfamide (Ifex, IFX, Isophosphamide)
- Lomustine (CCNU, CeeNU)
- Mechlorethamine (Nitrogen Mustard, Mustargen, HN2)
- Melphalan (Alkeran, L-PAM, Phenylalanine Mustard, L-Sarcolysin)
- Streptozocin (Streptozotocin, Zanosar)
- Thiotepa (Triethylene Thiophosphoramide, TSPA, TESPA)

Antimetabolite Agents

Antimetabolites are agents that interfere with the synthesis of RNA and DNA. By deactivating the synthesis of DNA, these agents prevent the cell from replicating. The antimetabolites are considered to be cell cycle phase–specific and work most often during the S phase of the cell cycle. These agents work best in rapidly dividing cells and fast-growing tumors. The most common cancers treated with the antimetabolites are leukemia, colon cancer, lymphoma, and others.

The most common side effects with the antimetabolites are stomatitis, myelosuppression, anorexia, nausea, vomiting, alopecia, and changes in skin and nails. Photosensitivity is increased with the administration of 5-FU, FUDR, and methotrexate. Patients receiving these medications will have increased skin sensitivity to sun and ultraviolet light exposure, and should be instructed on ways to decrease the risk for skin reactions and burns.

Gemcitabine (Gemzar) is one of the newest antimetabolite agents. Gemcitabine is currently being utilized to treat locally advanced or metastatic adenocarcinoma of the pancreas and bladder. The most common side effect of this agent is neutropenia and thrombocytopenia.

Common Antimetabolite Agents
- Cytarabine (ARA-C, Cytosar-U, Cytosine Arabinoside)

- Floxuridine (FUDR, 5-FUDR, 5-Fluoro-2'-Deoxyuridine)
- 5-Fluorouracil (Fluorouracil, Adrucil, 5-FU)
- Gemcitabine (Gemzar)
- Hydroxurea (Hydrea)
- 6-Mercaptopurine (Purinethol, 6-MP)
- Methotrexate (Amethopterin, Mexate, Folex)
- 6-Thioguanine (Thioguanine, Tabloid)

Antitumor Antibiotics

Antitumor antibiotic agents are actually isolated microorganisms (Knopf, Fischer, & Welch-Mc-Caffery, 1984). These agents have both antimicrobial and cytotoxic activity. The antitumor antibiotic agents are cell cycle phase–non-specific and have several mechanisms by which they chemically interact with the cell and alter its ability to survive or replicate.

Side effects that can occur with these agents include alopecia, anorexia, myelosuppression, nausea, vomiting, and pulmonary fibrosis. Some of these agents are considered vesicants and hold the potential for severe tissue and muscle damage if leakage occurs outside the vein. These agents must be given through a continuous infusion of intravenous fluid, to reduce the irritation to the vein and allow adequate flushing of the line.

Bleomycin is most often given first in a test dose, as it has the potential to cause anaphylaxis and very high temperatures. Doxorubicin (Adriamycin) and daunorubicin (Daunomycin) have the potential for cardiotoxicity, and patients may need a multigated angiogram (MUGA) scan done before the initial treatment to verify cardiac ejection fraction. Ejection fraction should be at least 50% for the patient to tolerate treatment with doxorubicin or daunorubicin.

Common Antitumor Antibiotics
- Bleomycin (Blenoxane)
- Dactinomycin (Actinomycin D, Cosmegen)
- Daunorubicin (Daunomycin, Rubidomycin, Cerubidine)
- Doxorubicin (Adriamycin)
- Idarubicin (Idamycin, 4 Demethoxydaunorubicin)
- Mithramycin (Mithracin, Plicamycin)
- Mitomycin (Mutamycin)

Plant Alkaloids

Plant alkaloids are cytotoxic agents derived from plant extracts. The plant alkaloids are considered cell cycle phase–specific and work during the M phase (mitosis), although the plant alkaloids teniposide and etoposide work mostly in the G2 phase.

Major side effects of the plant alkaloids include myelosuppression, except with the agent vincristine (Oncovin); neurotoxicities are most often seen with vincristine and are less likely with vinblastine. The potential for neuropathy must be forefront in the healthcare provider's mind and be assessed at every visit. Subtle signs of neuropathy include inability or difficulty in buttoning clothes or picking up coins or a feeling of numbness in fingers. These side effects can become dose-limiting toxicities and may result in the discontinuation of the agent.

Vincristine (Oncovin) and vinblastine (Velban) are considered to be vesicant agents. These agents must be administered through the sidearm of a continuous intravenous solution. If the agent leaks outside the vessel (extravasates), severe tissue and muscle damage may occur.

Common Plant Alkaloid Agents
- Etoposide (VP 16-213, Vepesid, Epipodophyllotoxin)
- Vinblastine (Velban, Vinblastine Sulfate)
- Vincristine (Oncovin, Vincristine Sulfate)
- Teniposide (VM-26)

Hormonal Treatment

Hormone therapy is not actually chemotherapy due to the fact that hormones are not considered to be cytotoxic. Many cancers that occur in the breast, prostate, and endometrium are somehow dependent on hormones. The hormones assist the cells to proliferate. These cells are then said to be hormone dependent, yet some cancer cells do not retain hormone dependency and lack the receptor for the hormone. If the receptor lacks hormone dependency, the value of altering the hormonal environment is nonexistent. If tumor cells are receptor positive to the hormone, these agents may be able to suppress the growth and proliferation of cancer cells (Brown & Hogan, 1990).

Common hormonal agents include estrogens (estradiol, diethylstilbestrol), androgens (testosterone, Halotestin), progestins (Megace, Provera) and corticosteroids (dexamethasone, prednisone, hydrocortisone). Drugs classified as antiestrogen (tamoxifen), antiandrogen (flutamide), and anti-adrenal (Cytadren) are not truly hormonal agents, but they have the capability of altering the hormonal environment of cancer cells that have the specific hormone-dependent receptor.

The side effects of hormonal therapy for cancer treatment are similar to their action in the human body for non-cancerous conditions. With sexual hormones effects can include fluid retention, change in libido, and sometimes a change in secondary sexual characteristics.

The corticosteroids can cause weight gain, fluid retention, euphoria, change in sleep habits, and increased appetite. If the patient is on high doses of steroids or is on them for a long period of time, tapering the dose before discontinuation is recommended to reduce withdrawal effects. A rapid drop in plasma level of the corticosteroid can result in mood changes and sometimes severe depression. For patients using corticosteroids over a long period of time, the risk can include hypertension, cushingoid syndrome, diabetes, and osteoporosis.

The use of antiestrogens can mimic the exact effects of low hormonal levels in normal life. Side effects can include hot flashes, mood swings, increased appetite, weight gain, nausea, and vomiting. Some retinal defects and an increased risk of endometrial cancers have been noted with long-term use. Premenopausal women will experience a chemically induced menopause upon taking the antiestrogen drug. Women should be instructed as to what effects and changes to expect when taking the antiestrogen agents.

Expected effects of the antiadrenal agents include lethargy, ataxia, and nystagmus. Most patients do very well on hormonal therapy. It is critical to assess patients routinely for any side effects and to provide education about the expected side effects.

Common Hormonal Agents
- Adrenocorticoids
  - Cortisone
  - Hydrocortisone
  - Dexamethasone
  - Methylprednisone
  - Methylprednisolone
  - Prednisone
  - Prednisolone
- Androgens
  - Testosterone propionate (Neo-hombreol, Oreton)
  - Fluoxymesterone (Halotestin, Ora-Testryl)
  - Testolactone (Teslac)
- Antiestrogens
  - Tamoxifen (Nolvadex)
- Estrogens
  - Diethylstilbestrol (DES)
  - Diethylstilbestrol diphosphate (Stilphostrol, Stilbestrol Diphospate)
  - Ethinyl estradiol (Estinyl)
  - Conjugated equine estrogen (Premarin)
- Progesterones
  - Medroxyprogesterone (Provera, Depo-Provera)
  - Megestrol acetate (Megace, Pallace)

Miscellaneous Agents

Paclitaxel (Taxol) is a semisynthetic product produced from the bark of the western yew tree or the needles and twigs of a more prevalent tree called the taxus baccata. Docetaxel (Taxotere) is also a semisynthetic product but is produced from the needles of the European yew tree. Both paclitaxel and docetaxel are antimicrotubule anticancer agents. They differ from other agents that affect the microtubles in that they promote rather than inhibit microtuble assembly and work to prevent the microtubule from disassembly. The microtubules are a key part of the mitotic spindle in mitosis.

Both paclitaxel and docetaxel are similar in action and effects. The decision to use one or the other is based on the patient's response as well as on possible drug resistance. The indication for use of docetaxel versus paclitaxel is related to the issue of anthracycline resistance of the disease. Patients may have a drug resistance to agents such as doxorubicin (Adriamycin) and no longer have a tumor response. Docetaxel may also be used in patients who do not show a response to paclitaxel. These agents are most commonly used to treat breast, ovarian, and lung cancers. Research is providing new indications for their use with other cancers, however.

Anticipated side effects include myelosuppression, alopecia, anaphylaxis, neuropathy, nausea, vomiting, hypotension, muscle and joint pain, and abnormal liver function. Both drugs must be administered through non–polyvinyl chloride (PVC) intravenous tubing. The use of such tubing is necessary due to leaching of diethylhexyl phthalate (DEHP), related to the chemical mixture of the agents. The infusion must be filtered with a .22-micron filter.

Due to the increased risk of severe hypersensitivity reactions with paclitaxel, the patient must be premedicated with corticosteroids, diphenhydramine, and an H_2 antagonist (i.e., cimetidine, ranitidine) before each dose. If signs and symptoms of severe reaction occur, such as hypotension, angioedema, urticaria, pruritus, or dyspnea, the infusion should be stopped immediately and aggressive therapy begun. Patients who experience a severe hypersensitivity reaction such as this should not receive further doses.

Premedication for docetaxel should include an oral dexamethasone regimen as per the manufacturer's guidelines. If severe hypersensitivity occurs, aggressive symptom therapy must be given and the infusion should be stopped immediately.

Topotecan is a semisynthetic agent produced from campothecin. Campothecins are alkaloids with anticancer activity that are derived from plants such as *Camptotheca acuminata*. Topotecan is used for patients with advanced ovarian cancer and in some protocols for the treatment of leukemia.

Topotecan can be administered by intravenous infusion only. Myelosuppression is the major side effect and can be a dose-limiting factor. In patients with renal or hepatic failure dosing adjustments should occur.

Miscellaneous Agents
- Docetaxel (Taxotere)
- Paclitaxel (Taxol)
- Topotecan (Hycamtin)
- Irinotecan (Camptosar)

Calculation of Dosing

Chemotherapeutic agents are ordered according to an algorithm for body surface area (BSA). Body surface area is calculated by patient height and weight, using the nomogram for determination of body surface area (Fig. 12-1); BSA is then stated in m^2. Accurate and current body height and weight measurements are crucial. To determine the BSA, find the markings for height and weight on Figure 12-1; using a straight-edged item, determine the intersection point on the middle column, which is the BSA.

Most chemotherapy is then ordered as milligrams per m^2. Before proceeding with the ordering of chemotherapy, it is critical to evaluate the patient's knowledge and understanding of the treatment, review the orders, determine the supplies needed, and begin to prioritize the care for the patient. A valuable community resource regarding medications is the pharmacist. Utilize the pharmacist within your agency or contact a pharmacist in your area who has expertise in cancer care. If none is available, contact the manufacturer of the chemotherapy agent and speak with the clinical consultant.

Clinical Trials

A clinical trial is a research study that is conducted with patients, most commonly to determine the value of a specific treatment or drug. Each study is developed to answer certain scientific questions and to assist in finding new and enhanced ways to treat a disease. The value of participating in a clinical trial is the access to treatments that may not otherwise be available. Clinical trials offer cutting-edge treatment opportunities to patients with a specific diagnosis and a particular clinical status.

Research trials begin with laboratory and animal studies long before they involve humans. Laboratory studies help provide information about safety, dosing, and effectiveness in treating specific disease processes. Once safety and efficacy are determined, trials can be conducted in humans to test the effectiveness of the agents, either alone or in combination with other therapies/agents. As with any treatment, there may be risks as well as benefits. Extensive education is provided to the patient and informed consent obtained by the clinical trial expert. Clinical trials are available at healthcare facilities across the nation. For more information about clinical trials, contact a Cancer Center Program and/or the local university medical center in your area.

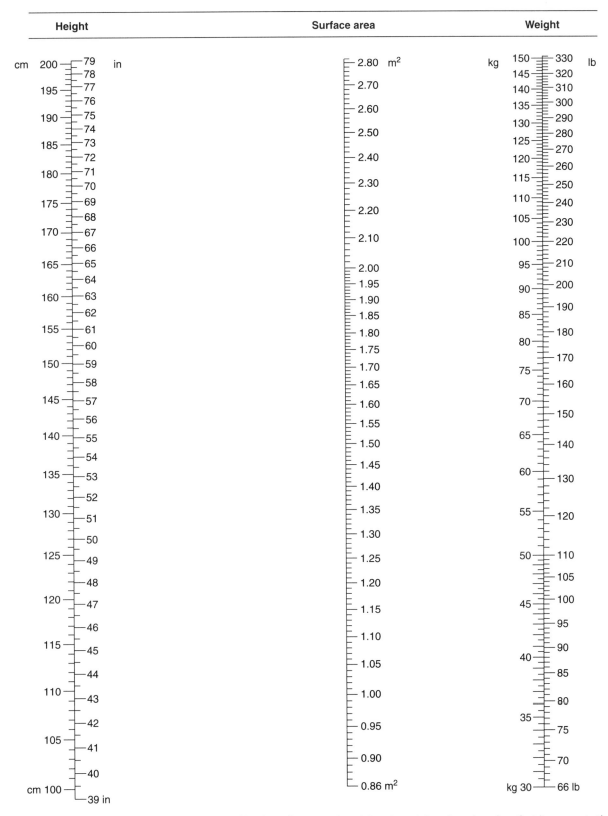

Figure 12-1 Nomogram for determination of body surface area in adults. A straight edge placed so that it connects the patient's height in the left column with the weight in the right column will intersect the center column at the point indicating the patient's body surface area.

Peripheral Stem Cell Transplant (Autologous Transplant)

With certain types of cancer, higher doses of chemotherapy are needed in order to treat the disease. A procedure called peripheral stem cell transplant or autologous bone marrow transplant allows the patient to receive higher than normal doses of chemotherapy without causing permanent damage to the bone marrow cells. This is done by first removing the stem cells via apheresis.

Peripheral blood stem cells are obtained using an apheresis procedure on a cell separation device (e.g., Cobe Spectra, Fenwal CS-3000). The patient is connected to the apheresis machine via a central venous catheter (usually a special apheresis catheter) for approximately 2 to 4 hours. During this time blood is automatically withdrawn and separated, and unneccessary components (i.e., red blood cells, platelets, and plasma) are returned to the patient. This type of collection process may need to occur several times over several days, in order to collect adequate numbers of stem cells (mononuclear cells). The apheresis can be efficiently performed on an outpatient basis, allowing the patient to be at home most of the time.

After each collection, the peripheral stem cells are specially processed and frozen with DMSO 10%, or treated and then frozen. The cells remain frozen at an approved location until the patient is ready for reinfusion of the cells.

After the apheresis procedures are completed, the patient receives high-dose (dose-intensive) chemotherapy to treat the particular type of cancer. The patient receives reinfusion of the stem cells within 48 to 96 hours of the completion of high-dose chemotherapy. The reinfusion occurs through the central line and is administered similarly to blood products.

Many institutions perform both apheresis and high-dose chemotherapy on an outpatient basis and admit the patient to an acute-care unit only if the need arises. The usual reasons for admission include sepsis, pain control, and other symptoms that cannot be managed effectively in the home.

Side effects of stem cell transplant include a variety of symptoms as discussed above with particular treatment agents; however, side effects in high-dose therapy patients occur to a greater degree. The most noted side effects of dose-intensive therapy include pancytopenia, mucositis, and alopecia.

Most patients are cared for in the home. Arrangements for home care visits and assessments are made with a home care agency competent in the care of these patients. Patient blood counts are checked on a frequent basis; monitoring for any sign of infection is critical. Patients receive instructions on dietary intake, avoidance of raw fruits and vegetables, and the use of special water products. Patients receive instructions on how to care for the central line and appropriate hygiene to reduce the risk of infection. Patients are often followed by an oncologist and a bone marrow transplant specialist.

Patients and families receive significant education from the nursing staff, physicians, dieticians, social service, and others related to apheresis and high-dose chemotherapy. Financial concerns and insurance coverage of this procedure remains an issue for many patients. It is critical in the planning phase to involve appropriate social service and financial counselors.

Educational Interventions for Patient and Family

Education of the patient and family is a critical component in providing psychological comfort and support. It is important to assess the knowledge level and understanding of both the patient and family, as well as to address the issues that are of utmost concern to them.

The timing and setting of the education are critical variables. Once a patient hears the word cancer, his or her ability to comprehend or absorb more information is greatly altered. The healthcare provider must be knowledgeable of the information related to prognosis and treatment options that the physician has shared with the patient and family. Such information will lay the groundwork for planning the educational intervention.

It has been shown that persons retain only about 10% of what is taught to them. However, retention is greatly increased if the information is shown to have value and meaning. Value and meaning are variables that can be influenced by the person's educational preparation and cultural, spiritual, religious, and familial background. Each person has differences in values, none being right or wrong, simply different. It is critical to respect these differences and customize education to reflect these variables, as what is important to one person may not be important to another.

Review the materials you have available about chemotherapy and cancer. Order brochures, videos, and tapes from other agencies or perhaps write one for your facility. In choosing brochures and pamphlets, it is key to select those with the lowest reading level, such as 4th or 5th grade. Even at this low reading level, often the information about chemotherapy is still difficult to understand.

Never assume that you have educated or taught a patient by merely handing him or her a book, pamphlet, or brochure. It is critical to ask the patient and family how they would like the information shared. Use of one-on-one teaching, brochures, videos, and tapes may work for many persons. One-on-one teaching and providing a time for questions and answers needs to occur for all patients; this allows not only for information sharing but also for the building of a relationship with the patient. Such a relationship may then provide knowledge and comfort to the patient and family.

Critical components of education about chemotherapy administration include (1) names of agents, (2) possible side effects, (3) when and how agents are administered, and (4) when and how to call the physician. Attempt to arrange a quiet place for the teaching to occur. Often the patient and family become emotional about the dramatic changes in their lives. Address each of these concerns as they arise, noting that each individual has his or her own set of fears, ideas, and concerns.

Always provide patients and families with information about resources and support systems within the community. Suggest that they utilize computers to access national data bases about cancer and treatments. If patients do not have access to computers, refer them to a local library where they can be assisted in using the computer technology. Remind patients that information given on the Internet often is non-professional in nature and may not be valid or accurate but merely personal opinion.

Suggest that the patient and/or family keep a journal or log of questions, concerns, or events that occur on a daily basis. By keeping a journal, the patient has a source of ventilation as well as a written document of questions to ask at the next appointment with the physician. It may also be helpful to family members.

Assessment of the Patient

Before ordering the chemotherapy, it is important to assess the patient. Assessment should include the following questions to gather information that will be helpful in planning care that is both time and cost efficient. Always review the patient medical record(s) from previous visits and treatments to verify crucial information. Key concerns are allergies, patient tolerance of previous treatment, symptom management, and venous access.

1. Has the patient received this medication before? If yes, when was the last dose? Is there a record of the treatment? Review the previous treatment documentation for doses, tolerance, and other care issues.
2. What is the patient diagnosis that requires treatment with chemotherapy? This is critical because many patients automatically assume that chemotherapy is used for cancerous conditions only and therefore are concerned about or perhaps confused by its use. Make sure to clarify this information with the patient and physician if necessary.
3. Has the patient received information and education about the chemotherapy? Education should focus on the medications, side effects, treatment schedule, and when and how to call the physician.
4. Did the patient experience any side effects, and what premedications worked well with their previous treatment(s)? What medications did not work? Did the patient have any reactions to the medications? Reactions to antiemetics can include extrapyramidal and severe hypersensitivity effects. These effects can intensify and worsen with future doses. Alert the physician to previous problems and verify whether these medications should be ordered.

5. Does the patient have a central venous access device? If yes, is the central line functioning adequately? Does it flush and draw well? Has the patient had any complications with the device? If the patient has a device that does not allow for blood withdrawal but flushes, verification of placement must occur before treatment. Verification by chest x-ray is strongly recommended and is a necessity if a chemotherapy agent is considered to be a vesicant.

6. Has the patient had peripheral intravenous lines before? What worked well? Has the patient had surgery or lymph node removal? If yes, this will affect the access to that extremity and limit the choices for intravenous sites.

7. Is the patient capable of tolerating the chemotherapy agents by the route ordered? For example, if the patient has a peg tube and cannot have oral intake, how should the chemotherapy be administered? It is critical to verify whether the agents can be crushed and administered in an alternative way. If crushing or altering the medication must be done, check with the pharmacy about whether this is possible.

8. What questions do the patient and family have? Allow the patient and family to voice their concerns and questions. Often patient, family, and healthcare provider have very different interpretations of what information is needed, yet each has merit and value.

9. Will the patient need medications for home use? Will the patient need symptom management medications for home? Will the patient/family be capable of handling such medications? What are the discharge plans for the patient? If the patient has specific needs, it is critical to address them as soon as possible so that appropriate services can be arranged that meet the patient and the payers requirements.

10. Does the patient have access to a pharmacy and a means of getting prescriptions filled as ordered? It is important to verify this with the patient. Many patients have financial and insurance coverage concerns and may not be able to get medications filled without some assistance. This should be arranged before discharging the patient. Many pharmaceutical companies have drug assistance programs, and paperwork must be done by either a pharmacist or social worker/case manager.

Organizing and Prioritizing Chemotherapy Orders

After assessing the patient, it is critical to review and organize the process for preparing the chemotherapy for administration. By reviewing the following questions, the process of chemotherapy administration should flow smoothly.

1. Are the orders complete with medication names, doses, route of administration, fluids, and premedications as needed? If not, contact the prescribing physician for clarification. It is critical to contact the ordering physician as practice patterns may vary between physicians.

2. It is recommended that telephone orders for chemotherapy not be accepted. Telephone orders should only be accepted for dose decreases or discontinuation. All orders need to be faxed to the nurse. Telephone orders received by someone who is unfamiliar with the chemotherapy agent(s) could be misinterpreted and place the patient, nurse, and healthcare facility at great risk.

3. Who will mix the chemotherapy agents? Guidelines by OSHA (Occupational Safety and Health Administration) and ONS (Oncology Nursing Society) recommend that all agents that are chemotherapeutic and/or cytotoxic should be mixed under a laminar flow hood to reduce exposure to the employee and the environment. Although a flow hood may not be available in all areas, it is the ideal. For some office practices, it may be possiblea to contract with a local infusion company so that mixing by staff would not be necessary. Contact an infusion company or local pharmacy to review available options.

4. Does the patient have appropriate lab work ordered? Most patients will need at least a complete blood count (CBC/Plt). The need for other laboratory tests will depend on

the specific medications ordered and the potential system effects. Many medications require baseline testing of renal, hepatic, and/or cardiac functions. If appropriate lab tests are not ordered, contact the ordering physician for further orders. If tests were done at an off-site location, ask for copies to be faxed to your facility to be reviewed and placed in the patient record.

5. What doses are ordered of each medication? Are the doses appropriate for this patient? Dosing of chemotherapeutic agents is based on the BSA; therefore, accurate height and weight measurements are key.

6. Is the patient capable of tolerating the route of administration ordered? Does he or she have adequate venous access?

7. Before mixing any chemotherapy medication, it is critical to have lab work and venous access verified. Is the lab work completed? Does the patient have venous access (central or peripheral)?

8. What equipment is required for administration of the chemotherapy? OSHA guidelines recommend that barriers be utilized, such as gown, gloves, and mask, to reduce the exposure to the employee.

Administration of Chemotherapy

The following procedure and steps are recommended to ensure safety and accuracy during administration of chemotherapy.

1. Verify that informed consent has occurred, if applicable. If the patient is in a clinical research trial, informed consent is mandatory.

2. Verify that the patient has received information pertaining to treatment and follow-up.

3. Check appropriate laboratory data prior to reconstitution of chemotherapy agent(s). Verify that the labs are within acceptable parameters.

4. Notify the ordering physician of abnormal lab/test results and receive orders as needed.

5. Verify the physician's written orders for specific dosage, route, and symptom management. If there are questions about the chemotherapy orders, contact the prescribing physician.

6. If lab and test values are all within acceptable parameters, the nurse may proceed with having the chemotherapy mixed. Never have the orders filled until all labs and tests are verified to be acceptable.

7. Verify that the patient has appropriate venous access before ordering chemotherapy to be mixed. If the patient has a central line that does not have a blood return, a chest x-ray will be needed to verify accurate placement. In particular, a vesicant should not be given without verifying the placement.

8. If the patient is to receive an oral chemotherapy agent that must be cut or crushed, it is critical to verify by checking with a pharmacist whether the drug can be cut or crushed. Cutting or crushing of any chemotherapy agent should be done under a flow hood to reduce environmental exposure.

9. Gather appropriate attire to administer chemotherapy, including a chemotherapy administration–approved gown (which should cover arms and the entire body), gloves (gloves without powder are recommended; some agencies double glove), and mask (many institutions do not use a mask). The key is to provide the nurse who is handling and administering the chemotherapy with barriers to protect him or her and the environment.

10. If a chemotherapy policy exists within your agency or facility, review it thoroughly before administering. If no policy exists, review current literature (see the reference list at the end of this chapter).

11. Review patient allergy/drug reaction history.

12. Explain the procedure for chemotherapy administration to the patient and answer questions.

13. Once chemotherapy has been prepared for administration, check the dose for accuracy and patient counts with another healthcare

provider (e.g., pharmacist, physician, nurse).

14. If the chemotherapy agent is a vesicant, verify that the appropriate equipment and antidotal agents are available in the immediate area in case of extravasation. (See the section below on extravasation.)

15. Verify the patient's identity before administration by checking his or her armband and asking the patient to state his or her name.

16. Assemble the equipment necessary for administration of chemotherapy. All intravenous tubing should be primed with a compatible solution. Never prime intravenous tubing with the chemotherapy agent as this can cause increased exposure to environment and persons. Many institutions have intravenous lines prefilled by the pharmacy under a flow hood to reduce the potential for exposure.

17. Intravenous lines should be functional with excellent blood return and without pain or swelling. The intravenous site should not be below the site of a recent blood draw (not less than 24 hours) or intravenous site. If peripheral intravenous lines are started below the site of a blood draw and a vesicant or irritant is administered, the risk of extravasation is higher. Never use an extremity that has had lymph node dissection; the risk of infection is high.

18. Chemotherapy agents that are ordered by intravenous push must be pushed through the sidearm of a continuous line of compatible fluid. Agents can be pushed in any order, but it is critical to flush the line well between each drug that is administered. If an infusion of vesicant agents is ordered, a central line is suggested to reduce the likelihood of extravasation. When infusing chemotherapy it is critical to verify the compatibility of all drugs before administration.

19. When administering an intravenous push, check the site for patency and infiltration every 2 to 3 cc by pulling back on the syringe plunger, then releasing to flush with compatible fluids. Note blood flashback and monitor for any signs of pain, swelling, or absence of blood return and/or infiltra-

tion. If the patient complains of discomfort, stop the infusion and verify intravenous placement.

20. Flush the sidearm of the intravenous tubing with 5 to 10 cc of normal saline or a compatible fluid upon completing each drug and before beginning another. This will reduce interactions and possible precipitant development.

21. Inject the drug(s) at the appropriate rate to prevent untoward sensations and complications. Patients may complain if drugs are administered too rapidly. Never administer more rapidly than the manufacturer's recommendations.

22. Observe the patient for allergic or any hypersensitive reaction to the drug(s) and take appropriate action(s) should either occur. If administering agents such as paclitaxel, docetaxel, bleomycin, and others that have the potential for severe hypersensitivity, appropriate premedications should be administered prior to treatment.

23. Upon completing the chemotherapy, flush the tubing and/or sidearm of the intravenous line with 5 to 10 cc of normal saline or a compatible solution. This is critical because it has been noted that if vesicant agents are not well flushed from the sidearm, extravasation can occur later due to residual drug in the sidearm hub.

24. Dispose of equipment in the appropriate chemotherapy disposal container. Chemotherapy wastes cannot be placed in regular trash, needle boxes, or other waste containers. Chemotherapy waste must be labeled and disposed of properly. All supplies such as gowns, gloves, masks, intravenous tubing, syringes, needles and needleless attachments must be disposed of in the chemotherapy waste container. Seek the advice of your local pharmacist or purchasing department to order such equipment. Many vendors carry such products. Verify with your waste management personnel and/or company about removal and disposal of the waste containers. It is critical to be in compliance with OSHA recommendations. Never recap or clip needles used for administration of chemotherapy. The needleless

systems available, such as those produced by Baxter, Becton-Dickinson, Abbott, and others, are the ideal for any healthcare system to reduce employee injury.

Documentation of Chemotherapy Administration

Documentation regarding the process of chemotherapy administration is critical. Documentation should occur on approved institutional forms and according to policies and procedures that govern practice within the specific facility or agency. Thorough documentation is a must! Charting must include all components in order to provide adequate legal documentation.

The following components must be included in the documentation by the nurse:

- Location of intravenous site
- Gauge of device used
- Number of attempts to start IV or access the device
- Patient tolerance
- Names of persons who verified lab/tests results and chemotherapy doses
- Premedications given
- Educational interventions
- Sequence of chemotherapy administration
- Intravenous fluids infused and rate of administration
- Assessment of site for pain, swelling, complaint by patient, and blood return
- Chemotherapy agents and medications charted on the medication record

Tissue Irritation and Extravasation

Vesicants are agents that are associated with severe necrosis, with possible damage to tendons, muscle, and surrounding tissue. Damage to the tissue and surrounding areas occurs as the result of leakage of the agent outside the vessel, which is known as extravasation. Irritant agents cause less severe reaction and burning sensation than vesicants.

The impact of the extravasation of the agent is directly correlated to the specific drug and the amount that was extravasated; therefore, meticulous intravenous assessment during administration is critical. Reactions to vesicant drug extravasations are often obvious in approximately 7 to 10 days, whereas the reaction to extravasation of an irritant drug occurs during the administration of the drug or within a few days following the administration. Vesicant and irritant agents should be administered through a continuous infusion of a compatible fluid. If vesicants are to be administered continuously, it is strongly recommended that this be done through a central venous access device. Administration of continuous vesicant infusions through a peripheral site holds a great potential for infiltration and requires constant monitoring. It is critical to note the assessment and verification of placement of any venous access device. Although infrequent, central lines can also have the potential for extravasation of fluids and drugs. Prior to the administration of any chemotherapy, verification of blood draw and flushing functions is critical. It is important to determine if the agents are vesicants. If so, it is key to ensure that the appropriate antidote is available. Vesicant agents should not be administered otherwise. Preparing an extravasation kit to have at all times would ensure the availability of appropriate materials.

A protocol or standing order must exist for the extravasation treatment process before administering any vesicant agent. The timeliness of treatment of an extravasation can reduce the degree of damage to the tissue and surrounding area(s). If the patient is receiving an investigational chemotherapeutic agent in a clinical trial, it is critical to have the information about the agent before administration. Information must be available to inform the healthcare provider of any vesicant potential with the agent and the recommended antidote.

The extravasation kit should include the following items:

- Ice pack or warm pack
- 3-cc syringes (two to three)
- .25-gauge needles (10)
- Needle or needleless supplies to draw from vials

- Alcohol swabs
- Band-Aids
- 2 vials of sterile water
- 2 vials of normal saline
- 1 vial of sodium thiosulfate 1 gm/1 cc
- 1 vial of hyaluronidase (Wydase) 150 U/mL
- 1 vial of hydrocortisone (Solu-Cortef) 50 to 100 mg

Antidote for Alkylating Agents

Sodium thiosulfate is the recommended antidote for the alkylating agents that are vesicants. Cold compresses should be used after the treatment of the extravasation site with the antidote. Cold compresses should continue for 24 hours unless contraindicated for another condition such as circulatory compromise.

Antidote for Antitumor Antibiotics

Hydrocortisone (Solu-Cortef) is the recommended antidote for the anthracycline agents that are vesicants. Cold compresses should be used after the treatment of the extravasation site with the antidote. Cold compresses should continue for 24 hours unless contraindicated due to another condition such as circulatory compromise.

Antidote for Plant Alkaloids

The appropriate antidote for the plant alkaloids is hyalouronidase (Wydase) for those that are vesicants. Warm compresses should be used for extravasation of these agents.

Extravasation Treatment Procedure

The nurse administering the chemotherapy should assess the intravenous site for pain, redness, swelling, and blood return. Remember that in persons with dark-pigmented skin, redness is not a reliable indicator.

Pain, burning, and stinging are common warning signs of extravasation. Redness may occur around the needle site; swelling may occur immediately or hours later. Blood return may still be present during extravasation. Patient tolerance and complaints are critical variables to consider. A rule of chemotherapy administration is "If in doubt about an intravenous line, take it out."

Treatment of Extravasation

1. Immediately stop the administration of the chemotherapeutic agent(s).
2. Leave the needle in place, but do not infuse any fluids through the line.
3. With a sterile syringe, aspirate any residual chemotherapy agent and blood in the intravenous tubing and the needle.
4. If able to aspirate residual agent from intravenous tubing, inject the appropriate antidote through the intravenous line. If unable to aspirate residual, do not inject the antidote through the intravenous line. Discontinue the IV line and proceed to step 5.
5. Using a syringe and 20-gauge needle or needleless adapter, draw up the appropriate antidote. Attach a sterile 25-gauge needle to the end of the syringe.
6. Cleanse the site of the extravasation with alcohol, then begin the process of injecting 0.1 cc of the antidote at five sites surrounding the circumference of the extravasation, changing the 25-gauge needle with each new injection site. This decreases the likelihood of tracking the vesicant agent further. If the site of extravasation is large, more injection sites may be necessary.
7. Apply a cold or warm pack to the extravasation site for at least 24 hours.
8. Notify the physician who prescribed the chemotherapy and inform him or her of what actions were taken; receive further orders if needed.

Documentation of Extravasation

Documentation of the extravasation event should include the following:

- Date
- Time
- Needle size and type
- Insertion site
- Drug administration sequence

- Drug administration technique
- Approximate amount of the drug extravasated
- Nursing management of the extravasation
- Patient complaints and/or statements
- Appearance of site
- Name of physician notified
- Follow-up measures
- Nurse's signature

Cleanup of Chemotherapy Spills

Spills and breaking of vials containing chemotherapeutic agents should be cleaned up immediately by personnel trained in the cleanup procedure. Every agency or healthcare facility must have an approved spill kit available to personnel administering chemotherapy. Information about spill kits and ordering may be obtained from purchasing or pharmacy departments or, in some institutions, from the safety and security department.

CONTAMINATION TO HEALTHCARE PROVIDER

Overt contamination of gloves and gowns or direct skin or eye contact should be treated as follows:

1. Immediately remove gloves, gown, mask or whatever equipment is contaminated with the chemotherapy agent.
2. Wash affected areas immediately with soap and follow with profuse amounts of water. For eye exposure, immediately flood the affected eye with water or isotonic eye wash designed specifically for this purpose; do so for at least 5 minutes.
3. Obtain medical attention immediately and complete appropriate facility forms for such an incident.
4. Report any chemotherapy waste or loss to the physician on call so that dosing corrections may be made.

PROCESS OF CLEANING SMALL SPILLS (<5 ML OR <5 CM)

1. Clean up the spill immediately wearing appropriate chemotherapy-protective barriers (gown, gloves [double], mask, and eye protection if needed).

2. Wipe liquids with absorbent gauze pads and solids with wet absorbent gauze pads, then cleanse (three times) using a detergent (hospital-approved disinfectant) followed by clean water. Place any glass fragments in the approved chemotherapy disposal container.
3. Dispose of all items in the chemotherapy disposal container.
4. For reusable items (infusion pumps, etc.) that have become contaminated, wash with a hospital-approved disinfectant in appropriate attire as above. Linens that are contaminated should be placed in a plastic bag and then sent for laundering with indication of contamination. Patient belongings should be placed in a plastic bag and laundered twice. Laundering should be done separately from other clothes.

PROCESS FOR CLEANING LARGE SPILLS (>5 ML OR >5 CM)

1. Obtain an approved spill kit for cleaning up large spills. A chemotherapy spill kit should be available at all times.
2. Wear appropriate chemotherapy barriers, gown, gloves (double), mask, and eye protection. Mask and eye protection should be worn when handling spills of powdered chemotherapy agents.
3. Limit the spill area by covering it immediately with absorbent sheets of disposable towels that are in the spill kit. Place disposable towels gently on the spill to avoid splashing or splattering.
4. If a powdered agent is spilled, cover the spill with a dampened disposable towel from the kit. Dampen the towel with water.
5. All contaminated surfaces should be thoroughly cleaned with a hospital-approved disinfectant and wiped clean with water. If a specific chemical inactivator is available in the spill kit for the substance that was spilled, it may be used as long as it is nontoxic and nondestructive to the surrounding area and does not cause the spill area to spread further.
6. All contaminated disposable materials must be discarded in the approved chemotherapy

disposal container. Non-disposable items such as reusable equipment should be wiped down first with water and then alcohol; personnel should wear the appropriate attire (described above).

7. Inform the ordering physician of the spill. Receive further orders if needed.

DOCUMENTATION OF SPILL/CONTAMINATION

Complete approved forms for the agency. Documentation on reports should include the location of the spill, date, time, approximate amount of spill, type of drug involved, action taken, and personnel and patient involved.

Summary

It is critical to note that many diagnoses, including cancer, may require the use of cytotoxic (chemotherapeutic) agents. Ideally these agents are administered by a nurse who is chemotherapy competent, but sometimes they need to be administered by a nurse who has little or no experience with them. It is key to note that all medications must be reviewed for appropriateness, dosing, side effects, and handling and disposal before administration. A nurse who is knowledgeable about the agents that are to be administered is enhancing the quality of patient care as well as demonstrating appropriate behaviors within the scope of nursing practice.

Regardless of the reason for use, the route of administration, or the dosage ordered, it is key to note that these agents must be administered, handled, and disposed of properly. This will ensure safety not only for the patient but for the nurse and the environment as well.

The use of cytotoxic (chemotherapeutic) agents —old and new, investigational and proven—will continue across the nation and around the world. The nurse must be diligent in verifying not only the information needed to provide safe and appropriate care, but also what resources exist that may offer support and assistance. Check with oncology nurses, healthcare facilities, and pharmacists within your area to receive more information. Remember that the patient is the focus for the care that nurses deliver, and each and every patient deserves appropriate, efficient, and compassionate care.

REFERENCES

Barton Burke, M., Wilkes, G.M., Berg, D., Bean, C.K., & Ingwersen, K. (1991). *Cancer chemotherapy: A nursing approach*. Boston: Jones & Bartlett.

Berg, D.T. (1997). New chemotherapy treatment options and implications for nursing care. *Oncology Nursing Forum*, 24(Suppl. 1), 5–12.

Brown, J.K. & Hogan, C.M. (1990). Chemotherapy. In S.L. Groenwald, M.H. Frogge, M. Goodman, & C.H. Yarbro (Eds.). *Cancer nursing: Principles and practice* (2nd ed.). Boston: Jones & Bartlett.

Miaskowski, C. & Viele, C. (1999). Cancer chemotherapy. In Miaskowski, C. & Buchsel, P. (Eds.). *Oncology nursing: Assessment and clinical care*. St. Louis: Mosby.

Occupational Safety and Health Administration (1995). Controlling occupational exposure to hazardous drugs. In *OSHA technical manual* (Chapter 21). CPL2-2.-OB-CH-4. Bethesda: OSHA.

Powell, L.L. (1996). *Cancer chemotherapy guidelines and recommendations for practice*. Pittsburgh: Oncology Nursing Press.

U.S. Department of Health and Human Services (1997). *What are clinical trials all about?* Bethesda: Office of Cancer Communications, National Cancer Institute.

Principles of Radiation Therapy

Karen E. Maher

Radiation therapy is the use of high-energy x-rays to treat cancer. Radiation oncology is a subspecialty that incorporates the science and clinical application of therapeutic radiation in cancer therapy. Approximately 60% of oncology patients will receive radiation therapy at some point in the cancer treatment continuum.

History

Radiation has been an ever-present ingredient in the evolution of life on Earth. It is not new and was not invented by the ingenuity of humans in the technological age—radiation has always existed. What is new and man made is the extra radiation given to people largely for medical purposes.

The use of therapeutic radiation has evolved dramatically over the past 100 years since the discovery in 1895, by Wilhelm C. Roentgen, of a fluorescent glow after an electrical charge was passed through a cathode ray tube. The powerful ray was given the designation X for the unknown, and later called roentgen rays. Only a few weeks after Roentgen discovered the x-ray, the chemical properties of naturally occurring elements were being studied by A. H. Becquerel and Marie and Pierre Curie in France. The natural radioactivity of uranium was discovered by Becquerel, of polonium and radium by the Curies (Bentel, 1996).

The discoveries of x-rays and radioactivity were promptly followed by their therapeutic application. Use of the x-ray evolved more quickly due to difficulty in obtaining adequate amounts of radium for therapeutic interstitial application. The radiation dose was measured by the degree of skin erythema. Cures, mainly for skin and superficial tumors, were documented; however, results could not be duplicated because there was no way of definitively measuring a given dose of radiation (Hilderley, 1997). From 1920 to 1940 much was learned, and the degree of skin erythema as a measure of radiation dose was replaced by the first physical unit, the roentgen (Bentel, 1996). The surge in technological research during World War II led to significant developments in the science of radiation. High-powered machines were produced, such as the linear accelerator that is still widely used today (Hilderley, 1997). Technical developments in electronics and computers have led to greater precision in the delivery of therapeutic radiation. It is possible to more accurately visualize the relationship of the tumor to normal structures, align and position the patient on the treatment table, and measure and calculate the dose (Bentel, 1996).

Basic Physics of Radiation Therapy

The radiation we are concerned with is radiation that will produce excitation and ionization during the absorption of energy in a biologic material (Figure 13-1). Excitation means raising an electron in an atom to a higher energy level without ejecting the electron from the atomic orbit. Ionization

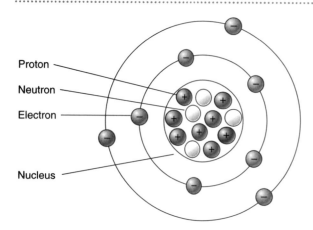

Figure 13-1 Basic structure on an atom. Protons, which are positively charged, and neutrons, which have no electrical charge, are the major components of the nucleus of an atom. The number of protons is equal to the number of negatively charged electrons orbiting the nucleus. Atoms of any given element may have different numbers of neutrons in the nucleus, thus giving atoms of the same element different atomic weights. An atom of a given element that differs only in its atomic weight is called an isotope. (Redrawn from Hilderley, L.J. [1997]. Radiotherapy. In S. L. Groenwald, M. Goodman, M. H. Frogge, & C. H. Yarbro [Eds.], *Cancer nursing: Principles and practice* [pp. 247–282]. Boston: Jones and Bartlett.)

is sufficient energy to eject one or more orbital electrons from an atom or molecule. The ejection of the orbital electron(s) causes a localized release of energy that is large enough to break chemical bonds. Thus, the process of excitation and ionization initiates a chain of events in cells that lead to a biologic effect that is defined as ionizing radiation. In the setting of therapeutic ionizing radiation, the goal is to produce sufficient damage such that the malignant cell cannot reproduce.

Radiation-induced cell kill occurs by primarily two mechanisms, the direct and indirect hit. In the direct hit, radiation primarily damages the DNA and the cell dies as it attempts to undergo mitosis. This is the most lethal injury to the cell and cannot be modified chemically. It accounts for approximately ⅓ of radiation-induced cellular damage. An indirect hit is when ionization takes place in the medium around the cell, which is most often water. The radiation absorbed by the water results in free radicals. A free radical is a very unstable

atom with a missing orbital electron. The atom is now looking for other atoms with which to bond and become stable (appropriate number of electrons in orbit). While the free radical is trying to bond, it causes chemical reactions that are damaging to cells and toxic enough to cause cellular death. Because of the higher proportions of water to DNA in a given cell, the probability of indirect damage through the ionization of cellular water is much greater and accounts for approximately ⅔ of radiation cellular damage (Figure 13-2).

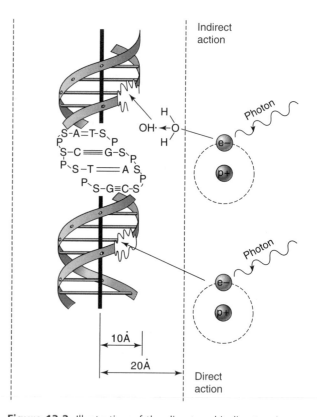

Figure 13-2 Illustration of the direct and indirect actions of radiation on cellular DNA. The structure of DNA is shown schematically; the letters S, P, A, T, G, and C represent sugar, phosphorus, adenine, thymine, guanine, and cytosine, respectively. *Direct action:* A secondary electron resulting from absorption of an x-ray photon interacts with the DNA to produce an effect. *Indirect action:* The secondary electron interacts with a water molecule to produce an OH radical, which in turn produces the damage to the DNA. (Adapted from Hall, E. [1994]. *Radiobiology for the radiologist.* Philadelphia: Lippincott-Raven.)

Therapeutic ionizing radiation is either electromagnetic or particulate (Figure 13-3). Electromagnetic energy is characterized by vibrations of electromagnetic waves. Electromagnetic waves are a form of energy, and, as the length of the wave increases, the intensity of the energy decreases. Ionizing radiation is electromagnetic energy with a very short wavelength and very high-energy intensity. Gamma rays and x-rays are two forms of electromagnetic energy that are roughly equivalent but differ in means of their production. X-rays are machine made; gamma rays are emitted by radioactive materials such as Co^{60} (Hilderley, 1997). Electromagnetic radiation, also called photon radiation, is used to treat parenchymal or deep-seated tumors such as those of the prostate, lung, and abdomen/pelvis. Electromagnetic radiation is skin sparing. The dose from an external photon beam builds up as it passes through the tissue of the patient, because of the increased number of particles set in motion distal to the patient's surface. This results in a low surface (skin) dose, which spares the patient significant radiation skin injury (Mackie, Liu & McCullough, 1998).

Particulate radiation, which includes electrons, neutrons, and alpha and beta particles, interacts with matter by direct collision. Electrons are the most common type of particulate radiation used in the therapeutic setting. The particulate radiation dose is designed to be given on or just below the skin because the electron loses its energy only a short distance within the target substance. For example, electrons are used to treat a skin cancer or a chest wall recurrence of breast cancer. Treatment with heavy charged particle beams, such as fast neutrons, protons, helium ions, and negative pi-mesons, remains largely investigational (Bentel, 1996).

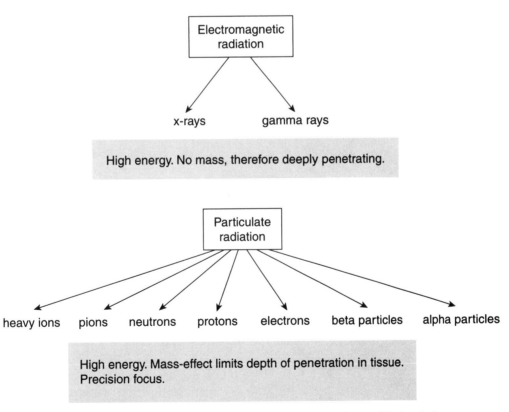

Figure 13-3 Characteristics of ionizing radiations. (Redrawn from Hilderley, L. J. [1997]. Radiotherapy. In S. L. Groenwald, M. Goodman, M. H. Frogge, & C. H. Yarbro [Eds.], *Cancer nursing: Principles and practice* [pp. 247–282]. Boston: Jones and Bartlett.)

Radiation Biology

Cellular response to radiation injury is related to the degree of mitotic activity. Actively replicating cells have four stages (Figure 13-4). The cell cycle is most sensitive to radiation during mitosis and the G2 phase, with the greatest resistance in the DNA synthesis phase (Hall, 1994). Poorly differentiated, immature cells, rapidly proliferating cells, and cells with a high mitotic potential are more radiosensitive. The term *radiosensitivity* refers to the response of the tumor to radiation in terms of degree and speed of response. Another frequently used term, *radiocurability*, refers to local or regional eradication of tumor cells, and means that the tumor-to-normal-tissue relations are such that curative doses of radiation can be applied regularly without excessive damage to normal tissues. Examples of radiocurable tumors are carcinomas of the cervix, larynx, breast, and prostate. These terms are not interchangeable; for example, non-Hodgkin's lymphoma is very radiosensitive but may not be radiocurable. All tissues have a degree of radiosensitivity, but it is the effect on normal tissue surrounding the tumor that largely determines the maximum radiation dose and resulting toxicities (Hellman, 1997).

The goal of radiation therapy is to destroy cancer cells while maintaining the integrity of normal tissue. This can be illustrated by the therapeutic ratio (Figure 13-5). Optimally, the therapeutic ratio will allow complete tumor eradication and minimal residual injury to surrounding normal tissues/structures. However, the radiation beam does not know the difference between normal cells and cancer cells; it kills them both. Thus, malignant and normal cells differ very little in their overall response to ionizing radiation. The goal is to destroy the tumor and cure the patient, but it is clear that the therapeutic ratio can be a delicate balancing of treatment outcome versus toxicities. Table 13-1 illustrates the cellular replacement times for selected systems.

Normal and cancer cells undergo some degree of repair of sublethal damage between doses of radiation. A single dose of ionizing radiation will have a greater effect on cells than the same dose divided into several fractions. If the goal is maximum tumor cell kill while sparing normal tissue, dividing the radiation into equal doses or fractions is crucial to achieving this goal. Radiation is most commonly administered once daily; however, hyperfractionation (two or more fractions per day separated by 4 to 6 hours) is used in selected cases. Fractionation is designed to take advantage of the *Four Rs of Radiobiology*:

1. *Repair:* This refers to the ability of cells to recover from sublethal radiation injury. Repair usually occurs within 24 hours but may take as little as 4 hours in some tissues. Normal cells repair between daily doses, whereas tumor cells may initially repair but their ability will decrease as radiation continues due to cellular damage, thus increasing the damage to tumor cells.

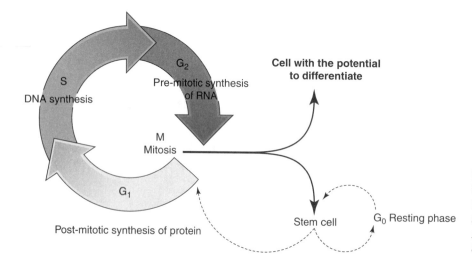

Figure 13-4 Cellular life cycle. (Redrawn from Maxwell, M., & Maher, K. [1992]. Chemotherapy-induced myelosuppression. *Seminars in Oncology Nursing,* 8[2], 113–123.)

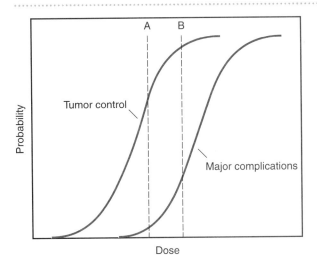

Figure 13-5 Therapeutic ratio. Sigmoid curves of tumor control and complications. (*A*) Dose for tumor control with minimum complications. (*B*) Maximum tumor dose with significant complications. (Redrawn from Hellman, S. [1997]. Principles of cancer management: radiation therapy. In V. T. DeVita, S. Hellman, & S. A. Rosenberg [Eds.], *Cancer: Principles and practice of oncology* [pp. 307–332]. Philadelphia: Lippincott-Raven.)

System	Turnover Time*
Blood	
RBC	120 d
Granulocyte	6–10 h in blood, 2–3 d in tissue
Lymphocyte	100–300+ d
Platelets	5–10 d
GI Tract	
Oral cavity	5 d
Stomach	3–9 d
Small intestine	1.5 d
Colon	10 d
Skin	20 d
Respiratory Tract	
Tracheal epithelium	50 d
Lung alveolar cells	10–30 d
GU Tract	
Urinary bladder	50 d
Testis	20 d
Eye	
Cornea	7 d

TABLE 13-1

SELECTED RENEWAL SYSTEMS AND THEIR APPROXIMATE TURNOVER TIMES

*Turnover time: Time for replacement of number of cells equal to that in the whole population.
(Adapted from Coia, L. R., & Moylan, D. J. [1994]. *Introduction to clinical radiation oncology*. Madison, WI: Medical Physics Publishing.)

2. *Repopulation* (regeneration): Normal irradiated cells are able to complete their cell cycle and undergo successful mitoses between radiation doses. Tumor cells are more likely to die as a result of radiation injury because of their abnormal features of growth and mitosis.

3. *Redistribution:* Fractionated radiation doses disrupt the tumor cell cycle, causing division delay of tumor cells. This, theoretically, enhances the effects of each succeeding radiation dose because more cells are likely to be in mitosis at the same time. Tumor cells may be more subject to redistribution, due in part to their erratic growth and development.

4. *Reoxygenation:* It is believed that, during radiation, well-oxygenated cells do not allow reversal/repair of the chemical changes produced by radiation. The reoxygenation process involves radioresistant hypoxic tumor cells becoming radiosensitive aerated or oxygenated cells between radiation doses. It has been stated that this may

be the most important advantage of fractionation. In large tumors with necrotic central components, the effect of radiation is to continuously destroy the outer layers (like peeling an onion) to allow the central core to be exposed to capillary oxygenation and thus be more radiosensitive. This theory assumes that there is adequate microcirculation of the tumor mass.

In summary, fractionation of the total radiation dose spares normal tissue because *repair* of sublethal damage allows *repopulation* between doses. The *redistribution* and *reoxygenation* that occur between the daily fractions increase the radiosensitivity of the tumor cells and improve overall treatment outcome. The goal is to kill tumor cells and allow normal cells to regrow and repopulate surrounding tissue (Hellman, 1997).

Role of Radiation in Cancer Treatment

The indications for radiation therapy are present throughout the cancer treatment continuum (Box 13-1). When radiation is the primary treatment, the goal is most often cure. In some cases, surgery or chemotherapy may achieve comparable responses and cure rates in some diseases, but radiation may offer some treatment advantages, such as improved cosmesis (early-stage breast cancer) or improved functional outcome (early-stage laryngeal cancer with preservation of voice and swallowing function). Also, some patients may not be able to undergo surgery or chemotherapy due to preexisting conditions such as cardiac or pulmonary disease.

Combined modality therapy (CMT) is becoming more widely used in cancer treatment. The premise of CMT is to combine surgery ± chemotherapy ± radiation, either in sequence or concurrently. The general rationale for combining radiation and surgery is that the mechanism of failure for the two techniques is different. Radiation rarely fails at the periphery of tumors, where cells are small in number and well vascularized. When radiation fails, it usually does so in the center of the tumor where there are large volumes of tumor cells, often under hypoxic conditions. Surgery, in contrast, is limited by the required preservation of vital normal tissues adjacent to the tumor. In resectable cancers the gross tumor can be removed, but these vital normal tissues limit the anatomic extent of the dissection. When surgery fails under these circumstances, it is usually due to microscopic tumor cells left behind. It is, therefore, logical to consider combining the two techniques (Hellman, 1997).

Radiation can be given pre- or postoperatively, and there are advantages and disadvantages of both techniques. Preoperative radiation may shrink a large tumor sufficiently to allow resection and preservation of organ function, as in rectal or laryngeal cancer. However, preoperative radiation prevents assessment of the tumor's initial anatomic extent and the careful staging available at surgical exploration. Some patients may undergo preoperative radiation but will not ultimately benefit from the treatment, such as a patient with rectal cancer in whom liver metastases are found at the time of resection. Postoperative radiation has the advantages of allowing smaller radiation treatment volumes and avoidance of unnecessary irradiation to patients who will not benefit. Indications for postoperative radiation ther-

---

BOX 13-1

The Indications for Radiation Therapy Span the Spectrum of Cancer Treatment. Some examples:

Cure	Primary treatment for early stage Hodgkin's disease, cervical carcinoma		breast radiation after lumpectomy, or to treat sanctuary sites such as the brain after definitive therapy for acute lymphocytic leukemia or small cell lung cancer
Control	To control the growth or spread of tumor mass. Generally not a cure but may afford local/regional control with minimal morbidity		
		Palliation	Pain control for sites of bony metastasis, control of bulky metastasis to reduce morbidity such as massive lymphadenopathy
Neoadjuvant	To "downstage" bulky tumors, such as large breast or rectal tumors. Intent may be curative and/or to allow less radical surgery		
		Oncologic emergencies	Spinal cord compression, and superior vena cava syndrome (selected cases)
Adjuvant	To reduce the risk of local recurrence at the site of tumor such as		

apy include decreasing the risk of local recurrence after resection, as in breast, lung, and brain cancers (Hellman, 1997).

The principles of combining radiation and chemotherapy are based on increasing the therapeutic index. Sequential or concurrent chemotherapy and radiation are used in treating multiple solid tumors, including lung, breast, head and neck, and gastrointestinal malignancies. The main advantage of CMT is that the target volumes are different; chemotherapy has systemic distribution, and the addition of local radiation gives a boost to the tumor bed and surrounding tissues. Systemic chemotherapy and radiation have different mechanisms of action and toxicities. Chemotherapy may be given in conventional tumoricidal doses and/or as a radiation sensitizer. When chemotherapy is administered as a radiosensitizer, the drug doses and administration schedules will vary. For example, a 24-hour continuous infusion of low-dose 5-fluorouracil may be given concurrently with radiation for patients with gastrointestinal or head and neck malignancies. It must be remembered that CMT will result in more severe and prolonged acute toxicities of each modality.

Approximately 50% of patients who receive radiation do so for palliative intent. Radiation therapy is effective for treating metastasis to multiple sites, including brain and bone, and for decreasing large tumor masses with the goals of managing pain and limiting disability caused by metastatic disease.

External Beam Radiation Therapy

Radiation can be administered by various methods. *External beam radiation* (teletherapy) is administered by a machine at a certain distance from the specific area of the body. External beam radiation is electromagnetic or particulate and is called megavoltage radiation.

External beam radiation is delivered using a linear accelerator that creates a high-energy x-ray beam (photons) (Figure 13-6). These machines allow precise therapy to deeply seated tumors with decreased damage to superficial tissues (skin sparing). The high-energy x-rays are made by accelerating electrons to the speed of light and then directing the electrons to strike a target. This process releases an enormous amount of energy that results in megavoltage or photon radiation. The maximum energy deposition occurs a few centimeters below the skin and depends on the megavoltage

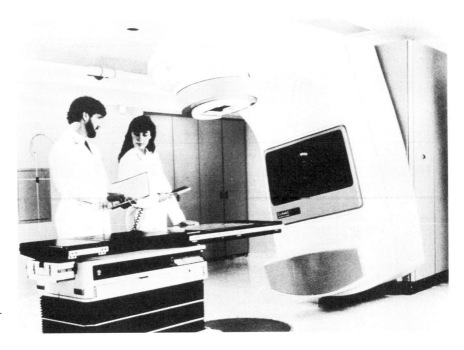

Figure 13-6 Linear accelerator. (Courtesy of Varian Associates Inc., Palo Alto, CA.)

energy used. Energies range from 4 to 25 MV (million volt potential). The linear accelerator is also able to generate more superficial radiation called electron therapy. Electron energies range from 6 to 20 MeV (million electron volt potential). Electrons are used when a greater radiation dose is needed on the skin. In this case, patients will have a more pronounced skin reaction during treatment.

Treatment Planning

The purpose of treatment planning, before initiating external beam irradiation, is to define the area to be treated and minimize radiation to surrounding tissues/organs. Treatment planning includes the following considerations: tumor histology, tumor size and location, route(s) of spread, anticipated toxicities, age and general health of the patient, stage of disease and prognosis, and type of available radiation equipment (Figure 13-7).

Before initiating external beam radiation, a *simulation* is performed. The simulation defines the target volume and surrounding normal structures. The simulator is a machine that reproduces the geometric arrangement of the treatment machine (linear accelerator) (Figure 13-8). Within the treatment room, light localizers describe the outline of the field, and small laser dots are used to accurately position the patient. It is important that the patient be put in a position that is comfortable and easily reproduced daily (Hellman, 1997). At

the time of simulation, the area to be treated (e.g., chest, abdomen/pelvis) is visualized with fluoroscopy to more accurately define the treatment volume. Oral or intravenous contrast material may be needed to highlight structures within the treatment field. The patient must lie on a narrow, hard table for 30 to 60 minutes, depending on the area being simulated. For some patients this is a difficult procedure, especially if they have pain or other conditions that make positioning difficult. Children younger than 3 years of age need sedation and frequently general anesthesia for simulation and daily treatments.

Positioning on the treatment table (also called the treatment couch) is tumor site dependent; the patient may be supine or prone, extremities can be abducted, and special material may be placed on the skin. Immobilization is important for accurate daily reproduction of the treatment field. This is accomplished most often by patient compliance; however, depending on the site to be treated, special devices may be used, such as a mask for treatment of head and neck cancers or a half-body cast for trunk or extremity immobilization.

Treatment field location and size can be determined using radiographic studies such as computed tomography (CT), magnetic resonance imaging (MRI), bone scans, or plain films of specific areas, such as an extremity or chest radiograph. When the treatment field has been determined, marks or small, permanent tattoos are placed on

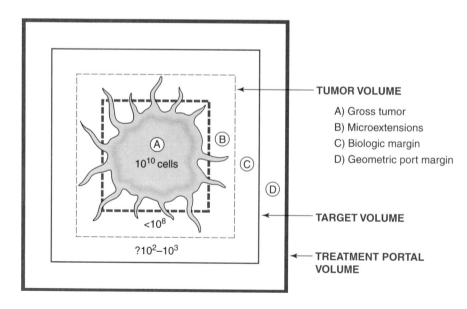

Figure 13-7 Definition of tumor volume and target volume. Target volume includes tumor volume, potential areas of local and regional microscopic disease around tumor, and margin of surrounding normal tissue. (Redrawn from Perez, C. A. & Purdy, J. A. [1992]. Rationale for treatment planning in radiation therapy. In S. H. Levitt, F. M. Khan, & R. A. Potish [Eds.], *Levitt and Tapley's technological basis of radiation therapy: Practical clinical applications* [p. 16]. Philadelphia: Lea & Febiger.)

TUMOR VOLUME

A) Gross tumor
B) Microextensions
C) Biologic margin
D) Geometric port margin

TARGET VOLUME

TREATMENT PORTAL VOLUME

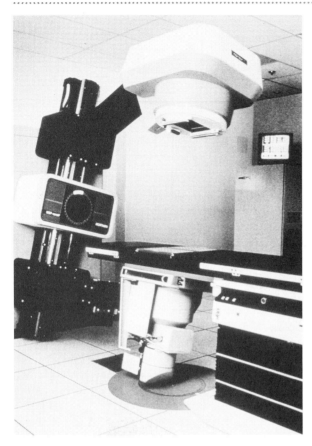

Figure 13-8 Varian Ximatron™ Radiation Therapy Simulator. (Courtesy of Varian Associates, Inc., Palo Alto, CA.)

specific points to define the field. These marks are lined up with coordinates on the machine and laser beams in the treatment room that intersect to confirm reproducible, exact daily positioning (Reinstein, 1998). Most treatments consist of opposed beams, such as anterior→posterior and posterior→anterior. However, multiple beams may be used at each treatment.

The linear accelerator only sees squares or rectangles. Most tumor volumes are not so geometrically arranged. Custom blocking, or shields, are used to individualize the treatment field to any shape and to spare normal tissue as much as possible. The radiation oncologist draws a line(s) on the simulation film around the structure(s) to be excluded. The films become a template for Styrofoam sheets on which the regions to be blocked are cut out, and the holes (3 inches thick) are filled

with a lead alloy with a low melting point. When the material has cooled, it is broken out of the Styrofoam sheets, mounted onto a clear plastic tray, and labeled with the patient's name. These blocks are placed in the path of the beam of the machine during treatment (Figure 13-9).

The next step in planning is formulating an isodose plan to optimize the irradiation technique and provide the best possible radiation dose distribution (Figure 13-10). Ideally, one would like to deliver the necessary dose to the tumor-bearing areas and spare all the normal tissue. However, due to limitations of present-day equipment, a certain amount of normal tissue radiation is unavoidable. In addition, because of the uncertainty of microscopic spread, targets are drawn more generously, at the risk of normal tissue injury (Khan, 1998). This planning is done by the physicist and dosimetrist using computer software programs. An isodose plan is printed and reviewed by the radiation oncologist. Sometimes, several different plans are formulated for comparison of the optimum beam arrangements. The goal is always to deliver the maximum radiation dose to the area of tumor and the minimum radiation dose to surrounding normal tissues and structures. This team effort must consider the best beam distribution, homogeneity within the target volume, and appropriate minimizing of dose in the transit volume (Hellman, 1997). The radiation oncologist then writes the radiation prescription, which includes the daily and total treatment dose, beam energy, and field arrangement. Directions for patient monitoring are also included, such as frequency of blood tests (e.g., CBC). Selected terms used in radiation therapy and radiation prescriptions are shown in Box 13-2.

Specialized Methods of External Beam Irradiation

Stereotactic radiosurgery (SRS) involves the precise delivery of radiation to a small, well-defined intracranial lesion in a *single dose*. It delivers this explicitly planned treatment to a target while adjacent normal brain tissue only millimeters away is spared from the radiation dose. SRS is most often administered using two types of treatment delivery machines. The gamma knife contains 201 separate sources of cobalt-60 (Co60) arranged 1 mm apart

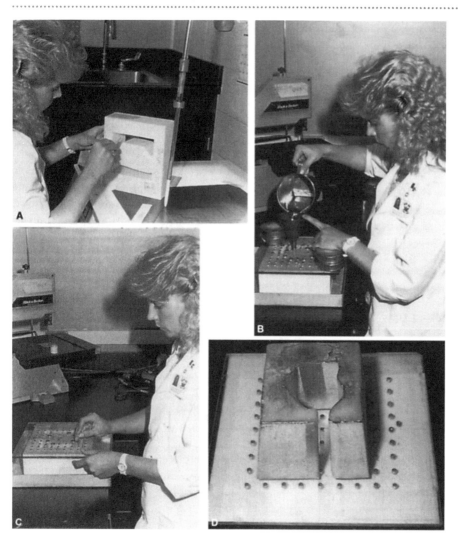

Figure 13-9 (*A*) The opening where the hot wire entered the Styrofoam is sealed with tape to prevent leaks. (*B*) The melted alloy is poured into the cavities left by the Styrofoam. (*C*) A tray is attached to the Styrofoam by pushing nails or screws through holes in the tray into the Styrofoam. (*D*) Finished block mounted on a tray. (Bentel, G. C. [1996]. *Radiation therapy planning.* New York: McGraw-Hill.)

in a large helmet structure. A linear accelerator can be modified to use four or five noncoplanar arcs to deliver precise photon beams. SRS technology requires rigid head immobilization; tumor localization with angiography, CT, or MRI with head frame in place; and sophisticated computer planning. This all requires the joint skills of the neurosurgeon, radiation oncologist, radiation physicist, and radiation therapists to plan for and deliver the precision required for radiosurgery treatment (Bucholtz, 1997) (Figure 13-11). The radiation oncology nurse is integral to caring for the patient throughout the pretreatment imaging, planning, and the SRS procedure, all of which may take 10 to 12 hours.

Patient eligibility indications for SRS treatment include a small primary brain tumor (generally ≤4 cm) or as boost treatment for solitary brain metastasis after whole brain irradiation. Nonmalignant lesions are also treated with SRS, such as arteriovenous malformations, acoustic neuromas, meningiomas, and pituitary adenomas (Bucholtz, 1997).

Stereotactic radiotherapy (SRT) uses sophisticated computer planning with precise delivery of the radiation to deliver *fractionated* radiation therapy to brain tumors. Head immobilization devices are used that are placed daily on the patient. As with SRS, this technique allows administration of radiation to intracranial structures while more

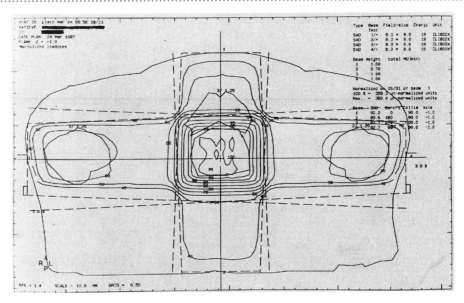

Figure 13-10 Isodose plan for four-field treatment of the prostate. In the lower left corner is the orientation of the diagram. The goal is to maximize the dose in the center (tumor volume) of the field, in this case the prostate, and minimize radiation to surrounding structures. Dotted lines outline the radiation beams, which will come from anterior-posterior opposed angles and opposed lateral angles. The various lines state the percent of radiation at each depth. The 99–100% lines are in the center. The round structures on the right and left of the center are the femoral heads (bone will slow down the beam) and must be calculated as a different density.

BOX 13-2

Terminology in Radiation Therapy

Becquerel (Bq): Unit of measure for the amount of activity of a radioactive nuclide in a particular energy state. One becquerel equals one nuclear disintegration per second. The becquerel replaces the former unit of designation *curie.*

Curie (Ci): Unit of measure formerly used to describe the rate of nuclear disintegration of a radioactive source.

Gray (Gy): Unit of radiation dose (one joule per kilogram). Unit of measure for the energy deposited by radiation in an absorbing medium. The gray has replaced the term *rad.* 1 gray equals 100 centigray (cGy) equals 100 rad (1 rad equals 1 cGy).

Rad (r): Acronym for radiation absorbed dose. In 1985, the term *gray* (Gy) became the official term for radiation absorbed dose, replacing the rad.

Roentgen (R): Unit of exposure to ionizing radiation: refers to the ability of x-rays to ionize air.

Sievert (Sv): The unit of dose equivalent of ionizing radiation is equivalent to one joule per kilogram. The Sv has replaced the term *rem* and is used in radiation protection and radiation safety when quantifying occupational exposure.

(Adapted from Hilderley, L. J., & Dow, K. H. [1996]. Radiation oncology. In R. McCorkle, M. Grant, M. Frank-Stromborg, & S. Baird [Eds.], *Cancer nursing,* [pp. 331–357]. Philadelphia: W.B. Saunders.)

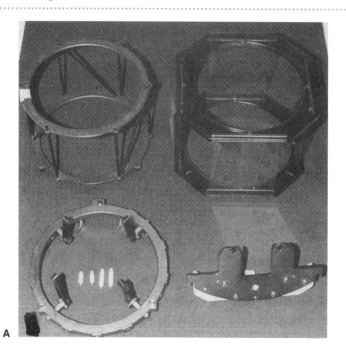

A

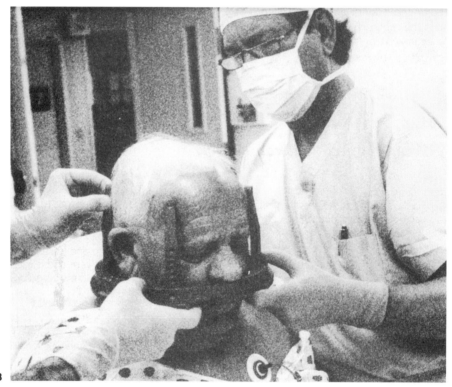

B

Figure 13-11 (*A*) Basic stereotactic system with angiographic localizer (*upper right*), computer tomographic localizer (*upper left*), head ring with post and pins (*lower left*), and a mount for positioning the patient onto the table (*lower right*). (Bova, F. J., Meeks, S. L., & Friedman, W. A. [1998]. Linac radiosurgery: System requirements, procedures, and testing. In F. M. Khan & R. A. Potish [Eds.], *Treatment planning in radiation oncology* [p. 218]. Baltimore: Williams & Wilkins.) (*B*) SRS head frame in place. (Courtesy of Legacy Emanuel Department of Radiation Oncology, Portland, OR.)

effectively sparing normal brain tissues. Indications for SRT include small-volume, well-defined brain tumors; brain tumors that are inoperable due to location deep in the brain or near critical structures; and pediatric brain tumors so as to decrease the possibility of late tissue effects (Bucholtz, 1997). Some examples of tumors treated with SRT are pituitary adenomas, meningiomas, craniopharyngiomas, low-grade astrocytomas, optic pathway gliomas, retinoblastomas, and acoustic neuromas.

Due to the fractionated schedule of SRT, head immobilization is not fixated with screws into the skull as it is with SRS, but is accomplished by a rigid, relocatable head immobilization device (Figure 13-12). The frame chosen may involve encasing the head, with the exception of the nostrils, in a cast that is rigidly fixed to the treatment table. Another system is a frame held in place by a rod in each external auditory canal and a clip molded to the bridge of the nose. A third device consists of a frame that is secured to the head by an impression of the upper teeth, an occipital tray with an impression of the occiput, and a strap that forcibly holds the dental and occipital impressions against the head (Bentel, 1996). Daily treatment time may be up to 1 hour, and patients may need analgesia if the immobilization device or treatment position is uncomfortable (Bucholtz, 1997).

Total body irradiation (TBI) is being used most commonly for the treatment of hematopoietic malignancies as part of the preparation regimen, with high-dose chemotherapy, for bone marrow transplantation, or for stem cell reinfusion. The goals of TBI include eradication of malignant cells throughout the body and suppression of the immune response to permit survival of the engrafted stem cell (Hilderley, 1997). TBI is usually administered twice daily (at least 6 hours between fractions) for 4 consecutive days. It is most often given before the high-dose chemotherapy portion of a transplantation regimen. The extent of TBI-related toxicity (acute and late) depends on several variables, including chemotherapeutic drugs used and the radiation dose rate. Box 13-3 outlines the acute and late effects of TBI.

Intraoperative radiation therapy (IORT) can be used to treat cancers in which local control is difficult to achieve and high radiation doses would damage adjacent structures. The major indications for use of IORT are to treat an exposed tumor bed or areas of unresectable gross tumors, and as a boost in combination with large-field external beam radiation therapy and surgical resection.

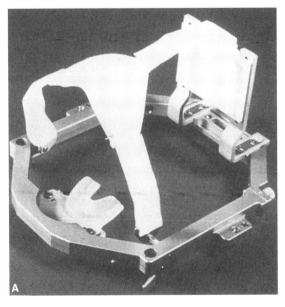
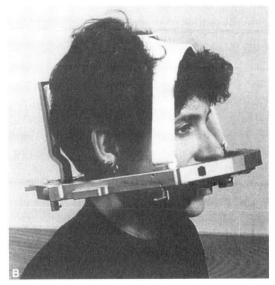

Figure 13-12 *(A, B)* Relocatable head immobilization device for stereotactic radiotherapy. (Bentel, G. C. [1996]. *Radiation therapy planning.* New York: McGraw-Hill.)

BOX 13-3

Acute and Late Toxicities of Total Body Irradiation (TBI)

Acute: Onset 24–72 h

- Nausea and vomiting
- Diarrhea
- Parotitis (usually resolves within 24 h)
- Xerostomia
- Ocular symptoms: conjunctival edema, lacrimation or dryness, photophobia
- Oral mucositis
- Alopecia
- Hyperthermia (T >38°C) associated with chills, usually resolves within 24 h
- Headache

Subacute: Onset weeks to months

- Veno-occlusive disease (5%–10% mortality)
- Interstitial pneumonitis

Late: Onset months to years

- Cardiac/renal failure: risk increased with high-dose chemo, especially cyclophosphamide
- Gonadal failure (40%–60%)
- Cataracts (~60% at 10 y)
- Disseminated necrotizing leukoencephalopathy (increased risk with intrathecal chemotherapy)
- Hypothyroidism (45% have elevated TSH)
- Pulmonary fibrosis

(Adapted from Ozsahin, M., Pene, F., Cosset, J., & Laugier, A. [1994]. Morbidity after total body irradiation. *Seminars in Radiation Oncology*, 4[2], 95–102.)

IORT has been used primarily for gastrointestinal cancers, especially of the stomach, pancreas, and colorectum. Implementation of IORT requires interdisciplinary collaboration with anesthesiology, radiation oncology, surgery, nursing, physics, and radiation safety. IORT is a very specialized procedure requiring dedicated equipment and facilities and currently is limited to a few centers (<10%) in the United States (Wojtas & Smith, 1997).

Brachytherapy

Brachytherapy is *internal radiation* and consists of temporary or permanent placement of a radioactive source on or within a tumor. The most common methods used to provide a therapeutic dose of internal radiation therapy include interstitial implant, intracavitary implant, and systemic therapy. It offers the advantage of delivering a high dose of radiation to a specific tumor volume, with a rapid falloff in dose to adjacent normal tissues. Brachytherapy may be used as a single treatment modality or in combination with external beam radiation, surgery, or chemotherapy. It can be delivered with curative intent or in the adjuvant setting,

such as postoperatively to an area that is at increased risk of local recurrence. It can also be used in the palliative setting to enhance comfort in accessible tumors. A wide variety of cancers are treated with brachytherapy. Most commonly, it is used in cancers of the endometrium, cervix, head and neck, and prostate and in extremity sarcomas. See Table 13-2 for specific isotopes.

Sealed brachytherapy sources are interstitial and intracavitary implants. In an interstitial implant, the radioactive source is contained in the form of a needle, seed, wire, or catheter that is implanted directly into the tumor. In an intracavitary treatment, the radioactive source is placed directly into the body cavity, as in treatment of endometrial or cervix cancer, and held in place by an applicator. The applicator and radioactive source are removed when treatment is complete. In some cases, the implant (seeds) are permanent (e.g., prostate, brain), while the radioactivity of the isotope decays over the period of time specific to the element. Patients' body fluids/secretions are not radioactive unless they have received a systemic radiation source.

Sealed sources are administered by two methods: low dose rate (LDR) and high dose rate

TABLE 13-2
RADIOACTIVE ISOTOPE CHART

Isotope	Emission	Half-life*	Source	Use	Administration
^{131}I (iodine)	Gamma rays[†]	8.05 days	Unsealed	Thyroid cancer	Oral, intravenous
^{32}P (phosphorus)	Beta particles[‡]	14.3 days	Unsealed	Malignant pleural or peritoneal effusion	Intrapleural; intraperitoneal in colloid form
^{192}Ir (iridium)	Beta particles Gamma rays	74.4 days	Sealed	Cancers of head and neck, breast, bronchus, brain; sarcomas	Interstitial and intracavitary
^{125}I (iodine)	Gamma rays	60.2 days	Sealed	Cancers of prostate, bladder, brain, bronchus	Interstitial
^{137}Cs (cesium)	Beta particles Gamma rays	30.0 years	Sealed	Gynecologic cancers	Intracavitary in an applicator
^{226}Ra (radium)	Beta particles Gamma rays	1602 years	Sealed	Head and neck cancer	Intracavitary and interstitial

*Time required for isotope to lose 50% of its radioactivity.
[†]Gamma rays: highly ionizing electromagnetic radiation emitted from radioactive isotopes; patient's body does not effectively shield gamma rays.
[‡]Beta particles: ionizing particles with moderate penetrating ability; the patient's body effectively shields the radiation when the isotope is injected.
(From Iwamoto, R. [1997]. Radiation therapy. In S.E. Otto [Ed.], *Oncology nursing* [p. 522]. St. Louis: Mosby.)

(HDR) brachytherapy. When a patient receives an LDR implant, he or she has the applicator inserted into the area to be treated while under anesthesia in the operating room. The patient then goes to the nursing unit, and the radioactive source is loaded. The duration of hospital stay depends on the isotope used and radiation dose required for tumor control. LDR requires hospital admission for 2 to 5 days as the radiation is continuously and slowly delivered to the tumor site. Depending on the site of the implant, the patient may be on complete bedrest, as with gynecologic brachytherapy, or ambulatory, as with head and neck implants. Some hospitals have specially designed rooms that are lead lined to minimize radiation exposure to staff and other patients. However, most institutions do not have special facilities, and the patient is placed as far from other rooms and patients as possible. The physicist will be integral to planning patient placement and monitoring radiation exposure to all who have patient contact. Radiation safety principles will be discussed later in the chapter.

HDR brachytherapy is an outpatient procedure. HDR units consist of a lead-shielded storage area for radioactive sources, several channels for source transport, a remote loading and unloading system, and a variety of applicators that are inserted (interstitial and intracavitary) into the area to be treated, such as the vaginal cuff after hysterectomy for gynecologic cancers, the bronchus for obstruction from lung tumor, or the site of excision of an extremity sarcoma.

The procedure is performed in the radiation oncology department. The patient is positioned and immobilized on a special table. The appropriate applicator is inserted and radiographic verification of applicator position is obtained. The optimal radioactive source configuration and dose distributions are then determined by the physicist and radiation oncologist using computer software programs. When the optimum dose arrangement is decided, the information is then programmed on a microcomputer that remotely operates the HDR machine. The sources, shaped as pellets or tubes, are automatically arranged as programmed within each channel. Each transport tube is attached to each receptor of the apparatus in the patient, who is lying on the treatment table in a lead- or concrete lined room. After all personnel have left the treatment room and the door is closed, the treatment is initiated from a remote-controlled switch. The radioactive source is transported by way of a wire into the applicator within a few seconds. The unloading of the sources is accomplished by remote control and requires only a few seconds (Bentel, 1996). Treatments are usually given weekly or biweekly for 3 to 4 weeks, with the number of treatments depending on the extent and type of tumor. The length of time that the patient is lying on the treatment table varies, but most often it is about 30 to 45 minutes, to allow for insertion of the applicator and verification by x-ray of proper applicator placement. The length of time that the door is closed and the patient is being treated (source is loaded/unloaded) also varies but averages 5 to 15 minutes. The advantage of HDR is that most patients do not need hospital admission and are able to continue activities of daily living. The ease with which the sources are loaded and unloaded makes it possible to return them to the shielded system while personnel work near the patient, essentially eliminating radiation exposure to staff (Bentel, 1996) (Figure 13-13).

Another sealed-source brachytherapy technique is the placement of radioactive plaques to treat choroidal melanoma. The most common isotope used is iodine-125. This method of brachytherapy can be used as an alternative to enucleation. Patients will have the procedure done with local anesthetic as an outpatient. The ophthalmologist extrudes the eye by loosening the muscles (rectus and oblique) and anchors a gold plaque containing the I-125 seeds over the melanoma on the sclera. The radiation oncologist and physicist are in attendance and have computed the dosimetric parameters and total radiation dose. There are few radiation precautions, and the patient returns within 5 days for plaque removal. Surprisingly, patients have little or no discomfort even with relatively large plaques that measure 2 to 3 cm.

Unsealed radiation sources are radioactive materials that are administered systemically, either intravenously or orally. An example is iodine-131, which is used therapeutically to treat diseases of the thyroid, including thyroid cancer. The isotope is administered systemically and is excreted in all body substances and fluids. Half of the I-131 is excreted within 48 hours of administration. Patients will be hospitalized and are a challenge for nursing because every article in the patient's room is considered contaminated. Articles are discarded but taken to a protected area until all detectable radioactivity decays. Thus, staff must remember not to leave a favorite stethoscope or pen in the patient's room because it will not be seen again for 2 to 3 months (see the section entitled "Radiation Safety").

Control of bone pain in patients with multiple bony metastasis is a significant clinical problem in patients with advanced cancer of the prostate, breast, and lung (Dunne-Daly, 1997). "Bone-seeking," systemically administered isotopes are being used in the palliative management of metastatic bone disease. These agents have proved effective for patients whose disease is too widespread for local radiation to achieve pain control (Held et al., 1994). The radiopharmaceutical strontium-89 (Sr-89) is a pure beta emitter with a half-life of 50.6 days. It is a calcium analogue that has increased uptake and retention at sites of increased bone metabolism, such as osteoblastic metastatic lesions. Retention of Sr-89 at metastatic sites may be indefinite and substantially longer than the radioactive half-life of the agent (Porter et al., 1993). Thus, Sr-89 can deliver therapeutic radiation for several months and can be repeated at 3-month intervals. Patients may also receive local external beam radiation concurrently with administration of Sr-89. Sr-89 is administered as a single intravenous injection, usually as an outpatient procedure, by the radiation oncologist or nuclear medicine physician. Toxicities include myelosuppression, primarily of leukocytes and platelets. An initial flare of bone pain may occur 2 to 3 days after injections and last 3 to 4 days. Radiation safety instructions are given to the patient and include double flushing of the toilet after use for the first 24 hours, frequent handwashing, and washing of linens or clothes that become exposed to body secretions. Instruct care providers regarding precautions and possible contamination from the patient's blood or excretions, especially if the patient is incontinent (Kan, 1995). Reassure the patient and family that he or she is not radioactive, only body excretions.

Radiation Safety

Radiation exposure to staff and patients is a highly regulated and monitored process. Essentially, there is no radiation exposure to staff when patients are treated with external beam linear accelerator machines. The machine does not have a live radiation source, and it does not turn on before the treatment room door is closed and the staff have left the room. The room in which the linear accelera-

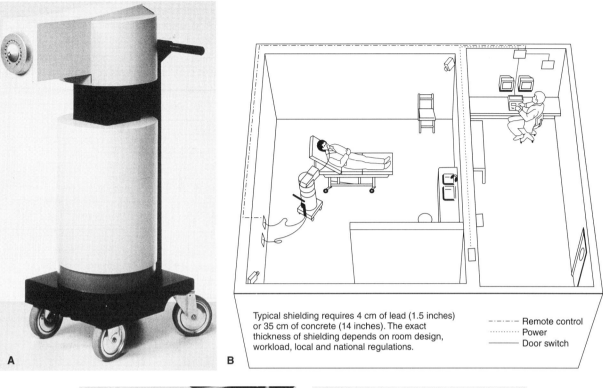

Typical shielding requires 4 cm of lead (1.5 inches) or 35 cm of concrete (14 inches). The exact thickness of shielding depends on room design, workload, local and national regulations.

—·—·— Remote control
·········· Power
———— Door switch

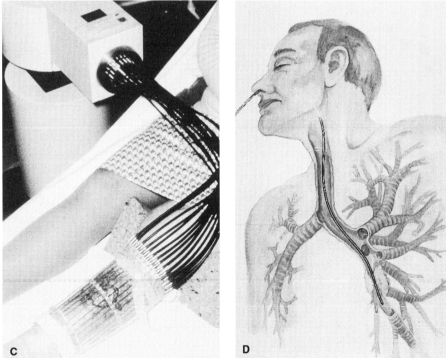

Figure 13-13 High dose rate brachytherapy (HDR). (*A*) HDR iridium containment machine. (*B*) HDR suite setup. (*C*) Interstitial HDR treating leg sarcoma. (*D*) Representation of bronchial HDR. (*A, B, D* courtesy of Nucletron Corporation, Columbia, MD.)

tor operates is protected by 3 to 6 feet of high-density concrete; depending on available space, lead or steel may be added to meet shielding requirements. Staff wear film badges that register radiation exposure and are checked monthly. Overall, there is very little risk of radiation exposure and few restrictions to staff, even if pregnant. The medical physicist is responsible for quality assurance and monitoring of safety of the linear accelerator. Radiation exposure to patients, outside the treatment field, is minimal because the beam is directed at the treatment field with blocks protecting surrounding tissues. Most states have well-defined guidelines that must be met to maintain facility licensing for operation of high-energy treatment machines and administration of radioisotopes.

Radiation safety is a different issue and of prime concern in caring for patients undergoing LDR brachytherapy. Nurses must know the specific radioisotope being used, whether it is sealed or unsealed, and whether it is temporary or permanent (Figure 13-14). There are multiple aspects of radiation safety and monitoring of staff. Guidelines are institution specific and should be clearly defined before admission and treatment of the patient. Radiation exposure depends on the type of implant and radiation source used. All personnel entering the patient's room wear a dosimeter that measures the radiation dose at each exposure. Each person's record is evaluated and recorded by the medical physicist.

The most important factors in radiation safety are the principles of time, distance, and shielding. The implementation of these factors is the most effective method to minimize radiation exposure when caring for patients undergoing LDR brachytherapy.

1. *Time:* Minimize time spent in close proximity to the patient. Radiation exposure is directly related to the time spent within a specific distance of the radioactive source. The key to using time efficiently when in the patient's room is to organize care activities and assemble necessary supplies before entering the patient's room. Before leaving the room, place items within easy reach of the patient to avoid needing to reenter the room (Iwamoto, 1997). Direct care is usually limited to ½ to 1 hour per person per shift (varies per state guidelines). Specific guidelines for staff and visitors should be posted conspicuously on the patient's door. Nurses and families are encouraged to use the hospital intercom system or telephone to communicate with the patient. This allows the nurse to "check in" with the patient and perform some assessment without radiation exposure, and help ease the patient's isolation.

2. *Distance:* Maximize the distance from the radioactive material. The amount of radiation decreases according to the inverse square law, which states that doubling the distance from the radiation source quarters the amount of radiation received. Thus, the further away from the source, the safer it is for everyone in contact with the patient (Box 13-4).

3. *Shielding:* In practice, the use of lead shielding has both advantages and disadvantages. When used properly, lead shielding can provide additional safety from radiation. When used improperly, it provides a false sense of security. Overall lead shielding can be cumbersome, and the nurse may spend more time in the room trying to work around the shields (Dunne-Daly, 1997). It may be said that the shield is a good thing because it is a constant reminder to the

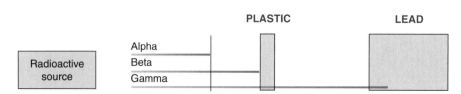

Figure 13-14 Range and penetration of alpha, beta, and gamma radiation. (Yasko, J. [1982]. *Care of the client receiving external radiation therapy.* Reston: Reston Publishing Company.)

BOX 13-4
Inverse Square Law

Radioactive Source

Meters	0	1	2	3	4	5	6	7	8
Exposure rate		$\frac{1}{1}$	$\frac{1}{4}$		$\frac{1}{16}$				$\frac{1}{64}$

If the exposure at 1 m from the radioactive source is *x*, the exposure at 2 m is one fourth of *x*, and at 4 m, one sixteenth.

According to the inverse square law, exposure decreases as the distance from the radioactive source increases.

$$\text{Exposure rate} = \frac{1}{(\text{distance})^2}$$

(From Iwamoto, R. [1997]. Radiation therapy. In. S.E. Otto [Ed.], *Oncology nursing* [p. 523]. St. Louis: Mosby.)

nurse to limit time spent near the radioactive source. Lead aprons, such as those used in diagnostic radiology, are insufficient to stop gamma rays and are not recommended (Iwamoto, 1997). The use of lead shielding varies according to institutional guidelines.

All of the above principles illustrate the importance of prebrachytherapy teaching for the patient and family. Patients are fearful of radiation and subject to many misconceptions. In addition, apprehension can be increased when they understand the radiation source will be *inside* their body and the radiation safety guidelines will affect nursing time spent in the room. Assure patients that they will receive the care they need because their well-being and safety are paramount. Because there is more than one nurse on the unit, exposure can be more easily divided to allow time with the patient if there is a need for additional nursing care. Pregnant staff are not allowed to care for brachytherapy patients. The teaching is best accomplished by the radiation oncology nurse in collaboration with inpatient nursing staff.

Toxicities of External Beam Radiation Therapy

Patients are at risk for multiple toxicities depending on the area treated. The radiation does not know the difference between tumor cells and normal cells, so all cells are vulnerable that are within the radiation beam. The specific tissue reactions to radiation are largely related to mitotic activity. Toxicities can be classified as acute, subacute, and late effects (Box 13-5). There is abundant literature documenting tolerance doses of tissues and structures within reasonably precise limits. However, this body of knowledge has required revision in recent years because of the advent of combined modality therapy. When chemotherapy and radiation are used concurrently, acute and late reactions in various tissues generally occur at much lower doses than when radiation is used alone. In addition, acute and late injuries can be produced that are not commonly seen with either modality alone.

Acute toxicities of radiation occur largely in rapidly renewing tissues (Hellman, 1997). When these rapidly proliferating cells are confronted with fractionated radiation, the Four Rs of Radiobiology apply. Because the response of rapidly renewing tissues depends on the balance between cell birth and cell death, acute tissue reaction is crucially affected by the time allowed for repopulation and therefore is dependent on field size, daily radiation dose, and overall length of treatment (number of treatments). It may appear that cancer cells are only considered active on Monday through Friday when patients are being treated; however, fractionation of treatment is crucial to allowing normal cell repopulation. Uninterrupted treatment would quickly surmount the body's ability to repair itself and cause overwhelming toxicities. Occasionally, treatment breaks are necessary to allow healing of normal tissue. Acute toxicities vary with each patient, are site specific, are generally short term, and resolve after completion

BOX 13-5

Phases of Radiation Injury

Acute Phase

- Evidence of radiation effect is seen in hours to days.
- Proliferating cells are more radiosensitive than quiescent cells.
- Brisk reactions heal completely, but significant residual damage may be present.
- Tissues most at risk:

Bone marrow	Ovary, testis
Bladder	Salivary gland
Colon	Skin
Esophagus	Small bowel
Lymph nodes	Stomach
Oral mucosa	Vagina

Subacute Phase

- Evidence of damage of clinical significance is seen in weeks to a few months after completing radiation.

- Tissues most at risk

Lung	Heart
Spinal cord	Brain
Liver	Kidney

Late Phase

- If given sufficient doses of radiation, all tissues can manifest late effects.
- Radiation causes injury to vasculoconnective tissue and parenchymal cell loss.
- Occurs in tissues with little cell turnover.
- Depends on fractionation, treatment volume, total radiation dose.
- Tissues most at risk:

Lymph tissue	Bone
Thyroid	Cartilage
Pituitary	Pancreas (endocrine)
Breast	Bile ducts
Brain	

---

of treatment. The time to complete resolution depends on the specific tissues in the radiation field and the degree of reaction to the radiation (Box 13-6).

Late effects are really the dose-limiting factor in radiation (Hellman, 1997). The extent and degree of late effects depend on the size of the daily fraction and the total radiation dose, total treatment time, size of the treatment field, type of radiation (photons vs. electrons), and concurrent chemotherapy. The mechanism of late radiation injury is not definitively known.

After whole or partial organ irradiation, the observed clinical and subclinical changes depend on the organ's inherent structure. Marks (1996) describes that at the tissue level radiation responses in normal structures and organs are largely based on damage to the stroma in which functional cells reside, such as blood vessels and connective tissue. These structures form the essential framework for more specialized cells and tissues. An organ can be considered to be made up of multiple functioning subunits (FSU). In a *paral-*

lel system, organ function is generally maintained if damage occurs because the remaining FSUs operate independently from the damaged regions, assuming there is adequate function in the remainder of the organ. What this means is that part of an organ can be sacrificed (damaged beyond repair) and the organ will still function adequately. The lung, liver, and kidney are all very sensitive to relatively low doses of radiation, but damage to part of the organ does not render it incapable of function. In a *series system,* damage to one portion of an organ may render the entire organ dysfunctional because it must work in sequence. If one piece of the organ is lost and cannot function, the entire organ/system shuts down. Examples include the gastrointestinal tract and neural tissues. This concept can be extended to encompass organ-to-organ interactions. Damage produced in one organ can have serious consequences in another, as in kidney failure leading to overall multisystem failure and death (Marks, 1996). Site-specific late effects are outlined in Box 13-7.

BOX 13-6

Site-Specific Acute Toxicities of Radiation Therapy

Acute toxicities depend on site treated (what normal structures are in the field), daily dose, radiation energy used, and volume treated (size of the field).

CNS (primary brain tumors, brain metastasis)

BRAIN
- Scalp, forehead erythema
- Alopecia
- External auditory canal irritation
- Nausea/vomiting (rare)

SPINAL CORD
- Lhemitte syndrome (subacute)

Head and Neck (nasopharynx, oro/hypopharynx, larynx)

- Skin erythema
- Oral mucositis
- Esophagitis → dysphagia → odynophagia
- Xerostomia
- Dysgeusia, ageusia → anorexia

Breast

- Skin erythema that may progress to moist desquamation

Chest/Lung (lung, esophageal, gastric cancers)

- Skin erythema (anterior and posterior fields)
- Esophagitis → dysphagia/odynophagia
- Dysgeusia → anorexia
- Gastric reflux symptoms

Abdomen/Pelvis (GI, GU, GYN cancers)

- Nausea/vomiting (radiation site dependent)
- Diarrhea
- Cystitis symptoms
- Mucositis of perianal region
- Vaginal dryness

Management of toxicities related to radiation therapy is similar to management of chemotherapy-related side effects. It may not always be clear if the chemotherapy or radiation is causing the specific toxicity. It is important to collaborate with medical and radiation oncology nurses in planning side-effects management. Specific recommendations are covered in other sections of the book. Although the side effects of radiation are site specific, most patients are at risk for some degree of skin reaction, fatigue, and, in selected cases, myelosuppression.

Skin Toxicity

The radiation beam must pass through the skin to reach the target. Normal skin response to radiation depends on numerous patient and treatment-related factors. Radiation factors include the use of beam type and energy, daily treatment dose, tissue equivalent (bolus), material on the skin surface during treatment, accelerated fractionation, and location and size of the treatment fields. Patient factors include skinfolds in irradiated volume, tangential fields, and poor nutritional status (Sitton, 1992).

Skin care management during radiation is still being researched. The goals of skin care management are to enhance patient comfort, promote healing, and prevent infection if skin breakdown occurs (Sitton, 1997). At this time, the optimum skin care regimen is unclear. Some general guidelines include gentle care to the skin in the treatment field, sun protection with sunblock products (SPF ≥15), and moist wound healing for wet desquamation (Dunne Daly, 1995; Strunk & Maher, 1993). Because of the lack of definitive data regarding the efficacy of skin care products and regimens, most skin care guidelines are institution specific and based on habit and anecdotal experience. The nurse should check with the radiation oncology nurse and/or physician treating the patient as to department policies.

BOX 13-7

Site-Specific Late Effects of Radiation Therapy

Because the tolerance levels of all tissues are known, the overall risk of radiation-related late effects to all sites is very low, but not zero. The percentage of risk varies by site, with bowel damage risk approximately 3% to 5%, and upper extremity arm edema with lymph node radiation approximately 10% to 15%.

CNS

BRAIN
- Focal/diffuse necrosis
- Leukoencephalopathy
- Pituitary/hypothalamic dysfunction
- Cognitive dysfunction

SPINAL CORD
- Myelopathy/necrosis

Head and Neck

MUCOSA
- Paleness, thinning, telangiectasias

SALIVARY GLAND
- Xerostomia

TEETH/MANDIBLE
- Caries
- TMJ fibrosis
- Osteoradionecrosis

THYROID
- Hypo/hyperthyroid
- Thyroid cartilage necrosis
- Laryngeal edema

EYE
- Cataracts
- Skin changes, loss of lashes
- Dry eye, corneal ulceration
- Visual loss/blindness

Chest

LUNG
- Pneumonitis (subacute)
- Pulmonary fibrosis

HEART
- Cardiomyopathy
- Pericarditis
- Coronary artery disease

BREAST
- Skin tanning, fibrosis, telangiectasias
- Breast fibrosis, contraction, edema
- Increased risk pathologic rib fracture
- Pneumonitis (subacute)
- Pulmonary fibrosis
- Pericarditis
- Arm edema if axilla ± supraclavicular LN treated

Bone
- Necrosis femoral head

Gastrointestinal

ESOPHAGUS
- Dysmotility
- Dysphagia/odynophagia
- Esophageal stricture

STOMACH
- Dyspepsia/gastritis
- Contracture

SMALL/LARGE BOWEL
- Mucosal injury
- Decreased motility, malabsorption
- Obstruction

RECTUM
- Proctitis
- Fistula

LIVER
- Radiation hepatitis
- Hepatic failure

Genitourinary

KIDNEY
- Anemia
- Chronic radiation nephritis
- Hypertension

BLADDER
- Mucosal injury: hematuria
- Fistula
- Fibrosis

PROSTATE
- Impotence

PENIS
- Mucosal changes
- Urethral stricture

VAGINA
- Thinning/atrophy/dry mucosa
- Narrowing, shortening, fibrosis

Reproductive

OVARIES/TESTIS
- Sterility

HEMATOPOIETIC
- Fibrosis
- Aplasia

CARCINOGENESIS
- Meningioma, nerve sheath glioma
- Sarcoma: bone/soft tissue
- Leukemias: AML

Fatigue

Fatigue during radiation is subjective, almost universal, and multifactorial (concurrent chemotherapy, weight loss, pain, anemia, and length of radiation treatment). The specific etiology of radiation-related fatigue is unclear. Frequently, patients have undergone a surgical procedure(s) and/or received chemotherapy before radiation therapy. Thus, when many patients come to the radiation experience, they are very familiar with fatigue and its impact on their life. Sitton (1997) has summarized the extensive research related to acute and chronic cancer-related fatigue. The impact of fatigue on a patient varies with multiple factors, including age, extent of disease, co-morbid conditions, and performance status. Fatigue is best measured by patient self-report (Piper, 1998). Patients describe their fatigue in many ways, including tiredness, weakness, exhaustion, lack of energy, malaise, impaired ability to concentrate, and overall impaired ability to complete activities of daily living. It follows that such a dramatic impact on physical and mental functioning will affect quality of life.

Patients and families should be taught that fatigue is an expected effect of treatment and may be increased when receiving CMT (Clark & Lacasse, 1998). The degree of fatigue-related symptoms increases over the course of radiation treatment (Greenberg, Sawicka, Eisenthal & Ross, 1992; Munro & Potter, 1996). An early study by King and coworkers (1985) examined 96 subjects weekly during radiation therapy, and then monthly for 3 months after completing treatment. The patients were receiving radiation for cancers of the chest, head and neck, prostate, bladder, and gynecologic tumors. Overall, from 65% to 93% of patients reported fatigue that gradually increased and was continuous by the last 2 weeks of treatment and persisted for several months after radiation. Patients receiving radiation to the head/brain are likely to experience fatigue that tends to manifest as increased sleepiness, drowsiness, lethargy, and anorexia. The symptoms of fatigue tend to persist after other treatment-related side effects have resolved. As expected, patients find fatigue and its impact on every aspect of their life a very difficult problem, and, due to the general lack of specific interventions, the patient and family may become even more frustrated and impatient. It is important to observe for symptoms of clinical depression, especially in the patient experiencing prolonged fatigue that may affect the ability to perform activities of daily living.

Graydon and associates (1995) evaluated the strategies patients use to manage fatigue while undergoing chemotherapy or radiation therapy. They identified four dimensions, including reducing or stopping activity, increasing activity (physical/social), distraction, and doing something different. Irvine and coworkers (1998), in a study of 76 women undergoing radiation therapy for breast cancer, reported that the strategies of sitting and sleeping were consistently the most frequently reported and were felt to be somewhat effective. What may make managing fatigue even more difficult is that it is a subjective experience. Patients can generally cope with other side effects, such as nausea, vomiting, diarrhea, and skin reactions, perhaps because there are concrete and effective interventions. Fatigue, on the other hand, does not lend itself to such techniques. Irvine and associates hypothesize that the decrease in psychological distress noted during radiation therapy, in their study, may have been because patients were receiving tangible aid in the form of treatment and/or support from health professionals. Acknowledging fatigue as a "legitimate" toxicity of radiation therapy may be as important as suggestions for management.

Myelosuppression

The bone marrow is an important dose-limiting cell renewal tissue for chemotherapy, wide-field irradiation, and autologous bone marrow transplantation (Mauch et al., 1995). The bone marrow is extremely radiosensitive to the degree that some injury is produced by any dose. Peripheral blood cells acutely respond by progressively decreasing in number due to the destruction of both mature and precursor cells. Lymphocytes are the most sensitive and can cause lymphopenia early in the course of therapy. The radiation dose, dose rate, and volume all affect the acute response of the bone marrow to therapy. When small radiation fields composing only 10% to 15% of the bone marrow are radiated, the unexposed bone marrow responds by increasing its population of progenitor cells meeting the demands for hematopoiesis. Thus, acute myelosuppression is usually not seen unless very large areas containing a substantial portion of marrow are within the radiation fields (Mauch et al., 1995). Approximately 40% of active bone marrow is in the pelvis, with the remaining 60% distributed as illustrated in Figure 13-15.

The chronic or late effects of radiation on the bone marrow are demonstrated by increased hematopoietic activity in unexposed marrow segments, followed by extension of functioning marrow into previously quiescent areas such as the femora and humeri (Mauch et al., 1995). Bone marrow regeneration is variable in each patient and generally lags behind the peripheral blood counts. Marrow recovery can occur over extended periods, with total recovery in 12 to 24 months, but this depends on the volume irradiated (Mauch et al., 1995). Generally, patients are not at greater risk for infection during the chronic recovery phase.

The combined effects of chemotherapy and radiation therapy on the marrow are complex. Any therapeutic regimen combining therapies must take into account potential increased dose-limiting marrow suppression (Mauch et al., 1995). Growth factors supporting all hematologic cell lines are seldom needed when radiation is used as a single modality. However, in CMT, they are frequently part of the treatment regimens due to the increased risk of pancytopenia.

What Happens When the Patient Enters the Radiation Oncology Department (Who Are All Those People in the Department That Is Usually in the Basement?)

Radiation oncology departments are multidisciplinary, and the team approach to cancer management is well illustrated. Staff members include physicians (radiation oncologist), radiation oncology nurses, radiation therapists, physicists, and dosimetrists. The radiation therapist is trained to set up and administer the daily treatments and monitor quality assurance of all aspects of therapy. Treatment planning is done by medical physicists and dosimetrists. Each staff member is integral to the administration of radiation and the care of patients during the treatment course.

When a patient is referred to radiation oncology, he or she first has a consultation with the radiation oncologist. Some radiation oncology departments have nurse practitioners and physician assistants who collaboratively consult, treat, and manage patients through a course of radiation therapy. Once the decision has been made to treat a patient with radiation, the next step is simula-

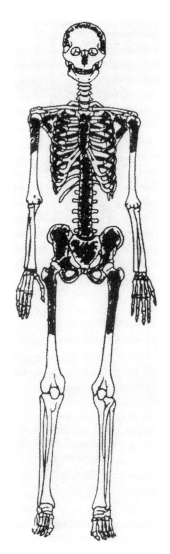

Figure 13-15 Bone marrow distribution. (Mauch, P., Constine, L., Greenberger, J., Knospe, W., Sullivan, J., et al. [1995]. Hematopoietic stem cell compartment: Acute and late effects of radiation therapy and chemotherapy. *International Journal of Radiation Oncology•Biology• Physics, 31*[5], 1319–1339.)

tion (see the section entitled "Treatment Planning" for further discussion of the simulation process).

The length of the course of treatment varies from a minimum of 2 weeks up to 7 weeks. Patients are treated 5 days per week (Monday through Friday). The daily treatment can be difficult, especially for the frail or elderly, patients with pain, and those who must travel extended distances to the treatment center. The first day of treatment takes longer due to the necessity of taking verification radiographs (portal films). Simulator films must be compared with the portal films made with the treatment machine, to verify the accuracy of field size and location as well as patient positioning. Portal films may be taken weekly and are repeated whenever adjustments in blocks or field parameters are requested. Patients will often ask if the portal films see the tumor and ask if the radiation is "working." Portal films do not visualize the tumor and are not designed to be diagnostic. Portal films can be compared with charting because they document the area treated as simulated and prescribed.

At the beginning of treatment, the patient has a teaching session with the radiation oncology nurse. This is when side effects are further explained and management techniques reviewed. Written information is given to the patient, along with telephone numbers and instructions for reaching assistance after hours. During the course of radiation, patients are evaluated at least weekly by the clinician (MD, NP, PA). The patient is examined for toxicities and sits with the clinician to discuss his or her progress and any problems or concerns. Other members of the cancer care team also interact with the patient as indicated, such as the radiation oncology nurse, oncology dietitian, physical therapist, social worker, or speech therapist. On the final treatment day, the patient also meets with the clinician for postradiation instructions, and a follow-up appointment is made.

Conclusion

Consider the scene of a patient entering the radiation therapy treatment room: the patient is directed to lie on a narrow, hard table with a very large machine looming above him or her. Staff position the patient and then leave the room; sometimes the room lights are left dim. The radiation

therapist then turns on the linear accelerator from a console outside the room, and the treatment machine begins emitting an invisible ray that cannot felt and that, at the least, is supposed to make the patient better and, at best, cure the cancer. Strohl (1988) has characterized this scene as epitomizing the loneliness of the cancer experience. It is, after all, the patient who must do the treatment alone. It does not take much to understand that patients must have considerable trust in the staff treating them.

Patients frequently have misinformation and are fearful regarding radiation, and patient's friends and family may reinforce their concerns due to their own lack of knowledge. It is essential that the radiation oncology nurse and physician educate the patient and family before beginning a course of treatment. Patient education should include the following: general issues, myths and misconceptions, information (include sensory information) on the actual treatments, the simulation process, expected outcome (cure, control, or palliation), adverse effects of treatment, and management of adverse effects (Dunne-Daly, 1994).

In a study by Christman (1990), the experience of cancer and its treatment was found to generate high levels of distress and difficulty in coping. Although cancer treatment is stressful, cessation of treatment was associated with emotional stress due to uncertainty about tumor recurrence. The staff in radiation oncology departments form short and intense relationships with patients and their families. Each staff member and radiation department deals with the ending of a course of therapy in a different way. Although patients are always pleased to be finishing treatment, it is important to acknowledge the ending of this portion of their cancer therapy. Radiation oncology staff members look forward to patient follow-up visits to renew friendships and hopefully celebrate a positive treatment outcome.

REFERENCES

Bentel, G. C. (1996). *Radiation therapy planning.* New York: McGraw-Hill.

Bova, F. J., Meeks, S. L., & Friedman, W. A. (1998). Linac radiosurgery: System requirements, procedures, and testing. In F. M. Khan & R. A. Potish (Eds.), *Treatment planning in radiation oncology* (pp. 215–242). Philadelphia: Lippincott Williams & Wilkins.

Bucholtz, J. D. (1997). Central nervous system tumors. In K. H. Dow, J. D. Bucholtz, R. R. Iwamoto, V. K. Fieler & L. J. Hilderley (Eds.), *Nursing care in radiation oncology* (pp. 136–151). Philadelphia: W. B. Saunders.

Christman, J. J. (1990). Uncertainty and adjustment during radiotherapy. *Nursing Research, 39*(1), 17–20.

Clark, P. M., & Lacasse, C. (1998). Cancer-related fatigue: clinical practice issues. *Clinical Journal of Oncology Nursing, 2*(2), 45–53.

Coia, L. R., & Moylan, D. J. (1994). *Introduction to clinical radiation oncology.* Madison, WI: Medical Physics Publishing.

Dunne-Daly, C. F. (1997). Principles of brachytherapy. In K. H. Dow, J. D. Bucholtz, R. R. Iwamoto, V. K. Fieler & L. J. Hilderley (Eds.), *Nursing care in radiation oncology* (pp. 21–35). Philadelphia: W. B. Saunders.

Dunne-Daly, C. F. (1995). Skin and wound care in radiation oncology. *Cancer Nursing, 18*(2), 144–162.

Dunne-Daly, C. F. (1994). Nursing care and adverse reactions of external radiation therapy: A self-learning module. *Cancer Nursing, 17*(3), 236–256.

Graydon, J. E., Bubela, N., Irvine, D., & Vincent, L. (1995). Fatigue-reducing strategies used by patients receiving treatment for cancer. *Cancer Nursing, 18*, 23–28.

Greenberg, D. B., Sawicka, J., Eisenthal, S., & Ross, D. (1992). Fatigue syndrome due to localized radiation. *Journal of Pain and Symptom Management, 7*, 38–45.

Hall, E. (1994). *Radiobiology for the radiologist.* New York: Lippincott-Raven.

Held, J. S., Osborne, D. M., Volpe, H., & Waldman, A. R. (1994). Cancer of the prostate: Treatment and nursing implications. *Oncology Nursing Forum, 21*, 1517–1529.

Hellman, S. (1997). Principles of cancer management: Radiation therapy. In V. T. DeVita, Jr., S. Hellman, & S. A. Rosenberg (Eds.), *Cancer: Principles and practice of oncology* (pp. 307–332). Philadelphia: Lippincott-Raven.

Hilderley, L. J. (1997). Radiotherapy. In S. L. Groenwald, M. H. Frogge, M. Goodman & C. H. Yarbro (Eds.), *Cancer nursing: Principles and practice* (pp. 247–282). Boston: Jones and Bartlett.

Hilderley, L. J., & Dow, K. H. (1996). Radiation oncology. In R. McCorkle, M. Grant, M. Frank-Stromborg & S. B. Baird (Eds.), *Cancer nursing: A comprehensive textbook* (pp. 331–358). Philadelphia: W. B. Saunders.

Irvine, D. M., Vincent, L., Graydon, J. E., & Bubela, N. (1998). Fatigue in women with breast cancer receiving radiation therapy. *Cancer Nursing, 21*(2), 127–135.

Iwamoto, R. (1997). Radiation therapy. In S. E. Otto (Ed.), *Oncology nursing* (pp. 503–529). St. Louis: Mosby.

Kan, M. D. (1995). Palliation of bone pain in patients with metastatic cancer using strontium-89 (Metastron). *Cancer Nursing, 18*, 286–291.

Khan, F. (1998). Introduction. In F. M. Khan & R. A. Potish (Eds.), *Treatment planning in radiation oncology* (pp. 1–10). Philadelphia: Lippincott Williams & Wilkins.

King, K. B., Nail, L. M., Kraemer, K., Strohl, R. A., & Johnson, J. E. (1985). Patients' descriptions of the experience of receiving radiation therapy. *Oncology Nursing Forum, 12*(4), 55–61.

Mackie, T. R., Liu, H. H., & McCullough, E. C. (1998). Model-based photon dose calculation algorithms. In F. M.

Khan & R. A. Potish (Eds.), *Treatment planning in radiation oncology* (pp. 89–112). Philadelphia: Lippincott Williams & Wilkins.

Marks, L. B. (1996). The impact of organ structure on radiation response. *International Journal of Radiation Oncology·Biology·Physics, 34*(5), 1165–1171.

Mauch, P., Constine, L., Greenberger, J., Knospe, W., Sullivan, J., et al. (1995). Hematopoietic stem cell compartment: Acute and late effects of radiation therapy and chemotherapy. *International Journal of Radiation Oncology·Biology·Physics, 31*(5), 1319–1339.

Maxwell, M., & Maher, K. (1992). Chemotherapy-induced myelosuppression. *Seminars in Oncology Nursing, 8*(2), 113–123.

Munro, A. J., & Potter, S. (1996). A quantitative approach to the distress caused by symptoms in patients treated with radical radiotherapy. *British Journal of Cancer, 74*, 640–647.

Ozsahin, M., Pene, F., Cosset, J. M., & Laugier, A. (1994). Morbidity after total body irradiation. *Seminars in Radiation Oncology, 4*(2), 95–102.

Perez, C. A., & Purdy, J. A. (1992). Rationale for treatment planning in radiation therapy. In S. H. Levitt, F. M. Khan, & R. A. Potish (Eds.), *Levitt and Tapley's technological basis of radiation therapy: Practical clinical applications* (p. 16). Philadelphia: Lea & Febiger.

Piper, B. F. (1998). The Groopman article reviewed. *Oncology, 12*(3), 345–346.

Porter, A. T., McEwan, A. J. B., Powe, J. E., Reid, R., McGowan, D. G. , Lukka, H., et al. (1993). Results of a randomized phase-III trial to evaluate the efficacy of strontium-89 adjuvant to local field external beam irradiation in the management of endocrine resistant metastatic prostate cancer. *International Journal of Radiation Oncology·Biology·Physics, 25*, 805–815.

Reinstein, L. E. (1998). Patient positioning and immobilization. In F. M. Khan & R. A. Potish (Eds.), *Treatment planning in radiation oncology* (pp. 55–88). Philadelphia: Lippincott Williams & Wilkins.

Sitton, E. (1992). Early and late radiation-induced skin alterations part 1: Mechanisms of skin changes. *Oncology Nursing Forum, 19*, 801–807.

Sitton, E. (1997). Managing side effects of skin changes and fatigue. In K. H. Dow, J. D. Bucholtz, R. R. Iwamoto, V. K. Fieler & L. J. Hilderley (Eds.), *Nursing care in radiation oncology* (pp. 79–100). Philadelphia: W. B. Saunders.

Strohl, R. A. (1988). The nursing role in radiation oncology: Symptom management of acute and chronic reactions. *Oncology Nursing Forum, 15*(4), 429–434.

Strunk, B., & Maher, K. (1993). A collaborative effort between radiation oncology and ET nurses in the care of a patient with esophageal cancer undergoing radiotherapy. *Journal of Enterostomal Therapy Nursing, 20*(4), 152–157.

Wojtas, F., & Smith, R. (1997). Hyperthermia and intraoperative radiation therapy. In K. H. Dow, J. D. Bucholtz, R. R. Iwamoto, V. K. Fieler, & L. J. Hilderley (Eds.), *Nursing care in radiation oncology* (pp. 36–46). Philadelphia: W. B. Saunders.

Yasko, J. (1982). *Care of the client receiving external radiation therapy.* Reston, VA: Reston Publishing Co.

Principles of Biotherapy and Gene Therapy

Elizabeth Abernathy

Biotherapy is the use of agents derived from biologic sources or of agents or approaches that affect the body's biologic responses. The biologic agents are referred to as biologic response modifiers (BRMs) and were defined in 1983 as "agents or approaches that modify the relationship between tumor and host by modifying the host's biologic response to tumor cells, with resultant therapeutic benefit" (Mihich & Fefer, 1983). Gene therapy may be included in this classification because it attempts to modify the body's biologic response through gene manipulation.

Over the years, as a treatment for cancer, biotherapy has had its successes as well as failures. This has been frustrating to clinicians and researchers, as well as to the general public who frequently read articles on biotherapy in the lay press announcing yet another "cure for cancer." However, the successes with biotherapy have led to its recognition by scientific and medical communities as the fourth treatment modality for patients with cancer, the other three being surgery, chemotherapy, and radiation therapy (Oldham, 1991).

Historical Perspective

The concept of manipulating the body's biology, especially the immune system, to treat cancer is not new. As far back as ancient China and Egypt, the power of the immune system to fight disease was recognized (Sell, 1987). In the late 1800s, a New York City surgeon, Dr. William Coley, after beginning frustrated with his failures in treating patients with cancer, searched his patients' records for clues to explain why some patients survived and others did not. He discovered that patients who developed life-threatening infections and high fevers after surgery and who survived the infection tended to have higher survival rates from their cancer. He hypothesized that the immune system was being stimulated by the infection and, once stimulated, it was better able to "fight" the cancer. He began injecting cancer patients with a live bacteria vaccine, referred to as Coley's toxins, in an effort to induce an increased immune response. His therapeutic responses were mixed; however, Coley's toxins stayed on hospital formularies until recent years (Jassak, 1995).

A core group of scientists remained very interested in biotherapy throughout the 1900s. However, it was not until the refinement of DNA technology and the advent of sophisticated computers in the early 1980s that researchers had the technology to isolate, understand, and produce the different components of the body's biologic systems crucial in the development and growth of cancer. These developments, along with new information on genetics, have given researchers the ability to explore the genetic basis of cancer as well as to attempt to treat cancer through the alteration or manipulation of genes (Farrell, 1996). Table 14-1 identifies the major biologic agents and their current regulatory approvals (Hood & Abernathy, 1996).

241

TABLE 14-1

APPROVED BIOLOGIC AGENTS

Agent	Trade Name	Generic Name	Approved Indications	Date
CSFs				
G-CSF	Neupogen	Filgrastin	Chemotherapy-induced myelosuppression	1991
GM-CSF	Leukine	Sargramostim	Post-ABMT for lymphoid malignancy engraftment failure	1991
EPO	Epogen	Epoetin alfa	Anemia; chronic renal failure; AZT-treated HIV infection;	
	Procrit		chemotherapy-related	1989
	Neumega	Oprelvekin	Chemotherapy-induced thrombocytopenia	
Interferon			Hairy cell leukemia, condyloma, AIDS-related Kaposi's sarcoma,	
Alpha			chronic hepatitis, melanoma	1986
Beta			Multiple sclerosis	1992
Gamma			Chronic granulomatous disease	1992
Interleukin				
IL-2	Proleukin	Aldesleukin	Metastatic renal cell carcinoma	1992
Monoclonal antibodies				
Oncoscint		Oncoscint	Diagnostic testing for ovarian and colorectal cancer	1993
OKT-3		Orthoclone	Treatment of acute cell-mediated rejection in organ transplant	
Rituxan		Rituximab	Refractory B-cell lymphoma	1997
Herceptin		Trastuzumab	Metastatic breast cancer	1998

(Hood, L. E., & Abernathy, E. [1996]. Biological response modifiers. In R. McCorkle, M. Grant, M. Frank-Stromborg, & S. Baird [Eds.]. *Cancer nursing: A comprehensive textbook* [2nd ed]. Philadelphia: W. B. Saunders.)

Overview of the Immune System

The immune system remains key in the body's ability to prevent, control, and destroy cancerous growth. An understanding of the concepts and components of this system is crucial to the understanding of biotherapy. The purpose of the immune system is threefold: to recognize, destroy, and clear that which is foreign from the body. To do this, the body must be able to determine what naturally belongs in the body and is not harmful (self) from that which is foreign and potentially harmful (antigen). It is believed that the body has or can have the ability to recognize cancer as foreign and can elicit an immune response in an attempt to destroy it, the same as it does against bacteria that has invaded the body.

The cells that carry out the functions of the immune system are primarily white blood cells (leukocytes). These cells are produced in the bone marrow and continuously circulate through the vascular and lymphatic systems, prepared to destroy any foreign invaders. The inflammatory response is the initial defense of the immune system to foreign invaders in the body. Neutrophils, a group of leukocytes, migrate to the area of the invasion, wall it off, and attempt to destroy the invaders. However, a more complicated response becomes activated once the inflammatory response is initiated. This is referred to as specific immunity and occurs when an antigen is recognized by a particular group of leukocytes, the lymphocytes, which in turn trigger a cascade of events to destroy the invader. One of the outcomes of this activation is that memory of the invader occurs for a group of lymphocytes, providing for a strong, rapid immune response if the same antigen is reencountered at some future time. This is the basis for immunization procedures such as for measles, tetanus, and polio.

Specific immunity can be divided into humoral and cell-mediated immunity (Figure 14-1). Humoral immunity refers to immunity conferred by a subset of lymphocytes, B-cells. Upon activation, B-cells secrete plasma cells, which in turn produce antibodies. Antibodies (immunoglobulins) have the ability to bind to surface receptors on antigens, either neutralizing the antigen or activating additional components of the immune system, such as complement, to destroy the antigen. The antigen–

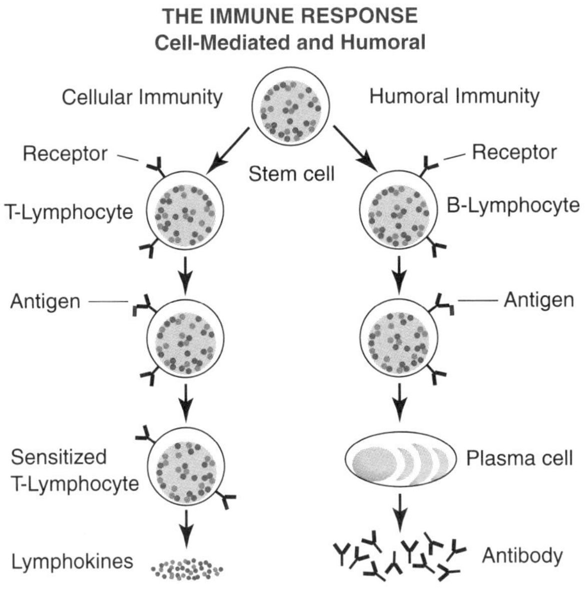

THE IMMUNE RESPONSE
Cell-Mediated and Humoral

Cellular Immunity   Humoral Immunity

Receptor   Receptor
                    Stem cell
T-Lymphocyte   B-Lymphocyte

Antigen   Antigen

Sensitized
T-Lymphocyte   Plasma cell

Lymphokines   Antibody

Figure 14-1 Differentiation of the lymphoid stem cell results in two distinct populations of lymphocytes. The B-cell system generates the humoral response, whereas the T-cell system generates the cellular response. (From National Institutes of Health. [1983]. *Understanding the immune system* [USDHHS Publication No. NIH 84-529]. Washington, DC: U.S. Government Printing Office.)

antibody interaction is highly specific, meaning that the antibody that binds to the antigen is only capable of binding to that particular type of antigen and no other.

One particular form of biotherapy, serotherapy, is modeled after the antigen–antibody interaction. Cancer serotherapy is the use of antibodies that have been created to recognize and bind with antigens expressed by a particular cancer.

The second type of specific immunity, cell-mediated immunity, refers to immunity conferred by T-lymphocytes. After activation, T-lymphocytes mature into cells with different functions, including:

- Memory cells: Remember the antigen
- Killer cells: Destroy antigens
- Helper cells: Activate humoral immunity
- Suppressor cells: Inhibit the immune response

Activated T-lymphocytes secrete proteins, called lymphokines, that mediate the behavior of the immune system cells. Many of the BRMs in clinical use today are lymphokines or cytokines,

which refer to all proteins released not only from lymphocytes but by any activated cell that mediates the activity of the immune system. Other cells such as macrophages identify and clear invaders from the body. It is critical that all components of the immune system are functioning fully and correctly for an immune response because of the interdependency of the reactions (Post-White, 1996a).

Cytokines

The majority of the BRMs in clinical use today are cytokines, proteins found naturally in small amounts in the body, which serve as important regulators and messengers of normal cellular function (Post-White, 1996a). Once the particular cytokine has been identified and its roles isolated, scientists are able to produce the cytokines in large, very pure quantities in the laboratory through the use of recombinant DNA (rDNA) technology. Recombinant DNA technology is the process of gene coding for a desired cytokine into another organism (e.g., *Escherichia coli*); as a result, the organism serves as a "factory" that produces the desired cytokine. All cytokines in clinical use are produced in this manner (Figure 14-2).

Cytokines have multiple actions, including the ability to regulate the production of other cytokines. Often when a cytokine is produced or administered, other cytokines are also produced. This may, in part, explain the similarities of some of the side effects patients experience after receiving cytokines. The most common side effect reported by patients receiving many of the cytokines is a flulike syndrome, including fever, chills, malaise, and fatigue.

Interferon

In 1957, two British virologists identified a substance that had the ability to interfere with viral replication, and named it interferon (Isaacs & Lindemann, 1957). Interferons are cytokines that have antiviral, antiproliferative, and immunomodulatory effects. These effects led researchers to discover interferon's antitumor activity (Oldham, 1985).

Interferons are a family of more than 20 different proteins produced by most human cells. There are three major types of interferon: alpha, beta,

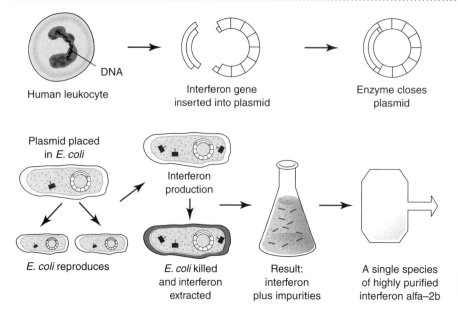

Human leukocyte

DNA

Interferon gene
inserted into plasmid

Enzyme closes
plasmid

Plasmid placed
in *E. coli*

Interferon
production

E. coli reproduces

E. coli killed
and interferon
extracted

Result:
interferon
plus impurities

A single species
of highly purified
interferon alfa–2b

Figure 14-2 Recombinant DNA production of highly purified human interferon-alfa-2b. (Schering Corporation. Reproduced by permission. Copyright © 1986. Shering Corporation. All rights reserved.)

and gamma. Each type has distinct abilities as well as similar properties and toxicities. Alpha interferon, the first BRM to receive FDA approval, was approved in 1986 for the treatment of a chronic form of leukemia, hairy cell leukemia. Of all the BRMs, alpha interferon has been researched the most extensively for cancer therapy. Since its initial approval, additional clinical indications have been added, including AIDS-related Kaposi's sarcoma, chronic myelogenous leukemia (CML), melanoma, and several noncancer indications (Borden, 1992).

Beta and gamma interferon have also shown antitumor activity in certain cancers and both have FDA approval, but for noncancer indications (Rao & Wadler, 1992). Research continues in this area to determine additional indications for the use of interferons, as well as to determine the optimal mode and timing of delivery of the agents. Currently being examined for its use in cancer therapy is combining interferon with other BRMs or with chemotherapy or radiation therapy.

Administration and Toxicities

Interferon, like all cytokines, is a protein and cannot be administered orally because digestive enzymes would destroy it. Subcutaneous injection is the most common route, but it can be administered by way of intramuscular, intranasal, intralesional, intrathecal, and intracavitary routes, as well as intravenously or by bolus infusion. The route of administration has been shown to alter the function and the toxicities of the cytokine. Constitutional side effects (flulike syndrome) are increased when it is administered intravenously (Skalla, 1996).

The toxicities of the interferons are dose and route dependent and affect multiple systems. Low doses are well tolerated, whereas high doses cannot be maintained because cumulative toxicities cannot be tolerated. The most common side effect is the flulike syndrome, which is associated with fever, chills, and muscle and joint aches (Table 14-2). Interferon is better tolerated if the dose is slowly escalated from an initial low dose. Patients who experience severe side effects early in therapy often continue to have difficulty; however, toxic effects generally lessen with dose reduction. Fatigue is often cumulative in its effect and may become so severe as to necessitate dose reduction or discontinuing therapy. Younger patients and those with a good performance status generally tolerate interferon the best. Toxicities associated with interferon gamma are more severe than interferon alpha and include (in addition to the flulike syndrome) hypotension, nausea, and vomiting (Skalla, 1996). Management of side effects from interferon requires a comprehensive nursing assessment and interventions based on minimizing the potentially debilitating effects of the therapy, as presented in Table 14-3.

TABLE 14-2

CLINICAL TOXIC EFFECTS OF INTERFERONS

	Interferon α and β	Interferon γ
Neurologic	FLS* Fatigue* Peripheral neuropathy* Confusion/dizziness Short-term memory impairment* Somnolence* Depression/personality changes* Decreased ability to concentrate* EEG abnormalities Coma[†] Seizures[‡]	FLS* Fatigue* Severe headache* Lethargy* Confusion[†]
Cardiopulmonary	Tachycardia[†] Hypotension/hyptertension[†] Atrial and ventricular arrhythmias[†] Acute cardiac failure[†] Acute pulmonary failure[‡]	Arrhythmias* Chest pain* Ischemia* Conduction abnormalities[†]
Gastrointestinal	Nausea/vomiting* Diarrhea* Altered taste* Increase in liver function tests Anorexia[†]	Increased nausea* Increased vomiting* Increase in liver function tests* Hyperbilirubinemia[†]
Integumentary	Rashes* Local inflammation* Urticaria* Mild alopecia* Increased eyelash growth* Enhanced radiation toxicity* Stomatitis[†] Reactivation of oral herpes simplex virus[†] Exacerbation of psoriasis[†]	
Hematologic	Bone marrow depression* Anemia[†]	Neutropenia* Coagulopathy[‡]
Musculoskeletal	Severe rigors[†]	Low back pain*
Renal	Proteinuria* Acute renal failure[†] Elevated BUN[†] Nephrotic syndrome[†]	Proteinuria* Renal insufficiency[†]
Metabolic	Hypercalcemia[†] Hypocalcemia[†] Hyperkalemia Hypertriglyceridemia[†]	Hypocalcemia* Hypertriglyceridemia*

Abbreviations: FLS, flulike syndrome consisting of fever, chills, myalgias; EEG, electroencephalogram; BUN, blood urea nitrogen.
*Low cumulative dose.
[†]High cumulative dose.
[‡]Rare.
(Skalla, K. [1996]. The interferons. *Seminars in Oncology Nursing, 12,* 97–105.)

TABLE 14-3

KEY POINTS FOR NURSING MANAGEMENT OF PATIENTS TREATED WITH INTERFERON

Flulike syndrome
  Premedicate with acetaminophen
  Increase fluid intake
  Administer interferon before bedtime
  Administer meperidine for rigors
Fatigue
  Maintain nutrition
  Encourage normal nightly sleep habits
  Encourage regular light exercise
  Prioritize activities
Fluid/electrolyte management
  Monitor electrolytes
  Encourage noncaffeinated fluids if dehydrated
Maximize dietary habits and hydration
  Perform dietary consult if necessary
  Review 48-h diet history for adequate caloric intake
Safety assessment/intervention
  Teach safe techniques of transfer/ambulation
  Reorient as necessary
  Make lists/calendars as memory aids for tasks/
    medications
  Teach safe administration techniques

(Skalla, K. [1996]. The interferons. *Seminars in Oncology Nursing, 12,* 97–105.)

Hematopoietic Growth Factors

Hematopoietic growth factors, also referred to as colony-stimulating factors (CSFs), are cytokines that regulate the production, maturation, and function of blood cells. The physiologic process of blood growth and development is called hematopoiesis. Blood cell formation occurs in the bone marrow and consists of cell production, differentiation, and maturation (Figure 14-3). All blood cells are derived from a pool of pluripotent "stem" cells, which are the body's most primitive blood-forming cells. The stem cell can either self-replicate or differentiate into either myeloid or lymphoid lineage. By binding onto specific receptors on stem cells, growth factors assist in the stem cell's lineage commitment. This binding activates the needed cell line to enter maturation. Because of the growth factor's role in stimulating maturation, the blood cell after maturation is released into circulation (DiJulio, 1991).

CSFs are generally named after the lineage they influence. Granulocyte–colony-stimulating factor (G-CSF) is a growth factor affecting the growth, maturation, and function of granulocytes, and granulocyte macrophage–colony-stimulating factor (GM-CSF) affects both granulocytes and macrophages. Four CSFs—G-CSF; GM-CSF; erythropoietin, a red blood cell growth factor; and Neumega, a platelet growth factor—have received FDA approval for use in patients with cancer (Table 14-4) (Abernathy, 1994). Several CSFs are in clinical trials, including interleukins, macrophage–colony-stimulating factor (M-CSF), and stem cell factor (SCF) (Pitler, 1996).

G-CSF, GM-CSF, and Neumega

The CSFs have dramatically influenced the treatment and care of patients with cancer and bone marrow failure disorders. Neutropenia is a common dose-limiting toxicity of chemotherapy and is associated with life-threatening infections, which continue to be the leading cause of death in people with cancer. Clinical trials have shown that G-CSF and GM-CSF have been effective in reducing the severity and duration of neutropenia after chemotherapy, thereby reducing hospitalizations and mortality from infections. When neutropenia is reduced, patients are better able to stay on schedule with their chemotherapy and not have to be delayed to allow for bone marrow recovery. This allows the patient's cancer to be optimally treated by eliminating a lag time for cancer regrowth to occur. In patients undergoing bone marrow transplants, G-CSF and GM-CSF have both reduced the length of time of bone marrow recovery after transplant (Abernathy, 1997).

Neumega (interleukin-II), a platelet growth factor, has been effective in reducing the number of platelet transfusions following myelosuppressive chemotherapy (Tepler, 1996).

Erythropoietin (EPO)

Anemia is a significant problem in patients undergoing cancer treatments, requiring many to receive multiple transfusions. The growth factor erythropoietin (EPO) provides valuable support by stimulating the production of red blood cells (erythrocytes) and diminishing anemia (Figure 14-4).

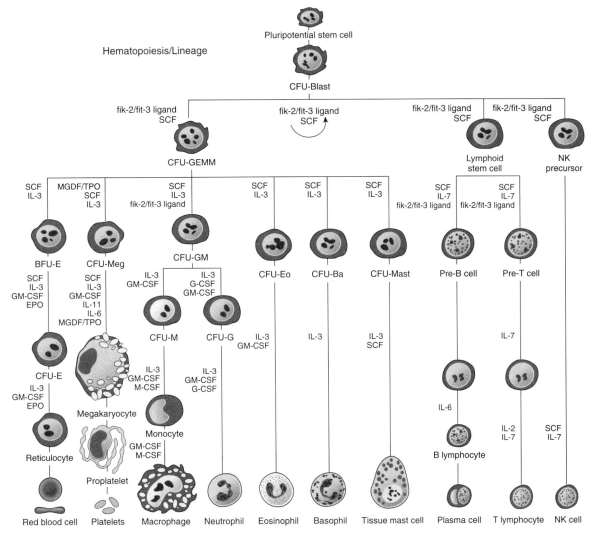

Figure 14-3 Hematopoietic growth chart depicting proliferation, differentiation, and maturation of the various cell lineages. (Reprinted with permission from Amgen Inc., Thousand Oaks, CA. All rights reserved.)

Erythropoietin is a protein that circulates within the bloodstream and is responsible for red blood cell production. It is produced mainly in the kidney, and its synthesis is based primarily on oxygen tension levels. The major function of the erythrocyte is to transport hemoglobin, which carries oxygen from the lungs to the tissue. When oxygen levels are decreased, the body responds by increasing its production of erythropoietin. Erythropoietin is carried to the bone marrow where it binds with erythroid precursor cells to stimulate the production of erythrocytes. Patients with anemia receiving EPO must have needed iron and other nutrients in order for their body to be able to correctly produce the new red blood cells (Rieger & Haeuber, 1995).

Administration and Toxicities

G-CSF, GM-CSF, EPO, and Neumega are most commonly given as a subcutaneous injection several times a week. Patients or caregivers are frequently taught to give the injections in the same manner that a diabetic self-injects insulin. The

TABLE 14-4
COLONY-STIMULATING FACTORS

	Epoetin alfa (Epogen)	Filgrastim (G-CSF, Neupogen)	Sargramostim (GM-CSF, Leukine)
What Is It?	A synthetic hormone produced by recombinant DNA technique	Hematopoietic growth factor, which promotes proliferation and maturation of neutrophil granulocytes	Hematopoietic growth factor, which stimulates production of monocytes, eosinophils, neutrophils, and megakaryocytes
Indications	Treatment of anemias associated with chronic renal failure and zidovudine therapy in patients with HIV infection; chemotherapy-induced anemia in patients with nonmyeloid malignancies receiving therapy with antineoplastic agents; autologous blood donation and presurgical blood loss; and other anemias of chronic disease	Prevent or reduce cytotoxic chemotherapy-induced neutropenia in cancer patients	Acceleration of myeloid recovery in patients with non-Hodgkin's lymphoma, acute lymphoblastic leukemia, and Hodgkin's disease undergoing autologous bone marrow transplant (ABMT), and persons with failed autologous BM engraftment
Dose	150 units/kg IV or SC 3 times/wk. Dose should be reduced when hematocrit reaches 30%–33% or there is an increase of more than 4 points during any 2-wk period. Hematocrit should not rise above 36%	5 µg/kg administered SC or IV by short infusion of 20–30 min; continue daily for up to 2 wk or until absolute neutrophil count (ANC) has reached, 10,000/mm^3, after the expected nadir	250 µg/m^2/d given SC or as a 1-h infusion. Begin 2–4 h after the ABMT infusion when ANC reaches 20,000 after the expected nadir
Onset of Activity	Approximately 7–10 d following 3 times/wk dosage	Rapid rise in neutrophil count within first 24 h following administration of IV filgrastim. Neutrophil counts continue to rise, reaching a plateau by day 3 of treatment, and remain continuosly elevated during treatment	Similar to filgrastim
Labs	Hematocrit should be determined 2 times/wk. Dose should be reduced when HCT reaches 30%–33% or if there is an increase of 4% in any 2-week period. This sharp rise can bring on hypertension. HCT should not rise above 36%	CBC with platelets should be obtained prior to starting filgrastim and 2 times/wk during daily therapy	CBC with platelets should be obtained prior to therapy and 2 times/wk during therapy
Contraindications	Uncontrolled hypertension	Drug should be given not less than 24 h after last dose of chemotherapy and should be stopped at least 24 h before chemotherapy	Drug should be given not less than 24 h after chemotherapy and 12 h after last dose of radiation therapy
Adverse Reactions	Hypertension, functional iron deficiency	Mild to moderate bone pain	Fever, chills, rash, fatigue, myalgia, bone pain, dyspnea, peripheral edema; use caution in patients with preexisting edema or pericardial effusion

(Abernaty, E. [1994]. Biotechnology: Exploring the fourth modality of cancer treatment. *Quality of Life: A Nursing Challenge, 3* [2], 30–38.)

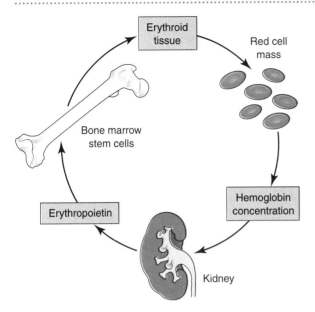

Figure 14-4 Erythropoiesis. The production of erythropoietin and the subsequent production of red blood cells occur as a result of the body's need for oxygen. (Reprinted with permission from Amgen Inc., Thousand Oaks, CA. All rights reserved.)

growth factors may also be given intravenously; however, side effects may be more severe when given by way of this route. In general, at approved doses, patients report few side effects. Higher doses of G-CSF and GM-CSF and combination therapy increase toxicities such as the flulike syndrome, bone pain, and headaches (see Table 14-4). EPO may result in hypertension for a small percentage of patients (Abernathy, 1994).

Interleukins

Interleukins are a group of cytokines named for their ability to "interlink" cells of the immune system and hematopoietic cells. They have been called the "hormones of the immune system." By interlinking the cells of the immune system, interleukins aid in the control of specific immune responses. Interleukins may directly influence hematopoiesis as CSFs, or they may indirectly aid in hematopoiesis by interacting with target cells to release CSFs. More than fifteen interleukins have been identified. They are referred to by number such as interleukin 1, interleukin 2, and so on.

This number refers to the order of approval of discovery applied by the International Congress of Immunology and does not imply ranking of importance or specific activity (Balkwill, 1989).

Interleukins are not directly cytotoxic to cancer cells, like chemotherapy, but are therapeutic through their ability to modulate the immune system. Interleukins achieve their therapeutic actions by stimulating other cytokines to become activated, and this stimulates a cascade of actions within the body's immune system (Wheeler, 1996).

Interleukin 2 (IL-2 or Aldesleukin) is the only interleukin with FDA approval as a cancer therapy (Parkinson & Sznol, 1995). Several of the other interleukins are in clinical studies to determine their role in cancer therapy, including, interleukin 1, interleukin 3, interleukin 4, and interleukin 6 (Table 14-5) (DeLaPena, Tomaszewski, Bernato & Kryk, 1996).

Interleukin 2 (IL-2)

IL-2, described originally in 1976 as the T-cell growth factor, is a protein released by activated T-lymphocytes that directs T-lymphocytes to clone and perform a variety of activities, including killing cancer cells. The cytotoxic activity is thought to be due to IL-2's ability to activate antitumor cells, which attack the tumor. These cells are mainly CD8+ (cytotoxic T-cells) and NK (natural killer) cells as well as B-cells, which secrete antibodies or immunoglobulins (Stadler & Vogelzang, 1995).

In 1986, the FDA approved a recombinant version of IL-2, Aldesleukin, for the treatment of renal cell cancer. Typically, renal cell cancer responds poorly to chemotherapy or radiation therapy, and research indicated that some patients, even with advanced renal cell cancer, were able to achieve prolonged remissions with IL-2 (Sznol & Parkinson, 1994). Clinical trials continue to evaluate the effectiveness of IL-2 in other cancers, such as melanoma and colon cancer, in bone marrow transplantation, and in patients with the human immunodeficiency virus (HIV) (Sznol & Parkinson, 1994).

Administration and Toxicities

IL-2 can be administered as a subcutaneous injection or intravenously as a bolus or continuous infusion. Clinical studies are evaluating the adminis-

TABLE 14-5

NAMES AND FUNCTIONS OF ILS

IL	Name	Produced by	Functions
IL-1 α, IL-1 β	Endogenous pyrogen, lymphocyte-activating factor	Monocytes, macrophages, B- and T-cells and NK cells	IL-1 α: cofactor for hematopoiesis: stimulates B-, T-, and NK cells. platelet and antibody proliferation IL-1 β: activates T- and NK cells, induces cytokines, acts in inflammation and disease mediation
IL-2	Killer helper factor. T-cell growth and activator	T-cells	Stimulates cytokine secretion, acts as growth factor and differentiation factor for T- and B-cells; enhances LAK, TIL, and NK cells
IL-3	Multi-CSF, eosinophil	T-cells	Stimulates pluripotent stem cells, pre-B (mast) cell growth, stimulates histamine
IL-4	B-cell growth factor	T-cells. mast cells, bone marrow	Growth factor for B-, mast, and resting T-cells: increases IgG and IgE secretion: enhances MHC Class II antigens on B cells: enhances phagocytic activity of macrophages and cytolytic activity of T-cells
IL-5	B-cell growth factor, eosinophil CSF	T- and mast cells	Stimulates growth and differentiation of B-cells and eosinophils; with IL-4 stimulates IgE
IL-6	B-cell stimulation factor	T-cells, monocytes, and macrophages	Increases secretion of immunoglobulins and antibodies. induces B-cell and myeloid stem cell differentiation, and stimulates T-cells
IL-7	Pre-B-cell growth factor	Bone marrow	Growth of B-cell precursors and thymocytes; increases the expression of IL-2 by T-cells
IL-8	Neutrophil chemotactic factor	Monocytes, macrophages	Chemotactic attracts neutrophils; aids adherence and migration of neutrophils
IL-9	40 kD protein	T-helper cells	Increases IL-4 secretion for T-helper cell growth factor, assists in growth of mast cells
IL-10	Cytokine inhibitor	T- and B-cells, macrophages	Stimulates cytotoxic T-cells; suppresses cytokine secretion by T-helper cells
IL-11	None	Stromal fibroblasts	Stimulates T-cell dependent B-cells; with IL-3 partcipates in growth of early hematopoietic cells and platelets; suppresses lipase activity
IL-12	Cytotoxic maturer, NK activator	B-cells	Stimulates CD4 and CD8, enhances NK and T-cell cytotoxicity
IL-13	P-600	T-cells	Increase B-cells
IL-14	B-cell growth factor	T-cells	B-cell proliferation

(De La Pena, L., Tomaszewski, J., Bernato, L., & Kryk, J. [1996]. Interleukins. *Oncology Nursing Forum, 19* [1], 60–75.)

tration of IL-2 in combination with other cytokines, chemotherapy, or radiation therapy to increase its therapeutic ability.

Multisystem toxicities that can endanger life may occur with the administration of IL-2. These toxicities are dose and schedule dependent. Low-dose therapy (e.g., <18 IU given subcutaneously) is generally well tolerated in the outpatient setting. However, high-dose therapy (e.g., 600,000 IU/kg given IV every 8 hours) is highly toxic and requires intense patient monitoring. The toxicities appear reversible once therapy is discontinued (Table 14-6) (Dudjack & Yasko, 1990). This is the only cytokine used clinically that produces such toxic side effects. Patients need to be prepared as to what to expect before receiving high-dose IL-2 therapy (Parkinson & Sznol, 1995). Comprehensive nursing assessments and interventions are critical in managing the toxicities of this therapy.

Serotherapy

Scientists have demonstrated that all cells, including tumor cells, have antigens on their surface that allow that cell to be identified by the immune sys-

TABLE 14-6
SIDE EFFECTS OF INTERLEUKIN-2

Signs/Symptoms	Comments
Flulike Syndrome	
Fever	Peaks at 39–40°C
Chills	Onset 2–4 h after administration; rigor possible; may be produced by a hypothalamic-based stress response or by release of lymphokines/monokines
Myalgia/arthralgia	At high doses, may be due to accumulation of IL-2-induced cells or cytokine deposits in joint spaces
Headache	Enhanced by fever
Malaise	
Gastrointestinal	
Nausea, vomiting, diarrhea, mucositis, xerostomia, anorexia	Acute or chronic, dose-related, cumulative toxicities; may produce generalized inflammation of mucosal lining; may require prophylaxis for GI bleeding
Integumentary	
Dryness, erythematous rash, pruritus, desquamation	Pruritus may occur without rash
Neurologic/Psychological	
Confusion, irritability, impaired memory, expressive aphasia, sleep disturbances, depression, psychoses, hallucination	Mental status changes may be enhanced by anxiety, sleep deprivation, and/or an intensive care environment
Cardiovascular	
Capillary leak syndrome	Dose-related (>100,000 U/kg)
Peripheral edema, ascites, weight gain	Decreased systemic vascular resistance results in shift of fluid from intravascular to interstitial spaces, including organs
Arrhythmias	Mostly atrial; occasional supraventricular tachycardia, myocarditis, chest pain; rare sudden cardiac death
Hypotension	Causes decreased tissue oxygenation and renal blood flow
Pulmonary	
Dyspnea, tachypnea	Dose-related
Pulmonary edema	Acute at onset; results in decreased oxygen diffusion to alveoli; occasional pulmonary infiltrates on chest x-ray; excessive fluid replacement is contraindicated
Cough	
Nasal congestion	
Renal/Hepatic	
Oliguria, proteinuria, increased serum creatinine and BUN, elevated liver function tests (serum bilirubin, SGOT, SGPT, LDH, alkaline phosphatase)	Direct tubular-cell toxicity and decreased renal blood flow; cumulative dose effect
Hematologic	
Anemia/thrombocytopenia	Cumulative, dose-related; occasional abnormalities in coagulation studies

(Dudjack, L. A., & Yasko, J. M. [1990]. Biological response modifier therapy. In L. A. Dudjack & J. M. Yasko [Eds.], *Biological response modifiers: Symptom management*. St. Louis: Park Row.)

tem. These surface antigens on cancer cells are referred to as tumor-specific antigens or tumor-associated antigens. Serotherapy, a biotherapy approach using principles of humoral immunity, is the ability to deliver a treatment or label through an antibody to tumor cells by binding with the specific antigens on tumor cells (Barquiran, Dantis & McKerrow, 1996). This approach is based on what is known about the antibody–antigen interaction, such as the specificity of that reaction and the ability of the immune system to destroy the antigen–antibody complex.

In 1975, Kohler and Milstein developed the hybridoma technique for producing monoclonal antibodies (MoAbs), as illustrated in Figure 14-5 (Kohler & Milstein, 1975; Schindler, 1988). This is a complicated technique to produce antibodies from the same clone specific to an isolated antigen. All antibodies derived from a single clone are identical, hence the term *monoclonal antibody* (MoAb) (Goldenberg, 1995). This procedure involves injecting a specified antigen into a mouse to elicit the production of antibodies, then retrieving the de-

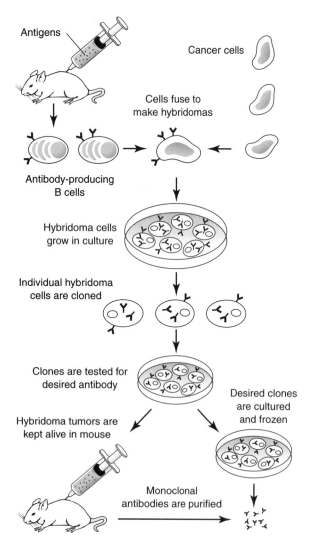

Figure 14-5 Use of hybridoma technique to make monoclonal antibodies.

sired antibody and fusing with a cancerous plasma cell to make a hybridoma, thus allowing for the continued production of the desired antibody.

Therapeutic possibilities of MoAbs are endless, but their production process is very complicated and many obstacles still impede their application. Potentially, MoAbs could be used to deliver toxic agents directly to tumor cells or for the identification of tumor cells (Oldham, 1983). A problem that researchers are working to solve is that tumor cells have the ability to shed their surface antigens, thus having these tumor antigens circulating in the bloodstream. If a patient receives an injection of MoAb for that tumor, the MoAb may bind to the circulating tumor antigens and not actually reach the tumor to bind with attached antigens (Goldenberg, 1995).

Two monoclonal antibodies, Rituxan and Herceptin, have been approved for therapeutic use in the oncology population. Rituxan is indicated for the treatment of patients with relapsed or refractory low-grade or follicular B-cell non-Hodgkin's lymphoma (Maloney et al., 1997). Herceptin is approved for treatment of metastatic breast cancer in patients who overexpress a certain protein receptor, HER2, and who have received chemotherapy to treat their metastatic disease (Neergaard, 1998).

An imaging MoAb, Oncoscint (Cytogen, Princeton, NJ), received FDA approval in 1993 for diagnostic imaging of colon and ovarian cancer. This MoAb is injected into a patient who has ovarian or colon cancer; because of the imaging particle attached to the antibody, when the MoAb binds with the patient's cancer cells, a radiograph is able to determine where the cancer is in the body (Cytogen Corp., 1997). Many clinical trials have tested MoAbs alone or in combination (conjugated) with radioisotopes, toxins, chemotherapy, or biologic agents. In vitro, they have been used to remove cancer cells from the bone marrow before autologous transplantation and to remove T-lymphocytes to lessen the incidence and/or severity of graft-versus-host disease (Goldenberg, 1995).

Administration and Toxicities

MoAbs are delivered intravenously to patients. Anaphylaxis, although rare, remains a potential risk associated with MoAb therapy, due to the delivery of a foreign serum (usually mouse) that contains the antibody into the body. Most associated toxicities are related to potential allergic responses or to what is conjugated with the antibody, such as a toxin or radioisotopes (Dillman, 1988). Nurses caring for these patients must be alert for hypersensitivity reactions and make certain that emergency drugs such as diphenhydramine, epinephrine, and solumedrol are at the bedside. If a patient shows signs of anaphylaxis, the first step is to stop the infusion, alert the physician immediately, and administer fluids and emergency drugs as ordered. Close monitoring of the patient's vital signs, including blood pressure and pulse, is mandatory.

Serum sickness, a delayed toxic effect caused by the accumulation of immune complexes (antibody–antigen formations), is rare but can occur 7 to 10 days after treatment. Joint pains, fever, rash, and generalized adenopathy are usually present. Treatments include hydration and nonsteroidal antiinflammatory agents and steroids.

Symptoms will resolve after the complexes are cleared from the circulation (Table 14-7).

Gene Therapy

Advances in genetics are allowing researchers to develop strategies to destroy cancer by correcting the genetic deficits and by manipulating genes to carry out cancer-killing activities (Robinson, Abernathy & Conrad, 1996). This approach, referred to as gene therapy, can be defined as an attempt to alter a patient's genetic material to fight disease. It is included in the biotherapy classification because of its ability to modify the body's biologic response by genetic manipulation. Gene therapy for cancer is complicated in that cancer is generally not thought of as a single genetic deficit but as a combination of gene mutations (Mitelmann, 1994).

It is helpful to understand the basics of genetics to comprehend how gene therapy may be use-

---

TABLE 14-7

SIDE EFFECTS OF MONOCLONAL ANTIBODIES

Signs/Symptoms	Comments
Anaphylaxis	
Generalized flush, urticaria, pallor, cyanosis, bronchospasm, hypotension, unconsciousness	Rare, even after HAMA* response is detectable; onset within 5 min of administration severe and life-threatening
Subacute allergic reactions	Infrequent and related to HAMA; onset within 24 h–1 wk unless otherwise noted
Flulike syndrome	
Fever, chills/rigor, diaphoresis, malaise, pallor, weakness	Onset 2–8 h after administration; most common of subacute signs/symptoms
Gastrointestinal	
Nausea, vomiting, diarrhea	
Integumentary	
Generalized erythema, urticaria, pruritus	
Cardiopulmonary	
Hypotension, dyspnea	
Delayed toxicity	
Serum sickness, flulike symptoms, malaise, arthralgia urticaria, pruritus, generalized adenopathy, pulmonary edema	Onset 2–4 wk after administration; caused by HAMA and circulating immune complexes deposited in tissues
Renal failure	Related to HAMA and caused by obstruction of renal tubules by immune complexes and tumor lysis metabolites

*HAMA = human antimouse antibodies.
(Dudjack, L.A., & Yasko, J.M. [1990]. Biological response modifier therapy. In L.A. Dudjack & J.M. Yasko [Eds.], *Biological response modifiers: Symptom management.* St. Louis: Park Row.)

ful as a cancer therapy. Genes are biologic units of heredity that determine simple traits, such as hair and eye color, as well as more subtle characteristics, such as the oxygen-carrying ability of the blood. Complex traits, such as IQ and physical strength, may be shaped by the interaction of several genes and environmental factors. Every human has more than 100,000 different genes that act as blueprints for producing specific enzymes or proteins that control physical characteristics and functions. Genes are located in the nucleus of each nucleated cell in the human body. Within the nucleus are 46 chromosomes, and each contains a single convoluted cord of DNA, the linear molecule that contains the genetic information (Engelking, 1995). A flaw in any of these genes or gene location can result in disease.

A group of genes, termed *oncogenes,* have been identified, which, on activation, can lead to the conversion of normal cells into cancer cells. Typically, oncogenes are involved in the growth and regulation of a cell. The mechanism for activating these genes is not fully understood. Another type of cancer-related gene, tumor suppressor gene, is known to suppress cellular growth and thus stop or control the action of the oncogene. However, when the tumor suppressor gene is damaged or absent, tumor development and growth are promoted due to the lack of ability to control the oncogene. Fewer than a dozen tumor suppressor genes have been identified; however, two of these, p53 and p16, are thought to be involved in the development of most of the human cancers (Weinberg, 1994).

With the explosion of knowledge in genetics and cancer development, coupled with DNA technology, the exploration of gene therapy is clinically possible in certain research settings. A variety of approaches are being tested in the laboratories and clinical research settings. Somatic cell gene therapy, an approach that involves the insertion of new therapeutic genetic information into a patient's nonreproductive cells, is the only type of gene therapy that is currently approved for human study. Germ-line gene therapy is not approved for clinical study in humans because it involves inserting new genetic information into reproductive cells (ova and sperm) with the intent of passing the changes onto the offspring (Wheeler, 1995). Some of the approaches in cancer therapy include gene

---

TABLE 14-8

APPROACHES OF GENE THERAPY IN CANCER TREATMENT

- Gene replacement—supply cells with healthy copies of missing or flawed genes
- Enhanced cytokine therapy—deliver cytokines by inserting their gene into either tumor cells or cells that infiltrate tumors
- Drug-targeting therapy—inject a tumor with a gene that renders the tumor cell vulnerable to a drug
- Oncogene inhibition—delivera synthetic agent capable of blocking the translation of an oncogene
- Gene marking—mark cells with a drug-resistant gene to determine if transduced cells are sensitive to therapy

---

replacement therapy, enhanced cytokine delivery, and drug targeting therapy (Table 14-8).

There are unknowns associated with any form of new therapy, and gene therapy is no exception. Possible associated risks include the chance of incorrectly inserting a gene that would trigger the development of cancer or other disease. With gene replacement therapy, transferred genes could be overexpressed, producing an excess of the missing protein and leading to disease (Hwu, 1995). Other risks are more involved with how the new genetic information is inserted into the DNA. A vector is what is used to carry the new information into the patient's genes. Typically in cancer studies, a deactivated retrovirus is most frequently used as the vector, because it will only infect dividing cells such as cancer cells. By infecting the cancer cells, the deactivated retrovirus, carrying the new genetic information, is able to attach to the cancer cell and empty its new genetic content into the cell's DNA. As the cancer cell then divides, each of its new offspring will contain the new genetic information. Risks associated with this include the chance that the retrovirus was not deactivated and might transfer its own genetic information (Figure 14-6) (Pizzo, 1993).

The possible benefits of gene therapy in cancer treatment may not be immediate; however, as our knowledge and understanding of molecular biology increase, applications for therapeutic interventions may be realized. Social and ethical issues have arisen from the possibility that genetically altering human egg and sperm cells could alter human genetic inheritance. Gene therapy for cancer therapy does not yet involve alterations in germ

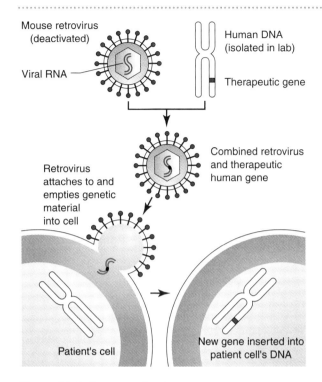

Mouse retrovirus (deactivated)

Viral RNA

Human DNA (isolated in lab)

Therapeutic gene

Combined retrovirus and therapeutic human gene

Retrovirus attaches to and empties genetic material into cell

Patient's cell

New gene inserted into patient cell's DNA

Figure 14-6 Gene transfer therapy.

cells; however, this may become an issue as more is learned about the genetic influence on cancer development (Jenkins, Wheeler & Albright, 1994).

Conclusion

Biologicals are frequently a routine part of the care and treatment of patients with cancer. They can vary widely in their actions, clinical applications, and side effects. Although they present challenges for the nurse to be able to fully understand their therapeutic abilities, it is imperative that nurses keep current on the roles and side effects of biologicals in cancer therapy. Every week articles appear in the lay press regarding new developments in biotechnology. Patients and their families often turn to the nurse to explain or interpret new information they have read about cancer therapy. This is a complex, difficult area to understand, often involving immunology, physics, genetics, and molecular biology. Nurses must meet this challenge by obtaining the education they need to better understand this emerging technology, so they can educate their pa-

tients, make astute observations of patients receiving BRMs, and participate in research to ensure the advancement of nursing care for these patients.

REFERENCES

Abernathy, E. (1997). Biotherapy. In C. Varricchio (Ed.), *A cancer source book for nurses* (pp. 122–138). Sudburg, MA: Jones and Bartlett.

Abernathy, E. (1994). Biotechnology: Exploring the fourth modality of cancer treatment. *Quality of Life: A Nursing Challenge, 3*(2), 30–38.

Balkwill, F. R. (1989). *Cytokines in cancer therapy.* New York: Oxford.

Barquiran, D. C., Dantis, L., & McKerrow, J. (1996). Monoclonal antibodies: Innovations in diagnosis and therapy. *Seminars in Oncology Nursing, 12*, 130–141.

Borden, E. C. (1992). Interferons: Expanding therapeutic roles. *New England Journal of Medicine, 326*, 1491.

DeLaPena, L., Tomaszewski, J., Bernato, L., & Kryk, J. (1996). Interleukins. *Oncology Nursing Forum, 19*(1), 6075.

DiJulio, D. (1991). Hematopoiesis: An overview. *Oncology Nursing Forum 18*(Suppl.), 3–6.

Dillman, J. B. (1988). Toxicity of monoclonal antibodies in the treatment of cancer. *Seminars in Oncology Nursing, 4*, 107–111.

Dudjack, L. A., & Yasko, J. M. (1990). Biological response modifier therapy. In L. A. Dudjack & J. M. Yasko (Eds.), *Biological response modifiers: Symptom management* (pp. 3–24). St. Louis: Park Row.

Engelking, C. (1995). The human genome exposed: A glimpse of promise, predicament, and impact on practice. *Oncology Nursing Forum, 22*(suppl.), 3–9.

Farrell, M. (1996). Biotherapy and the oncology nurse. *Seminars in Oncology Nursing, 12*, 82–88.

Goldenberg, D. M. (1995). New developments in monoclonal antibodies for cancer detection and treatments. *CA: A Cancer Journal for Clinicians, 44*, 43–64.

Hood, L. E., & Abernathy, E. (1996). Biological response modifiers. In R. McCorkle, M. Grant, M. Frank-Stromborg & S. Baird (Eds.), *Cancer nursing: A comprehensive textbook* (2nd ed., pp. 434–457). Philadelphia: W. B. Saunders.

Hwu, P. (1995). *Gene therapy of cancer. Principles and practices of oncology updates* (vol. 9, pp. 1–13). Philadelphia: J. B. Lippincott.

Isaacs, A., & Lindemann, J. (1957). Virus interference. *Proceedings of the Royal Society of London. Series B: Biological Sciences, 147*, 258–267.

Jassak, P. (1995). An overview of biotherapy. In P. T. Reiger (Ed.), *Biotherapy: A comprehensive overview* (pp. 3–13). Boston: Jones and Bartlett.

Jenkins, J., Wheeler, V., & Albright, L. (1994). Gene therapy for cancer. *Cancer Nursing, 17*, 447–456.

Kohler, G., & Milstein, C. (1975). Continuous cultures of fused cells secreting antibody of predetermined specificity. *Nature, 256*, 495–496.

Maloney, D. G., Grillo-Lopez, A. J., White, C. A., et al. (1997). IDEC-C2B8 (Rituximab) anti-CD20 monoclonal antibody therapy in patients with relapsed low-grade non-Hodgkin's lymphoma. *Blood, 90*(6), 2188–2195.

Mihich, E., & Fefer, A. (Eds.). (1983). *Biological response modifiers: A report* (pp. 3–31). National Cancer Institute Monograph No. 63 (NIH Publication No. 83-2606). Washington, DC: U. S. Department of Health and Human Services, Public Health Service. National Institutes of Health.

Mitelmann, F. (1994). Chromosomes, genes and cancer. *CA: A Cancer Journal for Clinicians, 44,* 133–135.

Neergaard, L. FDA approves new breast cancer drug. *AP Online,* accessed 26 September 1998.

Oldham, R. (1983). Monoclonal antibody in cancer treatment. *Journal of Clinical Oncology, 1*(9), 582–590.

Oldham, R. K. (1991). Cancer biotherapy: General principles. In R. Oldham (Ed.), *Principles of cancer biotherapy* (2nd ed., pp. 1–22). New York: Marcel Dekker.

Oldham, R. K. (1985). Biologicals for cancer treatment: Interferons. *Hospital Practice,* December, 71–95.

OncoScint (satumonmab pendetide) package insert. Princeton, NJ: Cytogen Corp, 1997.

Parkinson, D. R., & Sznol, M. (1995). High-dose interleukin 2 in the treatment of metastatic renal cell carcinoma. *Seminars in Oncology Nursing, 22,* 61–66.

Pitler, L. (1996). Hematopoietic growth factors in clinical practice. *Seminars in Oncology Nursing, 12,* 115–129.

Pizzo, P. A. (Ed.). (1993). *NIH Observer,* Sept/Oct, 13.

Post-White, J. (1996a). The immune system. *Seminars in Oncology Nursing, 12,* 89–96.

Post-White, J. (1996b). Principles of immunology. In R. McCorkle, M. Grant, M. Frank-Stromborg & S. B. Baird (Eds.), *Cancer nursing: A comprehensive textbook* (2nd ed., chap. 14). Philadelphia: W. B. Saunders.

Rao, S. V., & Wadler, S. (1992). Current use of interferons. *Contemporary Oncology,* December, 44–49.

Rieger, P. T., & Haeuber, D. (1995). A new approach to managing chemotherapy related anemia: Nursing implications of Epoetin alfa. *Oncology Nursing Forum 22,* 71–81.

Robinson, K., Abernathy, E., & Conrad, K. J. (1996). Gene therapy of cancer. *Seminars in Oncology Nursing, 12,* 142–151.

Schindler, L. W. (1988). *Understanding the immune system* (p. 88). Bethesda, MD: U. S. Department of Health and Human Services; NIH 28.

Sell, S. (1987). Introduction to immunology. In S. Sell (Ed.), *Basic immunology: Immune mechanisms in health and disease* (pp. 3–17). New York: Elsevier.

Skalla, K. (1996). The interferons. *Seminars in Oncology Nursing, 12,* 97–105.

Stadler, W. M., & Vogelzang, N. J. (1995). Low-dose interleukin 2 in the treatment of metastatic renal cell carcinoma. *Seminars in Oncology Nursing, 22,* 67–73.

Sznol, M., & Parkinson, D. R. (1994). Clinical applications of IL-2. *Oncology, 8,* 61–71.

Tepler, I., Elias, L., Smith, J. W. II, et al. (1996). A randomized placebo-controlled trial of recombinant human interleukin-II in cancer patients with severe thrombocytopenia due to chemotherapy. *Blood, 8,* 3607–3614.

Weinberg, R. (1994). Oncogenes and tumor suppressor genes. *CA: A Cancer Journal for Clinicians, 44,* 160–170.

Wheeler, V. (1996). Interleukins: The search for an anticancer therapy. *Seminars in Oncology Nursing, 12,* 106–114.

Wheeler, V. S. (1995). Gene therapy: Current strategies and future applications. *Oncology Nursing Forum, 22*(Suppl.), 21–26.

Oncologic Emergencies

CHAPTER
15

Barbara Fristoe

Oncologic emergencies are an assortment of complications often associated with advanced cancer or certain types of cancer. Early symptoms of serious or life-threatening conditions may be difficult to distinguish from problems common to cancer patients, such as pain, nausea, and headache. In caring for cancer patients, it is important for nurses to recognize and understand these complications. Accurate assessment, leading to prompt treatment, can positively affect patient outcomes.

Cancer emergencies are generally classified according to the system affected, such as cardiovascular, neurologic, metabolic, and hematologic emergencies. This chapter will discuss some of these complications as well as typical signs and symptoms, assessment, and treatment.

Cardiovascular Emergencies

Pericardial Disease and Tamponade

The pericardial sac surrounds the heart and consists of an outer parietal layer and inner visceral layer or membrane, with a small amount of fluid (15 to 50 mL) between the two layers. The pericardium is thought to serve a number of functions, including prevention of sudden dilatation of the heart with exercise or hypervolemia and maintenance of the position of the heart and great vessels. It decreases friction between the heart, lungs, and mediastinal structures, as well as helps to prevent spread of infection from the lungs

(Braunwald, 1994). Accumulation of fluid in the pericardial sac in excess of the normally small amount leads to the development of a pericardial effusion.

Spread of cancer to the heart occurs most often in advanced cancers of the lung, breast, gastrointestinal (GI) tract, melanoma, sarcoma, and in Hodgkin's and non-Hodgkin's lymphoma (Hancock, 1990; Kralstein & Frishman, 1987; Theologides, 1978). Cancer can spread to the pericardium by direct tumor extension or through the bloodstream, but the most common method of spread to the heart is thought to be through the lymphatic system, mainly from the mediastinal lymph nodes that are in close proximity to the heart (Hancock, 1990; Kralstein & Frishman, 1987). Pericardial fluid accumulates due to obstruction of lymphatics and veins that drain the heart (Theologides, 1978). The excessive accumulation of fluid in the pericardial sac interferes with cardiac contraction. Pericardial effusions may result from tissue damage with both chemotherapy and radiation therapy. Other causes include infection, pericarditis, and renal failure.

The pericardium is able to stretch to accommodate the buildup of fluid. Slowly developing effusions may cause few symptoms, whereas rapidly accumulating effusions can cause more severe symptoms. Cardiac tamponade occurs when the amount of fluid in the pericardial cavity obstructs blood flow to the ventricles leading to decreased cardiac output and, ultimately, to cardiac collapse. The occurrence of cardiac tamponade can be life threatening, requiring emergency treatment.

257

Symptoms of pericardial effusion can be relatively nonspecific and may develop over time. The most common patient symptoms are respiratory: dyspnea, cough, and orthopnea (Hancock, 1990). Chest pain may be present but may be described more as discomfort than pain. Pericardial effusion and even tamponade may not be obvious on physical and cardiac examination. Tachycardia may be present, but faint heart sounds and a pericardial friction rub are less common (Hancock, 1990).

Diagnosis

Physical assessment of the patient with pericardial effusion or tamponade may reveal jugular venous distention and liver enlargement (Braunwald, 1994; Steinherz & Yahalom, 1993). On cardiac examination, tachycardia, faint or muffled heart sounds, and pericardial friction rub may or may not be present (Stauffer, 1998). The paradoxical pulse, a decrease of systolic blood pressure more than 10 mm Hg during inspiration, is a cardinal sign of cardiac tamponade. This sign may be difficult to elicit due to concurrent cardiac or respiratory problems (Hancock, 1990).

Several tests are helpful in the diagnosis of pericardial effusions and tamponade. Electrocardiographic (ECG) changes consisting of ST-T segment changes and decreased QRS voltage are common. On chest radiograph, a pericardial effusion or tamponade shows as an enlarged, globular cardiac silhouette. Pleural effusions may also be evident on chest radiograph. Echocardiography is the best method for diagnosing and monitoring patients with pericardial effusions and tamponade. Analysis of fluid removed by pericardiocentesis, inserting a needle or catheter into the pericardial sac, may be necessary for definitive diagnosis. Fluid is cultured to determine if infection is present and sent for cytologic examination to determine the presence of cancer cells.

Treatment

Patients with symptomatic pericardial effusions or pericardial tamponade require immediate treatment to drain the pericardial fluid. Pericardiocentesis alone can be used to drain fluid and can be life saving. However, unless the underlying cancer is successfully treated or there is definitive treatment to prevent reaccumulation, fluid is likely to reaccumulate.

Pericardiocentesis with catheter placement for drainage and instillation of a sclerosing agent is a relatively safe and effective treatment (Kopecky, Callahan, Tajik & Seward, 1986; Kralstein & Frishman, 1987; Shepherd, 1997; Theologides, 1978). A pericardial catheter is placed under echocardiographic guidance and left in place for several days. After the fluid is drained, a sclerosing agent can be instilled into the pericardial space. Sclerosing initiates an inflammatory response, which causes the parietal and visceral membranes to adhere to each other and prevents further fluid reaccumulation. Chemotherapy drugs such as bleomycin, mitoxantrone, thiotepa, cisplatin, and vinblastine are used as sclerosing agents. Tetracycline and doxycycline are used but have no anticancer activity (Hancock, 1990; Kralstein & Frishman, 1987; Shepherd, 1997; Theologides, 1978).

Surgical procedures may be used to remove pericardial fluid and to prevent reaccumulation of an effusion. Pericardiectomy, removal of varying amounts by thoracotomy, requires a major surgical procedure (Tura & Danielson, 1990). This is often considered inappropriate treatment for many cancer patients who may be debilitated with advanced disease. Creation of a pericardial "window" to allow fluid drainage can be accomplished by less risky surgical procedures. Thoracoscopy allows direct visualization through a minimal thoracic incision and is often used for the creation of a pericardial "window" (Hancock, 1990; Kralstein & Frishman, 1987; Shepherd, 1997). Pericardiocentesis with placement of a drain by a subxiphoid approach is often effective with no further accumulation of fluid (Kralstein & Frishman, 1987).

The overall condition of the patient is considered when treatment for pericardial effusion and tamponade is undertaken. Effective palliative treatment is available for patients with malignant effusions. Some patients may also respond well to chemotherapy or hormonal treatment with good control of their underlying cancer. However, long-term survival is unusual in patients with pericardial effusions or tamponade because it generally represents advanced metastatic disease. Prolonged survival is more likely when an effusion is treatment related rather than a malignant effusion.

Superior Vena Cava Syndrome

The superior vena cava (SVC) drains the blood vessels of the head, neck, arms, and upper chest. It is a large but thin-walled vessel that is easily obstructed or compressed. The SVC is located in the mediastinum and is surrounded by more rigid structures such as the sternum, trachea, aorta, and mediastinal lymph nodes. Superior vena cava syndrome (SVCS) results from obstruction of the blood flow through the vessel. The most common cause of SVCS is malignancy with compression of the vessel by a tumor or lymph node mass. Superior vena caval thrombosis due to a central venous catheter can also cause obstruction.

Superior vena caval obstruction occurs most frequently in patients with lung cancer, particularly small cell lung cancer (Sculier et al., 1986). It may also occur in lymphoma, metastatic carcinoma, thymic carcinoma, and mediastinal germ cell cancer. Compression or obstruction of the vessel may result in increased venous pressure in the head and neck and upper extremities. This leads to common symptoms related to SVCS, including dyspnea, headache, feeling of fullness in the face or head, visual changes, and mental status changes. Facial edema as well as edema of the upper arms or chest may be present. Collateral veins in the neck or chest may be easily visible (Perez, Presant & Van Amburg, 1978).

For many years, superior vena caval obstruction was thought to represent a life-threatening emergency that required immediate treatment, often before a clear diagnosis of the cause of the obstruction was obtained. Radiation therapy was used empirically to relieve the obstruction and associated symptoms. However, once mediastinal radiation is completed, it may be difficult to obtain a definite histologic diagnosis from the irradiated area. More recently, studies have shown that in all but the most severe cases, it is preferable to obtain a tissue diagnosis before treating the underlying malignancy with the most effective therapy (Ahmann, 1984). In some situations, such as small cell lung cancer, chemotherapy may be used instead of radiation therapy. Metal stents can be placed percutaneously in the superior vena cava with effective relief of obstruction and symptoms (Nicholson, Ettles, Arnold, Greenstone & Dyet, 1997). Patients with mental status changes or other evidence of increased intracranial pressure, or upper airway obstruction will require emergency mediastinal radiation.

Neurologic Emergencies

Spinal Cord Compression

Epidural spinal cord compression (SCC) occurs in approximately 5% of patients who die of cancer (Byrne, 1992; Ratanatharathorn & Powers, 1991; Turner, Marosszeky, Timms & Boyages, 1991) and is usually an indication of late-stage disease. Epidural tumors causing SCC most frequently represent metastases from cancers of the lung, breast, and prostate. SCC can also occur with lymphoma, melanoma, kidney cancer, sarcoma, and multiple myeloma (Byrne, 1992; Ratanatharathorn & Powers, 1991). SCC usually develops as an extension of metastatic tumor in the vertebral column but may also arise from tumor spread through intravertebral foramina or, less commonly, arises directly in the epidural space (Byrne, 1992).

The thoracic spine is most often affected with SCC, occurring in approximately 70% of the cases. The lumbar spine is affected in 20% and the cervical spine in 10% of the patients with SCC (Byrne, 1992). In the thoracic spine, metastatic tumor that develops in the vertebral body compresses the spinal cord. Occasionally, there is fracture of the bone that directly impinges on the spinal cord. Metastatic tumor compression of the spinal cord leads to edema of the cord, ischemia, and loss of myelin (Byrne, 1992). Motor and sensory loss below the level of the compression as well as loss of bowel and bladder control can result. SCC can be a devastating complication of cancer. If left untreated or if diagnosis is delayed, paralysis and loss of bowel and bladder function can occur. In some cases, prompt treatment can reverse neurologic deficits.

The most frequent initial symptom of SCC is pain (Bruckman & Bloomer, 1978; Byrne, 1992). The pain may be localized in the spine, in the spinal nerve roots, or referred to the chest, abdomen, or extremities (Bruckman & Bloomer, 1978; Byrne, 1992). Pain associated with SCC is often worse with movement, with cough or having a bowel movement, with neck flexion, and when lying down (Ratanatharathorn & Powers, 1991). It is usually present with percussion or palpation of the spine over the involved area. Typically, the pain worsens over days to weeks. Motor deficits usually follow the onset of pain. Weakness is most often present in the lower extremities due to the distribution of spinal metastases to the thoracic and lumbar spine (Ratanatharathorn & Powers, 1991). Sensory deficit may occur at the same time or later than motor deficit. Patients may report numbness and tingling in the lower extremities. Urinary retention may be an earlier symptom of SCC, whereas loss of bowel function is a late finding (Bruckman & Bloomer, 1978).

Nursing assessment for SCC is multifaceted. Patient history reveals cancer diagnosis and previous treatment. Pain assessment for SCC includes onset, duration, location, quality, intensity, and aggravating and relieving factors. It is also important to assess the meaning of pain for that patient as well as effects of pain on relationships and activities of daily living. Physical examination with palpation and/or percussion of the spine can help locate areas affected by SCC. Sensory deficits are assessed by testing presence or absence of pain, and sharp, dull, hot, and cold sensations. Muscle strength can be documented for major muscle groups in the upper and lower extremities.

When SCC is suspected, a diagnostic workup may include a plain radiograph of the spine. Although not specific for SCC, the radionuclide bone scan is more specific in determining vertebral bone metastases than plain radiographs. Magnetic resonance imaging (MRI) is the most sensitive diagnostic imaging examination for SCC. MRI can detect epidural compression as well as vertebral bone metastases.

Prompt treatment of epidural SCC is essential to maintain neurologic function. SCC is usually treated with a combination of corticosteroids and radiation therapy. Dexamethasone is used to reduce edema and pain and improve neurologic function. The optimum dose of dexamethasone is unknown. Proposed treatment dosage ranges from a loading dose of 10 to 100 mg intravenously, followed by 4 to 6 mg orally four times a day (Byrne, 1992). Dexamethasone doses are tapered during treatment. Radiation is delivered in daily increments to a total of 3000 to 4500 cGy over about a 3-week period.

Although radiation therapy is most often employed to treat SCC, surgery is used in some cases. Multiple areas of SCC make surgery impractical. However, surgery is considered in several situations: (1) when the cause of epidural compression is unknown and there is no known diagnosis of cancer; (2) when there is progressive deterioration of neurologic function during radiation therapy despite high doses of corticosteroids; (3) if there is evidence of compression at a previously irradiated area; or (4) if there is spinal instability or bone applying pressure directly on the spinal cord. Additionally, surgery is indicated when a tumor is not responsive to radiation therapy (Bruckman & Bloomer, 1978; Ratanatharathorn & Powers, 1991). Although surgery alleviates SCC more rapidly than radiation, it does not eliminate microscopic foci of tumor cells. In most cases, surgery is followed by radiation therapy at similar doses to those used for primary treatment of SCC.

The goals of treatment of SCC are pain relief and maintenance of neurologic function. If left untreated, SCC progresses to motor and sensory loss with resulting paralysis and loss of bowel and bladder control. Most commonly, the patient's neurologic status at the onset of treatment is the best predictor of outcome (Harris, Sutcliffe & Robinson, 1996; Johnston, 1993; Ratanatharathorn & Powers, 1991; Turner et al., 1991). In one prospective study, Turner and associates reported that 81% of patients with SCC who were ambulatory before treatment were ambulatory after treatment, whereas only 16.5% of patients who were nonambulatory regained the ability to walk. In another study of 153 consecutive patients with SCC, 21% of those paralyzed at the time of diagnoses regained ambulatory function (Helwig-Larson, 1996).

Brain Metastases

Parenchymal brain metastases are the result of hematogenous spread from the primary tumor and occur in 20% to 30% of people with systemic cancer (Sundaresan & Galicich, 1985; Wright et al., 1993). Cancers of the lung and breast most commonly spread to the brain, but GI and genitourinary cancers, melanoma, and cancer of unknown primary may also metastasize to the brain. Many tumors that metastasize to bone, such as lung, breast, and prostate, can spread directly from the skull and compress brain parenchyma. Solitary metastatic tumors occur in about 50% of people, and two identifiable tumors are present in about 20% (Patchell et al., 1990).

Symptoms develop as the lesion increases in size, causing increased intracranial pressure. Nonspecific symptoms associated with increased intracranial pressure include headache, blurred vision, diplopia, nausea, and vomiting. The tumor mass interferes with the integrity of the blood–brain barrier by disrupting tight intercellular junctions and capillary walls (Weissman, 1988). This results in plasma leakage from the capillaries, causing edema around the tumor. Tumor mass and related edema compress adjacent areas of the brain, producing localized neurologic signs and symptoms such as motor and sensory changes, ataxia, dysphagia, personality changes, and seizures.

Leptomeningeal spread of cancer is less common than intracranial metastases. Leptomeningeal metastasis or meningeal carcinomatosis refers to tumor seeding of the meninges and cerebrospinal fluid (CSF). Leukemia; lymphoma; cancers of the breast, lung, and GI tract; and melanoma are most likely to spread to the meninges. Often, signs and symptoms of leptomeningeal metastasis correspond to more than one site in the cerebrospinal axis: the brain, cranial nerves, or spine. Typical symptoms include headache, ataxia, mental status changes, nausea, vomiting, diplopia, facial weakness, spinal pain, lower extremity weakness, and paresthesias (Wasserstrom, Glass & Posner, 1982).

Diagnosis

Parenchymal brain tumors are best diagnosed by contrast-enhanced computed tomography (CT) or MRI scan. The MRI is generally the favored imaging study. When a patient presents with a parenchymal tumor with no known systemic cancer, an evaluation to determine the site of the primary tumor is warranted. If no primary tumor is identified, the brain mass may be biopsied to determine if it represents metastatic disease or a primary brain tumor (Awan & Weichelsbaum, 1990).

Diagnosis of leptomeningeal metastasis is suspected when neurologic signs and symptoms related to involvement of more than one level of the cerebrospinal axis exist with no radiographic evidence of a parenchymal brain tumor or epidural spinal metastases (Kim & Bernstein, 1996; Wasserstrom et al., 1982). MRI of the brain and spinal cord is used in diagnosis. Cytologic analysis of CSF after lumbar puncture is performed to determine the presence of cancer cells, although malignant cells may not always be present in the CSF (Wasserstrom et al., 1982; Wujcik, 1983). Other characteristics of the CSF in meningeal carcinomatosis are elevated white blood cell count, increased protein loevels, and decreased glucose levels.

Treatment

The median survival for patients with no treatment for brain metastases is 1 month (Hoegler, 1997; Patchell et al., 1990; Weissman, 1988). When brain metastases are diagnosed, corticosteroid treatment is initiated to decrease edema. Dexamethasone is given in divided doses, up to 16 mg/day, generally with prompt relief of symptoms. Steroids are then tapered during the course of treatment. Patients are completely tapered off steroids or are maintained on the lowest dose that effectively controls neurologic symptoms. Anticonvulsants are given to patients with seizures. With steroid treatment alone, the expected survival with brain metastases is 2 months (Patchell et al., 1990; Weissman, 1988).

The best method of treating brain metastases is unknown. The number of intracranial tumors, the patient's age, and the extent and control of extracranial disease are important factors in determining treatment (Black, 1993). The standard treatment for brain metastases is whole brain radiation. The median survival with radiation therapy is 3 to 6 months (Patchell et al., 1990). Although most patients with brain metastases have advanced disease, approximately 50% will die of progressive intracranial disease (Hoegler, 1997). Surgical resection of a single metastasis to the brain followed by radiation therapy has been shown in two randomized studies to be more effective than radiation therapy alone. Patchell and associates (1990) found median survival to be 40 weeks with surgery and radiation therapy as opposed to 15 weeks with radiation alone. In a study by Noordijk and coworkers (1994), the median survival of patients treated with surgery and radiation was 10 months compared with 6 months in patients treated with radiation alone.

Stereotactic radiosurgery is a newer method of treating brain metastases that delivers high doses of radiation to a defined tumor area while sparing surrounding tissue. Radiosurgery may be used in patients with a single unresectable brain metastasis, with multiple or recurrent metastases, or in patients who have previously received whole-brain radiation (Adler, Cox, Kaplan & Martin, 1992; Breneman et al., 1997; Kim & Bernstein, 1996). Patients also receive whole-brain irradiation before or after radiosurgery unless they have been previously treated for brain metastasis. Currently, both surgical resection and radiosurgery are used as primary therapy for single brain metastases because longer survival and improvement in function are associated with both treatment methods.

Whole-brain radiation is associated with both acute and long-term toxicities. The most common acute side effects are alopecia and skin changes with erythema or skin breakdown. Less commonly, patients may experience headache, nausea, weakness, and otitis media (Kim & Bernstein, 1996). One to 4 months after whole-brain radiation, some patients experience a somnolence syndrome characterized by increased fatigue. Late effects of cerebral radiation may consist of dementia and neurologic deterioration (Kim & Bernstein, 1996).

Treatment of leptomeningeal carcinomatosis may include intrathecal chemotherapy and radiation to selected symptomatic sites (Kim & Bernstein, 1996; Shapiro, Posner, Ushio, Chernik & Young, 1977; Wasserstrom et al., 1982; Wujcik, 1983). Methotrexate and cytarabine are the chemotherapeutic agents most often administered intrathecally by lumbar puncture or into an Ommaya reservoir, an implanted port with a catheter that is placed in the lateral ventricle (Kim & Bernstein, 1996; Wasserstrom et al., 1982; Wujcik, 1983). Systemic chemotherapy is of little use in treating the CSF.

Treatment of brain metastases depends on several factors, including the patient's age and functional status, the extent and control of primary cancer, and the number of intracranial metastases. Good palliation of brain metastases is possible with the use of surgery, radiosurgery, and whole-brain radiation.

Metabolic Emergencies

Tumor Lysis Syndrome

Tumor lysis syndrome refers to rapid cellular breakdown with release of intracellular electrolytes and nucleic acids. The breakdown of malignant cells results in the release of purines, potassium, and phosphate. This may occur spontaneously in rapidly proliferating tumors or after chemotherapy (Sklarin & Markham, 1995). Pretreatment elevation of lactate dehydrogenase (LDH) and the uric acid level, as well as renal insufficiency, are risk factors for tumor lysis syndrome. Elevated levels of LDH and uric acid are indicators of a high tumor burden.

Tumor lysis syndrome is most commonly associated with rapidly growing, bulky tumors that are highly sensitive to chemotherapy treatment. Typically, these include acute lymphoblastic leukemia, Burkitt's lymphoma, and other high-grade aggressive lymphomas. Tumor lysis syndrome may also occur in acute myelogenous leukemia and chronic myelogenous leukemia in blast crisis. This syndrome has also been reported less frequently in other cancers, including breast cancer, chronic lymphocytic leukemia, metastatic seminoma, metastatic meduloblastoma, and small cell lung cancer (Drakos, Bar-Ziv & Catane, 1994; McCrosky, Mosher, Spencer, Prendergast & Longo, 1990; Sklarin & Markham, 1995).

The metabolic abnormalities associated with tumor lysis are hyperuricemia, hyperkalemia, hyperphosphatemia, and hypocalcemia. Excess uric acid and calcium phosphate may precipitate in the kidney, leading to renal insufficiency or failure. The development of renal insufficiency or failure worsens metabolic abnormalities. Hyperkalemia and hypocalcemia associated with tumor lysis can cause cardiac arrhythmia.

The diagnosis of tumor lysis syndrome is based on analysis of laboratory and clinical data. Risk factors for tumor lysis syndrome include pretreatment elevation of uric acid and LDH, renal insufficiency or failure, and volume depletion. Spontaneous tumor lysis may occur before cancer treatment is initiated, and hyperkalemia, hyperphosphatemia, and hypocalcemia are present at the time of diagnosis. Tumor lysis syndrome related to cancer treatment typically occurs within the first 72 hours of treatment.

Treatment

Identification of patients at risk for tumor lysis syndrome allows for initiation of preventive measures. Evaluation of renal function, hydration, and electrolytes allows for correction of abnormalities. Allopurinol is given to prevent the conversion of xanthines, products of the breakdown of purine, to uric acid. Hyperuricemia can lead to precipitation of uric acid crystals in the renal tubules. Alkalinization of the urine increases the solubility of uric acid and prevents its precipitation in the kidneys. Alkalinization is usually accomplished with the addition of sodium bicarbonate ($NaHCO_3$) to intravenous (IV) fluid. Fifty to 100 mEq of $NaHCO_3$ are added to each liter of 5% dextrose in water and administered at 200 to 300 mL/h to restore volume, to prevent precipitation of uric acid, and to reduce risk of renal failure (Arrambide & Toto, 1993).

For potential hyperkalemia, IV potassium supplementation should be avoided and patients should be monitored for cardiac arrhythmias. Hyperkalemia can be treated with a sodium–potassium exchange resin such as kayexalate (Arrambide & Toto, 1993; Warrell, 1993). Serum electrolytes, including potassium, calcium, phosphorous, and uric acid, should be monitored daily during treatment. Hypocalcemia causes increased nerve excitability with clinical manifestations that include skeletal muscle cramps, numbness and tingling, laryngeal spasm, carpopedal spasm, tetany, and abdominal spasms and cramps. Hypocalcemia can be treated with IV calcium gluconate (Arrambide & Toto, 1993). Hemodialysis should be considered early in the course of tumor lysis syndrome if the patient is not responding to more conservative treatment. This potentially life-threatening condition should be treated aggressively because the metabolic abnormalities associated with tumor lysis are easily reversed and the underlying tumor may be very responsive to treatment (Hande & Garrow, 1993).

Hypercalcemia

Hypercalcemia in malignancy refers to an elevated serum calcium level greater than 10.5 mg/dL. Hypercalcemia occurs in approximately 10% to 20% of patients with cancer and is seen most often in advanced stages of disease. Cancers most commonly associated with hypercalcemia are metastatic breast cancer, non–small cell lung cancer, multiple myeloma, squamous cell carcinomas of the head and neck, renal cell carcinoma, lymphoma, and gynecologic cancers (Goni & Tolis, 1993; Mundy, 1990). The exact mechanism of hypercalcemia is not entirely clear, and there appear to be different mechanisms in different malignancies (Ritch, 1990).

Serum calcium in healthy adults is maintained between 8.5 and 10.5 mg/dL. Serum calcium is highly bound to serum proteins, especially albumin (Porth, 1994). If the serum protein level is high, as in myeloma, or if serum albumin is low, as in malnourishment, the calcium level will reflect this. Formulas are available to estimate serum calcium when the albumin level is high or low. A measurement of ionized or free calcium will give a more accurate assessment of the degree of hypercalcemia.

Regulation of calcium is accomplished by complex mechanisms that include hormonal influence, GI absorption, bone activity, and kidney absorption and excretion. The hormonal regulators in calcium homeostasis are vitamin D (1,25-dihydroxyvitamin D), parathyroid hormone (PTH), and calcitonin. Normally, the amount of calcium absorbed from the GI tract is equal to the amount excreted by the kidneys (Mundy, 1990; Porth, 1994).

Approximately 99% of calcium is located in the bone and functions as storage for serum calcium. Bone undergoes a constant process of breakdown (resorption) by osteoclasts and formation by osteoblasts. A low serum calcium level stimulates the parathyroid gland to produce and release PTH. PTH maintains serum calcium in a normal range by regulating both bone resorption and calcium reabsorption from the kidney. It also stimulates vitamin D production in the kidney. PTH is regulated by a negative feedback loop. When the plasma calcium level is returned to normal, the production of PTH is inhibited (Mundy, 1990).

Calcitonin is a hormone produced and secreted by the thyroid gland. Its secretion is regulated by the serum calcium level that supplies the thyroid gland. It regulates serum calcium levels by inhibiting bone resorption and provides a feedback system that opposes the effects of PTH.

The kidneys participate in calcium regulation by controlling calcium excretion and reabsorption. The normal kidney filters large amounts of calcium in the glomerulus and selectively reabsorbs it in the renal tubules. PTH increases calcium excretion in the distal tubule. Although the kidney can increase calcium excretion approximately fivefold, this is usually not enough to counteract the hypercalcemia of malignancy (Mundy, 1990). Renal insufficiency can exacerbate hypercalcemia because of decreased ability of the glomerulus to filter calcium. With volume depletion, there is increased proximal tubular reabsorption of sodium as the kidney attempts to restore fluid volume. Calcium is reabsorbed along with the sodium (Ritch, 1990).

Clinical Manifestations

Because calcium is important in regulating many cellular functions, the effect of hypercalcemia may be evident in the GI, neurologic, renal, cardiovascular, and musculoskeletal systems. Early symptoms of hypercalcemia are often nonspecific and may include fatigue, lethargy, anorexia, nausea, constipation, and polyuria (Bajournas, 1990). These symptoms may be difficult to distinguish from symptoms of advanced cancer or cancer treatment. The severity of symptoms may be more related to how quickly the calcium became elevated than to the degree of elevation (Goni & Tolis, 1993).

Decreased autonomic nervous system activity in hypercalcemia affects the neuromuscular and GI systems. Typical neurologic symptoms include altered mental status, difficulty concentrating, confusion, and muscle weakness. Deep tendon reflexes are decreased. Some patients experience personality changes, hallucinations, and psychoses (Bajournas, 1990; Porth, 1994). Localized neurologic signs may occur but are not common. In the GI tract, hypercalcemia leads to anorexia, nausea, decreased gastric emptying, constipation, and abdominal pain (Bajournas, 1990; Goni & Tolis, 1993).

Cardiovascular consequences of hypercalcemia include increased cardiac contractility and irritability. Digitalis increases these responses (Bajournas, 1990; Porth, 1994). Electrocardiographic changes show slowed conduction with prolongation of PR and QRS intervals. With increased cal-cium levels, bradyarrhythmias occur and may lead to cardiac arrest (Bajournas, 1990).

High calcium concentration in the kidneys damages the proximal tubules, resulting in polyuria and loss of ability to concentrate urine. This leads to dehydration and hypovolemia, which, in turn, decreases glomerular filtration and leads to renal insufficiency. With renal insufficiency, calcium reabsorption is increased, resulting in progressively worsening symptoms.

Pathophysiology

There appear to be several mechanisms for the development of hypercalcemia in cancer. Hypercalcemia occurs in patients with and without bone metastases and in hematologic malignancies. The primary cause of hypercalcemia is bone resorption. Tumor cells are thought to release factors that act on bone to release calcium.

Many patients with widespread bone metastases develop hypercalcemia due to bone destruction, although the factors that lead to osteoclast activity and bone resorption are not entirely clear. Hypercalcemia of malignancy is primarily thought to be mediated by blood-borne substances that direct bone resorption. Parathyroid hormone-related protein (PTH-rP) has been found to be secreted by tumors. It exerts similar effects to PTH in that PTH-rP is able to bind to PTH receptors in bone and kidney and cause both bone resorption and calcium reabsorption in the kidney (Ikeda & Ogata, 1995; Muggia, 1990; Raue & Pecherstorfer, 1994; Ritch, 1990). Other factors implicated in bone resorption include the transforming growth factors, TGFα and TGFβ; tumor necrosis factors, TNFα and TNFβ; granulocyte and macrophage growth factors, GM-CSF and G-CSF; and interleukin-1 (IL-1) and interleukin-2 (IL-2) (Mundy, 1990; Ritch, 1990).

Hypercalcemia is usually a late event in breast cancer and is generally associated with widespread bone metastases. However, some patients with breast cancer who have no bone metastases develop hypercalcemia, and some patients with extensive bone metastases never develop hypercalcemia. It is thought that, particularly in breast cancer, prostaglandins secreted by tumor cells play a role in bone destruction (Goni & Tolis, 1993; Mundy, 1990; Ritch, 1990).

There is no evidence that dietary intake of calcium is a significant factor in hypercalcemia, and there is no need to restrict foods high in calcium.

Diagnosis

Hypercalcemia can occur in a number of conditions, the most common of which are hypercalcemia due to malignancy and primary hyperparathyroidism. Key to the diagnosis are the patient's history and physical examination and certain laboratory tests. Parathyroid hormone can be measured and is normal or low in hypercalcemia related to malignancy and elevated in primary hyperparathyroidism. The PTH-rP can also be measured, and elevation indicates cancer-related hypercalcemia. Certain electrolyte results are associated with hypercalcemia of malignancy, including hypokalemia, normal or elevated phosphorus, low or normal chloride levels, and normal or increased bicarbonate (Mundy, 1990; Ritch, 1990).

Treatment

The most effective treatment of hypercalcemia is successful treatment of the underlying cancer. However, hypercalcemia usually occurs in patients with advanced cancer, and the goal of treatment becomes symptom relief. Reduction in serum calcium is achieved by inhibiting bone resorption and increasing renal excretion of calcium.

Treatment of hypercalcemia begins with restoration of intravascular volume depletion, which is aggravated by nausea, vomiting, and polyuria. IV hydration with 0.9% saline is used to restore intravascular volume and glomerular filtration. Normal saline is infused rapidly, depending on the degree of hypercalcemia and dehydration and the renal and cardiac status of the patient (Mazzaferri, O'Dorisio & LoBuglio, 1978; Raue & Pecherstorfer, 1994; Ritch, 1990). Typically, at least 3 L of normal saline a day are administered. IV saline also promotes the renal excretion of calcium.

Fluid overload and electrolyte imbalances, particularly hypokalemia, may occur during rehydration. It is important to monitor cardiac status, urine output, and serum electrolytes during fluid administration. After fluid volume has been restored, diuretics are often used to increase renal calcium excretion. Loop diuretics, such as furosemide, interfere with calcium reabsorption in the kidney and assist urinary excretion of calcium. Furosemide is given at doses of 20 to 40 mg once or twice daily. Higher doses of 80 to 100 mg every 1 to 2 hours require more intensive monitoring of hydration, urinary output, and serum electrolytes (Ritch, 1990). Thiazide diuretics are always avoided because they enhance the kidney's reabsorption of calcium (Mazzaferri et al., 1978; Raue & Pecherstorfer, 1994).

Improvement in symptoms and calcium level may be seen quickly with rehydration, but the effects are not lasting. Drug therapy aimed at inhibiting bone resorption is often used to return the calcium level to normal. Several effective drugs are available, including calcitonin, bisphosphonates, gallium nitrate, and plicamycin.

CALCITONIN

Calcitonin is effective in limiting bone resorption and acts on the kidney to assist urinary excretion of calcium. Calcitonin is fast-acting and can be used safely in patients with dehydration and renal insufficiency. It is most often administered subcutaneously or intramuscularly at a dose of 4 to 8 U/kg every 6 to 12 hours (Raue & Pecherstorfer, 1994). Side effects are usually mild and consist of nausea, vomiting, abdominal cramps, and flushing. Unfortunately, the effects are short-lived because serum calcium may increase within 48 hours despite continued use (Raue & Pecherstofer, 1994; Ritch, 1990). Despite its limitations, calcitonin is effective and may be most useful in severe hypercalcemia when rapid response is indicated.

BISPHOSPHONATES

Bisphosphonates are potent inhibitors of bone resorption, although they do not directly affect renal tubular reabsorption of calcium (Rogers, Watts & Russell, 1997). The exact mechanisms of action are unknown. They are thought to be less effective in PTH-rP mediated hypercalcemia but are noted to be effective in some cases (Goni & Tolis, 1990; Raue & Pecherstorfer, 1994). Bisphosphonates appear to affect osteoclast differentiation and activity, and can cause cell death (Rogers et al., 1997). Because of these actions, the bisphosphonate pamidronate has been approved by the FDA for the prevention of osteolytic bone metastases and fractures in breast cancer and multiple myeloma. Two bisphosphonates are currently approved in the United States for the treatment of hypercalcemia, pamidronate (Aredia) and etidronate (Didronel). Both drugs are administered intravenously as an infusion over 2 to 4 hours. In a study by Gucalp and associates (1992), a single dose of pamidronate was found to be more effective than etidronate administered daily for 3 days in lowering calcium to normal levels.

GALLIUM NITRATE

Gallium was originally investigated in the 1960s as an antineoplastic agent. Although it did not have significant anticancer activity, hypocalcemia was noted as a side effect (Warrell, 1993). Its effect is due to inhibition of bone resorption. Gallium nitrate seems to be more active than bisphosphonates in restoring calcium to normal levels in PTH-rP mediated hypercalcemia (Warrell, 1997). Renal toxicity is a potential adverse effect. Gallium nitrate is administered by continuous IV infusion over 2 to 5 days.

PLICAMYCIN

Plicamycin (mithramycin) is an antitumor antibiotic that is active in testicular cancer. Hypocalcemia was found to be an unexpected adverse reaction, and the drug is now used primarily for hypercalcemia. Plicamycin works by directly damaging osteoclasts, leading to decreased bone resorption (Goni & Tolis, 1993). It is administered at a dose of 25 μg/kg body weight as an IV infusion over 30 minutes to 4 hours. Nausea is the most common side effect, but potential toxicities include thrombocytopenia and renal and hepatic damage. These are more common with repeated dosing (Goni & Tolis, 1993; Mazzaferri et al., 1978).

PHOSPHATES

Phosphates are effective in treating hypercalcemia by increasing the serum phosphate level, which decreases serum calcium and bone resorption, and increases urinary calcium excretion (Goni & Tolis, 1993; Mazzaferri et al., 1978). However, par-

enteral administration of phosphates can cause precipitation of calcium in the bone and in other tissues such as the heart, kidney, and other soft tissues (Mazzaferri et al., 1978; Mundy, 1990). Parenteral phosphate can have serious side effects including renal failure and severe hypocalcemia (Goni & Tolis, 1993). Oral phosphate, given in doses of 0.5 to 3.0 g/day, can be effective in mild hypercalcemia (Goni & Tolis, 1993; Ritch, 1990). Diarrhea is a common side effect of oral phosphates.

Treatment of hypercalcemia is challenging because it tends to be a recurrent and progressive problem unless the underlying cancer is effectively treated. This complication occurs most often in patients with widespread cancer who may already be debilitated. Immobilization due to pain or disability and dehydration due to anorexia or nausea can worsen hypercalcemia. When hypercalcemia is mild and the patient exhibits few signs or symptoms, outpatient treatment may be feasible with close monitoring and follow-up. Patients with severe symptoms or mental status changes need to be hospitalized for treatment. In some instances of end-stage cancer, if there are few effects from hypercalcemia and little hope of controlling the cancer, no treatment of the hypercalcemia may be the best option.

Hematologic Emergencies

Disseminated Intravascular Coagulation

Coagulation abnormalities are common in people who have cancer. This is frequently exemplified by elevated levels of factor VIII, fibrinogen, platelets, fibrin, and fibrin degradation products (Bunn & Ridgway, 1993). Abnormalities may be asymptomatic and evident only on laboratory tests. Coagulation defects tend to be greater with a large tumor burden and in advanced stages of cancer (Zacharski, Wojtukiewicz, Constatini, Ornstein, & Memoli, 1992).

Disseminated intravascular coagulation (DIC) occurs as a complication of serious conditions such as septicemia, trauma, obstetric complications, and malignancy. Abnormal activation of the coagulation process results in intravascular clot formation and/or uncontrolled bleeding. Multiple clots tend to form in the microvasculature of various organs, leading to ischemia. Activation of the fibrinolytic system to break down clots results in consumption of platelets and clotting factors with subsequent bleeding and thrombocytopenia.

In DIC, the underlying condition triggers an abnormal production of thrombin. Large amounts of circulating thrombin activate both the coagulation and the fibrinolytic system that breaks down clots. Circulating thrombin converts fibrinogen to fibrin. Some of the fibrin combines with fibrin degradation products to form a soluble form of fibrin. However, some of these complexes develop in the microvasculature where they can cause obstruction of blood flow, tissue hypoxia, and ischemia (Bick, 1978).

In malignancy, coagulation is thought to be activated in a number of ways: (1) growing tumor masses may invade or obstruct normal tissues; (2) tumor cells may have properties that induce coagulation; (3) release of cytokines by tumor cells that trigger coagulation; (4) tumor necrosis; and (5) infection or sepsis (Weick, 1978; Zacharski et al., 1992). In acute promyelocytic leukemia, the leukemic blast cells release procoagulant substances that initiate the coagulation process (Wilde & Davies, 1990).

DIC can occur in any type of cancer but is more common in adenocarcinoma, especially cancer of the pancreas and prostate. There is approximately an 85% incidence of DIC in acute promyelocytic leukemia. DIC may also occur in other subtypes of acute myeloid leukemia but is less common (Wilde & Davies, 1990).

Diagnosis

Chronic low-grade DIC is common in patients with disseminated cancer. It may be asymptomatic with little evidence of coagulation abnormality on laboratory tests (Colman & Rubin, 1990). Typical laboratory findings in chronic DIC include decreased or low-normal fibrinogen levels and elevated fibrinogen degradation products. These patients demonstrate a hypercoagulable state with recurrent thrombotic events. They may experience recurrent deep vein thrombosis, catheter-related thrombosis, or pulmonary embolus. Trousseau's syndrome, described by Armand

Trousseau in 1865, is a condition of migratory superficial thrombophlebitis. It is characterized by recurrent, superficial, and deep vein thrombosis. Treatment of Trousseau's syndrome with warfarin is rarely successful and requires long-term treatment with either subcutaneous or IV heparin (Bunn & Ridgway, 1993; Colman & Rubin, 1990).

With acute DIC, there is evidence of both abnormal thrombosis and bleeding. Bleeding is evident in areas of trauma or invasive procedures such as surgical wounds, venipuncture, or central line catheter sites. Bleeding can occur from the nose, mouth, GI tract, or bladder. Petechiae, purpura, hematomas, and acral cyanosis may be evident on inspection of the skin. Multiple areas may bleed or ooze simultaneously.

Thrombi in the microvascular circulation, with associated bleeding, cause ischemic injury to affected organs. The lungs, kidneys, and central nervous system are most often affected, but microthrombi may be present in any organ (Colman & Rubin, 1990). Pulmonary effects of DIC can lead to adult respiratory distress syndrome (Bunn & Ridgway, 1993; Colman & Rubin, 1990). Multiple organ failure can occur with acute hemorrhagic DIC.

Although there is no definitive laboratory test for DIC, this syndrome is likely when the platelet count and fibrinogen level are decreased and prothrombin time is prolonged. Often, the platelet count is below 50,000 mm^3. Fibrinogen is low because it is used in both clotting and fibrinolyis induced by thrombin and plasmin. Fibrin degradation products are increased to a level greater than 40 μg/mL. The prothrombin time is prolonged mainly due to decreased factor V and, to a lesser extent, decreased factors II and X, and fibrinogen (Zacharski et al., 1992).

Treatment

The presentation of DIC may occur in varying degrees. Some patients may have abnormal coagulation by laboratory determination but may be completely asymptomatic, with no clotting or bleeding. In others, clotting problems predominate with development of deep vein thrombosis or pulmonary embolus. Acute DIC with hemorrhage is a rare occurrence.

The most effective management of DIC is treatment of the underlying condition. If the cancer can be successfully treated, coagulation abnormalities will return to normal. If the cause of DIC is infection, sepsis, volume depletion, hypotension, or hypoxemia, correction of the specific condition will usually lead to resolution of the DIC.

When patients are asymptomatic with laboratory abnormalities diagnostic of DIC, careful observation alone may be sufficient, with interventions for any episodes of thrombosis or bleeding. Patients with recurrent thrombotic events can be treated with IV heparin by continuous infusion to maintain the partial thromboplastin time at one and a half to two times normal. Some patients may be maintained on low-molecular-weight heparin given as twice-a-day subcutaneous injection, which may be safer than IV heparin and does not require PTT monitoring. Cost and frequent injections are disadvantages of this method.

The best treatment for acute fulminant DIC is unknown and remains controversial (Bunn & Ridgway, 1993; Colman & Rubin, 1990). Although treatment of the patient's cancer and any contributing factors such as infection are considered standard, treatment with heparin is controversial (Bunn & Ridgway, 1993; Colman & Rubin, 1990). Heparin interferes with the coagulation process by binding to antithrombin III, thereby inhibiting thrombin activity. Thrombin formation leads to consumption of platelets and clotting proteins (Handin, 1994). However, because heparin is an anticoagulant, its use increases the risk of bleeding. Fresh frozen plasma and cryoprecipitate are standard treatment to replace clotting factors. Platelet transfusions are indicated when bleeding with thrombocytopenia is present (Bunn & Ridgway, 1993; Colman & Rubin, 1990; Handin, 1994).

In acute promyelocytic leukemia (APML), the incidence of DIC is very frequent and reported in approximately 85% of patients (Wilde & Davies, 1990). Blast cells in APML contain procoagulation factors that are released during chemotherapy treatment due to cell death. Heparin therapy was routinely administered with induction chemotherapy to prevent DIC and bleeding complications. More recent treatment with all-*trans*-retinoic acid (ATRA) results in rapid differentiation of cells in the bone marrow as well as correction of coagulation abnormalities (Keating, Estez, & Kantarjian, 1993).

When treatment of DIC is successful, coagulation abnormalities recover fairly quickly. Clinically, there is no evidence of thrombus formation or bleeding. The hemoglobin level and platelet count stabilize and recover without need for frequent transfusion. The prothrombin time and PTT will begin to normalize, although patients on heparin treatment will continue to have a prolonged PTT. The level of fibrin degradation products decreases with successful treatment. The plasma fibrinogen level is most likely to recover quickly and may be most useful in monitoring the patient's response to treatment.

Conclusion

Cancer and cancer treatment often lead to a variety of complications. Nurses encounter these patients in the doctor's office or outpatient clinic, the emergency room, the hospital, or in home or hospice care. Often, patients experiencing these problems have symptoms recognizable as a particular emergency situation, but in some circumstances symptoms may be vague and nonspecific. Accurate and timely nursing assessment as well as a low threshold for suspicion of a serious problem are important in diagnosing and treating the condition.

Nurses are continuously involved in patient and family teaching. Informing and encouraging patients to report key signs and symptoms to their nurse or doctor give patients the knowledge and permission to participate fully in their care. Teaching is very important in helping patients and families understand a current health crisis, the treatment plan, and expected outcomes. Nurses perform psychosocial assessment and provide emotional support to patients and families to help them cope with changes in health and functional status. Nursing care helps to guide patients and loved ones through very difficult decisions and treatments. Although the care of patients with cancer emergencies can be physically, intellectually, and emotionally challenging, it is tremendously rewarding in developing communication with and connectedness to patients with life-threatening illness.

REFERENCES

Adler, J., Cox, R. S., Kaplan, I., & Martin, D. P. (1992). Stereotactic radiosurgical treatment of brain metastases. *Journal of Neurosurgery, 76,* 444–449.

Ahmann, F. R. (1984). A reassessment of the clinical implications of the superior vena caval syndrome. *Journal of Clinical Oncology, 8,* 961–969.

Arrambide, K., & Toto, R. D. (1993). Tumor lysis syndrome. *Seminars in Nephrology, 13,* 273–280.

Awan, A. M., & Weichelsbaum, A. (1990). Palliative radiotherapy. *Hematology Oncology Clinics of North America, 4,* 1169–1181.

Bajournas, D. A. (1990). Clinical manifestations of cancer-related hypercalcemia: Epidemiology and etiology. *Seminars in Oncology, 17*(suppl. 5), 16–25.

Bick, R. L. (1978). Disseminated intravascular coagulation and related syndromes: Etiology, pathophysiology, diagnosis and management. *American Journal of Hematology, 5,* 265–282.

Black, P. McL., (1993). Solitary brain metastases. *Chest, 103*(suppl.), 367S–369S.

Braunwald, E., (1994). Pericardial disease. In K. J. Isselbacher, E. Braunwald, J. D. Wilson, J. D. Martin, A. S. Fauci & D. L. Kasper (Eds.), *Harrison's principles of internal medicine* (3rd ed., pp. 1094–1101). New York: McGraw-Hill.

Breneman, J. C., Warnick, R. E., Albright, R. E., Kukiatinant, N., Shaw, J., & Tew, J. (1997). Stereotactic radiosurgery for the treatment of brain metastases. *Cancer, 79,* 551–557.

Bruckman, J. E., & Bloomer, W. D. (1978). Management of spinal cord compression. *Seminars in Oncology, 5,* 135–140.

Bunn, P. A., Jr., & Ridgway, E. C. (1993). Paraneoplastic syndromes. In V. T. DeVita, S. Hellman, & S. A. Rosenberg (Eds.), *Cancer principles and practice of oncology* (4th ed., pp. 2026–2071). Philadelphia: J. B. Lippincott.

Byrne, T. N. (1992). Spinal cord compression from epidural metastases. *New England Journal of Medicine, 327,* 614–615.

Colman, R. W., & Rubin, L. N. (1990). Disseminated intravascular coagulation due to malignancy. *Seminars in Oncology, 17,* 172–186.

Drakos, P., Bar-Ziv, J., & Catane, R. (1994). Tumor lysis syndrome in nonhematologic malignancies. *American Journal of Clinical Oncology, 17,* 502–505.

Goni, M. H., & Tolis, G. (1993). Hypercalcemia of cancer: An update. *Anticancer Research, 13,* 1155–1160.

Gucalp, R., Ritch, P., Wiernek, P. H., Sarma, P. R., Keller, A., Richman, S. P, Tauer, K., Neidhart, J., Mallette, L. E., Siegel, R., & VancePol, C. J. (1992). Comparative study of pamidronate disodium and etidronate disodium in the treatment of cancer-related hypercalcemia. *Journal of Clinical Oncology, 10,* 134–147.

Hancock, E. W. (1990). Neoplastic pericardial disease. *Cardiology Clinics, 8,* 673–682.

Hande, K. R., & Garrow, G. C. (1993). Acute tumor lysis syndrome in patients with high-grade non Hodgkin's lymphoma. *The American Journal of Medicine, 94,* 133–138.

Handin, R. I. (1994). Disorders of coagulation and thrombosis. In K. S. Isselbacher, E. Braunwald, J. D. Wilson, J. D. Martin, A. S. Fauci & D. L. Kasper (Eds.), *Harrison's principles of internal medicine* (3rd ed., pp. 1804–1810). New York: McGraw-Hill.

Harris, J. K., Suttcliffe, J. C., & Robinson, N. E. (1996). The role of emergency surgery in malignant spinal extradural compression: Assessment of functional outcome. *British Journal of Neurosurgery, 10,* 27–33.

Harvey, H. A. (1997). Issues concerning the role of chemotherapy and hormonal therapy of bone metastases from breast cancer. *Cancer, 80*(suppl.), 27–33.

Helweg-Larson, S. (1996). Clinical outcome in metastatic spinal cord compression: A prospective study of 153 patients. *Acta Neurologica Scandinavica, 94,* 269–275.

Hoegler, D. (1997). Radiotherapy for palliation of symptoms in incurable cancer. *Current Problems in Cancer, 21,* 129–183.

Ikeda, K., & Ogata, E. (1995). Humoral hypercalcemia of malignancy: Some enigmas on the clinical features. *Journal of Cellular Biochemistry, 57,* 348–351.

Johnston, R. A. (1993). The management of acute spinal cord compression. *Journal of Neurology, Neurosurgery and Psychiatry, 36,* 1046–1054.

Keating, M. J., Estez, E., & Kantarjian, H. (1993). Acute leukemia. In V. T. DeVita, S. Hellman & S. A. Rosenberg (Eds.), *Cancer: Principles and practice of oncology* (4th ed., pp. 1930–1949). Philadelphia: J. B. Lippincott.

Kim, M., & Bernstein, M. (1996). Current treatment of cerebral metastases. *Current Opinion in Neurology, 9,* 414–418.

Kopecky, S. L., Callahan, J. A., Tajik, A. J., & Seward, J. B. (1986). Percutaneous pericardial catheter drainage: Report of 42 consecutive cases. *American Journal of Cardiology, 58,* 635.

Kralstein, J., & Frishman, W. H. (1987). Malignant pericardial drainage: Diagnosis and treatment. *Cardiology Clinics, 5,* 583–598.

Mazzaferri, E. L., O'Dorisio, T. M., & LoBuglio, A. F. (1978). Treatment of hypercalcemia associated with malignancy. *Seminars in Oncology, 5,* 141–153.

McCrosky, R. D., Mosher, D. F., Spencer, C. D., Prendergast, E., & Longo, W. R. (1990). Acute tumor lysis syndrome and treatment response in patients treated for refractory chronic lymphocytic leukemia with short-course, high dose cytosine arabinoside, cisplatin, and etoposide. *Cancer, 66,* 246–250.

Muggia, F. M. (1990). Overview of cancer-related hypercalcemia: Epidemiology and etiology. *Seminars in Oncology, 17*(suppl. 5), 3–9.

Mundy, G. R. (1990). Pathophysiology of cancer-associated hypercalcemia. *Seminars in Oncology, 17*(suppl. 5), 10–15.

Nicholson, A. A., Ettles, D. F., Arnold, A., Greenstone, M., & Dyet, J. F. (1997). Treatment of malignant superior vena cava obstruction: Metal stents or radiation therapy. *Journal of Vascular and Interventional Radiology, 8,* 781–788.

Noordijk, E., Vect, C., Haazma-Reiche, H., Padberg, G., Voormolen, J., Hoekstra, F., Tans, J., Netsaars, J., & Watendorf, A. (1994). The choice of treatment of single brain metastasis should be based on extracranial tumor activity and age. *Journal of Radiation Oncology, Biology and Physics, 29,* 711–717.

Patchell, R. A., Tibbs, P. A., Walsh, S. W., Dempsey, R. J., Maruyama, Y., Dryscio, R. J., Markesbery, W. R., Macdonald, J. J., & Young, B. (1990). A randomized trial of surgery in the treatment of single metastases to the brain. *New England Journal of Medicine, 322,* 494–551.

Perez, C. A., Presant, C. A., & Van Amburg, A. L. III. (1978). Management of superior vena cava syndrome. *Seminars in Oncology, 5,* 123–134.

Porth, C. M. (1994). Alterations in fluids and electrolytes. In C. M. Porth (Ed.), *Pathophysiology: Concepts of altered health states* (4th ed., pp. 591–627). Philadelphia: J. B. Lippincott.

Ratanatharathorn, V., & Powers, W. E. (1991). Epidural spinal cord compression from metastatic tumor: Diagnosis and guidelines for management. *Cancer Treatment Reports, 18,* 55–71.

Raue, F., & Pecherstorfer, M. (1994). Drug therapy of hypercalcemia due to malignancy. *Recent Results in Cancer Research, 137,* 138–160.

Ritch, P. S. (1990). Treatment of cancer-related hypercalcemia. *Seminars in Oncology, 17*(suppl. 5), 26–33.

Rogers, M. J., Watts, D. J., & Russell, G. G. (1997). Overview of bisphosphonates. *Cancer, 80*(suppl.), 1652–1660.

Sculier, J. P., Evans, W. K., Feld, R., DeBuer, G., Payne, D. G., Shepherd, F. A., Pringle, J. F., Yeon, J. L., Quirt, I. C., Curtis, J. E., & Herman J. G. (1986). Superior venal caval obstruction syndrome in small cell lung cancer. *Cancer, 57,* 847–851.

Shapiro, W. R., Posner, J. B., Ushio, Y., Chernik, N. L., & Young, D. F. (1977). Treatment of meningeal neoplasms. *Current Treatment Reports, 61,* 733–743.

Shepherd, F. A. (1997). Malignant pericardial effusion. *Current Opinion in Oncology, 9,* 170–174.

Sklarin, N. T., & Markham, M. (1995). Spontaneous recurrent tumor lysis syndrome in breast cancer. *American Journal of Clinical Oncology, 18,* 71–73.

Stauffer, J. L. (1998). Lung. In L. M. Tierney, S. J. McPhee, & M. A. Papandakis (Eds.), *Current medical diagnosis and treatment* (37th ed.). Stamford, CT: Appleton & Lange.

Steinherz, L. J., & Yahalom, J. (1993). Cardiac complications of cancer therapy. In V. T. DeVita, S. Hellman & S. A. Rosenberg (Eds.), *Cancer: Principles and practice of oncology* (4th ed., pp. 2370–2385). Philadelphia: J. B. Lippincott.

Sundaresan, N., Galicich, J. H. (1985). Surgical treatment of brain metastases. *Cancer, 55*(6): 1382–1388.

Theologides, A. (1978). Neoplastic cardiac tamponade. *Seminars in Oncology, 5,* 181–192.

Tura, I. C., & Danielson, G. K. (1990). Surgical management of pericardial diseases. *Cardiology Clinics, 8,* 683–696.

Turner, S., Marosszeky, B., Timms, I., & Boyages, J. (1991). Malignant spinal cord compression: A prospective evaluation. *International Journal of Radiation Oncology, Biology and Physics, 26,* 141–146.

Warrell, R. P. (1993). Metabolic emergencies. In V. T. DeVita, S. Hellman & S. A. Rosenberg (Eds.), *Cancer: Principles and practice of oncology* (4th ed., pp. 2128–2140). Philadelphia: J. B. Lippincott.

Warrell, R. P. (1997). Gallium nitrate for the treatment of bone metastases. *Cancer, 80* (suppl.), 1680–1685.

Wasserstrom, W. R., Glass, S. P., & Posner, J. B. (1982). Diagnosis and treatment of leptomeningeal metastases from solid tumors. *Cancer, 49,* 759–772.

Weick, J. R. (1978). Intravascular coagulation in cancer. *Seminars in Oncology, 5,* 203–211.

Weissman, D. E. (1988). Glucocorticoid treatment for brain metastases and epidural cord compression: A review. *Journal of Clinical Oncology, 6,* 543–551.

Wilde, J. T., & Davies, J. M. (1990). Haemostatic problems in acute leukemia. *Blood Reviews, 4,* 245–251.

Wright, D. C., Delaney, T. F., & Buchner, J. C. (1993). Treatment of metastatic cancer to the brain. In V. T. DeVita, S. Hellman, & S. A. Rosenberg (Eds.), *Cancer: Principles and practice of oncology* (4th ed.). Philadelphia: J. B. Lippincott.

Wujcik, D. (1983). Meningeal carcinomatosis: Diagnosis, treatment and nursing care. *Oncology Nursing Forum, 10,* 35–40.

Zacharski, L. R., Wojtukiewicz, M. Z., Constatini, V., Ornstein, D. L., & Memoli, V. A. (1992). Pathways of coagulation/fibrinolysis activation in malignancy. *Seminars in Thrombosis and Hemostasis, 18,* 104–116.

Helping Your Patients With Their Cancer Experience

Sexuality, Body Image, and Cancer

Cindi Bedell

Sexuality is an integral part of our humanness and is composed of some of our deepest desires and emotions. Sexuality is multidimensional, consisting of the act, our gender, our relationships, and our self-identity. The word *sex* came into the English language around the 15th century. Its origin is the Latin word *secare* or *sect,* which means to separate and then come together, as in animals joining together to reproduce and make clans.

Sexuality or sexual identity is the interrelationship of body image, functional capacity, social relationships, life roles, heritage, and religious background. Alteration of even one aspect of a person's life may alter his or her sexual self-perception. Figure 16-1 illustrates the dynamic interrelationships that make up a person's self-identity. Identifying the strengths and weaknesses in the self-identity can help develop plans and identify solutions for preventing and overcoming problems. Boosting body image can improve social relationships, sexuality, and functioning in everyday roles. Healthy social relationships and a rewarding career can improve body image, whereas losing a job or undergoing a separation from significant others can lead to questions about sexual identity or spirituality.

Nurse's Role

What is the nurse's role in dealing with sexuality and the cancer patient? Nurses have both the opportunity and the responsibility to discuss sexuality with their patients. Many nurses have expressed anxiety over bringing up this topic because of lack of knowledge about sexuality and their own insecurity in discussing sex with other people. The American Nurses Association and the Oncology Nursing Society Standard state that the patient should be able to identify "potential or actual changes in sexuality or sexual function related to disease and treatment" (American Nurses Association & Oncology Nursing Society, 1996). To fulfill this standard, the least a nurse should do is to inform a patient of potential side effects of treatment that may affect sexuality, ask whether he or she has any sexual concerns, and offer future assistance if needed. The nurse should learn basics about sexual development, normal reproduction, and the disease and treatment side effects specific for his or her patient population (Rabinowitz, 1994b).

PLISSIT

A very easy framework for sexual counseling that the nurse can follow is the PLISSIT model (Amon, 1976).

Permission—Often, the nurse can open the door to discuss sexuality by asking a few simple assessment questions, for example: "Many people on this chemotherapy or with this type of surgery experience a decrease in their sex drive or experience problems with their ability to enjoy sexual activities. Do you have any concerns you would like to discuss?" or "How have your treatments affected how you feel about yourself as a woman/man?"

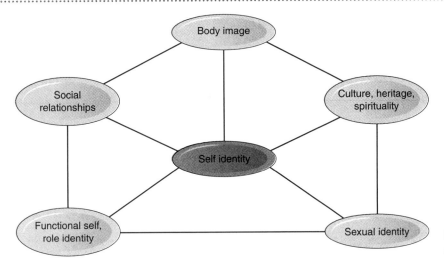

Figure 16-1 Interrelationships of components of self-identity.

The patient may or may not have any immediate questions or concerns to discuss with the nurse. However, by asking the questions, the nurse sends a message that sexuality is just as important as understanding pain, appetite, or sleep patterns. The patient is then more inclined to raise the issue if problems develop in the future.

Limited Information—Nurses do this best by teaching people and their partners what to expect from their disease and/or treatments. Nurses can also provide tips to prevent or overcome side effects, which may enhance sexuality or sexual response.

Judy informed all of her premenopausal breast cancer patients that chemotherapy could cause premature menopause, which could lead to vaginal dryness and painful intercourse. She instructed them to use vaginal lubrication on a regular basis and with intercourse to keep the vagina well moisturized. This limited amount of information prevented potential problems for the women she instructed.

M.C. was a 70-year-old newlywed who was about to have a radical prostatectomy. In preoperative teaching, the nurse mentioned that there was a potential for impotence after surgery. This opened a whole discussion with this gentleman and his bride who had engaged in sexual activities daily since their wedding 6 months earlier. The nurse informed the surgeon of their concerns before surgery, and alternative approaches to treatment were discussed.

Specific Suggestion—The nurse can problem solve with the patient when dealing with specific sexual concerns or complications.

Jerry was a 62-year-old male with lung cancer who told his nurse that he became too short of breath to have intercourse with his partner. The nurse suggested trying a new position in which he did not have to exert himself as much and/or changing the time of day such as early morning or after a nap when he was well rested.

Doug was a 42-year-old man who was terminally ill and wore an indwelling catheter. He was able to have an erection when his wife bathed him and wanted to know if they could have intercourse with the catheter. The nurse counseled him to either remove the catheter during intercourse or to clamp the catheter and use a condom over the catheter and penis for intercourse.

Intensive Therapy—The nurse also needs to know when more intensive counseling is required and what community resources are available. A bad relationship is not going to become better with the stress of illness and treatment.

Sandy was a 24-year-old woman diagnosed with lymphoma. She and Tom had only been married 3 months (and only dated for 6 months before that) when she was diagnosed. Tom began to go out dancing with his old buddies and would not sleep in the same room with Sandy after she began her chemotherapy. Whenever she tried to bring up the subject, he would storm out of the house, leaving her in tears. Her nurse referred her to a family and marriage counselor who had experience working with couples who had cancer. After just a few sessions, Tom was able to open up about his fears of losing Sandy and feeling left out of life when he was home taking care of her. With more open communication and realistic understanding of her prognosis, they were able to work through their feelings and grow as a couple together.

Normal Sexual Response

A normal sexual response is whatever is pleasurable and comfortable to an individual and his or her partner. The phases of human sexual response include desire, arousal, orgasm, and resolution. Desire, or libido, is the longing or need for the sexual connection with another person or the desire for sexual stimulation. Desire may be altered by illness, fatigue, emotions, medications, or endogenous hormones.

Arousal is the excitement phase of the response. In women, the vagina becomes larger and lubricated, the clitoris becomes engorged and enlarged, the nipples become erect, and the skin flushes. In men, the penis becomes engorged and enlarged, the testicles elevate and enlarge, the nipples become erect, and the skin flushes. The sexual response can be interrupted at this phase or can progress to orgasm.

Orgasm is the involuntary climax of tension that has built up, sending waves of pleasure through the pelvis and the rest of the body. In men, semen is ejaculated at this time.

Resolution is the return of all the body systems to the prearousal phase. Women can repeat this cycle of phases with very little recovery time, whereas men have a refractory period before arousal can occur again. Resolution and the refractory period vary between individuals and may increase with age, medications, and illness (Schover, 1988a; Schover, 1988b).

Body Image

Body image is a person's "mind's eye" or internal picture of self. Maintaining or returning to a healthy body image strengthens a person's self-identity and affects all aspects of his or her life, especially sexuality. The mind is the strongest sex organ of all.

"I miss the days when I felt comfortable lying across my bed naked and knew that I was attractive. Now all I have left is a furtive act done between covers."

A very attractive, 42-year-old woman with primary malignant hepatoma (carcinoma of the liver) said, "I feel dirty with this cancer growing inside of me and don't want anyone to touch me."

However, people's perceptions of how they look and how they react to their physical changes will be very different. Nurses need to be careful not to project their own feelings and beliefs onto what they expect from the patient.

M.M. was a 44-year-old woman who underwent a bilateral mastectomy with immediate reconstruction for a diagnosis of breast cancer. She was thrilled with her new shape. "I always hated my breasts. When I was younger, the boys made fun of me and, as I got older, they caused such back pain. Now, I have small, perky breasts and a flat stomach. I feel and look great! It is amazing, I have more energy now and even had the courage to quit my job and go back to school."

The person with cancer may experience many physical changes to his or her body. Some of these are preventable, some can be managed with cosmetics or camouflage, and others are as bad as they seem and may require more intensive therapy to overcome. Self-massage or touch to the physical changes, such as massaging a chest wall after a mastectomy, can help a person incorporate the changes into a new, healthy body image. Other methods to strengthen body image include spending time in front of a mirror speaking positive self-affirmations, visualizing self as an attractive sexual being, or physical exercise to improve physical conditioning.

Affirmation
The breasts are gone
But I am
Whole
Disfigurement
Need not include
My soul. *

Alopecia

Alopecia is complete hair loss. Although alopecia is not life threatening, it is often more devastating than any of the other changes caused by the cancer and/or its treatment. Women who have undergone mastectomy have stated that it was harder losing their hair than losing their breast because it was a much more visible reminder. Men often have a more difficult time than women because of the social stigma of wearing wigs, finding suitable appearing wigs, or problems with wearing a hat indoors (*Chemotherapy, radiation therapy, hair loss and you*, 1981).

Jack was a single, 62-year-old gentleman who used a motorized scooter to move around because of a lifelong problem with polio-induced leg weakness. He was very active socially at church and in older singles organizations. He took great pride in his thick, silver hair. When his diagnosis of lymphoma required chemotherapy that would cause complete hair loss, he refused treatment. "All I have left of me is my hair! The women love my hair. I will not give that up also!" Jack was sent to a hair replacement specialty shop, and he ordered a customized, human hair wig for men. His oncologist also modified his chemotherapy program to eliminate the worst alopecia-causing drug. Jack has had some thinning of his hair but proudly tells everyone that the wig is still in the box on his dresser.

Over 75% of hair follicles on the scalp are dividing at any one time. Dividing cells are the most vulnerable to chemotherapy and radiation therapy. Hair loss associated with radiation therapy is confined to where the radiation is aimed. So, a person receiving breast radiation therapy should only experience hair loss on the chest and axilla region, whereas whole brain radiation would cause complete loss of scalp hair. Hair loss begins 2 to 3 weeks after the initiation of the radiation therapy. Hair regrowth starts 8 to 9 weeks after completion of the therapy and may take up to a year to return to normal texture and thickness. Hair loss may be permanent if the total dose of radiation is greater than 5500 cGy.

Hair loss caused by chemotherapy can range from mild thinning to complete loss of all body hair. Body hair other than scalp hair is less vulnerable to chemotherapy because fewer of the hair follicles are in division at any one time. Chemotherapy agents differ in their capacity to cause alopecia. Hair loss is usually delayed 2 to 3 weeks after the start of chemotherapy. Regrowth usually begins 4 to 6 weeks after the completion of therapy and takes a year to return to normal thickness and texture.

There have been many attempts to find ways to prevent hair loss; however, none is completely successful. Although some shampoos are reported to strengthen the hair follicle and make it less vulnerable to the drugs, no clinical trials have been completed to document their effectiveness. Other methods to preserve hair have included minimizing the amount of drug that reaches the hair follicle. This can be done by a scalp tourniquet or by scalp hypothermia with a cold cap or ice cap. The tourniquet or cold cap needs to be applied before the drug administration and left in place for at least 1 hour after administration. If the person is receiving continuous infusion chemotherapy, taking oral agents or drugs with a long half-life, or receiving high-dose chemotherapy, this method will not work. Also, if the amount of chemotherapy to the scalp is minimized, cancer cells may survive the treatment in this area.

To minimize thinning and slow hair loss with some drugs, a person can:

Use a wide-tooth comb
Use a gentle shampoo and conditioner
Use a satin pillowcase
Avoid hot curlers, hair dryers, or curling irons
Avoid chemical processing, such as permanents and dyes
Avoid pulling the hair tight into elastics or barrettes
Avoid stiff hairsprays and mousse

Usually, the scalp begins to tingle and become slightly tender just before the hair begins to fall

---

*Excerpted with permission from Hjelmsted, L. (1993). *Fine Black Lines*. Englewood, CA.

out. At this time, if complete hair loss is expected, some people choose to take control of the situation by shaving their head or clipping their hair very short; this provides a sense of controlling their own destiny and is more manageable than hair falling out everywhere.

> *J.D. was a 21-year-old model with leukemia. When her scalp began to hurt, she shaved her head in a reverse mohawk and couldn't wait until morning rounds with her very conservative oncologist. Once her mohawk fell out, she had a daily ritual of drawing designs on her scalp with washable markers. She decided to have fun with her baldness and maintained a sense of control and dignity.*

Because the hair does not begin to fall out for 2 to 3 weeks, there is plenty of time for the purchase of whatever hair replacement items a person will use. Usually, more than one type of hair covering is needed, and caps, hats, or scarves are comfortable, attractive alternatives to wigs. Scarves are economical, can be styled and tied in many different fashions, can be worn under a hat for more color and head coverage, and can be easily made to match a wardrobe from many different fabrics. Some people use a sleep cap to help keep the head warm at night.

There are many different types of wigs, and they vary in price and care required. The cost can range from $30 to $3000. Although some insurance companies may cover a portion of the cost for wigs (cranial prostheses), Medicare and many HMO-type insurance companies do not.

- Synthetic wigs are the least expensive and the easiest to care for. They can appear very realistic if they are styled and fitted properly.
- Human hair wigs are more expensive and require more care. They need styling every time they are washed, just like real hair. They do allow for more flexibility because they can be styled in different fashions, permed, or even colored. This is often more appropriate for a longer period of hair loss.
- Custom-made wigs are fitted to a person's head. Hair (synthetic, mixed, or human) is woven in with a color mix that matches the person's hair. This is more expensive and often takes longer to obtain the wig.

During the period of alopecia, the scalp needs special care and attention. It is important to keep the scalp protected from the sun with hats or sunscreen. The scalp needs to be cleaned regularly with a gentle shampoo and conditioner. A cotton cap worn under the wig can help prevent irritation to the scalp by the wig material.

Skin and Nail Changes

Chemotherapy and radiation therapy can cause a change in the appearance and texture of the skin and nails. Changes may also occur due to low blood counts, a change in nutrition, and lack of fresh air and sunshine. Basic health practices including rest, fresh air, exercise, and hydration can keep the skin fresh and healthy. Drinking at least 2 quarts of liquids a day will help counter some of the drying and sallow appearance. Using perfume- and alcohol-free cosmetics, moisturizers, and sunscreen can also help keep the skin as fresh as possible (Table 16-1).

Nail changes are not life threatening but may cause embarrassment and are another visual reminder of what the person is going through. One patient described the white lines on her nails as tree rings that represented the number of chemotherapy treatments she had received. Another 34-year-old woman was upset that her son would not let her touch him because her nails looked so strange as they separated from the nail bed. Nail changes occur slowly but also take a long time to recover after the chemotherapy is over. Nails should be kept short and clean, and cuticles should not be cut or torn. Nail polish helps keep the nails strong and covers up blemishes. If the treatments cause neutropenia, then acrylic nails should be avoided to prevent fungal infections (Table 16-2).

A great program to teach women skin and nail care is the American Cancer Society "Look Good—Feel Better" program. Trained cosmetologists instruct women on the proper and safe use of cosmetics, including nail care, during cancer treatment. Women get the chance in a comfortable environment to learn how to apply makeup to overcome some of the physical aspects of the cancer. These programs often include free cosmetics and make-over. Call the local ACS office or 1-800-ACS-2345 for more information.

TABLE 16-1

SKIN CHANGES

Skin Change	High-Risk Drugs	Description/Characteristics	Care
Hyperpigmentation	Cytoxan Methotrexate Doxorubicin Caelyx 5-Fluorouracil Bleomycin Radiation therapy	• Entire body may become bronzed • Dark streaks along the vein • Dark discoloration along areas of trauma, such as scratch marks • Darkened areas where clothing is constrictive, such as along the elastic of the waist	• Inform patient that changes are normal • Wear loose-fitting clothing including undergarments • Avoid trauma such as scratching the skin • Avoid direct exposure to sunlight • Camouflage discoloration with makeup, long-sleeved clothing
Palmar plantar erythrodysesthesia/ acral erythema/ scleroderma	5-Fluorouracil Caelyx High-dose Ara C Bleomycin Taxotere Methotrexate	• Redness, pain, and swelling of palms of hands and soles of feet • Dryness and thickening of palms and soles • Peeling and cracking of the skin	• During and for 24–48 h after treatment, avoid overheating of hands and feet (no wool socks, gloves, etc.) • Pyridoxine 50–150 mg qd • "Bag balm" or "udder cream" from the drug store as an emollient • Cooling measures if painful (ice packs, cool water soaks) • Tylenol for pain
Acnelike rash	Steroids Estrogen	• Acne-looking rash on face and back	• Keep clean and dry • Dermatology consult
Blistering/moist desquamation	Radiation therapy 5-Fluorouracil Caelyx Ara C	• Fluid-filled sacs—may be clear or sanguineous • Sloughing of the skin without healthy skin beneath	• Keep skin clean and dry • Leave open to air as much as possible • Avoid contact with clothing or bed linens • May require topical antimicrobial agents

TABLE 16-2

NAIL CHANGES

Nail Change	High-Incidence Drugs	Description	Care
Hyperpigmentation	5-Fluorouracil Doxorubicin Doxil	A dark brown discoloration to the nail Dark-skinned people at increased risk	Cover nail with colored nail polish
Beau's lines	Doxorubicin Cytosar	White lines or stripes horizontal across nail	Cover nail with polish
Onycholysis	Taxotere Taxol	Nail separates from the nail bed	Keep nail short and trimmed to prevent snagging Keep hands clean and dry

Surgical Changes

Breast Surgery

Women who undergo any type of breast surgery may experience changes in body image. The breasts are tied to so many emotional and physical experiences and sensations. Shopping for a first bra, the touch of a lover's fondling, the letdown of milk, and the suckling of a child all are stored memories. It is no wonder that the loss of a breast causes such grief. Many women describe phantom sensations of arousal, milk letdown, and sometimes pain long after the breast is removed.

The most drastic change is for women who undergo mastectomy without reconstruction. Lois Tschetter Hjelmstad wrote:

Double Amputee
I have looked this way
Before—
Flat chested, pencil thin

When I was ten

Strange it is to seem
A sexless child
Again

(Too bad about
The graying hair
And slightly sagging chin)

July 1991*

A wide variety of breast prostheses are available for women today. It is very important to buy a prosthesis that fits well and is comfortable. Prostheses that are not fitted properly can cause back, rib, and shoulder strain and pain. Insurance will provide reimbursement for some of the cost of prostheses; however, insurance may dictate where a woman can purchase her prosthesis and may have a cap on the amount that is reimbursed. Very attractive intimate wear and swim wear are also available for women after mastectomy. The American Cancer Society can provide a list of local resources and also has a catalogue available by calling 1-800-ACS-2345.

The American Cancer Society provides a temporary prosthesis, affectionately called the

---

**Excerpted with permission from Hjelmsted, L. (1993). *Fine Black Lines*. Englewood, CA.

"fluffy," that women who undergo mastectomy can use while their chest is healing. This "fluffy" is also very useful for women who are undergoing reconstruction. It can be used for the breast that has a tissue expander in place, removing cotton from the "fluffy" as the breast is enlarged during the inflation process.

Women who have had a lumpectomy may have changes in their nipple, breast shape, and skin contour. With breast reconstruction and sometimes also with lumpectomy, there may be areas of the breast that are numb. A reconstructed nipple is not a sensate nipple and will not respond to stimulation; however, some women express phantom breast sensations when the other breast is being stimulated. For all women, massaging the breast or chest after surgery can increase sensation and help restore a woman's body image.

During sexual activity, if the chest wall is tender from surgery or radiation therapy, the woman may be more comfortable with a change in positions (side lying or on top) or with a small pillow placed between her chest and her partner during intercourse.

Gynecologic Surgery

Hysterectomy, the removal of the uterus, should not affect the woman's ability to have intercourse or achieve orgasm. Perceived body image changes may affect desire in some women. If the vaginal canal is shortened by surgery, there may be discomfort with full penetration of the penis. Changing positions and adequate lubrication may improve comfort and enjoyment.

If the ovaries are also removed and the woman is not receiving estrogen replacement, she may have difficulty with lowered libido or desire, vaginal dryness, and thinning of the vaginal wall. If her cancer allows, estrogen cream helps improve the integrity of the vaginal wall, making intercourse more comfortable. If she cannot use estrogen, lubrication with nonhormonal, water-based gels (e.g., Replens) on a regular basis can help keep the vagina hydrated. Extra lubrication (KY Jelly, Astroglyde) during intercourse is also helpful.

Radical vulvectomy removes all of the vulva, which includes the clitoris. Women may experience scarring, which could make penetration with the penis uncomfortable. Use of lubrication and vaginal dilators may help stretch and keep the opening to the vagina elastic and make penetration more comfortable. Changing positions or allowing more gradual introduction of the penis will also help. It may also be more difficult to achieve orgasm without the clitoris to stimulate. With experimentation and play, a woman may find other areas of her body that, when stimulated, can lead her to orgasm (Schover, 1988b).

Pelvic Surgery in Men

Prostatectomy, cystectomy (removal of the bladder), and abdominal perineal (A-P) resection all can lead to problems with impotence. Damage to the pelvic nerve plexus and/or scarring around the blood vessels may interfere with the stimulation and blood supply needed to engorge the penis during the excitement phase. Nerve-sparing surgeries may decrease the risk for some men, but it may take several months before complete recovery.

Many methods are available to treat impotence. An external vacuum system uses a hand-held vacuum device to engorge the penis and a tension ring to maintain the erection. Medication can be injected into the penis (Papavoron and Pentalomine or prostaglandin E) that causes vasodilatation and smooth muscle relaxation, thereby leading to an erection that lasts for about an hour. A new urethral suppository (alprostadil) acts like the penile injections to create an erection without having to use needles (*A patient's guide for the treatment of impotence*, 1995).

More recently, a new oral medication, sildenafil (Viagra) has been approved for the treatment of erectile dysfunction. Viagra leads to smooth muscle relaxation in the penis, thereby allowing a normal response to sexual stimulation and penile erection. It does not improve the sex drive or libido of a man. Viagra may not be as successful in men who are impotent due to nerve damage from radical prostatectomy, although some men who undergo nerve-sparing surgery may have slightly better results. Viagra should also be used with caution in men who have malignancies with increased blood viscosity, such as some leukemias or multiple myeloma, because this may lead to prolonged and painful erections (priapism) (Marks et al., 1999).

Men also may choose to have surgical implants placed, which can be manipulated to create an erect penis for intercourse. Implants can range from small, inflexible rods that are permanently erect, to flexible rods that can be bent, to different types of inflatable rods with implantable pumps.

Retroperitoneal lymph node dissection usually does not cause problems with impotence; however, it can cause retrograde ejaculation. When the man achieves orgasm, the semen goes into the bladder rather than out the penis (dry orgasm). This should not affect his pleasure from the orgasm but may make it more difficult to impregnate a woman. If he wishes to father a child, his sperm will need to be collected from his urine and artificially inseminated into the woman. Dry ejaculations also occur with any surgery that removes the seminal vesicles and prostate gland because no semen is produced.

Removal of one testicle (orchiectomy) should not affect a man's physical ability to have a healthy sexual response. However, body image changes may cause psychological inhibition, and some men may choose to have a testicular prosthesis implanted. The testicles are a man's main source of testosterone, which is necessary for desire and erection. So, with bilateral orchiectomy, testosterone levels are greatly diminished and sexual dysfunction may occur.

If a man has penile cancer, he may require partial or complete penile amputation. With partial amputation complete sexual response, including penetration and orgasm, can occur. With full amputation penetration is no longer possible; however, he can still achieve orgasm with masturbation or partner stimulation of the scrotum (Schover, 1988a).

Ostomies

Both urostomies and colostomies may cause problems with body image; however, they do not necessarily impede normal sexual relationships. Odor can be controlled by avoiding foods that cause odors in urine or stool, such as asparagus, beans, or broccoli. Also, eating applesauce, yogurt, and buttermilk can help counteract odors. Some people find that using sexy, cute, or humorous stoma covers can help them camouflage the physical changes. Some people with a colostomy can schedule sexual relationships around their normal bowel routine or may irrigate just before sexual activity. If bowel movement regularity is not possible, the appliance should be emptied just before sexual encounters. A sense of humor and a sense of self help overcome embarrassing moments of gas passing or leakage.

> *J. W., 23 years old, was a model before her diagnosis of leukemia, which led to an episode of ischemic bowel requiring a colostomy. She found that irrigating her colostomy and wearing a stoma cap and sexy crotchless lingerie allowed her to feel "normal" and engage in full sexual activity.*

Amputations

Removal of any body part requires adjustment both emotionally and physically. Prosthetics have come a long way with natural-appearing limbs and other missing body parts (e.g., nose, ears). Many of the prosthetic devices also are functional with feedback mechanisms for more realistic movement and sensation.

The actual loss of a limb should not interfere in the sexual response; however, problems with phantom limb sensations or pain may decrease de-

sire and arousal. Also, people may need to be creative with positioning and pillows for balance and movement during intercourse when a limb is missing.

Therapy-Related Effects on Sexuality

Many of the chemotherapy and hormonal agents as well as antiemetic, psychotropic, and antidiarrhea agents can cause changes in the sexual response and fertility. Often, things will return to normal after the therapy is discontinued, but some people will be receiving therapy for the rest of their lives and will need to learn how to overcome or minimize the effects of treatment (Table 16-3).

Radiation therapy can also cause body image changes and possible difficulty with sexuality. The skin may develop telangiectasia (spider veins), hyperpigmentation, dryness, loss of elasticity, and hair loss. Fatigue and malaise can decrease desire and arousal. The skin may be tender and need to be protected if experiencing redness or peeling. A

TABLE 16-3
MEDICATION EFFECTS ON SEXUALITY

Agent	Effect on Sexuality/Fertility	Treatment
Alkylating agents	Amenorrhea, azoospermia, vaginal dryness	Sperm or egg banking, estrogen creams if allowed, lubricants
Antiemetics	Impotence, decreased libido, decreased intensity of orgasm, dry ejaculation	Change types of antiemetics, testosterone preparations if allowed
Antiestrogens	Hot flashes, vaginal dryness, weight gain, decreased libido, decreased intensity of orgasm	Some physicians are allowing estrogen replacement with antiestrogen medications, vitamin E, flaxseed oil, testosterone cream
Antimetabolites	Stomatitis leading to pain during kissing, possibly pain on intercourse	Topical anesthetic for the mouth, lubrication for vagina or penis
Antitumor antibiotics	Impotence, decreased libido, nausea	Testosterone may help
Biologic agents	Decreased libido, depression	Antidepressants
Estrogen	Impotence, decreased libido, increased weight, gynecomastia (enlarged breasts)	Alternative forms of sexual expression, radiation therapy to the breast
Steroids	Acne, obesity, vaginitis, increased facial hair	Antibiotics, dermatology consult
Testosterone	Facial hair, increased libido, increased size of clitoris, weight gain, menopausal symptoms	Cosmetic therapy, explanations allow woman to feel normal with increased sex drive
Vinca alkaloids	Impotence, decreased libido, retrograde ejaculation, decreased peripheral sensation	Vitamin B_6, testosterone may help

change of position or use of pillow may help decrease trauma to the skin. Radiation to the head and neck may cause mouth and throat pain and dryness. Women who experience vaginal or pelvic radiation therapy may have vaginal stenosis requiring dilatation and lubrication. Men with pelvic radiation therapy may experience impotence due to sclerosis of the blood supply.

Special Populations

Teens

The adolescent years are challenging as teens develop their sexual identity ranging from experimentation and exploration to establishing mature, long-lasting relationships. Over 40% of teens are sexually active by the age of 16.

> *S. W. was a 16-year-old who had been undergoing chemotherapy for a year for acute lymphocytic leukemia. He had been instructed on proper use of contraceptives; however, he believed that after all of his chemotherapy he was sterile until his 15-year-old girlfriend became pregnant.*

> *M. P. was an 18-year-old with an aggressive lymphoma that required a large amount of blood product support. After she was in remission, she resumed her sexual activities with her boyfriend. Two years later, both she and her boyfriend tested positive for HIV.*

Nurses must ensure that teens fully understand the risk of pregnancy during treatment and the concepts of abstinence, safe sex, and contraceptives. They should also be allowed to express their feelings in a safe, accepting environment.

Immunosuppressed

Both cancer diagnoses and treatment may lead to periods of pancytopenia. Anemia can lead to weakness and fatigue. Taking a more passive role in sexual activities, changing positions, and planning on intimacies during high-energy times (first thing in the morning or after a nap) may help. With neutropenia, there is an increased risk for infection. Good hygiene is very important to prevent infection, and the use of condoms is highly recommended. Extra lubrication may be needed to prevent tearing of the vagina. Rectal intercourse is not recommended during periods of neutropenia.

> *C. T. was a 28-year-old woman hospitalized with pancytopenia for the treatment of Burkitt's lymphoma. It was feared that she would not leave the hospital. For her 1-year anniversary, the nurses chipped in and paid for a hotel room across from the hospital. They obtained a pass for her and her husband to spend the evening together. They gave platelets and all of her antibiotics before she left so she could have a 6-hour window of time with her husband. The clinical nurse specialist brought condoms for them to use and instructed C. T. on careful, gentle penetration with good lubrication. C. T. came back that night beaming and slept without pain medicine for the first time in days. She died 2 weeks later.*

Elderly

There is a myth that sex is only for the young and able bodied. Older adults may be reluctant to speak about their sexual experiences because of societal cues that it is inappropriate (e.g., the "dirty old man" label). Yet, today the image of older people being active and sexually alive into their 7th and 8th decade is more of a reality. Sexual activity is natural and spontaneous well into the later years, and information that is given to younger patients should also be shared with older people.

Terminally Ill

Patients who are dying may have decreased libido or energy needed to experience active sexual activities. However, they still need private time for intimacy, including skin-to-skin contact, cuddling, and closeness. Some hospices have waterbeds and double beds with rooms with doors that lock to allow for private, intimate moments.

Fertility

Chemotherapy leads to depletion of the germinal epithelium that lines the testicles and seminal vesicles. For women, it can lead to ovarian failure and sterility. The risk of infertility depends on the age of the person and the type and amount of drug received. The greatest risk for infertility is with alkylating agents, such as cyclophosphamide. A woman who is in her forties has a greater than 50% chance of entering menopause with chemotherapy, whereas a woman in her twenties may stop menstruating for a short time and then resume normal menstrual cycles. The long-term effects on eggs or sperm are not known; therefore, contraception should be used during and for at least a year after completing chemotherapy.

For men, sperm banking is a viable option to preserve the ability to father a child in the future. Unfortunately, many men who are ill do not have healthy sperm because of the effects of illness or fevers on spermatogenesis. Sperm should be banked every other day for a minimum of three samples. If time allows for the number of days to get the sample before starting chemotherapy, the man masturbates or with partner stimulation collects the semen, which is ejaculated into a sterile container. Tests are done on the initial specimen to determine sperm motility, sperm count (50 to 80 million/mm^3), and the presence of any sexually transmittable diseases. If the sample appears vital, it is frozen and can be stored for many years. To find out where a sperm bank is in your area, call fertility specialists in your telephone book (Honea, 1994; Smith & Babaia, 1992).

> *J. P. was 28 years old when he was diagnosed with Hodgkin's disease. He decided to sperm bank before his chemotherapy and radiation therapy. Five years later, he and his wife of 2 years found out that he was sterile and she was artificially inseminated with his sperm. After two attempts, they became parents of twin boys, both extremely healthy.*

For women, preserving fertility is much more difficult. Women can bank their eggs; however, they often need fertility drugs to stimulate multiple egg production and then need laparoscopic surgery to harvest the eggs. The procedure may be prohibited if hormonal therapy stimulates the cancer (breast cancer), if treatments need to be started before the stimulation and harvest can occur, or if the woman is too sick to undergo even a minor surgical procedure. For women with cancers that are not stimulated by hormones, oral contraceptives may help preserve ovarian function (Chapman & Sutcliffe, 1981).

Radiation therapy can also affect fertility if the testes or ovaries are within the field of radiation. If possible, attempts will be made to shield these organs during the treatments.

Moving On

In today's world, so much emphasis is placed on how we look and how we perform sexually. With all of the possible changes from a cancer diagnosis and treatment, people may have great difficulty in living up to society's norms. However, many people are able to overcome the emotional and physical challenges of cancer and go on to lead happy, fulfilling lives again. Using the acronym HAPPINESS, it is possible to find peace with self and intimacy with others again (Johnson, 1994; Leigh et al., 1993).

H—HOPE. Hold onto hope. There is always hope. Hope for a pain-free night. Hope for an evening of cuddling. Hope for a day without nausea.

A—ASK. Always ask your physician and/or nurse for suggestions to help you feel better physically, emotionally, and sexually.

P—PLAN. Plan time with your significant other, away from children, the phone or beepers and the television. Have a date night and maybe even go necking again.

P—PERMISSION. Permit yourself to experiment. Try a new style while shopping for a wig. Try something new with your partner during an intimate moment.

I—IMAGE. Get in touch with your new body image. Use touch, visualization, and affirmations to find the new you.

N—NEEDS. Communicate what you need and what makes you feel good. Make certain that you meet your own needs too, instead of always putting others' needs before yours.

E—EXPRESS. Express yourself fully. Do not hold back your feelings from yourself or your family. Try a journal if it is too hard to say things out loud.

S—SUPPORT. Find a support group for yourself and significant others. Not only will they help you feel better, they also may help you live longer. This is a great place to ask for helpful hints on improving body image and/or sexual intimacy.

S—SELF. Find and maintain a sense of self above all else. You need to love yourself before others can love you.

REFERENCES

American Nurses Association & Oncology Nursing Society (1996). *Statement on the scope of standards of oncology nursing practice.* Washington, DC: American Nurses Association.

Amon, J. S. (1976). *Behavioral therapy of sexual problems: Brief therapy.* Hagerstown, MD: Harper & Row.

Chapman, R., & Sutcliffe, S. (1981). Protection of ovarian function by oral contraceptive in women receiving chemotherapy for Hodgkin's disease. *Blood, 58,* 849–851.

Chemotherapy, radiation therapy, hair loss and you. (1981). Minneapolis, MN: Allen Arthur.

Cobleigh, M., Berris, R., Bush, T., et al. (1994). Estrogen replacement therapy in breast cancer survivors. A time for change. *Journal of the American Medical Association, 272,* 540–545.

Harwood, K., & O'Connor, A. (1994). Sexuality and breast cancer: Overview of issues. *Innovations in Oncology Nursing, 10,* 30–33, 51.

Honea, K. (1994). Fertility options for survivors. *Coping, 32.*

Johnson, J. (1994.) Enhancing sexuality and self-esteem after a breast cancer diagnosis. *Innovations in Oncology Nursing, 10,* 39–42.

Kaplan, H. S. (1992). A neglected issue: The sexual side effects of current treatment for breast cancer. *Journal of Sex and Marital Therapy, 18,* 1–18.

Leigh, S., Boyle, D., Loescher, L., et al. (1993). Psychosocial issues of long-term survival from adult cancer. In S. Groenwald, M. Frogge, M. Goodman & C. Yarbro (Eds.), *Cancer nursing: Principles and practices* (3rd ed., pp. 484–495). Boston: Jones and Bartlett.

Marks, L., Duda, C., Dorey, F., et al. (1999). Treatment of erectile dysfunction with Sildenafil. *Urology, 53,* 19–24.

Nishimoto, P. (1997). Sexuality. In R. Gates & R. Fink (Eds.), *Oncology nursing secrets.* Philadelphia: Henley and Belfus.

A patient's guide for the treatment of impotence. (1995). Augusta, GA: Osbon Medical Systems.

Rabinowitz, B. (1994a). Addressing unanswered questions about sexuality. *Innovations in Oncology Nursing, 10,* 37.

Rabinowitz, B. (1994b). Sexuality issues—The nurse's role. *Innovations in Oncology Nursing, 10,* 29, 38.

Schover, L. (1988a). *Sexuality and cancer: For the man who has cancer and his partner.* New York: American Cancer Society.

Schover, L. (1988b). *Sexuality and cancer: For the woman who has cancer and her partner.* New York: American Cancer Society.

Smith, D., & Babaia, R. (1992). The effects of treatment for cancer on male fertility and sexuality. *Cancer Nursing, 15,* 271–275.

Venous Access Devices

CHAPTER

17

Esther Muscari Lin

Types of Catheters

Venous access devices (VADs) can be classified into two general categories—central and peripheral. VADs are further categorized by how and where they are inserted and where the tip of the catheter is located. See Table 17-1 for defining characteristics of different VADs.

Peripheral

Although cancer care can extend for years, treatment periods can be limited to months. Therefore, a catheter may be chosen with a short time period in mind. Patients may even experience more than one type of catheter over the course of their disease process. Peripheral or short-term catheters can be used in both the inpatient and ambulatory settings. Peripheral catheters are placed by way of a peripheral vein and reside only in a peripheral vein. The most common peripheral catheters are inserted into oncology patients with a dwell time greater than 72 hours. The midline and midclavicular catheters are intended for ambulatory use.

Insertion

Midline catheters are inserted peripherally, most commonly in the antecubital fossa, and the catheter tip terminates in the proximal portion of the extremity (Intravenous Nurses Society, 1997a).

Midclavicular catheters are also inserted in a peripheral vein, like midline catheters, but the tip terminates in the proximal axillary or subclavian veins (Intravenous Nurses Society, 1997a) (Figure 17-1).

A variety of names have been applied to peripherally located catheter tips, including "halfway," "extended peripheral," and "peripherally inserted catheter" (PIC). PIC sounds the same as PICC (peripherally inserted central catheter). Emphasizing this point is warranted because the names are sometimes interchanged or incorrectly used. Because midline and midclavicular catheters terminate in peripheral veins, it is vital to distinguish what type of catheter is in place, because certain infusions can only be administered through a central vein. Midline and midclavicular infusions require an iso-osmotic or near iso-osmotic admixture (Intravenous Nurses Society, 1997a).

Duration

PICs often remain in place beyond the manufacturer's recommendation. This usually depends on patient status and need, the skill of caregivers, the infusion compositions, the patient's venous access status, skin integrity, and the condition of the vein in which the catheter is placed (Intravenous Nurses Society, 1997b). The Intravenous Nurses Society (1997a) recommends limiting midline catheter dwell time to 2 to 4 weeks and midclavicular dwell time to 2 to 3 months, because these catheters are still treated as *peripheral* catheters.

TABLE 17-1

VENOUS ACCESS DEVICES

	Catheter Tip Location	Therapy Duration	Required Insertion	Minimal Flush When Not in Use	Commonly Encountered Complications
Peripheral					
Smaller peripheral veins	Peripleural	<72 hours	Bedside	BID	Phlebitis
Midline	Proximal portion of extremity	Short-term/ acute	Bedside	BID	Thrombus
Midclavicular	Axillary or subclavian	Short-term/ acute	Bedside	BID	Thrombus
Central					
Subclavian/jugular	Superior vena cava (SVC)/right atria	Short-term/ acute	Bedside	BID or QD	• Infection • Thrombus
External, tunneled and cuffed	SVC/right atria	Long-term	Operating room	QD	• Fibrin sheath • Infection • Severed catheter has repair kit • Tip migration
Peripherally inserted	SVC/right atria	Extended or inter-mediate	Bedside Home Clinic Interven-tional radio-logy	BID or QD	• Catheter malposition • Infection • Rupture/break—Without repair kits for all the different types • Mechanical phlebitis
Subcutaneously implanted	SVC/right atria	Long-term	Operating room	Once a month	• Less risk of infection than external catheters • Tip migration

Maintenance

Flushing and dressing changes follow institutional protocols for peripheral lines because the tips of these catheters are in veins considered to be peripheral circulation, with smaller and narrower lumina.

Complications

Thrombus formation is at higher risk of occurrence because peripheral veins are smaller and are more easily influenced by the size and location of the catheter tip, patient coagulation status, and osmolality of the infusion (Intravenous Nurses Society, 1997b).

Central

A central venous catheter (CVC) or central venous access device (CVAD) refers to a catheter with tip location in a central vessel, most commonly at the junction of the superior vena cava and the right atrium. CVADs are either external or implanted ports and are either tunneled or nontunneled. CVADs are composed of either silicone or polyurethane. Silicone is a very soft, pliable material; polyurethane is slightly stiffer, resulting in more intimal vessel damage. Silicone is thicker and not as strong as polyurethane, but equally durable. Silicone and polyurethane are thromboresistant and nonhemolytic, thus making them less likely to harbor microbial colonization (Andris & Krzywda, 1997b; Macklin, 1997).

Duration

Central catheters can be categorized as either short term, intermediate, or long term.

Short-term CVADs are often used in critical care units or other inpatient units in which solu-

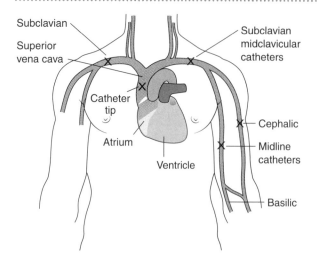

Subclavian
Superior vena cava
Catheter tip
Atrium
Ventricle
Subclavian midclavicular catheters
Cephalic
Midline catheters
Basilic

Figure 17-1 Catheter landmarks.

tions dictate central administration or peripheral access is limited and therapy duration is expected to be limited to the inpatient admission. Catheters used for short-term central access are percutaneous and nontunneled (Andris & Krzywda, 1997b).

Long-term CVADs have become almost routine in the care and treatment of patients with cancer because of a number of factors:

1. Central access allows infusion of high osmolar and vesicant solutions because the blood volume is high enough for instantaneous dilution and avoidance of intraluminal damage from these solutions (Andris & Krzywda, 1997b).
2. Long-term or "permanent" CVADs allow access to the bloodstream for blood aspiration, in addition to infusional therapies, without having to repeatedly "stick" a person's skin.
3. CVADs can have multiple lumina, which allow for multiple, noncompatible therapies to be infused simultaneously.
4. The length of time CVADs can remain in a person is indefinite, with the literature reporting up to 3 years.
5. Large-bore pheresis catheters required for stem cell harvesting can also be inserted with intended long-term dwell time and can be used for infusional therapies and blood aspiration after the pheresis period is completed.

There are four major types of long-term CVADs: the external, cuffed, tunneled, right-atrial catheter; the external, cuffed, tunneled, pheresis catheter; the subcutaneously implanted device; and the peripherally inserted central catheter (PICC). Regardless of the intended duration, the complications and general maintenance issues for each of the central catheters are the same and are summarized on the following pages.

Maintenance

It is necessary to have regular dressing changes and flushing protocols. CVADs require sterile dressing changes on some type of regular schedule or frequency and whenever they are soiled or wet, with at least daily flushing. The materials used for dressing changes and flushing vary among institutions and catheter manufacturing companies. The Centers for Disease Control recommend dressing changes only when they become wet or soiled. The Intravenous Nurses Society recommends regular changes without specifying frequency for transparent dressings and every 48 hours for gauze dressings. Due to the wide variety of recommendations, it is best to refer to individual institution policies and procedures for flushing and dressing standards.

There is agreement that appropriate cleansing when changing a dressing is 70% alcohol to remove *Staphylococcus epidermidis* and, when dry, iodophor to kill fungi, which occurs over time as the iodophor is allowed to sit on the skin (Andris & Krzywda, 1997b; Masoorli, 1996). The application of an antimicrobial ointment is controversial due to the potentially increased risk of contributing to bacterial resistance and/or *Candida* colonization (Andris & Krzwyda, 1997b; Masoorli, 1996; Masoorli, 1997b).

Complications

CVADs most commonly pose a risk for infection/sepsis, thrombosis, occlusion, and air embolism (Campbell, 1996; Macklin, 1997; Masoorli, 1997c; Ray, Stacey, Imrie & Filshie, 1996; Reed & Phillips, 1996). Infections can be either local or systemic. Local infections occur at the catheter exit site or along the tunnel in the case of tunneled catheters. Although the expected signs of localized infection, such as erythema, edema, tenderness, and drainage, may be absent in the neutropenic patient, infection may still be present. A tunnel infection is reflected in redness or tenderness along the catheter under the skin. When palpating the anterior chest, the subcutaneous catheter can be felt; as pressure is applied, the patient can report tenderness or pain and fluctuance may be noted. Systemic infections tend to be more obvious, with fever, malaise, hypertension, and possibly symptoms occurring within minutes of flushing or infusing into a catheter. Localized signs may be treated with oral antibiotics, but often, especially in the immunocompromised patient, the intravenous route is used. Warm, dry heat to the site and topical antibiotics may be helpful in addition to using other routes (Campbell, 1996; Masoorli, 1997b). Positive blood cultures from the central catheter always result in intravenous antibiotics. Difficulty in maintaining an infected line arises when culturing a fungus from the line because fungus-infected catheters tend to be resistant to antifungal therapy; this often results in catheter removal.

A thrombus develops from platelet and fibrin collection, usually at a site of injury or to a foreign body in a vein (Masoorli, 1997c; Reed & Phillips, 1996). Catheter tips can injure the intima or inner layer of a vein wall, whether it is during insertion, while indwelling, or after catheter migration (Andris & Krzywda, 1997b; Campbell, 1996; Collin, Ahmadinejad & Misse, 1997; Masoorli, 1997b; Reed & Phillips, 1996). The fibrin deposition can occur within the catheter or as a sheath along the length of the catheter or vein. A fibrin sheath along the catheter and near the tip can act like a one-way valve, allowing infusion of fluids inhibiting blood aspiration. A dye study of the catheter performed in interventional radiology, in which dye is injected into the catheter, will reveal the sheath and provide the details of location, length, and diameter of the long clot and if it is hanging over the catheter tip.

Blood clot formation within or at the end of the catheter can also occlude a catheter. Inadequate flushing or low-set alarm pressures can lead to blood backing into the catheter or blood not being adequately cleared from the catheter and resultant clot development (Harrison, 1997; Reed & Phillips, 1996). Once a chest radiograph confirms catheter tip placement, diagnosis can be made on clinical signs.

Signs and symptoms of a thrombosis can be obvious with catheter malfunction or more subtle when the thrombosis is in the superior vena cava, with difficult infusion, or blood withdrawal. Signs of superior vena cava syndrome can also begin subtly and progress to more obvious characteristics. Hand and/or arm swelling, a prominent venous pattern visible on the person's chest, distended neck veins, facial swelling, facial flushing or redness, dysphagia, or pain anywhere along the ipsilateral side of the patient's chest can be indicative of a thrombosis. Diagnosis is confirmed by fluoroscopy or venogram.

Difficulty flushing with or without the ability to aspirate blood suggests a clot and/or fibrin sheath, which can be confirmed with a dye study. Inability to flush or aspirate poses a much larger challenge (Figure 17-2). In cases of resistance with confirmed catheter tip location, the instillation of a thrombolytic agent such as urokinase is often successful in reducing a sheath or clearing a clot (Andris & Krzywda, 1997b; Reed & Phillips, 1996). If totally occluded, characterized by the inability to instill any fluid, the catheter is removed. If there is the ability to instill even a small amount, 0.5 cc of urokinase (5,000 U/cc), then it should be instilled and allowed to dwell for 15 to 30 minutes (urokinase has a short half-life of 6 to 14 minutes). This process should be repeated, gradually increasing the solution volume to the amount the catheter will allow, to a maximum of 1 to 2 cc (5,000 to 10,000 U/cc). It is crucial to not force any fluid into a catheter when solid resistance is met. The risk of shooting an emboli exists when pushing against a catheter occlusion. Therefore, when resistance is met after applying minimal pressure, there should be an attempt to aspirate and attempt to flush again (Macklin, 1997). It is also helpful to not use small syringes such as a 1-cc syringe when flushing or aspirating because the smaller the syringe, the greater the pressure that is exerted on the catheter (Masoorli, 1997b). There is also the risk of tearing the catheter when applying too much force against resistance. A hallmark sign that pressure has been applied against resistance is a longitudinal tear along the catheter. This can also be seen if a catheter is flushed with the clamp on.

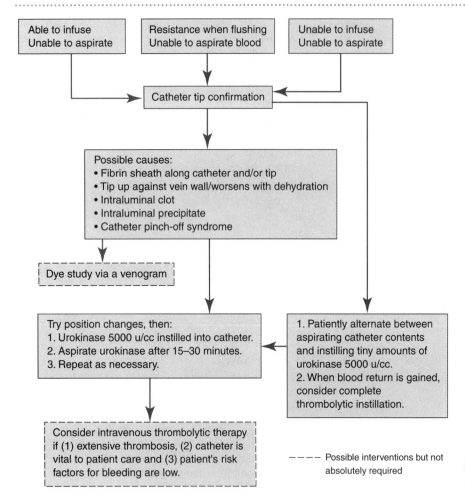

Figure 17-2 Troubleshooting catheter occlusion(s).

Management of a thrombosis depends on the severity of symptoms the patient is experiencing, the vessel(s) involved, the need for the indwelling device, and the extent of the thrombus. One may be less willing to try a course of an intravenous thrombolytic agent in oncology patients than in a different population because of other risk factors the oncology patient may have for bleeding.

An air embolus occurs if the catheter becomes disconnected from the cap or intravenous line or is severed or punctured. It can also occur during insertion or removal and when changing intravenous lines and catheter caps. Air is able to rush into the central vein at a rate commensurate with the length and diameter of the catheter. Signs and symptoms of an embolus include chest pain, short-

ness of breath, tachypnea, dyspnea, anxiety and/or feelings of impending doom, dizziness, hypertension, and tachycardia. Immediate action should include clamping the catheter above the opening and turning the patient on the left side with the bed in Trendelenburg position. Management is supportive of cardiopulmonary functions with intravenous fluids for hypertension, 100% oxygen, and cardiac monitoring (Campbell, 1996).

Other, less common complications include occlusion, catheter migration, and catheter breakage. In addition to clotting, catheter occlusion can also occur because of a precipitate within the catheter, catheter pinch-off syndrome, or a malpositioning of the catheter. Precipitates occur when incompatible drugs infuse together or the catheter is not properly flushed between drugs. A drug precipitate occlusion is difficult to resolve, and there have been some reports of instilling a small amount of hydrochloric acid (Campbell, 1996). The belief is that by decreasing the pH with the hydrochloric acid, the precipitate will dissolve (Andris & Krzywda, 1997b).

Catheter pinch-off syndrome occurs because of external compression of the catheter by the clavicle and first rib (Andris & Krzywda, 1997a). This can occur after a percutaneous placement of the catheter into the subclavian vein. As the catheter is compressed it becomes occluded, but occlusion is intermittent as the person moves and raises his or her arm. Over time, the catheter can become weakened from repeated compressions and eventually break, with the risk of the proximal catheter end embolizing into the central venous system. The key to detecting pinch-off syndrome is that the inability to flush or aspirate is alleviated when the person raises his or her arm. Confirmation is made with fluoroscopy or venogram with the patient's arms at the sides and then with arms raised (Andris & Krzywda, 1997a).

Catheter migration does occur in long-term CVADs but also occurs in a short-term catheter because it is not tunneled, is without a cuff for subcutaneous tissue to adhere to, and is not sutured. Although catheter tip position is confirmed at the time of placement, the location of the catheter tip is not reconfirmed over time unless signs and symptoms of malfunction occur. It is believed the CVADs, regardless of suturing or tunneling, are at risk for migrating because of the physical factors involved with a catheter in the superior vena cava (SVC). The high flow forces of the SVC; strong physical forces such as coughing, sneezing, or straining; repetitive raised arm movement (e.g., painting, hammering, tennis serve); and positive pressure ventilation can cause displacement (Collin, Ahmadinejad & Misse, 1996). Migration is confirmed on chest radiograph. Repositioning the catheter may be an option with use of a guidewire, but in many cases it is not possible, requiring removal.

Silicone catheters are at risk for being punctured, torn, or severed. Longitudinal tears along the catheter suggest excessive force used in flushing the catheter, as is the case when the catheter is flushed with the clamp closed. Sometimes, patients accidentally sever the catheter completely when using scissors near their chest. Fortunately, with many of the long-term catheters, if not damaged too close to the chest so that there is room to manipulate the old catheter, a new catheter can be reconnected.

Short-Term CVADs

INSERTION

Short-term CVADs are usually inserted by way of jugular, subclavian, or femoral veins because these veins are easy to find with physical landmarks, which assists in guiding the placement, and the veins are able to handle the large bore of the catheters (Levins, 1996). Short-term CVADs are often placed at the bedside using the Seldinger technique, in which the vessel is cannulated, a guidewire is inserted, and the catheter is threaded over the guidewire into the central circulation (Andris & Krzywda, 1997b; Levin, 1997). Patients are positioned supine in Trendelenburg position, occasionally with a rolled towel between the scapula if the subclavian or jugular vein is being accessed. The insertion procedure is a sterile procedure, requiring caps, masks, sterile drapes, gown, and gloves. The catheter is primed with sterile heparin before insertion, and IV solution should be on hand, primed and ready to be connected. Because positioning is uncomfortable, the patient's face is either partly or totally covered, and there can be discomfort with local anesthetic injections; some patients may benefit from a sedative or antianxiety agent. Radiographic documentation of catheter tip location is required after placement and should be documented in the patient's chart. Before placement documentation, infusions should be run slowly and be limited to an isotonic solution. Because of the insertion risks of arrhythmias, hemorrhage, hemothorax, and pneumothorax, reassessments should focus on vital signs, heart sounds, breath sounds, and pulses distal to the insertion site (Levins, 1996; Nightingale, Norman, Cunningham, Young, Webb & Filshie, 1995; Spies & Berlin, 1997).

DURATION

Short-term CVADs are generally intended for the time of a patient's hospitalization because they are nontunneled, without a cuff, and require suturing

(Reed & Phillips, 1996). The catheters tend to be stiffer than those used for long term; are located in difficult to reach areas for the patient, making self-care of the catheter very difficult; and, in some institutions, are changed over a guidewire on a regular basis or after a febrile episode.

COMPLICATIONS

The most common complications associated with short-term CVADs are infection and thrombus (Harrison, 1997). There are increased infection risks when the catheter is placed by a practitioner with minimal insertion experience; there is more than one lumen; or there are breaks in sterile technique, infrequent handwashing, and frequent hub manipulation (Andris & Kryzwda, 1997b; Harrison, 1997; Ouwendyk & Helferty, 1996; Smith & Shepard, 1995).

Intermediate and Long-Term CVADs

EXTERNAL, TUNNELED, CUFFED, RIGHT ATRIAL CATHETER

The external, tunneled, cuffed, right atrial catheter can have one to three lumina and was the first long-term CVAD developed in the early 1980s.

Insertion
The visible catheter is inserted into a major vein, and the tip is guided into the SVC, while the remaining lumina are tunneled under the skin and exited out onto the patient's chest. There is a Dacron cuff, sometimes with an antimicrobial covering that is just above the exit site (approximately 1 to 2 inches), which adheres to tissue and creates a mechanical barrier to bacteria entry. These catheters require surgical placement and are considered short or same-day procedures but can be removed in the ambulatory office. Common examples of external, tunneled, cuffed CVADs are the Hickman, Broviac, and Groshong (Bard Access Systems, Salt Lake City, UT).

Duration
External right atrial catheters can remain in place for many years (Masoorli, 1997c). The tunneling of the catheter and the placement of the cuff so that it adheres to subcutaneous tissue add to the

catheter's potential longevity by significantly reducing bacteria colonization (Masoorli, 1997c; Ouwendyk & Helferty, 1996). Removal is usually because the catheter is no longer needed or an unmanageable complication develops.

Maintenance
A heparinized flush solution maintains the patency of CVCs. A concentration of 10 U/mL in an amount to sufficiently match the catheter bore size and volume has been shown to be effective (Andris & Krzywda, 1997b; Clemence, Walker & Farr, 1995).

Flushing protocols vary among institutions and are also influenced by the type of catheter, intended function (whether for stem cell pheresis or blood aspiration), and if the patient has had previous fibrin sheaths or occlusions. After blood aspiration, an additional normal saline flush in varying amounts depending on institution protocol precedes the anticoagulant flush. In general, most catheters require daily anticoagulant flushing when not in use with the exception of the Groshong catheter, which has a one-way valve, blocking blood from flowing back into the catheter after it is flushed. The Groshong flush requirement is weekly as opposed to daily. When flushing a catheter, clamping the catheter just as the syringe plunger is infusing the last milliliter in the syringe can minimize the chance that the catheter will suck blood back into the tip, contributing to clotting (Harrison, 1997).

The required dressing for the right atrial, cuffed, external catheter promotes a good deal of discussion because the literature is abundant in comparing gauze and transparent dressing, yet the practical implications are not clear (Conly, Grieves & Peters, 1989; Masoorli, 1997a; Roach et al., 1995; Treston-Aurand, Olmsted, Allen-Bridson & Craig, 1997).

PHERESIS CATHETER

The pheresis catheter can also have multiple lumina and replaces the previously used femoral catheters.

Insertion
The large-bore pheresis catheters are similar in appearance to the above listed catheters but are considerably larger. These catheters are also placed by

surgeons in the operating room. An example of a combined pheresis/infusion catheter is the Horizon duration pheresis catheters, which are intended to be used for infusion therapy and blood aspirations after completion of pheresis and are meant to be long-term. In general, these catheters tend to be larger and heavier because of the necessary bore size for pheresis. Therefore, the exit site incision is slightly larger, resulting in a larger area for bacteria to enter. Also, because of the larger catheter size consuming more intravenous space, occlusions from clotting may also be a greater risk. Because this catheter is relatively new, was created for the dual purpose of stem cell pheresis and long-term therapy, and is used mainly in the bone marrow transplantation population, information about the complications, duration, and maintenance requirements is still being gained. The pheresis/infusion catheter requires similar flushing schedules as the right atrial catheters, but may require different heparin concentrations and fluid volumes. Variability among centers regarding maintenance standards and procedures is considerable.

IMPLANTED PORT DEVICE

The totally implanted device, or port, is not visible to the naked eyed and is composed of two parts, the reservoir (titanium or stainless steel) and the catheter.

Insertion

Subcutaneously implanted CVADs consist of a reservoir with a silicone self-sealing septum and a catheter attached to the reservoir. The catheter is inserted into a major vein, and its tip is also positioned in the SVC. The other end of the catheter is then attached to the reservoir, and the reservoir is placed in a created "pocket" in the subcutaneous tissue of the upper chest. The reservoir and vascular access are achieved by pushing a noncoring, bent, special needle (huber needle) through the skin and into the septum until the metal back of the reservoir is reached. Subcutaneously implanted devices or ports require surgical placement and a return trip to the operating room for removal.

Duration

Implanted CVADs are intended for long-term use. There may be a decreased risk of infection because the skin serves as the protective barrier against infection (Schwarz, Groeger & Coit, 1997).

Maintenance

The catheter is accessed under sterile technique, and a central line dressing covering the catheter needs to be maintained only while the needle is in place. The anticoagulation solution is the same as what is used for the right atrial catheter, but when the catheter is not in use, the flushing frequency is once a month (Brown, Muirhead, Travis, Vire, Weller & Hauer-Jensen, 1997).

Complications

Some complications unique to the implanted port include catheter migration and Twiddler's syndrome. Catheter migration in the implanted port has an additional risk factor for occurrence because the catheter is separate from the port reservoir. It is secured with a port-specific clip. The early cases of catheter migration in which the entire catheter separated from the port and migrated into the central circulation were due to securement technique, which has since been improved. Another complication unique to the port is called Twiddler's syndrome, in which the patient manipulates the port to the point that it flips over and the metal back rather than the septum is against the skin (Reed & Phillips, 1996). Twiddler's syndrome can be avoided by suturing the metal port to the tissue.

An additional risk accompanying the implanted port is that the port pocket the reservoir is sutured into carries the risk of becoming infected. Erythema, pain, drainage, and fever are signs of a pocket infection and can progress to the reservoir being pushed through the skin and out of the body. Although port infections are treated and respond to antibiotic coverage like other CVDs, pocket infections do not and usually lead to catheter removal (Schwarz, Groeger & Coit, 1997).

PERIPHERALLY INSERTED CENTRAL CATHETERS

Peripherally inserted central catheters (PICC) are "catheters inserted by way of a peripheral vein with the tip residing in the vena cava" (Intravenous Nurses Society, 1997b).

Insertion

The PICC has grown quickly in popularity because of easy insertion. Insertion can occur in the home, at the bedside, in the clinic, or in interventional radiology. Although sterile technique is required, venous access is by way of a peripheral vein, usually the basilic or cephalic vein, is threaded toward the heart, and does not require a surgeon or the operating room (Sansivero, 1995c). Chest radiographic confirmation of tip placement in the SVC–atria junction is required before using the catheter. Placement of a PICC line is considerably easier and quicker than other catheters for patients when they need central venous access.

Duration

PICC lines have potentially long dwell times with reports of over 2 years (Sansivero, 1997a). The ease in acquiring and placing PICC lines, combined with complications of other CVDs, has resulted in large increases in usage of PICC. This has led to growing amounts of information about duration, maintenance, and problems.

Maintenance

There is very little consensus concerning flushing and dressing change protocols (Sansivero, 1995). Depending on the PICC manufacturer, flushing requirements vary, but all require at least daily or, in some cases, twice-a-day flushing with an anticoagulant solution. Many PICC lines are open ended, requiring every-12-hour flushes with 3 cc of 10 U/cc when not in use (Sansivero, 1997b). Closed-ended PICCs, which have a valve that closes when fluid is not infusing, do not require anticoagulant flush solutions and can be flushed with normal saline solution after each use or once a week (Sansivero, 1997a). Dressing changes should be sterile and in accordance with other central lines in a institution. PICC dressing changes can occur as infrequently as every 7 days unless the dressing becomes wet (Sansivero, 1997a). A difference in dressing recommendations from other central lines is to coil the catheter under the dressing and cover it up to the hub, in an attempt to secure the catheter better and minimize migration (Sansivero, 1997a).

Complications

Flow rate is determined by the ratio of the infusing fluid's pressure against resistance. Factors that influence resistance are fluid viscosity, catheter length, and internal catheter diameter, or bore. The long length of the PICC, combined with the small diameter of some of the PICCs, adds to the resistance and can decrease the flow rate (Macklin, 1997).

There can also be resistance to PICC catheter removal. Resistance seems to occur because of venospasm, vasoconstriction, phlebitis, or valve inflammation (Masoorli, 1997b; Wall & Kierstead, 1995). If resistance is met, all attempts at removing the catheter should stop, a sterile dressing should be applied, and warm compresses should be placed on the vein for 60 to 90 minutes. If, on a second attempt, resistance continues, the procedure should be stopped and the physician should be notified (Masoorli, 1997b; Wall & Kierstead, 1995).

Documentation

Documentation begins with confirmation of all central line catheter placements. The type of catheter, manufacturer, lot number, catheter length, and internal diameter should be included in the initial notes after line placement. Each time a nurse accesses an indwelling device, a comment should be made on ease of flushing, blood aspiration, and type and volume of flush solution. A description of the catheter site should be included as well as the presence or absence of pain, blood, or drainage. Ongoing patient education should be described in terms of information provided, questions addressed, and patient and family responses and behaviors. Any maintenance care (dressing or cap changes) and interventions should be noted with a date and time.

In addition to the above information, PICC documentation should include insertion date, insertion location, insertion site, type of introducer used, catheter length, external catheter length, catheter brand, gauge and lot number, complications, and patient's comments and responses (Masoorli, 1997b; Sansivero, 1997b).

Choosing a Catheter

When deciding on the best type of catheter to recommend to a patient, the first and foremost criterion is the purpose of the catheter. Knowing this provides the time frame that the catheter will be needed. A number of factors to be considered are listed below:

Care provider—Who will be managing the catheter at home? Is there the ability and willingness to flush and change the dressing when needed?

Manual dexterity—Can the patient manipulate the syringes, tubing, etc., or does the patient suffer from arthritis or pain?

Financial—Does insurance cover the cost of maintenance materials or is the patient having to pay out of pocket? Can the patient afford the materials? Which catheter incurs the least number of dressing changes, flushes, and subsequent materials?

Body image—What does the patient do on a daily basis? Does he or she swim? Use the arms? Hold a job in which he or she is very visible to others? How does the patient feel about having a reminder of the disease in his or her arm or chest?

Skin pricks—How does the patient feel about having to access a port by placing a needle through the skin into the septum?

Safety—Is the patient physically active to the point that the external portion of a catheter is at high risk for dislodging? Is the patient around small children, frequently having to lift them or hold them?

Additional factors that influence catheter placement are previous surgery or radiation to the chest area, previous central access devices, obesity or cachectic state, previous history of superior vena cava syndrome or thromboses, metastatic disease or adenopathy in the anterior chest, anatomic abnormalities, bleeding disorders, or medications influencing bleeding times.

Patient Education

Patients need to understand the purpose of the catheter, what the maintenance implications are, and possible complications that can occur from the time of catheter insertion through catheter removal. Signs and symptoms of infections and other complications need to be understood and reiterated to patients so they react quickly and early to a complication. Patients need to be able to report to their health care provider any flulike symptoms, general malaise, chills, rigors, or fever as an indicator of an infection.

When patients are manipulating their catheters for cap changes or open-ended connections to intravenous lines, they need to consistently clamp their catheters before the next step in the procedure to minimize the risk of embolus. The nurse should explain to the patient that if he or she suspects air is entering the catheter, he or she should immediately clamp the catheter, lie on the left side with the head below the feet, and have someone call for help.

When a person is diagnosed with cancer and decisions are made about cancer therapies that will require multiple intravenous sticks, it is imperative for the provider to educate the patient about venous access device options. Once the patient has undergone the placement of the CVC, the provider will need to reinforce the education regarding care and the signs and symptoms of complications.

REFERENCES

Andris, D. A., & Krzywda, E. A. (1997a). Catheter pinch-off syndrome: Recognition and management. *Journal of Intravenous Nursing, 20*(5), 233–237.

Andris, D. A., & Krzywda, E. A. (1997b). Central venous access: Clinical practice issues. *Nursing Clinics of North America, 32*(4), 719–736.

Brown, D. F., Muirhead, J. J., Travis, P. M., Vire, S. R., Weller, J., & Hauer-Jensen, M. (1997). Mode of chemotherapy does not affect complications with an implantable venous access device. *Cancer, 80*(5), 966–972.

Campbell, P. M. (1996). Troubleshooting central venous catheters in the emergency department. *Journal of Emergency Nursing, 22*(5), 416–420.

Clemence, M. A., Walker, D., & Farr, B. M. (1995). Central venous catheter practices: Result of a survey. *American Journal of Infection Control, 23*, 5.

Collin, G. R., Ahmadinejad, A. S., & Misse, E. (1996). Spontaneous migration of subcutaneous central venous catheters. *The American Surgeon, 63*(4), 322–326.

Conly, J. M., Grieves, K., & Peters, B. (1989). A prospective randomized study comparing transparent and dry gauze dressing for central venous catheters. *Journal of Infectious Disease, 159*, 310.

Harrison, M. (1997). Central venous catheters: A review of the literature. *Nursing Standard, 11*(27), 43–45.

Intravenous Nurses Society. (1997a). Midline and midclavicular catheters. A position paper. *Journal of Intravenous Nursing, 20*(4), 175–178.

Intravenous Nurses Society. (1997b). Peripherally inserted central catheters. A position paper. *Journal of Intravenous Nursing, 20*(4), 172–174.

Lau, C. E. Transparent and gauze dressing and their effect on infection rates of central venous catheters: A review of past and current literature. *Journal of Intravenous Nursing, 19*(5), 240–245.

Levins, T. T. (1996). Central intravenous lines: Your role. *Nursing 96, 26*(4), 48–49.

Machlin, D. (1997). How to manage PICCs. *American Journal of Nursing, 97*(9), 27–32.

Masoorli, S. (1997a). Central lines: Controversies in care. *Nursing 97, 27*(3), 72.

Masoorli, S. (1997b). What to do about PICC line problems. *Nursing 97, 27*(2), 32aaa–32hhh.

Masoorli, S. (1997c). Managing complications of central venous access devices. *Nursing 97, 27*(8), 59–64.

Masoorli, S. (1996). Questions and answers about CVCs: How to minimize infection risks. *Nursing 96, 26*(11), 28–29.

Nightingale, C. E., Norman, A., Cunningham, D., Young, J., Webb, A., & Filshie, J. (1997). A prospective analysis of 949 long-term central venous access catheters for ambulatory chemotherapy in patients with gastrointestinal malignancy. *European Journal of Cancer, 33*(3), 398–403.

Ouwndyk, M., & Helferty, M. (1996). Central venous catheter management: How to prevent complications. *ANNA Journal, 23*(6), 572–577.

Ray, S., Stacey, R., Imrie, M., & Filshie, J. (1996). A review of 560 Hickman catheter insertions. *Anaesthesia, 51*(October), 981–985.

Reed, T., & Phillips, S. (1996). Management of central venous catheter occlusions and repairs. *Journal of Intravenous Nursing, 19*(6), 289–294.

Roach, H., Larson, E., Cohran, J., & Bartlett, B. (1995). Intravenous site care practices in critical care: A national survey. *Heart and Lung, 24*(5), 420–424.

Sansivero, G. E. (1995). Why pick a PICC? *Nursing 95, 25*(7), 34–42.

Sansivero, G. E. (1997a). Maintaining a PICC line: What you should know. *Nursing 97, 27*(4), 14.

Sansivero, G. E. (1997b). Taking care of PICCs. *Nursing 97, 27*(5), 28.

Schwarz, R. E., Groeger, J. S., & Coit, D. G. (1997). Subcutaneously implanted central venous access devices in cancer patients. *Cancer, 79*(8), 1635–1640.

Smith, R. L., & Sheperd, M. (1995). Central venous catheter infection rates in an acute care hospital. *Journal of Intravenous Nursing, 18*(5), 255–261.

Spies, J. B., & Berlin, L. (1997). Malpractice issues in radiology: Complications of central venous catheter placement. *American Journal of Radiology, 169*(August), 339–341.

Treston-Aurand, J., Olmsted, R. N., Allen-Bridson, K., & Craig, C. P. (1997). Impact of dressing materials on central venous catheter infection rates. *Journal of Intravenous Nursing, 20*(4), 201–206.

Wall, J. L., & Kierstead, V. L. (1995). Peripherally inserted central catheters: Resistance to removal, a rate complication. *Journal of Intravenous Nursing, 18*(5), 251–254.

CHAPTER

18

Nausea and Vomiting

Susan A. Ezzone

Among the many distressing side effects of cancer treatment, nausea and vomiting have been described as being the most feared, disruptive symptoms experienced (Rhodes, Johnson & McDaniel, 1995). Nausea and vomiting are known to occur as common side effects of many chemotherapeutic agents and radiation therapy but may also be symptoms of cancer, may occur postoperatively, or may be caused by complications of treatment. In many circumstances, nausea and vomiting may be dose-limiting side effects of treatment. Complications of nausea and vomiting may include anorexia, loss of appetite, dehydration, electrolyte imbalance, esophageal tears, and gastric irritation or bleeding. Although much progress has been made in the management of nausea and vomiting using new pharmacologic agents, patients continue to experience significant symptoms during treatment.

Pathophysiology

In recent years, the physiologic mechanisms of nausea and vomiting have become better understood. Often, the terms *nausea* and *vomiting* have been used interchangeably, contributing to confusion about the physiologic processes that cause each phenomenon. Rhodes, Johnson, and McDaniel (1995) most clearly define the difference between nausea, vomiting, and retching (Box 18-1). Nausea is often referred to as a subjective response that is unobservable but reported by patients. Vomiting is described as an objective response with the expulsion of stomach contents through the mouth. A less often subjective and objective response is retching, which is often referred to as "dry heaves." Understanding the physiologic mechanisms of nausea and vomiting is essential to the selection of appropriate antiemetic agents to be used.

The physiologic processes that lead to the symptoms of nausea and vomiting are due to the stimulation of neurologic mechanisms in the brain and gastrointestinal tract. In the brain, two areas called the vomiting center (VC) and the chemoreceptor trigger zone (CTZ) coordinate the nausea, vomiting, and retching response (Figure 18-1). The CTZ is located at the area postrema of the fourth ventricle of the brain and is stimulated by chemicals and neurotransmitters found in the cerebrospinal fluid (CSF) and blood. The CTZ and the VC are connected by the fasciculus solitarius. The VC is located near the medulla oblongata in the brain in the dorsal lateral reticular formation, and is close to centers responsible for respiration, salivation, and vasomotor and vestibular processes. The neurotransmitters that may stimulate the VC or CTZ include histamine, dopamine, serotonin, and acetylcholine (Fessele, 1996; Rhodes et al., 1995). The afferent fibers of the stomach and pharynx may be stimulated by neurotransmitters, which trigger the nausea and vomiting response by way of the vagus or glossopharyngeal nerve. Highly emetic chemotherapy is thought to cause a release of 5-hydroxytryptamine ($5\text{-}HT_3$) from the enterochromaffin cells in the gastrointestinal tract. The vagus nerve's $5\text{-}HT_3$ receptors are activated, which stimulate the VC, initiating the emetic re-

BOX 18-1

Definitions of Nausea, Vomiting and Retching

Nausea: A subjective, unobservable phenomenon of an unpleasant sensation experienced in the back of the throat and epigastrium that may or may not culminate in vomiting; it is synonymously described as feeling "sick at stomach." It is usually known through self-report but also may have some objective elements because of its intensity.

Vomiting: The forceful expulsion of the contents of the stomach, duodenum, or jejunum through the oral cavity. It may be objectively measured.

Retching: The attempt to vomit without bringing anything up; it is also called "dry heaves." Both subjective and objective measurements of this phenomenon are possible and useful.

(Rhodes, V. A., Johnson, M. H., & McDaniel, R. W. [1995]. Nausea, vomiting, and retching: The management of the symptom experience. *Seminars in Oncology Nursing Forum, 11* [4], 256–265.

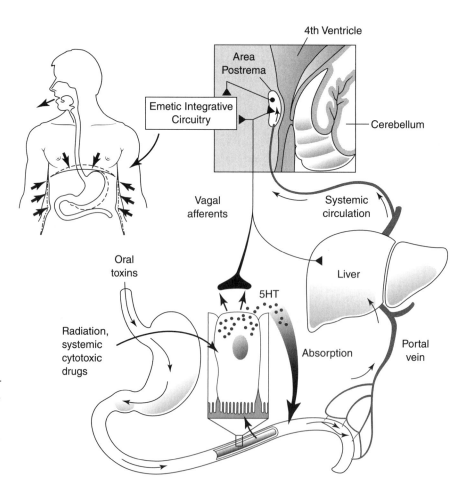

Figure 18-1 Neurologic pathways affecting the vomiting response. (Hogan, C.M. & Grant, M. [1997]. Physiologic mechanisms of nausea and vomiting in patients with cancer. *Oncology Nursing Forum, 24*[7], Suppl., 8–12.)

sponse (Dicato, 1996). A biphasic emetic response after chemotherapy has been described and refers to nausea during the first 12 hours, followed by a delayed response 2 to 5 days after administration of chemotherapy (Dicato, 1996). Delayed vomiting after chemotherapy administration may suggest that several emetic mechanisms occur and a combination of antiemetic agents should be used.

Etiology

During cancer treatment, nausea and vomiting most commonly are attributed to administration of chemotherapy and radiation therapy. The potential for chemotherapy to cause nausea and vomiting is based on the emetogenicity of the agent (Box 18-2). The more highly emetogenic chemotherapy agents cause the most severe symptoms of nausea and vomiting. Understanding the emetogenicity of each agent assists in establishing protocols for the management of nausea and vomiting.

The causes of nausea and vomiting have been described by Fessele (1996) as belonging to four different categories, including chemical, visceral, central nervous system (CNS), and vestibular mechanisms. Chemical causes of nausea and vomiting may be due to administration of narcotics, general anesthetics, or chemotherapy agents, which directly stimulate the CTZ. Other chemical causes may include metabolic abnormalities such as hypercalcemia and uremia, which can stimulate the CTZ and VC. Visceral causes of nausea and vomiting are usually a result of stimulation of the VC by the vagus nerve by physical or emotional mechanisms. CNS factors that may cause nausea and vomiting may be a result of psychological or physiologic changes. It has been estimated that anticipatory nausea and vomiting (ANV) occurs in one third of patients who receive chemotherapy, usually after one to two cycles (Rhodes et al., 1995). Because anticipatory nausea and vomiting is a conditioned response to the environment or experience of receiving chemotherapy, nonpharmacologic behavioral interventions may be useful in managing this response. Lastly, the vestibular center in the brain, which communicates to the inner ear, may be stimulated by neurotransmitters, causing a perception of imbalance and motion that leads to nausea and vomiting. Management of nausea and vomiting attributed to the four mechanisms described is based on the known neurotransmitters affected.

Anticipatory nausea and vomiting is a conditioned response that occurs before the second or

---

B O X   1 8 - 2

Emetogenicity of Chemotherapy Agents

Highly Emetogenic	**Moderately Emetogenic**	**Mildly Emetogenic**
Cisplatin	Cyclophosphamide	Methotrexate
Dacarbazine	Carboplatin	Mitomycin
Mechlorethamine	BCNU	Bleomycin
Dactinomycin	Procarbazine	Chlorambucil
	Cytosine arabinoside	Melphalan
	Doxorubicin	Hydroxyurea
		Etoposide
		Fluorouracil

(Fessele, K.S. [1996].Managing the multiple causes of nausea and vomiting in the patient with cancer. *Oncology Nursing Forum, 23* [9], 1409–1415.)

subsequent courses of chemotherapy (Morrow & Rosenthal, 1996). The mechanism of ANV is believed to be a result of a learned response. It has been observed in numerous studies that ANV does not occur in patients who do not experience side effects; it occurs more often with subsequent cycles of chemotherapy; and the more severe the side effects, the greater the incidence of ANV. Characteristics that predispose patients to develop ANV are listed in Box 18-3.

Radiation therapy may be associated with causing the symptoms of nausea and vomiting and is most common when treatment is given to the upper abdomen. Because the course of radiation may extend over several weeks, patients may experience nausea and vomiting for the duration of therapy. Factors that may contribute to the occurrence and severity of nausea and vomiting in patients receiving radiation therapy include single dose of greater than 8 Gy, cumulative dose greater than 30 Gy, total body irradiation (TBI), and hemibody irradiation (Schmoll & Casper, 1996).

Although nausea and vomiting in patients undergoing cancer treatment most commonly are side effects of chemotherapy and radiation therapy, other etiologies occur. Some patients experience these symptoms postoperatively and require management with antiemetics. Nausea and vomiting may be symptoms of metabolic abnormalities such as uremia, hypercalcemia, acute renal failure, or ketoacidosis due to the cancer or treatment.

Vestibular disorders or increased intracranial pressure related to primary or metastatic disease, meningitis, or other causes often lead to symptoms of nausea and vomiting. Disturbances of gastric motility or emptying usually cause nausea and vomiting and may include hepatomegaly, splenomegaly, bowel obstruction, surgical adhesions, and tumor involvement. Additionally, constipation may occur due to usage of opioids for pain management or as a side effect of vinca alkaloids, resulting in symptoms of nausea and vomiting (Axelrod, 1997; Hogan & Grant, 1997).

Assessment

For many years, efforts have been made to better identify the risk factors for nausea and vomiting in patients with cancer. A coordinated attempt among health care providers to assess possible causes and patient elements is necessary to determine the potential severity of symptoms that may be experienced. Most often, the interdisciplinary health care team assesses the risk of nausea and vomiting based on the emetic potential of the chemotherapy agent, site of radiation therapy, medications administered, or other causes as described above. Other elements that may increase the risk of nausea and vomiting in patients with cancer include a poor performance status, elderly, ANV, and a history of nausea and vomiting or al-

---

BOX 18-3

Patient Characteristics Associated With Development of ANV

Age less than 50 years
Nausea/vomiting after last chemotherapy
  session
Posttreatment vomiting described as "moderate,"
  "severe," or "intolerable"

Feeling warm or hot all over after last chemotherapy
  session
Susceptibility to motion sickness
Sweating after last chemotherapy session
Generalized weakness after last chemotherapy session

(Morrow, G.R. & Rosenthal, S.N. [1996]. Models, mechanisms, and management of anticipatory nausea and emesis. *Oncology, 53* [Suppl.], 4–7.)

coholism (Johnson, Moroney & Gay, 1997). Nurses often assume the responsibility to assess for these important potential risk factors. The assessment of patient elements that may contribute to the risk of nausea and vomiting can assist the interdisciplinary team in choosing the most appropriate antiemetic regimen for individual patients. It may be appropriate to combine pharmacologic and nonpharmacologic interventions to maximize antiemetic benefits.

Strategies to objectively assess the patient's experience of nausea and vomiting have been researched using a variety of tools. Self-report questionnaires are used to gather information related to the patient's perspective of the symptoms experienced. Tools that the observer (i.e., the nurse) uses to collect information focus on recording the number of vomiting and/or retching episodes in an 8-hour period. Nausea is difficult to assess using observation tools because it is subjective and based on the patient's perception of the symptom. An observational tool may not be practical in the clinical setting because an observer must be present to record information. Visual analog scales (VAS) quantify symptoms and are reliable, sensitive self-report tools (Ezzone, Baker, Rosselet & Terepka, 1998; Rhodes et al., 1995). An example of a VAS may be a 0 to 10 scale in which the patient is asked to report the severity of nausea at regular intervals. A VAS with zero or "0" meaning no nausea and 10 meaning the most severe nausea is useful to document the effectiveness of antiemetic agents. Rhodes and colleagues (1995) developed a monitoring tool that measures the symptoms of nausea, vomiting, and retching, as well as the associated distress and severity of each symptom. The occurrence of each symptom is measured, including the onset, duration, frequency, and amount experienced. Another tool is the Adapted Symptom Distress Scale-2, which measures a total of 14 symptoms including nausea and vomiting. The other symptoms measured with this tool are eating, pain, sleeping, fatigue, bowel elimination, breathing, coughing, lacrimation, concentration, changes in body temperature, appearance, and restlessness (McCorkle & Young, 1978). Measuring other symptoms along with nausea and vomiting is very important in understanding the complex of symptoms patients experience.

These self-report tools can be used during inpatient, outpatient, or home care treatment of patients with cancer. Patients can be taught these self-assessment techniques to use during treatment to provide useful information to the health care team when determining the effectiveness of antiemetics. The self-report tools should be brought back to the outpatient clinic setting so the health care team can understand the occurrence and severity of symptoms experienced. It is often also helpful if the patient is instructed to maintain a daily journal, diary, or log of symptoms experienced and effective interventions (Figure 18-2). The patient should record all interventions, including antiemetics, behavioral techniques, and alternative therapies used. In addition, the patient should record contributing symptoms or circumstances that affect the experience of nausea and vomiting.

Pharmacologic Agents

A variety of pharmacologic agents have been used to prevent and treat nausea and vomiting in patients receiving treatment for cancer. Most of the available literature on nausea and vomiting has focused on symptoms associated with the side effects of chemotherapy agents. Antiemetics are also often used to prevent nausea during treatment with narcotics or radiation therapy and postoperatively. Single or combination drugs used to prevent nausea and vomiting have been based on the emetogenicity of the chemotherapy agent and the stimulation of neurotransmitters during treatment. The drug, dose, frequency, and route of antiemetic may be adjusted according to the severity and occurrence of nausea and vomiting experienced. Occasionally, continuous intravenous administration or infusion of antiemetics has been used to control severe symptoms in highly emetic chemotherapy regimens (Johnson et al., 1997). Less often, continuous subcutaneous infusions of antiemetics have been used.

Traditionally, the most common antiemetic agents used were metoclopramide and phenothiazines combined with dexamethasone and lorazepam. Antihistamines, such as diphenhydramine, were used to prevent the extrapyramidal

Self-Care Journal

Date started   1/28/96
Time started   4:30 pm

Instructions

Please keep records in this journal for three days, beginning on the day of your outpatient clinic visit. Carry the journal and a pencil with you at all times so that you can record activities and results as they occur. The more detailed your journal is, the more valuable it will be in assessing your progress. In addition, your careful records will assist us in our research and in serving other patients. Your help is greatly appreciated.

The directions below will help you determine what information to put in each column of the journal. In addition, please refer to the sample entries on the next page.

Date, time	Record the date and time of each entry
How I felt before self-care activity	Record entries as often as desired and upon awakening, at noon, midafternoon or early evening, and before going to bed at night.
Self-care activity	Record the names of the medications taken and describe any action you took to improve how you were feeling.
Result	Describe how you felt an hour after completing the self-care activity; you may use the following code:

1 = I felt better
2 = no change
3 = I felt worse

Self-Care Journal Sample

Sample journal entries are shown below. Remember that details are important; if in doubt, include it.

Date	Time	How I Felt Before Self-Care Activity	Self-Care Activity	Result
1/28	4:30 pm	Restless	Listening to relaxing music	1
1/28	9 pm	Feeling okay	Took Kytril "po" as nurse directed	2
1/29	8 am	Hungry	Ate cream of wheat and toast	1
1/29	10:30 am	Tired	Napped in recliner	1
1/29	12:30 pm	Stomach feels empty	Sipped hot tea, ate chicken soup	1
1/29	4 pm	Bitter taste in mouth	Sucked on lemon drop	1
1/29	6:30 pm	Hungry but don't wish to smell hot foods	Enjoyed a turkey sandwich and applesauce	1
1/29	9:30 pm	Sleepy/tired	Warm bath and went to bed	2
1/30	8 am	Stomach feels "good"	Ate toast, fruit, and yogurt	1
1/30	10:30 am	Feel bloated, constipated	Took a stool softener	2
1/30	noon	Thirsty	Drinking tea, watching birds	1

Figure 18-2. Sample self-care assessment tool. (Rhodes, V. A. [1990]. Nausea, vomiting, and retching. *Nursing Clinics of North America, 25*[4], 893. Copyright 1990 by W.B. Saunders. Reprinted by permission.)

side effects of dopaminergic antiemetics. In the early 1990s, ondansetron dramatically changed the prevention, treatment, and patient experience of nausea and vomiting during cancer treatment. The effective use of ondansetron has been studied in children and adult patients undergoing treatment with chemotherapy, radiation therapy, and operative procedures (Simpson & Hicks, 1996). Currently the 5-HT$_3$ receptor antagonists available include ondansetron, granisetron, tropisetron, and dolasetron (Hesketh et al., 1996; Roila, Ballatori, Tonato & Del Favero, 1997). Before the development of these newer agents, the experience of nausea and vomiting often limited the doses of chemotherapy given to patients, thus affecting the ability to administer adequate treatment. Administration of the 5-HT$_3$ receptor antagonists in combination with traditional antiemetics has lessened the occurrence and severity of posttreatment symptoms. The most common drug used in combination with ondansetron has been dexamethasone (Dicato, 1996; Roila et al., 1997). Further research is needed to evaluate effective antiemetics for control of delayed-onset nausea and vomiting after chemotherapy; to refine dosing, scheduling, and routes of administration; to evaluate use of antiemetics alone or in combination; to evaluate use during multiple days and multiple cycles of chemotherapy; and to determine parameters to measure efficacy of antiemetics (Olver, 1996). In addition, 5-HT$_3$ receptor antagonists are significantly more expensive than traditional antiemetic agents and may be cost prohibitive in some cases. Common antiemetics used are described in Table 18-1.

A variety of interdisciplinary team approaches have been used to manage nausea and vomiting during cancer treatment. Johnson and associates (1997) describe an algorithmic approach to the management of nausea and vomiting based on the emetic potential of the chemotherapy agent(s) used. Treatment plans were developed for low-, moderate-, and high-risk emetogenic drug regimens and included specific recommendations for administration of antiemetic agents. In 1999, the American Society of Clinical Oncology developed recommendations for the use of antiemetics. They provide guidelines for the management of chemotherapy-induced acute and delayed emesis, anticipatory emesis, and radiation-induced emesis.

Nonpharmacologic Interventions

Nonpharmacologic interventions for the management of nausea and vomiting may be used alone or in combination, and also as an adjunct to pharmacologic agents (Table 18-2). The intent of these interventions is to focus attention on other stimuli rather than on the symptoms of nausea and vomiting. Because ANV cannot be controlled by antiemetics alone, nonpharmacologic interventions are particularly useful in managing this learned response. Most of the nonpharmacologic interventions are based on behavioral therapy, such as progressive muscle relaxation, imagery, or systematic desensitization. Distraction methods have also been effective when used alone or with other behavioral interventions and may include television, music, games, reading, and humor. Other nonpharmacologic interventions less frequently used include acupuncture, application of acupressure wristbands, hypnosis, massage, and aerobic exercise.

Progressive muscle relaxation (PMR) has been used in an attempt to decrease nausea and vomiting after chemotherapy and to prevent ANV. Patients are taught to actively tense and release major muscle groups to allow complete relaxation. It may be used in combination with other nonpharmacologic interventions such as imagery and systemic desensitization (Fessele, 1996; King, 1997).

Guided imagery has been used alone or in combination with PMR and music therapy. It is an intervention that can easily be learned and used by patients who experience ANV. Patients are instructed to choose an image that they find relaxing and safe and imagine what they usually associate with this place. Components of the image may be things relevant to all senses such as hearing, smelling, seeing, feeling, or tasting. The goal is to allow the image to replace the negative feeling of nausea and vomiting (King, 1997).

Systematic desensitization is a technique that can be learned to countercondition a response such as ANV. Patients are taught to imagine themselves going through the steps of chemotherapy administration: arriving at the clinic or hospital, entering the treatment room, talking with the

TABLE 18-1
SUMMARY OF ANTIEMETIC DRUGS

Drug	Form/Dose/Duration of Action	Route of Administration	Schedule	Comments
5-HT₃-receptor antagonists				*5-HT₃-receptor antagonists:* Indicated for moderate to highly emetogenic chemotherapy; causes minimal sedation; ideal for elderly and pediatric patients; use with stool softener, laxative, increased dietary fluids, and bran to prevent constipation; efficacy is increased in combination with dexamethasone; headache is common with ondanestron, and transient light-headedness may occur during infusion.
Ondansetron	0.15 mg/kg–0.18 mg/kg every 12 h × two doses; half-life, 3–4 h; onset, 30 min; duration, 8 h	Oral and IV	Every 12 h × two doses or 16–32 mg/24 h	
Granisetron	10μg/kg over 5 min IV or 1 mg orally; half-life, 8–10 h; onset, 30 min; duration, 12 h	Oral and IV	Every 12 h	
Phenothiazines				*Phenothiazines:* Use diphenhydramine or benztropine to prevent extrapyramidal symptoms; drowsiness, irritation, dry mouth, and anxiety may occur; hypotension occurs rarely with IV dosing; administer IV doses > 15 mg over 30 min; sustained-release on a regular basis may prevent delayed nausea and vomiting; may cause excessive drowsiness in elderly patients if given daily over 3–4 days; intramuscular route is painful; because prochlorperazine causes sedation, it is best given at hour of sleep.
Prochlorperazine	*Tablets:* 5, 10, or 25 mg; onset, 30 min; duration, 3–4 h	Oral	Every 4–6 h	
	Sustained release: 10 or 15 mg; onset, 30–40 min; duration, 10–12 h	Oral	Every 10–12 h	
	Rectal suppositories: 25 mg; onset 60 min; duration, 3–4 h	Rectal	Every 4–6 h	
	Parenteral: 5 mg/mL; onset, 10–20 min; duration, 3–4 h	Intramuscular	Every 3–4 h	
	IV: 20–40 mg; onset, 10–20 min; duration, 3–4 h	IV over 30 min as infusion	Every 3–4 h	
Thiethylperazine	*Tablets:* 10 mg; onset, 40 min; duration, 3–4 h	Oral	Every 4–6 h	Extrapyramidal symptoms may occur; use may potentiate central nervous system (CNS) depressants.
	Parenteral: 10 mg/2 mL; onset, 20 min; duration, 6–8 h	Intramuscular	Every 6–8 h	
	Rectal suppositories: 10 mg; onset, 30 min; duration, 6–8 h	Rectal	Every 6–8 h	
Trimethobenzamide	*Capsules:* 250 or 100 mg; onset, 30 min; duration, 3–4 h	Oral	Every 6–8 h	Drowsiness may occur; hypotension may occur with parenteral administration; intramuscular administration may cause pain and burning at injection site.
	Rectal suppositories: 200 mg; onset, 30 min; duration, 3–4 h	Rectal	Every 6–8 h	
	Parenteral: 200 mg/2 mL; onset, 30 min; duration, 3–4 h	Intramuscular	Every 6–8 h	

Drug	Formulation/onset/duration	Route	Schedule	Comments
Butyrophenones				
Haloperidol	Tablets: 0.5, 1, 2, or 5 mg; onset, 30–40 min; duration, 4–6 h	Oral	Every 4–6 h	Butyrophenones: May be as effective as phenothiazines; may have additive effects with other CNS depressants; extrapyramidal symptoms can be severe; use when anxiety and anticipatory symptoms aggravate degree and intensity of nausea and vomiting.
	Parenteral: 5 mg/mL; onset 20 min; duration, 3–4 h	Intramuscular	Every 2 h for two to three doses	
	IV: 0.5–2 mg; onset, 20 min; duration, 3–4 h	IV	Titrate to individual needs	
Droperidol	Parenteral: 1.25–2.5 mg; onset, 20–30 min; curation, 2–4 h	IV, intramuscular	Titrate to individual needs: 30 min prior to chemotherapy, 1 mg IV push to minimize anxiety	
Substituted benzamides				
Metoclopramide	Tablets: 5 or 10 mg; IV, 1–3 mg/kg; onset, 20 min; duration, 2–3 h	IV, oral	1–3 mg/kg IV piggyback 30 min prior to chemotherapy and every 2–3 h for three more doses; then 0.5 mg/kg orally four times on days 1 through 7 following chemotherapy	Substituted benzamides: Infuse over 30 min to prevent agitation and dystonic reactions; use diphenhydramine to decrease extrapyramidal symptoms; compatible with dexamethasone in solution; can cause diarrhea, headache, fatigue; works well to manage gastric stasis and delayed nausea.
Cisapride	Tablets: 10 mg	Oral	Three to four times/day; before meals and at bedtime	Increases gastric emptying and is associated with minimal extrapyramidal symptoms; indicated for heartburn.
Cannabinoids				
Dronabinol	Tablets: 2.5, 5, or 10 mg; onset, 30 min; duration, 4–6 h	Oral	Every 4–6 h	Cannabinoids: Second-line antiemetic; more effective in younger adults; side effects include CNS sedation, dizziness, disorientation, impaired concentration, dysphoria, orthostatic hypotension, dry mouth and tachycardia.

(continued)

TABLE 18-1

SUMMARY OF ANTIEMETIC DRUGS (CONTINUED)

Drug	Form/Dose/Duration of Action	Route of Administration	Schedule	Comments
Steroids				
Dexamethasone	*Tablets:* 4 mg	Oral	To prevent delayed symptoms: 2–4 mg four times/day × 2 days, 2–4 mg three times/day × 2 days, 2–4 mg two times/day × 2 days, 2–4 mg once a day × 2 days, then stop	*Steroids:* Compatible in solution with 5-HT$_3$-receptor antagonists or metoclopramide; taper dose to prevent insomnia, anxiety, and euphoria; to avoid perirectal burning, give as an infusion or slow IV push; vomiting may occur if dexamethasone is given too fast; may help to prevent delayed nausea when given in tapering doses.
	Parenteral: 10–20 mg	IV	10–20 mg prior to chemotherapy	
Benzodiazepines				
Lorazepam	*Tablets:* 1 or 2 mg	Oral	Every 2–3 h as needed	Benzodiazepines: Sedation, amnesia, and pleasant hallucinations in pediatric population; use with caution in patients with hepatic or renal dysfunction, who are debilitated, or are receiving ifosfamide; sublingual route provides rapid plasma levels and greater bioavailability; 1 mg prior to chemotherapy eases anxiety associated with treatment.
	Parenteral: 2–4 mg/mL; onset, 10 min; duration, 4–8 h	IV	0.025–0.04 mg/kg IV to mild-moderate sedation (maximum, 3 mg)	

(Goodman, M. [1997]. Risk factors and antiemetic management of chemotherapy-induced nausea and vomiting. *Oncology Nursing Forum, 24* [7], 20–32.)

nurses and doctors, and use of intravenous and drug administration equipment. The patient imagines this occurring in phases or hierarchies, moving closer to the location of chemotherapy administration. Progressive muscle relaxation is often used along with this technique (Morrow & Rosenthal, 1996).

Music therapy has been used in a number of studies to promote relaxation and distraction. It may be used alone or with pharmacologic or behavioral interventions. A recent study demonstrated that the use of music as an adjunct to antiemetic agents decreased the subjective perception of nausea and episodes of vomiting during the preparative regimen in patients undergoing autologous and allogeneic bone marrow transplantation (Ezzone et al., 1998).

Practice Setting

Nausea and vomiting are experienced by patients receiving treatment in the hospital, outpatient, and home care settings. The movement toward increased use of outpatient or home care settings for treatment has broadened the health care team's scope in providing adequate symptom management in alternative sites of care. Intravenous antiemetics are given most often in the hospital setting but may also be used in the outpatient or home care environment. Alternative routes such as oral, rectal, or subcutaneous are more frequently used in outpatient or home care settings. In some cases, continuous subcutaneous infusions of antiemetics have been used. Evaluation of the patient response to antiemetics is most important in continuing to manage these distressing symptoms.

Quality Improvement Indicators

Patient satisfaction surveys may provide the most insightful information about a patient's perception of cancer treatment and management of symptoms such as nausea and vomiting. The surveys are often a nonthreatening method to collect information about the experience of treatment in the hospital, outpatient, or home care setting. Samples of potential survey questions are listed in Box 18-4. These data can be used to evaluate antiemetic practice and update or change practices based on patient reports of relief of symptoms.

There is growing interest in conducting quality of life (QOL) studies during cancer treatment. A recent report summarized the assessment of QOL in patients receiving chemotherapy. Patients who experienced vomiting after receiving chemotherapy showed a decline in QOL scores (Osoba, Zee, Warr, Kaizer, Latreille & Pater, 1996). Incorporating QOL measurement into research protocols is necessary to better understand the effect of treatment-related side effects on daily functional activities of patients.

Documentation Examples

Numerous documentation tools are used in inpatient, outpatient, and home care settings when providing care to patients with cancer. It is important to document not only the information about cancer treatment (chemotherapy, radiation therapy, and surgery) but also the patient's response to treatment and strategies to manage symptoms. The drug, dosage, route, and frequency of anti-

---

B O X   1 8 - 4

Sample Patient Satisfaction Survey Questions

- I was educated about side effects of treatment.
- I was educated about management of side effects.

- My symptoms were managed adequately.

TABLE 18-2

NONPHARMACOLOGIC INTERVENTIONS FOR NAUSEA AND VOMITING

Technique	Description	Comments
Behavioral Interventions		
Self-hypnosis	Evocation of physiologic state of altered consciousness and total body relaxation. This technique involves a state of intensified attention and increased receptiveness to an idea	First technique used to control anticipatory nausea and vomiting Limited studies—mostly children and adolescents Easily learned No side effects Decreases intensity and duration of nausea Decreases frequency, severity, amount, and duration of vomiting
Relaxation	Progressive contraction and relaxation of various muscle groups	Often used with imagery Can use for other stressful situations Easily learned No side effects Decreases nausea during and after chemotherapy Decreases duration and severity of vomiting Not as effective with anticipatory nausea and vomiting
Biofeedback	Control of specific physiologic responses by receiving information about changes in response to induced state of relaxation	Two types: electromyographic and skin temperature Used alone or with relaxation Easily learned No side effects Decreases nausea during and after chemotherapy More effective with progressive muscle relaxation
Imagery	Mentally take self away by focusing one's mind on images of a relaxing place	Most effective when combined with another technique Increases self-control Decreases duration of nausea Decreases perceptions of degree of vomiting Feel more in control, relaxed, and powerful
Distraction	Learn to divert attention from a threatening situation and to relaxing sensations	Can use videos, games, and puzzles No side effects Decreases anticipatory nausea and vomiting Decreases postchemotherapy distress
Desensitization	Three-step process involving relaxation and visualization to decrease sensitization to adverse situations	Inexpensive Easily learned No side effects Decreases anticipatory nausea and vomiting
Other		
Acupressure	Form of massage using meridians to increase energy flow and affect emotions	Inconclusive literature support Acupressure wrist bands may be helpful to decrease nausea and vomiting
Music therapy	Use of music to influence physiologic, psychological, and emotional functioning during threatening situation	Often used with other techniques No side effects Decreases nausea during and after chemotherapy Decreases perceptions of degree of vomiting

(King, C.R. [1997]. Nonpharmacologic management of chemotherapy-induced nausea and vomiting. *Oncology Nursing Forum, 24* [7], 41–48.)

emetics used to manage symptoms of nausea and vomiting should be documented consistently to allow for comparison. Nonpharmacologic interventions used should also be documented in a manner that allows the nurse to communicate the patient's response to specific methods. It is often helpful to develop a documentation tool that can track the occurrence and severity of symptoms over time so that relief of symptoms by both pharmacologic and nonpharmacologic interventions is apparent (Table 18-3).

Patient Education Tools

Patients and families need educational materials to describe the side effects and management of side effects of cancer treatment. The National Cancer Institute, American Cancer Society, and Leukemia Society have a variety of materials available. Internet access has made it possible for patients to search for and find many resources quickly. Individual institutions often develop written patient educational pamphlets to suit spe-

cific practices and experiences related to cancer treatment and management of symptoms. An example of a patient education handout is shown in Box 18-5. Providing patients and families with reliable, consistent information is important to assist them in coping with the cancer treatment process.

Conclusion

Nausea and vomiting are difficult, distressing symptoms experienced by patients undergoing treatment for cancer. Over the past several years, much has been learned about pharmacologic and nonpharmacologic strategies to manage these symptoms. Advances in drug therapy for symptom management have improved the overall perception of nausea and vomiting and have promoted the completion of treatment regimens. Further research is still needed to maximize the benefits of drug therapy and behavioral interventions to manage nausea and vomiting during cancer treatment. Nurses play a significant role in assessment of

---

TABLE 18-3

PATIENT FLOWSHEET

Pain and Symptom Assessment

	23	24	01	02	03	04	05	06	07	08	09	10	11	12	13	14	15	16	17	18	19	20	21	22
10																								
9																								
8																								
7																								
6																								
5																								
4																								
3																								
2																								
1																								
0																								

Pain/Symptom Scale (0–10)   **0 = no pain/symptoms**   **10 = worst pain/symptoms imaginable**
Pain/Symptom Code   CP = chest pain   H = headache   P = Pain   N = Nausea   D = Diarrhea   C = Constipation   F = Fatigue/weakness
S = Sedation   X = Anxious   Other: _____

Sedation Scale (0–4)   0 = alert   1 = drowsy   2 = arousable   3 = arousable, but unable to orient   4 = unarousable

(The Ohio State University Medical Center, Arthur G. James Cancer Hospital & Research Institute, Columbus, OH.)

BOX 18-5

Cancer Therapy: Managing Side Effects—Nausea and Vomiting

Nausea is a sick, uncomfortable feeling in your stomach that often comes before you vomit, or "throw up." Nausea and vomiting are possible side effects of the medicines used for chemotherapy. These drugs can irritate your stomach or stimulate the vomiting center in your brain. The severity of stomach upset and how long it lasts depend on the medicines you take. Not all chemotherapy drugs can cause nausea and vomiting.

Radiation therapy also may cause nausea and vomiting. This is more likely to happen when your chest, stomach, or back is receiving radiation. Radiation treatment to other parts of your body should not cause nausea and vomiting.

Nausea and vomiting from these treatments are usually temporary.

> **If the nausea and vomiting last longer than 48 hours or are severe, call your doctor or nurse.**

Other causes of nausea and vomiting may include: your disease, infection, constipation, high blood sugar levels, low sodium (salt) levels, high calcium levels, and various medicines.

Ways to Reduce Nausea and Vomiting

FOODS AND LIQUIDS

- Eat lightly on the day you get chemotherapy or radiation therapy, or any time your stomach is upset. Try not to eat for 1 to 2 hours before and after your treatment.
- Eat small amounts often during the day instead of three large meals. Eat slowly, in a pleasant place. Give yourself plenty of time to eat. Eat whenever you feel like eating.
- Do not drink liquids with meals. Wait 30 to 60 minutes after eating. Clear, cool liquids are often tolerated well, especially fluids like Gatorade, Exceed, and Yoohoo. Try weak tea, clear soups, gelatin, or popsicles. Try ice cubes made from a favorite non-alcoholic beverage, 7-up, ginger ale, or cola.
- Eat bland, dry foods, such as unbuttered toast with jelly, saltine cracker, dry popcorn, or boiled/baked potatoes.
- Foods that digest easily include: skim milk, cereal, sherbet, fruit, plain vegetables.
- Eat foods that are cool or at room temperature. Do not allow refrigerated foods to sit at room temperature more than 30 minutes before you eat them.
- Avoid spicy "hot" foods, such as chili, hot peppers, or barbecue sauces. Do not eat fatty, fried, or greasy foods such as French fries, cheeses, butter, oil, cream, margarine, or red meats. Many patients do not like foods that are sweet.
- If foods with strong odors bother you, go into another room while these foods are cooking.
- Avoid your favorite foods during times of severe stomach upset. That way you will not connect them in your mind with nausea and vomiting.
- A metallic taste in your mouth may be relieved by sucking on hard candy such as lemon drops. Use plastic utensils whenever possible. Try citrus juice, pickles, relish, or cranberry juice.
- Family members should not coax, bribe, or threaten you about food. They can help best by cooking the foods for you so you will not have to smell the cooking odors.

ANTIEMETIC MEDICINE

(anti = against, emetic = vomiting)

- Take antiemetic medicine as it is ordered, about one half hour before eating. Take the medicine a day before treatment or for several hours before treatment, even if you feel fine. You may need to continue it regularly for a few days after treatment.
- If pills do not stay down, most antiemetic medicines can be given in another form, such as injections, suppositories, or under the tongue.
- **If your antiemetic medicine does not seem to be working, tell your doctor or nurse.** There are many antiemetic medicines and/or other drugs that may work better.
- Antacids such as Maalox or Mylanta may help mild nausea or heartburn.
- If you are weak, dizzy, or sleepy from the antiemetic medicine, ask someone to stay with you and help you walk.

OTHER WAYS TO HELP

- Rest before and after meals, but do not lie down for 2 hours after eating. Sit in a comfortable chair with your feet up.
- Slow, deep breathing through your mouth or swallowing will sometimes help the feeling of nausea to pass.
- Avoid unpleasant sights, sounds, and smells that might trigger nausea.

(continued)

BOX 18-5

Cancer Therapy: Managing Side Effects—Nausea and Vomiting (Continued)

- Do mouth care after every meal and before meals if you have a bad taste in your mouth.
- A bad taste in your mouth may be taken away by rinsing your mouth, removing and cleaning dentures, brushing your teeth, or sucking on hard candy such as peppermint.
- Open a window to get fresh air.
- Avoid strenuous exercise and sudden movements that may interfere with your sense of balance.
- Distract yourself by talking, reading, listening to music, playing games, doing handwork, watching TV, or working on a hobby.
- Learn how to do relaxation and guided imagery techniques (ask your nurse to teach you).
- Try to rest or take a nap during the nausea.
- To increase calories and maintain or gain weight, ask for the booklet *Eating Hints* from the National Cancer Institute. See your nurse or dietitian for this booklet or for more information.
- Even if you cannot eat foods, try to drink at least 1 to 2 quarts of fluid a day to avoid dehydration. Consider taking vitamins and nutritional supplements. If you have mouth pain:
  a. Try blended, smooth, creamy foods (e.g., eggs, soup, cheesecake, ice cream, pudding)
  b. Avoid hot foods
  c. Avoid acidic foods
- Take a mild laxative if you are constipated. Sometimes constipation can cause or add to your nausea. **Do not take a laxative if you are having belly pain. Call your doctor or nurse.**
- Take medications to keep pain under control.

- Provide comfort after nausea and vomiting by placing a cool cloth to the forehead or back of neck and by resting.
- Sit up and turn on your side when vomiting so you will not get any of it into your lungs.

When to Call Your Doctor or Nurse:

- Call your doctor or nurse if vomiting lasts longer than 2 days.
  Be prepared to answer these questions:
  - How often do you have nausea and vomiting?
  - About how much is coming up?
  - Does the vomit ever have blood or coffee ground-looking stuff in it?
  - Is the nausea and vomiting related to activity, food, medicines, pain, or coughing?
  - Do you feel better after vomiting?
  - Are your bowels moving? Are you passing water as usual?
  - What have you tried to decrease the nausea and vomiting?
  - What usually works best to control your nausea and vomiting?
  - Can you keep any food or fluid down?
- Weigh yourself once a week. **Report a loss of more than 5 lb in a week or 10 lb in a month.**
- **Report any of these signs of too much water loss (dehydration):**
  - **Dry eyes**
  - **Cracked lips/dry mouth**
  - **Dry, limp skin**
  - **Dizziness, especially when you stand up**

(©Copyright, NPEC, I A 12 [99] C, Department of Nursing; James Cancer Hospital: Columbus, OH.)

symptoms, evaluation of response to interventions, and providing patient/family education. Symptom management is a key component of nursing care during treatment.

REFERENCES

Axelrod, R. S. (1997). Antiemetic therapy. *Comprehensive Therapies, 23*(8), 539–545.

Baines, M. (1988). Nausea and vomiting in the patient with advanced cancer. *Journal of Pain and Symptom Management, 3*(2), 81–85.

Dicato, M. (1996). Mechanisms and management of nausea and emesis. *Oncology, 53*(Suppl.), 1–3.

Ezzone, S. A., Baker, C., Rosselet, R., & Terepka, E. (1998). Music as an adjunct for antiemetic therapy. *Oncology Nursing Forum, 25*(9), 1551–1556.

Fessele, K. S. (1996). Managing the multiple causes of nausea and vomiting in the patient with cancer. *Oncology Nursing Forum, 23*(9), 1409–1415.

Goodman, M. (1997). Risk factors and antiemetic management of chemotherapy-induced nausea and vomiting. *Oncology Nursing Forum, 24*(7), 20–32.

Gralla, R. J., et al. (1999). Recommendations for the use of antiemetics: Evidence-based, clinical practice guidelines. *Journal of Clinical Oncology, 17*(9), 2971–2994.

Hesketh, P., Navari, R., Grote, T., Gralla, R., Hainsworth, J., Kris, M., Anthony, L., Khojasteh, A., Tazoglou, E., Benedict, C., & Hahne, W. (1996). Double-blind, randomized comparison of the antiemetic efficacy of intravenous dolasetron mesylate and intravenous ondansetron in the prevention of acute cisplatin-induced emesis in patients with cancer. *Journal of Clinical Oncology, 14*(8), 2242–2249.

Hogan, C. M. & Grant, M. (1997). Physiologic mechanisms of nausea and vomiting in patients with cancer. *Oncology Nursing Forum, 24*(7), 8–12.

Johnson, M. H., Moroney, C. E., & Gay, C. F. (1997). Relieving nausea and vomiting in patients with cancer: A treatment algorithm. *Oncology Nursing Forum, 24*(1), 51–57.

King, C. R. (1997). Nonpharmacologic management of chemotherapy-induced nausea and vomiting. *Oncology Nursing Forum, 24*(7), 41–48.

Lichter, I. (1993). Which antiemetic? *Journal of Palliative Care, 9*(1), 42–50.

McCorkle, R. & Young, K. (1978). Development of a symptom distress scale. *Cancer Nursing, 1,* 373–378.

Mehta, N. H., Reed, C. M., Kuhlman, C., Weinstein, H. J., & Parsons, S. K. (1997). Controlling conditioning-related emesis in children undergoing bone marrow transplantation. *Oncology Nursing Forum, 24*(9), 1539–1544.

Morrow, G. R., & Rosenthal, S. N. (1996). Models, mechanisms, and management of anticipatory nausea and emesis. *Oncology, 53*(Suppl.), 4–7.

Olver, I. N. (1996). Antiemetic study methodology: Recommendations for future studies. *Oncology, 53*(Suppl.), 96–101.

Osoba, D., Zee., B., Warr, D., Kaizer, L., Latreille, J., & Pater, J. (1996). Quality of life studies in chemotherapy-induced emesis. *Oncology, 53*(Suppl.), 92–95.

Rhodes, V. (1997). Criteria for assessment of nausea, vomiting, and retching. *Oncology Nursing Forum, 24*(7), 13–19.

Rhodes, V. A., Johnson, M. H., & McDaniel, R. W. (1995). Nausea, vomiting, and retching: The management of the symptom experience. *Seminars in Oncology Nursing, 11*(4), 256–265.

Roila, F., Ballatori, E., Tonato, M., & Del Favero, A. (1997). 5-HT$_3$ receptor antagonists: Differences and similarities. *European Journal of Cancer, 33*(9), 1364–1370.

Schmoll, H. J., & Casper, J. (1996). Management of other non–cisplatin-induced emesis. *Oncology, 53*(Suppl.), 51–55.

Simpson, K. H. & Hicks, F. M. (1996). Clinical pharmacokinetics of ondansetron: A review. *Journal of Pharmacology, 48,* 774–781.

CHAPTER
19

Mucositis in Cancer Patients

Michelle R. V. Faber

Mucositis is one of the major dose-limiting toxicities of cancer treatment. It affects cancer patients' quality of life, their ability to proceed with treatment, and the cost of care. At least 40% of all patients newly diagnosed with cancer will experience oral mucositis related to their disease or its treatment (Beck, 1996).

Mucositis is the inflammation and/or ulceration and destruction of the mucosal cells in the body. Mucous membranes are found in the gastrointestinal, genitourinary, and respiratory tracts. In cancer and its treatment, the gastrointestinal effects of mucositis are the most common. This chapter will focus on the oral manifestations of mucositis.

Incidence

According to the National Oral Health Information Clearinghouse (NOHIC, 1999), oral complications occur in almost all patients receiving head and neck radiation, in 75% of patients who undergo bone marrow transplantation, and in 40% of patients who receive chemotherapy. With over 1 million new cancer cases per year, this adds up to hundreds of thousands of cases of mucositis. As growth factors are decreasing some dose-limiting toxicities of cancer treatment, such as neutropenia, mucositis is emerging as one of the three most common therapy-limiting side effects; the other two are thrombocytopenia and fatigue (Rubenstein, 1998).

A baseline understanding of mucosal cell reproduction is important in understanding how cancer and its treatment cause mucositis. In the mucosa, a basement membrane of stem cells constantly replicates and differentiates into the different types of mucosal cells. These new cells work their way to the surface layer of epithelial cells as the current epithelial lining is sloughed off or damaged. The average life of these mucosal cells is 3 to 5 days; thus, there is a new epithelial lining of cells every 7 to 14 days (Beck, 1996). It is this rapid replication cycle that makes the mucous membranes vulnerable to the cytotoxic effects of cancer treatment.

Risk Factors

The many risk factors for developing oral mucositis can be placed in four major categories: (1) cancer and its treatment, (2) side effects of disease and treatment, (3) other medical interventions, and (4) irritants.

Cancer and Its Treatment

Cancer itself causes disruptions in the integrity of the mucous membranes. Mucous membranes serve as the body's natural barriers against infection. Once a membrane is inflamed, it is more prone to infection. Oral cancers account for only 5% of all tumors and are not the most likely cause of mucositis. Much more common causes of mucositis are the treatments utilized to fight cancer, including chemotherapy, radiation therapy, and bone marrow transplantation.

311

Chemotherapy's antineoplastic effects are seen in all rapidly reproducing cells, as it interferes with cellular DNA, RNA, or protein synthesis. This interference causes a decrease in production and differentiation of the mucosal cells and promotes the early demise of the current epithelial cells. These factors impair the integrity of the membrane, which allows infection to occur. The peak effect of the chemotherapy on the mucosal cells is seen approximately 7 to 10 days after treatment. This is the same time period during which the chemotherapy has its peak effect on the white blood cell count. This lowered white blood cell count (nadir) further increases the risk for infection, as the body is less able to fight against infecting agents.

The categories of chemotherapy most toxic to the mucous membrane are as follows: the antimetabolites (e.g., 5-FU and methotrexate), antibiotics (e.g., doxorubicin, bleomycin, and mitomycin), alkylating agents (e.g., cyclophosphamide), and plant alkaloids (e.g., vinblastine and vincristine) (Box 19-1).

Radiation therapy causes mucositis by degrading the integrity of all the mucous membranes within the field of treatment. The radiation causes destruction of the epithelial cells and a corresponding inflammation. The extent of the damage to the mucosal cells depends on the amount, duration, and depth of the radiation treatments. The effect of the treatment on the mucosal cells is usually seen after the first week or two of treatment (Goodman, 1993). Radiation treatments can also affect the salivary glands. This condition, xerostomia, will be discussed in the next section.

Bone marrow transplant patients have a 70% chance of mucositis. The high-dose chemotherapy and radiation therapy before transplant and the prolonged effects of transplant on the bone marrow leave the patient's immune system unable to fight infection. The mucositis is usually at its worst 2 weeks after transplant and then slowly resolves. However, if the patient develops graft-versus-host disease, in which the patient's immune system

---

BOX 19-1

Chemotherapeutic Agents Likely to Cause Mucositis

Antimetabolites

5-Fluorouracil
Methotrexate
Floxuridine
Cyclocytidine
Cytosine arabinoside
6-Mercaptopurine
6-Thioguanine

Plant Alkaloids

Vincristine sulfate
Vinblastine sulfate
Etoposide

Antibiotics

Actinomicin D
Doxorubicin

Bleomycin sulfate
Daunomycin
Mithramycin
Mitomycin C
Mitoxantrone

Taxanes

Paclitaxel
Docetaxel

Miscellaneous

Hydroxyurea
Procarbazine hydrochloride

fights donor marrow rather than accepting it, the patient could experience chronic mucositis.

Side Effects of Disease and Treatment

Mucositis can also be caused by the side effects of cancer and its treatment. Dehydration, poor nutrition, and poor oral hygiene are among the side effects of oral cancer due to the discomfort associated with the impaired integrity of the oral mucous membranes. These three impairments may also be caused by the patient's inability to complete activities of daily living related to chemotherapy-induced fatigue. Dehydration causes dryness and cracking of the lips and mucous membranes, which increase the chances of infection and inflammation. In nasopharyngeal cancer the patient may be inclined to mouth breathe, which also dries the mucous membranes. Poor nutrition delays healing and increases the chances of infection. Poor oral hygiene can lead to infection due to the increased chance for bacteria to breed. Good oral hygiene actually stimulates circulation in the mouth, decreasing the chance for infection.

Radiation treatments can cause side effects of xerostomia (decreased functioning of the salivary glands) and ageusia (decreased functioning of the taste buds). Xerostomia causes dry mouth, which can lead to breakdown in the mucosa, and also causes dental caries if prolonged. Patients frequently require moistening agents for comfort when xerostomia occurs. Ageusia occurs when the taste buds are damaged by radiation. This can lead to poor nutrition. Ageusia usually resolves 2 to 4 months after treatment ends, but it is a permanent condition in some patients (Beck, 1996).

Other Medical Interventions

Medical interventions are the next category of risk factors for mucositis. Patients who are on oxygen therapy during their cancer treatment may need humidified oxygen to prevent drying of the mucous membranes. Mechanical trauma to the mucous membranes can occur in patients requiring repeated suctioning; this should be minimized if possible. Many patients take medications that can increase their risk for mucositis. For example, anti-cholinergics and antihistamines can dry the mucous membranes, which promotes breakdown, and steroids may allow fungal overgrowth in the mouth. Avoid drugs in these categories, if possible; otherwise, be sure that the patient is performing careful and frequent mouth care.

Irritants

Alcohol; cigarette and cigar smoke; hot, acidic, and spicy foods; and ill-fitting dental appliances, among other things, are irritants for everyone. Cancer patients, however, are more susceptible than most people to irritation of the mucosa, which leads to inflammation and increases the risk of infection.

Assessment

A good oral assessment is important in the care of each patient. Before looking in a patient's mouth, ask about mouth health. Especially important questions are about painful areas; any changes in taste, saliva, or sensation; ability to swallow and to speak; and any discolored areas. If the patient has noticed any changes, be sure to inquire about when they occured. Ask the patient if there is anything that makes these changes better or worse. A brief history will help you evaluate mucous membrane changes that may be subtle to you, but are not to the patient.

It is also important to know the cancer patient's treatment history as you evaluate the oral mucosa. Does this patient have a form of cancer that directly affects his or her oral mucosa? Has this patient received chemotherapy or radiation therapy for the cancer? If so, how many treatments has he or she received and when did they begin? The answer to those questions will tell you if and when the patient is likely to be immunocompromised (which is most likely to occur 7 to 10 days after treatment with chemotherapy).

To perform a good assessment, you will need appropriate tools; the most important tool is a good light source (Figure 19-1). The light source must be bright and movable, such as a gooseneck lamp or a flashlight. Other useful equipment includes gauze, a tongue blade, a disposable measuring device, and, if available, a dental mirror.

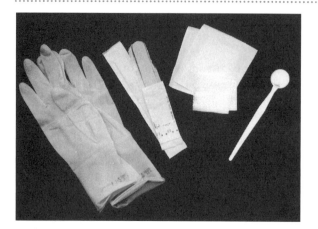

Figure 19-1 Tools for an oral assessment: light source; gloves; tongue blade; gauze; and dental mirror if available.

When you are examining the patient's mouth, always use universal precautions. Have the patient remove all appliances prior to your assessment. Look at the appliances and assess them for cleanliness. Be sure the patient has been maintaining them appropriately. As you start your oral assessment, look for changes in integrity, color, moisture, cleanliness, and perception. Start your oral assessment with the lips and note any dry or cracked skin, blisters, and edema (Figure 19-2). Raise the upper lip and pull down the lower lip to evaluate the teeth and mucosal lining of these areas (Figure 19-3). Next, have the patient open the mouth to assess the

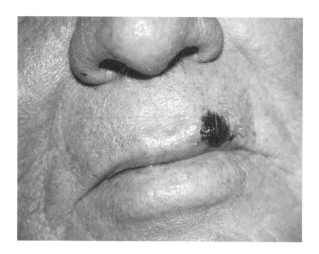

Figure 19-2 Herpes simplex lesion exacerbated by neutropenia.

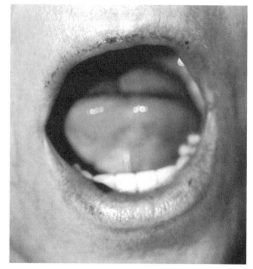

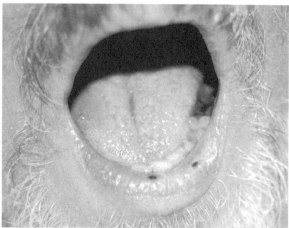

Figure 19-3 Mucositis may include the upper and lower lip areas.

hard and soft palate. Use the tongue depressor to move the cheeks outward to assess them. This is a good place to evaluate moisture and saliva. Normal saliva should be clear and watery. Look at the top of the tongue, then have the patient press the tongue to the top of the mouth and assess under the tongue (Figure 19-4). At this point you can use the gauze to move the tongue to either side to assess both lateral aspects. Once you are finished assessing the tongue, have the patient say "ahh" and assess the back of the oropharynx and uvula (Figure 19-5). If you cannot see these areas, use the tongue depressor and/or dental mirror to aid your assessment.

Although there are many assessment scales for categorizing mucositis, these are most commonly

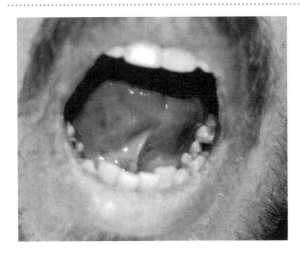

Figure 19-4 A complete oral assessment includes the oral mucosa beneath the tongue.

used by protocol nurses for research data collection. The best report is a thorough description of your assessment. Lesions, blisters, or other measurable irregularities should be monitored on a daily basis.

Treatment

Medical Intervention

The patient with mucositis will need medical intervention, with the stage of the treatment cycle and immune status determining the care required. An

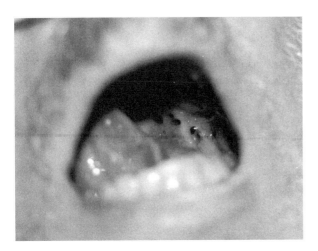

Figure 19-5 Mucositis on the anterior pillar of the oral cavity.

immunocompetent patient may require only comfort measures and empiric antibiotic therapy. Most often, however, the mucositis coincides with the patient's nadir and more intensive medical management will be required. Look for signs of infection such as fever, tachycardia, and an increased white blood cell count, but remember that the typical signs of infection may be absent in the immunocompromised patient due to his or her inability to produce white blood cells. Any lesions or open areas in the mouth should be cultured before starting antibiotic therapy. Culture results, although not necessary to begin therapy, are significant due to the potential for the oral infection to become systemic.

Patient Self-Care

Besides antibiotics, the patient will need meticulous mouth care and comfort measures (Box 19-2). Mouth care includes brushing the teeth and tongue, gargling, flossing, and moisturizing. NOHIC has an awareness program entitled "Oral Health, Cancer Care, and You," which is also sponsored by the National Cancer Institute, the National Institute of Nursing Research, and the Centers for Disease Control. Their patient teaching recommendations can be found on their Web site (http://www.aerie.com/nohicweb/campaign/den). NOHIC advises patients to brush their teeth, gums, and tongue with an extra-soft toothbrush after every meal and before bed. One suggestion is to soften the bristles in warm water before brushing. Brushing the tongue helps stimulate circulation to the tongue and remove any bacteria or debris. NOHIC also recommends flossing teeth every day. If the gums become sore or inflamed or are bleeding, the patient should avoid those areas but continue flossing other areas. Patients should also avoid using any mouthwash containing alcohol. These mouthwashes are acceptable for normal mouth cells but are too harsh and drying on the mucosa affected by chemotherapy or radiation therapy. Some products on the market are made without alcohol; these are acceptable for patient use. Patients can also make their own mouthwashes using 1/4 teaspoon of baking soda, 1/8 teaspoon of salt, and 1 cup of warm water. Rinsing with this mixture and then rinsing with plain warm water is very effective, both to prevent infec-

BOX 19-2

Daily Mouth Care

- Brushing the teeth and tongue with a soft toothbrush
- Gargling with saline, saltwater, or baking soda water

- Flossing (unless platelets are <40,000)
- Moisturizing

---

tion and to provide comfort for a painful mouth. Patients who are receiving chemotherapy should be instructed to begin saltwater gargles as a preventive for mucositis (1/4 teaspoon salt with 1 cup warm water).

To maintain healthy teeth and a healthy mouth while undergoing treatment, NOHIC also recommends avoiding candy and soda unless they are sugar-free and avoiding the use of toothpicks, tobacco products, and alcohol. Patients undergoing treatment should also be told to consult with their oncologist before seeing a dentist. This is to prevent dental work from being done during nadir when they are least able to fight infection. Necessary dental interventions can be scheduled around their treatments with the oncologist's help. If possible, however, extensive dental work should be postponed until after treatment is completed and the mucosa has had time to return to its normal state.

On the Horizon

Some new treatments in the research literature offer hope for prevention and improved treatment of mucositis. Amifostine, an organic thiophosphate, is a cytoprotective drug currently used for neurotoxicity caused by alkylating and platinum agents, paclitaxel, and radiation therapy. Griggs (1998) found that amifostine not only selectively protected neural cells from toxicity but also protected the oral mucosa. Amifostine has not been shown to diminish the effects of chemotherapy and radiation on the cancer cells.

Another recent study by Anderson, Schroeder, and Skubitz (1998) looks at the use of oral gluta-

mine supplementation during and after chemotherapy to decrease the duration and severity of mucositis. Ma, Ronai, Riede, and Kohler (1998) have found oral glutamine to be useful in increasing the comfort of many patients at high risk of developing mouth sores.

Mahood, Dose, Loprinzi, and Veeder (1991) studied the effectiveness of cryotherapy in reducing mucositis. Patients sucked on ice chips 5 minutes before and 25 minutes after bolus infusion of fluorouracil. This was a single study, however, and needs to be reproduced in order to test the findings.

Another familiar drug being studied in the treatment of mucositis is sucralfate, which is currently used to treat gastric ulcers. It works by binding to the damaged proteins in the mucosal surface. This drug action is now being applied to oral mucosa. The patients swish and swallow the sucralfate suspension. So far, however, this drug has been found to be effective as a comfort measure only, not as an effective prevention or treatment (Shenep, Kalwinsky, & Hutson, 1988). Thus, there are many potential additions to therapy for the treatment and prevention of mucositis.

Complications of Mucositis and Their Management

The most common complications of mucositis are infection, pain, and bleeding. Management of these complications can be as important as treatment of the mucositis itself.

The most life threatening of the common complications is infection. As mentioned in the treatment section, once the immunocompromised patient has developed mucositis, antibiotics are indicated. Oral cultures are indicated to determine whether the oral infection is viral, bacterial, or fungal in origin. Once cultures are taken, antibiotics should be started empirically. Antibiotics can be delivered in many forms: topically, swish and swallow, and troche. If the patient is neutropenic, a systemic oral antibiotic should be added to prevent systemic spread. If the patient is seropositive for herpes simplex virus, consider prophylactic antiviral therapy, such as acyclovir. All antibiotic therapy should be continued until the mucositis is resolved or the patient is no longer neutropenic.

In treating mucositis, it is important to remember the patient's comfort. Not only can mucositis put the patient at risk for infection, it can also be painful. Topical anesthetics that contain lidocaine or benzocaine will temporarily reduce oral pain. These topical agents also numb the mouth, however, which can cause other ill effects for the patient, such as decreased taste and thermal perception. Nelson (1998) found that taste loss can lead to compromised nutritional intake and therefore a worse outcome than for patients who do not experience taste loss. Oral gels that coat the mucosa can give pain relief for up to 6 hours. For moderate to severe mucositis pain, a systemic combination of an opioid and a nonopioid may be necessary. A combination of acetaminophen and codeine can be very effective and should be dosed for around-the-clock pain relief. If the mouth is too painful for the person to eat or drink, supplemental nutrition will be needed until the mucositis is resolved.

Bleeding is another mucositis complication. At the time when the mucosal cells and white blood cells are most affected by the cancer treatment, the platelets are also likely to be decreased. If the patient experiences oral bleeding, teach him or her to apply a cold gauze or use ice-cold irrigations to stop the bleeding. If this is ineffective, the patient may need a topical application of thrombin or systemic treatment in the form of a platelet transfusion.

Summary

Mucositis is a common cancer treatment toxicity, with as many as 75% of patients experiencing oral complications of their therapy. Its impact can be minimized, however, with appropriate preventive measures, meticulous mouth care throughout the cancer experience, and appropriate treatment and supportive measures. Research continues to investigate more effective treatments for, and even prevention of, mucositis. Caregivers can offer practical relief in the present and hope for the future.

REFERENCES

Anderson, P. M., Schroeder, G., & Skubitz, K. M. (1998). Oral glutamine reduces the duration and severity of stomatitis after cytotoxic cancer chemotherapy. *Cancer, 83,* 1433–1439.

Beck, S. L. (1996). Mucositis. In S. L. Groenwald (Ed.), *Cancer symptom management* (pp. 308–323). Sudbury, MA: Jones and Bartlett.

Goodman, M., Ladd, L. A., & Purl, S. (1993). Integumentary and mucous membrane alterations. In S. L. Groenwald, M. H. Frogge, M. Goodman, & C. H. Yarbro (Eds.), *Cancer nursing: Principles and practice* (3rd ed., rev., pp. 734–799). Sudbury, MA: Jones and Bartlett.

Griggs, J. J. (1998). Reducing the toxicity of anticancer therapy: New strategies. *Leukemia Research, 22* (suppl. 1), S27–S33.

Ma, L., Ronai, A., Riede, U. N., & Kohler, G. (1998). Clinical implications of screening p53 gene mutations in head and neck squamous cell carcinomas. *Journal of Cancer Research and Clinical Oncology, 124* (7), 389–396.

Mahood, D. J., Dose, A. M., Loprinzi, C. L., & Veeder, M. H. (1991). Inhibition of fluorouracil-induced stomatitis by oral cryotherapy. *Journal of Clinical Oncology, 9,* 449–452.

National Oral Health Information Clearinghouse (1999). Oral complications of cancer treatment [WWW document]. http://www.aerie.com/nohicweb/campaign/den

Nelson, G. M. (1998). Biology of taste buds and the clinical problem of taste. *Anatomical Record, 253* (3), 70–78.

Rubenstein, E. B. (1998). Evaluating cost-effectiveness in outpatient management of medical complications in cancer patients. *Current Opinion in Oncology, 10* (4), 297–301.

Shenep, J. L., Kalwinsky, D. K., & Hutson, P. R. (1988). Efficacy of oral sucralfate suspension in prevention and treatment of chemotherapy-induced mucositis. *Journal of Pediatrics, 113,* 758–763.

CHAPTER
20

Anorexia

Tracey Gosselin
Sharon Pitz

People diagnosed with cancer face not only physiologic and psychological distress but also nutrition issues that arise throughout the trajectory of their disease. Nutritional deficiencies may appear at the time of diagnosis, during the phase of active treatment, or at later stages as the disease progresses. The inability of the patient to tolerate nourishment not only affects the patient's perspective of the disease, but also the patient's family. The patient and the family may feel at a loss in trying to manage nutritional problems alone.

Anorexia is a common symptom of cancer and can often be overlooked by the family and patient as a symptom that will eventually go away. This symptom, unfortunately, has various contributing factors, such as chemical and metabolic changes, taste changes in relation to therapy, and pain that may be associated with the disease or the side effects of treatment. Patients complain of profound lack of appetite, nausea, fatigue, changes in body image with progressive generalized wasting, and ongoing decline in their ability to carry on their usual daily activities (Tchekmedyian, 1995).

Anorexia is seen in approximately 15% to 40% of cancer patients at the time of diagnosis and in 80% of patients who have advanced disease (Nelson, Walsh & Sheehan, 1994; Von Roenn & Knoph, 1996). When people think of anorexia, they commonly associate it with a disease called anorexia nervosa, which is an eating disorder characterized by a different set of symptoms. Many people are unaware that anorexia is a condition that also strikes cancer patients and has serious implications for overall long-term survival.

Severe malnutrition and cancer cachexia—a syndrome that includes a decline in food intake, depletion of essential nutrients, and changes in protein, fat, carbohydrates, mineral, and vitamin metabolism—leads to a loss of body mass, muscle wasting, and an increase susceptibility to toxicity. This syndrome is characterized by anorexia, weight loss, fatigue, and poor performance status (Figure 20-1). Severe weight loss (>10% of usual body weight) is associated with impairment and changes in vital organ function. If cachexia is allowed to progress, the patient's quality of life and, therefore, overall long-term survival will be affected. Malnutrition is reported as the cause of death in as many as 20% of cancer patients (Ottery, 1994). It is, therefore, important for us to understand the nutrition implications that cancer has on a person's body, as well as how to treat and manage side effects that arise from the disease.

Side Effects Associated With Cancer Therapies

Chemotherapy Side Effects

Chemotherapy represents a series of therapeutic drugs used to fight cancer cells in a person's body. These drugs not only kill cancer cells or "bad cells" but also affect healthy cells or "good cells." Certain types of chemotherapy work on fast-growing or rapidly dividing cells, such as hair cells, blood cells, and the entire lining of the gastrointestinal (GI) tract. The side effects specific to the

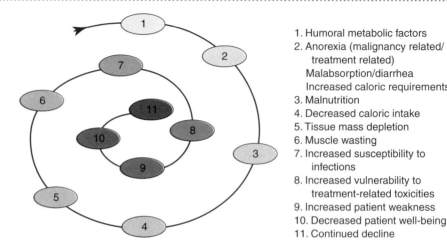

Figure 20-1 The spiral of cachexia and weight loss. (Redrawn from Cunningham, R. *The anorectic-cachectic syndrome in cancer.* A continuing education program by Bristol-Myers Squibb Oncology/Immunology.)

1. Humoral metabolic factors
2. Anorexia (malignancy related/ treatment related)
    Malabsorption/diarrhea
    Increased caloric requirements
3. Malnutrition
4. Decreased caloric intake
5. Tissue mass depletion
6. Muscle wasting
7. Increased susceptibility to infections
8. Increased vulnerability to treatment-related toxicities
9. Increased patient weakness
10. Decreased patient well-being
11. Continued decline

GI tract include mucositis, esophagitis, nausea, vomiting, constipation, diarrhea, and hypogeusia, which is a deterioration in taste perception, as well as dysgeusia, an alteration in sense of taste. Patients who receive platinum-based drugs generally complain of a metallic taste and should be educated about not eating foods with metal utensils and to avoid foods stored in metal containers. These patients sometimes have an aversion to red meat and usually tolerate cool, bland foods that have minimal to no aroma.

Nausea and vomiting are common side effects of chemotherapy. The use of antiemetics and nutrition counseling can help the patient and family maintain a sense of "normalcy" during treatment. The use of antiemetic drugs varies based on treatment regimen and type of cancer. Patients who receive chemotherapy may experience *acute* or *chronic* nausea depending on the drugs they receive. Acute nausea may arise during the infusion or within minutes or hours after the infusion has completed. Delayed nausea occurs 24 hours after chemotherapy is administered and can last up to several days. Therefore, it is important for patients to have antiemetic medications to use at home. Patients may also experience anticipatory nausea, which is a conditioning response that can be triggered by a sight, sound, or presence. For example, a patient may become nauseated after entering the clinic or seeing the chemotherapy bag.

During this phase of treatment, it is important to teach the patient relaxation and diversion techniques (Table 20-1). It is also important to teach the patient and family members who do the cooking that eating favorite foods during treatment may not prove to be beneficial.

Radiation Side Effects

Radiation therapy is a type of therapy used to treat a variety of cancers. Treatments typically last no longer than 3 to 5 minutes, depending on the disease, but the side effects from the treatment can be broken down into *acute* and *chronic* side effects. The nurse needs to be aware of the nutrition challenges that lie ahead for the patient who is undergoing radiation therapy and offer supportive measures to the patient and family. Patients who are able to maintain optimal nutrition intake during their therapy not only have a shorter recovery time from treatment, but are also able to handle additional types of treatment in the future. With the majority of cancer patients undergoing treatment at an outpatient facility, it is imperative that early nutrition counseling and intervention be provided.

The side effects of radiation therapy vary from patient to patient and depend on the dose of radiation, size of treatment field, and the site of therapy. It is important to remember that patients who

TABLE 20-1
NONPHARMACOLOGIC INTERVENTIONS FOR NAUSEA AND VOMITING

Technique	Description	Comments
Behavioral Interventions		
Self-hypnosis	Evocation of physiologic state of altered consciousness and total body relaxation. This technique involves a state of intensified attention, and increased receptiveness to an idea.	First technique used to control anticipatory nausea and vomiting Limited studies—mostly children and adolescents Easily Learned No side effects Decreases intensity and duration of nausea
Relaxation	Progressive contraction and relaxation of various muscle groups	Decreases frequency, severity, amount, and duration of vomiting Often used with imagery Can be used for other stressful situations Easily learned No side effects Decreases nausea during and after chemotherapy Decreases duration and severity of vomiting Not as effective with anticipatory nausea and vomiting
Biofeedback	Control of specific physiologic responses by receiving information about changes in response to induced state of relaxation	Two types: electromyographic and skin temperature Used alone or with relaxation Easily learned No side effects Decreases nausea during and after chemotherapy More effective with progressive muscle relaxation
Imagery	Mentally take self away by focusing one's mind on images of a relaxing place	Most effective when combined with another technique Increases self-control Decreases duration of nausea Decreases perceptions of degree of vomiting Feel more in control, relaxed, and powerful
Distraction	Learn to divert attention from a threatening situation and to relaxing sensations	Can use videos, games, and puzzles No side effects Decreases anticipatory nausea and vomiting Decreases postchemotherapy distress
Desensitization	Three-step process involving relaxation and visualization to decrease sensitization to aversive situations	Inexpensive Easily learned No side effects Decreases anticipatory nausea and vomiting
Other		
Acupressure	Forms of massage using meridians to increase energy flow and affect emotions	Inconclusive literature support Acupressure wrist bands may be helpful to decrease nausea and vomiting Often used with other techniques
Music Therapy	Use of music to influence physiologic, psychologic and emotional functioning during threatening situation	No side effects Decreases nausea during and after chemotherapy Decreases perceptions of degree of vomiting

(King, C. [1997]. Nonpharmacologic management of chemotherapy-induced nausea and vomiting. *Oncology Nursing Forum, 24* [7]; 41–48.)

receive radiation therapy have an exit site from the beam and, therefore, may experience side effects from the treatment in another location, different from the site being radiated. Most radiation therapy–induced nutrition difficulties are transient and subside about 2 weeks after treatments are finished (Nelson et al., 1994). For those patients who face long-term side effects, it is important for the nurse to be able to provide nutrition education to the patient and the family throughout the course of treatment and at follow-up. The use of a dietitian is also highly recommended for nutrition assessment, diet planning, and counseling.

Radiation therapy to the head and neck region can have acute and chronic side effects, depending on the site being irradiated (Table 20-2). It is important to encourage the patient to take antiemetics as ordered, usually 15 to 30 minutes before treatment if they are going to receive radiation to the stomach and small intestine region. Hydration

and the use of antidiarrheal medications are sometimes necessary to combat the symptoms patients experience.

Surgery Side Effects

Surgical intervention in cancer patients can sometimes be a difficult decision for the patient and family. The impact of surgery on a patient's nutritional status depends on whether the primary site of the cancer is in the GI tract. Many patients have already faced dramatic weight loss in lieu of a definitive diagnosis and struggle with the decision to proceed with surgery, considering their present nutrition state. In many GI cancers, the patient may need to consider having a diverting ileostomy or colostomy and the body image changes that may occur. If a patient is to undergo head and neck surgery, he or she may suffer from the inability to chew or swallow foods as in the past and may, therefore, need to have soft or blenderized foods. The issue surrounding the use of tube feeding at this point is also critical. After surgery, it is important for the patient to have an adequate nutrient intake to assist in the healing process. Patients who undergo partial or total gastrectomy have problems that revolve around consumption, absorption, and amount of food. Absorption difficulties are present when the greater portion of the stomach is removed. Vitamin B_{12} cannot be adequately absorbed, and pernicious anemia occurs. The absorption of fat is also affected, which hinders the absorption of fat-soluble vitamins. When a total gastrectomy is performed, the patient has to eat small, frequent meals due to the capacity he or she can hold and also due to the loss in appetite stimulus. Patients may experience dumping syndrome, which is characterized by nausea, cramping, and diarrhea when food is dumped into the jejunum after eating.

Nutrition Assessment of the Cancer Patient

The impact of cancer cachexia and anorexia on the patient's performance status justifies the need for early assessment and appropriate interventions based on the patient's nutritional status. It is im-

TABLE 20-2

ACUTE AND CHRONIC NUTRITIONAL PROBLEMS ASSOCIATED WITH RADIATION THERAPY

Site Being Irradiated	Acute	Chronic
Head and neck	Anorexia	Dental caries
	Discomfort/pain	Difficulty swallowing
	Dysgeusia	Dysgeusia
	Hypogeusia	Hypogeusia
	Inflammation and swelling	Osteoradionecrosis
	Oral infections	Trismus
	Stomatitis	Xerostomia
	Xerostomia	
Lung and esophagus	Anorexia	Decreased motility
	Discomfort/pain	Dysphagia
	Dysphagia	Esophageal strictures
	Dyspnea	Ulceration
	Esophagitis	
	Fatigue	
	Pharyngitis	
Stomach and intestines	Anorexia	Adhesions
	Diarrhea	Fistulas
	Discomfort/pain	Malabsorption
	Dyspnea	Obstruction
	Nausea	Strictures
	Vomiting	

portant to screen all patients, whether they are in an inpatient or outpatient setting, for nutrition difficulties before initiation of cancer treatment. In screening cancer patients, it is important to consider the unique needs of children and the elderly population. These populations are at higher risk for difficulties due to the physiologic changes that their bodies are undergoing (Table 20-3).

A three-stage approach to nutrition assessment should include the following:

1. A screening mechanism to identify patients potentially at risk for nutrition problems
2. A comprehensive nutrition assessment of patients found to be malnourished
3. A system to monitor a patient's nutrition status

The nutrition screening is designed to identify patients according to risk of malnutrition and is further divided into three categories: high risk, moderate risk, and low risk. The screen is based on clinical measures of nutrition status (Table 20-4).

Screening parameters are used to assess the likelihood of malnutrition and use the above risk factors as criteria (Table 20-5).

Patients at risk for protein-calorie malnutrition should be evaluated further to determine the type/degree of malnutrition. A nutrition assessment should include the following:

Medical history
Nutrition history
Anthropometric measurements
Laboratory data
Nutrient requirements
Physical assessment

Medical History

When reviewing issues regarding nutrition with the patient and family, it is important to also find out what other comorbid conditions the patient may have. Diseases and disorders such as diabetes, heart disease, and malabsorption disorders will all have an impact on the nutritional goals and interventions that you and the patient decide on together. In managing nutritional needs, these factors must be taken into account so the patient's health is not jeopardized.

TABLE 20-3
NUTRITIONAL ASSESSMENT COMPONENTS

Medical History

Date of diagnosis and type of malignancy
Type and duration of therapy
Prior therapies and surgeries
Current medications
Allergies
Side effects from past therapies
Side effects of current therapies
Other medical conditions and comorbidities

Nutritional History

24-hour food recall
Evaluation of food composition (calories and protein)
Food allergies
Food preferences based on religious and cultural beliefs
Use of mineral and vitamin supplements
Changes in eating habits based on disease/side effects of treatment
Preparation and cooking of food

Physical Assessment

Overall appearance
Skin integrity and turgor
Condition of hair
Performance status
Dentation and condition of oral mucosa
Alterations in healing

Anthropometric Measurements

Height
Weight
Weight changes as compared to ideal weight and weight before diagnosis
Midarm circumference
Skinfold thickness from abdomen, tricep, or subscapular area

Laboratory Data

Blood urea nitrogen
Creatinine
Creatinine height index
Glucose
Hematocrit
Hemoglobin
Potassium
Serum albumin
Serum transferrin
Sodium

Nutrient Requirements

Energy needs
Protein needs

TABLE 20-4
MALNUTRITION SCREENING CRITERIA

High-Risk Criteria*

Recent weight loss (≥5% loss of usual body weight in 1 month or ≥10% loss of usual body weight in 6 months)

Serum albumin ≤3.0 g/dL

Prealbumin ≤10mg/dL

Total lymphocyte count ≤1200/mm3

Patient receiving nothing by mouth for 5 days or maintained on 5% dextrose solution or clear liquids for ≥5 days

Current use of parenteral or enteral nutrition

Moderate-Risk Criteria

Recent involuntary weight loss (<5% loss of usual body weight in 1 month or <10% loss of usual body weight in 6 months)

Serum albumin 3.0–3.4 g/dL

Transitional feeding

Select dietary modification

Low-Risk Criteria (Not Compromised)

Weight stable

Serum albumin ≥3.5 g/dL

No indications for dietary modification

---

*If more than one high-risk criterion is observed, a comprehensive nutrition assessment should be performed.
(Detttoog, S. [1985]. Identifying patients at nutritional risk and determining clinical producivity: Essentials for an effective nutrition care program. *Journal of the American Dietetic Association, 85,* 1620–1622. Copyright 1985 by the American Dietetic Association.)

TABLE 20-5
NUTRITION SCREENING PARAMETERS

Subjective Data

Recent appetite changes (difficulty chewing or swallowing; nausea or vomiting)

Diarrhea or constipation (food allergies and intolerances)

Previous dietary modifications

Usual body weight

Objective Data

Diagnosis

Age

Height

Current weight (verify reported usual body weight)

Serum albumin

Prealbumin or total lymphocyte count (if available)

Diet order and duration (if appropriate)

Current or previous use of nutrition support

(Dettoog, S. [1988]. Nutrition screening and assessment in a university hospital. In *Nutrition screening and assessment as components of hospital admission: Report of the eighth Ross roundtable on medical issues* [pp. 2–8]. Columbus, OH: Ross Laboratories. Copyright 1988.)

Nutrition History

The nutrition history consists of a set of questions that are posed to the patient/family by the nurse and/or dietitian. The questions investigate the patient's ability to eat, including psychosocial factors such as living environment, cooking methods, and cultural beliefs about food preferences. It is also important at this juncture to ascertain what type of support mechanisms the patient and/or family have in place. Factors affecting nutrient intake such as food tolerances, food aversions, changes in taste, sense of smell, use of vitamin/mineral supplementation, nutrient supplements, herbal therapies, and "fad" diets should be addressed.

In a clinic or outpatient setting, a nurse may quickly assess the need for referral to a dietitian or nutritionist by using the tool shown in Figure

20-2. It is important in the outpatient setting to screen patients early in their treatment plan, so goals and interventions can be decided on while the patient is still doing well.

Anthropometric Measurements

Anthropometric measurements are physical measurements of a patient's body. These measurements are used to estimate body composition and include the patient's height, weight, usual weight, midarm circumference, and skinfold thickness measurements taken from the abdomen, triceps, or subscapular area. Accurate record-keeping and measurements will assist in verification of information provided by the patient and will also establish any patterns of weight gain or loss. In weighing the patient, it is important to try and do so at the same time daily. It is also important to take into account weight gain or loss that may be due to edema or diuretics.

Laboratory Assessment

Laboratory levels can be helpful in establishing deviations from normal parameters of key labora-

ONCOLOGY OUTPATIENT SCREEN FOR NUTRITION REFERRALS.

Patient Name _____ DX._____
Hx# _____ DOB _____ Treatment plan_____
Treatment Status: XRT _____ Chemo TX _____ Surgery _____

☐Initial   ☐Follow-up

WEIGHT HISTORY:
    Current weight _____ lbs   estimated   measured
    Height _____ inches   estimated   measured
    Usual weight _____ lbs   Weight at time of diagnosis _____ lbs
    Weight prior to beginning treatment _____ lbs
    Weight 1 year ago: _____ lbs
    Weight 6 months ago:_____lbs
    % of weight loss in last month _____%
    % of weight loss in last six months_____%
REFER PATIENT TO DIETITIAN FOR THE FOLLOWING
    weight loss greater than 5% in one month
    weight loss greater than 10% in six months
    feeding tube placement is planned: ☐PEG   ☐Enterflex/Dubhoff
                                    ☐G-Tube   ☐J-Tube

FOOD INTAKE
REFER TO THE DIETITIAN FOR ANY ITEM NOTED AS A SCORE OF 3 OR 4
Nutrient intake during the past month (compared to normal)

☐ No change		0
☐ Changed:	☐ more than usual	1
	☐ less than usual	1
	☐ much less than usual	2
I am now taking:	☐ little solid foods	3
	☐ only liquids	3
	☐ only nutritional supplements	3
	list products and usual amounts:	
	_____	
	☐ very little of anything	4

SYMPTOMS: NURSE TO GIVE *EATING HINTS BOOKLET* OR OTHER MATERIAL
APPROVED BY THE DIETITIAN
Gastrointestinal symptoms that persisted for more than 2 weeks (check all that apply):

☐ no problems eating   ☐things taste funny or have
☐ no appetite, just did not feel like eating   no taste
☐ nausea
☐ vomiting   ☐ smells bother me
☐ constipation   ☐other _____
☐ diarrhea   _____
☐ sore mouth
☐ sore throat

Nurses Signature _____ Date:_____

Figure-20-2. Oncology outpatient screen for nutrition referrals.

tory values. They can help in identifying or assessing a patient's nutritional status. However, one must be careful to consider all aspects of the patient's disease status, medications, and treatment plans because no single biochemical marker will identify the status of malnutrition. Major disease states may alter results by producing a false value through interference or by altering the result through a pharmacologic or toxic effect.

Albumin is used to measure the status of visceral protein stores. Albumin levels take longer to respond to increased protein intake, having a half-life of approximately 20 days. A prealbumin level is a more sensitive indicator (3- to 4-day marker) and a better indicator of visceral protein status. Serum transferrin reflects the body's ability to make serum proteins; this has a half-life of approximately 9 days. It is also a carrier protein for iron (Table 20-6).

TABLE 20-6
LABORATORY VALUES

Laboratory Values	Explanation for Deviations
Albumin	Increase in dehydration Decrease in tumor involvement of liver, ascites, edema, fluid overload, decreased protein intake, malnutrition/kwashiorkor, and malabsorption
Calcium	Calcium is albumin bound. If albumin is decreased, then calcium may be falsely decreased. Use the following formula for adjustment: $(4.0 - alb) * 0.8 = x$ $x + (calcium) =$ adjusted calcium
Transferrin	Increase in iron deficiency anemia and dehydration Decrease represents liver disease; increased iron stores and malnutrition/kwashiorkor
Glucose	Diabetes, tumor burden, and medications
BUN and creatinine	Antibiotics, kidney involvement, and malnutrition
Hematocrit and hemoglobin	Malnutrition, chemo/radiation, and blood transfusion
Lymphocyte count	Malnutrition, disease state (type of cancer), and chemo/radiation

Nutrient Requirements

To determine a patient's nutrient requirements, one must calculate the patient's energy needs and protein requirements. The formula to determine energy needs is the Harris-Benedict formula. This calculation assists the dietitian in planning adequate nutrition support to the patient.

The Harris-Benedict formula for men's BEE (basal energy expenditure) is calculated as follows:

BEE (men) = 66.47 + (13.75) (weight in kg) + (5.00) (height in cm) − (6.76) (age in years)

Women's BEE (basal energy expenditure) is calculated as follows:

BEE (women) = 655.1 + (9.56) (weight in kg) + (1.85) (height in cm) − (4.68) (age in years)

The BEE is also known as the BMR or basal metabolic rate.

Physical Assessment

The physical assessment provides the caregiver with a general overview of the patient's health status. It is important during the examination to look at the patient's hair, nails, skin, and oral mucosa. In assessing the patient's hair, the nurse should look for brittleness and sheen and note any alopecia the patient may have from therapy. When assessing the nails, distinguish between being pink and healthy versus dry, brittle, or discolored. When assessing the skin, the nurse should assess for easy bruising; dry, cracked or scaly skin; itchiness; or discoloration. To test the patient's skin turgor, pinch a small amount of skin on the forearm and see if there is a "tenting" effect, which may indicate dehydration. Lastly, when assessing the oral mucosa, look at the color of the lips, tongue, mucous membranes, and gingiva along with assessing the consistency of the patient's saliva. The oral mucosa should appear pink, moist, and clean, and the saliva should appear watery in nature. If the patient wears dentures, it is important to note whether the weight loss has occurred because the dentures may not fit as well. When doing the physical examination, the nurse can also assess the patient's mobility and ability to care for himself or herself.

Nutritional Management

Nutritional care and management of the anorexic cancer patient will depend on the cause of anorexia and the goals of the treatment team. Whenever possible, the patient should be involved in the treatment plan. General goals for nutritional care are:

1. To preserve lean body mass
2. To provide adequate nutrients
3. To minimize and control GI symptoms

Treatment plans may be:

1. Conservative—maintenance of a reasonable weight
2. Aggressive—prevent and/or correct nutrition-related imbalances and deficiencies
3. Palliative—comfort care and nonaggressive nutritional care

The oral route of feeding is always the preferred and most desirable method for nutrition support whenever possible. Patients with mild anorexia may respond well to nutrition counseling. Counseling should stress the importance of the following factors:

1. A balanced diet
2. Regular eating habits
3. Family involvement
4. Food safety/safe food handling, preparation, and storage
5. Ways to modify the diet when complications arise

A counselor should investigate for the use of excessive vitamin/mineral intake (pills or powders) and for fad or unproven diets, which may have a negative effect on the patient's nutritional status. Symptom management and a temporary change of food consistency, medication, physical surroundings, or eating plan often lead to an increase in oral intake.

Treatment modalities such as surgery or radiation therapy often necessitate a change in diet to promote symptom management/control or for increased absorption/digestion of nutrients (Table 20-7).

TABLE 20-7

DIETARY MODIFICATIONS BASED ON ABSORPTION/DIGESTION

Type of Surgery	Dietary Modifications
Esophagogastrectomy	Eat four to six small meals
	Limit fluids to 4–6 oz during meals
	Avoid lying down, reclining, bending over, or straining for 1½–3 h after meals
	Do not eat 2–3 h before bedtime
	Limit high-fat foods—cakes, cookies, pies, and fried foods
	Limit the amount of chocolate, alcohol, coffee, citrus juice, tomatoes, onion, peppermint, and spicy foods
	Select foods high in protein—fish, chicken, cheese, yogurt, and eggs
	Avoid chewing gum
	Do not smoke
Gastrectomy	Eat six small meals
	Eat soft, easy-to-digest foods
	Limit fluids to 2–4 oz with meals
	Avoid sugar—sweetened drinks, candy, and desserts
	Limit juice and fruit juices
	Avoid very hot or very cold liquids
	Use coffee, tea, milk, bread, potatoes, and spicy foods occasionally
Ostomy surgery	Eat meals at regular times
	Chew all foods thoroughly
	Drink 8–10 glasses of fluid a day. Avoid carbonated beverages
	Avoid gaining excessive weight
	Eat smaller evening meal to reduce stool output during the night
	Avoid nuts, raw fruits and vegetables, and mushrooms after surgery for 6 weeks

The degree of cachexia and tumor burden will need further investigation to determine the desired plan of nutritional care. Energy needs vary depending on the type of tumor present. Examples are hypermetabolic as with leukemia, normometabolic as with gastric, GI and mixed tumors, and, lastly, hypometabolic as with GI tumors. The percentage of weight change can assist in identifying patients at risk for malnutrition. Assessment of weight change is calculated as follows:

Actual weight ÷ Usual weight = % of usual weight

For example, Mr. A's current weight is 120 lb. His usual weight is 150 lb.

$$120 ÷ 150 = 80\%$$

Mr. A is at 80% of his usual weight or has experienced a weight loss of 20% of his usual weight (100% − 80% = 20% weight loss).

The percentage of usual weight should be further clarified to determine the length of time involved in the weight loss and to identify if it is a significant weight loss.

Time	Significant	Severe
1 week	1–2%	>2%
1 month	5%	>5%
3 months	7.5%	>7.5%
6 months	10%	>10%

It is also important to determine if weight loss is a continuing problem, if the loss has stabilized, or if the patient's appetite and oral intake are starting to improve and weight is gradually increasing. More aggressive nutrition care may be needed for the patient with no improvement or continued weight loss. The use of nutritional supplements (Table 20-8) and high-protein foods (Table 20-9) can help the patient maintain his or her current weight. The use of supplements and high-protein foods increases calorie and protein intake but does not always require the patient to eat more food. It is important to teach the patient and family the use of supplements in helping meet body needs.

Weight should be monitored two to three times a week to determine whether the patient's weight is stable, continuing to decrease, or increasing with the changes in eating. More frequent weights or daily weights show a more accurate change in fluid status. Sudden or rapid decreases in weight may alert one to the potential of dehydration and the need for more fluids. Patients receiving enteral feeds also need their weight monitored.

Use of Other Nutrition Supplements

When mechanical or physical complications prevent adequate oral intake and promote continued weight loss, rethinking the patient's nutritional

TABLE 20-8
NUTRITIONAL SUPPLEMENTS

Product	Serving Size	Calories	Grams of Protein
Boost	8 oz	240	10
Boost Energy Bar	1 bar	190	4
Carnation Instant Breakfast (plus milk)	8 oz	280	12
Ensure	8 oz	254	9
Ensure Plus	8 oz	360	13
Equate (WalMart)	8 oz	250	9
Equate Plus (WalMart)	8 oz	250	13
Resource	8 oz	180	9
ScandiShake (plus milk)	8 oz	600	16
Sustacal	8 oz	240	15
Sustacal Plus	8 oz	360	14
Sustacal Pudding	5 oz	240	9

TABLE 20-9

HIGH-PROTEIN FOODS

Food Choice	Serving Size	Calories	Grams of Protein
Dairy			
Most cheeses	1 slice	60	4
Cottage cheese	1 cup	239	30
Yogurt (plain)	1 cup	150	8
Powdered milk (nonfat, dry)	3.2 oz	325	32
Custard	1/2 cup	218	10
Whole milk	8 oz	150	8
Lowfat milk	8 oz	100	8
Skim milk	8 oz	90	8
Meat and Eggs			
Beef	3 oz	172	14
Poultry	3 oz	85	17
Fish	3 oz	144	21
Pork	3 oz	220	14
Egg	1 medium	75	6
Nuts, Seeds, and Beans			
Peanut butter	1 tbsp	94	4
Peanuts	1 oz	165	8
Sunflower seeds	1 oz	160	6
Pumpkin seeds	1 oz	155	7
Dried beans, cooked	1 cup	213	14

needs and goals should be considered (Figure 20-3). Enteral nutrition is preferred for feeding when the GI tract is functional because it helps to maintain digestion, absorption, and gut motility.

Enteral Feeding Considerations
- Route for feeding
- Type of feeding tube
- Formula selection
- Feeding program
- Complications
- Monitoring

Route of Feeding
- Short term: <6 weeks
- Gastrostomy or PEG tube
- Jejunostomy
- Gastrojejunostomy

See Figure 20-4.

The gastrostomy or PEG tube is indicated for use when an obstruction prevents the insertion of a nasal tube. It is more desirable for long-term use and gives the patient increased mobility because he or she is not constantly in need of an IV pole or pump to do the feedings. Loose-fitting clothing will conceal the tube. Jejunostomy or "J" tubes should be considered for use in patients who have chronic aspiration or gastric obstruction problems. They are small tubes that require continuous feeding and frequent flushing to prevent clogging. Pills should not be crushed and put down the "J" tube because this could cause clogging; if medications cannot be given by any other route, consult with a pharmacist.

Formula Selection

A complete nutritional evaluation is recommended before selecting and initiating tube feeding. Considerations that the provider needs to take into account include gut function, tube placement, organ function, formula composition, osmolarity, kcal/protein content, and volume of the formula needed to meet the recommended daily allowances (RDAs) for vitamin and mineral needs. The treatment plan and goals should also be considered.

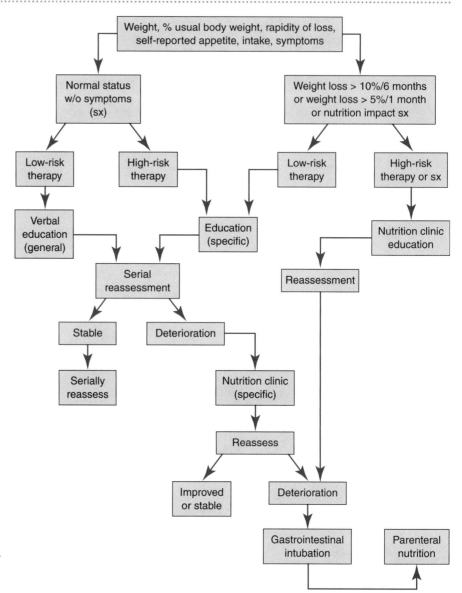

Figure 20-3 Rethinking the patient's nutritional needs. (From Rethinking nutritional support of the cancer patient: The new field of nutritional oncology. *Seminars in Oncology, 21*[6], 774.)

Feeding Schedule and Plan

Continuous feedings are usually infused over a 24-hour period for full nutritional support. Consideration should be given to the degree of cachexia and the length of time a person has gone without oral intake before starting the feeding. In general, it is recommended to start a continuous feeding with full-strength formula, at approximately 50% of the goal rate, but not more than 50 cc/hour. After the feeding has been well tolerated for 8 to 12 hours, one may increase the feedings by 10 to 25 cc every 4 to 8 hours. This will help to reach the patient's goal rate with minimal side effects.

Once the tube feed is tolerated at the goal rate, cyclic feeding may be attempted to allow the patient more freedom and "off time" to perform activities of daily living. It is important to slowly increase the volume and decrease the time of the feeding to determine the level best tolerated by the patient. If a hospitalized patient is discharged before the cyclic goal is reached, ask the dietitian to

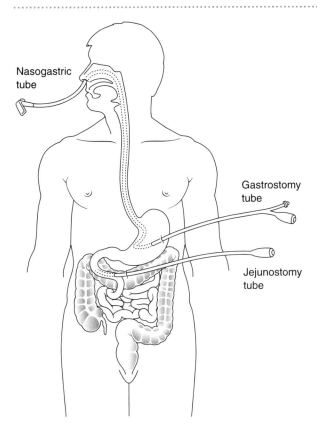

Nasogastric
tube

Gastrostomy
tube

Jejunostomy
tube

Figure 20-4 Types of feeding tubes. (From Anderson, L., & Ward, D. [1997]. Nutrition. In S.E. Otto [Ed.], *Oncology nursing* [3rd ed.]. St. Louis: C.V. Mosby.)

formulate a plan with the patient and family. This plan should include several hourly rate options for the patient to use at home. An example is shown in Table 20-10.

The patient may have to slowly adjust the on/off time so as to best determine his or her tolerance. It is also important for the patient to decrease the "on" time slowly (about every 2 to 3

TABLE 20-10		
SAMPLE FEEDING PLAN		
Feeding Formula	x cc/h ×	22 h on and 2 h off
	x cc/h ×	20 h on and 4 h off
	x cc/h ×	18 h on and 6 h off
	x cc/h ×	16 h on and 8 h off
	x cc/h ×	14 h on and 10 h off
	x cc/h ×	12 h on and 12 h off

days) and not to predetermine the "on" time. This way the patient and family will not be disappointed if the patient is unable to reach a goal. The importance of meeting nutritional needs should be stressed and reinforced with the patient and family.

Bolus feeds should be started with full-strength formula, giving the patient approximately 100 cc every 3 hours for the first 24 hours. If this is tolerated well by the patient, the volume can then be increased by 10 to 30 cc every three feedings. This increase in volume can be done until the goal volume is reached. After the goal is reached, it is necessary to change the formula to a normal day's activity schedule to allow the patient and caregivers time for normal activities and sleeping through the night.

Once the feeding schedule has been established, it is important for the patient and family to learn the following about the formula:

1. How to store the formula after opening the can.
2. When giving formula, it should be at room temperature to avoid GI cramping.
3. They should not change the formula without consulting a dietitian.

Case Study

P. W. is currently receiving combined-modality treatment of his head and neck cancer with chemotherapy and radiation. You know that he completed his first cycle of chemotherapy last week, consisting of 5-FU or fluorouracil with cisplatin, as well as radiation treatments delivered twice a day. During your weekly treatment check, you notice that P. W. has lost a total of 15 lb since beginning treatment. He tells you that he is having difficulty swallowing food and also that food just doesn't taste the same. After further assessment, you note that he has a white coating in his mouth and a stage II stomatitis. He complains of constipation that you think is related to his pain medication. P. W. tells you he is just not hungry. You note that P. W. has another cycle of chemotherapy to receive in 2 weeks and also 3 more weeks of radiation treatments. You discuss your findings with P. W.'s health care provider, and the following labs are ordered, which you draw and send to the laboratory: CBC, calcium, total protein, albumin, magnesium, potassium, sodium, chloride, BUN, and creatinine.

P.W.'s laboratory tests return with abnormal values, including an albumin of 2.7. You let the health care provider know of the multiple issues that P. W. is dealing with. The following nursing interventions and education are provided to P. W. and his family:

1. You establish how P. W. and his family learn best and what types of educational materials you need to provide them. Examples are videos, pamphlets, recipes, teaching displays, and booklets. You also want to establish if they have any learning and/or language barriers that might affect their comprehension of what you teach.
2. You review with P. W. the use of his pain medications and the frequency of taking them. You instruct him to use a daily stool softener and to increase his fluid intake, fiber, and activity. You review with him how constipation occurs and how it affects his appetite by causing abdominal discomfort and a full feeling, thereby making him not feel hungry.
3. You teach P. W. and his family about the viscous lidocaine that he is to use before eating. You instruct him to use it right before he eats because the numbing effect in his mouth and throat will only last for 10 to 15 minutes. You also review with him how to take his antiemetic 20 to 30 minutes before eating.
4. You discuss his current eating habits and reinforce the need for high-protein meals and snacks. You review that, if early satiety is a problem, six small meals a day may be helpful in maintaining P.W.'s nutritional status without overwhelming him. You discuss the use of an attractive eating environment that is nonthreatening and soothing.
5. When discussing food selection, you encourage them to avoid fatty, spicy, and acidic foods and to also avoid gas-forming foods. You encourage them to use sauces and gravies to assist with making foods moist and to serve bland, cool foods if the pain gets worse.

Later that week, you learn that P. W. is admitted to the hospital for a gastrostomy tube. Before P. W. is discharged, the dietitian assists him in planning for his home care needs. The dietitian shares the following information:

P. W.'s feeding formula will be at full strength. He is receiving 1920 cc in a 24-hour period to meet his calorie/protein needs and to also provide 100% of the RDAs for vitamin and mineral needs. This volume provides 2035 kcal, 84 g of protein, and 1632 cc of water. To meet his fluid needs of 1 cc/kcal of formula, P. W. will require an additional 403 cc of water. This free water need can be met by flushing the tube after feedings in full or part, based on his oral intake. P. W. will still be able to take oral nutrition with his gastrostomy tube in place, although it may be minimal.

Upon discharge, the dietitian reviews the plan for P. W.'s home feeding schedule. He will start his feeding with full-strength formula. P. W. will give himself 100 cc every 3 hours times 8 feeds for the first day. He will then increase by 30 cc every 3 hours to a goal of 320 cc every 3 hours. Once the goal is reached, the schedule can be changed to 320 cc every 3 hours from 7 AM to 10 PM. P. W. can then flush the tube with 70 cc of water after each feeding, for a total of 420 cc of water. This will meet the patient's fluid needs as well as flush any residue from the tube. It is important that P. W. and his family are able to verbalize/demonstrate the following before discharge:

1. Rationale for purchasing same formula each time
2. How to flush gastrostomy tube and give formula
3. Care of the gastrostomy tube
4. Storage of formula

Resources

With the rapid changes occurring in health care, it is imperative that patients and their families have the necessary resource support to help them through this difficult time. If patients and families are linked to the appropriate resource support, they will be empowered to make decisions that they feel comfortable with as well as have the knowledge necessary to make them. As noted in the inside front and back covers of this book, many private and public agencies assist patients and families at minimal cost to no cost.

Home care services and hospice care can be a great resource to patients and families who are in need of assistance after they have been hospitalized or during active treatment in an outpatient facility. They can assist the patient and family by reinforcing prior nutritional counseling; review techniques of G-tube, J-tube, and Dubhoff feeding; and, lastly, assist the patient and family with developing creative nutritional strategies to use at home.

The use of a social worker during this time is also critical. For patients and families who are socioeconomically challenged, the social worker can assist them with filing for free medication programs, assist with acquiring meals and nutritional supplementation, and also link the patient/family with support groups in the area.

REFERENCES

Bloch, A. (1994). Feeding the cancer patient: Where have we come, where are we going? *Nutrition in Clinical Practice, 9*(3), 87–89.

Grant, M. M., & Rivera, L. M. (1995). Anorexia, cachexia, and dysphagia: The symptom experience. *Seminars in Oncology Nursing, 11*(4), 266–271.

Kaempfer, S. H., & Lindsey, A. M. (1986). Energy expenditure in cancer. *Cancer Nursing, 9*(4), 194–199.

Nelson, K. A., Walsh, D., & Sheehan, F. A. (1994). The cancer anorexia-cachexia syndrome. *Journal of Clinical Oncology, 12,* 213–225.

Ottery, F. D. (1995). Supportive nutrition to prevent cachexia and improve quality of life. *Seminars in Oncology, 22*(2; suppl 3; April), 98–111.

Ottery, F. D. (1994). Cancer cachexia: Prevention, early diagnosis and management. *Cancer Practice, 2*(2), 123.

Puccio, M., & Nathanson, L. (1997). The cancer cachexia syndrome. *Seminars in Oncology, 24*(3), 277–287.

Ross, B. T. (1990). Cancer's impact on the nutritional status of patients. In A. S. Bloch (Ed.), *Nutrition management of the cancer patient.* Rockville, MD: Aspen.

Tchekmedyian, N. S. (1995). Cost and benefits of nutrition support in cancer. *Oncology, 9*(11 suppl.), 79–84.

Tisdale, M. J. (1997). Cancer cachexia: Metabolic alterations and clinical manifestations. *Nutrition, 13*(1), 1–7.

Von Roenn, J. H., & Knoph, K. (1996). Anorexia/cachexia in patients with HIV: Lessons for the oncologist. *Oncology, 10,* 1049–1056.

Constipation and Diarrhea

Dawn Camp-Sorrell
Rebecca Hawkins

A diagnosis of cancer and the treatment of cancer can affect the gastrointestinal (GI) system in various ways, including constipation and diarrhea. At some point on the cancer continuum, the patient will experience difficulties with bowel habits. If not managed appropriately, devastating outcomes can occur, such as bowel obstruction, electrolyte imbalance, dehydration, pain, and laxative dependence. Some patients may abandon or delay cancer treatment or managing symptoms, resulting in inadequate treatment of the cancer or symptoms such as pain.

Symptoms such as constipation and diarrhea are well known to health care providers as well as the general public. Less understood is the ability to successfully manage these symptoms. This chapter reviews constipation and diarrhea associated with cancer treatment and cancer. The assessment and nursing management of these symptoms are presented.

Normal Bowel Function

Normal bowel habits vary widely among individuals and are particularly influenced by dietary patterns. The absorption of water into the colon regulates bowel function. Nutrients taken in by the diet are absorbed within the small intestines, whereas the colon absorbs water and electrolytes. Consequently, alterations in intake or in the GI mucosa influence the consistency of the stool. The three distinct processes of normal bowel function are colonic motility, defecation, and continence.

Colonic motility refers to the transport of fecal material from the colon to the rectum. Within the colon, three separate peristalsis movements move the stool to the rectum. Segmental contractions do not propel the feces; these contractions mix the colonic content and bring material to be absorbed into the lumen. The fecal material is pushed back into the right colon by retrograde peristalsis. Propulsive movements push the stool forward to the large segment of the colon. Peristaltic activity within the colon only occurs several times within a 24-hour period.

Defecation and continence functions depend on the integration of complicated sensorineural and motor reflex functions. When the rectal ampulla is approximately one fourth full, the urge to defecate is felt. If the urge is voluntarily overridden, the sensory nerves in the rectum become desensitized to the fullness and do not initiate the reflex activity necessary for evacuation.

Definition

Constipation is defined as the infrequent passing of hard and dry stool usually associated with abdominal or rectal discomfort or pain (Gootenburg & Pizzo, 1991; Levy, 1991). A feeling of incomplete evacuation may also be associated with constipation. If constipation is not managed appropriately, bowel obstruction, increased pain, and improper use of laxatives can occur. Constipation is often accompanied by nausea, anorexia, and lethargy.

Diarrhea is an increase in frequency of stool, usually three to four times a day, and an increase in stool volume with a liquid consistency (Levy, 1991). At times, diarrhea is confused with pseudo-diarrhea, which is an increase in defecation without a change in consistency. Fecal incontinence is the inability to control the passage of stool. If diarrhea is not managed successfully, electrolyte imbalance, dehydration, and abdominal cramping occur. Unsuccessful management of either symptom can result in impaired skin integrity or decreased social interaction.

Etiologies

Constipation can result from decreased fiber in the diet, decreased fluid intake, lack of exercise, or immobility. Constipation can also be a symptom of diseases such as hypothyroidism, depression, hypercalcemia, hypokalemia, or bowel obstruction by tumor. Numerous types of drugs can contribute to constipation, such as opioids, anticholinergic drugs, antidepressant drugs, anticonvulsants, sedatives, diuretics, and aluminum-containing antacids. Treatment-related causes include the neurotoxic effects of cancer chemotherapy agents (e.g., vincristine, vinblastine, nalvabine). Chemotherapy agents stimulate the nerves along the GI tract, resulting in a decrease in peristalsis or paralytic ileus. After abdominal or pelvic surgery, an ileus or decrease in mobility is the major cause of constipation. The exact mechanism for the decrease in bowel motility is unknown but appears to be related to opening of the peritoneal cavity and the manipulation of the bowel. Adhesions that can develop after abdominal surgery can hamper the motility of the bowel, resulting in constipation. Other factors, which are individualized, include lack of privacy, interruption in normal bowel patterns, and failure to respond to the defecation reflex.

Depending on the cause of diarrhea, this symptom can be classified as acute (24 to 48 hours) or chronic (Wadle, 1990). Diarrhea may occur as a result of osmotic transport, abnormal absorptive mechanisms, inflammation, altered intestinal motility, or secretion of fluid and electrolytes (Stegbauer, 1995). In osmotic abnormalities, substances (such as food or drugs) in the intestines are not fully absorbed. Therefore, the unabsorbed substances have an osmotic pull effect, drawing fluid into the intestinal lumen, which increases the weight and volume of stool. Secretory abnormalities result from the intestinal mucosa secreting excessive amounts of fluid and electrolytes, thus increasing the weight and volume of stool. Bacterial invasion by organisms such as *Escherichia coli* or *Clostridium difficile* causes this type of diarrhea. Inflammatory disorders such as Crohn's disease within the bowel affect the motility, increasing the weight and volume of stool.

Disorders induced by chemotherapy or radiation affect the motility of the colon by disrupting the rapidly dividing epithelial cells that line the GI tract. Chemotherapy agents such as 5-fluorouracil and cisplatin can induce diarrhea (Casscinu, Feldeli, Feldeli & Catalano, 1994; Petrelli et al., 1990). The incidence of biotherapy-induced diarrhea from interleukin-2 is as high as 84% (Sharp, 1994). However, the mechanism of action is unknown.

Radiation to the lower abdomen can induce diarrhea, with an incidence of up to 80% (Danielson et al., 1990). Diarrhea can occur from radiation administered to the lower thoracic and lumbar spine. A radiation dose of 18 to 22 Gy to the bowel induces diarrhea, which occurs usually in the second week of radiation. Damage to the epithelial cells during radiation causes edema of the intestinal wall, resulting in changes of motility that cause diarrhea. Epithelial cells within the bowel are highly sensitive to radiation because of their short cell cycle (Henriksson, Franzen & Littbrano, 1991). Unfortunately, radiation-induced diarrhea can be chronic in nature, persisting 5 to 15 years after radiation completion.

After abdominal surgery, diarrhea can occur until the GI tract returns to normal (Clarke-Pearson, Olt, Rodriguez & Boente, 1993). However persistent, diarrhea usually represents bowel obstruction, colitis, or bacterial infection. Diarrhea can occur from graft-versus-host disease in a bone marrow transplantation patient. The mechanism occurs when the patient's GI cells recognize the donor cells as foreign, thus initiating an immune reaction leading to a sloughing of the GI cells or diarrhea. Multimodal treatments such as combination chemotherapy with lower abdominal radiation increase the intensity and duration of the diarrhea (Hawkins, 1996).

Nutritional supplements as well as enteral tube feeding can cause diarrhea. A paradoxical diarrhea can occur from a fecal impaction. Acute diarrhea can be a result of antibiotic therapy. Antibiotics frequently cause an alteration of the normal GI flora or cause a transient inflammation of the intestinal mucosa. Other types of drugs can cause acute diarrhea as well, such as lactulose, potassium supplements, digitalis, and antihypertensives (Wadle, 1990).

Nursing Assessment of Constipation and Diarrhea

Bowel function assessment is vital in managing the patient experiencing constipation or diarrhea (Bisanz, 1997; Canty, 1994; Hawkins, 1996). An assessment should be performed initially to serve as a baseline to determine the degree of alteration when it occurs. Elimination varies greatly among individuals, ranging from one to three bowel movements per day to one every 3 days (Canty, 1994). A change in a person's daily bowel habits is more important than the actual number of stools per day.

Because many drugs are known to cause an alteration in elimination, a drug history should be obtained, including the use of laxatives. An accurate diet recall must be taken to have a record of a daily fluid and dietary intake. Caffeine and alcohol can induce diarrhea, whereas cheese and chocolate can cause constipation. Mobility and exercise patterns need to be assessed. Serum electrolytes should be obtained to rule out metabolic abnormalities. Box 21-1 summarizes the information needed to accurately assess bowel function. The abdomen should be assessed for bowel sounds, tenderness, masses, distention, and stool-filled colon.

Nursing Management of Constipation and Diarrhea

Anticipating situations that will cause constipation or diarrhea can minimize the occurrences. For instance, all patients requiring narcotics for pain control must be placed on a stool softener and laxative to minimize constipation. Although prevention is the best method, when not possible, other interventions can be implemented to alleviate the symptom. Unfortunately, dietary interventions alone are not successful in reversing bowel problems. Pharmacologic interventions along with nonpharmacologic approaches are usually required.

BOX 21-1

Nursing Assessment Guidelines for Bowel Function

- Cancer history
  - Type of cancer
  - Potential for disease invasion of bowels
  - Presentation with bowel obstruction
- Elimination patterns
  - Baseline (before cancer)
  - Current pattern of elimination
  - Character, frequency, and time of day of elimination
- Medication use
  - History of laxative use or abuse
  - Current medication history

- Current and past cancer treatment (location of surgery and/or radiation therapy and types of chemotherapeutic agents)
- Diet history
  - Dietary fiber intake (6–10 g of dietary fiber/day is recommended)
  - Fluid intake (eight 8-oz glasses of fluid/day is recommended)
- Exercise and activity
  - Daily exercise helps to increase peristalsis
- Potential metabolic sources
  - Risk of hypercalcemia
  - Risk of hypocalcemia

Cancer therapies such as radiation or chemotherapy may need dose reduction or may need to be held until the symptoms are managed. If the patient is undergoing antibiotic therapy, a change in drug therapy may be warranted.

The use of laxatives or stool softeners usually relieves constipation. Defecation is stimulated by laxatives in three general mechanisms. The first is through osmotic properties, which cause fluid absorption into the bowel and soften the stool for easier travel. Laxatives decrease net absorption of water by directly acting on the intestinal mucosa and increasing the intestinal motility. This results in a decrease in salt and water absorption because of decreased transit time (Canty, 1994). Table 21-1 lists specific laxatives and their mechanism of action.

Suppositories, such as glycerin and bisacodyl, or enemas are other types of pharmacologic therapies. Elimination is induced within 30 minutes

TABLE 21-1

CLASSIFICATION AND PHARMACOLOGIC PROPERTIES OF LAXATIVES

Laxative	Onset of Action (h)	Site of Action	Mechanism of Action	Comments
Saline				
Magnesium sulfate	0.5–3	Small and large intestine	Attract/retain water in intestinal lumen increasing intraluminal pressure; cholescystokinin release	Laxative may alter fluid and electrolyte balance. Sulfate salts are considered the most potent.
Magnesium hydroxide				
Magnesium citrate				
Sodium phosphate				
Sodium phosphate/ biphosphate enema	0.03–0.25	Colon		
Irritant/stimulant				
Cascara	6–10	Colon	Direct action on intestinal mucosa; stimulates myenteric plexus; alters water and electrolyte secretion	Bile must be present for phenolphthalein to produce its effects. Castor oil may be preferred when more complete evacuation is required.
Senna				
Phenolphthalein				
Bisacodyl tablets				
Casanthranol				
Bisacodyl suppository	0.25–			
Castor oil	2–6	Small intestine		Castor oil is converted to ricinoleic acid (active component) in the gut.
Bulk-producing				
Methylcellulose	12–24 (up to 72)	Small and large intestine	Holds water in stool; mechanical distention; malt soup extract reduces fecal pH	This is the safest and most physiologic laxative.
Psyllium				
Polycarbophil				
Lubricant				
Mineral oil	6–8	Colon	Retards colonic absorption of fecal water; softens stool	Laxative may decrease absorption of fat-soluble vitamins.
Surfactants				
Docusate	24–72	Small and large intestine	Detergent activity; facilitates admixture of fat and water to soften stool	Laxative is beneficial when feces are hard or dry or in anorectal conditions where passage of a firm stool is painful.
Miscellaneous				
Glycerin suppository	0.25–0.5	Colon	Local irritation; hyperosmotic action	Presence of sodium stearate in the preparation causes the local irritation.
Lactulose	24–48	Colon	Delivers osmotically active molecules to colon	This also is indicated in portal-systemic encephalopathy

(From *Drug Facts and Comparisons* [1999]. Copyright 1999 by Facts and Comparisons, a Division of Lippincott Williams & Wilkins. Reprinted by permission.)

after the use of glycerin suppository stimulates fluid retention in the colon. The rectal mucosa is stimulated by an increase in contractility from a bisacodyl suppository within 15 to 60 minutes of insertion. Sodium phosphate enemas add bulk to the stool. The stool can be lubricated by a mineral oil enema for ease of passage through the colon. Fluid retention into the intestinal lumen is caused by a saline enema, thus allowing the stool to move easier. Irritation to the intestinal mucosa will stimulate defecation, which can be induced by a soap sud enema. If the patient's white blood cell and platelet count are within a safe range, a manual dislodgement of the impaction may be necessary to relieve the constipation.

Prevention strategy begins with recommending a bowel program and reevaluating the program with every contact with the patient. When the bowel program is no longer successful, the regimen should be altered to meet the patient's needs (Hawkins, 1996). The most important consideration is retention and augmentation of normal bowel motility and function. Without proper management, the patient could suffer from internal and external hemorrhoids, which could cause bleeding or infection. The most frequent bowel regimens include a stool softener with a bulking agent, which is available in combination products.

Diarrhea induced by cancer therapies usually requires pharmacologic therapy. Before initiating therapy, other causes of diarrhea, such as infection, intestinal obstruction, laxative abuse, or tumor recurrence, should be ruled out. Small-bowel infection usually produces nonbloody, watery diarrhea and a low-grade fever with leukocytes in the stool specimen. Infections in the colon produce fever as well as blood, mucus, and leukocytes within the stool (Wadle, 1990). To prevent dehydration, electrolyte imbalance, and skin breakdown in the perianal area, prompt management is essential.

Drugs that slow peristalsis, such as anticholinergic agents and opiates, are not recommended for use in infectious diarrhea because they slow elimination of pathogens from the GI tract and make

TABLE 21-2

CLASSIFICATIONS OF ANTIDIARRHEAL AGENTS

Drug	Dosage	Mechanism of Action
Opiate		
Loperamide (Imodium)	Two 2-mg tablets PO up to maximum of 8/day	Binds to opiate receptor on smooth muscle of the bowel and slows motility and fluid absorption
Diphenoxylate (Lomotil)	1–2 tablets PO three to four times/day maximum of 8 tablets/day	
Codeine	30–60 mg PO every 4–6 h as needed	
Absorbents		
Pectin		
Aluminum hydroxide (Mylanta)	2 tablets or 30 cc prn	
Bulking Agents		
Psyllium (Metamucil, Citracil)	1 tsp–1 Tbsp in 8 oz of liquid	A natural fiber that provides bulk to the colon. Effective in mild diarrhea
Bismuth Products		
Pepto-Bismol	2 Tbsp Q 30 min to 1 h prn maximum of 8 doses/24 h	Normalizes fluid movements in bowel and binds bacterial toxins and antimicrobial activity
Somatostatin Analogues		
Octreotide	50–200 µg SQ two to three times/day or 50–150 µg/h IV titration	Used in chemotherapy-induced diarrhea. Decreases intestinal motility, reduces intestinal fluid volume

TABLE 21-3
COMMON TOXICITY CRITERIA OF THE EASTERN COOPERATIVE ONCOLOGY GROUP (NATIONAL CANCER INSTITUTE)

Grading	0	1	2	3	4
Diarrhea	None	Increase of two to three stools/day over pre-RX	Increase of four to five stools/day or nocturnal stools or moderate cramping	Increase of seven to nine stools/day or incontinence or severe cramping	Increase of >ten stools/day or grossly bloody diarrhea, or need for parenteral support
Constipation	None or no change	Mild	Moderate	Severe	Ileus >96 h

symptoms more severe and longer lasting (Wadle, 1990). When the diarrhea is induced from cancer treatment, the drug of choice is loperamide. This drug differs from diphenoxylate and codeine in that it has no systemic effects in a normal dose (Levy, 1991). Diphenoxylate is another antidiarrheal agent; when combined with atropine, it is marketed as Lomotil. Interestingly, atropine was added to the combination in an attempt to decrease narcotic abuse rather than for antidiarrheal properties. A drug with a powerful constipating effect that should be considered is codeine. However, this drug is usually not first-line therapy because of its systemic effect. A useful antidiarrheal agent for high-volume diarrhea is octreotide. Usually, this drug is the treatment of choice when endocrine or anatomic secretory diarrhea is not responsive to other agents (Levy, 1991). Psyllium, a bulking agent, is used for watery diarrhea to create a gel, thereby thickening and slowing the diarrhea.

BOX 21-2
Patient Education Guidelines for Constipation and Diarrhea

Diarrhea
- Eat foods high in fiber.
- Notify your nurse or physician if you have more than three watery stools per day.
- Eat foods high in sodium and potassium if you are experiencing diarrhea.
- Drink at least eight 8-oz glasses of fluid a day to prevent dehydration.
- Avoid the following:
  - Milk products
  - Raw fruits and vegetables
  - Beans and peas
  - Spicy or fatty foods
  - Caffeine
  - Alcohol and tobacco
- Take antidiarrheal medication as ordered.
- Be sure your rectal area is clean and dry after each episode of diarrhea.
- Nutmeg added to foods may decrease diarrhea.
- A & D ointment may be used to soothe the rectal area

Constipation
- Report to your nurse or physician when stools are hard to pass, or if you do not have a bowel movement for 2 days.
- Drink at least eight 8-oz glasses of fluid/day. Hot liquids are best.
- Try to exercise daily.
- Use medications for your bowel as instructed by your physican or nurse.
- Eat foods high in fiber.

Permission granted to reproduce these guidelines for educational purposes only.
(From Liebman, M.C., & Camp-Sorrell, D. [1996]. *Multimodal therapy in oncology nursing* [pp. 342–343]. St. Louis: Mosby.)

Table 21-2 list antidiarrheal agents and their dosage and mechanism of action.

Documentation

Documenting the patient's normal bowel function is necessary to evaluate for abnormalities. When bowel alterations are related to cancer treatments or to management of symptoms, documentation of these side effects is beneficial in evaluating treatment methods. Several tools have been developed to define the degree of toxicity experienced by the cancer patient in an attempt to provide documentation consistency. Table 21-3 gives an example of grading diarrhea and constipation. Frequently, the nurse must screen the patient for symptoms and

initiate appropriate therapy over the phone. Most patients can be managed without the patient being seen by the health care provider. It is vital that the nurse gather sufficient information to determine the needs of the patient. Figures 21-1 and 21-2 show a sample phone triage flow sheet.

Patient Education

To minimize the effects of constipation and diarrhea, careful patient education is required. Pharmacologic as well as nonpharmacologic methods must be taught to the family and patient to prevent or minimize these effects. Box 21-2 provides patient and family education tips to use in management of constipation and diarrhea.

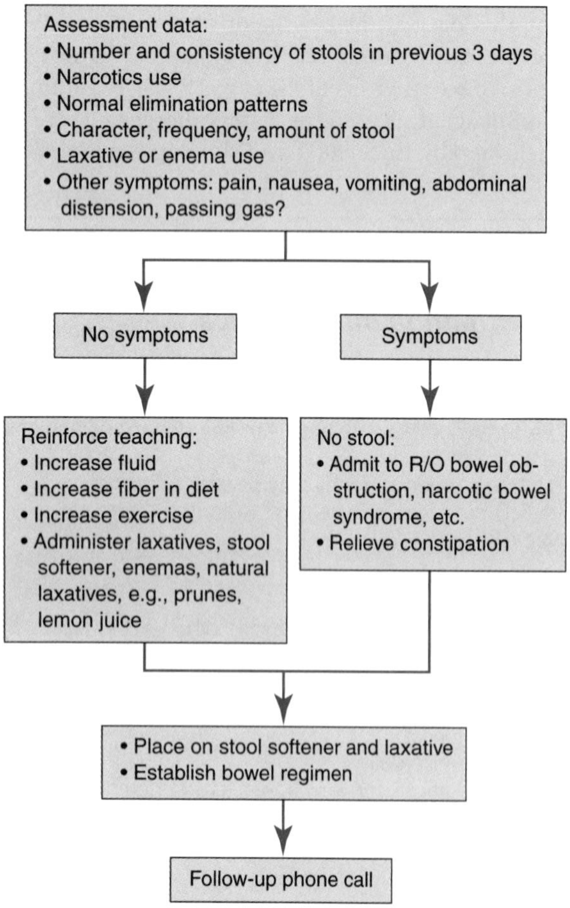

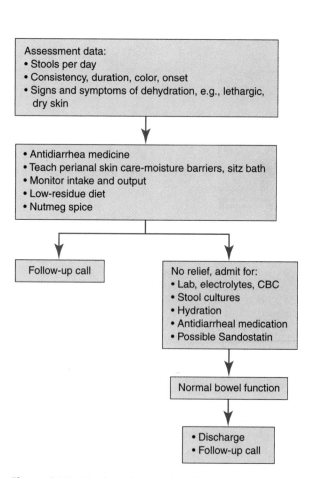

Figure 21-1 Constipation phone triage flow sheet. (Camp-Sorrell, D. [1997]. *Cancer nursing: Principles and practice* [4th ed.]. Boston: Jones & Bartlett.)

Figure 21-2 Diarrhea phone triage flow sheet. (Camp-Sorrell, D. [1997]. *Cancer nursing: Principles and practice* [4th ed.]. Boston: Jones & Bartlett.)

Case Study

My Experience With Constipation as a Chemotherapy Patient

When you first realize that you are going to need to go through chemotherapy, you feel overwhelmed trying to take in all the information, digest it, and decide what the best treatment plan is for you. The oncologist discusses the litany of side effects with you: infertility, hormonal changes and all that accompanies those changes—hair loss, nausea, constipation, diarrhea, mucositis, neutropenia, and so forth. It is overwhelming even to a health care professional who works in the oncology arena. It's different when it's suddenly happening to you.

Some of these side effects are more serious and distressing than others, and certainly you would think that constipation would be one of the less serious and more manageable side effects. However, my experience proved to me that constipation can become a major problem very quickly, with long-term consequences if not managed early.

When I first began chemotherapy, my oncologist informed me that some patients on chemotherapy experience diarrhea and others constipation. There was no way to predict if I would experience either of these side effects. I anticipated that I would be more likely to experience diarrhea because I have had loose stools a few times in my life when I was under stress.

What my oncologist failed to warn me about is how quickly constipation can creep up on you and become a problem. I received four cycles of Adriamycin and cyclophosphamide. After my second cycle, I did not have a bowel movement for 3 days. This was not unusual for me. I frequently would not have a bowel movement for 3 days without any problems. What I didn't realize was that I was becoming dehydrated. I was also taking in less fluid than normal because my appetite for everything had decreased, and I wasn't as active because I was feeling some fatigue. Together, this created decreased motility of my intestinal system, resulting in constipation.

By the fourth day, I decided to take some action. This was really too late. I began taking Senokot and bisacodyl as the nurse recommended. She warned me against taking any harsher laxatives. I was also warned by both the nurse and the oncologist not to use any form of suppository because of the chance harboring infection by using anything inserted rectally.

I didn't realize how serious the problem was at first, so I started with the lowest doses of the drugs. Nothing happened. I increased the dose. Nothing happened. I began to feel desperate, bloated, and cramped. Finally, after increasing the doses to the maximum over the next 2 days and kneeling on the floor in the fetal position, I began to get some movement. By this time, I also began to try to increase my intake of fiber in my diet and was trying to force down Metamucil, which was not easy to do when even food was sometimes not appetizing.

To describe that first bowel movement as painful would be putting it mildly. As disgusting as it sounds, I had to physically assist it. That day, I think I went to the bathroom all day. By the sixth bowel movement, I was no longer completely filling the toilet.

Although I religiously began to monitor and increase my water and fiber intake after that, it took months before I could get my intestinal system back in order. I remained on Senokot and bisacodyl, trying to reduce the dose and discontinuing it every now and then to see if I could get along without it. I needed the drugs for the remainder of my chemo treatments and about a month to a month and a half after chemotherapy to keep me regular.

As a result of straining, I developed what I thought were hemorrhoids that were bleeding. I finally made an appointment with my gynecologist and her nurse practitioner and found out I not only had hemorrhoids, but I had also developed an anal fissure. The nurse practitioner recommended that I wait a couple of weeks and see if it healed on its own and, if not, go to see a surgeon. She informed me that fissures are very difficult to heal on their own because each time you have a bowel movement, they tear open again. They can actually get worse and tear further.

The last thing I wanted to do was see a surgeon. I had talked with friends who had experienced this type of surgery, and they encouraged me to do anything to avoid it. I was afraid if I went to the surgeon that the recommendation would be surgery because that's what they know. I knew it would not heal in 2 weeks. I had already had it for at least 12 weeks, and it had not healed yet. I had gotten better and then worse depending on how loose I could keep my stools and how often I had a bowel movement. It was a constant dilemma. If I had frequent bowel movements, the fissure never had time to heal. If I didn't have frequent bowel movements, I faced the fear of having constipation. Having a bowel movement was always painful, yet, if I missed a day without one, I became very anxious, anticipating another problem. Worst of all, my system was still not regular, although I was taking drugs and trying to eat as much fiber as possible.

I decided to see a gastroenterologist, thinking that I might get some good advice and an alternative to surgery. I did not return after the first appointment because the physician did not examine me, yet wanted me to go through a magnitude of tests. At this point in my therapy, the last thing I wanted to do was get some invasive tests when I already know what the problem was. I just wanted a solution.

My radiation oncologist was actually the health care provider who helped me get through this situation. I was almost ready to throw in the towel and go to see the surgeon when I discussed my dilemma with him. He recommended that I use baby wipes, preferably with aloe, each time I had a bowel movement and afterwards apply Neosporin ointment to help keep out any bacteria and enable it to heal. I had to sit in a warm, not hot, tub of water for 10 to 15 minutes a day. He suggested that I continue the high-fiber diet and drink as much water as I could handle. Although it seemed that this was not helping, he indicated that it may take a couple of months to get my system back in working order. I just needed to be patient. If I didn't have a bowel movement for 2 days in a row, I should start taking Senokot and bisacodyl again, and if I haven't had a bowel movement by the third day, I should start milk of magnesia.

This gave me hope that I could do something, and the advice worked! Within a couple of weeks, the bleeding stopped. It did take weeks before my system was regular, and I still have to be careful. I make sure I eat lots of fruits and vegetables and a bowl of the highest-fiber cereal (8 g or more per serving). I still have problems when I travel. If I am away from home for more than 4 days, my hemorrhoids will flare up. It is difficult to find high-fiber cereals in restaurants and hotels. I try to carry a bottle of water and packets of cereal with me. Even so, the flights and the disruptions in my regular schedule tend to make me irregular.

My recommendation to nurses as managers of supportive care for patient on chemotherapy would be to take this side effect more seriously and be proactive. Let your patients know when they are on chemotherapy that they may have a tendency to experience dehydration, which can quickly cause constipation. If they do not experience a bowel movement over a couple of days, they should start on medication because constipation can quickly get out of control. This is a time to be proactive because, once the situation gets out of control, it is not fun to deal with and causes life-long problems.

Summary

Bowel elimination problems can cause distress and discomfort for the patient with cancer. Prevention is the key to managing bowel alterations and begins with an in-depth assessment of normal bowel patterns. Changes must be made based on individual responses to the treatment plan. Assessing and managing patients with elimination problems are challenges for all nurses who provide care to cancer patients.

REFERENCES

Bisanz, A. (1997). Managing bowel elimination problems in patients with cancer. *Oncology Nursing Forum, 24,* 679–686.

Canty, S. L. (1994). Constipation as a side effect of opioids. *Oncology Nursing Forum, 21,* 739–745.

Casscinu, S., Feldeli, A., Feldeli, S. L., & Catalano, G. (1994). Control of chemotherapy-induced diarrhea with octreotide. *Oncology, 51,* 70–73.

Clarke-Pearson, D. L., Olt, G. J., Rodriguez, G., & Boente, M. (1993). Preoperative and postoperative care. In D. M. Gershensen, A. L. Dechenney & S. L. Currey (Eds.), *Operative gynecology* (pp. 29–83). Philadelphia: W. B. Saunders.

Danielson, A., Nyhlin, H., Persson, H., et al. (1990). Chronic diarrhea after radiotherapy for gynecological cancer: Occurrence and etiology. *Gut, 32,* 1180–1187.

Gootenburg, J. E., & Pizzo, P. A. (1991). Optimal management of acute toxicities of therapy. *Pediatric Clinics of North America, 38,* 269–297.

Hawkins, R. (1996). Gastrointestinal side effects. In M. Liebman & D. Camp-Sorrell (Eds.), *Multimodal therapy in oncology nursing* (pp. 325–349). St. Louis: Mosby.

Henriksson, R., Franzen, L., & Littbrano, B. (1991). Prevention of irradiation-induced bowel discomfort by sucralfate: A double-blind placebo-controlled study when treating localized pelvic cancer. *American Journal of Medicine, 91*(suppl 2a), 151s–157s.

Levy, M. H. (1991). Constipation and diarrhea in cancer patients. *Cancer Bulletin, 43,* 412–422.

Petrelli, N. J., Rodriguez-Bigas, M., Rustum, Y., et al. (1990). Bowel rest, intravenous hydration, and continuous high-dose infusion of octreotide acetate for the treatment of chemotherapy-induced diarrhea in patients with colorectal carcinoma. *Cancer, 72,* 1543–1550.

Sharp, E. (1994). Case management: Hospitalized IL-2 patients. *Seminars in Oncology Nursing, 9*(suppl. 1), 14–19.

Stegbauer, C. C. (1995). Bacterial overgrowth in a patient with chronic diarrhea. *Nurse Practitioner, 20,* 60–63.

Wadle, K. R. (1990). Diarrhea. *Nursing Clinics of North America, 25,* 901–908.

Pain Assessment and Management in People With Cancer

Terry Ashby
JoAnn Dalton

The incidence of pain in patients with cancer is significant. Studies estimate that approximately one third of cancer patients receiving treatment and as many as 90% of patients with advanced cancer experience moderate to intense pain (Ahles et al., 1984; Bonica, 1990). By effectively assessing and controlling cancer pain, nurses can return function and even quality of life to a patient whose life is being controlled by the illness. This should be the primary goal for the nurse caring for a patient with chronic pain.

Pain is defined by the International Association for the Study of Pain as an unpleasant sensory and emotional experience associated with actual or potential tissue damage, or it is described in terms of such damage (Merskey & Bogduk, 1994). Developing a definition potentially more useful to nursing, McCaffery describes pain as "whatever the experiencing person says it is, existing whenever the experiencing person says it does" (McCaffery & Beebe, 1989). The latter definition emphasizes the importance of "self-report" in assessment of pain and the need for the nurse to believe the patient's report. Camp (1988) compared nurses' recorded assessments of pain with perceptions of pain as described by cancer patients using 30 nurse–patient dyads in the hospital. A lack of agreement between the nurse's documentation of pain and cancer patients' descriptions of their pain was found. Furthermore, it was reported that nurses were not documenting their assessments of patients' pain, and, when they did, it lacked important information. It is important to note that, in this study, the documentation took place in the nurses' notes because there was no pain assessment tool in place. The patient is the leading authority on how he or she feels. Without pertinent information related to the patient's pain status, the physician has insufficient data with which to make critical judgments about treatment. The patient's description of the pain, using his or her exact words, is often the key necessary for correctly identifying the cause of the pain and, consequently, the appropriate treatment.

Is controlling the pain of a person with cancer different from controlling that of a surgical patient or a patient with a chronic illness? Nurses experienced in pain management would reply, yes and no. Although the goal of providing comfort for the patient is the same, the management of chronic pain requires more intensive decision making over a longer period of time.

Only in recent history has the science of cancer pain management become conspicuous at a multidisciplinary level. This science was generated, for the most part, because of ineffective pain management by both nurses and physicians, thus prompting the patient to demand improved techniques and understanding of pain management. This underscores the importance of the nurse becoming educated in the nuances of cancer pain syndromes and the specialized pharmacology needed to care for these patients. This brings us squarely back to the importance of the role of the nurse.

The Nurse's Role in Pain Management

The primary role of the nurse in caring for the person experiencing cancer pain is that of practitioner, skilled in assessment of the pain status of the patient. Without this proficiency in recognition of specific symptoms relating to pain, the entire medical team, including the patient, suffers.

The nurse as educator needs to enlist the help of the patient and caregiver in both assessment and management of the pain situation if there is any hope of dealing with it realistically. Addiction is not a common problem in patients using opiates on a daily basis. In fact, it is rare. Thus, in speaking to the patient and family, the nurse should emphasize that the intended purpose of analgesics (including opiates) is to maintain comfort so the patient can go on with his or her life. Dispelling common misconceptions such as addiction and overcoming the negative reputation of "narcotics" are barriers the nurse must face in educating the patient and family. Other barriers encountered are misunderstandings, such as believing that pain is a sign that the disease is worse or that the patient will develop a tolerance to the medication and then not have it when it is really needed. As the patient, family, and nurse agree on the goal of preventing suffering, the nurse forms an empathic bond with them that brings about an acceptance of the information given. To the extent that the nurse can elicit the family's help in assessment and management, there will most likely be a successful outcome. To the extent that the nurse cannot win their support or tries to manage the problem in an authoritarian manner, there may be a poor outcome, with all parties involved working against each other. One way to keep the family involved in the process is to elicit their help in the assessment process. Families caring for patients at home should be encouraged to keep a pain log or diary that describes episodes of breakthrough pain when the nurse is not at the scene.

Finally, the role of the nurse should be that of a patient advocate and liaison between the patient and the physician. Studies have shown that when patients and physicians differ on their estimation of pain intensity, then pain control suffers. The nurse, through diligent and detailed pain assessment, can supply the physician with the data necessary to make the best decision possible related to pharmacologic control. Important overall trends that the nurse should monitor for the physician include:

1. Compliance—Whether the patient is receiving the appropriate dosages at the right times and in the prescribed manner

   "Mrs. Johnson is getting her Percocet, 2 PO every 6 hours around the clock."

   "The reason Mr. Atkins was sleeping so much is that he was taking his sustained-release morphine on an as-needed basis. He is now taking it BID as ordered with the immediate-release morphine used q4h. For breakthrough as ordered."

2. Effectiveness of the current regimen—Is the current level of pain acceptable to the patient? How many times in a 24-hour period is the patient requiring a medication for breakthrough (acute) pain?

   "Mr. Hamilton's pain is down to a 3, but he is still alert and active. He is satisfied with his pain control."

   "Mrs. Frazier is now taking her immediate-release morphine seven to ten times per day and is still having levels of pain as high as 8 on the 10-point scale. It may be time to increase her sustained-release medication."

3. Is the medication regimen well tolerated by the patient?—Are the side effects of the regimen diminishing the quality of life you are trying to preserve?

   "Mr. Clifton feels so much better. He even took a walk in his garden this morning."

   "Jason is sleeping up to 14 hours per day. His mother says that when he is awake he is hallucinating most of the time and will not eat."

These concepts, coupled with specific details about the nature of the pain problem, are crucial if the physician is going to make rational decisions regarding the medication regimen.

Pathophysiology

In the nurse's role of clinician, involved in pain assessment and management, pathophysiology gives us the rationale for the decisions we make. Pathophysiology is important to study because it gives us clues to the etiology of the person's problem. Pain is initially felt in the nociceptor, or sensory, neurons throughout most the body that detect tissue damage and transmit the impulse along pathways to the spinal cord and, eventually, the brain. The brain interprets the stimuli as painful and stimulates the release of serotonin, norepinephrine, and dopamine, which can act to moderate the perception of pain (Paice, 1996). This mechanism for acute pain can sometimes be overridden by permanent damage to neurons or infiltration of a tumor, resulting in chronic pain, which may last from months to a lifetime. It is important for nurses to differentiate between acute and chronic pain because they are treated differently and they present in patients in dissimilar ways. Acute pain is of relatively short duration, is frequently a result of a treatment or intervention, and is often managed by moving from stronger to weaker analgesics. It may cause the patient to exhibit symptoms of increased blood pressure, tachycardia, and a visible reaction. Chronic pain, on the other hand, is of a duration usually greater than 6 months, is often treated by moving from weaker to stronger analgesics, and may produce little to no overt physiologic change in the patient. Short-acting opioids such as meperidine (Demerol), although useful in acute pain, usually are not used in chronic pain due to a buildup of toxic metabolites. Chronic pain syndromes are defined as associations of particular pain characteristics with the specific consequences of the disease and its treatment (Cherny & Portenoy, 1994). For example, diabetes is often associated with a painful peripheral neuropathy. In oncology, medications in the vinca alkaloid class can also be responsible for a peripheral neuropathy that may cause numbness, tingling, or burning in the periphery of the extremities. Identification of these syndromes is the best direct evidence for the underlying cause and treatment of the specific pain problem. The following case study illustrates the complexity of a cancer pain problem.

The first point to be made is that this case is not unusual. Cancer pain rarely, if ever, develops into a pain situation that is easily recognized or treated with a single medication or technique. In the case of this young woman, her disease progression has resulted in a number of different pain syn-

Case Study

Janice is a 46-year-old mother of four who was diagnosed with stage II adenocarcinoma of the breast 18 months ago. She and her oncologist decided on an aggressive regimen of a modified radical mastectomy followed by a five-drug regimen of chemotherapy, including cyclophosphamide, methotrexate, 5-fluorouracil, vincristine, and prednisone. The chemotherapy lasted an entire year with many ups and downs in her treatment, but, when it was finished, Janice was told that there was no detectable disease in her body. Last week, during a monthly self breast exam, she discovered a lump the size of a pea in her other breast. Unlike the first lump, this one seemed attached to her chest muscle and caused an intermittent "burning" pain in the area. Fearing the worst, Janice was sent for a CT scan where it was discovered that she had a recurrence of her breast cancer. Janice also noted that over the past month she has been having a dull, unrelenting pain in her back and in her right leg, which she had attributed to arthritis and getting older. While she is in the hospital receiving tests, Janice is given Percocet 1 to 2 tablets q4h for pain. After entering her room to assess Janice's comfort level, the nurse is told that she is still having significant pain in her spine and a nagging "numbness and tingling" in her feet and toes. The area of recurrence on her breast has begun to "ache" on a more regular basis.

dromes that need to be identified and treated in a deliberate manner. The nurse may opt to simply ask the physician for an order for a stronger analgesic, but a regimen that would be more beneficial to the patient can be arrived at by identifying the component parts of the pain problem. In this case, the most significant problem is coming from her bone metastasis causing pain in her spine and legs. Her site of recurrence is an example of somatic pain caused by direct tumor invasion of a peripheral nerve. The pain is radicular and well localized. Her neuropathy is the probable result of vincristine, a chemotherapy agent with this known side effect.

Pain can be loosely divided into nociceptive and neuropathic designation. Nociceptive pain is pain caused by tissue damage from either a somatic or visceral lesion. Somatic pain (in body structures) is characterized by sharp, aching, throbbing, or pressure-like pain and is usually well localized. Visceral pain arises from visceral structures and can be described as gnawing or cramping and may be poorly localized (Cherny & Portenoy, 1994). Neuropathic pain is thought to arise from damage to the peripheral or central nervous system and is typically resistant to opioids. It is often described as burning, numbness, or tingling and may be treated with adjuvant medications such as the tricyclic antidepressants, anticonvulsants, or local anesthetics.

Table 22-1 lists some common cancer pain syndromes.

Assessment

Nurses in pain management agree that pain assessment is absolutely the cornerstone of effective pain management. Imagine a patient going to a physician's office for the first time after finding out from a neighbor (who is a nurse) that her blood pressure is dangerously high. After a period of time, the

---

TABLE 22-1
COMMON CANCER PAIN SYNDROMES DUE TO PERIPHERAL NERVE INJURY

Pain Syndrome	Associated Signs and Symptoms	Affected Nerves
Tumor infiltration of a peripheral nerve	Constant, burning pain with dysesthesia in an area of sensory loss. Pain is radicular and often unilateral.	Peripheral
Post radical neck dissection	Tight, burning sensation in the area of sensory loss, dysesthesia, and shocklike pain may be present. Second type of pain may occur mimicking a drooped shoulder syndrome.	Cervical plexus
Postmastectomy pain	Tight, constricting, burning pain in the posterior arm, axilla, and anterior chest wall. Pain is exacerbated by arm movement.	Intercostobrachial
Postthoracotomy pain	Aching sensation in the distribution of the incision with sensory loss with or without autonomic changes. Often exquisite point tenderness at the most medial and apical points of the scar with a specific trigger point. Secondary reflex sympathetic dystrophy may develop.	Intercostal
Postnephrectomy pain	Numbness, fullness, or heaviness in the flank, anterior abdomen, and groin. Dysesthesia are common.	Superficial flank
Post limb amputation	Phantom limb pain usually occurs after pain in the same site before amputation. Stump pain occurs at the site of the surgical scar, several months to years after surgery. It is characterized by a burning dysesthetic sensation that is exacerbated by movement.	Peripheral endings and their central projections
Chemotherapy-induced peripheral neuropathy	Painful paresthesia and dysesthesia. Hyporeflexia. Less frequently: motor and sensory loss; rarely autonomic dysfunction. Commonly associated with the vinca alkaloids, cisplatin, and taxol.	Distal areas of peripheral (e.g., polyneuropathy)
Radiation-induced peripheral nerve tumors	May promote malignant fibrosarcoma. Painful, enlarging mass in a previously irradiated area. Patients with neurofibromatosis more susceptible.	Superficial and deep
Cranial neuropathies	Severe head pain with cranial nerve dysfunction. Leptomeningeal disease. Base of skull metastasis.	Cranial V, VII, IX, X, XI, XII are common
Acute postherpetic neuropathy	Painful paresthesia and dysesthesia. Constant burning and aching pain. Shocklike paroxysmal pain. Immunosuppression from disease or treatment is a risk factor. Postherpetic neuropathy incidence increases with age.	Thoracic and cranial (VI) are most common

(Jacox, A., Carr, D. B., Payne, R., et al. [1994]. *Management of cancer pain: Clinical practice guideline No. 9.* Rockville, MD: Agency for Health Care Policy and Research.)

nurse comes out to the waiting room. "The doctor is behind schedule and will not be able to see you today. Here is a prescription for a blood pressure medication. Make an appointment in 1 month." As ridiculous as this scenario sounds, every day nurses try to manage a patient's pain, or relay information to the physician, with as little information as was described in the previous scenario.

Excellent general guidelines for assessment can be found in the Agency for Health Care Policy and Research (AHCPR) guidelines for the Management of Cancer Pain (Jacox et al., 1994).

A Ask about pain regularly.
Assess pain systematically.
B Believe the patient and family in their reports of pain and what relieves it.
C Choose pain control options appropriate for the patient, family, and setting.
D Deliver interventions in a timely, logical, and coordinated fashion.
E Empower patients and their families.
Enable them to control their course to the greatest extent possible.

Lack of consistency in assessment has been shown to be one of the obstacles in effective pain management (Camp, 1988; Lee, McPherson & Zuckerman, 1992). Often, pain is assessed during the initial assessment or only when there is an acute problem. Despite this, many settings fail to use an assessment tool at all or, if assessment is provided, it is used inconsistently. The initial assessment should be more detailed than subsequent assessments and should attempt to paint a clear picture of the origin of the pain. Pain should be assessed on a regular basis due to nature of chronic pain, which is frequently changing. The following components should be part of a clinical pain assessment:

Description of the pain—This should be in the patient's own words. Do not try to translate the description into medical jargon, but ask a question such as "What does your pain feel like?" or "How would you describe your pain?" Often, the patient's description is representative of a specific pain syndrome.
Location—Should be elicited from the patient and documented on a human figure that is part of a pain assessment instrument. Be aware that there can be multiple pain sites.

Intensity—On a 0- to 10-point scale, have the patient rate pain by telling him or her that 0 means "no pain at all" and 10 is "the worst pain imaginable."
Exacerbating and alleviating factors—Ask the patient, "What makes your pain better?" "What makes your pain worse?" Do not discount home remedies or nonpharmacologic modes of pain relief.
Onset/duration—When does the pain begin? What precipitates the pain? How long does it last? Is it intermittent or continuous?

Other factors important in the assessment can be added to a pain assessment instrument or documented in a narrative portion of the instrument. Among the most important of these would be the recording of any side effects the patient may be experiencing from the pain medication. Another important factor to be assessed is how the patient and the family cope with the pain problem. Is the patient depressed, despondent, or exhibiting unrealistic goals for treatment of the pain problem? For example, it is unrealistic for the patient who is on 90 mg of sustained-release morphine BID to state that he should be able to think clearly and go back to work as a taxi driver. Figure 22-1 is a sample clinical pain assessment instrument that can be used in a variety of settings.

As nursing is moving increasingly into the home setting, any discussion of pain assessment would be incomplete without mentioning the family's role. In a hospital setting, the nurse can focus primarily on the patient because the nurse controls the medications as well as the assessment. In the home setting, the patient caretaker is often the most important gatekeeper of the patient's analgesia. If the family caretaker is not convinced of the patient's need or the benefit derived from the analgesic regimen, then he or she is unlikely to give the medication correctly. Simply put, to neglect the family's role in pain assessment and management is to ensure a poor outcome for the patient. On the other hand, to teach, involve, and empower the family in the process greatly enhances the chances for a favorable outcome for the patient and fosters a feeling of usefulness on the part of the family. When the patient and the patient's caretaker are persuaded to take part in the assessment process (Figure 22-2), then a more accurate picture of the pain situation is achieved.

Name _____   Date _____   Nurse _____

Diagnosis (list all) _____   Pt. # _____

1. Location: On the figures below, indicate areas where pain occurs. Use A,B,C,D etc. to indicate more than one area of pain.

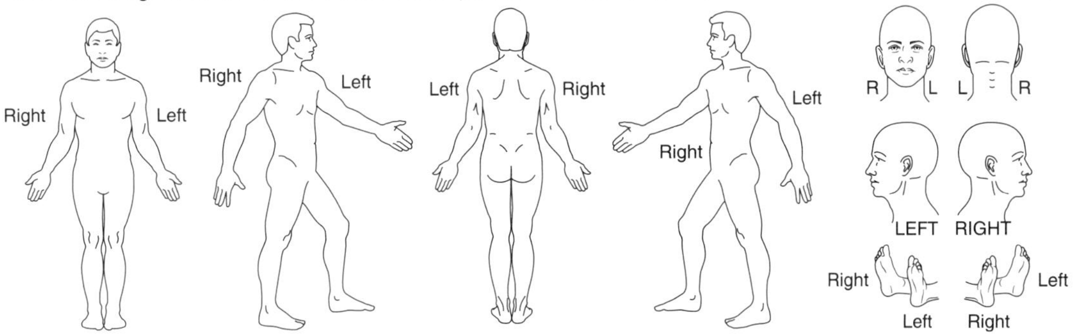

2. Describe your pain (or areas of pain) in your own words: _____

_____

3. Intensity: On a 0–10 scale (0 being no pain and 10 being the worst pain imaginable) rate area(s) of pain

_____

4. A) What is an acceptable level of pain? _____
   B) What will this level allow you to do? _____

5. What do you think causes or increases your pain? _____

6. What relieves your pain? _____

7. What times of the day is your pain more severe? _____

8. What helps you cope with your pain? _____

9. What effect does your pain have on:

   Sleep _____   Activity level _____

   Relationships _____   Other _____

10. What problems do you notice when you take your pain medication?

   ☐ Vomiting   ☐ Drowsiness   ☐ Confusion   ☐ Decreased activity level
   ☐ Nausea   ☐ Sleep   ☐ Hallucinations   ☐ Constipation   Other: _____

11. Current Pain Medications (include adjuvant medications):

Medication	Dose	Route	Times

12. Plan/Comments: _____

_____

Figure 22-1 Pain assessment chart. (Adapted by the HFC research committee from *Pain: Clinical manual for nursing practice.* St. Louis: C.V. Mosby.)

You can use a chart like this to rate your pain and to keep a record of how well the medicine is working. Write the information in the chart. Use the pain intensity scale to rate your pain before and after you take the medicine.

Pain Intensity Scale

```
      0      1      2      3      4      5      6      7      8      9     10
      I------I------I------I------I------I------I------I------I------I------I
      No                                                            Worst
      pain                                                           pain
```

Date	Time	Pain intensity scale rating	What I was doing when I felt the pain	Medicine I took	Pain intensity scale rating 1 hour after taking the medicine
9/20/95 example	2:30	6	Sitting at my desk reading	2 Percocet	2

Medication Problems:
(check all that are appropriate)

Date/Time	Nausea/Vomiting	Constipation	Drowsiness	Confusion	Hallucination	Sleep	Activity	Mood

Figure 22-2 Example of a Home Pain Assessment Log that can be given to the family to enlist their help in assessment. (Adapted by the HFC research committee from AHCPR Pub. # 94–0595.)

Often, family teaching involves the issues of tolerance and addiction. Although the patient may develop dependence on the medication, addiction is a craving for the drug for reasons other than pain relief and, as such, should not be a factor in treating patients (Miaskowski, 1993). The nurse can ask the patient, "Would you be taking these medicines if you were not in pain?" The answer, invariably, is no. Tolerance is feared by family members due to the misconception that, if a person uses opioids early in an illness, he or she will need so much more later that they will question if the patient will be able to get enough, or that the medication will be ineffective when the patient "really needs it." However, there is virtually no ceiling or maximum dosage on the opioids, so they can be increased as needed.

Principles of Pain Management

As mentioned earlier, the first step in effective management is to assess the pain problem. Aside from the medical treatment of the disease process through chemotherapy, radiation, or surgery, the mainstay of pain management is pharmacotherapy. In addition to these modalities, nonpharmacologic methods of pain relief are often used in concert with medical and pharmacologic interventions. For chronic cancer pain, medications should be given on an around-the-clock basis, with the addition of breakthrough medications as needed.

Routes of Administration

Whenever possible, the oral route of medication administration should be employed because of low cost and convenience for the patient. There are times, however, when the patient is no longer able to take medications by way of an oral route. In these cases, rectal or transdermal routes may be used, but rectal medications should not be looked on as a long-term solution or used when diarrhea is present. This may cause undue discomfort for the patient and is labor intensive for the patient caretaker. The transdermal route is useful in that it can be easily administered by the family and can last up to 3 days. The disadvantage is that the transdermal route has the problems of lack of control over the dosage given and the patient will still

need a medication for "breakthrough" pain. The subcutaneous route has the advantage of a continuous administration of the medication without having to have vascular access. In patients with cachexia, finding adequate subcutaneous tissue can be problematic, causing irritation and frequent site changes. Parenteral routes should only be used as a last resort (e.g., when other routes cannot be used or are ineffective).

When converting from one route to another, it is critical for the nurse to consult a chart of equianalgesic dosages to ensure a smooth transition from one route to another while maintaining the dosage. In rare cases of intractable pain, intraspinal administration of opioids or anesthetics should be considered. This route may be expensive as well as laden with the possible complications.

The World Health Organization's Three Step Analgesic Ladder provides a guideline for determining which class of medications should be used for different pain situations (Figure 22-3).

STEP 1. Nonopioid analgesics to be combined with an adjuvant medication if one is indicated. This group of medications consists of acetaminophen and the nonsteroidal antiinflammatory drugs (NSAIDs) and is appropriate for mild pain and as

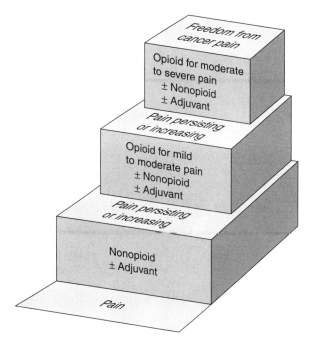

Figure 22-3 World Health Organization three-step analgesic ladder. (World Health Organization, 1990.)

an adjuvant medication when combined with the opioids for moderate pain (Table 22-2). The following are general guidelines when using this class of analgesics:

- Unlike opioids, acetaminophen and the NSAIDs have maximum daily dosages with definite contraindications for some patients. They can be used without concern for tolerance or dependence (Cherny & Portenoy, 1994).
- The NSAIDs can cause gastric irritation and should be given with food. If one NSAID is not found to be effective, it is worth trying another medication in this class.
- The NSAIDS can inhibit platelet aggregation and should not be given in the presence of a low platelet count or to a patient on anticoagulants.
- The NSAIDs should be given with caution in the elderly, people with impaired renal function, or people with gastric ulcers.

- Acetaminophen is metabolized by the liver and, as such, should not be given to people with liver disease.

STEP 2. Opioids for mild to moderate pain with a nonopioid and/or adjuvant medication if indicated.

As the patient's pain increases or is no longer controlled with nonopioids alone, an opioid may be used, often in a combination preparation with a nonopioid. When opioids are used, their effectiveness must be evaluated with regards to the side effects that will occur. These may include constipation, nausea, vomiting, mental clouding, sedation, hallucinations, and lethargy. In addition to these, the nurse now has to deal with tolerance and dependence, which are not characteristic of the nonopioid medications. Because the side effects of opioids will occur in all patients to some degree, it is wise for the nurse to be proactive regarding side effects as soon as the first dose is administered. Table 22-3 lists some common side effects associ-

TABLE 22-2

NONOPIOIDS USED FOR CANCER PAIN

Drug	Trade Names	Adult Dose (Initial)	Duration of Action	Maximum Dose/Day	Comments
Acetaminophen	Tylenol	650 mg q4h	3–4 h	4000–6000 mg/day	Use caution with liver disease
Acetylsalicylic acid	Aspirin	650 mg q4h	3–4 h	5200 mg/day	Avoid use in gastric ulcers, clotting disorders, or with anticoagulants
Ibuprofen	Motrin, Advil, others	200 mg q4h	4 h	3200 mg/day	May cause GI irritation
Ketoprofen	Orudis	25 mg q6h	4–6 h	300 mg/day	May cause GI irritation
Naproxen	Aleve, Naprosyn	250 mg	up to 7 h	1500 mg/day	Over the counter; GI irritation
Diclofenac sodium	Voltaren	25 mg q8h	6–12 h	200 mg/day	Need prescription
Indomethacin	Indocin	25 mg q6h	4–6 h	200 mg/day	More GI and CNS effects than other NSAIDs
Sulindac	Clinoril	150 mg q12h	up to 12 h	400 mg/day	Need prescription; low side effect profile
Etodolac	Lodine	200–400 mg q6–8h	6–12 h	1200 mg/day	Need prescription; low side effect profile
Piroxicam	Feldene	20 mg	48–72 h	20 mg	Long acting; may cause GI irritation, ulcers

(Amadio, P., Cummings, D., & Amadio, P. [1993]. Nonsteroidal antiinflammatory drugs. *Postgraduate Medicine, 4*, 73–97.)

TABLE 22-3

MANAGEMENT OF COMMON SIDE EFFECTS ASSOCIATED WITH OPIOIDS

Constipation	• Start patients on a bowel regimen containing docusate sodium 100–200 mg BID or TID and senna 1–2 tablets at HS.
	• Maintain adequate fluid intake.
	• Provide increased roughage, if the patient can tolerate this in the diet.
Respiratory depression	• Not a major problem in patients who are taking opioids chronically.
	• If respiratory depression occurs, withhold a dose of the opioid and stimulate the patient.
	• If an opioid antagonist is required, dilute 1 ampule (0.4 mg) of naloxone in 10 mL of normal saline and administer slowly, titrating the drug to the patient's respiratory rate.
Sedation	• Sometimes this side effect is difficult to avoid.
	• Dextroamphetamine in doses of 2.5–5 mg BID may be helpful.
Nausea and vomiting	• Administer antiemetic as needed.

(Miaskowski, C. [1993]. Current concepts in the assessment and management of cancer-related pain. *MEDSURG Nursing, 2*[2], 113–118.)

ated with opioids and some suggested interventions.

Analgesics, in particular the opioids, should be titrated to the effect rather than a specific dose. The fact that there is no ceiling on this class of medications is beneficial for two reasons. First, the effectiveness of the medication can be maintained by increasing the dosage as tolerance develops or the disease process necessitates more medication. Second, as the dose is escalated, there is not a corresponding escalation in the side effects. In fact, there is typically a tolerance to the side effects that occur after a period of time. The exception to this is constipation. This requires ongoing assessments of bowel function and placing the patient on a bowel regimen as soon as opioids are started. The process of determining the appropriate dosages of pain medication involves a continuous negotiation between the nurse and the patient. An important point to consider when titrating dosages is that the medication regimen used should be given by the clock to ensure consistent blood levels of the medication. So a QID regimen becomes 12 AM–6 AM–12 PM–6 PM as opposed to 9 AM–1 PM–5 PM–9 PM.

STEP 3. Opioids for moderate to severe pain with or without a nonopioid and an adjuvant medication.

As the pain becomes more severe, either a more potent opioid or higher dosages become necessary. Although morphine is still the drug of choice for severe pain, it is often useful to change from one opioid to another because some patients tolerate some opioids better than others, or may have an idiosyncratic reaction to a specific medication. Although some of the side effects of the opioids are unavoidable, and to be expected along with analgesia, the nurse needs to assess the severity of the effect and determine if a change in medication is warranted. Tolerance to many of the opioid side effects occurs rapidly and can be managed while remaining on the medication (Cherny & Portenoy, 1994, p. 285). Other potential side effects of opioids include hallucinations, pruritus, CNS irritability, tremors, twitching, urinary retention, and myoclonic seizures. Often, switching to a different class of opioids may alleviate these symptoms because cross reactions are less likely between classes (Young & Koda-Kimble, 1995).

Table 22-4 lists opioids commonly used for moderate to severe cancer pain.

Adjuvant Medications

Adjuvant medications encompass a variety of different classes of medications and are used alone or in addition to opioids to treat a specific type of pain. They may be used at any step of the analgesic ladder.

TABLE 22-4
OPIOIDS USED FOR SEVERE CANCER PAIN

Drug	Equianalgesic Dose (mg)		Duration of Effect (h)	Comments
	PO	Parenteral		
Codeine	200	130	2–4	Usually combined with a nonopioid. May cause nausea and vomiting in some people.
Oxycodone with a nonopioid	30	15	2–4	May be used in step 2 of the ladder or in higher doses as a single agent. Adverse effects milder than morphine.
Hydrocodone with a nonopioid	30	15	2–4	Usually combined with a nonopioid. Must watch acetaminophen dosages with ATC dosing.
Propoxyphene	50	NA	2–4	Usually combined with a nonopioid. Should be used with caution in the elderly, and patients with renal impairment.
Morphine	30	10	3–4	The drug of choice for chronic pain due to low cost and availability.
Hydromorphone	7.5	1.5	2–4	May be useful in patients intolerant to morphine.
Methadone	20	10	4–8	A long half-life can lead to higher than desired plasma levels.
Meperidine	300	75	2–4	Not recommended for cancer pain due to toxic metabolites that can build up in a short period of time.
Fentanyl transdermal	100 µg/h = morphine 2 mg/h	NA	48–72	Patches available to deliver 25, 50, 75, and 100 µg/h.

(Adapted from Cherny, N., & Portenoy, R. [1994]. The management of cancer pain. *CA: A Cancer Journal for Clinicians, 44*[5], 262–303.)

The tricyclic antidepressants, most notably amitriptyline, are used for treating neuropathies. It has both a direct analgesic effect, as well as a potentiating effect when used in conjunction with opioids. Amitriptyline has been the most widely studied, but it has anticholinergic properties that can cause symptoms such as dry mouth, constipation, and urinary retention (Jacox, Carr, & Payne, 1994). Sedation and anticholinergic effects are less in the tricyclic agents desipramine and nortriptyline (Young & Koda-Kimble, 1995).

Another class of medications used to treat neuropathies are the anticonvulsants. Medications such as Tegretol, Dilantin, and clonazepam can be effective for lancinating or burning neuropathic pain (Jacox, Carr, & Payne, 1994).

Topical agents used to treat neuropathic pain, such as capsaicin cream, have been used to treat postherpetic neuralgias. They are limited by a delay in their effect, which may be weeks, and by inconvenient application. Mexiletine is a local anesthetic agent that should be a third-line agent, after the antidepressants and the anticonvulsants, due to its side effects of cardiac arrhythmias, nausea, vomiting, constipation, and tremor (Paice, 1996).

Bone pain, usually caused by the cancer metastasis to the bone, is a significant problem in many cancers. Often, the pain is resistant to opioids. The biphosphonates, calcitonin, and strontium-89 (a radionuclide) treat bone pain by reducing osteoclastic activity. Although clinical trials are equivocal, these medications clearly benefit some people with bone pain due to metastasis.

Corticosteroids have a variety of beneficial effects in addition to their powerful anti-inflammatory properties. They act as an appetite stimulant and antiemetic and can decrease swelling in the central nervous system. They are adjunctive therapy in spinal cord compression and in primary brain tumors. Adverse effects include hypertension, elevated blood glucose, psychiatric symptoms, and immunosuppression. Long term, these

Case Study

D. J. is a 42-year-old male who was diagnosed 2 years ago with metastatic prostate cancer, which is rare in men of his age. After undergoing a radical prostatectomy, he has undergone three different courses of chemotherapy. Of the medications used, all have had either minimal or no effect in slowing the spread of the cancer. D. J.'s last cycle of chemotherapy caused him to break out in a rash that became vesicular and was located on his lateral chest and extended around to his spine. He has learned that the rash was herpes zoster (shingles), and, although it has gone now, he is bothered by a stinging pain in the same area. D. J. was recently advanced to MS Contin (a sustained-release morphine) 30 mg PO BID with MSIR (immediate-release morphine) 15 mg q4h for breakthrough pain. He describes a dull pain in his hips, ribs, and lower back. On her first visit to his home, Julie, a home health nurse, is concerned that he is taking too much morphine. He is using the MSIR four to five times per day. He is alert and still performs small chores around the house, with a pain level of a 3 on a 0 to 10 scale.

medications are known to cause osteoporosis and Cushing's syndrome (Paice, 1996).

Before discussing the specifics of D. J.'s pain medication regimen, let us look at the overall goal of his care. Simply put, the goal is the comfort of the patient, not an arbitrary amount of the medication. If the patient is functioning on an adequate level, although he displays signs of side effects that would hamper his quality of life, then the goal is being achieved. Julie proceeded to do a thorough pain assessment and, in contacting the physician, was able to suggest an NSAID for his bone pain and amitriptyline at bedtime for his postherpetic neuralgia. With the use of adjuvant medications, the likelihood that his opioid will have to be raised rapidly to levels that would affect his ability to perform ADLs is decreased.

Nonpharmacologic Pain Control

Some pain researchers have stated that psychological interventions should be used as an adjunct only in severe pain. However, if a person learns the techniques when the pain is mild, and he is more alert when not on opioids, then these methods will be beneficial for the duration of the pain problem. These methods and techniques should be taught to both the patient and the family, because they can assist the patient with a number of the interventions. An important point to consider is that these techniques are best used in addition to pharmacologic modalities, not in place of them. These methods should be documented in the medical record with the same care as the medications are afforded to ensure continuity between care providers.

Heat and Cold

Heat is an effective method of reducing pain that can also reduce inflammation and speed healing by increasing the flow of blood to the surface of the skin. It can also relieve joint stiffness or soreness. Methods for administering heat include warm baths, heating pads, and warm, moist towels wrapped around an area. General guidelines for application of heat include:

- Do not use heat over skin that has been irradiated.
- Use heat with extreme caution and for brief periods in patients with vascular disease or decreased sensation.
- Use heating pads on the *low* setting, and use a towel or pillowcase between the pad and the patient.
- If the patient is taking a bath, make sure the patient caretaker uses a thermometer to check the temperature of the water. It should not be above 101°F (Jacox, Carr, & Payne, 1994).

Cold therapy can, like heat, reduce pain and swelling (if used within the period when swelling begins) by causing peripheral vasoconstriction to the area. It can be applied through ice bags, commercial gel packs that can be frozen, or by cold, moist washcloths. Of these methods, the gel pack lasts the longest. Here are some general guidelines for application of cold:

- Do not use cold over skin that has been irradiated.
- If using ice bags, crushed ice will cover more surface of the skin than will ice cubes.
- Use a towel or pillowcase between the ice pack and the patient.
- Ice should not be used in patients with peripheral vascular disease and for no longer than 15 minutes in other patients (Jacox, Carr, & Payne, 1994).

Relaxation, Distraction, and Imagery

These psychological techniques are an effective adjunct to medication, however are best employed in the patient whose cognition is intact. They have an added benefit of relieving anxiety and are based on the scientific basis that the mind is a necessary component of pain perception. To the extent that patients can distract themselves, or be distracted, the pain perception is lessened. Here are some general guidelines for using and instructing patients in these techniques:

- Music is one form of distraction. Ask the patient his or her preference for music, keeping in mind that soothing music seems to work better at relaxation than loud music with a rapid beat.
- Conversation, humor (in conversation, audio-, or videotapes), and prayer can all be used to distract someone from concentrating on the pain.
- Imagery can be facilitated by using a quiet room or a soothing setting and asking the patient to picture in his or her mind a place he or she has been (or wants to go) that is quiet, peaceful, and brings about warm feelings. For many people, it is a place near the ocean or a body of water, and, for others, it may be a place in a field of grass or wild flowers.
- Often, slow rhythmic breathing can be used to promote relaxation as can closing your eyes. These techniques work best before pain becomes too intense.

- The nurse should assess how well the form of relaxation/distraction is working to evaluate its usefulness in the plan of care.

Invasive Procedures

There are a number of invasive procedures that are highly effective in the relief of high levels of pain. For the most part, they are interventions that are made by the physician when the pain situation is severe and the patient is critically ill. They include radiation therapy, neurolytic blocks, implantable pumps for epidural opioids, neuroablation (destruction of nerve conduction for pain relief), and surgery for debulking a tumor (Jacox, Carr, & Payne, 1994).

Pain Management in the Home

Although pain assessment and management in acute care settings have the obvious benefits of control over the medication regimen, a readily accessible medical professional, and easy access to a variety of medications, pain management in the home setting is a completely different experience. One has only to consider that the patient at home may not have any of the above situations, presenting a number of challenges for the home health nurse. This is a brief list of some of the issues that should be considered when managing the pain of a home-bound cancer patient:

- **Cost**—Many medications, including pain medications, are beyond the financial resources of many patients. The nurse must take into consideration whether the patient will be able to afford the medication before suggesting it to the physician, or communicate this information to the physician. Medicaid, indigent programs from pharmaceutical companies, and private donations from churches or other groups can all be used to help with medication expenses.
- **Adequate care provider**—Is there a care provider in the home who can assess pain, or at least dispense the medication? At some point, many patients on opioids become unable to keep track of their medications due to the nature of opioids' cognitive effects.

- **Willingness of the patient or care provider to learn**—Is the care provider receptive or able to be taught about the medication regimen or nonpharmacologic techniques? Are there misconceptions about addiction, tolerance, or reporting pain that need to be addressed?
- **Diversion**—In the home, diversion of opioids is more of a problem than in controlled settings. There is no substitute for the nurse keeping track of the number and frequency of use of the medication. Does the patient, inexplicably, run out of medications too soon or lose the prescription more than once? Is there a person who has taken on a sudden concern for the care and medication of the patient? Although not a regular occurrence, diversion should be expected if opioids are being diminished without a rational explanation.
- **Supply of medication**—The home health nurse needs to ascertain, during the visit, if the patient has enough pain medication to last until it is reordered. Often, patients will wait until they are out of medication before determining that they need more; if it is on a weekend, this can be problematic. It only takes a minute for the nurse to count (or estimate) the number of pills that are left and determine if a call to the physician is necessary.

This is by no means an exhaustive list and the only thing that is certain in the home setting is uncertainty.

Teaching the family should be the primary concern when they are managing the patient's care; this cannot be emphasized enough. One does not have to be an expert in the field to teach patients about cancer pain. The National Cancer Institute, as well as the American Cancer Society have free, or low-cost booklets that discuss cancer pain and its treatment. This information is written for the patient, and the content appropriately augments what should be taught.

Box 22-1 is a list of the educational points that should be addressed with the family.

Conclusion

Although this chapter is not intended to be an exhaustive study on the topic of cancer pain management, it should provide the basic tools necessary to

---

B O X   2 2 - 1

Patient Education Program Content

General overview

Pain can be relieved.

Defining pain.

Understanding the causes of pain.

Pain assessment and use of pain-rating scales to communicate pain.

Talking to doctors and nurses about pain.

Using a preventive approach to pain control.

Pharmacologic Management

Overview of drug management of pain.

Overcoming fears of addiction and drug tolerance.

Understanding drug tolerance.

Understanding respiratory depression.

Controlling common side effects of drugs (e.g., nausea and constipation).

Nonpharmacologic Management

Importance of nonpharmacologic interventions.

Use of nonpharmacologic modalities as adjuncts to analgesics.

Review of previous experience with nonpharmacologic modalities.

Peer support groups and pastoral counseling.

Demonstration of heat, cold, massage, relaxation, imagery, and distraction.

(Ferrell, B.R., Rhiner, M., & Ferrell, B.A. [1993]. Development and implementation of a pain education program. *Cancer, 72*[11 suppl.], 3426–3432.)

effectively manage the person with cancer-related pain. There are a number of ways that one can validate the effectiveness of pain management strategies. One method is to survey patients to determine how satisfied they are/were with the pain management they received. Another way a nurse can gauge the effectiveness of current treatments is to compare them with other professionals working with the same type of patients. The state cancer pain initiatives are groups of nurses, physicians, and pharmacists who have as their goal to learn more about the proper treatment of cancer pain. It is a goal that is not only beneficial to us as professionals, but speaks to who we are as a profession.

REFERENCES

Ahles, T. A., Ruckdeschel, J. C., & Blanchard, E. B. (1984). Cancer-related pain. I. Prevalence in an outpatient setting as a function of stage and type of cancer. *Journal of Psychosomatic Research, 28,* 115–119.

Amadio, P., Cummings, D., & Amadio, P. (1993, March). Nonsteroidal anti-inflammatory drugs. *Postgraduate Medicine, 4,* 73–97.

Bonica, J. J. (Ed.). (1990). *The management of pain* (2nd ed.). Philadelphia: Lea & Febiger.

Camp, L. D. (1988). A comparison of nurses' recorded assessments of pain with perceptions of pain as described by cancer patients. *Cancer Nursing, 11,* 237–243.

Cherny, N., & Portenoy, R. (1994). The management of cancer pain. *CA: A Cancer Journal for Clinicians, 44*(5), 262–303.

Ferrell, B. R., Rhiner, M., & Ferrell, B. A. (1993). Development and implementation of a pain education program. *Cancer, 72*(11 suppl.), 3426–3432.

Jacox, A., Carr, D. B., Payne, R., et al. (1994). *Management of cancer pain: Clinical practice guidelines No. 9.* Rockville, MD: Agency for Health Care Policy and Research.

Lee, D. S., McPherson, M. L., & Zuckerman, I. H. (1992). Quality assurance: Documentation of pain assessment in hospice patients. *The American Journal of Hospice and Palliative Care,* January/February, 28–43.

McCaffery, M., & Beebe, A. (1989). *Pain: Clinical manual for nursing practice.* St. Louis: C. V. Mosby.

Merskey, H., & Bogduk, N. (1994). *Classification of chronic pain: Descriptions of chronic pain syndromes and definitions of pain terms.* Seattle, WA: IASP Press.

Miaskowski, C. (1993). Current concepts in the assessment and management of cancer-related pain. *Medsurg Nursing, 2*(2), 113–118.

Paice, J. A. (1996). Pain. In S. Groenwald, M. Frogge, M. Goodman & C. Yarbro (Eds.), *Cancer symptom management* (pp. 100–125). Sudbury, MA: Jones & Bartlett.

Young, L. Y., & Koda-Kimble, M. A. (1995). *Applied therapeutics: The clinical use of drugs* (6th ed.). Vancouver, WA: Applied Therapeutics Inc.

CHAPTER

23

Mood Alterations

Barbara Warren

Anxiety, fear, denial, depression, crisis, anger, frustration, acceptance. All of these emotionally charged words are often related in some way to the diagnosis of cancer. Patients and family members experience a multitude of emotional reactions throughout the course of the illness that frequently lead to the nursing diagnosis of mood alteration. This chapter describes variations in mood commonly seen in patients diagnosed with cancer and their family members. Guidelines for providing care to these clients both in hospital or at home are presented.

The diagnosis of any life-threatening situation is sure to evoke an emotional response in all but the extremely young or the cognitively impaired. Although the attention of the media has over the past decade been highly focused on the relatively new disease of AIDS, cancer remains a significant player in the cast of life-threatening diseases. Look in any health or self-help section of the local library or book store and there is a multitude of resources for people with cancer. In the last 30 years, cancer has come out of the closet. Although people may be more willing to use the word "cancer" and may actually admit to having been diagnosed with cancer, the fear and anxiety surrounding such a diagnosis have changed little.

Over the past 20 years, this author has asked large groups of nursing students, volunteers, and health professionals to do a brief word association exercise as an introduction to lectures on cancer and cancer treatment. Asked to write down the "first word that comes to your mind when you hear the word `cancer,'" the majority of partici-

pants invariably identify words such as "pain" and "death." When asked to freely associate with the words "chemotherapy" and "radiotherapy," participants' responses have included such things as "painful," "nausea and vomiting," "hair loss," "debilitating," "anxiety," and "fear." Seldom are either of these words immediately associated with positive concepts such as "treatment" or "cure." If these words produce this type of response in potential caregivers and those directly involved in patient care, how much of that attitude or feeling must also exist in the patients and families for whom the association is more direct? Mcfarland (1993, p. 4) writes:

> *. . . Cancer is the answer.*
>
> *That's what a friend told me when she first heard that word. "I've been looking for something all my life. I've tried booze and drugs and whatever else I could think of. I've been depressed for forty years. I prayed to die. Now, cancer is the answer."*
>
> *I think I know what she meant. As I sat in my hospital bed invaded by tubes and lost in a cloud of uncertainty, I had that same feeling. Oh, that wasn't all I felt. Anger and fear and despair and lostness and sadness and hope all called for their turn, too.*

Living with a cancer diagnosis is not a static thing; it is a process. A process of adjustments and readjustments. At times, the reactions experienced by patients may go beyond that which would be described as a normal adjustment to a life-threatening diagnosis. There is a growing body of psychiatric literature that focuses on pathologic responses, which are classified in the current *Diagnostic and Statistical Manual of Mental Disorders* (American Psychiatric Association, 1994). This chapter will not attempt to describe these responses but will explore the variety of normal emotional reactions or mood alterations patients and family members may experience as they adjust to living with cancer.

Grief Response to Diagnosis

The word "cancer" continues to evoke images of pain, suffering, and death. Virtually every patient with cancer experiences some distress during the first 3 months after learning of his or her diagnosis (Weisman & Worden, 1976). One patient's wife remembers being told about the diagnosis:

> *The neurologist in charge of my husband's case came in to see us. He pulled the curtains around the bed, sat down beside me and began to cry. I went cold with fear, but nothing could have prepared me for the words, "I'm sorry, but we've found malignant cells in your spinal fluid. We suspect a lymphoma." . . . I can still remember how I felt. It was as if someone had punched me hard in the stomach—it was physical pain. . . . Numbly we listened as the doctor outlined the proposed treatment . . . and all the while I kept looking at my husband, imagining him wasting away before me, seeing the shock and fear in his eyes and the despair I felt was unimaginable. I wanted to run and hide, but there was nowhere to run and no place to hide. It was my worst nightmare come true.*

McFarland (1993) also describes the impact of the diagnosis:

> *I understood . . . that I would be dead in a year or two. I would have thought it even had he (the oncologist) not spoken the words. In our society, we equate cancer with death.*

Physical pain, shock, fear, despair, anticipated wasting and death—all reactions to hearing the diagnosis of cancer. Many of the same type of reactions have been associated with learning about the death of a loved one. Lindemann (1944), in his classic article on grief, described the acute reactions of people who had survived the Coconut Grove nightclub fire. The symptoms described included physical symptoms such as sighing, a tightness in the throat, shortness of breath, weakness, tears, loss of appetite, and inability to sleep; emotional symptoms such as shock, disbelief, denial, numbness, anger, guilt, fear, depression, helplessness; mental symptoms such as visual, auditory, and olfactory hallucinations, disorganization, restlessness, and apathy; and, finally, spiritual symptoms that included reassessment of one's own values. These symptoms, directly related to acute grief, are frequently observed in patients or their family members as they adjust to hearing they have a cancer diagnosis. Sometimes, patients are led to believe that some of these symptoms are disease related—"what do you expect, you've got cancer." It's crucial that we acknowledge and recognize that these symptoms may be more directly related to a grief response to the diagnosis rather than the diagnosis itself. In 1917, Freud described the normal process of grief and mourning as a reaction to loss in his classic paper "Mourning and Melancholia." Since that time, grief theorists have asserted that grief is a natural and normal response to any significant loss suffered by a person. A multitude of losses are associated with a diagnosis of cancer (Box 23-1). Some losses are more obvious than others, but each of these losses or anticipated losses, if significant to the person diagnosed (or his family members), can activate a grief response.

Since Lindemann's classic study, a variety of theorists have described the process of grief. Lindemann (1944) described three stages including an early phase of shock, disbelief, or denial; a second phase of acute mourning; and a final phase of resolution. Bowlby (1961), Engel (1964), Parkes and Weiss (1983), and Rando (1984) also describe grief as a process involving several stages (Table 23-1). Worden (1991) and Parkes and Weiss (1983) describe specific tasks that must be accomplished to complete the work of grieving (Table 23-2).

If we accept the premise that cancer involves losses, we must also accept the conclusion that each significant loss will subsequently be grieved. What signs of grieving can be anticipated? Rando (1984) summarizes the psychological reactions to loss under three broad categories: avoidance, confrontation, and reestablishment.

Avoidance responses include shock, denial, and disbelief. This is a time when patients or their

BOX 23-1

Losses Associated With Cancer Experience

Cancer Trajectory	Real and Anticipated Losses
Diagnosis	Health Identity Future Stability/work Sense of control Body image
Treatment: Surgery	Limbs Breast Organs/body parts Functions (colostomy) Sense of control Body image
Treatment: Radiotherapy/chemotherapy	Hair Appetite Weight Body image Normal daily life pattern Skin integrity Social/recreational acitivities Work patterns Libido Body function Self-esteem
Remission/end of treatment	Contact relationships with health professionals Perceived "life line" "Sick role"—attention and concern of family or friends
Recurrence/treatment failure, "terminal" phase	Hope Future orientation Faith/belief Body functions/abilities Comfort Anticipation of "total loss" or death

family members may not want to talk about the diagnosis or use the word "cancer." In the past, patients might have been said to be in denial. We can now recognize this reaction as a normal grief response, which will generally decrease in intensity as the reality of the diagnosis sets in. Assessment of the individual and his or her family is crucial at this stage. Total avoidance (seldom seen clinically) might mean that the person ignores all signs and

symptoms and virtually avoids any attempts by medical professionals to assess or treat the disease. More commonly, we will see people who want to run and hide, to pretend it is not happening but actually continue to seek medical attention and tend to follow medical advice. During the avoidance phase, people may question the results of tests, asking if there is any possibility they might be incorrect or wanting different tests to prove the

TABLE 23-1
GRIEF RESPONSES

Lindemann (1944)	Bowlby (1961)	Engel (1964)	Parkes and Weiss (1983)	Rando (1984)
Shock and disbelief	Urge to recover lost object	Shock and disbelief	Numbness	Avoidance
Acute mourning	Disorganization and despair	Developing awareness	Pining and disorganization	Confrontation
Resolution	Reorganization	Resolution	Reorganization	Reestablishment

first ones were incorrect. They may put forward alternative explanations for their illness: "I'm just under stress" or "It could be just a tumor, not cancer, right?" This effort to deny the diagnosis is a step in the grieving process that allows the person to work through the first task of grief in his or her own time and should not be viewed negatively. It is not uncommon for patients to ask different people the same questions in an attempt to get a different answer. This practice, although sometimes frustrating for the caregivers involved, can be likened to the process most people go through when they lose an object of some significance. For example, how often do we go back to the same place over and over again when we have misplaced something, constantly hoping it will magically reappear in the place we have already looked? Patients are doing the same thing—looking for that which they have lost, although they know intellectually that they cannot find it.

Rando (1984, p. 30) describes the *confrontation* phase as the time when grief is experienced most intensely.

> *The individual has recognized that there has been a loss and the shock has worn off to a great degree. Denial and disbelief may still occur, but a whole host of new reactions arise that spring from the individual's confrontation with the loss and its implications.*

During this time, we see extremes of emotion—anxiety, fear, depression, anger, panic, and guilt. Patients may be irritable with their families or caregivers. They may be angry with their health care providers, the health care system, or even with God. They may find it difficult to concentrate and fail to remember important instructions given by their health care providers. This is often the most distressing time for patients and their families as the awareness of the impact of the diagnosis and subsequent treatment becomes more clear.

Reestablishment is the time when the person begins the "emotional and social reentry back into the every day world" (Rando, 1984, p. 35). Emotionally, the person regains an interest in day-to-day activities unrelated to their cancer or its treatment. The disease begins to take its place in their

TABLE 23-2
TASKS OF GRIEVING

Lindemann (1944)	Parkes and Weiss (1983)	Worden (1991)
Emancipation from the bondage of that which was lost	Intellectual recognition and explanation of the loss	Accepting the reality of the loss and working through the pain of grieving
Readjustment to the environment in which that which is lost is missing	Emotional acceptance of the loss	Adjusting to an environment in which that which is lost is missing
Formation of new relationships	Assumption of a new identity	Emotionally "relocate" that which is missing and move on with life

life without being overwhelming or all consuming. Some patients have even described the cancer as having been beneficial to their lives. Gardiner (1994) writes:

> *Everyone should be diagnosed with cancer!*
> *That's right! Think of it! Think what*
> *the world would be like!*
> *Picture all people actually facing their*
> *own mortality! The world would be a*
> *much better place.*
> *Think how everyone's lives would change!*
> *Think how their life's priorities would change.*
> *Instantly, all things that were "SO*
>   *IMPORTANT"*
> *would suddenly be re-evaluated.*
> *Time would be more precious!*
> *Families and friendships would be sacred.*
> *The world would be as it was meant to be.*
> *Everyone would be equal. There would be*
> *more honesty, tears, laughter and love.*
> *People might actually reach out and*
> *help one another.*
> *People would learn to enjoy every minute of*
> *every day in case it was their last.*
> *They would learn the true meaning of life.*
> *Yes! I think everyone should be diagnosed*
> *with cancer!*

Not all patients or their families will come to this degree of acceptance. As the grief response progresses, however, most people will come to incorporate the cancer experience into their identity in one way or another.

Living With Cancer Treatment—Effect on Mood

Surgery, radiotherapy, chemotherapy, immune therapy, gene therapy, and who knows what the future holds! Aggressive treatments for aggressive diseases. All of these treatments for cancer evoke some kind of emotional or psychological response. The person diagnosed with cancer experiences not only the assault of the disease but the additional assault of treatments designed to rid the body of cells not responding to its own normal regulatory mechanisms.

Everyone knows someone who knows someone who experienced horrific side effects of one treatment or another, and no one is afraid to share that information with a newly diagnosed patient. Fear of the unknown is a common reaction for those facing treatment for cancer. Patients hear stories from friends of friends and with their own imaginations build more stories about the possible effects they might experience while they undergo treatment for cancer. Fear of what lies ahead is a natural consequence. Clear, concise information about what to expect is an essential antidote to this problem.

There are, however, specific effects of treatment that do have a direct or indirect impact on the patient's mood—fatigue, medication-related anxiety syndromes, and "treatment exhaustion."

Fatigue and Depression

> *Being tired depresses me. Even the simplest tasks are hard to do. The tiredness and depression are mostly from the chemo, I know, but I have almost a year of that to go. Just about the time I get a little energy back, I have to go back for more chemo. I'm just so sick and tired of being sick and tired (McFarland, 1993).*

Surgery, chemotherapy, and radiation therapy are all associated with fatigue (Greenberg, 1998). Many treatment-related factors play a role in fatigue. After surgery, patients face the body's response to injury and repair, effects of general anesthesia, deconditioning by bedrest, pain, and relative anemia. Radiation treatment has long been associated with fatigue although the exact causation factors are not clearly defined. Most chemotherapy protocols are associated with fatigue. Some drugs have a direct side effect of fatigue such as 5-fluorouracil, the vinca alkaloids, or biologic treatments like interferon and interleukin-2, whereas others such as the corticosteroids may cause insomnia, which increases fatigue. (For more information on fatigue, see Chapter 24.)

Regardless of the cause, fatigue, like pain, can greatly interfere with a person's quality of life and adversely affect mood. In fact, fatigue has a strong correlation to measures of depression, somatization, and anxiety (Wessely, 1998). Patients readily identify fatigue as interfering with their normal activities of life. Inability to complete tasks, whether physical or mental, along with an overwhelming and often constant sense of exhaustion will certainly interfere with one's sense of well-being and ultimately one's mood. Feeling "down" or feeling "blue" often cannot be distinguished from being totally exhausted. Patients, families, and caregivers may need some assistance in differentiating between cancer and treatment-related fatigue and depression.

The grief response as described above is similar to depression with the symptoms of sadness, tearfulness, and yearning. However, depression is accompanied by increasing dysfunction, feelings of worthlessness, and even suicidal preoccupation (Lovejoy & Matteis, 1997). The incidence and prevalence of depression in patients with cancer are unclear. A multitude of studies using a variety of measurement tools have produced results ranging from 1.5% to 55% (Massie & Popkin, 1998). Fincannon (1995) found that 31% of referrals to a psychiatric liaison nurse for patients with cancer were related to what nurses described as perceived symptoms of depression. Of those patients, 23% actually met the DSM-IV criteria for the diagnosis of major depression, whereas 53% were actually experiencing an adjustment disorder or grief response. Fincannon (1995, p. 89) suggests that "feeling sad and crying once a week about the stressors resulting from the illness could be considered normal behavior. However, if patients cry most of every day and are unable to function, they may require further psychiatric evaluation." Staff members and patients may not always agree in their perceptions of anxiety or depression (Lampic, von Essen, Peterson, Larsson & Sjoden, 1996). These findings would support the need for systematic and thorough assessment of patients' emotional states to avoid overestimating or alternatively minimizing the presence of anxiety or depression in individual patients.

Medication-Related Anxiety

Anxiety in the face of a life-threatening illness is not an unexpected reaction. For most patients, anxiety occurs at the time of diagnosis or transition periods throughout the illness and may be considered a "normal" grief response as described above. However, medication-related anxiety disorders are also seen in patients with cancer.

Steroids are known to produce minor mood disturbances, including anxiety symptoms, restlessness, emotional lability, insomnia, and agitation (Noyes, Holt & Massie, 1998). Up to 10% of patients on high doses of steroids may also experience major psychiatric disturbances. If the onset of symptoms is sudden in a patient receiving steroids as a part of their treatment, consider the possibility that the steroid is responsible.

Another common cause of anxiety-like symptoms are antiemetic drugs such as metoclopramide and prochlorperazine. Up to 50% of patients treated with these drugs may experience a motor restlessness or akathisia several hours or days after treatment, which may be accompanied by anxiety (Fleishman, Lavin, Sattler & Szarka, 1994). This side effect may be disturbing to some patients who may describe it as "I just couldn't sit still. My legs just needed to move" or "I felt like jumping out of my skin." These symptoms can be rapidly controlled by administering a benzodiazepine or β-blocking drug, by reducing the dose, or substituting a different antiemetic (Noyes, Holt, & Massie, 1998). The nurse's assessment of the patient is a critical factor in ensuring that this side effect is controlled quickly and efficiently.

Treatment Exhaustion

Treatment with radiation and/or chemotherapy can be administered over extended time periods. A course of radiation may cover up to 6 or even 8 weeks, and a schedule of chemotherapy may last several months. The side effects of treatment seldom decrease as treatment progresses and may be cumulative with some regimens. Patients and family members may mark the calendar, looking forward eagerly to the final treatment. Delays may occur due to lowered blood counts or other side effects, extending treatment times even further. For some patients, it begins to feel like the end will never arrive. At the half-way mark, patients and family may celebrate, thinking treatment will soon be over, only to find the second half of the treatment plan even more difficult than the first. Patients may express the feeling that "I just can't complete this. It's too long...too difficult" and be tempted to stop treatment early.

Although noncompliance is not considered to be a major problem (Richardson & Sanchez,

1998), family members as well as patients may be become tired of the routine and wish it to be over. This is a time when ongoing support from nurses and other health professionals and volunteers is crucial. Completion of the treatment regimen is often critical to the anticipated outcome. Assisting patients/family members to weigh the cost versus benefits is paramount. If the benefit of completing treatment outweighs the costs, patients may still require added assistance or incentives to carry on. One analogy that may be helpful to assist patients and families is that of running a marathon. It's well known that marathon runners "hit the wall" somewhere around the 20- to 23-mile mark of a 26-mile run. This happens even with well-trained athletes. They feel they can go no further. One well-prepared athlete described it as "I just need to keep putting one foot in front of the other and I know that somehow I'll get past that wall." Sometimes, simply knowing that this is a common phenomenon is enough to help the patient to "put one foot in front of the other" and keep going. Advance preparation may also make a difference. Listen to patients and families to determine what their expectations are. If the expectation is that the second half of treatment will be much easier than the first half (just because it is almost complete), help them to be prepared for "hitting the wall." Just knowing it can happen may make the difference.

Treatment Completion and Long-Term Survival

Completion of treatment may be greeted with some ambivalence. Although people may look forward to being free of daily, weekly, or monthly clinic or treatment visits and the effects and side effects of treatment, being on treatment may also provide a sense of security. Some patients may view the end of treatment with a feeling of being abandoned by their professional caregivers. One patient described it as having her "life line severed." Patients worry that, without further treatment, their disease may recur. Once again, there may be a grief response to the losses associated with treatment completion (see Table 23-1).

Spiegel (1993, p. 32) points out that, after diagnosis with a life-threatening illness, people are faced with a sense of vulnerability that most

would like to ignore: "The *comfortable* sense of invulnerability is taken away. Life after such a realization can be rich, rewarding, even improved, but it will not be the same. It is laced with the knowledge that it can and will slip away." Family members who expect life to return to "normal" immediately after treatment completion may be disappointed when the patient does not immediately return to their prediagnosis self. In fact, if we accept the premise of the grief process, it is entirely possible that people will never return to who they were before but will, in time, develop a new identity—one that incorporates the cancer experience.

Posttraumatic Stress Syndrome

The experience of being diagnosed and treated for cancer includes a variety of painful, intrusive procedures, hospital stays, and a sense that one's life is out of control. A variety of researchers have reported the presence of stress or trauma-related symptoms such as avoidant behaviors, intrusive thoughts, and heightened arousability in survivors of cancer. These symptoms, similar to those seen in people who have experienced extreme stress related to combat or natural disaster, are recently being referred to as posttraumatic stress disorder (PTSD) (Passik & Grummon, 1998). According to the DSM-IV classification, the symptoms of PTSD may wax and wane throughout the cancer experience and beyond. The difficulty in diagnosing this disorder in people with cancer is compounded by the fact that patients may be experiencing a variety of other reactions of normal adjustment. Clinicians, however, should be aware of some of the symptoms that may be associated with a diagnosis of PTSD (Box 23-2). In comparing Lindemann's description of the grief response in Table 23-1 with Box 23-2, it is easy to see why a diagnosis of PTSD might be difficult to make in this situation.

In fact, it is common for patients to find themselves experiencing many of these same symptoms as the time approaches for their next follow-up appointment. The anxiety and stress generated by returning to the treatment center or undergoing tests that may indicate recurrence of the illness are often unanticipated by patients or their families. Once again, normalizing these reactions for patients is an important supportive role for the nurses who provide outpatient or home care for these people.

BOX 23-2

Symptoms of Posttraumatic Stress Disorder

DSM-IV Criterion	Possible Symptoms
Persistent reexperiencing of the traumatic event	Recurrent, intrusive thoughts, images, or perceptions Recurrent dreams or reliving of the cancer diagnosis or treatment Intense distress when exposed to cues/symbols of the cancer Physiologic reactivity when exposed to cues/symbols of the cancer
Persistent avoidance of stimuli associated with the trauma and numbing of general responsiveness	Efforts to avoid thoughts, feelings, or conversations associated with the cancer Efforts to avoid activities, places, people that arouse recollections of the cancer Inability to recall aspects of the cancer experience Diminished interest in usual activities Feelings of estrangement/detachment from others Restricted range of effect Sense of foreshortened future
Symptoms of increased arousal	Difficulty sleeping Irritability or angry outbursts Difficulty concentrating Hypervigilance Exaggerated startle response

Duration is more than 1 month
Clinically significant distress or impairment in social occupations, or other important areas of functioning

(Adapted from Passik, S., & Grummon, K. [1998]. Posttraumatic stress disorder. In J. C. Holland [Ed.]. *Psychooncology.* New York: Oxford University Press.)

Recurrence

About the beginning of May, the doctors pronounced [my husband] miraculously cured, sent him home, and advised him to forget his experience and get on with his life. All we had to do was report back for bi-monthly check-ups. We felt very much in limbo. For one thing, we couldn't "forget" and, for another thing, D. wasn't getting better. His walk was slow and shuffling, he couldn't bend over, and he gained very little weight. He was in constant pain. This period of so-called remission, which lasted about a year, was a time of tremendous tension for us. It was like waiting for the other shoe to drop—and it was almost a relief when it did. It's strange, but living with cancer is easier than living with the fear of its return. (Flynn, unpublished)

For some people, the diagnosis of a recurrence may legitimize the way they have been feeling. For others, it may come as a complete shock. Whatever the initial response, the period of adjustment to this "new identity" is seldom without difficulty. The critical difference between an initial diagnosis and a recurrence is that the goal of treatment for most cancers shifts from one of cure to one of control and/or palliation. This change of focus is a significant loss, which will once again evoke the grief response, which may be even more intense than that which followed the initial diagnosis.

Advancing Disease

When cure and control are no longer possible, patients and their families are faced with the reality that the disease will progress and eventually cause the person's death. Some patients or families may seek further treatment even if the likelihood of benefit is small. This is a time of upheaval and distress, and patients and family members may not always agree on which direction care should take.

> *Dennis chose to take the treatments. At this point he didn't believe he was going to die and so he would sort through what the doctors said and pick out what he wanted to hear. But I knew. . . . I have to tell you that I prayed hard for Dennis to reject this course of treatment. I had enough of pain and sickness and suffering, and I missed my kids. I was just plain exhausted, and I felt so guilty for feeling that way. I guess there's always guilt when you lose someone. If it's a sudden death, it's guilt over things not said or quarrels not resolved. But a terminal illness, a death by inches, so to speak, has its own terrible kind of guilt. It's guilt for being exasperated, frustrated and tired. For unkind thoughts and for wanting it to be over. It's present guilt, that must be faced every day, as well as future guilt, when you think "if only I had more patience, been kinder, more loving." Sometimes it's feeling guilty for wanting to eat, or sleep, or be alive, when it seems so unfair. (Flynn, unpublished)*

Family dynamics may be strained, and everyone needs more support during this transition time. Once again, the period of grieving over the additional losses (of hope, of future orientation) may be one of turmoil for everyone. For some families, however, the grief work may eventually be accomplished by the major players.

> *After about a month, Dennis told me the time had come to let go, but he wanted to continue taking the treatments a while longer. Once he had reached that point of acceptance, things became much easier for both of us. It was a great relief for him to be able to quit fighting and he became very calm and relaxed. Unfor-*

> *tunately for us, other people were not as ready to accept his decision and they seemed determined to convince us of the error of our ways. . . . Now I'm not saying that everyone who receives a diagnosis of cancer should instantly resign themselves to death—but I am saying that when the patient has reached the point that Dennis had, this decision should be respected and accepted by those close to him.*
>
> *Dennis and I grieved together during the last two months of his life. We mourned for what would never be, we were thankful for the time we'd had, and we cried together. We also did practical things—he told me things I should know about the car, the insurance policies and the will, and together we planned his funeral. He picked his pall bearers and the music, and lectured me about spending too much money. He told me he wanted me to marry again, because he didn't want me to be alone. All of these things helped me through the months following his death, and I count it a great honor to have shared part of my life with such a brave and caring man. (Flynn, unpublished)*

Pain

Throughout this period of the disease, mood alterations can be influenced not only by the obvious grieving but by symptoms of the disease. Pain, in particular, has a strong influence on mood and quality of life. Cancer or cancer-related pain is a significant problem for many patients. Cancer pain may be due to a variety of causes, including tumor progression and related pathology, operations, and other invasive diagnostic or therapeutic procedures, toxicity of chemotherapy and radiation, infection or muscle aches due to limited physical activity (Foley, 1979). The importance of pain control cannot be overestimated.

> *Unrelieved pain causes unnecessary suffering. Because pain diminishes activity, appetite, and sleep, it can further weaken already debilitated patients. The psychological effect of cancer pain can be devastating. Patients with cancer often lose hope when pain emerges, believing that pain heralds the inexorable progress of a feared, destructive and fatal disease. . . . Pain can exacerbate individual suffering by worsening helplessness, anxiety and depression. (Agency for Health Care Policy and Research, 1994)*

Glover and associates (1995) found that patients with pain had significantly higher scores on all of the subscale scores of the Profile of Mood states (except vigor) and had a significantly higher total mood disturbance score than did pain-free patients. They also found that the subscale scores of tension, depression, anger, fatigue, and confusion were moderately correlated with increases in pain intensity. Velikova and colleagues (1995) found that there was a significant relationship between pain and anxiety in a group of patients undergoing active treatment for their cancers. Zimmerman, Story, Gaston-Johnasson & Rowles (1996, p. 51) identified that "cancer patients with pain were more anxious, depressed and hostile and had more somatic complaints than cancer patients who did not have pain. . . . Additionally, patients with pain reported interference with sleep, activity and enjoyment of life."

> *I just feel down when I can't get rid of the pain. I know I'll feel better if I just take my [analgesic]. I took it yesterday and had a really good day (an 80-year-old woman with multiple myeloma).*

The quality of life of cancer patients with pain is significantly worse than that of cancer patients without pain (Ferrell, Rhiner, Cohen & Grant, 1991). Pain interferes with all aspects of quality of life, including physical, psychological, social, and spiritual. Assessing and treating pain (see Chapter 22) may make significant impact on the patient's mood.

Nursing Interventions

Grief Response (Table 23-3)

If grief is a natural reaction to loss, what is the role of the caregiver in assisting patients or family members who are experiencing the grief response? Worden (1991) suggests that for uncomplicated grief, guiding the person through the tasks of grieving can by accomplished within a reasonable time frame. Nurses are in an optimal position to guide patients through the grief they experience in response to learning of their diagnosis or throughout their illness as they face secondary losses. Nurses who recognize and acknowledge this grief response can normalize the experience for patients and their families. Unfamiliar emotions and reactions can be frightening not only for the family who observe the response but also for the patients themselves. A little anticipatory guidance can go a long way to overcoming the fear that one may be "going crazy" or that the disease may be affecting the brain.

During the early phase of the grief response, the nurse may need to answer questions over and over again as the patient seeks a different answer. Clarifying questions before answering is an important practice, which often helps the patient to put into words what he actually knows already.

During the confrontation phase, the nurse can be most supportive with an accepting, nonjudgmental attitude. Listening to the patient and family and providing opportunities for them to express their feelings openly without fear of reprisal allow them the freedom to begin adjusting to the diagnosis and what it means in their lives. This is often an opportune time to introduce the patient and family to a volunteer who has "been there," who cannot only accept and understand the feelings but can help the person to realize that there is life after a cancer diagnosis.

Nurses help patients adjust to their losses by listening to them talk about the losses they are experiencing and the circumstances surrounding them. This may mean hearing the same story time after time as patients reconstruct the events leading up to their diagnosis. Encouraging expression of feelings related to the diagnosis is also therapeutic. Tears, anger, frustration, fear are natural expressions of grief and should not be discouraged with attempts to encourage "positive thinking." Successful resolution of the grief response will not be accomplished by attempting to avoid the grieving. Continual avoidance through a guise of positive thinking does not allow movement through the grief work. Positive thinking may emerge gradually as people begin to develop a new image of themselves.

The expression of the emotions of grieving often includes the expression of anger. This response is often the most difficult for everyone involved—patients, family members and health care professionals. Recognizing anger as an expected consequence of grieving can help nurses to maintain their own objectivity in the face of a blaming, often overwrought patient or family member. Not

TABLE 23-3

GRIEF RESPONSES IN PEOPLE DIAGNOSED WITH CANCER

Type of Grief Response	Task to Be Accomplished	Manifestations in Patients/Families
Avoidance behaviors • Denial • Disbelief • Numbness	Accepting the reality of the diagnosis	Seeking alternative options Not believing test results; asking for more tests to confirm the diagnosis Asking that patient not be informed of diagnosis
	Explanation of the meaning of the loss	Refusing to use word "cancer"—substituting "growth," "tumor," "lesion" Refusing tests/treatments Asking the same questions over and over again
	Attempting to recover the lost object	Seeking alternative explanations Reviewing lifestyle patterns and risk profiles
Confrontational behaviors • Emotional responses • Preoccupation with that which was lost • Disorganization and despair	Experiencing the "pain" associated with the loss	Expressions of anger, frustration with caregivers or health care system, God, or higher power Anger over "misdiagnosis" or late diagnosis Irritability with family and friends
	Adjusting to the environment in which that which was lost is missing	Seeking information about disease and possible treatments Reviewing events around diagnosis/treatment Expressing fear of treatment/future treatment/outcomes May seek alternative/adjunctive treatment plans Preoccupation with treatment regimen, blood tests, managing side effects Expressing sense of despair, depression Crying, tears Experiencing sense of confusion/memory lapses/disorganization Confronting one's own mortality Seeking support from volunteers, support groups
Reestablishment phase • Reorganization	Formation of new identity	Talking freely and openly about impact of diagnosis and treatment Supporting others newly diagnosed with similar disease
	Formation of new relationships	Volunteer activities with American Cancer Society Returning to work/recreational/family activities
	Reinvestment in life	Reestablishing life priorities "beyond" cancer diagnosis and treatment

reacting personally to expressions of anger or distrust is crucial. Accepting the patient's emotions and remaining calm and unprovoked by angry responses will assist in the resolution of this well-documented grief response. Assisting the person to identify the source of their anger and redirecting their energies toward problem solving can be accomplished once the emotional response has dissipated.

Even as patients readjust to their diagnosis and develop a new identity that incorporates the illness into their life, they may continue to need support and guidance to understand that grief is not a constant progression. Each person will follow his or her own pattern. The theorists' descriptions of stages or tasks provide only a framework to better understand the individual response. They do not provide a recipe book that can or should be followed on a step-by-step basis.

Anxiety/Fear

High levels of anxiety interfere with the person's ability to hear instructions or accept guidance. When selecting appropriate interventions to allay anxiety, it may be helpful to consider specific assumptions about the anxiety state and allow your actions to be modified by those assumptions (Box 23-3). According to Fincannon (1995), only 50% of patients referred for a psychiatric consultation for symptoms of anxiety were indeed experiencing pathologic anxiety. Lampic and associates (1996) also showed that staff's perception of patient anxiety levels was often higher than that of the patient himself. These studies support the need for thorough and concise assessment of patient mood. Not all patients exhibiting signs of "anxiety" will need psychiatric attention. Interventions by the primary nurse may be all that is necessary (see Box 23-3).

BOX 23-3

Interventions for the Anxious Patient

Assumptions	Actions
It is easier to allay a known fear than to ease anxiety from an unknown source.	Assist patients to clarify their concerns. Determine specific fears and help to allay. Help to reduce problem to a manageable size.
People generally feel less anxious when they know what is going to happen to them.	Explain, explain, explain. Provide information in a variety of ways: verbally, in writing, by video. Determine patients' learning style and make information appropriate to their style. Keep explanations concise and consistent. Include sensory information about tests or treatments whenever possible.
Anxiety is lessened when people believe they have some control over their situation.	Present patient with options. Assist them to understand that they are constantly making choices. Use patient-controlled analgesia as much as possible for pain relief.
Loneliness aggravates anxiety.	Assess social support levels. Encourage family to accompany patient whenever possible. Provide volunteer support if necessary.
A feeling of depersonalization contributes to anxiety.	Respect patient's individuality.
Anxiety and muscular tension often coincide.	Provide opportunities for the relief of muscular tension through physical activity or relaxation exercises.
Anxiety can often be relieved by diversional activity.	Assess individual's interests and help to provide opportunities for related diversional activities. Consider also relaxation exercises, social contacts, music, story telling.

Depression

Lovejoy and Matteis (1997, p. 155) suggest that the incidence of depression among cancer patients will rise coincidentally with the worldwide incidence of depression among the world's population. These authors conclude that "nurses can take an active role in preventing and managing cancer-related depression in direct care environments by developing critical pathways for screening, prevention, treatment and outcome assessment using theory-based research." Clearly, it is essential to determine if the patient is indeed "depressed" or if he or she is experiencing the normal sadness of grieving or physiologic fatigue related to the disease or treatment (see earlier discussion). If nurses understand the cognitive-behavioral theory of depression, they may be able to prevent and treat early signs of depressive mood without intensive psychiatric involvement (Box 23-4).

Conclusion

Mood alterations in response to the diagnosis and treatment of cancer are common. Most of the mood changes can be considered as part of the

BOX 23-4

Prevention and Treatment of Cancer-Related Depression

Assumptions Based on Cognitive-Behavioral Theory

Depression is mediated by individual's attendance to selected stimuli within the environment, which reinforces errors in information processing or perceptual distortions.

Patient Outcomes

Patients may:
- Make arbitrary inferences based on evidence
- Take information out of context
- Overgeneralize
- Magnify trivia
- Inappropriately attribute situations as being "their own fault" (e.g., low counts delay treatment)

Nursing Strategies

Assess patient's perception of information and provide accurate interpretation.

Ask patients to "reframe" situation from an unconsidered but equally plausible viewpoint.

Clarify the meaning of the illness, breaking areas of concern into incremental problems and solutions.

Provide opportunities for relaxation and positive imagery techniques to redirect negatively focused thoughts to more positive experiences.

Provide distraction techniques to block negative thoughts with absorbing mental activities.

(Adapted from Lovejoy, N. C., & Matteis, M. [1997]. Cognitive-behavioural interventions to manage depression in patients with cancer: Research and theoretical intitiatives. *Cancer Nursing, 20* [3] 155–167.)

normal adjustment to a life-threatening situation. This chapter covered these normal alterations rather than provide in-depth discussion of the pathologic reactions seen in a small percentage of patients. Early intervention on the part of the nurse involved in the patient's care may be instrumental in assisting the patient to work through the anticipated grief response to a life-threatening diagnosis and to prevent further complications of pathologic mood states.

BIBLIOGRAPHY

Aass, N., Fossa, S. D., Dahl, A. A., & Moe, T. J. (1997). Prevalence of anxiety and depression in cancer patients seen at the Norwegian Radium Hospital. *European Journal of Cancer, 33*(10), 1597–1604.

Agency for Health Care Policy and Research. (1994). *Clinical practice guideline no. 9. Management of cancer pain: Adults.* Washington, DC: U. S. Department of Health and Human Services.

American Psychiatric Association (1994). *Diagnostic and statistical manual of mental disorders: DSM-IV* (4th ed.). Washington, D.C.: American Psychiatric Association.

Bowlby, J. (1961). Processes of mourning. *International Journal of Psycho-analysis, 42,* 317–340.

Chochinov, H. M., Wilson, K. G., Enns, M., & Lander, S. (1997). Are you depressed? Screening for depression in the terminally ill. *American Journal of Psychiatry, 154,* 674–676.

Du Gas, B. W., & Knor, E. R. (1995). *Nursing foundations: A Canadian perspective.* Scarborough: Appleton & Lange Canada.

Engel, G. (1964). Grief and grieving. *American Journal of Nursing, 64,* 93–98.

Ferrell, B. R., Rhiner, M., Cohen, M. Z., & Grant, M. (1991). Pain as a metaphor for illness. Part I: Impact of cancer pain on family caregivers. *Oncology Nursing Forum, 18*(8), 1303–1309.

Fincannon, J. L. (1995). Analysis of psychiatric referrals and interventions in an oncology population. *Oncology Nursing Forum, 22,* 87–92.

Fleishman, S. B., Lavin, M. R., Sattler, M., & Szarka, H. (1994). Antiemetic-induced akathisia in cancer patients. *American Journal of Psychiatry, 151,* 763–765.

Foley, K. M. (1979). The treatment of cancer pain. *New England Journal of Medicine, 313,* 845.

Friedman, L. C., Lehane, D., Webb, J. A., Weinberg, A. D., & Cooper, H. P. (1994). Anxiety in medical situations and chemotherapy-related problems among cancer patients. *Journal of Cancer Education, 9*(1), 37–41.

Gardiner, N. (1994). *Thoughts–while travelling my cancer journey.* Calgary: West Canadian Graphic Industries Inc.

Glajchen, M., Fitzmartin, R. D., Blum, D., & Swanton, R. (1995). Psychosocial barriers to cancer pain relief. *Cancer Practice, 3*(2), 76–81.

Glover, J. (1995). Mood states of oncology outpatients: Does pain make a difference? *Journal of Pain & Symptom Management, 10*(2), 120–128.

Greenberg, D. (1998). Fatigue. In J. C. Holland (Ed.), *Psychooncology.* New York: Oxford University Press.

Kornblith, A. B. (1998). Psychosocial adaptation of cancer survivors. In J. C. Holland (Ed.), *Psychooncology.* New York: Oxford University Press.

Lampic, C., von Essen, L., Peterson, V. W., Larsson, G., & Sjoden, P-O. (1996). Anxiety and depression in hospitalized patients with cancer: Agreement in patient–staff dyads. *Cancer Nursing, 19*(6), 419–428.

Librach, S. L. (1991). *The pain manual. Principles and issues in cancer pain management.* Toronto: Pegasus Healthcare.

Lindemann, E. (1944). Symptomatology and management of acute grief. *American Journal of Psychiatry, 101,* 141–148.

Loscalzo, M., & BrintzenhofeSzoc, K. (1998). Brief crisis counseling. In J. C. Holland (Ed.), *Psychooncology.* New York: Oxford University Press.

Lovejoy, N. C., & Matteis, M. (1997). Cognitive-behavioural interventions to manage depression in patients with cancer: Research and theoretical initiatives. *Cancer Nursing, 20*(3), 155–167.

Lupi, R. S. (1998). Classics revisited: Freud's "Mourning and Melancholia." *Journal of the American Psychoanalytic Association, 46*(3), 867–883.

Lynch, M. E. (1995). The assessment and prevalence of affective disorders in advanced cancer. *Journal of Palliative Care, 11*(1), 10–18.

Massie, M. J., & Popkin, M. K. (1998). Depressive disorders. In J. C. Holland (Ed.), *Psychooncology.* New York: Oxford University Press.

McFarland, J. R. (1993). *Now that I have cancer I am whole.* Kansas City: Andrews and McMeel.

Noyes, R., Jr., Holt, C. S., & Massie, M. J. (1998). Anxiety disorders. In J. C. Holland (Ed.), *Psychooncology.* New York: Oxford University Press.

Parkes, C. M. (1970). The first year of bereavement. *Psychiatry, 33,* 444–467.

Parkes, C. M., & Weiss, R. S. (1983). *Recovery from bereavement.* New York: Basic Books.

Pasacreta, J. V., & McCorkle, R. (1998). Bedside interventions. In J. C. Holland (Ed.), *Psychooncology.* New York: Oxford University Press.

Passik, S. & Grummon, K. (1998). Posttraumatic stress disorder. In J. C. Holland (Ed.), *Psychooncology.* New York: Oxford University Press.

Rando, T. A. (1984). *Grief, dying and death.* Champaign: Research Press Company.

Richardson, J. L., & Sanchez, K. (1998). Compliance with cancer treatment. In J. C. Holland (Ed.), *Psychooncology.* New York: Oxford University Press.

Spiegel, D. (1993). *Living beyond limits.* New York: Random House.

Velikova, G, Selby, P. J., Snaith, P. R., et al. (1995). The relationship of cancer pain to anxiety. *Psychotherapy and Psychosomatics, 63*(3-4), 181–184.

Weisman, A. D., & Worden, J. W. (1976). The existential plight in cancer: Significance of the first 100 days. *International Journal of Psychiatric Medicine, 7,* 1–15.

Welch-McCaffrey, D. (1985). Cancer, anxiety and quality of life. *Cancer Nursing, 8*(3), 151–158.

Wells, M. E., McQuellon, R. P., Hinkle, J. S., & Cruz, J. M. (1995). Reducing anxiety in newly diagnosed cancer patients: A pilot program. *Cancer Practice, 3*(2), 100–104.

Wessely, S. (1998). Nonpharmacological interventions for fatigue. In *Proceedings of 1st International Conference on Research in Palliative Care,* May 7–9, 1998. Bethesda, Maryland.

Worden, J. W. (1991). *Grief counseling and grief therapy.* New York: Springer Publishing Company.

Zimmerman, L., Story, K. T., Gaston-Johnasson, F., & Rowles, J. R. (1996). Psychological variables and cancer pain. *Cancer Nursing, 19*(1), 44–53.

Fatigue

Lillian M. Nail

CHAPTER
24

Fatigue is a common and troubling side effect of cancer treatment (Nail, 1997b; Richardson, 1995; Smets et al., 1993; Winningham et al., 1994). Cancer treatment modalities that produce fatigue include surgery, chemotherapy (CTX), radiation therapy (RT), and biologic response modifiers. Although fatigue is an important part of the treatment experience of many people with cancer, it is poorly understood by health care providers and often is ignored in clinical practice. The research base on fatigue as a side effect of cancer treatment is constantly expanding and suggests several different approaches to managing cancer treatment-related fatigue (CRF). The cause of CRF is not known; it is likely that there are several different causes. Identification of the causal mechanisms will provide direction for approaches to preventing and treating CRF.

Background

The research on fatigue in cancer patients focuses on fatigue as a side effect of treatment. Fatigue may also be a presenting symptom, most often in lung cancer when obstruction leads to hypoxia (Sarna, 1993a, 1993b), hematologic cancers that result in decreased red blood cell counts, or as a component of the debilitation associated with advanced cancers (Donnelly & Walsh, 1995). Because most patients with cancer are diagnosed with local or regional disease (Parker et al., 1997), stage of disease at diagnosis does not explain the high prevalence of fatigue among people with cancer.

Defining Cancer Treatment— Related Fatigue

Fatigue, like pain, is a self-perceived state. Some of the synonyms for CRF used by people undergoing cancer treatment include tired, exhausted, weary, drained, overcome, lazy, slow, droopy, weak, dense, worn out, listless, dragged out, pooped, sluggish, run down, and used up (Ferrell et al., 1996a; Pearce & Richardson, 1996; Ream & Richardson, 1996; Schwartz, 1997a). The literature on fatigue often confuses the sensation with a response to the sensation, such as decreased activity or increased rest (Tiesinga, Dassen & Halfens, 1996). It is important to recognize that responses to sensations are a result of a cognitive process and reflect the outcome of a complex series of appraisals and decisions. Assessment of a self-perceived state, such as CRF, should focus on the intensity of the sensation, not on assumptions about the relationship between the intensity of the sensation and behavioral responses.

Another confusing aspect of the literature on fatigue is the fact that most of the research on fatigue is on muscle fatigue and muscle weakness. The focus of most of this research was on improving the performance of elite athletes, with a few studies addressing rehabilitation of people with chronic neurologic problems resulting from illness or injury. The sensation of fatigue in cancer patients is not tied to muscular performance or focal neurologic damage. Although muscle weakness probably contributes to the sensation of fatigue, it is not a prerequisite for the sensation of fatigue experienced as a side effect of cancer treatment (Nail & Winningham, 1995).

Fatigue experienced as a side effect of cancer treatment differs from the fatigue experienced by healthy people on several dimensions. First, CRF is not fully relieved by sleep and rest. People receiving cancer treatment consistently rate sleep and rest as helpful, but not completely effective, in relieving fatigue (Foltz, Gaines & Gullatte, 1996; Graydon et al., 1995; Nail et al., 1991; Richardson & Ream, 1997). Second, CRF is not necessarily linked to activity. In healthy people, the sensation of fatigue is attributed to sustained physical or mental effort. People undergoing cancer treatment may experience sudden, overwhelming waves of fatigue that are not linked to effort or activity. Third, healthy people view fatigue as a warning that they are pushing themselves to their limit. CRF becomes a background sensation that is present upon awakening, it varies in intensity throughout the day, and the pattern is linked to the phases of cancer treatment. People who experience fatigue as a side effect of cancer treatment make mental adjustments in their standard for fatigue. The state they previously defined as "a little tired" is redefined as "not tired," and the sensation of extreme tiredness is reset to a new point that is higher than the previously experienced maximum (Breetvelt & Van Dam, 1991).

A peculiar phenomenon in defining fatigue is the belief that you can tell how tired a person is based on physical appearance. Although the "look" of fatigue has not been studied, anecdotes from patients argue against the idea that there is a universal appearance of fatigue. Cancer patients complain that health care providers, friends, and family tell them that they do not look tired at times when patients feel quite fatigued. However, there may be subtle indicators in posture, muscle tone, voice, and facial expression that have not been identified.

Prevalence of CRF

Data on the proportion of people with cancer who experience CRF during treatment are difficult to interpret. In studies based on self-reported measures of the sensation of fatigue, the proportion varies from 40% to 100% depending on study design, instrumentation, diagnosis, and type of treatment (Irvine et al., 1991; Irvine et al., 1994; Jacobs & Piper, 1996; Nail, 1997b). The lowest proportions are obtained when health care provider ratings are used, such as those that form the basis for toxicity reporting in many cancer treatment trials.

Patterns of CRF

Surgery

Most people with cancer enter the cancer care system after at least one surgical procedure. Postoperative fatigue is common and may take several months to resolve (Salmon & Hall, 1997). It is important to recognize that the majority of cancer patients begin another form of treatment before postoperative fatigue from diagnosis and initial surgical treatment is resolved.

Radiation Treatment

Patients receiving RT usually notice increased fatigue the second week of treatment. The sensation of fatigue increases over the course of treatment, peaks near the end of RT, and gradually declines over the months after (Figure 24-1) (Fieler, 1997; Greenberg et al., 1992; Haylock & Hart, 1979; King et al., 1985; Walker et al., 1996).

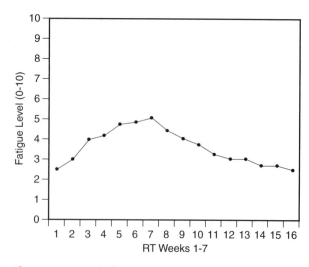

Figure 24-1 Typical pattern of CRF with radiation treatment (RT).

Chemotherapy

The pattern of CRF associated with CTX is linked to the administration of CTX (Figure 24-2) (Berger, 1998; Jones, 1993; Piper, 1992; Richardson & Ream, 1997; Sitzie & Huggina, 1998; Sitzia et al., 1997; Smets et al., 1996). Patients report peak fatigue in the days immediately after CTX. CRF gradually decreases until the next treatment is administered. Some patients find that the level of CRF immediately before the next treatment gradually increases over the cycles of CTX. After the peak in the days after the final treatment, CRF gradually decreases over the months after treatment. The pattern of fatigue experienced by patients who receive CTX over several days has not been characterized.

Biologic Response Modifiers

Biologic response modifiers such as interferon alpha cause intense fatigue. CRF associated with these agents is cited by patients as a reason for stopping treatment (Borden & Parkinson, 1998; Dalakas, Mock & Hawkins, 1998; Dean et al., 1995; Licinio, Kling & Hauser, 1998; Valentine et al., 1998). Patients describe the sensations associated with biologic response modifiers as flulike with aching in the muscles and joints. Some agents produce acute fatigue, chills, and fever soon after administration, whereas others have a more chronic pattern of side effects.

Bone Marrow or Peripheral Stem Cell Transplantation

Fatigue is an important lingering side effect of bone marrow transplantation, with patients experiencing fatigue years after transplantation (Bush et al., 1995; Molassiotis et al., 1995; Whedon & Ferrell, 1994). Although the pattern of CRF during the acute phase of marrow transplantation is not clearly described in the literature, variables such as type of transplantation and speed of engraftment are believed to influence the sensation of CRF.

Impact on Quality of Life

CRF is a problem both because it is an unpleasant sensation and because it diminishes quality of life. The negative impact of CRF involves all aspects of quality of life (Dean & Ferrell, 1995; Ferrell et al., 1996a, 1996b; Fieler, 1997; Harpham, 1994; Longman, Braden & Miskel, 1997; Nail & Jones, 1995; Pater et al., 1997; Steginga & Dunn, 1997.

Physical Activity

The most common advice given to people experiencing CRF is to decrease activity, which is a natural response to fatigue irrespective of the cause. Winningham (1994) proposes a model of CRF that addresses decreased activity as both a consequence of CRF and a contributor to further CRF (Nail & Winningham, 1993). In this model, decreased physical activity leads to decreased muscle mass and initiates a cycle of decline with decreased strength making activity more difficult. People receiving catabolic steroids as part of their cancer treatment regimen or as a component of a side effect management plan are extremely likely to experience loss of muscle mass as are those who decrease their physical activity or experience deficits in nutrition (see Chapter 20).

Examples of the changes experienced in physical activity include making one trip from the car to the house for each bag of groceries rather than carrying two bags at once, limiting the number of

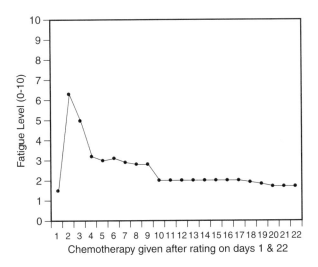

Figure 24-2 Typical pattern of CRF during one cycle of chemotherapy.

trips up and down stairs, and paying attention to previously automatic functions like sitting upright in a chair without arms. Some activities can be interrupted by frequent rest periods. Activities of daily living, like getting dressed, will take much longer than usual when CRF dictates frequent rest periods. More subtle changes in activity, especially in recreation or leisure activities, may not be noticed by the person who has decreased the activity at the time the change occurs.

Emotional Stability

CRF can contribute to irritability, lapses in attention, and mood swings (see Chapter 23). A comment frequently heard by people with cancer who report fatigue to friends and family members is, "You're not tired—you're just depressed." This comment is based on the knowledge that fatigue is a sign of depressed affect in people who do not have physical illness. In physical illness, the diagnosis of depression is based on evaluation of mood, not physical symptoms. It is important to recognize that CRF and any changes in usual life due to CRF or other side effects and symptoms may result in negative mood, but that CRF is not caused by depression and is not a sign of depression. Careful evaluation of affect by a mental health professional who is knowledgeable about side effects of cancer treatment is required when depression is suspected (Nail, 1996; Valente & Saunders, 1997).

Loss of Concentration

Fatigue interferes with information processing. The extent to which changes in cognition reported by cancer patients are due to CRF or to other effects of cancer treatment is not known, but CRF appears to be a contributing factor (Cimprich, 1992a; Licinio et al., 1998). Specific strategies for restoring concentration are being tested in people undergoing cancer treatment (Cimprich, 1993, 1995). CRF has important implications for patient education, obtaining history information, and patient assessment because incomplete information or decreased ability to process information may result in inappropriate treatment, failure to recognize and report treatment toxicity, and inadequate self-care (Cimprich, 1992b).

Assessment

A variety of tools have been developed and applied as measures of CRF in a research context. However, measurement tools for research are not necessarily appropriate for clinical practice. The foundation of clinical assessment is the recognition that CRF is a self-perceived state and can be assessed by asking about the amount or intensity of the sensation. The approach to assessment in the clinical setting can be parallel to that used for pain assessment (Box 24-1), based on a numeric

---

BOX 24-1

Fatigue Assessment Items

Directions: Each day, write in the number that represents how much fatigue you experienced and write in the number that best describes how much fatigue interfered with your life.

0 = not at all . . . . 10 = the most possible

	M	T	W	Th	F	S	Su
Amount of fatigue today:	__	__	__	__	__	__	__
Amount fatigue interfered today:	__	__	__	__	__	__	__

rating of 0 through 10. It is essential to have data from patients over time, and the time frame for assessment needs to be tailored to the treatment. For example, patients receiving cyclic CTX should be asked about their level of fatigue in the days after the previous treatment and the day they arrive at the clinic for the next treatment, not just at the time they have a treatment appointment, which is likely to reflect the lowest level of fatigue. The impact of fatigue can be assessed separately by asking for a 0 to 10 rating of "How much has fatigue interfered with your life?" Patients who report low fatigue but high negative impact may want to explore structured exercise or energy conservation, whereas those who have higher levels of fatigue but less negative impact may not be interested in an active approach to CRF management. Recognizing unusual spikes in CRF is important in triggering evaluation for febrile neutropenia, anemia, and other physiologic problems. In some settings, patients are encouraged to use daily diaries to establish the intensity and pattern of their fatigue and to report sudden increases that do not fit the pattern.

Preparing for Fatigue

Because of the high prevalence of CRF across different types of cancer treatment, all people beginning treatment should get information about fatigue. A common concern of health care providers about warning patients of impending experiences is that "If I tell them about it, they'll have it." It is essential for health care providers to recognize the value of providing people with accurate information about impending experiences documented in an extensive body of research testing informational interventions in a variety of physical illnesses (Johnson, 1997; Johnson et al., 1988). An additional consistent finding in this work is that preparatory information does not cause side effects, but people who get accurate preparatory information are better able to plan for the experience and tend to experience less disruption in usual activity.

An additional concern about the information provided to cancer patients revolves around what happens when information about expected treatment side effects is withheld. People with cancer monitor the way they feel. When a symptom appears, the person experiencing it will interpret it (Skelton & Croyle, 1991). If the symptom is known to be an expected side effect of treatment, it will be interpreted as such. If no information was provided about fatigue, the natural conclusion is that it is a symptom of the disease or an indication that something is wrong with the treatment. The meaning attached can be that the treatment is not working, that the person is not tolerating the treatment and will die, or that the prognosis presented at the time of making the treatment decision was a lie. Accurate information about expected treatment side effects prevents inaccurate interpretation.

Interventions for Cancer Treatment-Related Fatigue

The approaches to managing CRF available to clinicians are diverse but limited by lack of knowledge of the underlying mechanism of CRF. Examples of the use of selected intervention techniques are displayed in Table 24-1.

Correcting Physiologic Problems

ANEMIA

Preventing or correcting anemia through the administration of erythropoietin consistently improves self-perceived energy level and quality of life in cancer patients receiving CTX (Glaspy et al., 1997; Henry & Abels, 1994). The extent of decline in hemoglobin varies, with an average of about 3 g in outpatients receiving standard CTX regimens (Del Mastro et al., 1997; Dunphy et al., 1997). Controversies associated with preventing or correcting anemia include the risks of using transfusion, lack of specific guidelines for treatment based on relative change in hemoglobin versus transfusion trigger points, and the cost-effectiveness of maintaining hemoglobin level using transfusions or erythropoietin. When anemia is due to a cause other than myelosuppression, the approach to treatment needs to be appropriate to the etiology of the problem (Spivak, 1994).

TABLE 24-1

SUGGESTED APPROACHES TO CARE

Action	Rationale	Example
Arrange care to fit pattern of rest and activity	Energy conservation	Schedule procedures to fit preference for morning activity and afternoon rest
Encourage reasonable level of physical activity	Exercise associated with lower levels of CRF	Assist patient to identify an indoor walking track to continue daily walk during inclement weather
Take history information once, asking clear, simple questions	Energy conservation, avoid problems with attentional fatigue	Confirm medication allergies based on chart information rather than asking patient to generate list again
Consolidate appointments, limit travel when possible	Energy conservation	Blood tests drawn at laboratory near home, x-rays scheduled just before clinic visit (2-hour drive to medical center)
Support patient in ongoing monitoring of fatigue level and pattern identification	Early detection and intervention for physiologic problems	Daily diary, patient calls with marked increase in CRF 14 days after CTX, seen in clinic with elevated temperature and neutropenia

HYPOXIA

Hypoxia may be present in patients with pulmonary problems such as obstruction by tumor, radiation pneumonitis, pulmonary fibrosis, or underlying lung disease. The approach to treatment needs to be appropriate to the underlying pathophysiology (Farncombe, 1997). Supplemental oxygen may be helpful for some patients but will not correct any of the underlying pulmonary problems.

LOSS OF MUSCLE MASS

Decreased muscle mass contributes to fatigue, but the extent to which people receiving cancer treatment experience changes in muscle mass is unknown (Fredrix, Staal-van den Brekel, & Wouters, 1997; Kalman & Villani, 1997). It is clear that cancer cachexia, often seen as a result of the disease process rather than cancer treatment, involves loss of muscle mass. The primary intervention used to prevent cancer cachexia is aggressive nutritional support (see Chapter 20), but success in maintaining muscle mass is limited and the relationship to CRF is not known (Kalman & Villani, 1997; Simons et al., 1998).

Another factor that contributes to loss of muscle mass is the use of catabolic steroids, administered as a component of the treatment regimen or as part of a side effect management regimen. The magnitude of muscle mass loss that accompanies the use of catabolic steroids in cancer treatment regimens has not been established. The primary intervention directed at preventing these losses in other populations is resistance training (weight training). This intervention has not been tested systematically with cancer patients and is an area where research is needed.

OTHER PHYSIOLOGIC PROBLEMS

Increased fatigue that is not part of the person's usual pattern may indicate a variety of other physiologic problems (Jacobs & Piper, 1996). Dehydration and electrolyte imbalance may cause fatigue. A sudden overwhelming sensation of fatigue may be an early indicator of infection in immunocompromised cancer patients. Careful assessment is needed to identify these changes and prevent complications.

Exercise

In studies comparing subjects assigned to various forms of aerobic exercise (walking, riding a stationary bicycle, walking on a treadmill), those who exercised had less fatigue than those who did not exercise (Dimeo et al., 1996, 1997; MacVicar & Winningham, 1986; Mock et al., 1994, 1997; Schwartz, 1997b). Subjects in these studies were mostly women with breast cancer receiving CTX or RT or people who recently underwent bone marrow transplantation. The findings of these studies suggest that physical activity is helpful in managing fatigue and indicate that it is safe in the populations studied. These studies have excluded subjects with advanced disease and those at risk of injury due to skeletal metastases. Exercise programs require consideration of other illnesses, previous fitness level, and safety issues. The program should be designed by someone with a background in exercise physiology and based on standard recommendations for exercise among those with physical illness (American College of Sports Medicine, 1995).

The recommendation to use exercise to treat fatigue is one that does not make sense when people view fatigue as a result of physical activity, and it may be difficult for patients and staff to accept the idea that exercise is an intervention for CRF. However, the consistent findings across studies provide strong support for using exercise during treatment. It is also important to consider the issue of patients who are physically active before cancer treatment and the recommendations made to them at the time they begin treatment. Surveys of physically active cancer patients indicate that many continue their programs of activity during treatment, with some maintaining their usual level, some decreasing activity, and others increasing activity (Schwartz, 1997b). It is not known if ceasing activity influences fatigue among physically active cancer patients. In some treatment settings, active patients are supported in their efforts to continue their exercise programs, whereas in others they are actively discouraged. The research on positive effects of exercise in cancer patients undergoing treatment reported to date raises serious concerns about the wisdom of routinely advising patients to abandon their programs of physical activity.

Energy Conservation

Prioritizing activities and changing the way activities are performed are standard approaches to dealing with fatigue. Despite the frequency with which energy-conservation strategies are suggested to cancer patients, there are no studies with cancer patients or patients experiencing fatigue with other illnesses that examine the effects of energy conservation. There is strong clinical anecdotal support for using energy-conservation techniques with patients experiencing CRF. The challenge in clinical practice is in defining and applying these techniques.

There are many different components of energy-conservation interventions, all of which depend on assessment of the nature, extent, and approach to the patient's usual activity. The conceptual basis for energy conservation is that fatigue increases with increased energy expenditure. Consequently, decreasing the quantity of activity, substituting less strenuous activities, or changing the way an activity is performed to require less work constitute the components of energy-conservation interventions.

Decreasing activity requires that the patient decide which activities can be safely abandoned or performed by someone else. Substituting a less strenuous activity requires that the relative energy investment of each type of activity be recognized. For example, walking on a flat surface requires less physical work than walking uphill, playing tennis, swimming, or skating. Performing an activity in a different way is much more subtle and requires careful evaluation. The general principles for changing the way activities are performed include doing the activity from a seated position rather than a standing position, arranging materials needed for the job so the most frequently used tools and materials are closest to the person doing the task and the longest reach is to the least frequently used materials, and the number of times standing is required is limited. Mobility and stability aids commonly used in home care, such as raised toilet seats, chairs with arms, furniture that has a high enough seat to facilitate rising from a seated position, and using a wheelchair when long walks are required, are approaches used for energy conservation. In the palliative care setting, home care and hospice programs are skilled in evaluating the home and suggesting simple modifications that are extremely helpful in energy conservation.

When the energy conservation plan involves transferring activities to others, the person who is to take on the activity must be willing and able to complete the activity. In addition, transferring the activity needs to actually relieve the patient of the activity without substituting orientation tasks, supervision, preparation, or socialization. When having someone come over to "help" requires straightening the house, preparing refreshments, and giving up an afternoon nap that has become part of the fatigue management routine, the visit may end up being more tiring than helpful.

Sleep and Rest

People experiencing fatigue as a side effect of cancer treatment consistently rate sleep and rest as helpful, but not completely effective, in managing CRF (Berger, 1998; Graydon et al., 1995; Nail et al., 1991; Richardson & Ream, 1997). There is very little research on sleep problems in cancer patients, and the extent to which the disease, treatment, and treatment side effects change sleep patterns is unknown (Hu & Silberfarb, 1991). It is clear that various aspects of the treatment regimen, treatment side effects, self-care measures, and symptoms of cancer can all disrupt sleep. Around-the-clock medication administration, forcing fluids, pain, coughing, shortness of breath, diarrhea, nausea, hot flashes, urinary frequency, beeping intravenous fluid pumps, and mucositis may all disrupt sleep. Sleep aids include effective management of side effects and symptoms, minimizing sleep disruption by carefully scheduling medications, organizing care by professionals and family members to allow sleep, and judicious short-term use of sleeping medications (Nail, 1997a). Periods of especially high risk for sleep disruption include times when pain management is ineffective, when postoperative pain is triggered by movement, in the days immediately after administration of CTX, and during times when patients are considering treatment options or awaiting information about disease status.

Rest periods are also rated as helpful in dealing with CRF. The need for rest interrupts activity, and pacing activity to allow for rest is a skill that can be learned. In situations such as the extreme fatigue and sleepiness that accompany cranial irradiation, patients may report needing several rest periods to complete the task of dressing themselves. Patients who are accustomed to using pastimes like reading or sewing as restful activities may find that they are unable to concentrate enough to allow their usual rest activity to be effective or satisfying. There are no standard guidelines for using rest periods as an intervention for CRF. The current recommendation for clinical practice is to individualize rest based on patient preference. Documenting the current pattern of rest and having the patient evaluate the efficacy of rest for relieving CRF are important steps in evaluating the use of rest by individual patients.

Nutrition

As mentioned in Chapter 20, many people with CRF use nutritional supplements or specific dietary strategies to manage fatigue. The approaches used by the public vary and are based on a variety of rationales such as "candy is a high-energy food," "iron supplements boost the blood," "fluids flush out toxins," "heavy meals make you tired," and "vitamins make you less tired." No dietary strategies or supplements have been studied to determine if they are effective in improving CRF in patients with localized cancer who do not have nutritional deficits. The standard recommendation for cancer patients is that they eat a balanced diet, avoid foods that they find unpalatable or that taste or smell different from usual, and use vitamin and mineral supplements to make up for deficiencies in dietary intake. Additional research is needed to determine if specific dietary interventions influence CRF.

Summary and Conclusions

CRF is an important challenge in providing nursing care to people with cancer. As the most frequent side effect of treatment, CRF has a major negative impact on quality of life, but there is no single approach to preventing or managing it that is completely effective. Careful planning of care to make the demands of the treatment regimen as simple as possible, limit demands on the patient's concentration, and allow maximum flexibility in scheduling are important regardless of the setting of care or the specific cancer diagnosis. Routine assessment is important in defining the pattern of CRF, identifying the relationship between exacerbations of CRF and changes in physiologic parameters, and evaluating the efficacy of intervention. The key concepts used in caring for people who are at risk of CRF are summarized in Box 24-2. Remembering that the fatigue experienced as a side effect of cancer treatment is markedly different from fatigue experienced by healthy people is the first step in addressing the problem.

BOX 24-2

Key Concepts

- Fatigue is the most common side effect of cancer treatment.
- Not all people who are treated for cancer have fatigue, but most experience it at some point during treatment.
- The best way to assess fatigue is to ask patients how tired or fatigued they are, using a 0 to 10 scale.
- A sudden increase in fatigue that does not match the patient's usual pattern needs aggressive evaluation.
- Appearance, activity, and affect are *not* valid indicators of the intensity of fatigue.
- Most people will use a variety of approaches to minimizing CRF.

REFERENCES

American College of Sports Medicine (1995). *ACSM's guidelines for exercise testing and prescription* (5th ed.). Baltimore: Williams & Wilkins.

Berger, A. (1998). Patterns of fatigue and activity and rest during adjuvant breast cancer chemotherapy. *Oncology Nursing Forum, 25,* 51–62.

Borden, E.C., & Parkinson, D. (1998). A perspective on the clinical effectiveness and tolerance of inteferon-alpha. *Seminars in Oncology, 25*(1 Suppl.1), 3–8.

Breetvelt, I.S., & Van Dam, F.S. (1991). Underreporting by cancer patients: The case of the response-shift. *Social Science and Medicine, 32,* 981–987.

Bush, N.E., Haberman, M., Donaldson, G., & Sullivan, K.M. (1995). Quality of life of 125 adults surviving 6–18 years after bone marrow transplantation. *Social Science and Medicine, 40*(4), 479–490.

Cimprich, B. (1992a). Attentional fatigue following breast cancer surgery. *Research in Nursing and Health, 15,* 199–207.

Cimprich, B. (1992b). A theoretical perspective on attention and patient education. *Advances in Nursing Science, 14,* 39–51.

Cimprich, B. (1993). Development of an intervention to restore attention in cancer patients. *Cancer Nursing, 16,* 83–92.

Cimprich, B. (1995). Symptom management: Loss of concentration. *Seminars in Oncology Nursing, 11,* 279–288.

Dalakas, M.C., Mock, V., & Hawkins, M.J. (1998). Fatigue: Definitions, mechanisms, and paradigms for study. *Seminars in Oncology, 25*(1 Suppl.1). 48–53.

Dean, G.E., & Ferrell, B.H. (1995). Impact of fatigue on quality of life in cancer survivors. *Quality of Life: A Nursing Challenge, 4,* 25–28.

Dean, G.E., Spears, L., Ferrell, B.R., Quan, W.D.Y., Groshon, S., & Mitchell, M.S. (1995). Fatigue in patients with cancer receiving interferon alpha. *Cancer Practice, 3*(3), 164–172.

Del Mastro, L., Venturini, M., et al. (1997). Randomized phase III trial evaluating the role of erythropoietin in the prevention of chemotherapy-induced anemia. *Journal of Clinical Oncology, 15*(7), 2715–2721.

Dimeo, F., Berzt, H., Finke, J., Fetscher, S., Mertelsmann, R., & Keul, J. (1996). An aerobic training program for patients with haemotological malignancies after bone marrow transplantation. *Bone Marrow Transplantation, 18,* 1157–1160.

Dimeo, F., Tilmann, M., Bertz, H., Kanz, L., Mertelsmann, R., & Keul, J. (1997). Aerobic exercise in the rehabilitation of cancer patients after high dose chemotherapy and autologous peripheral stem cell transplantation. *Cancer, 79,* 1717–1722.

Donnelly, S., & Walsh, D. (1995). The symptoms of advanced cancer. *Seminars in Oncology, 22*(2 Suppl.3), 67–72.

Dunphy, F.R., Dunleavy, T.L., Harrison, B. R., et al. (1997). Erythropoietin reduces anemia and transfusions after chemotherapy with paclitaxel and carboplatin. *Cancer, 79*(8), 1623–1628.

Farncombe, M. (1997). Dyspnea: Assessment and treatment. *Supportive Care in Cancer, 5,* 94–99.

Ferrell, B.R., Grant, M., Dean, G.E., et al. (1996a). "Bone tired": The experience of fatigue and its impact on quality of life. *Oncology Nursing Forum, 23,* 1539–1547.

Ferrell, B.R., Grant, M., Funk, B., Garcia, N., Otis-Green, S., & Schaffner, M.L.J. (1996b). Quality of life in breast cancer. *Cancer Practice, 4*(6), 331–340.

Fieler, V.K. (1997). Side effects and quality of life in patients receiving high-dose rate brachytherapy. *Oncology Nursing Forum, 24*(3), 545–553.

Foltz, A.T., Gaines, G.G., & Gullatte, M. (1996). Recalled side effects and self-care actions of patients receiving inpatient chemotherapy. *Oncology Nursing Forum, 23,* 679–683.

Fredrix, E., Stall-van den Brekel, A., & Wouters, E. (1997). Energy balance in non-small cell lung carcinoma patients before and after surgical resection of their tumors. *Cancer, 79,* 717–723.

Glaspy, J., Bukowski, R., Steinberg, D., Taylor, C., Tchekmedyian, S., & Vadhan-Raj, S. (1997). Impact of therapy with epoietin alfa on clinical outcomes in patients with nonmyeloid malignancies during cancer chemotherapy in community oncology practice. *Journal of Clinical Oncology, 15*(3), 1218–1234.

Graydon, J.E., Bubela, N., Irvine, D., & Vincent, L. (1995). Fatigue-reducing strategies used by patients receiving treatment for cancer. *Cancer Nursing, 18*, 23–28.

Greenberg, D., Sawicka, J., Eisenthal, S., & Ross, D. (1992). Fatigue syndrome due to localized radiation. *Journal of Pain and Sympton Management, 7*, 38–45.

Harpham, W.S. (1994). *After cancer: A guide to your new life.* New York: W.W. Norton.

Haylock, P.J., & Hart, L.K. (1979). Fatigue in patients receiving localized radiation. *Cancer Nursing, 2*, 461–467.

Henry, D.H., & Abels, R.I. (1994). Recombinant human erythropoietin in the treatment of cancer and chemotherapy-induced anemia: Results of double-blind and open-label follow-up studies. *Seminars in Oncology, 21*(2 Suppl.3), 21–28.

Hu, D.S., & Silverfarb, P.M. (1991). Management of sleep problems in cancer patients. *Oncology Huntington, 5*(9), 23–27.

Irvine, D., Vincent, L. Graydon, J.E., Bubela, N., & Thompson, L. (1994). The prevalence and correlates of fatigue in patients receiving treatment with chemotherapy and radiotherapy: A comparison with the fatigue experienced by healthy individuals. *Cancer Nursing, 17*(5), 367–378.

Jacobs, L.A., & Piper, B.F. (1996). The phenomenon of fatigue and the cancer patient. In R. McCorkle, M. Grant, M. Frank-Stromborg, & S.B. Baird (Eds.), *Cancer nursing: A comprehensive textbook* (2nd ed., pp. 1193–1210). Philadelphia: W.B. Saunders.

Johnson, J.E., Fieler, V. K., Jones, L. S., Wlasowicz, G. S., & Mitchell, M. L. (1997). *Using self-regulation theory in your clinical practice.* Pittsburgh: Oncology Nursing Press.

Johnson, J.E., Nail, L.M., Lauver, D., et al. (1988). Reducing the negative impact of radiation therapy on functional status. *Cancer, 61*, 46–51.

Jones, L.S. (1993). *Correlates of fatigue and related outcomes in individuals with cancer undergoing treatment with chemotherapy.* Unpublished doctoral dissertation, SUNY Buffalo, Buffalo.

Kalman, D., & Villani, L.J. (1997). Nutritional aspects of cancer-related fatigue. *Journal of the American Dietetic Association, 97*, 650–654.

King, K.B. Nail, N.M., Kreamer, K., Strohl, R., & Johnsonl, J.E. (1985). Patients' descriptions of the experience of receiving radiation treatment. *Oncology Nursing Forum, 12*(5), 55–61.

Licinio, J., Kling, M.A., & Hauser, P. (1998). Cytokines and brain function: Relevance to interferon-alpha-induced mood and cognitive changes. *Seminars in Oncology, 25*(1 Suppl.1), 30–38.

Longman, A.J., Braden, C.J., & Mischel, M.H. (1997). Pattern of association over time of side-effects burden, self-help, and self-care in women with breast cancer. *Oncology Nursing Forum, 24*(9), 1555–1560.

MacVicar, M.G., & Winningham, M.L. (1986). Promoting the functional capacity of cancer patients. *Cancer Bulletin, 38*, 235–239.

Mock, V., Burke, M.B., Sheehan, P., et al. (1994). A nursing rehabilitation program for women with breast cancer receiving adjuvant chemotherapy. *Oncology Nursing Forum, 15*, 447–450.

Mock, V., Dow, K., Meares, C., et al. (1997). Effects of exercise on fatigue, physical functioning, and emotional distress during radiation therapy for breast cancer. *Oncology Nursing Forum, 24*, 991–1000.

Molassiotis, A. Boughton, B. J., Burgoyne, T., & van den Akker, O.B.A. (1995). Comparison of the overall quality of life in 50 long-term survivors of autologous and allogeneic bone marrow transplantation. *Journal of Advanced Nursing, 22*, 509–516.

Nail, L.M. (1996). Differentiating between fatigue and depression in cancer patients. In C.M. Hogan & R. Wickham (Eds.), *Issues in managing the oncology patient* (pp. 36–41). New York: Philips Healthcare Communications.

Nail, L.M. (1997a). Fatigue. In R.A. Gates & M. Fink (Eds.), *Oncology nursing secrets.* Philadelphia: Hanley & Belfus.

Nail, L.M. (1997b). Fatigue. In S.L. Groenwald, M.H. Frogge, M. Goodman, & C.H. Yarbro (Eds.), *Cancer nursing: Principles and practice* (4th ed., pp. 640–654). Boston: Jones & Bartlett.

Nail, L.M., & Jones, L.S. (1995). Fatigue as a side effect of cancer treatment: Impact on quality of life. *Quality of Life: A Nursing Challenge, 4*, 8–13.

Nail, L.M., Jones, L.S., Greene, D., Schipper, D., & Jensen, R. (1991). Use and perceived efficacy of self-care activities in patients receiving chemotherapy. *Oncology Nursing Forum, 18*, 883–887.

Nail, L.M., & Winningham, M.L. (1993). Fatigue. In S.L. Groenwald, M.H. Frogge, M. Goodman, & C.H. Yarbro (Eds.), *Cancer nursing: Principles and practice* (3rd ed., pp. 608–619). Boston: Jones & Bartlett.

Nail, L.M., & Winningham, M.L. (1995). Fatigue and weakness in cancer patients: The symptom experience. *Seminars in Oncology Nursing, 11*, 272–278.

Parker, S.L., Tong, T., Bolden, S., & Wingo, P.A. (1997). Cancer statistics, 1997. *CA: A Cancer Journal for Clinicians, 47*(1), 5–27.

Pater, J. Zee, B., Palmer, M., Johnston, D., & Osoba, D. (1997). Fatigue in patients with cancer: Results with National Cancer Institute of Canada Clinical Trials Group studies employing the EORTC QLQ-C30. *Supportive Care Cancer, 5*, 410–413.

Pearce, S., & Richardson, A. (1996). Fatigue in cancer: A phenomenological perspective. *European Journal of Cancer Care, 4*, 20–32.

Piper, B.F. (1992). *Subjective fatigue in women receiving six cycles of adjuvant chemotherapy for breast cancer.* Unpublished doctoral dissertation, University of California at San Francisco, San Francisco.

Ream, E., & Richardson, A. (1996). Fatigue: A concept analysis. *International Journal of Nursing Studies, 33*, 519–529.

Richardson, A. (1995). Fatigue in cancer patients: A review of the literature. *European Journal of Cancer Care, 4*, 30–32.

Richardson, A., & Ream, E. (1997). Self-care behaviors initiated by chemotherapy patients in response to fatigue. *International Journal of Nursing Studies, 34*, 35–43.

Salmon, P., & Hall, G.M. (1997). A theory of postoperative fatigue: An interaction of biological, psychological, and social processes. *Pharmacology, Biochemistry, and Behavior, 56*(4), 623–628.

Sarna, L. (1993a). Correlates of symptom distress in women with lung cancer. *Cancer Practice, 1*(1), 21–28.

Sarna, L. (1993b). Fluctuations in physical function: Adults with non–small cell lung cancer. *Journal of Advanced Nursing, 18*(5), 714–724.

Schwartz, A.S. (1997a). Reliability and validity of the cancer fatigue scale [meeting abstract]. *Oncology Nursing Forum, 24*(2), 331.

Schwartz, A.S. (1997b). *Exercise, fatigue, and quality of life in women receiving adjuvant chemotherapy for breast cancer.* Unpublished doctoral dissertation, University of Utah, Salt Lake City.

Simons, J.P., Schols, A.M., Westerterp, K.R., ten Velde, G.P.M., & Wouters, E.F.M. (1998). Effects of medroxyprogesterone acetate on food intake, body composition, and resting energy expenditure in patients with advanced, non–hormone sensitive cancer. *Cancer, 82,* 553–560.

Sitzia, J., & Huggina, L. (1998). Side effects of cyclophosphamide, methotrexate, and 5-fluorouracil (CMF) chemotherapy for breast cancer. *Cancer Practice, 6,* 13–21.

Sitzia, J., North, C., Stanley, J., & Winterberg, N. (1997). Side effects of CHOP in the treatment of non-Hodgkin's lymphoma. *Cancer Nursing, 20,* 430–439.

Skelton, J.A., & Croyle, R.T. (1991). Mental representation, health, and illness: An introduction. In J.A. Skelton & R.T. Croyle (Eds.), *Mental representation in health and illness* (pp. 1–9). New York: Springer-Verlag.

Smets, E., Garssen, B., Cull, A., & de Haes, J. (1996). Application of the Multidimensional Fatigue Inventory (MFI-20) in cancer patients receiving radiotherapy. *British Journal of Cancer, 73,* 241–245.

Smets, E.M.A., Garssen, B., Schuster-Uitterhoeve, A.L.J., & de Haes, J.C. (1993). Fatigue in cancer patients. *British Journal of Cancer, 68,* 220–224.

Spivak, J.L. (1994). Cancer-related anemia: Its causes and consequences. *Seminars in Oncology, 21*(2 Suppl.3), 3–8.

Steginga, S.K., & Dunn, J. (1997). Women's experiences following treatment for gynecologic cancer. *Oncology Nursing Forum, 24*(8), 1403–1408.

Tiesinga, L.J., Dassen, T.W.N., & Halfens, R.J.G. (1996). Fatigue: A summary of the definitions, dimensions, and indicators. *Nursing Diagnosis, 7*(2), 51–62.

Valente, S.M., & Saunders, J.M. (1997). Diagnosis and treatment of major depression among people with cancer. *Cancer Nursing, 20*(3), 168–177.

Valentine, A.D., Meyers, C.A., Kling, M.A., Richelson, E., & Hauser, P. (1998). Mood and cognitive side effects of interferon-alpha therapy. *Seminars in Oncology, 25*(1 Suppl.1), 39–47.

Walker, B.L., Nail, L.M., Larsen, L., Magill, J., & Schwartz, A. (1996). Concerns, affect, and cognitive disruption following completion of radiation treatment for localized breast or prostate cancer. *Oncology Nursing Forum, 23*(8), 1181–1187.

Whedon, M., & Ferrell, B.R. (1994). Quality of life in adult bone marrow transplant patients: Beyond the first year. *Seminars in Oncology Nursing, 10,* 42–57.

Winningham, M.L., Nail, L.M., Burke, M.B., et al. (1994). Fatigue and the cancer experience: The state of the knowledge. *Oncology Nursing Forum, 21,* 23–36.

CHAPTER
25

Myelosuppression

Jeanne Erickson

The person with cancer can experience myelo-suppression from the disease process as well as from the prescribed therapy. Myelosuppression, or bone marrow suppression, is the decreased production of blood cells in the bone marrow, manifested as anemia, thrombocytopenia, and leukopenia. As a result, the patient is at risk for altered tissue perfusion, bleeding, and infection. These episodes can be life threatening, and caregivers must be knowledgeable in the assessment, prevention, and management of these complications.

Hematopoiesis

Hematopoiesis is the complex process of blood cell production in the bone marrow (Rothstein, 1993). A primitive pluripotent stem cell in the bone marrow is the progenitor for all blood cell lines (Figure 25-1). The stem cells differentiate and mature into functional white blood cells (WBCs), red blood cells (RBCs), and platelets, regulated by various hematopoietic growth factors. Mature blood cells are then released into the circulation as needed.

White blood cells include granulocytes, monocytes, and lymphocytes. Granulocytes are the body's primary defense against infection and are categorized as neutrophils, basophils, and eosinophils. The most important and most common granulocytes are neutrophils, which phagocytize microorganisms that enter the body through the skin, gastrointestinal mucosa, and lung tissue. Monocytes also phagocytize microorganisms as well as play a role in the immune function of lymphocytes. B-lymphocytes and T-lymphocytes are responsible for the body's immune function. B-lymphocytes produce antibodies and are responsible for humoral immunity, which provides for protection against foreign antigens, such as viruses, bacteria, and toxins. T-lymphocytes provide cellular immunity through the production of various cytokines, which initiate or regulate inflammatory responses. Cellular immunity provides for protection against fungi, viruses, and intracellular bacteria; it also initiates transplantation rejection. Platelets or thrombocytes develop from megakaryocytes, which differentiate from the stem cell. Platelets play a central role in hemostasis, initiating the clotting mechanism in conjunction with numerous clotting factors in the blood. Erythrocytes or RBCs carry hemoglobin, which delivers oxygen to body tissues and returns carbon dioxide to the lungs for elimination. The hematocrit and hemoglobin are the measures used to determine values for RBCs. Table 25-1 lists the normal range of blood cells in the adult.

Etiology

Hematopoiesis can be disrupted by cancer and cancer therapy (Rostad, 1991). Cancers that originate in the bone marrow, such as leukemia, interrupt normal blood cell production and result in the proliferation of abnormal cells and a deficiency of normal blood cells. Solid tumors, such as lung cancer, breast cancer, and prostate cancer, may

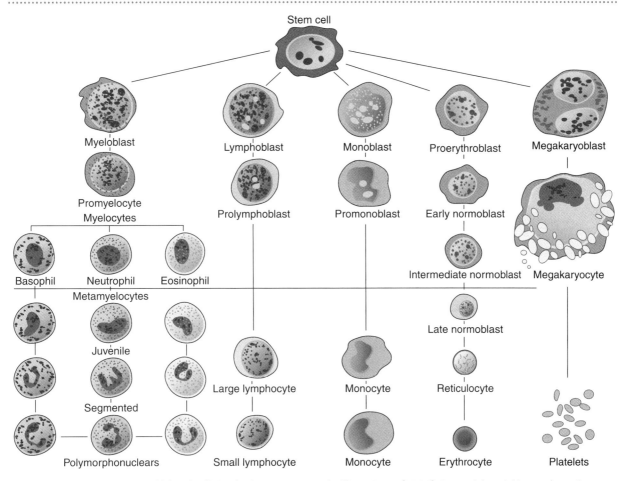

Stem cell

Myeloblast Lymphoblast Monoblast Proerythroblast Megakaryoblast

Promyelocyte Prolymphoblast Promonoblast Early normoblast
Myelocytes

Basophil Neutrophil Eosinophil Intermediate normoblast Megakaryocyte
Metamyelocytes

Juvenile Late normoblast

Segmented Large lymphocyte Monocyte Reticulocyte

Polymorphonuclears Small lymphocyte Monocyte Erythrocyte Platelets

Figure 25-1 Development of blood cells in the bone marrow. (Wilkes, G. M. [1996]. Potential toxicities and nursing management. In M. B. Burke, G. M. Wilkes, & K. Ingwersen [Eds.]. *Cancer chemotherapy: A nursing approach.* Boston: Jones & Bartlett.)

spread to the bone marrow, and malignant cells then replace normal hematopoietic tissue.

Myelosuppression is an expected side effect of many chemotherapy agents. Chemotherapy is toxic to rapidly dividing cells, stopping cell growth, division, and replication. Hematopoietic tissue is rapidly growing and, hence, is susceptible to the effects of chemotherapy. The production of granulocytes and platelets is affected most severely because of their rapid turnover rate, but other blood cell lines are affected as well. Most chemotherapy agents cause a slight decrease in granulocytes and platelets for a few days after treatment, followed by a dramatic drop to a low point 7 to 14 days after treatment, with a gradual recovery within 21 to 28 days (Camp-Sorrell, 1997). This

lowest point that the blood count reaches after chemotherapy administration is called the *nadir*. The decreased blood cell counts occur when the bone marrow, temporarily affected by the chemotherapy, cannot replace the normal circulating blood cells that have completed their life span. After the chemotherapy is metabolized and excreted from the body, the bone marrow resumes normal blood cell production and reestablishes normal blood cell counts. The bone marrow is affected by both the dose and frequency of chemotherapy treatments. Higher doses of chemotherapy cause more profound drops in the blood counts, and more frequent treatments allow less time for the bone marrow to recover between treatments. Although most chemotherapy drugs cause a nadir

TABLE 25-1
NORMAL VALUES FOR ADULT COMPLETE BLOOD CELL COUNT (CBC)

Laboratory Test		Normal Value
White blood cell count		$3.8 - 10.6 \times 10^3/\mu L$
Neutrophils		45.5%–73.1%
Eosinophils		0.0%–4.4%
Basophils		0.2%–1.2%
Lymphocytes		18.3%–44.2%
Monocytes		2.6%–8.5%
Red blood cell count	male	$4.4–5.9 \times 10^6/\mu L$
	female	$3.8–5.2 \times 10^6/\mu L$
Hemoglobin	male	13–18 g/dL
	female	12–16 g/dL
Hematocrit	male	40%–52%
	female	35%–47%
Platelets		$150–440 \times 10^3/\mu L$

μL = microliter, dL = deciliter.

(Adapted from Kjeldsberg, K. [1993]. Normal blood and bone marrow values in man. In G.R. Lee, T.C. Bithell, J. Foerster, et al. [Eds.], *Wintrobe's clinical hematology* [pp. 2297–2309]. Philadelphia: Lea & Febiger.)

TABLE 25-2
DISTRIBUTION OF ACTIVE BONE MARROW IN THE ADULT

Site	Percentage of Total Red Marrow
Head	13.1
Upper limb girdle	8.3
Sternum	2.3
Ribs (all)	7.9
Vertebrae	
Cervical	3.4
Thoracic	14.1
Lumbar	10.9
Sacrum	13.9
Lower limb girdle (os coxae and femoral head and neck only)	26.1

(Haeuber, D. & Spross, J. [1994]. Protective mechanisms—bone marrow. In J. Gross & B. Johnson [Eds.], *Handbook of oncology nursing* [pp. 373–399]. Boston: Jones & Bartlett)

at 7 to 14 days, some drugs have a delayed effect on the bone marrow, with a nadir at 3 to 4 weeks after treatment.

Radiation therapy as a treatment modality also affects the growth of rapidly dividing cells. Unlike the systemic effects of chemotherapy, however, radiation affects only the function of the bone marrow that is included in the irradiated body segment (Haeuber & Spross, 1994). Table 25-2 outlines the sites of active bone marrow in an adult. The treatment area predicts how much, if any, myelosuppression will result from a course of radiation therapy. If only a small percentage of active marrow is included in the treatment site, for example, the person likely will not experience significant myelosuppression.

Today, cancer treatment commonly combines chemotherapy with radiation therapy, giving a greater risk of myelosuppression. Patients who have received multiple treatment courses may develop bone marrow atrophy or fibrosis, with a decreased bone marrow reserve and a diminished ability to recover from further myelosuppressive therapy.

Neutropenia

The most serious complication of bone marrow depression is leukopenia (neutropenia), or a low level of white blood cells, which increases the patient's susceptibility to infection (Rostad, 1991). Infection is the leading cause of morbidity and mortality in patients with cancer, and the incidence of infection as well as treatment costs continue to increase (Tooney & Parker, 1996). It is essential for nurses to successfully assess and manage patients at risk for infections.

Of the white blood cells, neutrophils form the front defensive line against bacterial infections. Because the circulation life of a neutrophil is less than 8 hours, rapid proliferation from the bone marrow is essential to maintain a normal level in the blood. Rapid production of this cell line, however, makes them most sensitive to the effects of chemotherapy. Neutropenia, or a low number of neutrophils, is a critical risk factor for infection.

Normal levels of white blood cells are shown in Table 25-1. When neutrophils are reported as a percentage of the total white blood cell count, the absolute neutrophil count must be calculated with an equation. To determine the absolute number of neutrophils, the percentage of neutrophils and bands (immature neutrophils) in the total white blood cell count is multiplied by the total white blood cell count. For example, if the neutrophil is reported to be 57%, the bands are 3%, and the total white blood cell count is 5,000/mm^3, the formula would be 60% × 5,000/mm^3 = 3,000/mm^3. The risk of bacterial infections increases as the absolute neutrophil count decreases. The patient is at a moderate risk of infection with a neutrophil count between 500 and 1000/mm^3 and is at a severe risk with a neutrophil count < 500/mm^3 (Camp-Sorrell, 1998).

Infection occurs when pathogens overcome host defenses. Without adequate neutrophils as a defense, virtually any organism is capable of causing an infection. Bacteria are the most frequent cause of infections in neutropenic patients. The most common causes of infection include the gram-negative organisms *Escherichia coli, Klebsiella pneumoniae, Enterobacter,* and *Pseudomonas aeruginosa* and the gram-positive organisms *Staphylococcus aureus* and *Streptococcus.* The frequency of infections caused by gram-positive bacteria, as well as strains of *Staphylococcus* and *Enterococcus* that are resistant to usual antibiotic therapy, has increased at many cancer centers (Pizzo, 1993; Warnick, 1997). The patient's own normal flora is suspected to cause approximately 85% of infections in the neutropenic patient. Sites frequently infected include the respiratory tract, urinary tract, skin wounds, intravenous or indwelling catheters, the mouth and esophagus, and the perianal/rectal area.

With a drop in the lymphocyte count, the patient develops immunodeficiency and also becomes susceptible to infections from various fungi, protozoa, and viruses, such as cytomegalovirus and herpes.

Management of Neutropenia

Interventions to manage the patient at risk for infection are aimed to maximize the patient's own defenses against infections, to minimize sources of infection, and to treat infections as aggressively as possible (Camp-Sorrell, 1998; Ellerhorst-Ryan, 1997; Rostad, 1991; Wilkes, 1996). Because infection in a neutropenic patient can progress rapidly to septic shock and death within a matter of hours, signs of infection in a neutropenic patient must be considered an emergency.

Patients should be educated about their risk of infection and important symptoms to report. Because the majority of patients receive treatment in an outpatient setting, they are likely to be at home when symptoms of infection develop. Patients must know that a fever greater than 101°F must be reported immediately, as well as any new sign or symptom of infection.

Many interventions are aimed at maintaining intact skin and mucous membranes. Personal hygiene should be emphasized. Invasive procedures should be minimized, and protocols for mouth, skin, rectum, and IV catheters should be strictly enforced. Persons at a high risk for infections should limit contact with external sources of infection, such as other people with infectious diseases and items with a high microbe count. If the patient is hospitalized, a private room is preferable, but other types of isolation have not shown benefit except for those undergoing bone marrow transplantation. Thorough handwashing by caregivers before patient contact is essential to prevent the spread of microorganisms in patient care.

Without adequate neutrophils, neutropenic patients do not develop the classic and common signs of infection. Commonly, fever is the only sign of infection; any other signs and symptoms, such as redness, swelling, drainage, or pus formation, are subdued or absent. Frequent and detailed physical assessments are imperative in neutropenic patients, but the findings may be lacking despite the presence of fever.

The first sign of infection in a neutropenic patient requires immediate treatment. After a careful history and physical examination to identify the source of infection, a urinalysis and chest radiograph, as well as routine bacterial and fungal cultures of body fluids, should be obtained to identify an organism and guide the choice of antibiotics. Antimicrobial therapy is generally instituted immediately after blood cultures are obtained. A broad-spectrum antibiotic regimen is necessary to cover the commonly infecting bacteria. The combinations of an aminoglycoside and a beta-lactam antibiotic, or the combination of an extended-spectrum penicillin and a third-generation cephalosporin or an aminoglycoside, are effective antibiotic regimens. The regimen can be adjusted if culture results reveal a specific organism. If a patient remains febrile or has symptoms of sepsis while already on broad-spectrum antibiotics, the drug regimen can be expanded to cover fungi. Antibiotics should be continued until the neutropenia is resolved (Pizzo, 1993).

Most recently, colony-stimulating factors (CSFs) have been used to greatly reduce the severity and duration of chemotherapy-related neutropenia. These naturally occurring glycoproteins act on hematopoietic cells and accelerate the production of granulocytes in the bone marrow. G-CSF and GM-CSF are two growth factors that are commonly prescribed to shorten the period of neutropenia. Given as subcutaneous injections for several days after chemotherapy administration, these growth factors have been shown to decrease complications related to neutropenia with minimal side effects (Camp-Sorrell, 1998; Haeuber, 1991). Table 25-3 outlines nursing management of patients with neutropenia.

Anemia

Myelosuppression also results in anemia, with an inadequate production of RBCs in the bone marrow. Anemia, defined as a reduction in the number of RBCs, can also result from a shortened RBC survival or from hemorrhage. Vitamin and iron deficiencies, as well as a number of chronic and hereditary conditions, may contribute to the picture of anemia in the patient. These causes should also be considered when planning care for the person with anemia.

Anemia from myelosuppression occurs later and less dramatically than the decreases for granulocytes and platelets because the life span of the RBC is 120 days (DiJulio, 1991). Anemia may occur, for example, after several courses of chemotherapy or radiation therapy, or when the cumulative effects of blood loss from surgery or inadequate nutrition are combined with other treatments.

The clinical presentation of the person with anemia varies depending on the severity of the RBC deficiency. Because the role of RBCs is to transport oxygen, the physiologic effect of anemia is tissue hypoxia, which can affect every organ system and cause a variety of symptoms. Patients with mild anemia may appear pale and may com-

plain of fatigue and shortness of breath on exertion. Patients with severe anemia may have headache, irritability, dizziness, dyspnea at rest, and significant activity intolerance as well as ischemic events to major organs (Rieger & Haueber, 1995).

In anemia related to bone marrow depression, laboratory assessment reveals a low number of normally shaped and formed RBCs. Corresponding values for hemoglobin and hematocrit are also low. Hemoglobin measures the total amount of this iron-carrying molecule in the peripheral blood, and hematocrit is the percentage of RBCs in the total blood. Other laboratory tests that evaluate the size, shape, and hemoglobin content of RBCs are essential to diagnose other types of anemia if these are suspected.

Management of Anemia

Management of the patient with anemia includes interventions related to symptom management. Blood transfusions and pharmacologic therapy with erythropoietin (EPO), an RBC growth factor, may also be indicated (Haueber & Spross, 1994; Matthews, 1998; Rostad, 1991). Patients should be educated about their risk of anemia and important symptoms to report. They require strategies to manage fatigue and dyspnea related to anemia. Symptomatic patients with severe anemia may be treated with RBC transfusions, which can temporarily relieve the complications of anemia until RBC production is restored. Adult patients usually receive 2 units of packed red blood cells, which is expected to raise the hematocrit by three points per unit. Patients receiving transfusions must be monitored for risks of fluid overload, transfusion reactions, and transmission of various infections. Most recently, therapy with EPO, an endogenous growth factor that regulates RBC production, is being used to prevent as well as treat chemotherapy-related anemia (Glaspy, 1997; Rieger & Haueber, 1995). EPO therapy is given as subcutaneous injections one to three times weekly to maintain adequate hemoglobin and hematocrit values. Benefits of EPO include improved RBC values, decreased transfusion requirements, and improved quality of life with few side effects. Table 25-4 lists guidelines for the management of the patient with anemia.

TABLE 25-3
NURSING MANAGEMENT OF THE PATIENT WITH NEUTROPENIA

1. Maximize the patient's own defenses against infection.
   a) Implement skin care regimen to maintain skin integrity.
   b) Implement mouth care regimen to maintain integrity of oral mucous membranes (i.e., normal saline rinses four times/day).
   c) Avoid IM and SQ injections, rectal temperatures, and rectal medication administration.
   d) Avoid invasive procedures, such as urinary catheterization.
   e) Implement bowel regimen to prevent constipation and perirectal care regimen to promote perirectal skin integrity.
2. Minimize patient's exposure to sources of infection in the environment.
   a) Enforce thorough handwashing for all persons who have physical contact with the patient.
   b) Restrict persons with colds and infections from physical contact with patient.
   c) Limit dietary intake of fresh fruits and fresh vegetables with thorough cleansing of those items consumed.
   d) Limit patient contact with obviously infected items, such as cat litter, bird cages, and so forth, related to risk of fungal and parasite infections.
   e) Admit to a private room in the hospital if possible.
   f) Change IV sites and dressings at regular intervals.
3. Assess for signs and symptoms of infection.
   a) Monitor VS every 4 h or more frequently if temperature is elevated.
   b) Monitor total WBC count and neutrophil count.
   c) Inspect potential sites of infection, including lungs, skin, IV, catheter sites, mouth, and perirectum.
   d) Question patient about symptoms of infection, such as fever, chills, pain on elimination, cough, sore mouth or throat, drainage or swelling.
4. Implement antimicrobial therapy aggressively.
   a) Report temperature greater than 101°F or any new sign of infection.
   b) Obtain bacterial and fungal cultures of body fluids (urine, blood, any drainage) before starting initial antibiotic therapy.
   c) Obtain chest radiograph.
   d) Administer antimicrobial therapy as soon as possible and adjust regimen as necessary. Check drug allergies and monitor for side effects.
   e) Administer G-CSF or GM-CSF therapy as prescribed.
      i) Implement a teaching plan that includes:
         a) Goal, dose, schedule, and side effects of therapy
         b) SQ administration technique if applicable
         c) Laboratory tests used to evaluate response to therapy
5. Educate patient and family about the risk of infection.
   a) Inform the patient about the relative risk of infection from the diagnosis and therapy.
   b) Explain the importance of WBC and neutrophil counts during the period of infection risk.
   c) Implement a teaching plan that includes:
      i) Symptoms of infection (fever >101°F, chills, cough, sore mouth or throat, pain on elimination, or swelling)
      ii) Self-care measures to prevent infection
      iii) When and how to report symptoms of infection
      iv) How potential infections will be treated

(From Camp-Sorrell, 1998; Ellerhorst-Ryan, 1997; Rostad, 1991; Wilkes, 1996.)

Thrombocytopenia

The third complication of myelosuppression is bleeding related to thrombocytopenia, or an inadequate number of platelets. The platelet count falls to a predictable nadir approximately 7 to 14 days after most chemotherapy, with a gradual recovery similar to that of white blood cells in 21 to 28 days (Camp-Sorrell, 1998). The patient is at a significant risk for bleeding when the platelet count is <50,000/mm^3 and at risk for spontaneous bleeding with a count <20,000/mm^3. Other clinical conditions may add to the risk of hemorrhage; these include various coagulopathies, such as disseminated intravascular coagulation (DIC), tumor lysis syndrome, and septic shock.

When thrombocytopenic, the patient is at risk for minor bleeding or life-threatening episodes of

TABLE 25-4

NURSING MANAGEMENT OF THE PATIENT WITH ANEMIA

1. Assess for signs and symptoms of anemia.
   a) Monitor RBC, hemoglobin, and hematocrit values.
   b) Question patient about symptoms of fatigue, dyspnea, headache, palpitations, dizziness, and activity intolerance.
   c) Assess patient for paleness, tachycardia, tachypnea, and mental status changes.
2. Manage symptoms related to anemia.
   a) Guide patient to identify a safe and realistic activity level to conserve energy. Enlist assistance with activities as necessary.
   b) Teach patient to change positions slowly to prevent dizziness and loss of balance.
   c) Teach breathing exercises and optimal positioning if patient complains of dyspnea.
   d) Arrange and maintain supplemental oxygen if patient has symptoms of hypoxia.
3. Educate the patient and family about the risk of anemia.
   a) Inform the patient about their relative risk of anemia from their diagnosis and therapy.
   b) Explain the importance of RBC, hemoglobin, and hematocrit values.
   c) Implement teaching plan that includes:
      i) Symptoms of anemia (fatigue, activity intolerance, dyspnea)
      ii) Self-care measures to manage symptoms of anemia
      iii) When and how to report symptoms of anemia
      iv) How severe anemia would be treated
4. Administer RBC transfusions as prescribed.
   a) Prepare the patient.
      i) Obtain the patient's transfusion history and consent. Identify patient per institutional policy.
      ii) Establish IV site and flush IV line with normal saline.
      iii) Record baseline VS. Premedicate patient before transfusion, if appropriate.
      iv) Explain purpose, procedure, and adverse reactions related to transfusion. Teach patient what signs of reaction to report.
   b) Mange the transfusion.
      i) Prepare the product with appropriate tubing and filter. Identify the patient per institutional policy.
      ii) Begin the transfusion slowly. Monitor for signs of acute transfusion reactions and manage reactions appropriately.
      iii) Complete transfusion within 4 hours. Document VS and patient response at completion.
5. Administer EPO therapy as prescribed.
   a) Implement teaching plan regarding EPO therapy including:
      i) Goal, dose, schedule, and side effects of therapy
      ii) SQ self-adminstration technique
      iii) Laboratory tests used to evaluate response to therapy

(From Haeuber & Spross, 1994; Matthews, 1997; Rostad, 1991.)

hemorrhage, which may occur from the gastrointestinal tract, skin and mucous membranes, genitourinary tract, respiratory tract, or in the central nervous system. Nursing assessment should include emphasis on these potential sites of bleeding as well as close monitoring of the platelet count.

Management of Thrombocytopenia

Interventions for the patient with thrombocytopenia aim to prevent problems with bleeding (Camp-Sorrell, 1998; Gobel, 1997; Rostad, 1991). Bleeding precautions should be instituted to maintain integrity of skin and mucous membranes and minimize episodes of trauma to the patient. Transfusions of platelets are indicated when there is active bleeding associated with thrombocytopenia or as a prophylactic measure when the platelet count is <10,000/mm³. Under optimal conditions, a platelet transfusion (6 units) will increase the count by 30,000 to 60,000/mm³, and platelet transfusions are usually required every 2 to 3 days in the absence of platelet production (Rostad, 1991). Various clinical factors adversely affect the desired increment from a platelet transfusion, including fever, infection, and the presence of antibodies on the surface of the platelets. A posttransfusion platelet count is recommended to verify the therapeutic effect of the transfusion. Current research with platelet growth factors offers potential therapy to stimulate the production and maturation of platelets during a period of myelosuppression. Table 25-5 summarizes interventions for the patient with thrombocytopenia.

Conclusion

Nurses are challenged to provide comprehensive and cost-effective care to patients with myelosuppression. Patient education is critical to the successful prevention and early detection of infectious and bleeding complications, especially in the growing population of patients who are treated in outpatient settings. Patients and family members

---

TABLE 25-5
NURSING MANAGEMENT OF THE PATIENT WITH THROMBOCYTOPENIA

1. Minimize sources of trauma as cause of bleeding.
    a) Avoid IM and SQ injection, rectal temperatures, and rectal medication administration.
    b) Avoid aspirin, aspirin-containing products, and nonsteroidal antiinflammatory drugs, which may increase bleeding tendency.
    c) Minimize venipunctures and other invasive procedures, such as urinary catheterizations, enemas, douches, and dental procedures.
    d) Apply pressure to venipuncture sites for 5 minutes.
    e) Implement mouth care regimen with soft brushing and avoid flossing.
    f) Use only electric shavers for hair removal.
    g) Provide assistance with activities as necessary to prevent falls. Maintain an environment free of obstacles.
    h) Limit activities likely to cause trauma, such as contact sports.
2. Assess for signs and symptoms of bleeding.
    a) Inspect potential sites of bleeding, including skin, nose, mouth.
    b) Question patient about blood in sputum, urine, stool, or emesis.
    c) Check sputum, urine, stool, emesis, and other fluids for occult blood.
    d) Monitor platelet count frequently during period of bleeding risk.
3. Administer platelet transfusions as prescribed.
    a) Prepare the patient.
        i) Obtain patients's transfusion history and consent.
        ii) Establish IV access with large-gauge catheter.
        iii) Record baseline VS.
        iv) Explain purpose, procedure, and adverse reactions related to the transfusion. Teach patient what signs and symptoms of reaction to report.
    b) Manage the transfusion.
        i) Prepare product with appropriate tubing and filter. Identify patient per institutional policy.
        ii) Flush line with normal saline. Premedicate patient before transfusion if appropriate.
        iii) Begin transfusion slowly. Monitor for signs of acute transfusion reaction and manage reactions appropriately.
        iv) Complete transfusion within 1 h. Document VS at completion.
        v) Draw posttransfusion platelet count. Document patient response.
4. Educate patient and family about the risk of bleeding.
    a) Inform the patient about the relative risk of bleeding related to the diagnosis and therapy.
    b) Explain the importance of platelets and platelet counts during the period of bleeding risk.
    c) Implement a teaching plan that includes:
        i) Symptoms of bleeding, such as bruises, petechiae, nose bleeds, blood in urine, stool, sputum, or emesis
        ii) Self-care measures to prevent bleeding
        iii) When and how to report symptoms of bleeding
        iv) How potential episodes of bleeding would be treated

(From Camp-Sorrell, 1998; Gobel, 1997; Rostad, 1991.)

must be informed when to notify their health team of critical symptoms that require medical interventions. Nurses who see patients in ambulatory settings or at home must be knowledgeable and vigilant about assessment parameters to detect infections, bleeding, and compromising anemia. Nurses play a major role in the treatment of myelosuppression through interventions related to pharmacologic therapy, transfusion therapy, and symptom management.

REFERENCES

Camp-Sorrell, D. (1998). Myelosuppression. In J. K. Itano & K. N. Taoka (Eds.), *Core curriculum for oncology nursing* (pp. 207–219). Philadelphia: W. B. Saunders.

Camp-Sorrell, D. (1997). Chemotherapy: Toxicity management. In S. L. Groenwald, M. H. Frogge, M. Goodman & C. H. Yarbro (Eds.), *Cancer nursing: Principles and practice* (pp. 385–425). Boston: Jones & Bartlett.

DiJulio, J. (1991). Hematopoiesis: An overview. *Oncology Nursing Forum, 18*, 3–6.

Ellerhorst-Ryan, J. M. (1997). Infection. In S. L. Groenwald, M. H. Frogge, M. Goodman & C. H. Yarbro (Eds.), *Cancer nursing: Principles and practice* (pp. 585–603). Boston: Jones & Bartlett.

Glaspy, J. (1997). The impact of epoetin-alfa on quality of life during cancer chemotherapy: A fresh look at an old problem. *Seminars in Hematology, 34*(suppl 2), 20–26.

Gobel, B. H. (1997). Bleeding disorders. In S. L. Groenwald, M. H. Frogge, M. Goodman & C. H. Yarbro (Eds.), *Cancer nursing: Principles and practice* (pp. 604–639). Boston: Jones & Bartlett.

Haeuber, D., & Spross, J. (1994). Protective mechanisms—Bone marrow. In J. Gross & B. Johnson (Eds.), *Handbook of oncology nursing* (pp. 373–399). Boston: Jones & Bartlett.

Haeuber, D. (1991). Future strategies in the control of myelosuppression: The use of colony-stimulating factors. *Oncology Nursing Forum, 18*, 16–24.

Kjeldsberg, K. (1993). Normal blood and bone marrow values in man. In G. R. Lee, T. C. Bithell, J. Foerster, et al. (Eds.), *Wintrobe's clinical hematology* (pp. 2297–2309). Philadelphia: Lea & Febiger.

Matthews, L. V. (1998). Alterations in ventilation. In J. K. Itano & K. N. Taoka (Eds.), *Core curriculum for oncology nursing* (pp. 281–296). Philadelphia: W. B. Saunders.

Pizzo, P. A. (1993). Management of fever in patients with cancer and treatment-induced neutropenia. *New England Journal of Medicine, 328*, 1323–1332.

Rieger, P. T., & Haeuber, D. (1995). A new approach to managing chemotherapy-related anemia: Nursing implications of epoetin alfa. *Oncology Nursing Forum, 22*, 71–81.

Rostad, M. E. (1991). Current strategies for managing myelosuppression in patients with cancer. *Oncology Nursing Forum, 18*, 7–15.

Rothstein, G. (1993). Origin and development of the blood and blood-forming tissues. In G. R. Lee, T. C. Bithell, J. Foerster, et al. (Eds.), *Wintrobe's clinical hematology* (pp. 41–78). Philadelphia: Lea & Febiger.

Tooney, J. F., & Parker, M. M. (1996). New perspectives in the management of septic shock in the cancer patient. *Infectious Disease Clinics of North America, 10*, 239–253.

Warnick, E. (1997). Vancomycin-resistant enterococcus. *Clinical Journal of Oncology Nursing, 1*, 73–77.

Wilkes, G. M. (1996). Potential toxicities and nursing management. In M. B. Burke, G. M. Wilkes & K. Ingwersen (Eds.), *Cancer chemotherapy: A nursing approach* (pp. 97–186). Boston: Jones & Bartlett.

Complementary and Alternative Therapies for Cancer

Jon Seskevich

Many people with cancer have no interest in complementary and alternative therapies and are very comfortable following conventional medical advice. There are a million new diagnoses of cancer in the United States each year. Mainstream Western medicine is able to improve the prospects of long-term survival for half. The rest will die of their disease within a few years (Office of Technology Assessment [OTA], 1990; Bailar & Garnik, 1997). A significant and growing minority of patients with cancer and their families are actively pursuing therapies outside the mainstream of medicine as is reflected in the general population (Ernst & Cassileth, 1998). Most are seeing conventional medical providers as well as using complementary and alternative therapies and therapists (Eisenberg et al., 1993).

A diagnosis of cancer sends one's life into a new direction, one that is not asked for. It is like being pushed out of a helicopter into a jungle war with no training, no maps, and no idea how to survive, according to Michael Lerner. Lerner is a former Yale professor, recipient of a MacArthur Foundation "genius" fellowship, and one of the country's leading authorities on complementary therapies for cancer. Nurses in all clinical settings who provide compassionate and comprehensive health care education furnish needed maps and survival training for patients with a new diagnosis or in any phase of cancer treatment.

The subject of alternative therapies for cancer stirs quite a debate within the field of oncology. Viewpoints range from an enthusiastic acceptance of complementary therapies to the belief that they are all quack medicine. For example, two leading oncologists at major comprehensive cancer centers reflect this continuum. William R. Fair, chief of Urological Surgery at Sloan-Kettering Cancer Center, states that, "Every oncologist should recognize the importance of diet, nutritional supplementation, physical activity, stress reduction, social and spiritual support and non-pharmacologic therapies as vital parts of cancer treatment" (Gordon, 1998). Edward C. Halperin, chairman of the Department of Radiation Oncology at Duke University Medical Center, has written, "The Office of Alternative Medicine is far more than an amusing federal boondoggle; it is a shameful diversion of taxpayer dollars to foundationless pseudo-science instead of biomedical research" (Halperin, 1998).

With such divergent opinions by experts in oncology, what instruction and support can nurses provide when patients or their families ask, "What about alternative therapies for this cancer?"

This chapter provides information and insight regarding complementary and alternative cancer treatments. It is not all encompassing but serves as an introductory survey. It gives definitions, practical guidance, resources, "how-to's," background, and research information about many popular modalities in this important field. The role of a nurse as patient-advocate mandates that we offer patients either direct education or referral to appropriate education or resources. In the highly charged area of alternative treatments for cancer, nurses need to have information beyond what is in the popular press to counsel patients appropriately.

Definitions of Therapies

Conventional Therapy (Proven Cancer Treatment)

Conventional therapies for cancer are surgery, chemotherapy, and radiation therapy. In general, oncology clinical practice is based on the national consensus protocols for the treatment of specific staged cancers. These mainstream medical modalities have been tested using the research model against biopsy-proven cancer(s) and have proved effective. There is peer review of medical records and reports. Results of controlled studies are reported and published in refereed journals. The results of the treatment are compared with therapies that are already standard. A conventional therapy's results are reproducible by different scientists. The treatment material and any medical equipment or devices (with copyright protection) are available for independent analysis.

Research Therapy

The research process is a rigorous evaluation and review designed to meet the criteria for a conventional therapy. Research therapies are treatments that have benefit suggested by animal and laboratory research. Research of drug efficacy goes through three phases. In phase I clinical trials, new investigational drugs are tested in a very few human volunteers for safety. This is a carefully structured and closely monitored process. As safety is maintained, the dosages in these studies are increased. The ability to demonstrate efficacy increases with higher dosages, as do the risks of severe or unexpected side effects. Phase II clinical trials use information gained from phase I studies and test for safety in larger groups, and look to see if the drug works with different types of cancer. Phase III clinical studies look at whether the drug is superior to current standard medicines and check further for side effects. An advisory panel of doctors appointed by the U. S. Food and Drug Administration (FDA) reviews the data and recommends whether a drug should be approved to become a standard treatment for a specific cancer, or submits further questions to the developers. The

FDA then either approves a drug or not. There is continuous monitoring by companies and the FDA for side effects. Sometimes, these adverse reactions only become clear after a drug has been taken by thousands or even millions of people.

Unconventional Therapies

Any cancer treatment used that is not yet proven therapy by research review is called an unconventional therapy. Also, any proven therapy used in a way that has not been proven is an unconventional therapy. Unconventional therapies for cancer need to increase the research knowledge base to add credibility with providers of conventional medicine.

Alternative Medicine

Alternative medicine is defined many ways in the professional and popular press. Eisenberg and colleagues (1993), in their ground-breaking study, defined alternative medicine functionally, as therapies not traditionally taught in U. S. medical schools or generally available in hospitals. This definition is becoming obsolete, because over 30 academic medical schools offer at least one course in the area of alternative medicine. Many professional academic nursing programs have had holistic/complementary therapies classes or modules since the late 1970s and early 1980s. Alternative therapies that were once disregarded, such as mind–body relaxation techniques and acupuncture for pain management, are now demonstrating proven quality outcomes in studies. These therapies only recently have started to become part of conventional medical practice. No biopharmacologic, herbal, or combination therapy for cancer has moved into the mainstream.

Alternative systems of medical practice are any therapies initiated or prescribed by practitioners outside American biomedicine, such as chiropractors, herbalists, naturopaths, traditional Chinese medicine practitioners, homeopaths, lay healers, and shamans. These practitioners have long been a part of the world health care system. Alternative medical practices have not yet met scientific criteria for efficacy and safety (Eisenberg, 1997).

It is important to note that an alternative therapy is not the same as "alternative treatments" within conventional medicine. Alternative treatments in the conventional understanding simply refers to equivalent choices available, such as aspirin or acetaminophen for headaches. Within conventional oncology practice, a discussion of "alternative treatments" has a standard of equivalence in safety and efficacy with each treatment option. For example, a lumpectomy with radiation for breast cancer may be a safe and effective alternative treatment to mastectomy. The long-term health benefits for a person with breast cancer may be equivalent with either treatment. Unconventional cancer therapies alone do not hold the same promise as proven cancer treatments except in palliative care.

Complementary Therapy

Eisenberg and colleagues found that 96% of patients using "alternative therapies" were also under the care of a conventional medicine provider (Eisenberg et al., 1993). Rather than using alternative therapies instead of conventional medicine, patients use them in addition to conventional medicine. This has given rise to the term *complementary therapies:* therapies that complement conventional medical treatments. Proponents believe they complement the body's ability to regain and maintain health. Some complementary cancer therapies help people deal with the stress of illness and conventional treatments, thereby improving the quality of a person's life. Some complementary therapies can help improve functional status. The American Cancer Society (ACS) considers the following modalities "helpful complementary approaches": aromatherapy, art therapy, biofeedback, garlic, herbal teas, massage therapy, meditation, music therapy, prayer, spiritual practices, tai chi, and yoga (American Cancer Society, 1998). An important point is that cancer patients who have improved quality of life and better functional status do better overall. Certainly, most oncologists would prefer that their patients have good quality of life and functional status. There may, indeed, be an adjunctive effect for conventional cancer treatment with some complementary therapies. More research needs to be done to confirm this hypothesis.

Disproved Therapy

The ACS defines unproven therapies as: "Therapies such as lifestyle practices, clinical tests or therapeutic modalities that are promoted for general use for the prevention, diagnosis, or treatment of cancer, and which are, *on the basis of careful review by scientists or clinicians* [italics added] deemed to have no real evidence of value" (American Cancer Society, 1998). Quack therapies are treatments proved to be worthless for cancer but which are still recommended as effective by a provider. Fortunately, they represent a small portion of today's alternative and complementary medicines. It is important to note there are clinics (in Mexico and the United States) that still give Laetrile as a therapy, although it has been proved ineffective in cancer treatment and can cause arsenic poisoning. Other quack therapies are openly or clearly phony. An example of this is psychic surgery. The James Randi Foundation has offered $1 million to anyone who can demonstrate psychic surgery without sleight of hand and with tissue sample analysis. Some alternative and complementary medicine skeptics include all unconventional treatments in the category of quack medicine because of the lack of completed research that proves effectiveness.

Questions for Unconventional Cancer Therapy Providers

The following questions can help a patient differentiate complementary therapies from quack treatments:

- Are there patients who have undergone the therapy who can share their experience?
- Can you ascertain if the therapy is potentially dangerous?
- What are the side effects?
- Does the therapy operate according to known or plausible principles of science?
- What are the claims of practitioners, and is there any scientific literature that supports or justifies the assertions?
- Is information about the therapy available to you, or is it a closed, secret system?

- Are patients encouraged to reject conventional therapies or shamed for coming too late because of the use of conventional therapies?

Recognizing Potential Signs of Deception

Unscrupulous alternative promoters typically use fiction to steer patients away from conventional medicine and toward useless and potentially dangerous treatments. Precious time can be lost as a patient avoids proven methods and explores useless therapies. One sign of deceptive practices is a claim of miraculous cures in promotional material. Real cures for cancer would be found on the front pages of major newspapers and journals with documented data, not in advertisements in the back of magazines. The use of patient testimonials in advertising and publicity without reliable published data in peer-reviewed publications raises more questions.

A warning sign of deceptive practice is the suggestion that a cure for cancer is being suppressed. This gives quack sources credibility through the diversion of anger at the "establishment." There is broad media exposure whenever there is even a hope of a new scientific breakthrough in the war on cancer. Another challenge to the conspiracy claim is the competition of scientists throughout the world for peer-reviewed success. This drives people through painstaking, good quality control to find a cure for serious illness. There may be some fair criticisms of conventional medicine (Lazarou, Pomeranz, & Corey, 1998), but suppressing a cure for cancer is not one of them.

Skeptics of unconventional cancer therapies believe that reported cures from these therapies typically fall into one of the following categories: (1) the patient never had cancer; (2) the cancer was cured or put into remission by a proven therapy, but the unconventional therapy is given the credit; (3) the cancer is progressing but is erroneously represented as slowed or cured; (4) the patient may have died or is unavailable for long-term follow-up and counted as cured; (5) rare cases of spontaneous remission or a slow-growing cancer that are publicized as a cure (Barrett & Herbert, 1998).

The National Center for Complementary and Alternative Medicine (NCCAM)

With growing public interest in alternative therapies comes increased recognition of the need for quality scientific review of these treatments. The National Institutes of Health (NIH) established the Office of Alternative Medicine (OAM) in 1992 through an act of Congress. The OAM provided a variety of functions: "(1) the awarding of grants for basic science and clinical research, (2) the coordination of research activities within the NIH, (3) the development of a national data base and informational clearinghouse, (4) the institution of 'field investigations' whereby provocative findings are more thoroughly evaluated, (5) the delivery of technical assistance to researchers of alternative therapy, and (6) the development and oversight of 'centers' devoted to various aspects of alternative medicine research, education and policy development" (Eisenberg, 1995).

The NCCAM was established by Congress in 1998. The center, with increased funding of $50 million a year, will further the work of the OAM and be devoted to carrying on and supporting basic and applied research and academic training. It will distribute information on complementary and alternative medicine (CAM) to researchers, health care providers, practitioners, and the general public. It will also set up and carry out other projects that will further the investigation and application of CAM treatments demonstrated to be effective.

The University of Texas Center for Alternative Medicine (UT-CAM) is one of 10 research centers established by the OAM to evaluate alternative therapies. The University of Texas Center is the first OAM-supported center focused solely on alternative and complementary treatments for cancer. The National Cancer Institute (NCI) is co-funding the center. One of the center's main missions is to facilitate scientific evaluations of biopharmacologic, herbal, and combination therapies. The hope of the center is to assist patients and health care providers in thinking critically about the options in cancer care today. Their website (*http://www.sph.uth.tmc.edu/utcam/*) posts all research information available on the most popular biopharmacologic, herbal, and combination therapies for cancer. The NCCAM is establishing a second center for CAM in oncology in 1999.

Knowledge Is Power: The Vital Quartet of Complementary Therapies

> *We do not let health professionals treat cancer without training. Patients need training too. It's crucial to making the many choices the disease imposes. In my experience training often improves cancer patients' quality of life and there is increasing, though not conclusive evidence that it may extend survival (Lerner, 1994).*

From his research, Lerner believes that

> *There is no complementary/alternative therapy that has been shown to cure cancer. There are conventional therapies that sometimes cure cancer. There are different rates of cure among the many types of cancer. Although research is just building into many nontraditional healing therapies, evidence exists of quality of life improvement with an ensuing possible extension of life for some complementary adjunctive therapies (Lerner, 1994).*

Andrew Weil is director of the Program in Integrative Medicine at the University of Arizona in Tucson and author of six books, including *Spontaneous Healing.* He concisely advises a cancer patient, "If you have cancer, it is important to work to improve overall health and resistance on all levels." Lerner seconds this statement with an encouragement to interested patients to use what he calls "the vital quartet." These are lifestyle practices that are intrinsically health promoting. Scientific evidence exists of health benefits for these modalities. The quartet consists of (1) mind–body medicine, behavioral and psychological approaches, (2) spiritual or religious practices, (3) good nutrition, and (4) exercise, body work, and physical approaches.

For many, "cure" and "healing" are synonyms. Within holistic treatments and approaches that focus on the whole person, there is an important distinction. *Cure* means restoring the body to physical health. Biomedicine seeks to cure disease

and alleviate pain. A cancer cure, therefore, means the illness is gone and a person lives as long a life as he or she would be expected to in the absence of the cancer. (Some measure a cure for cancer at the 5-year point after treatment began without a recurrence.) A biopsychosocial, holistic approach includes treating the response to the illness and alleviating suffering. *Healing* is a dynamic approach to improving and nourishing all facets of a person. Body, mind, spirit, family, work, creative expression, and community make up who we are. Healing approaches may or may not have an impact on physical survival; coping with the effects of the illness may, for example, be the goal. Even death, surrounded by love, with psychological acceptance, pain control, and meaning, can be a "healing" experience.

Mind–Body Medicine, Behavioral, Psychological Approaches

Psychoneuroimmunology (PNI) is a recent field in medicine, with the first major text edited by Ader published in 1981. The Oncology Nursing Society, the main professional organization for nurses who work with cancer patients, has a special interest study group in PNI. A main idea in PNI is that there are complex interrelationships among behavioral, neural, endocrine, and immune systems. Research in this field "supports, though not conclusively, that psychosocial factors, including psychosocial interventions, may contribute to the extension of life with cancer" (Lerner, 1994). Social support is positively associated with better psychological adjustment and longer survival (Holland & Rowland, 1989). Studies by Fawzy and colleagues (1993) and Spiegel (1989) have suggested that cancer support groups contribute to life extension. Reducing the sense of helplessness or hopelessness in cancer patients may also extend life (Greer & Silberfarb, 1982). However, the only published research by Siegel, a popular cancer self-help promoter, does not support imagery or support groups contributing to a longer life, let alone curing cancer (Gellert & Siegel, 1993). It remains a worthy postulate that psychosocial interventions to increase social support could improve survival statistics.

Patients and families report turning to popular inspirational books for guidance and information.

In these books, there may be "pearls of wisdom." However, there can also be difficulties. Some well-known practitioners have claimed for years that stress or personality characteristics cause cancer, yet solid research, including a study of almost 10,000 women, shows that psychological traits do not play a role in cancer development (Cassileth, 1998). Inherited genetic mutations cause many types of cancer. Tobacco and dietary factors are other contributors. Promoters of the idea that a person "gives himself or herself cancer" or that patients should investigate why he or she might "need" their cancer are misguided and have contributed to feelings of guilt and inadequacy in patients. Science is not averse to seeing psychological factors as a cause of disease if the evidence is there. For instance, research is available that suggests anger, hostility, and depression contribute to the development of coronary artery disease (Williams, 1993). LeShan, a psychologist and well-respected leader in the field of mind–body medicine, wrote, "I have been working with people faced with catastrophic illness for over forty years. Thoughts and feelings do not cause cancer and can not cure cancer. They are, however, important factors in the total ecology that makes up the human being" (LeShan, 1998). Stephen Levine (1987), a well-known author on conscious living and dying, encourages the viewpoint that a person is not responsible for his or her cancer but responsible to it, to do what he can do to contribute to health and healing.

INDIVIDUALIZED PSYCHOLOGICAL SUPPORT

Well-meaning friends and family often encourage patients to "think positive." This can slow or even prevent the healthy grieving of the loss of health, life direction, and control that often happens with a cancer diagnosis. Nurses can provide key support for this grieving process. In the field of PNI, dealing with honest feelings of sadness, anger, and frustration can strengthen the immune system. If these feelings are not worked with, depression can result, which weakens the immune system. Positive thinking can be a helpful tool to help manage worry.

Nurses can encourage social support that is personally meaningful to the individual patient.

Case Studies

A 55-year-old male patient with sarcoma was in tears the day before his leg was to be amputated. A nurse, although well meaning, was concerned about "how he can beat this cancer" when having such negative feelings. On the contrary, honest grief reaction, especially in an older man (conditioned to be strong and keep feelings to himself) might have been physiologically the most healthy, positive thing he could do for himself.

A 68-year-old female with breast cancer has a son who, over the phone, is strongly encouraging her to begin a macrobiotic diet, despite her expressed lack of interest. The tension about the issue is palpable at times. Psychobiologically, she might benefit more if she had her wish of more friendly and supportive, personal visits from that son!

Provide opportunities and support for a patient's emotional expression. Recognize that every person is unique, and that psychological coping styles vary. Support groups with skillful leaders may be helpful for some people with cancer. Others may find listening to another group member's problems depressing and counterproductive. Some find the best support from confiding in a close friend; others find going to a professional therapist an answer. Quiet, alone time may meet the reflective needs of some. Journaling about one's experiences and feelings can provide a therapeutic outlet.

HOPE

For the cancer patient who wants to live, it is important to maintain hope. Never take away someone's hope. People continue to fight for their lives even if the odds are stacked against them. Many people over the years have extended survival beyond what was expected. Hope is a feeling beyond simple efforts to "think positively." O'Regan and Hirshberg (1993) found more than 1000 articles in the world medical literature about the "rare but spectacular phenomenon of spontaneous remission of cancer."

A way to help a person with cancer maintain hope is to explore meaning in his or her life. Frankl, in *Man's Search for Meaning,* found that people with a deep core of meaning in their life were more likely to have survived the tragedy of Auschwitz in World War II. Family, unfinished life work, and God are sources of meaning for people. Cancer brings a person face to face with the possibility of his or her own death. People do not want to talk about death because they are afraid that acknowledging the possibility is giving up or will somehow make death happen. It is important to help a patient face death on his or her own terms. As one puts affairs in order, more energy is available for fight or for acceptance in the next phase of life. If death is inevitable, hope can shift—hope for a death with dignity without too much suffering; a hope for final days that do not place too much of a burden on family or loved ones; a hope of being united with loved ones who have already died. Even for someone who longs for death, a question could be, "While you're still here, what gives you meaning in life?"

STRESS MANAGEMENT

Stress and personality factors are not causes of cancer, but they may have an effect on the cause of cancer. Smoking and high-fat diets used by many to manage life stressors can have a carcinogenic effect, as 50% of cancers are induced through smoking and fat-filled diets (Cassileth, 1998). It is safe to say that, regardless of *why* a person got cancer, this serious, potentially life-threatening or chronic illness is stressful to patients and families. Stress simply comes from change. It is present whenever there is a change in life, even with good events (holidays, a wedding, having a child or grandchild).

Oncology nurses, social workers, or psychologists experienced in working with cancer patients may have good stress management ideas to offer. There are many behavioral medicine approaches that can have positive outcomes on symptoms and side effects of cancer and its treatment. Identify resources for techniques for the patient, such as progressive muscle relaxation, meditation, and imagery. As mentioned, talk therapy and grief work are productive ways to work with feelings. Balancing activity and rest helps patients cope with fatigue. Encourage assertive communication, such as learning to say no and asking for what one wants and needs. Learning to receive can be a valuable lesson for patients with cancer. Many independent people have difficulty receiving support. Encourage them to reflect on the happiness they felt when they gave to others. As the person with cancer receives from family and friends, there is also the opportunity for loved ones to find meaning and contribute.

RELAXATION TECHNIQUES, MIND–BODY SELF-REGULATORY SKILLS

Patients are often told to relax, but no one then says how to do it. Unfortunately, the word *relax* has been abused. Shouted as an order, guiltfully implored, or pleadingly requested, "Just relax!" can increase tension. Learning to relax is an art. Regular practice can yield many benefits.

Relaxation techniques are exercises done that reverse the physical stress response. The belly softens, the breathing deepens, muscles ease, digestion improves, the heart slows, and blood pressure lowers. Pain can be decreased, or the duration of a severe pain flare-up can be lessened.

Relaxation techniques involve concentration or mindfulness and differ from daydreaming and watching television. There have been 2,500 research studies suggesting the effectiveness of mind–body self-regulatory skills.

What are key common elements to learning most of the relaxation techniques? Find a comfortable position; be in a quiet environment; have an object of concentration; and, when the mind wanders, gently return to the object of concentration.

Some good stress management techniques:

- *Relaxation response:* Focusing on a word or phrase that has meaning to you. As the mind wanders, notice "thinking" and return to the phrase or word. Combine this with soft abdominal breathing. See practice section below.
- *Biofeedback (BFB):* Uses machine feedback that helps a person learn that he or she is relaxing. It trains you to systematically relax your muscles.
- *Prayer:* Most religions teach this practice. It can bring physical and mental benefits as well as spiritual ones.

- *Meditation:* Sitting, standing, moving, or lying down and using concentration points. Awareness and mindfulness bring a person's experience into the present moment. Greater clarity and equanimity can be fostered to cope with life's changes.

- *Visualization or imagery:* Uses the imagination to bring on a calm, relaxed feeling. A peaceful, nurturing place, a healing force at work on the cancer, or goals after treatment are all possible therapeutic images. If you can worry, you could have the ability to use imagery for stress management.

- *Positive thinking or affirmations:* Use calming words and self-talk to reverse the body's stress response.

- *Guided relaxation, nature and music tapes:* Practice listening, gently returning to the sound from the tape as the mind wanders.

- *Lamaze and Bradley breathing and point concentration:* These help to release the body's natural pain medicine and promote muscle relaxation.

- *Progressive muscle relaxation:* Slowly scan through the body, head to feet or feet to head, intentionally relaxing muscle groups.

Choose one or two preferred techniques and begin practice with 10 to 20 minutes once or twice a day.

Relaxation Technique Practice

For some, religion or spirituality is important. If so, choose a meaningful spiritual phrase. If not, choose a personally significant phrase. Sit or lie comfortably and let your abdomen gently rise with the inhale and fall with the exhale. When you are sitting, it is easier to stay awake. Repeat your phrase with the inhale and with the exhale, silently to yourself. Each time the mind wanders, make a mental note "thinking" and gently return to the phrase or word. If the mind is very restless and continues to wander, be patient, gently returning to the phrase. This quiets the mind and brings on the positive physical effects (Seskevich, 1997).

Spirituality

See Chapter 28 for related information regarding spirituality.

Nutrition and Diet

Controlled clinical trials in nutrition and cancer are urgently needed. The conventional medical approach that there is "no evidence" that nutrition makes any difference in cancer is changing. Evidence exists that prevention of cancer can happen through healthy eating. Diet is being explored as a possible modality to help prevent recurrence of cancer. In 1995, an NCI-sponsored research study began with Le Marchand of the University of Hawaii as the principal investigator. The team is investigating the effect of a daily diet that includes nine fresh fruits and vegetables for participants who have had an early stage head, neck, or lung cancer that was successfully treated with surgery or radiation. Participants in the study will be followed for 5 years. Data exist that a low-fat diet may be beneficial for breast and prostate cancer patients, but weight loss (less than high school or college weight) needs to be closely monitored (Lerner, 1994).

When judging a complementary nutritional program, patients need to investigate the program's credibility. Trustworthy nutritional programs do not claim to be a cure for cancer. Those that claim to be must be viewed with great caution. Block integrates diet, fitness, and psychological support into his conventional oncology practice. He states that

> Although the nutrition and diet part of my clinical program has received the widest attention, it is neither more nor less important than the other components. I am not a nutritionist or dietitian, nor do I claim that the diet has miraculous or curative powers. I believe strongly that diet is a critical factor in health and that what we eat makes a significant difference in our body's ability to resist disease and maintain health. I believe that diet can act therapeutically as well as adjunctively in treatment. (Lerner, 1994)

For the nutritional component of the vital quartet, nurses can educate patients about moderation and variety in diet. The U. S. Department of Agriculture (USDA) publishes guidelines for healthy eating that represent the best consensus-based information on good nutrition. Six to eleven servings of grains and grain products (rice, pasta, bread, and cereals); three to five vegetables; two to four servings from the fruit group; two to three servings from the milk, yogurt, and cheese group; and two to three servings from the protein group of dry beans, nuts, eggs, fish, poultry, and meat make a strong nutritional program for cancer. Fats, oils, and sweets are to be used sparingly. This guide can help any person or family interested in complementary nutritional therapies for cancer.

If one eats an adequate diet as identified above, nutritional needs will be met. Cassileth, a conservative but well-respected scientist in the field of alternative medicine, says,

> *The inescapable fact is that how we eat influences how we feel and how well our bodies are equipped to ward off major disease. As important as diet turns out to be, the companion fact is that food does not cure serious illness. Don't be fooled into substituting a special diet for real medical treatment when it is needed to save your life. (Cassileth, 1998)*

Eating and good nutrition can be a challenge for a cancer patient during treatment. Commercial supplements such as Ensure or Sustacal are options when eating is problematic. Consultation with a registered dietitian with experience in cancer care may provide many helpful tips for getting the needed calories and nutrition that your patient needs.

For those patients with cancer who ask questions about the latest research findings on vitamin and mineral supplements, Lerner writes, "A reasonable hypothesis exists that there may be some benefit for some cancer patients with some cancers from dietary and nutritional supplements. Also it is probable that some diets, vitamins, and supplements have a negative effect in some individuals with some types of cancer." Lerner concludes the following from the vitamin and mineral research in oncology:

- Vitamins A (with the retinoids and carotenoids), C, and E and several of the B vitamins have shown significant anticancer effects in experimental, epidemiologic, and clinical studies. The most significant vitamins for general anticancer effect are the antioxidant vitamins A, C, and E. The use of these vitamins should be considered in both prevention and treatment.

- Vitamin C has been the subject of a great controversy. It is not yet clear whether, in pharmacologic doses, it enhances survival, as Cameron and Pauling (1976) claim. More recent studies do indicate that it may have a protective effect against cancer and some antitumor effects, and the capacity to diminish side effects of radiotherapy and chemotherapy and improve outcomes. A few recent studies support Pauling and Cameron's hypothesis that vitamin C may be powerfully potentiated when administered in combination with vitamin K.

- Patients with leukemia should be cautious in taking vitamin C. One study shows that it enhanced leukemia development in some human leukemia cell lines and inhibited leukemia development in other cell lines. This raises the more important proposition that nutrients, in general, may act to enhance or inhibit histologically identical cancers in different patients. However, this capacity of some nutrients to affect the same cancer in different directions is probably relatively rare, in comparison with the ability of specific nutrients to inhibit or enhance cancer unidirectionally.

- Vitamin E has a wide range of positive effects in cancer—particularly vitamin E succinate. It enhances the effects of selenium and enhances some chemotherapies, radiotherapy, and hyperthermia. It also may help prevent hair loss, and it protects the heart (in animal studies) from cardiac toxicity from doxorubicin.

- B vitamin supplementation should be approached with care. Vitamin B_{12} can act as both a tumor promoter and a tumor inhibitor; its tumor-enhancing activities are partially controlled by methionine. Vitamin B_6 (pyridoxine) is deficient in many cancer patients and has been used to enhance the outcome of radiotherapy in a controlled prospective trial.

- Among the minerals, selenium has broad immunopotentiating and anticancer effects, whereas zinc is a selenium antagonist. Although zinc is an essential nutrient for life, great care should be taken in using zinc supplements with cancer (Lerner, 1994).

Physical Exercise, Body Approaches

There have been no studies that assess the effect of exercise on people who already have cancer. However,

> *Studies suggest that exercise therapy can decrease pain, nausea, fatigue, and depression. It may reduce the increases in weight and body fat often seen after adjunctive chemotherapy in women with breast cancer. While preventing gains in body fat, it also decreases loss of muscle tissue, helping to maintain strength and function. Studies also indicate that exercise influences the immune system. Moderate exercise appears to improve the functioning components of the immune system such as natural killer cells and monocytes. This could theoretically assist the body in fighting off cancer recurrence. (Lerner, 1994)*

Aerobic exercise involves taking part in physical activity that raises the heart rate and maintains an increased heart rate for a sustained period of time. Reasonable goals based on current health status should be the expectation. Develop a safe and appropriate exercise plan. Monitor the heart rate. A person in cancer treatment or in a debilitated state may begin by walking as little as 5 minutes twice a day. A patient should consult with the primary care provider before beginning an exercise program.

Eastern physical exercise practices such as yoga, tai chi, qi gong, and martial arts often combine a mind–body component with the exercise. There can be much less aerobic intent with these modalities. Stretching, movement, balance, and strength are cultivated. It would be important for a person with cancer to discuss with the teacher his or her physical condition and limitations before starting to practice. Physical exercise is most safely undertaken with the approval of the licensed care provider. Recognize the body's signals to decrease or stop the exercise and report any problems to one's doctor.

Massage can be a treasured form of nurturing and relaxation. There can be so much painful touch in the treatment of cancer that a therapeutic massage session offers a welcome contrast. The literature on massage in cancer is mostly positive. In nursing literature, studies show massage produces enhanced relaxation, increased sense of well-being, and less tension and tiredness. The major concerns come from the possibility of helping a cancer spread because of increases in circulation. Also, pressure massage to bony metastases is a risk. It is important to encourage a patient to seek the physician's approval before taking massage therapy.

Implications for Effective Caregiving

As the discussion of the vital quartet concludes, it is time to turn the focus to the emotional challenges a nurse caring for the cancer patient may experience. It is important for nurses to do inner work regarding the clients' shocking or difficult life situations. It may be a natural emotional response to feel pity, unfairness, anger, or "thank God it's not me." How can nurses be psychologically supportive to someone else when awash in feelings? Picture a 28-year-old woman with two children and a serious diagnosis of cancer. How does this make you feel? Now, imagine you are the patient sitting in a hospital room trying to have a good day. Many who walk in may smile, but underneath the surface all these feelings swirl. Examining one's feelings about death and dying, grief, loss, and hope is valuable for all caregivers.

A first step is to become aware of the feelings that arise. Is there helplessness, frustration, or confusion? Although these are normal feelings to have in response to suffering, it is important for nurses to inspect whether their sensitivities might block the ability to be present for the patient. Honesty and mindful awareness of the feelings allow some emotional equanimity, providing an ability to reach out and give care, support, and respect.

Herbal Remedies, Pharmacologic, Biologic, and Miscellaneous Treatments

This group of treatments represents a large and controversial group of unconventional cancer treatments. Most of these treatments do not have the intrinsically health-promoting actions that the vital quartet have.

Herbal Remedies

> *The FDA is not required to regulate herbal preparations, and manufacturers are not obliged to specify their ingredients. Therefore consumers cannot know whether a product for sale on a store shelf contains what it says it does, whether it is pure, or whether it includes potentially dangerous elements or contaminants. (Cassileth, 1998)*

In the past 10 years, more than 53,000 natural products were tested by the Natural Products Branch of the NCI, including 36,000 plants from 25 countries around the world. Fifteen hundred marine plants, 6,000 marine invertebrates, and 7,000 fungi and bacteria were also tested. Approximately one third of all new cancer therapies originate from a natural source. Herbs, tree bark, and flowers have all produced proven cancer therapies. Examples include camptothecin, paclitaxel (Taxol), cytosine arabinoside, and the AIDS drug AZT (azydothymidine) (Cassileth, 1998).

Herbal treatments for cancer are part of the over-the-counter supplement industry that has yearly sales of $6 billion in the United States alone (*Washington Post*, 1998). Profit from the sales of these products can be lucrative. In general, many herbal products can be used safely for minor ailments. It is important that the primary health care provider ask patients, "Is there anything else you're taking or thinking of taking other than what I prescribe?" This open-ended question and resulting dialogue can bring to light supplements, herbs, vitamins, home remedies, and alternative/complementary therapies.

Within unconventional cancer treatments, some herbal products are promoted as cures for cancer. Essiac, Blue Green Algae, mistletoe (also known as iscador), Pau D'Arco tea, Chaparral tea, sassafras, and others do not cure cancer as proponents may claim. "Best case" research needs to be gathered, at the least, before any of these therapies can be taken seriously as having curative powers. Serious toxic effects can occur with some herbal therapies for cancer. In preliminary studies, Matol and Chapparral were shown to stimulate malignancies. Research of these herbal treatments, concerning tumor reduction and quality-of-life improvement, is needed as well. Science is willing to use any natural substance that is beneficial in the war on cancer. However, the "natural" label is sometimes used as a sales promoter. Natural does not always mean safe and benign. Coumadin is a natural plant product; however, taking too much is poisonous. Obviously, this is a hot political subject that revolves around freedom of choice on the one hand and truth in advertising on the other.

ESSIAC TEA

What it is: The original formula consisted of four ingredients: Burdock root, slippery elm bark, sheep sorrel, and Turkish rhubarb. In 1922, Rene Caisse, nurse manager at a hospital in Ontario, Canada, began using the original herbal formula. Her source was a cancer survivor who was treated with this tea by "an old Indian medicine man" of the Ojibwa tribe. Dr. Charles Brusch was an associate of Caisse in the early 1960s. He also was a physician of John F. Kennedy. Caisse and Brusch decided to alter the original formula by adding "potentiating" herbs consisting of watercress, blessed thistle, red clover, and kelp.

What practitioners say it does: Published claims about Essiac tea in the promotional material include curing cancer and rebuilding the immune system to help the body fight cancer. Brusch is quoted in the promotional material on Essiac tea as saying, "Essiac is a cure for cancer, period. All studies done at laboratories in the United States and Canada support this conclusion" (OTA, 1990).

Research evidence: The NIH and the NCI have attempted to document Essiac's efficacy with information from various Canadian groups.

> *In 1983, Canadian federal health officials requested that NCI test Essiac for antitumor effects in animals. Caisse submitted three samples of Essiac (two dried samples used to make an extract and one liquid sample), which Memorial Sloan Kettering Cancer Center tested in the S-180 mouse sarcoma test system. This test is intended to detect immunotherapeutic effects (indicated by the occurrence of tumor regression) or chemotherapeutic effects (indicated by a diminished tumor growth rate). The results of six immunotherapy tests and two chemotherapy tests of Essiac samples using the S-180 system all showed no activity. MSKCC tested Resperin's sample of Essiac in a variety of other animal leukemic and solid*

tumor test systems in 17 separate chemotherapy experiments and found no antitumor activity in any of these tests. No evidence of acute toxicity was found in any of these tests, although some evidence of subacute toxicity (slight weight loss in treated animals) was found (OTA, 1990).

The UT-CAM center was not able to obtain any of Brusch's research on which he based his claim of cure. Essiac is widely used among cancer patients in Canada and the United States. Sales are beyond $8 million annually.

It is produced in liquid and dry herbs for wholesale and mail order customers. The ESSIAC product by Resperin estimates sales of approximately $3.2 million/year, whereas sales of Flor-Essence, marketed by Flora, Inc. in the US are estimated at $4.5 million. Herbal-Essence & E-tea herbal capsules are other brands of the product (UT-CAM website, 1998).

HOMEOPATHY

What it is: Homeopathy was developed in the late 18th century by a German physician named Samuel Hahnemann. It first served as a humane treatment approach in a world of bloodletting and purging. It is a liquid preparation of a substance that creates the symptoms it is designed to treat. These remedies are made from plants, minerals, and other natural materials. Homeopathy uses a super-dilute mixture of water or alcohol that probably does not contain a molecule of the original substance.

What practitioners say it does: The dilution and vigorous shaking of the mixture transform it into a medicine that helps the body fight an illness. As a part of an intensive "do it all" program, it is believed that homeopathy can contribute to healing as a body–mind–spirit tool. Homeopathic providers usually do not claim this treatment is a cure for cancer. Additionally, practitioners believe there can be an aggravating effect that makes cancer worse if the wrong remedy, the wrong potency, or the wrong sequence is given. Homeopaths also report that if the wrong remedy is given, there is no reaction.

Research evidence: There have been no studies using homeopathy as a treatment for cancer. Hahnemann's "vital force" theory is a subtle energy example that has not been scientifically shown to exist. Most scientists believe homeopathic remedies are essentially water and their only action is as a placebo.

HOXSEY HERBAL TREATMENT

What it is: John Hoxsey, a veterinarian horse surgeon, developed the treatment as a cancer cure after watching horses' cancers reverse after eating herbs growing wild in a field. His grandson, Harry Hoxsey, made the treatment popular. The first clinic offering the Hoxsey tonics and salves opened in the early 1920s. The ingredients of his treatments were potassium iodide, combined with some or all of the following substances: licorice, red clover, burdock root (*Arctium lappa*), stillingia root (*Stillingia sylvatica*), berberis root (*Berberis vulgaris*), poke root (*Phytolacca americana*), cascara (*Rhamnus purshiana*), Aromatic USP 14 (artificial flavor), prickly ash bark (*Zanthoxylum americanum*), and buckthorn bark (*Rhamnus frangula*; Hoxsey, 1956). After Hoxsey was forced to quit practicing this unconventional treatment in the United States in 1963, the Hoxsey treatment has been offered at a clinic in Tijuana, Mexico, under the direction of Hoxsey's longtime chief nurse, Mildred Nelson (OTA, 1990). The American Medical Association and the American Cancer Society have viewed the Hoxsey therapy as a prototypical cancer quackery treatment.

What practitioners say it does:

Nelson claims that about 80 percent of the cancer patients who take her herbal treatment are cured. She believes that a "bad attitude" is usually responsible for the "20 percent failure rate," and that she can tell who will get well and who will not, based on their attitude when they first arrive at the clinic. A patient's strong belief that the treatment is going to lead to recovery is the best predictor of success, she says. It "normalizes and balances the chemistry within the body," a process she believes results in tumor regression (OTA, 1990).

Research evidence: In 1957, a committee of faculty members of the University of British Columbia conducted a review of the Hoxsey treatment and facilities (OTA, 1990). They visited Hoxsey's Dallas clinic. They were particularly interested in following up on patients from British

Columbia who were treated at the clinic. The clinic gave the committee members records for 78 patients from their "active" files. The committee was able to follow up on 71 of these patients, using British Columbia's cancer registry, death registry, and physician records. Their detailed findings were summarized as follows:

> For over one-half of the [cancer] patients from British Columbia, the result [of treatment with the Hoxsey method] has been either death or progression of the disease. In nearly one-quarter there was no proof that the patient ever had cancer. Nearly one in ten of the patients had curative treatment before going to the Hoxsey Clinic. The data indicate that many of the herbs used in the Hoxsey internal tonic or the isolated components of these herbs have antitumor activity or cytotoxic effects in animal test systems. The complete Hoxsey herbal mixture has not been tested for antitumor activity in animal test systems, with human cells in culture, or in clinical trials, however. It is unknown whether the individual herbs or their components that show antitumor activity in animals are active in humans when given in concentrations used in the Hoxsey tonic. It is also unknown whether there might be synergistic effects of the herbs used together (OTA, 1990).

MISTLETOE (ISCADOR)

What it is: Mistletoe (*Viscum album L*), a familiar Christmas plant, contains an extract that is manufactured and marketed in Europe as a cancer treatment. Widely used in Europe as an unconventional cancer treatment, it is also available in the United States. The mistletoe treatment for cancer was first proposed in 1916 by Rudolf Steiner, the founder of a system of thought known as anthroposophy. This system seeks to understand the physical world by studying the spiritual realm using principles of modern science. The extract is administered as a SQ injection three to seven times a week, for many months and sometimes years. Anthroposophy clinics are holistic and use mistletoe along with diet, artistic activities, light exercise, hyperthermic or oil baths, and massage.

What practitioners say it does: For 75 years, mistletoe has been used as a cancer treatment.

Research evidence: The UT-CAM website states that mistletoe "has been reported to reduce tumor size and improve the quality of life and survival of some cancer patients" (UT-CAM website, 1998). Very few side effects have been recorded, except for the rare case of allergic reaction. Eating the berries of the plant can be dangerous because they are highly toxic. Clinical trials are underway in the United States. There is extensive German research literature on this treatment. Possible mechanisms of action have been identified.

TRADITIONAL CHINESE MEDICINE (TCM)

What it is: In the United States, TCM is the best known traditional medicine of the world. Herbal medicines, acupuncture, acupressure (massage therapy), moxibustion (heat therapy), and qi gong (exercise, energy medicine, and meditation) are components of this therapy. It comprises most elements of the vital quartet.

What practitioners say it does: Unlike many practitioners of alternative therapies in oncology, providers of TCM often make modest claims concerning the efficacy of their therapy for cancer. Treatments are seen as compatible with conventional therapies and can be helpful with the side effects of chemotherapy and radiation. Qi or vital energy is said to be restored through the treatments. David Eisenberg, of Beth Israel Hospital and Harvard Medical School in Boston, was the first U. S. medical exchange student to China and is one of the leading popularizers of TCM today.

Research evidence: Most research evidence comes from Asia. There has been a concerted effort to conduct quality research into the components of TCM. Seventy-six human studies, including 25 randomized controlled studies of TCM, have been gathered by the UT-CAM. In conventional Western medicine, chemotherapies have been developed from Chinese herbal medicines. The energetic components of TCM are outside of Western scientific understanding. Qi, in other traditions known as chi, prana, or subtle energy, has not been proven.

Pharmacologic, Biologic, and Miscellaneous Treatments

These therapies have a central component of a pharmacologic or biologic substance, including biochemical agents, vaccines, blood products, and synthetic chemicals (OTA, 1990). Some of these therapies are presented openly, and the components are verifiable. Others are made up of secret ingredients that, unfortunately, are all too easily accepted by many proponents of alternative cancer therapies. These therapies can be expensive and difficult to access. Cost is also a factor in generating evidence about the efficacy of alternative cancer therapies. For example, an academic medical center recently received a $4.3 million grant for a 3-year study of St. John's wort for depression. The high cost of quality research is a major impediment to the full investigation of alternative pharmacologic and biologic treatments.

It takes many years for a drug to get onto the market in the U.S. In the developed world, the U.S. has the most rigorous safety and efficacy testing standards. This fact can create anxiety for someone with a shortened life expectancy searching for a cure for his or her illness. However, advocates of any cancer therapy who make health claims bear the burden of proof. It is an ethical and legal responsibility to conduct proper studies and report them in sufficient detail to permit evaluation and confirmation by others.

ANTINEOPLASTONS

What it is: Antineoplaston treatments are offered by Stanislaw Burzynski at his clinic in Houston. Burzynski came to the United States from Poland in 1970 and became assistant professor of medicine at the Baylor School of Medicine. He left Baylor and began a clinic and research institute to independently work on his theories. Antineoplastons are peptide fractions originally derived from human blood and urine. It has now been synthesized in the laboratory. Phenylacetate, a fatty acid, is the main ingredient. Burzynski's treatment is popular and very expensive, but because of the unsubstantiated claims of a cancer cure, Burzynski has been in ongoing conflict with the government. In 1996, a judge ordered him to stop selling his unproven treatment. Charges were then filed, including violating FDA and U.S. Postal Service requirements and rules. In 1997, Burzynski was found not guilty of the 75-count federal indictment.

What practitioners say it does: Burzynski believes that the peptides convert cancer cells into normal cells and are deficient in people with cancer. By supplementing the antineoplastons, the person is able to cause the cancer to go into remission. Burzynski claims thousands of people have been cured of cancer by his treatment. There have been strong claims made in Congress and the media by Burzynski's supporters concerning government suppression of his therapy.

Research evidence: Despite Burzynski's claims, there have been no research data or records from him to prove his assertions of a cure for cancer. There have been a few unsuccessful attempts made to research antineoplastons over the years. Because this is a popular and unproven therapy for cancer, the NCI is conducting serious research into antineoplastons now. The FDA has granted permission for the Houston Institute to conduct clinical trials of antineoplastons. Real documentation of patients' cancer conditions and their response to the treatment will be gathered.

CANCELL (ENTELEV)

What it is: Cancell is a dark brown liquid made up of four common chemicals (sulfuric acid, nitric acid, potassium hydroxide, sodium sulfite). Treatments are administered orally or rectally every 6 hours, night and day, for 45 days or more. It is also applied externally on the skin.

What practitioners say it does: In 1936, James Sheridan, a chemist, had a dream and was inspired by God, he said, to make Cancell. Sheridan claimed Cancell digests cancer cells and renders them harmless. It claims to change the vibratory rate of cancer cells.

Research evidence: The ingredients of Cancell that have been analyzed by the FDA and the NCI have no evidence to claim any action against cancer or other disease.

COENZYME Q10

What it is: A coenzyme dietary supplement that has been looked at with cancer since 1972. Dr. Karl Folkers began exploring CoQ10 based on the unexpected and unusually long survival for his cancer patients who were using CoQ10 for cardiac problems. It is an antioxidant and was first isolated from the mitochondria of beef heart.

What practitioners say it does: Folkers suggested that CoQ10 might control cancer either by helping antibody synthesis or by attacking tumor cell operation with a CoQ10 antimetabolite 17.

His later work focused on supplementing CoQ10 to facilitate antibody production and antioxidant protection.

Research evidence: Although 25 human studies of the supplement have been done, the studies' outcome measures have been assorted. The studies have assessed survival (n = 2), disease response (n = 4), blood levels (n = 8), protection against heart damage (n = 9), protection against radiation pneumonitis (n = 1), and effect on immune system (n = 1; UT-CAM website, 1998). Only one study has been a randomized clinical trial. Evidence exists for its cardioprotective capacity with a couple of chemotherapies. Minor side effects, if any, have been reported.

COFFEE ENEMAS

What it is: Coffee enemas are given up to two to four times daily. Not seen as curing cancer, they are a component of many alternative cancer therapy programs that seek to build the body's immunity in order to fight cancer.

What practitioners say it does: Enthusiasts proclaim coffee enemas restore function to poisoned cells, which then mobilize to fight tumors. There are claims that coffee enemas detoxify the liver and other organs. The notion that the linings of the intestines suffer buildup of impacted waste is proffered.

Research evidence: There is no scientific support for the claims of proponents. The physiologic fact is that the colon sheds its lining every day and regenerates it. It is impossible for anything to build up on its walls. Coffee enemas are stimulating and addicting; the sensation may be a pleasurable experience for some people.

DMSO

What it is: Dimethyl sulfoxide is an industrial solvent, similar to turpentine. It is given as an unproven cancer treatment intravenously, usually in combination with other therapies such as Laetrile. DMSO is approved for interstitial cystitis in humans and as a veterinary medicine to reduce swelling in dogs and horses.

What practitioners say it does: There is the claim that it can penetrate the shell around cancer cells. The DMSO acts as a vehicle for the other treatments to attack the cancer.

Research evidence: There is no evidence that DMSO has any anticancer activity. Human studies have been discontinued by researchers due to safety issues based on eye changes in experimental animals.

HYDRAZINE SULFATE

What it is: Hydrazine sulfate is a cancer treatment developed by Joseph Gold, a cancer researcher in Syracuse, New York, around 1970. It is an industrial chemical used as rocket fuel in World War II.

What practitioners say it does: Gold, through his studies, came to believe that hydrazine sulfate could slow the weight loss and wasting away of the body that many cancer patients faced. He felt it could enhance the effect of other drugs. This therapy, made popular in the media, has long been waiting for scientific research to back proponents' claims.

Research evidence: In 1994, three methodologically sound studies found no positive effects from hydrazine sulfate (Cassileth, 1998). Therefore, it is a disproved therapy for cancer.

IMMUNOAUGMENTATIVE THERAPY (IAT)

What it is: In the Bahamas, Lawrence Burton offered an alternative cancer treatment. He died in 1993, but clinics in the Grand Bahamas, West Germany, and Mexico still exist. The main treatment consists of daily injections of cancer immune therapy, derived from processed blood products. It contains secret blood components added to pooled human blood from people without cancer. Proponents of IAT discourage active participation in conventional treatments.

What practitioners say it does: In a detailed table appearing in his IAT Patient Brochure, Burton lists a large number of human malignancies for which "at least 50% of patients have responded to immuno-augmentative therapy with long-term regression of tumors and/or remission of symptoms" (OTA, 1990). Burton and his staff would not and could not provide any studies or patient records to the NIH OTA that would verify this.

Research evidence: In the late 1980s, Congress, under pressure from many interested patients and supporters, asked the NIH OTA to offer Burton assistance in developing clinical trials of his treatment. He declined to participate with this and all government organizations. A by-product of his cooperation would have been a model of how an alternative cancer treatment could effectively be studied. A major opportunity for humane and ethical investigation of his work was lost, according to the NIH (OTA, 1990).

IAT clinics have resisted any independent, confidential assessment of the treatment's ingredients or safety. HIV and hepatitis B have been found in samples of his treatment obtained from patients. Burton's claimed rationale for building the immune system has not withstood investigation. Therefore, no scientific evidence exists that this treatment is safe or effective in the treatment of cancer. Burton was charismatic and has a loyal following. His treatment is expensive and administered at a vacation resort. The resort environment could be responsible for the increase in well-being reported by patients. In a 1987 survey of IAT patients by Cassileth and colleagues (1987), the IAT patients were more likely to be ambulatory, younger, better educated, and of higher socioeconomic status than cancer patients in general.

LAETRILE (AMYGDALIN, VITAMIN B$_{17}$)

What it is: Laetrile is a natural substance made from apricot pits. It was a popular alternative cancer treatment during the 1970s and was thoroughly investigated by the FDA.

What practitioners say it does: It releases cyanide into the body, which is thought to target and kill cancer cells. It is also claimed to weaken the cell membranes of cancer cells and allow other alternative therapies to work against the cancer.

Research evidence: Many reports exist in medical journals of cyanide poisoning and damage to the neuromuscular and respiratory systems due to Laetrile. Scientific studies have been conducted for over 20 years into the efficacy of this product. No evidence of an effect in animal or human cancers has been detected. Due to the strong research data, the U.S. Supreme Court ruled that it is illegal to bring Laetrile into the United States.

REVICI BIOLOGICALLY GUIDED CHEMOTHERAPY

What it is: This cancer therapy was developed by Emanuel Revici at his clinic in New York. He practiced until he was close to 100 years of age.

Other physicians today continue to operate his clinic. The Revici theory of tumor origin and development is scientifically very complex. Some believe his ideas are sophisticated and ahead of their time; others believe this is another in the line of the so-called cancer cures such as Laetrile.

What practitioners say it does: Revici believed tumors are either catabolic or anabolic. After determining which type of tumor is present, it is then treated with either lipids (sterols) or fatty acids. Specially formulated substances are given either orally or by injection. They are said to fight cancer.

Research evidence: In 1963, a Clinical Appraisal Group in New York City, made up of experienced researchers, studied Revici's method. They found it to be without merit in the treatment of cancer. No other reviews of the treatment have taken place, and no clinical studies have been done on the treatment. Despite the poor scientific review of his cancer therapy, several mainstream scientists have found his understanding of lipid chemistry sound, especially on the properties of fatty acids.

714-X

What it is: Gaston Naessens, a French microbiologist now living in Quebec, developed an unconventional cancer therapy. A nitrogen-providing compound (nitrogen with camphor as a delivery agent) is injected into the lymph system near the abdomen to treat cancer. The name, "714," is from his initials, which are the 7th and 14th letters of the alphabet. X is the 24th letter for the year of his birth, 1924.

What practitioners say it does: Naessens invented a microscope he claimed allows one to see otherwise invisible blood particles he called "somatids." Some scientists believed his somatids were simply cell fragments. He theorized that cancer cells are deficient in nitrogen, and that injecting 714-X into the body would reconvert cancer cells to normal cells. He used the special microscope to follow individual patient process.

Research evidence: Scientists can find no evidence in support of this theory or efficacy of this method. Because of the popularity of this therapy in Canada, the Canadian Breast Cancer Research Initiative is moving forward to further study this treatment. Members of the medical establishment, however, do not favor this continued effort, or, for that matter, Naessens' hypothesis. Richard Fishel, director of the DNA Repair and Molecular Carcinogenesis, Thomas Jefferson University School of Medicine, Philadelphia, Pennsylvania, says, "Naessens' theory appears eclipsed by the developments in the science of cancer genetics of the last 20 years. While our knowledge is far from complete, it is clear that cancer develops as a result of acquired genetic defects in the machinery that controls the cell cycle and cell division." Alterations in the workings of the cells can be "due to environmental influences, such as cigarettes, dietary compounds, sunlight, and oxygen which is the most mutagenic substance on the face of this earth" (Holzman, 1998).

SHARK CARTILAGE AND BOVINE CARTILAGE

What it is: Dr. John F. Prudden, associate professor of Clinical Surgery at Columbia Presbyterian Medical Center, discovered the effectiveness of bovine cartilage during his work on wound healing and arthritis in the early 1950s. Cartilage for therapeutic use is derived from cattle, sheep, sharks, and chickens. It is a pill, powder, or suppository (Office of Alternative Medicine [OAM], 1992).

What practitioners say it does: There are several theories about how it is effective. Shark cartilage is thought to prevent angiogenesis, the process of the body creating new blood vessels that feed a tumor. If angiogenesis is prevented, a cancer would starve. Bovine cartilage is thought to strengthen the immune system. Cartilage is believed to be nontoxic. Long-term effects from exposure to the suggested dosage (22 times the required daily dosage of calcium) are unknown.

Research evidence: Prudden, the NCI, and the ACS all criticize William Lane whose ideas in the best-selling 1992 book *Sharks Don't Get Cancer* popularized this therapy for cancer. In fact, sharks do get cancers—malignant melanoma and brain tumors. The two research studies Lane refers to in the book that "prove" the efficacy of shark cartilage were not scientifically sound (McCutcheon, 1997). No clinical trials have been completed on cartilage as a treatment for cancer. No statistically

significant results were reported in the five human studies reported in the literature (UT-CAM website, 1998). Nine studies are in progress. One is a multicenter, phase I/II trial of cartilage extract for prostate patients, under way at the University of Texas MD Anderson Cancer Center. All interested in cartilage therapy are awaiting the results of top quality, long-term, double-blind, randomized clinical trials in which cancer patients are given shark cartilage or a placebo agent. Results may come from some of the studies in progress now.

Combination Metabolic and/or Unconventional Dietary Approaches

When pharmacologic and/or biologic treatments are used in various combinations and with special diets, enemas, and instructions about avoiding substances thought to be harmful, these treatments become part of a general approach often referred to as "metabolic therapy." *Metabolic* is a nonspecific term used by many unconventional practitioners to refer to a combination of unconventional approaches aimed at improving the physical and mental condition of cancer patients (OTA, 1990). Many of the best known "metabolic clinics" are located in or near Tijuana, Mexico, not far from the U.S. border. These clinics make strong claims that they can "cure" or effectively treat cancer. They often dismiss conventional therapies, and they conduct little if any scientific research on their own treatments (Lerner, 1994). Hoxsey therapy, Manner metabolic diet therapy, Kelley metabolic therapy, "Eumetabolic" treatment offered by Hans Nieper, and chelation therapy are some of the many metabolic or unconventional dietary approaches in use today. A few of the most popular approaches are discussed in more detail.

THE GERSON TREATMENT

What it is: The Gerson treatment is one of the oldest and best known of the American alternative nutritional therapies for cancer. The therapy was developed by Max Gerson in the 1930s and 1940s. His clinic in the United States opened in 1977. He had a very controversial career that was at odds with the medical establishment. The Gerson therapy is an intensive cancer treatment program available in San Diego, California and Mexico. It uses a special juice diet, coffee enemas, simple vegetarian foods, "nontoxic medicines," and alignment with nature as a treatment for cancer. Thirteen glasses daily of various fresh, raw juices are prepared hourly from organically grown fruits and vegetables. It is an intensive program for anyone.

What practitioners say it does: Many cancer cures are claimed from this treatment. The purpose of the therapy is to detoxify the body so it can cure itself. Easily accessible program information claims that the Gerson treatment "can save about 50 percent or more of advanced 'hopeless' cancer patients" and that "the percentage who recover can exceed 90 percent for early cancers and some 'early terminal' cancers" (OTA, 1990).

Research evidence: The clinic in San Diego, according to one report, treats approximately 600 patients per year. Two reviews by the NCI have shown no life extension or cure benefit attributed to the treatment. Gerson did not supply more requested data during the first review. The second study was challenged by the Gerson Clinic staff as being based on technicalities (OTA, 1990). A British insurance company with qualified researchers investigated the clinic, reviewed best case scenarios, and found little objective evidence of benefit in the clinical outcomes. They did find high psychological scores for patients who were participating in the clinic at the time. The intensive self-participatory nature of the treatment, being in control of their health, and the support from family and friends could explain the benefit. The researchers believed conventional medicine should pay attention to that finding (Reed & Sikora, 1990).

LIVINGSTON-WHEELER THERAPY

What it is: This therapy is an autogenous vaccine, nutritional supplementation, antibiotic, and dietary program, developed by the late Virginia C. Livingston, a physician and microbiologist. She believed a microbe caused cancer and prescribed treatments to fight it. She named it *Progenitor cryptocides* (PC), meaning "the ancestral, or primordial, hidden killer" (OTA, 1990). It invades the body when the immune system is weakened.

What practitioners say it does: Her treatment goal is to build the immune system to help it fight the cancer. Throughout her career, in books and publications, she suggested high success rates. She died in 1990, and her clinic, which first opened in 1968 in San Diego, remains open.

Research evidence: The *P. cryptocides* culture examined by other scientists was found to be "different species of the genus *Staphylococcus* and *Streptococcus*" (OTA, 1990). Livingston published no data in scientific journals to support her claims of success with the treatment. Only one case-controlled study has been published. Terminal cancer patients without any proven treatment options received either the Livingston program or conventional therapy. The groups did not have a difference in survival time. Quality of life was lower originally in the Livingston treatment group and continued to stay lower (Cassileth, 1991).

MACROBIOTICS (MACROBIOTIC DIET)

What it is: The original macrobiotic diet was very strict, with brown rice and some liquids. Modifications to the macrobiotic diet have evolved. Today, it is mostly a vegetarian diet that can contain adequate amounts of nutrients. The diet can provide the cardiovascular benefits of a low-fat, low-calorie diet. It consists of 50% to 60% whole grains and cereals, 25% to 30% vegetables, 5% to 10% sea vegetables and beans or soybean products like miso and tofu, and 5% soups. Some fish and nuts are allowed. No nutritional supplementation is encouraged.

What practitioners say it does: The macrobiotic philosophy and diet developed in the 1930s in Japan and was transplanted to Boston. George Ohsawa and Michio Kushi were the original proponents of this way of life and diet. The lifestyle and spirituality are based on ancient Chinese thinking. Yin and yang are opposite forces in the universe. They symbolize the essential balance that keeps nature and the universe maintaining itself. Yin–yang values are assigned to cancers, food, geography, and food preparation. Treatment is prescribed to bring the body back into balance so it may fight the illness.

Research evidence: There are three components to macrobiotics that can be taken into account independently: merits of the nutritional value of the diet, the value of individual ingredients, and the philosophy. The macrobiotic diet has a low-fat cancer prevention benefit. There is no evidence that macrobiotics, or any other diet, cures cancer. The macrobiotic community claims it does. There are testimonials of people in remission, but many have also taken conventional treatments. Scientists are investigating a component of soybeans, genistein, for potential anticancer properties.

The macrobiotic diet is low in calories and may be deficient in nutrients. This can mean that a cancer patient may undergo serious weight loss and imbalances that can challenge an already compromised person. Studies of infants and children

---

BOX 26-1

Complementary and Alternative Cancer Treatments

More information concerning complementary and alternative cancer treatments is available from:

The National Cancer Institute Cancer Information Service

1-800-4-CANCER. Phone information and written material on alternative therapies and general information about cancer is available.

The American Cancer Society

For conservative, realistic information.
(*http://www.cancer.org*)
Monographs on most unconventional cancer therapies with rankings of "highest concern," "high concern," and "of concern." This material is available by calling your local ACS office. Their viewpoint is often discouraging about most unproven therapies, although their website now recommends a few complementary therapies.
(*http://www.cancer.org/alt_therapy/index*)

The University of Texas Center for Alternative Medicine (UT-CAM)

Given the widespread interest in unconventional cancer treatments and the public demand for information on research, the UT-CAM team values and continues to seek outpatient experiences with these therapies. PO Box 20186; #434 Houston, Texas 77225. E-mail: utcam@utsph.sph.uth.tmc.edu. The website address is: *http://www.sph.uth.tmc.edu/utcam*

The National Center for Complementary and Alternative Medicine (NCCAM).

NCCAM website is *http://altmed.od.nih.gov/nccam/*

Medical School Libraries

These can provide computer access to information, medical journals, and textbooks on cancer therapies. Ask the librarian for assistance.

Comprehensive Cancer Centers

The NCI has designated cancer centers around the country as leaders in multiple aspects of cancer care. Patient resource libraries are often available at comprehensive cancer centers. Call 1-800-4CANCER for locations.

Internet

There are no quality controls for information on the Internet. It is an open marketplace with (bizarre to interesting) information available on alternative therapies for cancer.
The 300-page, out-of-print book, *Unconventional Cancer Treatments,* Office of Technology Assessment, Congress of the United States. (GPO stock number 052-003-01207-3). Washington, DC: U. S. Government Printing Office, 1990, has been posted on the Internet.
Special consultants were made up of scientists, skeptics, proponents and researchers. This fascinating document is at: *http://www.quackwatch.com/01QuackeryRelatedTopics/OTA/ota00.html*
Quackwatch is a website for the most hard-nosed skeptical viewpoints on alternative medicine. *http://www.quackwatch.com.*

on macrobiotic diets have turned up serious deficiencies (Cassileth, 1998).

There are many components of macrobiotic philosophy that involve "energy-based theories" that cannot be measured or detected scientifically. For believers, this is not a problem. Skeptics, however, believe that if it cannot be measured it does not exist. The diagnostic tools of macrobiotic practitioners include pulse diagnosis, iridology, study of the tongue, aura, and vibrational assessment. These tools have no known therapeutic value. Iridology has been disproved.

Where Is More Information Available on Alternative and Complementary Cancer Treatments?

The American Cancer Society states, "Knowledge is power. For the cancer patient, knowledge means the power to understand your specific disease and the best treatment options available. It also means taking control and learning how to deal with cancer's devastating effects on you and your family." (See Box 26-1.)

REFERENCES

American Cancer Society. (1998). Alternative and complementary therapies. *http://www.cancer.org/alt_therapies/overviews/alttreatments.html*.

Bailar, J. C. III, & Gornik, H. L. (1997). Cancer undefeated. *New England Journal of Medicine, 336*(22), 1569–1574.

Barrett, S., & Herbert, V. (1998). Questionable cancer therapies. *http://www.quackwatch.com/01QuackeryRelatedTopics/cancer.html*.

Cameron, E., & Pauling, L. (1976). Supplemental ascorbate in the supportive treatment of cancer: Prolongation of survival times in terminal human cancer. *Proceedings of the National Academy of Sciences USA, 73*, 3685–3689.

Cassileth, B. (1998). *The alternative medicine handbook: The complete reference guide to alternative and complementary therapies.* New York: W. W. Norton.

Cassileth, B., et al. (1991). Survival and quality of life among patients receiving unproven as compared with conventional cancer therapy. *New England Journal of Medicine, 325*, 1180–1185.

Cassileth, B., et al. (1987). *Report of a survey of patients receiving immunoaugmentative therapy, September 1987.* Philadelphia: University of Pennsylvania Cancer Center.

Eisenberg, D. M. (1997). Advising patients who seek alternative medical therapies. *Annals of Internal Medicine, 127*(1), 61–69.

Eisenberg, D. M. (1995). *Syllabus of alternative therapies and clinical implications.* Boston: Harvard Medical School.

Eisenberg, D. M., Kessler, R. C., Foster, C., Norlock, F. E., Calkins, D. R., & Delbanco, L. T. (1993). Unconventional medicine in the United States—Prevalence, costs and patterns of use: Results of a national survey. *New England Journal of Medicine, 328*, 246–252.

Ernst, E., & Cassileth, B. D. (1998). The prevalence of complementary/alternative medicine in cancer: A systematic review. *Cancer, 83*(4), 777–782.

Fawzy, I., Fawzy, N. W. et al. (1993). Malignant melanoma: Effects of an early structured psychiatric intervention, coping, and affective state on recurrence and survival 6 years later. *Archives of General Psychiatry, 50*, 681–689.

FDA rules to restrict herbal remedy claims. *Washington Post*, April 24, 1998.

Frankl, V. (1998). *Man's search for meaning.* New York: Washington Square Press.

Gellert, G., Siegel, B., et al. (1993). Survival of breast cancer patients receiving adjunctive psychosocial support therapy. *Journal of Clinical Oncology, 11*(1), 66–90.

Gordon, J. S. (1998). *Conference brochure for comprehensive cancer care: Integrating complementary and alternative therapies.* Washington, DC: The Center for Mind-Body Medicine.

Greer, S., & Silberfarb, P. M. (1982). Psychological concomitants of cancer: Current state of research. *Psychological Medicine, 12*, 567–568.

Halperin, E. C. (1998). Let's abolish the Office of Alternative Medicine of the National Institutes of Health. *North Carolina Medical Journal, 59*(1), 21–26.

Holland, J., & Rowland, J. (1989). *Handbook to psychooncology.* New York: Oxford.

Holzman, D. (1998). Canada promotes research on alternative treatments for breast cancer. *Alternative and Complementary Therapies, 4*(2), 8–12.

Hoxsey, H. M. (1956). *You don't have to die.* New York: Milestone Books.

Lane, I. W., & Comae, L. (1992). *Sharks don't get cancer.* Garden City Park, NY: Avery.

Lazarou, J., Pomeranz, B. H., & Corey, P. N. (1998). Incidence of adverse drug reactions in hospitalized patients: A meta-analysis of prospective studies. *Journal of the American Medical Association, 279*(15), 1200–1205.

Lerner, M. (1994). *Choices in healing: Integrating the best of conventional and complementary approaches to cancer.* Cambridge, MA: MIT Press.

LeShan, L. (1998). *Conference brochure for cancer as a turning point.* Asheville, NC.

Levine, S. (1987). *Healing into life and death.* Garden City, NY: Anchor Press/Doubleday.

McCutcheon, L. (1997). Taking a bite out of shark cartilage. *Skeptical Inquirer, 21*(5), 44–48.

Office of Alternative Medicine, National Institutes of Health. (1992). *Alternative medicine: Expanding medical horizons. A report to the National Institutes of Health on alternative medical systems and practices in the United States.* Washington, DC: U.S. Government Printing Office.

Office of Technology Assessment, Congress of the United States. (1990). *Unconventional cancer treatments.* Washington, DC: U.S. Government Printing Office.

O'Regan, B., & Hirshberg, C. (1993). *Spontaneous remission: An annotated bibliography*. Sausalito, CA: Institute of Noetic Sciences.

Reed, A., James, N., & Sikora, K. (1990). Mexico: Juices, coffee enemas, and cancer. *Lancet, 336*, 676–677.

Seskevich, J. (1997). Reprinted from booklet *Stress Management Education*. Durham, NC: Duke University Medical Center Patient Education.

Spiegel, D., Bloom, J. R., Kraemer, H. C., & Gottheil, E. (1989). A psychosocial intervention and survival time of patients with metastatic breast cancer. *Lancet, 2*(8668), 888–891.

The University of Texas Center for Alternative Medicine Research in Cancer. (1998). *http://www.sph.uth.tmc.edu/utcam/*.

Williams, R., & Williams, V. (1993). *Anger kills*. New York: Random House.

CHAPTER 27

Dying

Carla Jolley

"Dying is the process of moving into the state of death. Dying still has movement, death is static."

—*Patricia Weenolsen in* The Art of Dying

During the last decade, advances in cancer diagnosis and cancer treatments have had a positive impact on the morbidity and mortality of cancer patients. For the first time ever, the American Cancer Society's (ACS) Department of Epidemiology and Surveillance (1998) reported a reduction in the total number of new cancer cases and a decline in cancer deaths in the United States. Nevertheless, the number of cancer-related deaths remains sobering, and after heart disease cancer continues to be the second cause of death. The ACS 1998 Cancer Statistics estimates that 564,800 Americans can be expected to die of cancer—more than 1,500 people a day. This is a staggering statistic, and it is these patients who challenge nurses to support and guide them, their caregivers, and their families in the dying process.

The ability to support and to meet the needs of dying patients and their support systems is affected by a multitude of factors. These factors include the initial stage at the time of diagnosis, past and present treatments, whether the patient is experiencing a recurrence or progression of the disease, the patient's relationship with the health care provider, the health care provider's experience and comfort level with death and dying issues, the patient's family/support system or lack thereof, the symptoms he or she is experiencing, and his or her own fears and concerns about death.

In the midst of this, nurses who are caring for the dying patient, not dependent on the practice setting, have an opportunity to enter into a profoundly intimate time in the life of the patient and his or her loved ones. Nurses can support the patient in a process of dying well in many ways. Byok (1997) states, "Dying well can be thought of as a subjective personal experience which embodies a sense of meaning and purpose and sense of completion, at times even fulfillment." To be able to achieve this goal of dying well, patients need to have their physical symptoms controlled, to be allowed opportunities to address emotional and spiritual concerns, and to be provided with anticipatory guidance for the journey ahead. For the nurse who is caring for the dying patient, there are many opportunities for personal and professional growth, but most of all the opportunity to make a difference.

The Role of the Nurse in an Office-Based Practice/Ambulatory Clinic

The nurse in an office-based practice or ambulatory clinic has the initial opportunity to participate in supporting the patient who has moved into the realm of issues related to dying and his or her impending death. The nurse has had the opportunity to establish his or her relationship with the patient through multiple interactions: phone triage as medical problems occur, administering chemotherapy and/or blood products, greeting and attending to him or her during the frequent doctor appointments, and engaging in creative problem-solving to address concerns. This relationship allows the nurse to be a key player for the patient who is entering the terminal stages of his or her illness.

The exact timing of when the terminal stage of illness begins in a patient with advanced cancer is very difficult to define. Signs and symptoms of the advanced disease and the continuing deterioration that comes as the body systems are no longer able to compensate often result in more distressing symptoms and decreased functional status. Palliative treatment for the patient with far advanced disease changes the goal for the patient from curative treatment to a focus on quality of life (Conhill et al., 1997). Primary physicians or oncologists may stay actively involved with the patient by providing symptom management and support, but patients and families can feel despondent and abandoned if they feel "there is nothing else to do." The nurse can reassure patients and families that they may continue their relationship with the office or clinic, that the focus will be active symptom management, and that support and communication can continue on the phone even though they may no longer be able to leave their home.

Making appropriate and timely referrals for this patient is an important intervention that can never be underestimated. The nurse is positioned to facilitate these referrals. Becoming educated on what resources are available for patients and knowing the viable and appropriate support resources in the community immensely benefits these patients. Although patients and families often are reluctant to let strangers in at such an intimate time, the nurse is often very familiar with the patient and how he or she thinks, and their caregivers may be able to transcend this barrier. If the nurse can feel confident in the information he or she is providing, it allows a smoother transition through the continuum of care. Each community has its own unique options available, and it is important to become familiar with them. Hospice and home care nurses can provide a satisfactory option in this continuum. They work very closely with the referral source in providing an often complex plan of care and support. The insights that the referring nurse can provide, based on his or her involvement in the patient's current care up to this point, are invaluable to the nurse who will be treating the patient in the home setting.

In assessing when to make the referral, it is necessary to address issues beyond symptoms. For instance: How are they coping? Is the primary caregiver getting any respite or rest? Is there a primary caregiver or support system? How will they cope as things change at home? Do they have equipment they need? What is the patient's functional status, and what are the primary concerns that are being expressed? Identify a concrete problem (e.g., the patient is getting a bedsore because he is sleeping in the recliner for dyspnea, or the daughter is getting overwhelmed with the medication schedule and doesn't want to give her dad bowel care) that can be addressed by the referral source. This approach can allow the patient and family permission to transition smoothly to addressing care at home. These services can offer support for the patient and family in the dying process, even if the patient and their family do not identify this as the primary reason for the initial referral. A persuasive point in presenting these options is that most home health care and hospice agencies provide 24-four hour call and weekend coverage. Another helpful strategy is to educate the patient and family before the referral becomes necessary, with the expectation the referral will be made at a more timely or critical moment as it is needed. When the time does occur, it can be introduced easily with the statement, "I think this is a good time to make that referral for services we had talked about earlier." The patient and family will also be able to identify the transition time themselves if given some specifics about what might initiate a referral in their specific case. A timely referral allows more to happen in preparation for the impending decline and death; appropriate services and support can be accessed, and issues can be identified and addressed by the interdisciplinary team. It allows for the outcome to be dying well rather than a crisis admission with minimal time to prepare for both the patient, the caregivers, and the family.

A Death at Home

For the patient who chooses to die at home, the support available in the community needs to be identified. The two options are usually hospice home care and home health care services. Hospice home care is a purposeful referral for end-of-life care; most hospices' admission criteria include that the patient is no longer receiving any active treatment and has a life expectancy of 6 months or less. Home health care services may have been involved with the patient before the focus was terminal care or may receive a referral for a specific skilled need. Some agencies oversee both home care and hospice services.

Hospice is essentially a philosophy of care that emphasizes quality of life when the quantity of life is limited by a terminal disease. In the United States hospice has been primarily a social movement, developing programs to enable patients to die well (Corliss, 1991). The 1994 survey by the National Center for Health Statistics found that 59% of persons discharged from hospice agencies had conditions related to cancer (Hospice Association of America, 1997). A fundamental principle of hospice care is that the patient and family together compose the unit of care (Reimer, Davies, & Martens, 1991). Hospice is thought to be the gold standard of end-of-life care. Hospice services are provided by an interdisciplinary team of healthcare providers, including the patient's physician, and volunteers. The goal is to provide symptom management and supportive psychosocial, emotional, and spiritual care services. Bereavement care after a patient's death is provided to the family and caregivers.

The role of the hospice nurse is to coordinate and oversee the plan of care for the patient. The professional expertise of the hospice nurse is in pain and symptom management. The approach is a holistic one, including addressing emotional and spiritual needs. Patient and family education is an important aspect of every visit (Corliss, 1991). Referrals are made to other team members as appropriate. The key component of hospice nursing is the interaction between the nurse, the hospice patient, and the family (Raudonis & Kirschling, 1996). Raudonis and Kirschling (1996) found in their study of nine bereaved family caregivers that they characterized the hospice nurses as respectful, kind, caring, clinical experts whose presence and interventions helped meet the needs of the family experiencing death. These attributes are the essence of the art of nursing, no matter the setting, and are invaluable in the eyes of the patient and family. Care for the dying must always be done with a mindful approach and a sensitive heart.

There are a variety of models and diversity of arrangements with hospice services today. Congress enacted legislation in 1982 creating a Medicare hospice program or the Medicare Hospice Benefit for those patients with Medicare A. It covers the services of the interdisciplinary team, physician services, medications, medical supplies and equipment, and some episodes of continuous care for crisis or respite. The hospice is reimbursed at a fixed rated for each day the patient is enrolled. The patient does sign an "election" statement waiving traditional Medicare benefits. The Hospice Association of America (1997) reports that the Medicare hospice program participation has grown at a dramatic rate. From 1984 to 1996 the total number of hospices participating in Medicare rose from 31 to 2154—a 70-fold increase. Of the 2154 Medicare-certified hospices, 815 are home care agency based, 526 are hospital based, 22 are skilled nursing facility based, and 791 are free standing. There are also an estimated 746 non–Medicare certified hospices. Many of these, however, are certified by the state in compliance with the Medicare conditions of participation. Medicaid in most states covers hospice, many private insurances have a hospice benefit, and hospices are beginning to negotiate in the market of managed care. It is important when learning about local resources to be aware of the standards of care and to identify what accreditation the hospice has achieved. Some community hospices may have a limited range of services.

The home health nurse may be the other caregiver involved in supporting a death at home. The home health nurse will become involved when the cancer patient's functional status has become compromised. For a home health admission to home care the patient needs to meet certain criteria: the patient must be "homebound," require skilled intermittent services, and the services need to be ordered by the physician. The referral may be initiated by the physician, nurses, discharge planners, medical social workers, the family, friends, or the patient. The admission most likely is precipitated by an identified concern that requires skilled nursing intervention. For cancer patients with advanced disease, it often is symptom management, nutritional/fluid assessment and monitoring, wound care, and providing education to the caregivers to meet the needs of the patient as he or she is deteriorating. The admission for home care may come after a hospitalization; patients are experiencing shorter stays and returning home much less stable. Currently, reimbursement for Medicare patients covers skilled nursing home health care services and other members of the interdisciplinary team (physical therapists, occupational therapists, speech therapists, medical social workers, and home health aides). Most private insurance and managed care plans have some level of home health care coverage, especially if it is in lieu of hospitalization.

Mulhern (1998) identifies two obstacles to home care adequately addressing end-of-life issues, which must continually be addressed and managed in the acute home care model. The first is making a conscious effort to focus on palliation and spiritual and psychosocial concerns. In effective terminal care, addressing painful end-of-life issues cannot be rushed. With home care reimbursement decreasing, home care staff are required to make more visits each day, reducing the length of time available to spend with each patient. Also, spiritual counseling and bereavement services are not usual components of a home care team, and it often takes time to identify and make outside referrals. The second obstacle is that palliative care requires a specialized body of knowledge and skill that can be difficult to obtain and retain if one is not routinely applying it. In addition, some patients with advanced disease continue to seek treatment options, and others are unable to face the terminal nature of their disease and do not elect hospice. These patients challenge home care nurses to prepare the patient and family for a future death while still supporting their active treatment choices or the patient's choice not to acknowledge the inevitable. Mulhern concludes that in such cases, by working within the interdisciplinary team, using specialty consultants and community resources, and providing continuity of care to the patient and family over various phases of the illness trajectory as needs change, patients and families can and do experience a high level of support and satisfaction at the end of life.

The main component for a death at home, whether the hospice or home health care team is providing the services, is the identification of a primary caregiver. This may be a spouse or other family member. In today's society the definition of family does not necessarily follow traditional lines of being a blood relative or spouse; it is the person the patient identifies and describes as family. Those who function as family are part of a social system in which members have ties to one another, have ongoing interactions with one another, are interdependent, have some common history or frame of reference, and share some goals (Germino, 1991). It is on this unit of care—patient and family—that interventions and support must be focused. The caregiver is the critical element making it possible for a death to occur at home, and if the caregiver becomes too stressed by the burden of patient care the arrangement may collapse (McMillan & Mahon, 1994). It becomes imperative to find ways to support and enhance families coping with the caregiving situation.

Hull (1992) found that families relied on a repertoire of coping strategies to help them maintain caregiving. These included creating "windows of time" for themselves away from caregiving responsibilities; social comparison—evaluating their situation in reference to others they considered less fortunate; cognitive formulation—minimizing the negative and finding benefits from situations; and avoidance—directing energy away from the inevitable death, over which they had no control, to aspects of care that were within their control. Nursing interventions need to focus on assisting families to identify resources within their own network and community resources to provide opportunities for respite from caregiving duties. This study also supports assisting families to find meaning in the situations they are facing and to equip them with the knowledge and tools they need to assist with a feeling of control over, if not the situation, symptoms or changes they may be addressing.

A Death In the Hospital

The first task of the inpatient nurse may be to identify the dying patient when he or she is admitted to the hospital. Hospitalization under Medicare's Diagnosis Related Groups does not permit admission for terminal care; the brief stabilization of a medical problem is permitted, but then the person must be discharged either to the home, an inpatient hospice, or a skilled nursing facility (Zerwekh, 1991). For example, admissions for dying patients may have been precipitated by an exacerbation of uncontrolled pain, dyspnea, severe side effects from bowel obstruction, or hemorrhaging. The family may have become overwhelmed with the multiple tasks and symptoms that needed to be attended to, especially if support is lacking or the illness and decline has been drawn out. In such a case the admitting diagnosis for the dying patient may be more subtle, such as dehydration, weakness, fever of unknown origin, or metabolic imbalances. Lack of awareness or acceptance of death can lead to unplanned emergency admissions to the hospital that end in death (Seale & Kelly, 1997). Depending on the institution, there may be an area or service identified for terminal patients such as an inpatient hospice unit, an oncology ward, a palliative care team to oversee care, or a special room set aside for the dying patient and the family (Box 27-1). Generally (especially in light of changes in the health care environment), cancer patients who are dying are admitted to a medical service.

The role of the nurse in facilitating appropriate care is important. It is the holistic assessment of that patient, the circumstances of the admission, the patient's support system or lack of one, and the patient's and family's understanding of the goals of care that the nurse must integrate into the care plan of the dying patient. The focus of the care plan needs to include the family and identified caregivers. If the original plan had been a death at home, the patient and family may feel that they failed. This concern needs to be addressed not only by the nurse but also the entire health care team, and positive feedback given for caring for the patient up to this point. If the patient is not imminently dying, discharge planning follows closely on the heels of the admission. The patient may return home with a new referral or to previously established hospice or home care, a skilled nursing facility, or an inpatient hospice if available. Referrals to social work, discharge planners, and case managers need to be facilitated as quickly as possible if this is the case.

The patient who is imminently dying and is expected to expire in the hospital presents a special challenge in the health care environment of today. Families may experience a new set of caregivers every 8 hours, therefore making continuity of nursing staff, if possible, a priority. In the case

---

BOX 27-1

Creating a Hospice Room

Choose a room away from the nurse's station, with low traffic flow
One with windows, view if able
A private room, larger in size
Furnish it with a recliner
Provide an alternative for sleeping, e.g., cot, futon
Paint in soft hues
Choose soothing artwork
Explore the limitations of your system; consider a washable quilt

Provide soft and alternative lighting, floor lamps
Furnish a tape/CD player
Have a bookshelf with books for reading aloud, CDs, inspirational music
Gain administrative support; can use for other patients in times of increased census
Approach hospital foundations, guilds for monetary support

of the terminal cancer patient, it is very easy to focus discussion on the things that are not being done or will not be done. Patients and families will be more comforted by discussions of what will be done: a pain-free state will be maintained, frequent oral and skin care given, and privacy, support, and anticipatory guidance provided (Goetchieu, 1997). With administrative and collegial support, the nurse can create a caring and supportive environment in which the patient will spend his or her final days.

Clinical Issues Across Settings

Anticipatory Guidance

Anticipating both the physical and emotional changes that a patient will experience with progressive disease will help the nurse prepare families for what to expect and how to intervene. By guiding the patient and family through the possible complications or symptoms that may occur, they will feel less frightened when and if they occur. Such anticipatory guidance is most likely to succeed when it matches a family style that copes by problem solving and planning ahead; it will be least successful with people who have lived their lives from crisis to crisis (Zerwekh, 1991).

Preparing families and patients for the inevitable death is somewhat paradoxical in nature. The preparation of the concrete tasks for inevitable death itself needs to be completed, while at the same time supporting the hope that there will be time enough to resolve unfinished business and for the opportunity to complete developmental tasks for the end of life. When discussing this paradox, present the information about progressive deterioration that comes with advanced disease at an almost predictable pace until death occurs. Although there can be plateaus of time without any changes, there is seldom improvement. What if there were sudden changes, because cancer can be unpredictable at times, and death came quickly? The patient and family need to have made the basic preparations: no code status established, a plan for where death will occur, education on the limited options if death is not to occur at home, what to do when death occurs, how to

diagnose when death has occurred, whom to call, and the funeral home/arrangements desired.

In contrast to the unpredicted or sudden death, the patient and family have a definite time frame within which they may choose whether to participate in a variety of options to complete unfinished business and end-of-life tasks. Byok (1996) offers "task work" in Table 27-1 to represent various means through which the patient may develop a sense of completion, satisfaction, and even mastery within areas of life that are of subjective importance to him or her. Exploring what is important to the patient to complete or resolve before death and how he or she envisions spending his or her last days will help the family and patient set goals. The nurse can offer suggestions, help identify opportunities, and sometimes facilitate some of this work when the nurse–patient relationship allows and if the patient is interested. Sometimes patients and/or their families find this too painful or are unable to even consider addressing these issues; this too needs to be respected as an active choice. Human beings are unique, and it is often stated that they die as they have lived. It is important to get a sense of who the person is, to allow for the opportunities to be available for growth, and to respect and support his or her wishes in a nonjudgmental way.

Anticipatory guidance about physical changes, possible symptoms, and complications may involve some research for the nurse. The nurse can draw from past experiences and knowledge about basic physiology. It is important to get a sense of the expected trajectory of the disease. Using this information and clinical experience can help the nurse identify symptoms or difficulties expected. This allows the nurse to obtain the tools and equipment to have readily available to address these possible symptoms and concerns. For example, if the patient has liver metastases and is expected to obstruct at the biliary tree, he or she may have symptoms of jaundice, pruritus, and mental changes as the bilirubin level climbs and most likely will need something for restlessness and comfort.

Anticipatory guidance is used to address the clinical issue that more often than not comes up— that of "terminal dehydration." This is an expected universal symptom for most patients and very troublesome for families to understand without some education.

TABLE 27-1
DEVELOPMENTAL LANDMARKS AND TASKS FOR THE END OF LIFE

Sense of completion with with wordly affairs
Transfer of fiscal, legal, and formal social responsibilities
Sense of completion in relationships with community
Closure of multiple social relationships (employment, commerce, organizational, congregational): Components include expressions of regret, expressions of forgiveness, acceptance of gratitude and appreciation.
Leave-taking: the saying of goodbye
Sense of meaning about one's life
Life review
The telling of one's "stories"
Transmission of knowledge and wisdom
Experienced love of self
Self-acknowledgement
Self-forgiveness
Experienced love of others
Acceptance of worthiness
Sense of completion in relationships with family and friends
Reconciliation, fullness of communication and closure in each of one's important relationships.
Component tasks include expressions of forgiveness and acceptance, expressions of gratitude and appreciation, acceptance of gratitude and appreciation, expressions of affection.
Leave-taking: the saying of goodbye
Acceptance of the finality of life—of one's existence as an individual
Acknowledgement of the totality of personal loss represented by one's dying and experience of one's personal pain of existential loss
Expression of the depth of personal tragedy that dying represents
Decathexis (emotional withdrawal) from worldly affairs and cathexis (emotional connection) with an enduring construct
Acceptance of dependency
Sense of a new self (personhood) beyond personal loss
Sense of meaning about life in general
Achieving a sense of awe
Recognition of a transcendent realm
Developing/achieving a sense of comfort with chaos
Surrender to the transcendent, to the unknown—"Letting Go"

(Byock, I. [1996]. The nature and suffering and the nature of opportunity at the end of life. *Clinics in Geriatric Medicine, 12* [2], 237–252.)

Terminal Dehydration

One of the more difficult issues facing the nurse in any setting is addressing the issue of terminal dehydration. This term is commonly used to refer to the process that occurs when a dying person's condition causes him or her to gradually reduce fluid intake (Zerwekh, 1997). Sometimes dehydration can be exacerbated by the disease process itself, especially if there is vomiting, diarrhea, or excessive wound or fistula drainage. The burdens and benefits of initiating artificial hydration (or to continue in some cases) for each patient and their family need to be considered individually. For most patients close to death, hydration offers little or no known benefit, and terminal dehydration may have many benefits that add to decreasing the suffering of dying patients.

The intake of foods and liquids as desired or tolerated by the patient is termed "patient endorsed intake." This is the usual course for most patients dying from their advanced disease. Although they are not denied anything they wish to ingest, neither is anything forced on them (Smith,

1995). As their body continues to deteriorate and operate less effectively, eventually their desire for any kind of intake is lost. This process usually happens over an extended period of time. The complications of postural hypotension noted as a side effect of acute dehydration are not usually a problem because most terminal cancer patients at this point are bedridden (Musgrave, 1990). Accordingly there is a strong cultural norm that compels us to link nurturing, eating, and drinking lest our loved one "starve to death." This powerful norm of nurturing associated with feeding and the notion of suffering associated with starvation and dehydration are deeply rooted in our sense of how to nurture (Byok, 1995). Byok (1995) suggests that this may especially be true for those patients who lived through the world wars and the Great Depression of this century. This can become a very distressful time for families and caregivers unless they are prepared for the expected course of the progressive deterioration and the expected decrease of food and fluids in the dying process.

Numerous articles and chapters (Burge, 1993; Byok, 1995; Dunphy et al., 1995; McCann et al. 1994; Musgrave, 1990; Smith, 1997; Twycross & Lichter, 1998; Zerwekh, 1997) about terminal dehydration identify the benefits (Box 27-2). The decreased intake results in decreased urine output, decreasing the need for the bedpan, urinal, com-

mode, incontinence, and/or sometimes catherization. Terminal dehydration results in decreased gastrointestinal fluid, reducing episodes of vomiting. In bowel obstructions, common in advanced and end-stage ovarian cancer and some gastric/colorectal cancers, it can allow the forgoing of a nasogastric tube for decompression. It may result in a reduction in pulmonary secretions, which in turn leads to less coughing and choking and decreased need for suctioning. Pharyngeal secretions are diminished, and patients who are too weak to swallow are less likely to experience the feeling of drowning. Peripheral edema and ascites often gets reabsorbed, resulting in decreased discomfort. Pain relief can occur with a reduction in the edematous reaction surrounding tumors. Patients with raised intracranial pressure may regain lucidity for a time as they dehydrate. There is thought to be a natural anesthesia that appears to occur near death, which decreases suffering.

The logistics and invasiveness of the infusion itself need to be considered. If there is no central line, painful needle sticks are required. The family may experience additional financial burdens and increased stress with the added care needs for maintaining the infusion if artificial hydration is being delivered at home (Zerwekh, 1997). The possible psychological effects on the patient of being "tied down" or "hooked up" need to be ex-

---

BOX 27-2

Benefits of Dehydration

Decreased urine output, resulting in the need for the urinal, bedpan, commode and/or catheterization

Decreased GI fluid, resulting in decreased episodes of vomiting, need for nasogastric tubes

Decreased pulmonary secretions, resulting in decreased cough, coughing, choking, and suctioning

Decreased pharyngeal secretions for those too weak to swallow; less likely to feel like drowning

Decreased fluid overload, resulting in decreased peripheral and pulmonary edema

Reabsorption of fluid, resulting in decreased ascites, decreased peritumor edema with decreased pain

Decreased wound and fistula drainage

Decreased intracranial pressure in some patients, resulting in increased lucidity

Decreased care, cost, and burden of maintaining hydration

(Adapted from Zerwerkh, 1991, 1997; Twycross & Lichter, 1998; Taylor, 1995; Smith, 1995,1997; Musgrave, 1990; Byok, 1995.)

plored (Zerwekh, 1997). Artificial hydration is a complex issue without distinct research support to offer clear direction.

The most commonly cited side effect of terminal dehydration is a dry mouth or a feeling of thirst. This is often exacerbated by side effects of medications and altered oral mucosa. This symptom can be addressed with good oral hygiene, frequent sips of fluid, use of saliva substitutes, ice chips, and treatment of oral infections as needed.

The possible benefits of hydration in selected terminal patients are to correct a fluid or electrolyte imbalance and/or stabilize the patient's condition and reverse certain symptoms, especially if they are induced by causes such as hypercalcemia, diarrhea, or diuretic therapy, though these improvements are most likely transient with the expected progression of the disease (Zerwekh, 1997). Sometimes artificial hydration can be reduced gradually or even dramatically if signs and symptoms of fluid overload occur after hydration has already been initiated; it does not always have to be an either/or decision. This can ease the transition for patients and families who are trying to let go and need to make some very difficult decisions. Ongoing nursing assessment becomes crucial as feedback is needed to ensure that patients are kept as comfortable as possible.

The nurse caring for the terminally ill patient has a fundamental obligation to respect the wishes of each patient while keeping in mind the goal of comfort (Taylor, 1995). The nurse can participate in the task of educating patients, families, and colleagues about a systematic analysis of the benefits and burdens of artificial hydration. Writing an order for artificial hydration is ultimately the physician's responsibility, but physicians can be influenced by the nurse's assessment of the patient's condition and the nurse's concerns for the patient's comfort (Zerwekh, 1997). Finally, it is a nurse's obligation not to pass judgment on any decisions made to withhold or continue the hydration of a terminally ill patient (Taylor, 1995).

End-Stage Symptom Management

It is important for nurses to understand the physiology of dying, what some end-stage symptoms may be for their patient, and how they might intervene to ease suffering and to prepare families for the inevitable end of life. In *How We Die*, Nuland (1994) describes the destructive nature of cancer—how its twin forces of local invasion and distant metastasis gradually interfere with the functioning of the various tissues of the body. Tubular organs can become obstructed, metabolic processes are inhibited, blood vessels can erode sufficiently to cause minor and sometimes major bleeding, the vital centers are destroyed, and delicate biochemical balances are destroyed. He identifies other less direct ways for cancer to take its toll also: debilitation, poor nutrition, and susceptibility to infection.

The actual last few days of life have been the subject of study by multiple authors (Conhill et al., 1997; Lichter & Hunt, 1990; Turner et al., 1996; Ventafridda et al., 1990). Table 27-2 presents a summary of symptoms identified. The attributed cause for exacerbation of symptoms or new symptoms is usually the effects of multisystem organ failure, metabolic changes, progressive tumor growth, and immobility. The type of cancer will greatly influence more specific symptoms that may develop. Problems with dyspnea and secretions are more likely to develop in a patient with lung cancer. Patients with end-stage ovarian cancer are at very high risk for obstruction and severe symptoms of nausea and vomiting. Patients with liver metastases may have more symptoms related to metabolic changes. Durham and Weiss (1997) identify the "irrevocable" events that occur near the time of death: the lungs become unable to take in enough oxygen for adequate gas diffusion and binding with hemoglobin; the heart and blood vessels become unable to maintain adequate circulation to tissues; and the brain ceases to regulate vital centers to maintain life.

Creating a normalcy about changes expected can allow families to continue care (Kemp, 1997). Most caregivers will not have cared for a dying person before, and anticipatory guidance about changing physical symptoms becomes a necessary intervention for the nurse to offer. The family teaching sheet (Box 27-3) provides not only the expected symptoms or changes but also simple interventions to address these concerns.

For as long as possible, administering medications orally remains the preferred choice in terminal care. It combines the reliability of absorption,

TABLE 27-2
SUMMARY OF SYMPTOMS AT THE END OF LIFE

Authors	Number of Patients	Timing of Assessment	Symptom Prevalence
Conhill et al (1997)	176	56% within 48 hours, the rest within the week	Asthenia—80.18% Anorexia—80.1% Dry mouth—69.9% Confusional status—68.2% Constipation—55.1% Dyspnea—46.6%
Turner et al. (1996)	50	Final 72 hours	Pain—56% Lethargy/weakness—36% Dyspnea—26% Restlessness/terminal agitation—18% Emotional distress—12% Nausea/vomiting—12%
Licther & Hunt (1990)	200—36% experienced symptoms	Final 48 hours of the 36% with symptoms	Noisy or moist breathing—56% Pain—51% Restlessness/agitation—42% Incontinence of urine—32% Dyspnea—22% Retention of urine—21%
Ventafridda et al. (1990)	120—52.5% with "unendurable" symptoms requiring sedation-inducing sleep	Average last 2 days before death of 63 patients with "unendurable symptoms"	Dyspnea—52% Pain—49% Delirium—17% Vomiting—8%

ease of titration, simple administration, and lower cost than most other routes (Warren, 1996). However, preparing for symptom management for the last few hours or days includes considering alternative routes of delivery if the patient is unable to sustain oral medications, particularly for those medications needed for symptom management. Transdermal application, subcutaneous injections or infusions, intravenous administration, and rectal administration become the most common alternative options. Dahl (1996) states that most cancer pain can be relieved by relatively simple measures: 75% to 85% of patients receive adequate pain control with oral, rectal and transdermal drugs. Although the rectal route of drug administration has its drawbacks, it has a number of advantages, especially in the home setting: limited patient/family education is required; no high technology is involved; it is the least expensive for the limited time needed; and it is particularly useful when the oral route is acutely unavailable, allowing for a longer-term plan to be established if

needed (Warren, 1996). Box 27-4 instructs on ways to maximize rectal administration of medications.

Many terminal cancer patients who have undergone chemotherapy treatments have a venous access device (VAD) in place (see Chapter 17 for more information on VADs). This can be a viable route for intravenous delivery of medication if needed for delivery of a continuous infusion or intermittent dosing. Home infusion services make it possible for placement of a percutaneous intravenous central catheter (PICC) or a midline catheter if needed. The burden of care increases dramatically when IV medications are involved, increasing both cost and caregiver stress. It is important to evaluate the appropriateness of the intervention.

If a VAD is not available and a parental infusion is needed, especially for pain management, another route is the use of a subcutaneous infusion. Continuous subcutaneous infusion of opioids and other medications has proved to be safe and

BOX 27-3

Handout: Preparing for Death—Common Signs and Symptoms

The Home Health and Hospice staff recognizes that this particular time period for you and your loved one will be one of the most difficult times you will have ever to experience. Our approach in all matters affecting you and your loved ones during this time is to be as honest and straightforward as possible. In this way the team members can establish a trusting relationship and open communication with both you and your loved one. Our philosophy of care is that the "fear of the unkown" is always greater than the "fear of the known." We offer this information to help you prepare and anticipate symptoms that you may experience as the dying progresses. Your nurse and your physician are your best resources to help you clarify your concerns about this information presented. These changes are a normal, natural way in which the body prepares itself for the final stage of life, death. *Not all these symptoms will occur with every person, nor will they occur in this particular sequence.* We want to relate each possible symptom to you in order to decrease your fear if they should occur. After each symptom are some suggestions to enhance comfort, or ask your nurse for further assistance.

1. The person may have a decrease in appetite and thirst, wanting little or no fluid. The body will naturally begin to conserve energy that is expended on these tasks. The person may have difficulty swallowing.
   *Do not force food or drink on your loved one. Offer food and fluids in small portions if they are interested. Small chips of ice, frozen Gatorade, or juice may be refreshing. If the person is able to swallow, fluids may be given in small amounts by a syringe. Toothettes moistened with water or saliva substitute will keep the mouth moist and comfortable if they are unable to swallow.
2. The person will gradually spend more and more time sleeping during the day and appear to be uncommunicative or unresponsive and difficult to arouse at times. This symptom is due in part to change in the body's metabolism.
   *Plan to spend time with your loved one on those occasions when he/she seems most alert or awake. Sit with your loved one, hold his or her hand; do not shake it or speak loudly.
3. The person may become increasingly confused about time, place, and identity of close and familiar people. Again, this is due in part to body metabolism changes.

*Remind your loved one frequently: what day it is, what time it is, and who is in the room talking to them. Explain softly, truthfully, and clearly when you do something for them, e.g., reposition or encouraging them to take medication or sip of water.

4. You may notice the person becoming restless or doing repetitive motions such as pulling at bed linen or clothing. These symptoms may be due in part to a decrease in the oxygen circulation to the brain and decrease in metabolism.
   *Do not try and restrain or interfere with such motions. Speak in a calming way, lightly massage the forehead, recall a favorite person or experience, play some calming music.
5. The person's urine output will decrease. The person's urine may become more concentrated, very dark in color. Incontinence (loss of control) of urine and/or bowel movements may occur as the muscles in that area begin to relax or are too weak. Sometimes there is a need to insert a foley catheter into the bladder.
   *Your nurse will help guide you and your loved one in how to best manage your loved one's incontinence if needed, and hygiene techniques for cleanliness. The nurse can insert a catheter if it is appropriate, and teach you how to manage it easily.
6. The arms and legs of the person may become increasingly cool to the touch and you may notice skin color changes. This is a normal indication that the blood circulation is slowing and is decreasing to the body's extremities and being resent to its most vital organs.
   *Keep warm blankets, but not electric, on the person to prevent him/her from feeling overly cold. Down comforters or cotton blankets or quilts work best.
7. Sometimes secretions may collect in the back of the throat and may make a gurgling sound or rattling sound as air flows past them. You may have heard this referred to as the "death rattle." This symptom is a result of a decrease in the body's intake of fluids and inability to cough up normal secretions. This symptom is often more distressing to the caregiver listening than it is to the person.
   *Providing a humidifier to increase the humidity in the room is helpful; often the person is breath-

(continued)

Handout: Preparing for Death—Common Signs and Symptoms (Continued)

ing through their mouth. Elevating the head of the bed with pillows or raising the head of a hospital bed and repositioning the person's head to the side allows gravity to aid with the drainage of secretions. Your nurse will evaluate if medication is needed.

8. During sleep, at first, you will notice breathing patterns in the person change to an irregular pace where there may be 10–30 seconds of "no breathing." This pattern may continue for hours or even days. Your nurse and doctor refer to this as periods of "apnea." This symptom is very common and indicative of a decrease in circulation and buildup in body waste products. Your loved one may also experience periods of rapid, shallow, pant-like breathing.
   *Elevating the head of the bed and/or turning them on their side often may bring comfort.

9. Clarity of vision may dim or become blurred; hearing usually remains very clear until the end.
   *Keep soft lights on in the room; never assume your loved one cannot hear you. Continue to talk softly to them, *if you can* give them permission to go, reassure them, and let them know how much they mean to you.

It may be helpful for you and your family to think about and discuss what you will do at the time of death. Identify whom you would like to be with you or whom you would like to have called. If there are children, ask selected adults to be "on call" for support at that time. You may like to discuss and decide if clergy or the patient's identified spiritual support person should be called before or at the time of death. It can be helpful to contact the funeral home ahead of time; with an expected death, some decisions can be made and information relayed ahead of time.

How Would You Know That Death Has Occured?

An expected death is not an emergency. Do not call 911. Call your home health or hospice nurse if you think or suspect a death has occurred. Signs of death include such things as:

1. No breathing
2. No heartbeat
3. Loss of control of bladder and/or bowel
4. No response to stimulation
5. Eyelids slightly open
6. Eyes fixed on a certain spot
7. Jaw relaxed and mouth slightly open

Please know that although this information may feel frightening or overwhelming, the team's first goal is to help prepare you for what to expect. Your physical and emotional well-being is as important to us as the dying person's. It is important not to expect that all of these symptoms of approaching death will occur. The focus of this paper is to help you prepare for when or if they do occur. Remember that a member of Home Health or Hospice team is always available to help you.

02/98 Home Health and Hospice of Whidbey General Hospital, Coupeville, WA.

efficacious, offering economic as well as physiologic advantages (Poniatowski, 1991; Storey et al., 1990; Kemp, 1997; Vila & Zarek, 1992). It has volume limitations of no more than 2 mL/h, but high concentrations of the medication can address this as well as connecting two separate sites to a Y connector to the infusion. Poniatowski (1991) cautions, however, that if there is not adequate subcutaneous tissue the patient may experience poor absorption and perfusion.

Pain

The principles of pain management are addressed in Chapter 22, but end-stage pain management requires continuing evaluation and planning for how to maintain a therapeutic level for continued relief as the patient's condition deteriorates and as he or she is unable to swallow and becomes less and less responsive. The patient's source of pain does not go away; his or her ability to communi-

BOX 27-4

Rectal Administration

1. Ensure adequate hydration of the dosage form. If tablets or capsules are being inserted and the rectum is very dry, insert 10 mL warm water to help with dissolution.
2. Insert the dosage form about a finger's length into the rectum. Insertion higher allows a larger part to be absorbed into the superior rectal vein and from there into the portal circulation. Important with drugs that are quickly metabolized by the liver, such as morphine.
3. Keep volumes of drug preparations less than 60–80 mL. This will decrease the chance of spontaneous expulsion from the rectum.
4. When administering multiple tablets into the rectum for a single dose, enclose them in a single gelatin capsule to eliminate the need for multiple insertions.
5. Rectal irritation, while a concern when administering any medication by the rectal route, should not be viewed as a limiting factor when administering commercially prepared suppositories, tablets, or capsules.
6. Avoid repeated rectal instillation of solutions of drugs with alcoholic vehicles or drugs that use glycols as solubizing agents, such as many parenteral forms.
7. Avoid rectal use of enteric-coated tablets. They need an acidic environment for the coating to be dissolved and the active drug to be released.

(Warren, D. [1996]. Practical use of rectal medications in palliative care. *Journal of Pain and Symptom Management, 11*(6), 378–387.)

cate the pain response, however, can become severely compromised. It is important to watch for cues for increased distress. Lichter and Hunt (1990) report that patients may appear to suffer only from movement when they are unresponsive. Even if they are deeply unconscious, they may moan or call out. He encourages gentle, passive range of motion earlier in the trajectory when the patient becomes bedbound to decrease the severity of pain from immobility and joint stiffness. When addressing the pain regimen and delivery, the least complicated alternative route must be considered.

In caring for patients at home, transdermal fentanyl has eased the burden for patients and caregivers in end-stage pain management. Transdermal fentanyl's unique delivery system allows continuous opioid concentration for 72 hours, and it comes in varying strengths from 25 µg/hr to 100 µg/hr. Multiple patches can be applied to achieve higher levels of concentration as needed. Herbst and Strause (1992), who studied transdermal fentanyl use in eleven hospice home care patients, found that they were satisfied with their pain management and, after completing the study, chose to continue this treatment. The major difficulty identified in their study was the obtaining of relief in the first 72 hours with the patch alone. Korte and coworkers (1995) addressed this in their study, which looked at day-to-day titration with fentanyl. The study was based on visual analogue scales and the use of rescue doses of morphine. Fifty-one percent did not need dose increases during days 1 to 3; 49% did need dose increases once or twice. Ahmedzai and colleagues (1997) did a cross-over study in 202 patients comparing oral sustained-relief morphine with transdermal fentanyl, looking at the issues of preference, efficacy, and quality of life. Patients received one treatment for 15 days, then the other for 15 days. Both were equally effective for pain relief. Less constipation ($p < 0.001$) and less daytime drowsiness were noted, and there were no differences in their measurements of quality of life. At the conclusion of the study, 54% preferred the fentanyl because it caused less constipation and decreased interruption of daily activities and was more convenient. Thirty-six percent still preferred the sustained-release morphine.

Because of variability of patient response to transdermal fentanyl, it is preferable to switch while the patient can communicate his or her responses. Also, the caregiver can use breakthrough medications adequately. The conversion in the package insert for transdermal fentanyl equilanalgesic is safe but probably is low at 1:150. Donner and colleagues (1996) started at 1:100 in a direct conversion study of morphine to transdermal fentanyl in 38 patients and, through regression analysis, calculated a mean transdermal/morphine ratio of 1:70. Difficulties with transdermal fentanyl include the equianlagesic conversion, difficulty with adhesion if patients are diaphoretic, increased rate of absorption with fevers; also, because it uses

subcutaneous fat, some cachectic patients may have altered pharmacokinetics. It is important to evaluate patterns of relief; occasionally patients need to be switched to every-48-hour dosing for adequate coverage.

In the algorithm (Figure 27-1) the initial assessment addresses the most common reason for needing to alter the current regimen, difficulty swallowing. Many patients may already have short-acting morphine tablets that can be dissolved easily or liquid morphine, which allows for easy conversion to an around-the-clock (ATC) regimen. The ATC regimen is an option in the short term or as an interim measure while switching to an alternative route. The sustained-released formulations of morphine and oxycodone (Oxycontin) can be used rectally, if multiple pills are used.

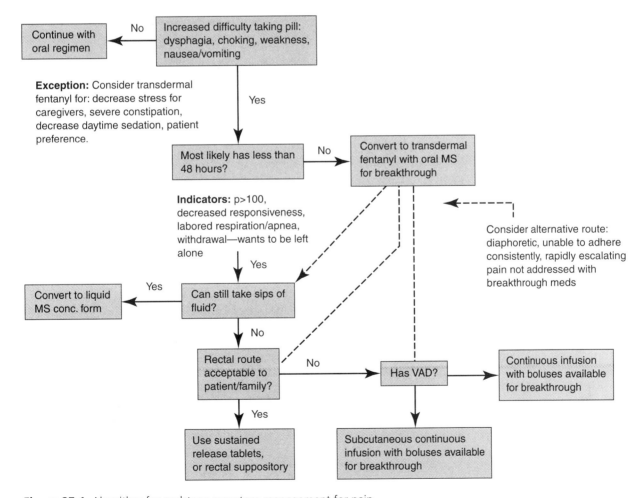

Figure 27-1 Algorithm for endstage symptom management for pain.

Placing these medications in a gel cap eases administration. Commercial rectal suppositories are available for morphine and hydromorphine, but they are low doses and their duration is 4 to 6 hours. Another alternative is the use of transdermal fentanyl (discussed above) if the patient is projected to have a life expectancy greater than 48 hours. (Lindley-Davis [1991], in her study of 11 hospice patients, looked at the dying process and identified that an apical pulse of greater than 100 was a strong indicator that death was imminent, especially when combined with changes in respiratory status and evidence of withdrawal from surroundings and company—wanting minimal visitors and no new introductions.) Other routes for pain medications that can be considered are parenteral, a VAD, or subcutaneous infusion if needed or indicated.

Pain relief is possible in dying patients. Grond (1991) studied cancer pain relief in 401 dying patients. At the time of death, 52% had no pain at all, 24% experienced only mild or moderate pain, 20% were unable to rate their pain, and 3% experienced severe pain.

The nurse is key to providing ongoing evaluation and education to patients and families about their pain regimen and management. Patients and families often have fears that pain will become unbearable and that there will be no way to address the suffering. Reassuring patients that they will continue to receive pain medication even as they deteriorate, that it can be increased as it is needed—that there is no limit, and that as professional caregivers we will evaluate and address it frequently—can ease the burden of the unknown.

Dyspnea

Dyspnea is the subjective feeling of breathlessness, of not being able to get enough air. It is complex, multifactorial, difficult to define, and difficult to relieve completely (Twycross & Lichter, 1998).

Ripamonti and Bruera (1997) state, from the pathophysiologic view, that the symptom of dyspnea is associated with three main abnormalities: (1) increased respiratory effort to overcome a certain load (i.e., pleural effusion), (2) increased proportion of respiratory muscle required to maintain normal workload, and (3) increased ventilatory requirements (i.e., hypoxia, anemia). They identify that the specific reasons cancer patients experience dyspnea may be directly related to the effect of the tumor, the effect of therapy, or other causes (anemia, ascites, fever, infection, heart failure, cachexia).

Treatment of dyspnea is directed at the cause, if possible; in terminal patients these treatment decisions need to be considered carefully. For example, what is the cost/benefit ratio of a pleurodesis for a malignant pleural effusion? Can the patient tolerate the procedure? Can he or she physically get to the clinic? How fast is the effusion expected to reaccumulate? How much relief is expected? Then, most importantly, there is the need to address the symptom.

Supportive measures include placing the patient in an upright position, limiting and pacing activities, and performing regular and frequent oral care (Kemp, 1997). Altering the environment can be helpful by finding the comfort range for room temperature (often a cool range is preferred), eliminating irritants, increasing ventilation, and using a fan (Kemp, 1997; Twycross & Lichter, 1998; Lichter & Hunt, 1990). Relaxation techniques and guided imagery may be used to help control both anxiety and rate of breathing (Twycross & Lichter, 1998).

Medical treatment includes using medications for anxiety (lorazepam, alprazolom, diazepam). Anxiety is a large component of dyspnea. Morphine has been found to work both on anxiety and dyspnea (Kemp, 1997; Twycross & Lichter, 1998). Bruera (1990), in one of the first studies to actually measure morphine's effect on dyspnea, found that morphine could improve the symptom without significantly changing respiratory rate, saturation of O_2, or expiratory CO_2. Oxygen can be helpful, especially if the patient is cyanotic, but not usually as often or as much as the patient would hope. Morphine sulfate at 2 to 5 mg every 4 hours for the opiate-naive patient is the standard starting dose. If the patient is on opioids, he or she may need up to a 50% increase to achieve the desired effect (Twycross & Lichter, 1998; Bruera, 1990; Lichter & Hunt, 1990). Nebulized morphine is reported to relieve breathlessness in the terminal patient (Twycross & Lichter, 1998). There have not yet been any larger prospective studies. Other medications to consider are bronchodilators for chronic obstructive disease and steroids (Kemp, 1997).

The nurse needs to remember how frightening the experience of dyspnea is for patients and their family members. Maintaining a calm and reassuring approach, explaining symptoms experienced, and advocating for aggressive medical management to lessen discomfort is warranted.

"Death Rattle"

"Death rattle" is the term used to describe the noisy ventilation that is heard when patients are unable to clear secretions (Bennett, 1996). It does often occur when death is imminent, but it can come and go through the last several days.

Bennett (1996) explains that the secretions are produced and retained from two sources, the salivary glands and the bronchial mucosa. When patients are no longer able to swallow and have no cough reflexes, supine or semi-recumbent positions allow secretions to pool in the oropharnyx and bronchi. Turbulence of air created by breathing over these secretions creates the death rattle. He proposes that there are two types of death rattle. In the first, predominantly salivary secretions accumulate when the swallowing reflexes are inhibited; this becomes clinically apparent in the last few hours of life. The second type is predominantly bronchial secretions accumulating over several days as the patient becomes too weak to cough; this becomes apparent even earlier in the trajectory with an infection.

Scopolamine works by inhibiting salivary secretions and depressing ventilation and, probably to some degree, bronchial dilation. In Bennett's study of 100 patients (1996), scopolamine was likely to give a good response in the first type of secretion, but with the second type it was much more difficult to get any response at all. Lichter & Hunt's (1990) study found that in the 55% of their patients who experienced the death rattle, 94% found effective relief from only one dose of scopolamine and only 6% needed repeated dosing. The dose for intermittent dosing is O.4 mg SC every 4 hours; also, use of the transdermal patch is easy and can be effective.

Atropine can also be used. It tends to be excitatory but its action does decrease sputum production (Bennett, 1996). The recommended dose is usually 0.4 to 0.6 mg parenteral solution either orally or subcutaneously. Small doses of furosemide may be helpful if there is a heart failure component.

If necessary, morphine can be administered at doses large enough to reduce the depth of breathing to 12 to 15 per minute so that breathing becomes quieter (Lichter & Hunt, 1990).

Delirium/Restlessness

Defining the mental changes that occur when a patient is imminently dying generates several different labels: confusional status (Conhill et al., 1997), terminal agitation (Turner et al., 1996; March, 1998), or end-stage delirium (Ventafidda et al., 1990). Whatever it is called, the symptom of altered mental status is often feared by the patient and very distressing to families. Restlessness more often than not accompanies these mental changes. The first intervention is to determine if there is a treatable cause. Look for things such as pain, bladder or rectal distention, or the need to be repositioned (March, 1998). Review and readjust medications if indicated; with multisystem failure it may be necessary to pare down the list to symptom-management medications only.

Often at this point in deterioration, when death is most likely imminent, the oral route is not an option. If pain or discomfort may be adding or compounding the difficulty and symptoms, titrating opioids upward may give the patient relief. If the patient is not on an opioid, start with a low dose of morphine, 2.5 to 5 mg, using a concentrated solution or commercially prepared or dissolving tablets, and slowly administer toward the back of the throat if tolerated. An effective and versatile medication is lorazepam 0.5 to 2 mg PO or bucally every 4 to 6 hours. The tablet is easily dissolved and absorbed; it works especially well if there is an anxiety component. Other medications that may be effective are alprazolam, diazepam, and chlorpromazine. Diazepam and chlorpromazine are available in rectal suppositories. Midazolam SC is an effective but expensive option (March, 1998).

Supporting the family when the patient is experiencing these symptoms is imperative. Encourage them to use a calm and accepting approach with their loved one and to be a presence. Explore with the patient and family whether there is any underlying unfinished business that the patient is trying to communicate. Review the phenomenon of near-death awareness with the family to facilitate these explorations.

Case Study:

Near-Death Awareness

Richard recognized and greeted me with an engaging sweet smile. He was a young and bright 40-year-old hospice patient being cared for at home by his wife and family and had been on my caseload for about 3 months. He had advanced pancreatic cancer and had deteriorating rapidly over the last week. The first task after the assessment was to reaccess his catheter. He was on a continuous Dilaudid infusion. As I was bending over him, he was looking past me over my shoulder. He had a glassy-eyed look, unfocused. I asked him what was it that he saw. He told me he was trying to see through the fog; his plane didn't know which way to go and he needed help from the cockpit crew. I asked him who was in the cockpit. He laughed and said Darlene, his wife, but I could be too if I wanted. Darlene was a retired nurse and had been a very attentive caregiver, open to suggestions and some assistance, but she definitely was in charge. Though she knew he was dying, she wanted to have as much time with him as possible. I asked him what the fog meant to him. He was quiet while I was finishing my task, adding the new bag of medication and helping his wife turn and position him. I sat beside him in his hospital bed when we were finished, and his wife sat on the other side. He then began to articulate that he needed to understand the changes he was experiencing, that the fog was the unknown. Richard was able to say he knew he was actively dying and that he needed Darlene to understand, that it was going to be okay "in the cockpit," that the journey he was on now needed to be acknowledged. This symbolic interchange allowed for a very meaningful conversation about the things he was experiencing, how we thought from the best of our knowledge it would continue, and for his wife to be able to say she was going to be able to continue to support him in the dying process and to let him go now that the time was at hand. He died about 2 weeks after that conversation had occurred.

Patients who are in the final hours, days, or weeks often undergo a period of seeming confusion. In their book *Final Gifts*, Callahan and Kelly explore and identify a phenomena called "Nearing Death Awareness"—when the patient may be trying to communicate what is happening to him or her or is making a request for something that person needs for a peaceful death. In the experience described above, Richard uses a common metaphor often found in these communications, that of travel. He is describing his journey and is conveying what he needs to get there from both the nurse and his wife.

Callahan and Kelly state that nearing death awareness resembles in some ways the near-death experiences reported by people who have been resuscitated after being clinically dead. These people report similar events of seeing bright lights, traveling through a tunnel, being in the presence of a supreme being—all very comforting phenomena. The distinction is that the near death experience happens suddenly, while nearing death awareness happens slowly as the process of leaving this world occurs. The person is aware of a dimension that lies beyond. He or she may also see, hear, or talk to people or family members from the past or who have died before.

For nurses who care for patients who are dying, being aware of the many different ways the patient may be communicating can allow for messages or requests that otherwise may be ignored or attributed to confusion or hallucination, rather than interpreted and responded to. The "Nearing Death Awareness" handout for families allows them to participate in those periods (Box 27-5). It is a useful tool to review for the nurse too. Often it is modeling by the nurse that gives the family permission to participate in a meaningful way when these conversations occur.

Creating a Supportive Physical Environment

The environment can be created to attend to the different senses of the patient. Creating rituals that include the different senses of touch, smell, sight, sound, and taste can be both comforting and supportive. These interventions can occur whether in the hospital, inpatient hospice, skilled nursing facility, or at home.

BOX 27-5

Family Handout: Nearing Death Awareness

"Nearing death awareness" is the phenomenon a person may experience in the process of dying. As a person is nearing death in the final hours, days, or weeks of their life, they may make statements or gestures that seem to make no sense. Sometimes they are trying to communicate what they are experiencing or their "awareness" of approaching death. By keeping opend minds and listening carefully, we can begin to understand messages they are conveying through symbols or suggestion. Often these messsages fall in two categories: what they are experiencing while dying, or requests for what they need for a peaceful death. They may see visions of loved ones or spiritual beings or make reference to travel, change, or things in their past. Sometimes the dying person's messages are difficult to understand or decipher. It may be difficult for them to communicate; try not to be frustrated. Here are some suggestions to keep in mind. (Please substitute in your reading your family member or your loved one for "the patient" to personalize it for your situation.)

- Attend to everything the dying person says. Keep pens and paper close by so that anyone can jot down notes about gestures, conversations, or anything out of the ordinary said by the patient. Talk with one another about these comments and gestures.
- Remember that there may be important messages in any communication, however vague and garbled. Not every statement made by the patient has significance, but heed them all so as not to miss the ones that do.
- Be open for key signs: a glassy-eyed look; the appearance of staring through you; distractedness or secretiveness; seemingly inappropriate smiles or gestures, such as pointing, reaching toward someone or something unseen, or waving when no one is there; efforts to pick at the covers or get out of bed for no apparent reason; agitation or distress at your inability to comprehend something the patient has tried to say
- Respond to anything you don't understand with gentle inquiries, for instance, "Can you tell me what's happening?" This is sometimes a helpful way to initiate this kind of conversation. You might also try saying, "You seem different today. Can you tell me why?"
- Pose questions in open-ended, encouraging terms. For example, if the patient whose mother is deceased says, "My mother is waiting for me," turn that comment into a question: "Mother's waiting for you?" or "I'm so glad she's close to you. Can you tell me about it?"
- Accept and validate what the patient tells you. If he/she says, "I see a beautiful place!", say, "I'm so pleased. I can see that it makes you happy," or "I'm so glad you're telling me this. I really want to understand what's happening to you. Can you tell me more?"
- Remember that the patient may employ images from life experiences like work or hobbies.
- Be honest about having trouble understanding. One way is to say, "I think you're tryiing to tell me something important and I'm trying very hard, but I'm just not getting it. I'll keep trying."
- Don't push. Let the patient control the breadth and depth of the conversation—they may not be able to put their experiences in words; more talk may frustrate or overwhelm them.
- Avoid instilling a sense of failure. If the information is garbled or the delivery impossibly vague, show that you appreciate the effort by saying, "I can see that this is hard for you; I appreciate your trying to share it with me," "I can see you're getting tired/angry/frustrated. Would it be easier if we talked about this later?", or "Don't worry. We'll keep trying and maybe it will come."
- If you don't know what to say, don't say anything. Sometimes the best response is simply to touch their hand or smile and stroke his or her forehead. Touching gives the important message "I'm with you."
- Remember the patient sometimes chooses an unlikely confidant. Those close to death often try to communicate important information to someone who makes them feel safe who won't get upset or be taken aback by such confidences.

(Adapted from Callahan, M. & Kelly, P. [1992]. *Final gifts: Understanding the special awareness, needs, and communications of the dying.* New York: Bantam Books.)

Touch is a unique way to share presence and love from the heart when words are meaningless (Achterberg et al., 1994). Families and those who sit with the dying may be overwhelmed and confused how best to initiate touch. Often they are afraid they are going to hurt their loved one or may be uncomfortable touching the deteriorating body. Bottlifk (1997) has identified the five types of touching nurses can and do use as interventions when caring for cancer patients: comforting, connecting, working, orienting, and social touch. Nurses use touch in many therapeutic interactions and are in the unique position of being able to model this behavior for caregivers. Encouraging and allowing families to participate in some of the rituals of bathing, positioning, and personal care can be a nonthreatening way to begin. Massage can be offered to ease discomfort, be incorporated into passive range of motion, and used for painful peripheral edema, reducing swelling by increasing blood and lymph flow (Urba, 1996). It is important to elicit feedback from the patient about what may or may not be comfortable and to tell the patient before you initiate any kind of contact.

Touching also includes hugging, holding, and cuddling as powerful ways to break the illusion of separateness, loneliness, and fear that surfaces during "deathing" (Achterberg et al., 1994). Encouraging families and caregivers to simply sit and hold the hand of their loved one can often be enough to help establish a caring and intimate connection. A soft stuffed animal or the warmth of a real pet can be a sweet source of touch as well (Furman & McNabb, 1997).

Smell is a very personal matter. The offensive smells of illness can add to the discomfort and be overwhelming at times. Nausea can be easily induced. A complementary therapy that is gaining popularity is aromatherapy, the use of essential oils obtained from plants in order to obtain physical, emotional, or aesthetic well-being (Urba, 1996). For the immediate environment the use of vaporization, in which a few drops of oil are placed in water over a small candle burner, can add a hint of fragrance to the room. Oils as a vehicle for the essential oils can be used for massage. Many scents are thought to elicit different emotional responses; relaxing oils include lavender, tangerine, sandalwood, and clary sage. Sometimes fresh linens, fresh air, or lightly scented flowers are

enough (Achterberg et al., 1994). It is important that caregivers and nurses are mindful and avoid using strongly scented perfume, soaps, and hairsprays.

The use of lighting is important to the sense of sight. Soft lighting is usually the preference. Unfortunately, most hospitals have fluorescent lighting, but indirect lighting and night lights can be used as an alternative. In the home setting, shaded lamps at eye level are more comfortable than overhead lights (Furnam & McNabb, 1997).

Provide familiar and favored articles to surround the patient, such as family pictures or a favorite knickknack. Favorite bedclothes or lingerie or new, more comfortable and practical clothing to lounge in should be encouraged. Baggy sweats and cotton tube socks keep patients warm and ease the difficulty of dressing.

Furman and McNabb (1997) describe the use of color, which can be stimulating or soothing. Generally, they report, soft, muted tones are best, with watercolors of greens and blues as soothing. Colors to avoid are red, yellow, and orange; they may invoke anxiety. Patients' preferences should be explored. At home, personal linens can be used very creatively. Children's sheets can be used for those with a sense of humor. Favored quilts and the use of lap blankets can also be considered.

Sound may be used in a variety of ways. Encourage the patient and family to use what makes sense for that individual. Many types of soothing music selections for relaxation and meditation can be used as an intervention or to provide a pleasant background, depending on the patient's likes or dislikes. He or she may prefer gospel, jazz, classical, folk, or perhaps the quiet. The noise of the television can even be comforting, especially if it is part of the patient's normal routine. Some patients enjoy being read to. If the patient is too weak to participate in conversation, storytelling around the bedside can be meaningful. Family members are continually reminded that the patient can continue to hear even after he or she cannot respond and to continue to talk to the patient until death occurs.

The most distressing symptom for some patients is the taste changes. Cool sips of flavored fluids, diluted juices, ice chips, sherbets, and ices can sometimes pacify the discomfort of taste alterations. The patient may be at the point at which he or she is not eating or drinking. As reviewed above, mouth care becomes very important for comfort. Peppermint-flavored toothettes are refreshing and require minimal effort.

Involving the family in creating individualized strategies in addressing the senses is very important. It provides validation of their relationship and history with the patient. It allows for reflection on who that person is, his or her likes and dislikes, and what may be meaningful and symbolic to incorporate into care at the end of his or her life.

Case Study:

After-Death Care

Julie paged the hospice nurse on call, "I think my mom is gone." A visit was offered as it was evident she was extremely upset and uncertain of herself. Julie had been the primary caregiver to her mother, who had been diagnosed with lung cancer and widespread metastatic disease a few months ago. Upon the nurse's arrival, both Julie and her college-aged daughter Cindy were there at the mother's bedside, crying softly and comforting each other. The nurse listened with her stethoscope, and the mother had indeed died. The nurse sat down with them both and asked them what she could do for them now and offered to have them help prepare the body before the mortician arrived. Julie had a pretty gown that she wanted to have put on her mother, and Cindy said she had promised Grandma that she would paint her toenails. Julie's mother had some severe neuropathies, which had made it difficult in those last few months to get her weekly pedicure, and she was such a proper "little old lady" that details were important to her. Julie and the nurse bathed her with water laced with her favorite perfume, brushed her white hair and tied it with a ribbon, and dressed her in the chosen gown. Cindy meanwhile painted her toe nails in bright pink. It was a meaningful time for this family. The nurse facilitated the conversation to review this passing life and to physically prepare the body. They laughed and cried as they were able to take the time to reflect on their loved one's life and death, to say good-bye.

After-death care, whether done by the nurses or the family, can be symbolic and respectful. The nurse's attitude towards the patient's body is likely to be more memorable for the family than the attention that they themselves receive (Hill, 1997). The family should be invited to participate if they would care to and, if they would not like to, be invited back to the patient's bedside after the care is done. It is important to return the body to as close to its natural state as possible—to remove the foley catheter, disconnect IVs and pumps, and remove the oxygen tubing. It is important to lay the body nearly flat. Wash at least the face and comb the hair. Close the eyes if possible. Check with family members, but replacing dentures (if possible) can improve the contours of the face, which are often sharp from weight loss. The jaw often stays relaxed. Remove any jewelry the family would like to keep in their possession. Sometimes it is necessary to use lotion to slip rings off. Straighten the bedding, and dim the lights. Offer the family a chance to sit with the body, and make sure there is no one else who would like to see the body before it is removed by the mortuary or taken to the morgue. If a death has occurred at home, the family may want to light some candles to create a soft lighting. They may want to have prayer, a reading, or just quiet, reflective moments before their loved one is taken away. In asking about these things, permission is given and opportunities offered that they may have not thought of in the midst of their grief.

Funeral homes usually place the body in a body bag. This can be very upsetting to families, especially if they are not aware that this may happen. In explaining this to families before the funeral home arrives, you can ask them if they would like to go to another room. Some funeral homes ask families to leave; most give them a choice.

There may or may not have been an opportunity to have the patient participate in his or her funeral planning. Some patients have strong feelings or beliefs about preferences: burial or cremation, a service or no service, and where they would like their final resting place to be. Funeral directors are trained in assisting families through the process and are very helpful if no directions have been left. There are many types of services: a funeral service has the body present and is held at a place of worship or at the funeral home; a memorial service is a service without the body present; a private service is by invitation only and may be held at a place of worship, a funeral home, or a family home. These services vary in ceremony and procedures according to community affiliations and religion, denomination, and belief system.

The funeral ceremony provides an opportunity for the survivors and others who share in the loss to express their love, respect, grief, and appreciation for the person's life. It is a significant event for the bereaved and the beginning of their journey without their loved one.

Case Study:

Bereavement Care

I remember vividly one of the first bereavement visits I made as a young nurse. I was so nervous about what I was going to say or what I could possibly offer Anna Mae in the face of losing her spouse, Ralph, of 67 years. From my perspective he had a rapid decline. He had been diagnosed with liver cancer only 2 months before. At 88 years of age Ralph had multiple chronic health problems: CHF, atrial fibrillation, and diabetes. It was difficult for his body to accommodate to the rapidly accumulating ascites and metabolic changes. Ralph died in his sleep and pain never became an issue. Anna Mae was saddened and grieving the loss of her companion of almost 70 years, but the story she needed to tell that day was the decline and death of her daughter who had died 20 years earlier of a brain tumor. She eloquently recounted the suffering, the aching sense of loss, and the numbing sadness of the "lack of order" in losing a child. As I listened to her story, it was as if I could almost touch the pain that Anna Mae expressed. It made little sense to me then. I know I must have looked a bit bewildered as she explained to me that Ralph and she understood one of them would need to go first and they had both lived for such a very long time. She assured me she missed him dearly, but the waves and tears of anguish about her daughter were so prominent in her thoughts. Years later, I have now done this for many years, and have children of my own. I understand the loss of a child is inexplicably painful and that with each loss the winds of grief and memories are stirred, and so it is important to be prepared to explore previous losses in the context of the current situation. Anna Mae grabbed my arm as I bid her farewell and said ". . . it's all in the telling of the story. Thank you for listening to mine."

The nurse often provides care to the bereaved, whether she is present at the time of death, answering the page, or providing a follow-up bereavement visit. The nurse will respond to the bereaved depending both on her relationship with the patient and family and her own issues concerning death and dying. Although grief is a deeply personal experience, it most often occurs within the context of a family and therefore inevitably is influenced by and, in turn, influences the grieving experience of other family members (Kissane et al., 1997). Energy must be focused on the family unit, whether it will be only a brief encounter or a more focused course of intervention with follow-up visits.

Grief is a profound personal emotion, influenced by past losses and the meaning of the relationship lost, along with the survivor's personality, coping mechanisms, and level of faith. It is difficult to explain or describe the feelings that accompany a death, and can be altogether too overwhelming and unexpected. Therefore, providing normative information to families about grief both verbally and in writing is extremely important in bereavement care (Kemp, 1997). Whereas for some bereavement can provide opportunities to find new directions that may lead to psychological, social, and spiritual growth (Parkes, 1998), for others it may trigger a cascade of negative events or outcomes.

Some individuals are at high risk for poor bereavement outcome. Cooley (1992) presents seven major predictors of poor bereavement outcome of which nurses should be aware. First is the circumstances that surround the death. People who had less than 2 weeks to prepare for the death had more difficulty coping than those who had more time. Second is the nature of the relationship with the deceased; negative consequences result when there has been a highly dependent and clinging relationship with the deceased or ambivalence. The third predictor is previous difficulty with coping or poor coping skills. The fourth predictor is age; younger persons experienced more difficulty in adjusting compared with older individuals, especially if there were young children at home. The most important indicator of positive bereavement outcome is social support. Remarkably, it is perceived social support more than the actual received support that is most helpful. The final two indicators are previous physical and mental health problems that predispose individuals to greater risk during bereavement. These predictors can allow the nurse to identify those who will most likely need or benefit from ongoing bereavement support or a referral to a community resource or program.

In the hospital setting it is sometimes difficult to provide a comprehensive bereavement program. Referrals to community resources are appropriate. Some hospice bereavement programs are open to the community, and many churches have developed and provided resources. There may also be formal groups available in the community for those who have lost children or spouses. Burke and Gerraghty (1994) describe the process their oncology unit experienced developing and implementing a program that offered both educational and emotional support for recently bereaved families. It was initiated with an act as simple as sending bereavement cards and went on to provide biannual survivor support programs. Addressing some level of bereavement care is important to incorporate into care of dying patients.

The nurse often provides a follow-up visit to the bereaved for a death at home, though some programs have specific bereavement counselors. The goal for the initial visit is to evaluate coping, identify those at high risk for poor bereavement outcomes, allow for the storytelling, and provide referrals as indicated or as the program dictates. The consensus is that the best time to start or initiate a follow-up visit is 3 to 8 weeks after the event (Parkes, 1998).

Parkes (1998) provides some guiding principles for a bereavement visit, but cautions that there are no rules of thumb because every situation is different. The most important principle is to take adequate time and listen. The bereaved should do most of the talking, and the nurse must not talk too much. The best way to facilitate grief and begin the visit is to ask them to tell their story. Parkes' insight is important here. He explains that while the bereaved are explaining themselves to the nurse, they are explaining themselves to themselves. The event they describe becomes more real and the implications are clearer. The other intervention to offer is positive reassurance about the normality of grief and simple explanations of any symptoms that are frightening or bothering them.

Kemp (1997) identifies other tasks besides telling the story that should be incorporated into bereavement care. One task is encouraging the bereaved to express and accept sadness. Another task is to express and accept guilt, anger, and other feelings perceived as negative. Expressing and acknowledging these feelings allows for exploring, understanding, and addressing them. Reviewing the family's relationship with the deceased is similar to a life review and can incorporate other tasks in the telling of the story. Finally, exploring possibilities of life after death is important. He points out that in the early days after the death with the pain of acute grief, the future seems horrible because the feelings of despair and emptiness are so overwhelming. Experiencing the suffering associated with grief is a necessary precursor to looking into the future. He points out there is no specific point or estimated time line for the grief response, but there is usually a gradual awareness that the future possesses hope.

The nurse as the bereaved should not be overlooked, and a personal inventory should be initiated upon the death of a patient. Lev (1994) points out that establishing an effective and rewarding relationship with a dying patient requires some level of self-protection. The more intense the caregiving, the more intense the nurse–patient relationship can become, and greater care-related strain is often a predictor of greater strain during bereavement.

Finding ways to address and support grieving as an individual is important in allowing the nurse to continue working with dying patients and to prevent burnout. The nurse needs to explore her own reactions and feelings about the death, find ways to achieve closure, and validate the relationship with the patient and family. This might occur in many ways. Attending funerals, making follow-up calls to the family, providing an initial bereavement visit, and addressing it in a work group context, either formal or informal, are pathways to provide closure for the nurse. Creating a ritual that makes sense to the nurse can ensure consistency in acknowledging grief. A ritual may be as simple as lighting a candle, writing a goodbye note in a journal, or buying a flower in remembrance to keep on a bedside table for a time.

Conclusion

Caring for the dying is a difficult but rewarding part of nursing. The patient who is dying of cancer needs the very best of what nursing has to offer. Compassion and clinical competence play a significant role in assisting the patient and family in the process of dying. Many complicated and difficult physical and psychosocial issues will challenge the patient, the family, and the nurse. Anticipating the changes, being open to the mysterious and the spiritual, and taking opportunities to validate another's existence become the focus of both nursing care and care for the dying.

> *. . . being present as someone is dying tears the boundaries between the personal and professional realms of my being. The experience of a patient dying challenges me to accept a more intimate, and yet more deeply respectful, relationship with that person. I do not know how it could be otherwise. While I may bring clinical skills and years of experience to the task, ultimately I am simply present, offering to help and wanting to learn.*
>
> Ira Byock, MD, author of Dying Well

REFERENCES

Achterberg, J., Dossey, B. & Kolkmeier, L. (1994). *Rituals of healing: Using imagery for health and wellness.* New York: Bantam Books.

Ahmedzai, S., & Brooks, D. (1997) Transdermal fentanyl versus sustained-release oral morphine in cancer pain: Preference, efficacy, and quality of life. *Journal of Pain and Symptom Management, 13*(5), 254–261.

American Cancer Society (1998). *Cancer facts and figures.* Atlanta: Author.

Bennett, M. (1996). Death rattle: An audit of hyoscine (scopolamine) use and review of management. *Journal of Pain and Symptom Management, 12*(4), 229–233.

Bruera, E. Macmillan, K., Pither, J., & MacDonald, R. (1990). Effects of morphine on the dyspnea of terminal cancer patients. *Journal of Pain and Symptom Management, 5*(6), 341–344.

Burke, C. & Gerraughty, S. (1994). An oncology unit's initiation of a bereavement support program. *Oncology Nursing Forum, 21*(10), 1675–1679.

Burge, F. (1993). Dehydration symptoms of palliative care cancer patients. *Journal of Pain and Symptom Management, 8*(7), 454–464.

Byock, I. (1995). Patient refusal of nutrition and hydration: Walking the ever-finer line. *American Journal of Hospice and Palliative Care, 12*(2), 8–13.

Byock , I. (1996). The nature of suffering and the nature of opportunity at the end of life. *Clinics in Geriatric Medicine, 12*(2), 237–252.

Byock, I. (1997). *Dying well: The prospect for growth at the end of life.* New York: Riverhead Books.

Callahan, M. & Kelly, P. (1992). *Final gifts: Understanding the special awareness, needs, and communications of the dying.* New York: Poseiden Press.

Cooley, M. (1992). Bereavement care: A role for nurses. *Cancer Nursing, 15*(2), 125–129.

Conhill, C., Verger, E., Henriquez, I., Saiz, N., Espier, M., Lugo, F., & Garrigos, A. (1997). Symptom prevalence in the last week of life. *Journal of Pain and Symptom Management, 14*(6), 328–331.

Corliss, I. (1991) Dying well: Symptom control within hospice care. *Annual Review of Nursing Research, 12,* 125–146.

Dahl, J. (1996). Effective pain management in terminal care. *Clinics in Geriatric Medicine, 12*(2), 279–298.

Donner, B., Zenz, M., Tryba, M. & Strumpf, M. (1996). Direct conversion from oral morphine to transdermal fentanyl: A multicenter study in patients with cancer pain. *Pain, 64,* 527–534.

Dunphy, K., Finley, I., Rathbone, G., Gilbirt, J., & Hicks, F. (1995). Rehydration in palliative and terminal care: If not—why not? *Palliative Medicine, 9*(3), 221–-228.

Durham, E. & Weiss, L. (1997). How patients die. *American Journal of Nursing, 97*(12), 41–46.

Furman, J. & McNabb, D. (1997). *The dying time: Practical wisdom for the dying and their caregivers.* New York: Bell Tower.

Germino, B. (1991). Cancer and the family. In S. Baird, R. McCorkle, & M. Grant (Eds.), *Cancer nursing: A comprehensive textbook.* Philadelphia: W.B. Saunders.

Goetschuis, S. (1997). Families and end-of-life care: How do we meet their needs? *Journal of Gerontological Nursing, 23*(3), 43–49.

Grond, S., Zech, D., Schug, S., Lynch, J., & Lehmann, K. (1991). Validation of World health Organization guidelines for cancer pain relief during the last days and hours of life. *Journal of Pain and Symptom Management, 6*(7), 411–422.

Herbst, L. & Strause, L. (1992). Transdermal fentanyl use in hospice home-care patients with chronic cancer pain. *Journal of Pain and Symptom Management, 7*(3), S54–S57.

Hill, C. (1997). Evaluating the quality of after death care. *Nursing Standard 12*(8), 36–39.

Hospice Association of America (1997). *Hospice facts and figures.* Washington, D.C.: Author.

Hull, M. (1992). Coping strategies of family caregivers in hospice homecare. *Oncology Nursing Forum, 19*(8), 1179–1187.

Korte, W., Stoutz, M., & Morant, R. (1995) Day-to-day titration to initiate transdermal fentanyl in patients with cancer pain: Short- and long-term experience in a prospective study. *Journal of Pain and Symptom Management,11,* 139–146.

Kemp, C. (1995). *Terminal care: A guide to nursing care.* Philadelphia: J.B. Lippincott.

Kemp, C. (1997). Palliative care for respiratory problems in terminal illness. *American Journal of Hospice and Palliative Care, 14*(1), 26–30.

Kissane, D., McKenzie, D., & Block, S. Family coping and bereavement outcome. *Palliative Medicine, 11*(3), 191–201.

Lev, E. (1994). Issues for the nurse caring for dying patients. In S. Hubbard, P. Green, & M. Knobf (Eds.), *Oncology nursing: Patient treatment and support.* Philadelphia: J.B. Lippincott.

Lichter, I. & Hunt, E. (1990). The last 48 hours of life. *Journal of Palliative Care, 6*(4), 7–15.

Lindley-Davis, B. (1991). Process of dying: Defining characteristics. *Cancer Nursing, 14*(6), 328–333.

March, P. (1998). Terminal restlessness. *American Journal of Hospice and Palliative Care, 15*(1), 51–53.

McCann, R., Hall, W., & Groth-Juncker, A. (1994). Comfort care for terminally ill patients: The appropriate use of nutrition and hydration. *Journal of the American Medical Association, 272*(16), 1263–1266.

McMillan, S. & Mahon, M. (1994). The impact of hospice services on the quality of life of primary caregivers. *Oncology Nursing Forum, 21*(7), 1189–1195.

Muhlhern, P. (1998). Point...counterpoint: Can homecare services adequately address end-of-life issues? *ONS News, 13*(2), 8, 12.

Musgrave, C.F. (1990). Terminal dehydration: To give or not to give intravenous fluids? *Cancer Nursing, 13*(1), 62–66.

Nuland, S. B. (1994). *How we die: Reflections on life's final chapter.* New York: Alfred A. Knopf.

Ontario Funeral Service Association (1997). *Funeral etiquette.* Ontario: Author.

Parkes, C. (1998). Bereavement. In D. Doyle, G. Hanks, & N. MacDonald (Eds.), *Oxford textbook of palliative medicine.* Oxford: Oxford University Press.

Poniatowski, B. (1991). Continuous subcutaneous infusions for pain control. *Journal of Intravenous Nursing, 14*(1), 30–35.

Raudonis, B., & Kirsching, J. (1996). Family caregivers' perspectives on hospice nursing care. *Journal of Palliative Care, 12*(2), 14–19.

Reimer, J., Davies, B., & Martens, N. (1991). Palliative care: The nurse's role in helping families through the transition of "fading away." *Cancer Nursing, 4*(6), 321–327.

Ripamonti, C., & Bruera, E. (1997). Dyspnea: Pathophysiology and assessment. *Journal of Pain and Symptom Management, 13*(4), 220–232.

Seale, C. & Kelly, M. (1997). A comparison of hospice and hospital care for people who die: Views of the surviving spouse. *Palliative Medicine, 11*(2), 93–100.

Smith, S.A. (1995). Patient-induced dehydration—Can it ever be therapeutic? *Oncology Nursing Forum, 22*(10), 1487–1491.

Smith, S.A. (1997). Controversies in hydrating the terminally ill patient. *Journal of Intravenous Nursing, 20*(4), 193–200.

Storey, P., Hill, H., Louis, R. & Tarver, E. (1990). Subcutaneous infusions for control of cancer symptoms. *Journal of Pain and Symptom Management, 15*(1), 33–41.

Taylor, M.A. (1995). Benefits of dehydration in terminally ill patients. *Geriatric Nursing, 16,* 271–272.

Turner, K., Chye, R., Aggarwal, G., Philip, J., Skeels, A., & Lickiss, J. (1996). Dignity in dying: A preliminary study of patients in the last three days of life. *Journal of Palliative Care, 12*(2), 7–13.

Twycross, R. & Lichter, I. (1998). The terminal phase. In D. Doyle, G. Hanks, & N. MacDonald (Eds.), *Oxford textbook of palliative medicine.* Oxford: Oxford University Press.

Urba, S. (1996). Nonpharmacologic pain management in terminal care. *Clinics in Geriatric Medicine, 12*(2), 301–311.

Ventafridda, V., Ripmonti, C., De Conno, F., Tamburini, B, & Cassilieth, B. (1990). Symptom prevalance and control during cancer patients' last days of life. *Journal of Palliative Care, 6*(3), 7–11.

Villa, E. & Zarek, J. (1992). Clinical pharmacology and the management of pain. In J. Kornell (Ed.), *Pain management and care of the terminal patient.* Seattle: Washington State Medical Association.

Warren, D. (1996). Practical use of rectal medications in palliative care. *Journal of Pain and Symptom Management, 11*(6), 378–387.

Weenolsen, P. (1997). *The art of dying.* New York: St. Martin's Griffin.

Zerwekh, J. (1991). Supportive care of the dying patient. In S. Baird, R. McCorkle, & M. Grant (Eds.), *Cancer nursing: A comprehensive textbook.* Philadelphia: W.B. Saunders.

Zerwekh, J. (1997). Do dying patients really need IV fluids? *American Journal of Nursing, 97*(3), 26–30.

Spirituality

Jill Nuckolls

CHAPTER

28

Spirituality—it is a word that speaks volumes, and means something different to all. One's spirit is one's soul. It is the essence of one's being, all that one is. It seeks to look beyond the physical and into the heart. It is all the emotions, all the experiences, all the values held by that person. It is that person. It is also what makes that person unique, yet bound to all humans. If a person allows us into that realm of his or her being, it is an honor and a sacred place because it is a place where there are no facades to protect. It is a place where all the scars, the tears, the fears, and the joys are laid out to be rejected or loved. We, as nurses, are on occasion allowed into this sacred spot and, thus, we must know how to react and how to heal this dimension of our patients as well as healing their physical illnesses.

Definition of Spirituality

Physicians, too, are beginning to move into examining the spiritual as well as the physical realms. Michello's 1988 work cited physician studies that showed involvement with religious activities acted as buffers against some illnesses, concluding that, "No person can be well physically if he is sick spiritually." In 1997, a review showed that spirituality had again risen to the forefront of the medical field. It was discovered that more than 200 articles had been published based on spirituality. Statistically significant associations have been found between religious belief and health. It has been shown that spiritual practice promotes

health-related behaviors and lifestyles, thus reducing disease risk, enhancing well-being, and providing social support (Levin, Larson & Puchalski, 1997). A recent survey conveyed that 80% of Americans believe that God or prayer can improve the course of illness. However, only 10% of physicians will actively inquire as to a patient's belief system (Levin et al., 1997). This means that, although physicians are aware of the statistics, few act on them. Thus, the nurse should be available and willing to assess and intervene on the patient's behalf.

All disciplines have struggled with the definition of spirituality, and nursing is no exception. Nursing's part in this movement came with the emergence of holistic nursing. The holistic nursing movement acts on an approach that includes caring for the mind, body, and spirit (Dossey et al., 1988). Although seemingly a new idea, this is not the case. As early as Florence Nightingale's era, nurses have been aware of a higher law needing attention. Nightingale applied her spiritual beliefs to her model of practice by stating the need for nurses to "place the patient in the best possible condition for God to act" (McQuiston & Webb, 1995). This statement showed her belief that medicine is only part of the cure and the sense that there is more to a person than the body. She was, in essence, caring holistically for her patients.

Since Nightingale's time, we have expanded the view of what spirituality encompasses. Spirituality is defined by Webster (1988) as "a sensitivity or attachment to religious values." Certainly religion is a component of spirituality. Studies have been conducted on religiousness in terminal illnesses, such as the much-cited research by Reed (1986). This study focused on spirituality from the religious aspect, using a definition that conceptualized spirituality or religiousness as "the perception of one's beliefs and behaviors that express a sense of relatedness to spiritual dimensions or to something greater than the self" (Reed, 1986). Since that point, the view of spirituality has expanded, including those who approach religion through nonorganized views, thus preserving respect for varying viewpoints. This change shows a trend to conceptualizing spirituality as separate from religiousness. Religion is often defined throughout the latest literature as being based on practices and beliefs (Cobb & Forman, 1997). In essence, it is a means to show the values one holds. Other studies conceptualized spirituality more broadly, such as that conducted by Michello in 1988, which stated spirituality to be "an affirmation of life in a relationship with God, self, community, and environment that nurtures and celebrates wholeness."

So what is the "real" definition of spirituality? The quest for a unified definition of spirituality is still fraught with debate. Research has created many definitions. However, a few key components seem to be embedded in most definitions. One of the common threads in studies defining spirituality showed spirituality as involving a search for meaning, in life, death, and/or illness (Copp, 1994; Hungelman et al., 1996; O'Connor et al., 1990; Smucker, 1996; Thompson & Pitts, 1993). Another commonality is the broader view discussed earlier of having a connectedness with God, others, and self. Further consideration of the definition has also revealed many who believe that hope is an important piece of spirituality as a means of coping, in order to find the meaning desired. Carni (1988) posed a definition that faith comes from hope, which is rooted in the psyche of early relationships. Carni focused her research on Erikson's developmental stages of growth, leading her to conclude that regression work may be needed with some patients who did not work through trust issues as children. Owen (1989) posed that hope simply plays a therapeutic role in cancer coping through the spiritual realm. As shown, everyone has a different opinion, just as spirituality encompasses different aspects for various people. In this chapter, spirituality is conceptually defined as a multidimensional concept involving a connectedness between oneself and a higher being, between oneself and the environment in which one participates, and between oneself and the inner being of one's soul, as well as involving a search for the meaning of distressful circumstances with the concept of hope being prominent in this search. This concept arises from Reed's (1992) view of the changing paradigm of spirituality and Parse's conceptual framework of human becoming (McQuiston & Webb, 1995).

By viewing spirituality in this manner, one will transcend the possibilities by stretching the boundaries inward, outward, and upward. By imagining the not yet, as described by Parse, one can connect with a higher being that is not tangible in this life. This part of spirituality includes the organized religiousness many accept into their lives.

An interpersonal connectedness is formed with the environment, including other human beings, by people revealing and concealing who they are and who they are becoming. It is in this dance that we interact with our environment. This dance is never static, as is described by Parse in discussing "human unfolding" (McQuiston & Webb, 1995). She suggests that this changing interpersonal connectedness is part of human becoming and grows through the human "synergistically becoming more complex and more diverse in coexistence with others" (McQuiston & Webb, 1995).

Intrapersonal connectedness involves discovering what Parse calls "valuing." It is the process of sorting through beliefs, deciding which are important, and living life as a testimony to those beliefs. This is another area of spirituality that can incorporate the religious viewpoints one holds. In essence, it is the development of a personal world view, integrating the new into the established belief system and finding a sense of peace with that system.

The Importance of Spirituality in a Cancer Diagnosis

"Isn't that depressing? You must be an angel to take care of cancer patients." These are words nurses hear often when telling people what they do for a living. Most respond, "No, it's not depressing, although it can be sad, and the nurse is not the angel—the patients are." The courage patients display often reveals the deeper struggle of their spirit. The thought of a diagnosis of cancer creates a knot in the pit of most people's stomachs. Despite the facts of survivorship, a cancer diagnosis ignites the possibility of death. Of course, everyone knows that death is the end of life and that all will eventually arrive at that point. However, most do not go through life thinking about death. The diagnosis of cancer provokes a mental response that may cause patients to reevaluate their life and entertain thoughts of death. This response may be followed by a process of existential questioning, such as, "Is my faith strong enough to support me in times of distress?" or "What is the purpose in my life and sufferings?" This process occurs during the first 100 days after diagnosis (Weisman & Worden, 1976). It may also recur as the disease progresses or relapses. Physicians have indicated that this process occurs even without the prognosis of death (Smith et al., 1993). The answers to these existential questions will bring inner peace to some through periods of introspection and examination of their spirit, whereas others will struggle and sink into spiritual despair. These thoughts of death lead patients to decipher what death means to them personally. The search for meaning causes them to question and explore the traditional values and spiritual beliefs they have held (Smith, 1993). Turmoil may occur as patients reevaluate their belief system. Patients may experience guilt, frustration, or depression in trying to sort out the feelings they have regarding their beliefs. Many people will ask "Why me?" or "Where is God in all of this?" Often, patients will return to the spiritual beliefs they held as youngsters, thus creating a need for nurses to meet the patient wherever he or she is along the spiritual continuum (Smith et al., 1993). It is at these moments that it is necessary for nurses to be responsive because the patient needs a sense of peace, whether that means knowing it is all right to question long-held beliefs or coming to terms with the meaning spirituality holds in his or her life and death.

Imagine then what it would be like, sitting in a doctor's office, somehow knowing, yet hoping beyond all hope that it's not true. Hearing the words as if in a tunnel. They echo through your very soul. "It's cancer." You remember all the TV shows about cancer patients and their deaths, you may even remember a family member or a friend with cancer and relive the anguish of the diagnosis for them as you hear it being told to you. It becomes you. Suddenly, your life has changed. You are no longer just average Joe; you are a cancer patient. Despite all the facts the doctor may be giving you about the success rate of treatment, your mind is still turning over the diagnosis and its meaning. Its meaning for many, although there are many cancer survivors, is the possibility of death. How would that feel? What questions would arise for you? Those are probably some of the same questions your cancer patients are asking.

Another aspect of the importance spirituality holds in a cancer diagnosis is that often the spiritual realm of a person's being holds many coping strategies. Coping is adapting to situations in a way that limits the potential threats and the stress associated with those threats. Lazarus states that people use four coping strategies: information seeking, direct action, inhibition of action, and intrapsychic. Direct action could be a person's desire to exercise their faith through certain rituals (Sodestrom & Martinson, 1987). These rituals may include the "religious" applications of reading the Bible, praying, receiving communion, attending chapel services, or simply sharing their faith with others. Jenkins and Paragament (1995) found "religious" coping to be of great importance when patients were undertaking a new diagnosis of cancer or cancer relapse, and in situations where cancer altered their body image. They also showed that religious coping appears to be used more by women, African Americans, elders, and those with lower socioeconomic status. This provides some clues as to those patients more likely to employ "religious" coping. Meyer (1992) noted that patients who are intrinsically religious, meaning they see religion as the driving motivator in life, used religious means and direct action more than their extrinsic or nonreligious counterparts. However, those patients seeking their spiritual realm outside of organized religion must also be remembered. They may have other ways of exhibiting their faith. They may have a special stuffed animal representing hope and love that must go with them to all treatments. They may find they can use meditation and guided imagery to reach a sense of spiritual peace during times of pain. Even joking when the time seems inappropriate may be one's means of retaining joy and hope in a devastating moment. Although these may not seem like traditional spiritual coping strategies, the assumption that all persons are spiritual applies, and nurses may need to look beyond the obvious to see how the patient's soul, or spirit, is using beliefs to cope. This shows the need for nurses to consider spirituality as a means of coping. These means of direct action, using spiritual means to cope, creates a sense of peace, strength, and hope in stressful situations. It may even lessen the impact of the cancer diagnosis for some (Sodestrom & Martinson, 1988).

Hope also becomes an integral part of a person's spirit. Several studies discussing the concept of hope imply that there is a component of faith in some spiritual sense within this concept (Carni, 1988; Nowotny, 1989; Owen, 1989). According to Nowotny (1989), in order to have hope, one must be able to have a relationship with others or a higher being. Others suggest that obtaining an inner peace is necessary for hope to prevail (Owen, 1989). Regardless of how it is written, hope comes from within, is related to the spirit by way of peace or relationships, and is needed in order to cope with changing life events such as cancer. The importance of this component of spirituality is that the nurse needs to be able to support or provide hope at all times to patients. This does not mean reassuring a patient who is dying that a cure is possible. Sometimes, hope is in the form of hoping for a peaceful death or a good day

to enable visits with family. It has been stated that hope should be based on reality. This seems true. At the same time, the question arises as to whose reality is it—the nurse's or the patient's? That may be a question that patients have to answer for themselves.

Spirituality and You

To care for a patient's spiritual aspect of being, nurses must first evaluate their understanding of their own spiritual realm. Boutell and Bozett (1987) studied 238 registered nurses in Oklahoma and found an amazing 78% assessing and acting on patient's spiritual needs often or at least occasionally. It was also noted that 74% of the sample were involved in some form of religious activities themselves. This does not mean that nurses not involved in organized religion did not assess patients' spiritual needs, but it does lend credence to the idea that understanding one's own spirituality is important for assessing and being aware of patient's spiritual needs.

Parse's concept of human becoming is one framework for developing awareness of one's spirituality. Parse values "living authentically." This means exploring one's beliefs and evaluating which ones are most important. A world view then develops based on those values. Finally, living authentically is derived from using those principles and values. To come to terms with those values, introspection can be used. Box 28-1 is an exercise to practice introspection and to begin evaluation of a personal spirituality.

BOX 28-1

Beginning Your Own Spiritual Journey

Think back to a significant moment in life where something "just felt right." Ask yourself why. What was it about that experience that created such emotions and memories? What meaning did you find in that situation? What values did it speak to, and did it enhance or change the values you previously held? Did it change the way you viewed the world or the way you conducted your life? These are ways to begin your own spiritual journey.

My moment of true spiritual identity came this past summer. I had traveled to Zdvizhovka, a remote village in the Ukraine. The village houses many refugees from the Chernobyl accident, and our team was there to provide medical care for the poor and the sick of the village. We set up a makeshift clinic in the church. For 2 weeks, we labored, treating those we could with the limited resources we had. Because we had only 2 weeks, we worked long hours, making every minute count. We learned quickly how to make home remedies from household products we had around the church. On occasion, we were frustrated because although we had means of treating certain diseases, the necessity of obtaining blood levels prevented us from being able to provide the medicine to cure the disease. I realized how poor in material items those people were. They lacked even the most basic medical care. The only blood pressure cuff available in the local hospital was broken. At times, I wondered if we could ever make a difference. However, I found I could make a difference with my knowledge and my love. The children of the village were attention deprived and starved for love. The few days we were there provided them with that love and attention, and miraculously they blossomed into happy, smiling children. Although we could not speak their language, we found the language of the spirit was enough. The final day of our stay brought many tears and a little girl named Ala to say "I love you" in English, just as the van was pulling away.

It was the experiences I had in the Ukraine that caused me to reevaluate the values and tangibles in my life that I held as important. Through this reflection, I gained insight into my own beliefs and spirituality. It changed my life and my direction. Now I look at nursing as a gift, not a career. Every day, I look for ways to make that day count, just as we did in the Ukraine.

A trip to another country is definitely an eye-opening and heart-opening experience. However, one does not need to travel to a distant land to have meaningful experiences that can show awareness of spirituality. Those experiences can come in the middle of the busiest shift or on the worst day. Experiences with cancer patients have guided many nurses' thoughts and values about spirituality for years. Simply watching and listening to a patient's struggle with finding that meaning in life and death creates questions that will nag the mind until attention is paid to them. The following case study will provide an opportunity to question personal beliefs about a coping style as well as some spiritual questions that arose in this situation.

Case Study:

Susan and John were married only 3 months when John was diagnosed with leukemia. John was a bright, blue-eyed jokester. Although hoarse from the ET tube, he would still roll his eyes for sarcastic effect in response to a comment. For 8 months, we treated John in a race against time. The cancer eventually won. However, the struggle Susan and John went through spiritually was classic. Initially, they were both angry. They were angry at God and at the cancer. Susan and I became close and would spend time just sitting after hours, talking. She struggled with why God had done such a thing. She expressed anger at Him and often took that anger out on the staff. Then her attitude began to change. She relied heavily on prayer and pastoral support. That seemed to bring comfort to the whole family. Then, finally, when death became imminent, she told me she guessed it was God's will and that maybe He just needed an angel that would make him laugh.

Those words often lay on my mind. Think about that situation. Do you think death is God's will? How do you perceive that style of coping? How would you have handled the situation? These questions will lead you to discover your own beliefs and will guide you to respond to the patients and their families when they struggle with spiritual issues.

Piles' (1990) study showed that the other issue for nurses in providing spiritual care was education. More nursing schools are integrating spirituality into their curriculum in the form of nursing diagnoses. However, several studies show that nurses still feel inadequate in their preparation to provide spiritual care (Dettmore, 1986; Narayan-asamy, 1993). These and other studies show that with increased education, the likelihood that spiritual care will be provided and the comfort level with this care will increase. Therefore, the need exists for continuing education to focus on spiritual issues.

Assessing Spiritual Needs and Nursing Diagnosis

How often has a patient been admitted and been asked the question, "Do you have any religious beliefs we should be aware of?" or "Do you want to see a member of the clergy while you are here?" This is often the extent of a spiritual assessment in the hospital. In the clinic setting, the limited amount of time negates getting much more information than vital signs. How, in the cost-effective atmosphere of today's health care world, can the spiritual needs of patients be assessed and interventions offered?

A few questions posed to a patient on admission may open the door for further discussion of spirituality. However, admission time is not always the best time to approach such a subject. In the admission stage or in the initial meeting with a patient, there is no previous knowledge of that person. Part of adequately assessing spiritual needs is knowing the appropriate time to assess. Gaining trust and establishing rapport are necessary steps before probing into the deep waters of a patient's spiritual being. Only when a solid rapport has been etched will the patient feel able to allow the nurse into his or her spiritual life. It is, as was discussed previously, a sacred place where there are no facades to protect oneself. Therefore, trust in the nurse is an important step. Once that rapport has been established, the nurse can then begin asking questions. "Is religion or God important to you?" and "Do you find a source of strength or meaning in another area?" are two opening questions that will start a spiritual conversation. Mentioning one's own spirituality and how it is expressed can provide the patient with the knowledge that this is not a taboo subject. Evidence of a patient's spirituality may be seen in the form of tangible items—a cross necklace, a rosary, a Bible, or icons. Home clergy or spiritual advisors may provide suggestions about how to support the patient spiritually. The following is an exercise to begin assessing a patient's spirituality.

> When speaking about spirituality, use your observation skills. Is the patient uncomfortable, anxious, angry, or depressed? These may be clues to spiritual distress. Another suggested question to provoke spirituality discussions is, "How does this diagnosis or disease affect your spiritual practices or beliefs?"

If, during conversations, the patient responds by discussing doubt, worthlessness, spiritual ambivalence, or a sense that his or her beliefs are not good enough, then the nurse is provided subjective data that the patient is experiencing some form of spiritual distress. Objective data that would accompany the spoken words may be symptoms of depression, an unwillingness to discuss beliefs, or a change in spiritual practices, whatever they may be. There is a nursing diagnosis for spiritual distress created by Carpenito (1992):

Focus	Outcome Criteria/Goals
Spiritual distress related to crisis of illness	1. Patient will express feelings related to change in beliefs 2. Patient will describe spiritual belief system positively 3. Patient will describe satisfaction with meaning and purpose of illness

In research, there are a few measures of spirituality. The Spiritual Well Being (SWB) Scale has been used often to research spirituality. It consists of three subscales to measure the spiritual, religious, and existential well-being of patients. Its internal consistency has been shown at 0.89 (Kaczorowski, 1989). However, other research has shown that the SWB scale is lacking in construct validity with regard to the hospice population (Kirschling & Pittman, 1989). Another popular scale is the Intrinsic/Extrinsic Religiosity (I/E-R) scale, which has been shown to be reliable and valid (Fehring et al., 1997; Meyer, 1992). The main drawback of using this scale is that it focuses on religion, not spirituality in the broad concept. Many who do not affiliate themselves with a religion may feel unable to complete the questionnaire because they believe the questions do not pertain to their view of spirituality. The JAREL spiritual well-being scale is a more recent addition to nursing research. It was developed in 1996, and factor analysis tests proved its use. However, because of its newness, more testing must be done to confirm its reliability and validity (Hungelman et al., 1996). The Spiritual Health Inventory is another such scale, used to determine if nurses actually assessed their patient's spiritual needs accurately. Construct and content validity was simply through expert panel review (Highfield, 1992). Therefore, once again, more extensive testing of the scale is needed.

Two other measures commonly in use relate to spirituality through mood states and hopefulness. The Profile of Mood States (POMS) is a well-known measure of six moods, and internal consistence of all is 0.90 or above (Fehring, Miller & Shaw, 1997). POMS has been used to show connections between spirituality and moods. Several studies have shown that depression is inversely related to strong religious faith (Fehring et al., 1997; Smith et al., 1993). Although, once again, the focus of these studies was religiousness, not spirituality, they still provide a basis for the need to care spiritually for patients. The Nowotny Hope Scale is often used to show the connection between spirit and hope. It was developed in 1989 and shows promise because its validity and reliability were tested and found adequate (Nowotny, 1989). Despite several measures of spirituality, most have significant limitations, thus suggesting the need for either retesting or development of new scales. In addition, most research articles reviewed concluded that to gain insight into the spiritual dimension of patients, longitudinal qualitative methods would be the better measures. In truth, several research articles have used qualitative means, all providing insight as to how the spirit is involved with illness, death, and healing. However, only a few describe the method of obtaining data and show adequate rigor to ensure accurate results. Those few have enlightened the nursing world as to the depth of the human spirit and have provided invaluable and empirical data (O'Connor, Wicker, & Germino, 1990; Sodestrom & Martinson, 1987). Because so few are adequate in their processes, there is a need within the research arena to focus on qualitative methods that will provide an accurate assessment of spirituality. Undertaking the longitudinal studies would provide nursing with explicit empirical data over time describing the changing human spirit because, as Parse has stated, the act of becoming is never static.

Interventions

Once assessment has occurred, the nurse can plan interventions to assist a patient through a spiritual crisis or simply to maintain spirituality through the course of a cancer diagnosis. The nurse can refer the patient to the pastoral care department or provide resources to continue expression of spirituality (e.g., times of chapel services or allowing privacy for meditation). Emblen and Halstead (1993) found that, although nurses believed praying, listening to patients, and referrals were adequate spiritual care, patients also felt that showing compassion, being "present," talking, touching, smiling, and good physical care were parts of spiritual care as well.

How to intervene can be remembered by using the the acronym REST.

R = Respect. One must respect a patient's spirituality in the realm of his or her practices, beliefs, and culture. Without respect, there will be no open communication between the nurse and the patient in which to discuss questions or distresses.

E = Encourage. Encouraging patients to discuss personal spiritual beliefs means providing a listening ear, a sense that they are cared for, a sense that they are important to the nurse, and a safe place to discuss perhaps their deepest fears or doubts.

S = Support. Supporting the patient through whatever questions or concerns are expressed is of great importance. It is the time in the patient's life when nothing seems stable. The patient is questioning the very core of his or her being. As mentioned before, patients may be feeling guilt for questioning beliefs or may be finding that beliefs are not strengthening them as previously they had. This can be disconcerting, and patients need someone to provide assurance that they are still important people and are still acceptable to a higher power although they question and doubt. Perhaps the nurse will be the only one to behave in such a way that the patient knows he is acceptable as he was and as he is now.

T = Trust. Trust has two components. The first is the trust the nurse has of his or her own instincts and "gut feelings." Often, the nurse may have a gut feeling about a patient situation. That feeling is considered to be intuition. Intuition forms from experience. Personal experience that leads to intuition is considered a form of knowledge in the nursing profession. One's intuition can help guide the decision of when to talk and when to be a silent presence.

The second part of trust is that the patient must have trust in the nurse and the relationship that has been forged. The first way to establish this trusting relationship is through basic care. Building blocks for trust are (1) giving accurate and honest information to the patient and following through on requests, (2) being one's self and being genuine in caring, and (3) developing knowledge of the patient and who he or she is. This can be accomplished through listening to his or her journey—all the different events that have now brought the patient to this point in life.

Spirituality and the Family

Spirituality affects more than just the patient. It also affects everyone involved with that person. Family members and friends may encounter their own spiritual crises while their loved one is dealing with cancer. Often, if the patient is faced with a terminal illness, the family is faced with guilt from feeling tired or feeling as if they would like the patient to die instead of suffering. These people are the support system for the patient. The patient needs strength from them, yet they need to gain strength from somewhere themselves. The nurse can play many roles in the spiritual care of not only the patient but also the family, thus continuing to help the patient receive what is needed.

The feelings encountered by family members may create tension within the family system that the patient will sense, thus causing increased dis-tress for him or her. One study examined the issues that were most important to caregivers versus the patient. It was found that, although both suffer, the issues may be entirely different. The patients were more focused on relationships and finding meaning, whereas the caregivers worried over finances, daily activities, and the comfort of the patient (Swenson, 1993). This situation could set up a milieu that throws both the patient and the caregiver into conflict by not realizing the focus issues each has. The nurse can play the role of mediator and counselor during this time. Often, nurses are the ones who see the deep-seated hurts within family groups, and sharing in these hurts, although uncomfortable, allow the patients permission to discuss what they need from the family to be at peace. Perhaps then the nurse can take that information and guide the family members to gain strength and supply the patient's needs. One such example would be sharing encouraging words with the family outside the patient's room or before bringing them into the office. The same implications apply for family as for the patient. Listen actively, permit the family to express their concerns or even anger, do not judge their responses, and remember that silence and touch are important aspects of spiritual care, perhaps more so than having divine wisdom.

In the Christian tradition, there is a belief that life is eternal and that once one passes through this earthly life, he or she will experience a closer life with God. If patients and family have this belief, death is then viewed as part of God's design for creation, and the caregivers may feel more freedom to care for the patient throughout the transition from life to death without a sense of failure (Bryant, 1991). Other traditions hold different views. Jehovah's Witnesses believe that death is the enemy. The Jewish tradition sees death as an end point with no eternal life. Most other religions view death as a passover into another life. Catholics need to be anointed and experience the Eucharist and Reconciliation before death, whereas the Islamic faith requires special washing and shrouding of the body. It is essential for the nurse to understand these needs and to provide an opportunity for them to be accomplished. Other issues that may arise involve regular religious practices. Meditation is an essential part of the Hindu philosophy. The nurse can help the patient continue religious practices through the illness by providing time alone for meditation. Table 28-1 describes some of the most common religions and their beliefs. This can serve as a beginning guide to ensure that cultural and religious practices are not impeded, thus providing a sense of relief and respect to the patient and family.

Many family members, regardless of their religious affiliation, will experience a period of struggle. They will often ask the same questions the pa-

TABLE 28-1
COMMON RELIGIONS AND BELIEFS

Religion	Illness Beliefs	Diet	Death	Other Beliefs
Baptist	May practice laying on of hands, healing through prayer, Bible reading for comfort/guidance	Usually alcohol abstinence	Belief that soul goes to heaven if one is saved through Jesus May like pastor present for prayer and comfort	Bible reading, visitation from clergy, friends and family, and time for prayer may be desired Believer's Baptism practiced
Buddhism	Illness result of sin, medical treatment accepted, family assists with care	Primarily vegetarian	Belief in afterlife as reincarnation Autopsy allowed	Should confront individual situation First noble truth is that life is out of joint, therefore suffering exists Overcoming selfishness is key
Catholic	Illness is part of life	No meat on Ash Wednesday and Fridays during Lent for those age 14 and up	Need to be anointed, experience the Eucharist and Reconciliation	May have tangible items of faith such as rosary, scapular, and other icons used for prayer May request communion
Mormon	Blessed by laying on of hands	Abstinence from alcohol, tobacco, and caffeine	Burial is preferred	A sacred undergarment may be worn and should only be removed in emergency
Eastern Orthodox	Oppose abortion and euthanasia	Fast from meat and dairy, Fridays and Wednesdays in Lent.	Last rites are mandatory	Baptism within 40 days of birth
Episcopal	May believe in spiritual healing		May like priest present	Infant baptism—lay person may perform in emergency
Islam	Women must not sign consent forms—husbands will make decisions Suffering is predestined Stoicism important	No pork Meat must be blessed Daytime fasting during month of Ramadan	Special procedures for washing and shrouding the body Belief in afterlife in form of reincarnation	Surrender to the will of Allah is supreme virtue Women cover head and face
Jehovah's Witness	Belief that soul is in the blood—usually refuse blood transfusions	No food that has blood (e.g., sausage, luncheon meat)	See death as enemy	Do not celebrate holidays
Jewish	When women menstruate, men may not touch them Medical procedures avoided on Sabbath if possible	Meat kosher Fasting during Yom Kippur No shellfish or pork, and no leavened products during Passover	Do not believe in brain death Someone should be present when soul leaves the body Taharah—washing of the body and burial must occur within 24 h	Men wear skull cap Women cover hair after marriage May wish rabbi to pray

tient asks: Why them? Why would God let this happen? Others with strong religious backgrounds may present with different thoughts. Islamics believe that life is a gift from Allah, and surrendering to His will is considered a supreme virtue (Halstead & Mickley, 1997). This may sound similar to some Christians who believe that illness and death are God's will. In the academic world, this is called fatalism, the belief that no matter what is done, God will decide either to heal or to take a patient. This can cause some to discontinue medicines or refuse treatment. Those who are steeped in the mind-set of the medical field may have a conflict with this thinking if they believe medicine is the ultimate cure. Regardless of bias, one is responsible for presenting the facts, possibly suggesting what seems best, and ultimately allowing the patient to make the decision. A case in point comes from a conversation with an oncologist. He responded to a question of how to convince a patient to take chemotherapy despite the fact that the patient felt strongly that God did not wish chemotherapy for him. The oncologist answered the question by saying, perhaps the patient is right. It is his choice and his belief, and we would do a disservice to strip him of that. He also added a case study of his own that taught him if the patient is at peace with the decision, it is the right decision. On occasion, the decisions made by the family based on beliefs may be confusing to the staff or even cause conflict. A case in point is Margaret.

Case Study

Margaret was Joe's wife. They had two teenage boys. Joe was a nurse and was diagnosed with leukemia the day before Christmas. He never fully achieved remission throughout the several different chemotherapy regimens he received. Finally, it became apparent that death was imminent. His wife became quite hostile. She permitted only positive affirmations to be spoken in the room with Joe. She often spoke of God's healing power and stated that because she "claimed" Joe's healing, he would be healed. This was to be a testimony to his brothers who did not share their faith. "If he wasn't healed," she asked, "What kind of God would God be?" She would request that we pray for Joe, and, on

some occasions, we did have bedside prayer. The hospital chaplain also became involved with Joe's care and was a strong source of strength for Margaret. However, I noticed that Joe did not often suggest prayer or ever claim he would be healed by God. What he did say was that he only wanted to take his boys to the beach—one last time. We planned a beach party on the unit for him and his family. His wife agreed that would brighten his spirits, and she and her sons helped us plan. We had the Beach Boys playing on the tape player and crepe paper suns hung across the workroom. Beach towels were tablecloths, and laughter was the main course. It was after this party that Joe expressed that he was ready to stop. His cognition began to deteriorate, and it was difficult to discern exactly what he meant. But, on several occasions, he would comment about stopping the car because he didn't want to drive anymore or that he was tired and wanted to lie down and rest. From these comments, the team determined that he was asking to stop any heroic measures. The subject was broached with his wife. She refused to sign a Do Not Resuscitate order because she still believed that, although it appeared he was dying, she had to hold to her faith that he would be healed. The story ended with a messy code and finally Joe's death. Margaret never accepted that God did not heal her husband and seemed to lose her faith in many things. I could not help this situation. I found myself struggling with my own faith and working through to find peace with how I perceived Joe's death. When I expressed my belief, Margaret rejected it, because it did not end with Joe's healing.

As nurses, although we try to heal, we must realize that we are not going to ease all the pains and see all happy endings. I still do not know what could have made a difference to Margaret in this situation, maybe nothing. Maybe I did make a difference simply by caring enough to listen and to hear the concerns, not only of her but of Joe as well.

The suffering of one person has an effect on others in his or her world. These others are the family and friends, but also the nurse. There is a risk in becoming fully present with a patient. The relationship with the patient may end in joy or in sorrow. Being able to discuss feelings about death, cancer, cancer treatments, spiritual concerns, and how to intervene is necessary to create a milieu of self-care. To be fully present with many patients, the nurse must be well-grounded in his or her own sense of spirituality and well-being. The old adage that good nurses do not get attached is no longer accurate. Instead, nurses who do allow themselves to be present with patients and hear their physical, emotional, and spiritual needs are those who receive a sense of truly making a difference and "being" a nurse.

Conclusion

Spirituality is a concept many disciplines hold dear, yet struggle to define. It is a broad concept involving all persons, not simply those relying on organized religion.

All persons have a spiritual component, and this component needs to be addressed to ensure the most positive outcomes for that patient. The definition that comes closest to incorporating all the various definitions of spirituality is in viewing spirituality as a multidimensional concept involving a connection between oneself and a "higher being," between oneself and the environment in which one participates and between oneself and the inner being of one's soul, as well as involving a search for the meaning of distressing circumstances with the concept of hope being prominent in this search.

In a cancer diagnosis, spirituality is an essential aspect of care. Research has shown that a cancer diagnosis causes patients to reflect and explore their spirituality, thus perhaps causing times of distress. The nurse's role is to assess the patient's spiritual needs and intervene as needed. To adequately accomplish this, the nurse must first have participated in introspection to determine his or her spiritual beliefs and to know his or her own biases. Then, a trusting relationship must be formed with the patient. Once there is assurance that the patient will be listened to nonjudgmentally, discussions can occur about spiritual issues. Using the acronym REST, the nurse can know to respect the patient's views of spirituality and take into consideration factors such as culture, encourage the pa-

tient to talk and share about the life journey that has brought that patient to that point in time and the concerns he or she has, and support the patient during times of struggle when he or she is questioning long-held beliefs.

The cancer diagnosis also incorporates family and friends as well as the patient. Sometimes, the best help the nurse can be to the patient is to provide support for the family. Spiritual issues can be fairly similar for family members and patients. The same interventions would apply to both. The nurse should realize that the family may need to be given permission to be angry or may need to know they are acceptable although they have feelings of guilt, just as the patient needs these same reassurances. However, the caregivers may be experiencing stressors that the patient is not. This can create tension within the relationships. It is important for the nurse to recognize these situations as well as play the role of mediator in helping each to understand the other.

In essence, caring for a cancer patient and the family involves the holistic approach: Caring for the mind, body, and spirit. In doing this, the interventions intermingle. Using the simple therapeutics of touch, sharing, and silence, the nurse can accomplish care of all the aspects of the person. Many nurses do not assess spirituality needs because of a fear of not knowing how. Several possibilities exist. Following the REST acronym will aid in assessing and intervening. Observing signs of certain religious faith may enable the nurse to provide adequate time and means for the patient to continue in his or her practices. The nurse may also use a patient's spirituality as a means to help the patient cope. The nurse needs to be aware that many use religion as a means of direct action coping. Above all, the nurse should remember that spirituality does not necessarily mean religiosity. All persons are spiritual and, thus, should be cared for spiritually. This means needing to respond appropriately with regards to culture and individual spiritualness. What is a normal tradition for one may seem uncomfortable and odd to another. However, the goal is to ensure the patient's spiritual aspect is cared for, not the nurse's own comfort level. By participating in spiritual care, the nurse will find a greater sense of purpose in being a nurse. It may become a gift given from which one can share and guide others, instead of only a career.

REFERENCES

Boutell, K., & Bozett, F. (1987). Nurses' assessment of patients' spirituality: Continuing education implications. *Journal of Continuing Education in Nursing, 21,* 172–176.

Bryant, C. (1991). Said another way, death from a spiritual perspective. *Nursing Forum, 26*(4), 31–34.

Carni, E. (1988). Issues of faith and hope in cancer patients. *Journal of Religion and Health, 27*(4), 285–290.

Carpenito, L. (1992). *Nursing diagnosis.* New York: J. B. Lippincott.

Chinn, P., & Kramer, M. (1995). *Theory and nursing.* St. Louis: Mosby.

Cobb, M., & Forman, D. (1997). The meaning of spirituality. *Journal of Advanced Nursing, 26,* 1183–1188.

Copp, L. (1998). Illness and the human spirit. *Oncolink* (1998). *http://oncolink.upenn.edu/psychosocial/qol/qol_5.html.* Cerenex.

Dettmore, D. (1986). Nurses' conceptions of and practices in the spiritual dimension of nursing. *Dissertations Abstracts International, 47B,* 2370.

Dossey, B., Keegan, L., Guzzetta, C., & Kolkmeier, L. (1988). *Holistic nursing.* Rockville, MD: Aspen.

Emblen, J. (1992). Religion and spirituality defined according to current use in nursing literature. *Journal of Professional Nursing, 8*(1), 41–47.

Emblen, J., & Halstead, L. (1993). Spiritual needs and intervention: Comparing the views of patients, nurses, and chaplains. *Clinical Nurse Specialist, 7,* 175–182.

Fehring, R., Miller, J., & Shaw, C. (1997). Spiritual well being, religiosity, hope, depression, and other mood states in elderly people coping with cancer. *Oncology Nursing Forum, 24*(4), 663–671.

Halstead, M., & Mickley, R. (1997). Attempting to fathom the unfathomable: Descriptive views of spirituality. *Seminars in Oncology Nursing, 13*(4), 225–230.

Highfield, M. (1992). Spiritual health of oncology patients. *Cancer Nursing, 15*(1), 1–8.

Hungelman, J., Kenkel Rossi, E., Klassen, L., & Stollenserk, R. (1996). Focus on spiritual well being: Harmonious interconnectedness of mind–body–spirit—Use of the JAREL spiritual well being scale. *Geriatric Nursing, 17*(6), 262–266.

Hutchins, D. (1991, May). Spirituality in the face of death. *The Canadian Nurse,* 30–33.

Jenkins, R., & Paragament, K. (1995). Religion and spirituality as resources for coping with cancer. *Journal of Psychosocial Oncology, 13*(1/2), 51–74.

Kaczorowski, J. (1989). Spiritual well being and anxiety in adults diagnosed cancer. *Hospice Journal, 5*(3/4), 105–115.

Kirschling, J., & Pittman, J. (1989). Measurement of spiritual well being: A hospice caregiver sample. *Hospice Journal, 5*(2), 1–11.

Lazarus, R. (1980). The stress and coping paradigm. In L. Bonde & J. Rosen (Eds.), *Competence and coping during adulthood* (pp. 28–69). Hanover, NH: University Press of New England.

Levin, J., Larson, D., & Puchalski, C. (1997). Religion and spirituality in medicine: Research and education. *Journal of the American Medical Association, 279*(9), 792–793.

McQuiston, C., & Webb, A. (1995). *Foundations of nursing theory.* Thousand Oaks, CA: Sage.

Meyer, M. (1992). Religious orientation and coping with cancer. *Journal of Religion and Health, 31*(4), 273–279.

Michello, J. (1988). Spiritual and emotional determinants of health. *Journal of Religion and Health, 27*(1), 62–69.

Narayanasamy, A. (1993). Nurses' awareness and educational preparation in meeting their patients' spiritual needs. *Nurse Educator Today, 13,* 196–201.

Nowotny, M. (1989). Assessment of hope in patient with cancer: Development of an instrument. *Oncology Nursing Forum, 16*(1), 57–61.

O'Connor, A., Wicker, C., & Germino, B. (1990). Understanding the cancer patient's search for meaning. *Cancer Nursing, 13*(3), 167–175.

Owen, D. (1989). Nurse's perspectives on the meaning of hope in patients with cancer: A qualitative study. *Oncology Nursing Forum, 16*(1), 75–79.

Piles, C. (1990). Providing spiritual care. *Nurse Educator, 15*(1), 36–41.

Reed, P. (1992). An emerging paradigm for the investigation of spirituality in nursing research. *Research in Nursing and Health, 15,* 349–357.

Reed, P. (1986). Religiousness among terminally ill and healthy adults. *Research in Nursing and Health, 9,* 35–41.

Smith, E., Stefanek, M., Joseph, M., Verdieck, M., Zabora, J., & Fetting, J. (1993). Spiritual awareness, personal perspective on death, psychosocial distress among cancer patients: An initial investigation. *Journal of Psychosocial Oncology, 11*(3), 89–102.

Sodestrom, K., & Martinson, I. (1987). Patients' spiritual coping strategies: A study of nurse and patient perspectives. *Oncology Nursing Forum, 14*(2), 41–46.

Swenson, C. (1993). Stages of religious faith and reactions to terminal cancer. *Journal of Psychology and Theology, 21*(3), 238–245.

Thompson, S., & Pitts, J. (1993). Factors relating to a person's ability to find meaning after a diagnosis of cancer. *Journal of Psychosocial Oncology, 11*(3), 1–21.

Varricchio, C., Pierce, M., Walker, C., & Ades, T. (1997). *A cancer source book for nurses.* London: Jones and Bartlett.

Webster, M. (1988). *Webster's ninth new collegiate dictionary.* Springfield. Merriam Webster.

Weisman, A., & Worden, J. (1976). Existential plight in cancer: Significance of the first 100 days. *International Journal of Psychiatry in Medicine, 7*(1), 1–15.

Issues of Today and Tomorrow

Changes in Cancer Care Reimbursement

Laura Adams

Significant gains are being made in the 1990s in fighting the war on cancer. The cancer death rate in the United States fell 2.6% between 1991 and 1995. This decrease in cancer deaths was the first of its kind since record-keeping began in the 1930s (National Cancer Institute [NCI], 1998). Even with this decline, however, in 1999 more than 1.2 million new cases of cancer are expected to be diagnosed, and 563,100 people—more than 1,500 per day—are expected to die of cancer (American Cancer Society [ACS], 1999). Today, men have a one in two chance of developing cancer in their lifetime, and women have a one in three chance (ACS, 1989).

While cancer death rates were rising during the 1970s and 1980s, so, too, were health care expenditures. In 1960, health care expenditures were $26.9 billion, 5.1% of the gross domestic product (GDP). By 1980, they had increased 820% to $247.3 billion, 8.9% of the GDP, and in 1990 they rose to $699.5 billion and 12.2% of GDP. Health care expenditures broke the $1.0 trillion mark in 1996. However, as a percentage of GDP, they remained stable at 13.6%, a level they had maintained since 1993 (Health Care Financing Administration [HCFA], 1998).

Rising health care expenditures during the 1970s and early 1980s were cause for national concern. The emergence of managed care organizations (MCOs) was largely attributable to the need to control health care costs.

Managed Care Organizations

The term *managed care* refers to any form of insurance company or health plan that employs one or more (but usually all) of the following:

- Selective contracting to direct patients to a limited number of health care providers (health care provider refers to those entities that bill directly for their services: hospitals, physicians, skilled nursing facilities, home care and home infusion agencies, and so forth)
- Compensation to its contracted health care providers in such a way that it provides incentives to control costs
- Utilization review to control unnecessary use of health care services

The three primary types of MCOs are health maintenance organizations (HMOs), preferred provider organizations (PPOs), and point-of-service (POS) plans. HMOs are the most restrictive plans and have the most rules, but also offer the most extensive benefits and the lowest amount the patient must pay out of his or her own pocket (*out-of-pocket expenses*). POS plans are the least restrictive and most flexible, and PPOs fall between the two.

1. Health maintenance organizations (HMOs) —An HMO is a health plan that offers comprehensive health care provided by a

limited number of hospitals, physicians, and other health care providers. HMOs have several key components:

A comprehensive range of covered services from specialty care to preventive care (immunizations, well-child care, annual gynecologic visits), prescriptions, and routine eye examinations.

Members must choose a primary care physician (PCP)—usually an internist, family practitioner, pediatrician, or general practitioner—who either directly provides, or coordinates and authorizes, all of the patient's health care. PCPs are often referred to as "gatekeepers" because they direct all of the patient's care that is to be paid for by the HMO.

PCPs are generally compensated on a prepaid basis, whereas specialist physicians, hospitals, and other providers may be reimbursed on a prepaid basis or by other discounted reimbursement models.

There are three traditional models of HMOs, all of which are considered organized, prepaid health care systems. A *staff* model HMO delivers services through a salaried physician group that is employed by the HMO and treats only the HMO's patients. Kaiser is probably the most well-known staff model. A *group* model HMO contracts with one or more physician group practices, and each group primarily treats the HMO's patients. An *independent practice association* (IPA) contracts directly with physicians who are in private practice, and/or with one or more multispecialty group practice(s). Most of these physicians participate with multiple MCOs and also see patients with other types of insurance.

2. Preferred provider organizations (PPOs)—A PPO is a health plan that has contracts with a large network of private practice physicians, hospitals, and other health care providers. The plan compensates the health care providers using one or more discounted reimbursement model(s). PPOs have no "gatekeeper," and the patient may elect to see any health care provider. However, the patient will pay more out of pocket if the provider does not participate in the PPO.

3. Point-of-service (POS) plans—A POS is a health plan in which patients are enrolled in an HMO or a PPO and receive the high level of benefits that those plans offer as long as they use the proper health care providers and follow the procedures for receiving care. In a POS plan, the patients also have the option of self-referring to any health care provider outside of the HMO or PPO, but they will have to pay much more out of pocket.

How Does Managed Care Control Health Care Dollars?

Reimbursement or payment structure is one way that MCOs have successfully encouraged health care providers to control costs. Other cost-containment mechanisms employed by MCOs include preauthorization of defined services and case management programs. Preauthorization requires obtaining approval in order for the health plan to pay for the services. Approval may come from the PCP in the form of a referral for certain services, or it may involve a hospital calling the health plan before an inpatient admission. Case management programs are often used to manage complex cases and emphasize resource management with a goal of producing high-quality, cost-effective outcomes within and across inpatient and outpatient delivery settings (Bedell & Mroz, 1997).

Growth and Enrollment in Managed Care

In 1980, only 10 million Americans were enrolled in HMOs (Bodenheimer & Sullivan, 1998); by 1998, that number had increased to over 80 million (National Committee for Quality Assurance [NCQA], 1998). In 1997, the American Association of Health Plans reported that over 150 million Americans were enrolled in some type of managed care organization, including HMOs, PPOs, and POS plans. The growth patterns are also reflected in the employer segment—in 1993, only 53% of all insured employees were enrolled in a managed care organization, but by 1998 that percentage had increased to 85% (Gorman, 1998). As the enrollment in MCOs continues to increase, so too does the number of Americans without any health insurance. An estimated 44.3 million people in the United States, or 16.3% of the population, had no health insurance coverage in 1998 (U.S. Census Bureau, 1999).

Current Reimbursement for Health Care Services

Providers today receive most of their payments for health care services from the following sources: government programs (including Medicare, Medicaid, CHAMPUS), MCOs, self-insured employers, and, in decreasing numbers, traditional indemnity insurance.

The move to manage health care costs and the increasing power of MCOs have fundamentally and significantly altered compensation for health care services, including cancer services. Cancer care, whether provided in the physician's office, outpatient clinic, or hospital inpatient unit, is affected by the general trends that are affecting reimbursement. Cancer care and its complexities also face additional reimbursement issues that are discussed later in this chapter.

Reimbursement Terminology

In any discussion about health care reimbursement, it is useful to be familiar with the following terms:

Charges—Charges are the amount that a health care provider—hospital, physician, home care agency, hospice—bills for providing services. The amount that appears on the bill is referred to as the charge.

Costs—Costs are defined as the expenses incurred to provide a service. Costs are almost always lower than the charges, because the charges include a margin of profit.

Current Procedural Terminology (CPT)—Physicians Current Procedural Terminology (CPT) is a systematic listing and coding of procedures and services performed by physicians. It is published annually by the American Medical Association.

Net revenue—Net revenue is the money that is actually received from the insurance company or other payor for providing the services.

Professional component—Portion of reimbursement for which a physician bills (using CPT coding).

Profit—Profit is the money remaining after all costs have been deducted from the net revenue.

Provider—Entity, in relation to the insurance company, that provides medical services to the patient and bills for those services. In the context of insurance and managed care reimbursement, nurses are not considered providers because they do not bill directly for the care they provide.

Relative weight—An assigned weight that is intended to reflect resource consumption.

Reimbursement Models

MCOs and other payors continue to modify the way in which they pay providers in order to further reduce payments. Lawyers and other business professionals must often assist health care providers in interpreting and understanding the different reimbursement methodologies. In this section, examples of the primary reimbursement methodologies are described. However, there are many more variations that exist, and new methodologies are constantly under development.

FEE-FOR-SERVICE

Fee-for-service reimbursement is most frequently associated with indemnity insurance plans and, at one time, meant that the insurer paid the provider the amount that was billed. However, full payment of billed charges rarely occurs today, and the indemnity plans that remain have implemented means to control expenditures. The most common means of controlling payments, particularly for services provided in physician offices, are fee schedules. Fee schedules are listings of predetermined payments that establish a maximum payable amount for each billable CPT code. The insurer pays no more than the stated maximum amount. Each insurance company has its own fee schedule (Box 29-1).

How Are Resources Managed Within Fee-for-Service Reimbursement?

Fee-for-service is a retrospective payment system that reimburses providers after the services have

BOX 29-1

Fee Schedule Reimbursement for Physician Services

Example: Patient Q has a visit in the office of his hematologist, Dr. Plasma. In addition to the office visit, Dr. Plasma performs a skin biopsy. (Dr. Plasma sends the sample to pathology at the local hospital, and they will bill the insurance company a technical and professional fee for processing and interpreting the specimen.) Dr. Plasma bills the insurance company for the office visit and the biopsy using CPT codes. The insurance company pays Dr. Plasma according to their allowable fee schedule:

CPT CODE	DESCRIPTION	DR. PLASMA'S CHARGE	INS. CO. FEE SCHEDULE/PAYMENT
99214	Office visit, established pt.	$130.00	$95.50
11100	Biopsy of skin; single lesion	$125.00	$102.00
	TOTAL:	$255.00	$197.50

Dr. Plasma will be reimbursed 78% of billed charges, which is a 22% discount.

Fee Schedule Payment/Dr. Plasma's Charge	=	Reimbursement as % of Charge
$197.50/$255.00	=	78%

---

been rendered. Fee-for-service does not have any controls against overuse of health care resources—preauthorization of services is not required for reimbursement, and there is a financial reward, by way of payment, to provide more services. In this system, the more services the provider performs and bills for, the greater the payment.

DISCOUNT FROM CHARGES

Discount from charges refers to a reimbursement model in which a contractually agreed upon discount is applied against billed charges. MCOs usually use discount from charges methodology as well as other reimbursement methodologies. The level of discount that physicians and hospitals agree to accept continues to increase as managed care companies demand greater discounts. A discount from charges is a reimbursement model that can be used for inpatient and outpatient hospital services, physician services, and other ancillary services. On the West Coast and in regions of the country where managed care is particularly aggressive, the levels of discount can approach 40%, 50%, and even 60% (Box 29-2).

How Are Resources Managed With a Discount From Charges Reimbursement?

Discount from charges is similar to fee-for-service methodology in that it is a retrospective payment system. Preauthorization of services may or may not be required for reimbursement, and there is a financial reward, by way of payment, to provide more services *and* have high charges. The higher the dollar amount of the bill, the more you get paid (Box 29-3).

In the example in Box 29-3, HMO Help U will pay more to Hospital Hippocrates than it did to Hospital Healer for the same service. Fewer and fewer payors will agree to a discount from charges because it does not provide an incentive to the provider to control costs.

Payment Caps and Ambulatory Payment Classification (APC) Systems

In an effort to control the amount paid under a discount from charges model, some MCOs have implemented payment caps, whereby payment per day for outpatient services will never be more than a certain dollar amount. In the examples in Boxes 29-2 and 29-3, HMO Help U might implement an

BOX 29-2

Discount From Charges Reimbursement for Outpatient Hospital

Example: Patient J receives outpatient chemotherapy at Hospital Healer, and the charges for one day of treatment are $1489. Hosptial Healer has a contract with HMO Help U that reimburses 75% of charges for outpatient services.

Hospital Healer Charge	×	Reimbursement Percentage	=	Reimbursement
$1489		75%		$1117

outpatient payment cap per day of $1000, so payment to both Hospital Healer and Hospital Hippocrates for outpatient services would never exceed $1000 per patient per day. With a payment cap, HMO Help U will never pay more than the agreed-upon cap, regardless of actual charges.

An outpatient, diagnosis-related, prospective payment system has been developed, called the Ambulatory Payment Classification (APC) system. The APC system combines procedural codes and diagnostic codes into groups that are clinically related. Reimbursement in this system is tied to the group in which the patient is categorized and limits reimbursement through this means.

HOW ARE RESOURCES MANAGED WITH PAYMENT CAPS AND APCS? When outpatient reimbursement has a payment cap or is through an APC system, there are distinct incentives to manage resources. These flat payments provide a financial incentive for the hospital to provide the most appropriate care while managing the costs and resulting charges. Hospitals are discouraged from ordering extra tests, performing extra procedures, or increasing charges because the reimbursement will never be more than the set amount, regardless of the actual charges.

INPATIENT PER DIEMS

Most MCOs today use per diems to compensate hospitals for providing inpatient health care services. A per diem is a set amount per day and is paid for each day that the patient is in the hospital. Per diems are usually acuity based, meaning there are different rates for different classifications of service. The basic breakdown of per diems can include many levels of acuity and types of services, depending on which services a hospital provides.

BOX 29-3

Discount from Charges Reimbursement for Outpatient Hospital

Example: Patient J went to the Hospital Hippocrates instead of Hospital Healer for the same outpatient chemotherapy treatment. Charges at Hospital Hippocrates are $1623, $134 more than at Hospital Healer. Hospital Hippocrates also has a contract with HMO Help U that reimburses 75% of charges for outpatient services. Reimbursement to Hospital Hippocrates will be:

Hospital Hippocrates Charge	×	Reimbursement Percentage	=	Reimbursement
$1623		75%		$1217

A per diem contract may have as few as two or three per diems (OB, Medical/Surgical, ICU) or more than twenty if it is a large hospital providing the full range of adult and pediatric inpatient services (Box 29-4).

Most hospitals also negotiate some kind of *stoploss provision* in their per diem contracts. Seriously ill patients with long hospital stays, clinically complex cases, and patients with high, intense resource utilization can have hospital bills that are in the hundreds of thousands of dollars or, in some cases, upwards of a million dollars. Stoploss provisions protect a hospital from the potential financial losses associated with these high-dollar cases by literally stopping or limiting the loss at a predetermined level. In the contract examples from Box 29-4, Hospital Healer and BabiesBeWell have the following stoploss provision in their contract with HMO Help U:

> If charges for an inpatient admission exceed $75,000, Hospital Healer or Hospital Babies-BeWell will be reimbursed 70% of charges for the entire stay in lieu of the per diem payment.

In the examples in Boxes 29-5 and 29-6, Hospital Healer and Hospital BabiesBeWell each have a contract with HMO Help U that reimburses the hospital with the inpatient per diems and stoploss provision as described earlier in this section.

In catastrophic cases when a patient is receiving intensive services, the charges can increase disproportionately to the length of stay. The stoploss provision becomes even more important in protecting a hospital against the financial impact of these types of cases.

How Are Resources Managed
With Per Diem Reimbursement?

Per diem payments are another prospective payment system. The hospital knows how much it will be paid each day based on the patient's per diem classification. Like other models that limit payment—diagnosis-related groups (DRGs), case rates, and payment caps—per diem payments provide clear financial incentives to effectively manage resources and control costs. Because the hospital is paid a set amount each day, performing many tests and procedures only increases

---

BOX 29-4

Per Diem Contracts for Adult and Pediatric Hospitals

Example: Hospital Healer and Hospital BabiesBeWell are full-service adult and pediatric hospitals, respectively, in a large hospital chain. They both have contracts with HMO Help U that provide per diem payments for inpatient services.

HOSPITAL HEALER SERVICES	PER DIEM CONTRACT WITH HMO HELP U
Newborn Nursery	$400
Obstetrics (Mother and Baby)	$1200
Medical	$1400
Surgical	$1800
ICU/CCU	$2000
Cardiovascular Surgery	$2200

BABIESBEWELL SERVICES (children's specialty hospital)	PER DIEM CONTRACT WITH HMO HELP U
Medical/Surgical	$1500
Pediatric Intensive Care Unit (PICU) Level 1	$1800
Neonatal Intensive Care Unit (NICU) Levels 1 and 2	$3300
PICU Levels 2 and 3, NICU Level 3	$3500

BOX 29-5

Per Diem Reimbursement

Example: Patient Y was admitted to Hospital Healer for removal of his prostate. Patient Y was in the hospital for 5 days for the surgery and recovery. The charges for the 5-day length of stay were $16,000.

HMO Help U will reimburse Hospital Healer with the Surgical Per Diem of $1,800 for each day of Patient Y's inpatient hospital stay.

Length of Stay	×	Surgical Per Diem	=	Reimbursement
5	×	$1,800	=	$9,000

In this case, Hospital Healer will be reimbursed 56% of billed charges from HMO Help U.

HMO Help U Reimbursement/Hospital Healer Charge		=	Payment as % of Charges
$9,000/$16,000		=	56%

BOX 29-6

Per Diem Reimbursement with Stoploss Provision

Example: Patient U was admitted to BabiesBeWell Hospital for leukemic induction chemotherapy. Patient U became septic and developed other complications, which resulted in a hospital stay of 32 days. Patient U was in the Medical Unit for 20 days and in the Pediatric Intensive Care Unit, Level 1, for 12 days. Total charges for the patient's 32-day length of stay were $98,000. BabiesBeWell Hospital will be paid, under the stoploss provision, 70% of charges in lieu of the per diem because charges were more than $75,000.

Charges	×	Stoploss Percentage	=	Payment
$98,000	×	70%	=	$68,600

If BabiesBeWell did not have this stoploss provision in the contract and was paid only by per diems, payment would have been:

Length of Stay	×	Medical Per Diem	=	Reimbursement
20	×	$1,500	=	$30,000

Plus

Length of Stay	×	PICU Level 1 Per Diem	=	Reimbursement
12	×	$1,800	=	$21,600
		TOTAL REIMBURSEMENT	=	$51,600

BabiesBeWell would have only received 53% of charges without the stoploss provision.

charges—payment remains the same. However, the hospital has a financial incentive to keep the patient in the hospital as long as possible because the hospital is paid on a per day basis. To prevent this from happening, MCOs that use per diem contracts have aggressive case management programs that only authorize the hospital to be paid for those days that the case management team deems are *medically necessary.*

DIAGNOSIS-RELATED GROUPS (DRGS)

Medicare was introduced by the government in the mid-1960s to provide health care coverage for persons over the age of 65 (and was later expanded to include long-term disabled persons). Like systems for the employed, Medicare was designed to offer health care coverage to enrollees, incorporating a compensation arrangement with the physicians and hospitals. In the 1970s, there were increases in health care expenditures, the number of people over the age of 65, and the number of people enrolled in Medicare. These factors led to the government facing Medicare expenditures far exceeding the amount it had budgeted. Congress stepped in and reduced the amounts paid hospitals for care provided to patients with Medicare. However, by fiscal year 1982 the aggregate Medicare/Medicaid

underpayment to hospitals still reached $6 billion (Hall, 1989).

Medicare introduced a new payment system designed to better control expenditures for inpatient hospital stays in 1983. This system, known as the diagnosis-related group (DRG) system, is still in effect today and pays hospitals a flat amount based on a patient's diagnosis. The DRG system assigns an expected length of inpatient hospital stay and relative weight for each of the 503 DRGs. Each hospital is assigned a unique base rate based on geographic location, status (urban/rural location, teaching hospital, and so forth), and local labor costs. Payment is calculated by multiplying the DRG relative weight by the hospital's base rate. There are some cases when the costs for treating a patient are significantly higher in relation to the costs of other patients within the DRG. Certain payment adjustments exist for such cases (Box 29-7).

How Are Resources Managed With DRG Payments?

DRGs are a prospective payment system (PPS) because the expected payment can be calculated before providing the service. DRGs and similar "case rate" methodologies are designed to provide a financial incentive for the hospital to provide the

---

B O X   2 9 - 7

DRG Payment for Inpatient Hospital Services

Example: DRG 410, Chemotherapy Without Acute Leukemia as Secondary Diagnosis

The relative weight for DRG 410 is 0.7968. Assume Hospital Healer has been assigned a DRG base rate of $3900. An oncology patient receiving inpatient

chemotherapy is in the hospital for 3 days and is classified in DRG 410. The patient's charges for the 3-day inpatient stay are $6200. Medicare reimbursement is calculated as follows:

Relative Weight	×	Hospital Healer DRG Base Rate	=	Payment
0.7968	×	$3,900	=	$3,108

In this example, Hospital Healer will be paid 50% of billed charges.

DRG Payment/Hospital Healer Charge	=	Payment as % of Charge
$3108/$6200	=	50%

most appropriate care while managing the costs and resulting charges. This incentive works as follows: If the patient recovers quickly and is ready to be discharged sooner than the expected length of stay for the patient's DRG, the hospital will benefit because it will still receive the payment that was based on a longer length of stay. The system discourages hospitals from keeping patients unnecessarily because it will not make additional payments for a length of stay and resulting charges beyond the assigned number of days.

CASE RATES

Case rates are a reimbursement model used by MCOs and other payors. A case rate is a flat rate that is paid for all hospital and physician services provided during a defined treatment course or for a specific DRG. Case rates are more commonly used to reimburse for complex high-cost services, such as bone marrow/stem cell transplantation, solid organ transplantation, and cardiac surgery. Many MCOs are increasingly trying to negotiate case rates for other services, including cancer care and neonatology.

When case rates are negotiated for transplant services, the case rate generally includes all inpatient and outpatient, hospital and physician services, often beginning with the evaluation and continuing through the transplantation and follow-up care until discharge back to the referring physician. The case rates are often referred to as "global" or all-inclusive case rates because they include all hospital, physician, and ancillary services. A stoploss provision may or may not be part of the methodology.

Hospital Healer has a contract with HMO Help U to provide autologous bone marrow transplantation services. HMO Help U will pay Hospital Healer a case rate of $100,000 to provide all inpatient and outpatient, hospital, physician, and ancillary services, beginning at the point the patient is accepted as a candidate and continuing through transplantation and follow-up care until the patient is discharged home to her or his referring physician. Services covered by the case rate include (but are not limited to) catheter placement, mobilization of stem cells, pheresing or harvesting of stem cells, the preparative regimen, and inpatient transplantation admission including room

and board, nursing care, pharmaceuticals, blood and blood products, all outpatient follow-up care until discharge home including any home infusion services, and any readmissions before discharge home (Box 29-8).

Contracts with case rates may also incorporate a stoploss provision to provide financial protection when charges are extremely high, as in the case of a seriously ill patient or an extremely complex case. An example of a type of stoploss provision with a case rate contract would be:

> *If charges for the transplantation case rate period exceed $140,000, HMO Help U will reimburse Hospital Healer 70% of charges for the entire stay in lieu of the case rate payment (Box 29-9).*

Not all case rates incorporate stoploss provisions, and when they do, they can use a variety of often complex methodologies.

How Are Resources Managed With Case Rates?

The financial incentives with case rates are to effectively manage resources and control costs. These are also the financial incentives for other methodologies that limit payment—outpatient payment caps, inpatient per diems, and DRGs. However, with case rates, the need to effectively manage resources and control costs applies equally to the hospital, the physicians, and the ancillary providers because payment to all of them must be split based on the lump sum case rate payment. This financial model discourages providers from keeping patients in the hospital too long, from ordering unnecessary tests and procedures, and from raising charges.

CAPITATION

Capitation is a prospective, per-member-per-month (PMPM) payment methodology used by MCOs. Ten years ago, capitation payment was used principally for PCP services. Today, it is employed for payment of hospital services as well as physician services, and even used for ancillary services such as home infusion, home care, and laboratory. Under a capitated system, a provider receives a set payment each month for every member and agrees that the capitation amount provides compensation for performing an agreed-upon listing of services.

BOX 29-8

Case Rate Payment

Example: Patient C has non-Hodgkin's Lymphoma and is undergoing an autologous bone marrow transplantation (BMT) at Hospital Healer. She begins her course of care by receiving injections of growth factor to mobilize her stem cells. After mobilization, she is pheresed to collect the cells. Patients are usually pheresed two to four times to obtain an adequate collection, and Patient C is pheresed four times. During the mobilization, she develops a catheter site infection and is hospitalized for 2 days. Patient C later goes back into the hospital for her transplantation and stays for 22 days. After discharge, she is treated in the outpatient BMT clinic and receives daily supportive care. Hospital Healer's home infusion agency makes visits to Patient C in her hotel to provide IV hydration and pain medication. Patient C is readmitted to the hospital for fever and stays 3 days. Finally, after 35 days of follow-up care, Patient C is discharged back to the care of her referring physician. Hospital Healer prepares to bill HMO Help U for Patient C's transplantation course of care:

Inpatient Charges	2 days, pretransplantation, catheter infection	$ 6,000
	22 days, transplantation admission	$ 92,000
	3 days, posttransplantation, fever	$ 7,500
Outpatient Charges	Pretransplantation (mobilization, pheresis)	$ 14,400
	Posttransplantation—clinic visits during 35 days f/u period	$ 11,300
Physician Charges	All physician services from acceptance until discharge back to referring MD	$ 15,000
Home Infusion	Posttransplantation supportive care	$ 3,500
	TOTAL CHARGES	$149,700

HMO Help U will reimburse Hospital Healer the agreed-upon case rate of $100,000, 33% less than the actual billed charges. Hospital Healer, the BMT physicians (and physicians from other specialties who provided services to Patient C), and the home infusion agency will divide the case rate based on either a percentage of the amount collected (whereby all entities would receive 67% of their charge) or some other agreed-upon distribution formula.

BOX 29-9

Case Rate Payment With Stoploss Provision

Example: If the stoploss provision is applied to the case rate payment example from Box 29–8, HMO Help U would pay Hospital Healer 70% of charges because the total charges were above the stoploss threshold of $140,000.

Charges	×	Stoploss Percentage	=	Payment
$149,700	×	70%	=	$104,790

The basic principles of capitation are the same, whether being used to compensate physician, hospital, or ancillary services:

- The capitation rate is prepayment for an agreed-upon listing of services.
- Some services may be "carved out" of the capitation rate and paid through a different reimbursement methodology.
- Capitation is a financial incentive to control costs. If providing care costs the provider more than the monthly capitation payment, the provider loses money. Conversely, if providing the care costs less than the capitation payment, the provider makes money.
- Capitation models include other financial incentives to control costs, including "risk pools." With risk pools, some monies from the capitation payments are set aside and, if total health care expenditures for the MCO are less than expected, monies are returned to the providers. If expenditures are more than expected, the monies are retained by the MCO. A full discussion of risk pools is beyond the scope and intent of this chapter.

Primary Care Physician Capitation

In an HMO, members must select a PCP or "gatekeeper" who provides for or coordinates all of the members' health care. The HMO determines its PCP capitation rates based on a number of factors, including member sex and age, and the frequency of services provided to its members (Box 29-10).

Services covered by the capitation rate are identified by CPT code and are generally inclusive of all services provided by PCPs. Because HMOs cover preventive care, the capitation rate includes well-care services and immunizations (Box 29-11).

Specialist Physician Capitation

Most HMOs and other MCOs pay specialist physicians according to a fee schedule. However, capitation for specialist physicians is increasing in use as MCOs continue to reduce payments (Box 29-12).

As with PCP capitation, each hematology/oncology practice is given financial incentives to make sure providing care to HMO Help U members does not cost more than their monthly payment.

BOX 29-10

PCP Capitation Rates

Example: PCP capitation scheduled from HMO Help U:

Member Age	Member Sex	PCP Capitation Rate
Less than 2	Male or female	$29.74
2–4	Male or female	$16.35
5–19	Male or female	$7.82
20–44	Male	$5.83
20–44	Female	$10.62
45–64	Male	$10.13
45–64	Female	$10.13
65+	Male or female	$19.70

BOX 29-11

Capitation Payment for PCP Services

Example: Assume primary care physician group Family Health has 2000 members from HMO Help U who have selected Family Health physicians as their PCPs.

Family Health, Monthly Capitation Report From HMO Help U

MEMBER AGE	MEMBER SEX	PCP CAPITATION RATE	NUMBER OF HMO HELP U MEMBERS	MONTHLY CAPITATION
2–4	Male or female	$16.35	50	$817.50
5–19	Male or female	$7.82	100	$782.00
20–44	Male	$5.83	500	$2,915.00
20–44	Female	$10.62	470	$4,991.40
45–64	Male	$10.13	420	$4,254.60
45–64	Female	$10.13	460	$4,659.80
MONTHLY TOTAL CAPITATION PAYMENT			2000	$18,420.30

Family Health receives $18,420 per month in capitation, or $221,000 per year. Family Health has a financial incentive to make sure that it costs no greater than $221,000 per year to provide primary care services to HMO Help U members. If it costs Family Health more than $221,000 per year, they will have to make up lost revenue from another source, or suffer a financial loss.

Hospital Capitation

Hospital capitation is similar to physician capitation. When an HMO uses hospital capitation, the members from that HMO must receive all of their care from one hospital, and that hospital is paid a set amount per member per month for all inpatient and outpatient hospital services. The hospital partners with a group or groups of physicians from the HMO, and the partner physicians are capitated for each member who selects a PCP from the partner physician group. Some highly specialized services, such as transplantation, may be excluded from the capitation payment and reimbursed under a different methodology.

A typical capitation to a full service hospital may range from $35 to $50 per member per month (Box 29-13).

How Are Resources Managed With Capitation?

Under a capitation model, if Hospital Healer implements strategies to reduce the inpatient length of stay, they will make more money because their costs will be reduced but the monthly payment will remain constant. Similarly, if costs increase to greater than $80,000 per month they will lose money.

The reimbursement models used by MCOs include built-in incentives for providers to reduce costs and manage resources. The six models that were reviewed in this section were discussed in order of financial risk. Fee-for-service reimbursement has the lowest level of financial risk to the provider, and capitation has the highest. In parts of the country where MCOs have a large share of the market, providers are faced with reimbursement methodologies that demand controlling costs—capitation, case rates, inpatient per diems, DRGs, and outpatient discount from charges with payment caps. In markets where managed care has fewer members, the reimbursement methodologies that are used—fee-for-service, discount from charges for inpatient and outpatient services—do not have strong built-in incentives to control costs.

BOX 29-12

Capitation Payment for Specialist Physician Services

Example: One model of capitating hematology and oncology specialty physicians with an HMO would be as follows: HMO Help U has established a hematology/oncology capitation rate of $0.31 per member per month. The rate includes all services provided by the hematologists and oncologists except drugs, ad-ministration of drugs, and supplies. There are four (4) hematology/oncology practices participating with HMO Help U—Practices A+, O–, AB–, and O+. HMO Help U has 200,000 enrolled members, of which 3,500 receive services from the four hematology/oncology practices during a specific month.

Hematology and Oncology Monthly Capitation Report

Hem/Onc Capitation Rate	×	HMO Help U Total Members	=	Monthly Hem/Onc Budget
$0.31		200,000		$62,000

The four hematology/oncology groups decided they would split the monthly budget based on the percentage of HMO Help U members that they provide services to during a month.

HEMATOLOGY/ONCOLOGY PRACTICES		NUMBER OF HMO HELP U PATIENTS SEEN IN A MONTH	PERCENTAGE OF TOTAL PATIENTS SEEN
Practice	A+	1,500	43%
Practice	O–	1,000	28%
Practice	AB–	750	22%
Practice	O+	250	7%
TOTAL MEMBERS SEEN		3,500	100%

The monthly hematology/oncology capitation from HMO Help U would be split among the practices as follows:

HEMATOLOGY/ONCOLOGY PRACTICES		PERCENTAGE OF TOTAL PATIENTS SEEN	(×) MONTHLY BUDGET	= MONTLY PAYMENT
Practice	A+	43%	$62,000	$26,660
Practice	O–	28%	$62,000	$17,360
Practice	AB–	22%	$62,000	$13,640
Practice	O+	7%	$62,000	$4,340
		100%		$62,000

BOX 29-13

Capitation Payment for Hospital Services

Example: Hospital Healer capitation payments from HMO Help U for the 2000 members who have se-lected Family Health physicians as their PCPs.

Hospital Healer Monthly Capitation Report

Hospital Capitation Rate	x	HMO Help U Members	=	Monthly Revenue
$40		2000		$80,000

Special Reimbursement Considerations for Cancer Care

All of the current reimbursement issues that affect physician and hospital reimbursement also affect reimbursement for cancer care. However, cancer care reimbursement faces even greater challenges that affect patients and providers alike.

Clinical Trials

Most of the major advances in cancer treatment are a result of clinical trials. The treatments that have improved cancer survival rates in childhood leukemia, Hodgkin's disease, breast cancer, and other cancers over the last few decades have all been developed through clinical trials. To continue this progress, it is imperative that patients are able to participate in such trials (NCI, March 26, 1998). Yet, it is estimated that only 3% to 5% of adult cancer patients participate in clinical trials (NCI, September 19, 1997). Many factors may prohibit a patient's participation in a trial, including denial or limited payment by a patient's health plan.

There are three primary costs associated with clinical trials:

1. Routine costs for the treatment of the patient, which occur whether or not the patient is enrolled in the trial. These costs have historically been paid for by the third-party payor.
2. Extra costs to patient care generated as a result of the trial, such as medication, laboratory studies, and diagnostic studies. These costs may or may not be paid for by the trial sponsor or through a grant, and are not likely to be paid for by a health plan or third-party payor.
3. Administrative costs of the study, including data gathering, statistical study, meetings, and travel. These costs are usually borne by the sponsor of the trial (e.g., a pharmaceutical company) or through a grant (through the National Cancer Institute or similar entity). These costs will not be paid for by a health plan or third-party payor.

Today, most health plans contain language in their benefit contract that specifically denies bene-

fits for services or procedures that are experimental or investigational in nature. As William T. McGiveny, chief executive officer of the National Cancer Care Network (NCCN), states, "The sharp lines between investigational and established therapies do not fit the reality of cancer treatment" (NCCN Forum to Air Issue, 1998). Many MCOs have established independent review panels to help them determine when investigational care is appropriate. Meanwhile, physicians have developed detailed documentation to assist patients in fighting such denials. Appeal packets usually include a letter from the treating physician stating why the proposed trial is the best treatment option for the patient and any peer-reviewed studies or other publications that support the treatment.

Under current Medicare policy, there is no coverage for patient care costs if a beneficiary chooses to enroll in a trial (NCI, January 29, 1998), but, ironically, Medicare will cover the cost of treating adverse events such as fever and neutropenia that may result from treatment received during a trial (Bailes, 1997).

There are many discussions and proposals in federal and state legislatures and the private sector regarding coverage and payment for patients enrolled in clinical trials, and it is not likely to be an issue that is quickly resolved. Limiting access to clinical trials prevents patients from receiving state-of-the-art care, hinders researchers' understanding of cancer treatment, and ultimately limits advances in cancer treatment for all patients (Bailes, 1997).

Off-Label Drug Use

"Off-label" drug use is the use of a drug for an indication not included on the drug label approved by the U.S. Food and Drug Administration (FDA). Once the FDA has approved a drug for human use, there are no limitations on the indications for which it may be prescribed. Many third-party payors refuse to pay for "off-label" drug use. Benear (1997) states that more than half of all patients with cancer receive at least one drug off label during the course of their treatment.

As reported by Benear (1997), a General Accounting Office (GAO) survey in 1990 showed that the prescribing of drugs for off-label use was widespread. Among the 1470 clinical oncologists surveyed:

- One third of drug administrations were given for off-label use.
- 56% of patients had at least one off-label drug included in their treatment regimen.
- Off-label use occurred twice as often for patients being treated for palliative care as for those receiving curative treatment.
- Off-label use was more prevalent for patients with malignancies that had metastasized than for earlier disease stages.
- The extent of off-label drug use was higher for cancers for which there was no standard therapeutic regimen.

Medicare, some individual states, and some insurance companies have developed guidelines for approval of certain off-label drugs. Effective with the Omnibus Reconciliation Act of 1993, Medicare covers off-label drug use for anticancer drugs as long as the uses are documented in certain publications. However, the inconsistency of coverage for off-label drug use continues to present difficulties for patients and providers alike.

Uninsured and Underinsured Patients, Denials for Treatment

Patients who do not have insurance (uninsured), those who have benefit caps and/or high coinsurance or other out-of-pocket responsibilities (underinsured), and those whose treatment is denied by the insurance company often face insurmountable obstacles to receiving treatment for cancer.

Uninsured patients may qualify for government assistance programs such as Medicaid. However, an increasing number of people are above the income criteria for Medicaid yet cannot afford to pay for health insurance coverage. Unfortunately, after a patient without insurance is diagnosed with cancer, he or she is usually unable to obtain insurance coverage, even if able to pay the monthly premium, because of "preexisting condition" clauses. Preexisting condition clauses state that an insurance company will not cover treatment for a condition that a patient had before enrolling with the insurance company. When patients are uninsured and do not qualify for Medicaid, many times the only way to receive treatment is by paying for the

total cost of treatment themselves. Due to the high cost of cancer care, patients without insurance usually do not have the money to pay for the treatment and are frequently unable to raise large amounts of money.

Underinsured patients are those whose insurance does not adequately cover the cost of the treatment, leaving the patient financially responsible for large portions of his or her bill. Few patients realize they are underinsured until they need to use their insurance, and then they discover that their policy does not offer full coverage. Ways in which patients are underinsured include:

- *Lifetime maximum payment limits*—All insurance policies define the lifetime maximum payment. A lifetime maximum means that the insurance company will only pay up to the defined amount, and the patient is responsible for any charges above the lifetime maximum. The best insurance plans have unlimited lifetime payments, whereas other plans have $1 million, $2 million, or more in lifetime maximums. Plans that have less than $1 million in lifetime maximum payments are problematic for patients with cancer because years of treatment can often cost more than the lifetime maximum payment. In these instances, the patient is basically left without insurance because he or she is then responsible for bills. Once the lifetime maximum payment has been made, the patient can change to another insurance company but often this is not feasible because of preexisting condition clauses or the employer does not offer more than one insurance company or health plan.
- *Benefit caps*—Some policies have payment caps on specific procedures, like transplantation. A patient who recently required an allogeneic bone marrow/stem cell transplantation thought he had full insurance coverage. However, when his benefits were verified, he learned that his plan had a cap on transplantations of $150,000, and an annual follow-up cap of $10,000 per year, up to a maximum payment of $50,000. This patient will be financially responsible for all charges for the transplantation that are greater than $150,000, and for every year

after for any transplantation-related follow-up charge greater than $10,000. In this example, the patient could very well be responsible for more than $100,000 to $200,000.

Patients undergoing cancer treatment also face having treatment denied by insurance companies, particularly for treatment provided when the patient is enrolled in a clinical trial (see previous section on clinical trials) or for treatment that may not routinely be accepted as a standard of care, like bone marrow/stem cell transplantation for certain diagnoses. In these cases, the patient and provider can appeal directly to the insurance company, or the patient can hire an attorney to appeal the insurance company's denial. Both of these actions take time, and many patients may require treatment before resolution of the appeal.

Before managed care, hospitals and physicians could provide more free care to patients with financial limitations by a practice known as "cost shifting." Cost shifting simply meant that third-party payors reimbursed hospitals and physicians at a high enough level that there were profit margins that allowed them to provide indigent care for those patients without insurance. In the current reimbursement environment, many third-party payors do not cover the costs of the care that hospitals and physicians currently provide, and most hospitals do not have the financial reserves to provide free care for patients without insurance or with limited coverage. Patients in these situations must either pay for treatment, choose alternative/less costly treatment, or, in some extreme cases, forego care.

Current and Future Challenges

Revenue to hospitals, physicians, and other health care providers is diminishing due, in large part, to MCOs and their reimbursement levels. Health care providers are faced with providing high-quality, cost-effective care while payments continue to decrease. In some cases, providers are being paid less than what it actually costs to provide the care.

Many wonder if there is a growing backlash against the managed care industry. Health care providers, consumers, lawmakers, and journalists are now routinely posing questions about whether the cost-containment efforts used by MCOs are going too far. Headlines from the last several years include:

- Many doctors tell of denial of coverage by HMOs (Toner, 1999)
- Cancer researchers plead for funds. Refusal of insurers, managed-care companies to pay for patients in studies criticized (Rosen, 1998)
- The soul of an HMO: Managed care is certainly bringing down America's medical costs, but it is also raising the question of whether patients, especially those with severe illnesses, can trust their doctors (Larson, 1996)
- Backlash against HMOs: Doctors, patients, unions, legislators are fed up and say they won't take it anymore (Church, 1997)
- Must good HMOs go bad? The commercialization of prepaid group health care (Kuttner, 1998)
- Calls growing for HMO reforms: State residents are worried about both the quality of health care and its rising costs (Clabby, 1998)

Paul Ellwood, the man who coined the term *health maintenance organization* nearly 30 years ago and developed many of the concepts associated with managed care, was recently quoted in *Time*, "The idea was to have health-care organizations compete on price and quality. The form it took, driven by employers, is competition on price alone" (Gorman, 1998).

It is difficult to predict the path that health care will follow, particularly given the current climate. Most health care providers acknowledge that health care costs need to be controlled, and many are implementing creative new strategies that control costs while continuing to provide high-quality patient care. If reimbursement to providers continues to decrease, however, there are grave concerns that patient care will suffer, if it has not already.

The war against cancer will rage on. Science and medicine will continue to make great strides in treating and preventing cancer. In the new millennium, we can hope that the effort and energy that patients and health care providers exert battling insurers and MCOs will one day yield a truce—a truce in which the health plans can offer coverage for their members while adequately reimbursing the health care providers; in which health care providers can cost-effectively treat patients without sacrificing quality; and in which the patients can focus on fighting their disease, not their insurer.

REFERENCES

American Association of Health Plans. (1997, August 15). AAHP Fact Sheets: Access. *http://www.aahp.org/services/consumer_information/facts/access.html.*

American Cancer Society (1999). Cancer facts and figures 1999: Basic cancer facts. *http://www.cancer.org/statistics/cff99/basicfacts.html.*

Bailes, J. S. (1997, June). Reimbursement for patient care costs in cancer clinical trials. *Journal of Care Management, 3*(3, Suppl.), 11–15.

Bedell, M. K., & Mroz, W. T. (1997). The bone marrow and blood stem cell marketplace. In M. B. Whedon & D. Wujcik (Eds.), *Blood and marrow stem cell transplantation* (p. 462). Sudbury, MA: Jones and Bartlett.

Benear, J. B., III. (1997, June). Reimbursement for the use of "off-label" drugs in oncology. *Journal of Care Management, 3*(3, Suppl.), 3–10.

Bodenheimer, T., & Sullivan, K. (1998). How large employers are shaping the health care marketplace (first of two parts). *New England Journal of Medicine, 338*(14), 1003–1007.

Church, G. J. (1997, April 14). Backlash against HMOs: Doctors, patients, unions, legislators are fed up and saying they won't take it anymore. *Time, 149*(15), 32–36.

Clabby, C. (1998, October 11). Calls growing for HMO reform. *The Sunday News & Observer* (Raleigh, NC), p. 1A, 12A.

Gorman, C. (1998, July 13). Singing the HMO blues. *Time, 152*(2), 22–28.

Hall, C. P., Jr. (1989). Hospital plans. In J. S. Rosenbloom (Ed.), *The handbook of employee benefits: Design, funding, and administration* (2nd ed., p. 133). Homewood, IL: Dow Jones-Irwin.

Health Care Financing Administration. (1998). *National health care expenditures: National health expenditures aggregate, per capita, percent distribution, and annual percentage change by source of funds: Calendar years 1960–96* [data file posted on the World Wide Web]. *http://www.hcfa.gov/stats/nhe-oact/nhe.htm.*

Kuttner, R. (1998). Must good HMOs go bad? (first of two parts): The commercialization of prepaid group health care. *New England Journal of Medicine, 338*(21), 1558–1563.

Larson, E. (1996, January 22). The soul of an HMO. *Time, 147*(4), 44–52.

The National Cancer Institute. (1998, March 26). *The nation's investment in cancer research: A budget proposal for fiscal year 1999, executive summary* [report posted on the World Wide Web]. Bethesda, MD: Author. *http://wwwosp.nci.nih.gov/bypass99/index.html.*

The National Cancer Institute. (1998, January 29). *Questions and answers about the proposed Medicare coverage for NIH-supported cancer clinical trials* [press release backgrounder posted on the World Wide Web]. Bethesda, MD: Author. *http://rex.nci.nih.gov/massmedia/backgrounders/medicarecov.html.*

The National Cancer Institute. (1997, September 19). *Health plans in Midwest agree to cover patient costs of NCI cooperative group sponsored clinical trials* [press release posted on the World Wide Web]. Bethesda, MD: Author. *http://rex.nci.nih.gov/massmedia/pressreleases/healthplants.htm.*

National Committee for Quality Assurance. (1998, September 23). *State of managed care quality press release* [press release posted on the World Wide Web]. *http://www.ncqa.org/news/sofmcrel.htm.*

NCCN forum to air issue of who pays for clinical trials. (1998, February). *Oncology News International, 7,* 2, 3, 29.

Rosen, J. (1998, July 21). Cancer researchers plead for funds. Refusal of insurers, managed-care companies to pay for patients in studies criticized. *The News & Observer* (Raleigh, NC). *http://news-observer.com.*

Toner, R. (1999, July 29). Many doctors tell of denial of coverage by HMOs. *New York Times,* p. A18.

United States Census Bureau. (1999, October 4). *Increase of 1 million uninsured people, Census Bureau says.* [press release, CB99-189, posted on the World Wide Web]. Washington, DC: Author. *http://www.census.gov/Press-Release/www/1999/CB99-189.html.*

Ethical Dimensions in Cancer Care

Carol Sheridan

As we enter the new millennium, and as science and technology continue to advance at a staggering pace, ethical issues will continue to challenge nurses who provide care to cancer patients and their families. Recent shifts in health care reimbursement from a fee for service to a managed care model, with capitated reimbursement contracts and health maintenance organizations (HMOs), have, in many instances, resulted in downsizing of hospitals. In some cases, the care of the cancer patient and family has shifted from the cancer center and oncology unit to medical/surgical units. The convergent forces of emerging technology, changes in reimbursement, and the consumer movement have driven cancer care from dedicated cancer units and hospitals to office practices, ambulatory centers, and home health settings. In these diverse settings, nurses provide care to cancer patients and their families, as the patient moves along the disease trajectory, and will confront ethical dilemmas that may occur anywhere along this trajectory (Figure 30-1). The ability of the nurse to recognize early these ethical dilemmas and to apply ethical precepts and principles using the nursing process will ensure ethical, compassionate, and quality cancer care for patients and their families.

Ethical Principles

A central tenet of cancer nursing practice is an understanding and application of ethical principles. Everyday ethical principles assist nurses in identifying and resolving ethical dilemmas related to clinical practice, and individual professional conduct. Ethics has been defined as "the study of the *right* and *wrong* in human interactions" (Winters, Glass & Sakuri, 1993). An ethical issue or dilemma is recognized by the nurse when, in the course of providing care, the nurse experiences discomfort, and "something does not feel right about the interaction or situation" (Scanlon & Glover, 1995). This emotional response is the first step in beginning to identify an ethical dilemma. Six general ethical principles have been identified (Table 30-1): autonomy, beneficence, fidelity, justice, nonmalifience, and veracity (Fry, 1991; Thomasma, 1997).

Autonomy

Autonomy refers to the ability of a person to independently exercise free will, based on his or her particular beliefs and values. Free will is associated with responsibility for independent autonomous decision making and is predicated on two assumptions. First, before the decision, all relevant information has been provided and is understood by the person. The second assumption recognizes that there are societal constraints that limit individual autonomy. For example, if an individual decision or act does harm to others, society restricts this level of autonomy (e.g., a person screaming "Fire" in a crowded movie theater).

Beneficence

Beneficence is the principle of doing good. It is characterized by kindness and charity and fre-

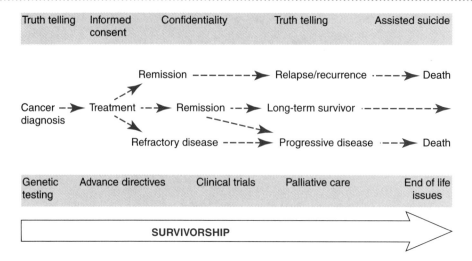

Figure 30-1 Ethical dilemmas along the cancer trajectory.

quently thought of as acting in the best interests of others. This principle has the potential for conflict with autonomy because it does establish that nurses and other health care members will always act in the best interest of the patient. This is a common belief held by some patients. A comment such as, "Oh, the doctor and nurse will do what is best for me" is not uncommon. Beneficence, like the other ethical principles, cannot be used in isolation. All must be incorporated into the assessment, diagnosis, interventions, and evaluation of clinical situations.

Fidelity

Fidelity is the principle of being faithful in the discharge of our professional duties and obligations to our patients, families, and colleagues.

Justice

Justice as an ethical principle speaks to ensuring that each person is given his or her due. In the current health care environment, justice as an ethical principle applies to issues of access to care, the al-

TABLE 30-1		
ETHICAL PRINCIPLES AND PRACTICE EXAMPLES		
Ethical Principle	*Definition*	*Clinical Practices*
Autonomy	A person's right and ability to choose	A cancer patient's decision to have a PICC line versus a Hickman catheter for infusional chemotherapy
Beneficence	The act of doing good	The act of allowing a child to accompany the parent to the OR before cancer surgery
Fidelity	Being faithful to the discharge of our professional duties	Adminstering all medications that have been ordered to control a cancer patient's symptoms (e.g., pain and/or nausea and vomiting)
Justice	Ensuring each person receives his or her due	Providing quality care to all patients equally regardless of their insurance coverage and ability to pay
Nonmaleficence	Above all else, do no harm	While administering chemotherapy, the nurse should be confident in his or her knowledge and skill to safely administer antineoplastics to all patients
Veracity	The act of truth telling	Truthfully answering the patient's questions about side effects of therapy and strategies to address these side effects

location of scarce resources, and health policy that may result in health care rationing.

Nonmaleficence

Nonmaleficence is associated with the Hippocratic oath, "above all else, do no harm." Nonmaleficence as an ethical principle guiding nursing practice means that nurses will, in all interactions with patients and families, give thoughtful consideration and attention to all interventions and ministrations to ensure there is never any harm intentionally inflicted on patients or family members.

Veracity

Veracity as an ethical principle addresses the act of truth telling and honesty in all professional interactions with patients, families, and professional colleagues. Veracity has also been associated with or interwoven with fidelity.

On a daily basis, nurses are called upon to provide care to patients. Many of these ethical principles guide the nurses' decision making.

Professional Nursing

Nursing's commitment to ethical behavior and practice has a long history and has been shaped and influenced by a multitude of forces. Some of the historical roots for nursing's commitment to ethical behavior can be found in the 1893 Florence Nightingale Pledge (Scanlon & Glover, 1995). Sixty years later, in 1950, the American Nurses Association's House of Delegates approved the first *Code for Nurses*. This document outlined the creation and maintenance of a code of ethical behavior for nurses. The American Nurses Association continues its commitment to ethical practice, updating in 1992 the *Code for Nurses With Interpretive Statements* (American Nurses Association, 1992). This code outlines eleven areas with interpretive statements that provide further clarification and direction for nurses in daily clinical practice.

In the early 1970s, the American Hospital Association drafted its first *Patient's Bill of Rights* to promote open and honest communication between health care providers and patients. The *Patient's Bill of Rights* supports respect for personal and professional values with sensitivity to patient differences. Ultimately, this document promotes the patient's role in decision making around health care. The updated version (American Hospital Association, 1992) outlines a number of patients' rights that, in particular, pertain to the care of the cancer patient (e.g., obtaining information that is understandable concerning diagnosis, treatment, and prognosis; the right to have an advance directive; and the right to consent or decline to participate in proposed research studies).

The Oncology Nursing Society, incorporated in the mid-1970s, collaborated toward the end of that decade with the American Nurses Association to publish the first *Outcome Standards for Cancer Nursing Practice* (American Nurses Association and Oncology Nursing Society, 1979). In the revised 1987 *Standards of Oncology Nursing Practice* (American Nurses Association and Oncology Nursing Society, 1987), oncology nurses were called on to use both the ANA *Code for Nurses* and the *Patient's Bill of Rights* as guides for ethical decision making in practice. A few years later, a dramatic shift took place—a legislative shift from paternalism and beneficence to the promise of full and complete autonomy in decision making regarding health care. The Patient Self-Determination Act enacted as a federal law in 1991 required all health care institutions (including hospice and home care agencies) on admission to notify patients of their right to accept, refuse, and/or to execute an advance directive (Berrio & Levesque, 1996; Scanlon, 1998). Legal requirements may vary from state to state, but the Joint Commission for Accreditation of Healthcare Organizations (JCAHO) currently incorporates this advance directive requirement in their standards. This shift from paternalism to full and complete autonomy for patients and their families lends support for the advocacy role nurses have continuously provided patients and their families as they seek health care. The Oncology Nursing Society (Table 30-2) has continued to recognize and support nurses in developing ethical competence while providing quality cancer care to patients and their families (Ersek et al., 1995; Ferrell & Winters, 1993).

TABLE 30-2
SELECTED ONCOLOGY NURSING SOCIETY ACTIVITIES SUPPORTING ETHICS AS AN IMPORTANT COMPONENT IN THE CARE OF CANCER PATIENTS

Year	Activity
1991	A resolution was approved to support: "The Oncology Nurses' role in dealing with Ethical decision making"
1991–92	ONS Board established the Ethics Task Force
1993	Ethics Task Force report published (Ferrell & Winters, 1993)
1993–94	ONS Board established the Ethics Advisory Council
1995	Ethics Advisory Council published a list of priority ethical issues (Ersek et al., 1995)
1997	**ONS Published Position Statements** "Use of Placebos for Pain Management in Patients With Cancer" ONS's endorsement of the ANA Position Statement on Active Euthanasia and Assisted Suicide
1998	**ONS Published Position Statement** "Cancer Genetic Testing and Risk Assessment and Counseling"

Nursing Process

There is a strong professional and, in some cases, legislative imperative that nurses caring for cancer patients identify, address, and attempt to resolve ethical dilemmas that arise through the course of a cancer patient's care. But how does the nurse do this? Where does one begin? Using the nursing process, the framework that is integral to professional nursing practice, assists nurses in organizing their thinking (Box 30-1). The nurse will use the nursing process In gathering information, differentiating subjective and objective findings, diagnosing or labeling the problem, planning and implementing solutions, and, ultimately, in evaluating outcomes (McCash, 1996). The five phases of the nursing process may overlap and in many ways can parallel an ethical and clinical judgment model (Meares, 1997). In fact, the discipline of clinical ethics has been described by Jonsen and associates (1998) as "a practical discipline that provides a structural approach to assist physicians in identifying, analyzing and resolving ethical issues in clini-

BOX 30-1

Utilizing the Nursing Process with Ethical Dilemmas

"Something does not feel right" (Recognizing an Ethical Dilemma

Assess	Gather subjective and objective information
	Clarify values and beliefs of the patient/family and involved staff
	Determine competence re: decision making
	What is the patient's understanding of the situation?
	Provide information re: treatments and alternatives
	Examine the patient's/family's fear
	Identify who is the decision maker
	Determine religious/cultural beliefs that may influence the decision-making process
	How does the patient/family define Quality of Life?

Diagnosis	Define the dilemma and who "owns" the dilemma
	Name or label the dilemma
Plan	With the interdisciplinary team and the patient and family, identify and weigh alternatives
Implement	Carry out the decision
	Support the patient and family in the decision
	Minimize distress for the patient and staff
	Provide emotional support
Evaluate	Was the objective or goal achieved?
	Was the patient/family satisfied with the process and outcome?

cal medicine." When "something does not feel right," the nurse can use the nursing process to:

1. Assess and identify the issue or dilemma
2. Plan for an interdisciplinary discussion with the identification of possible solutions
3. Implement the solution and evaluate the outcome for the patient, family, and staff members involved

Priority Ethical Concerns in Cancer Care

In addition to providing competent and compassionate care to cancer patients, the nurse should be able to recognize areas where ethical dilemmas are

likely to occur. Ersek and colleagues (1995) identified nine priority ethical issues that should be addressed when providing care to cancer patients. They are:

1. Assisted suicide
2. End of life care
3. Pain management
4. Health care reform
5. Access to care
6. Truth telling
7. Scientific integrity
8. Confidentiality
9. Advance directives (Table 30-3)

Although ethical dilemmas are not limited to these nine areas, these are considered high inci-

TABLE 30-3

PRIORITY ETHICAL ISSUES IN CANCER CARE

Priority Area	Clinical Examples	Clinical Tips and Tools to Use
Assisted suicide	A patient requests help from a nurse to get prescriptions in order to plan a suicide	ANA/ONS position statements on euthanasia and assisted suicide
End of life decisions	A terminally ill patient decides he or she wants no more "blood draws" and intravenous therapy	ANA *Code for Nurses With Interpretive Statements*
Advance directives	Newly diagnosed lung cancer patient returns to your office for blood counts after receiving therapy at the local cancer center	*Patient's Bill of Rights*
Pain management	The physician orders a placebo for Mr. X for the next 48 hours to determine his actual need for analgesia	ONS position statement on the use of placebos for pain management *AHCPR guidelines for cancer pain*
Health care reform Access to Care	A patient is enrolled in a local health plan and is unable to see a breast cancer specialist because the physician is not a member of the plan	ONS position statement on quality cancer care AFCOS Consensus Statement: *Access to Quality Cancer Care*
Truth telling	A physician asks you not to discuss with Mr. Smith the results of his recent CT scan (advanced disease that has progressed through the past 3 months of treatment). The family feels "it will be too depressing for him"	ANA *Code for Ethics with Interpretive Statements* NCI Publication: *What Are Clinical Trials All About?* (# 97-2706)
Scientific integrity	You are asked to collect blood samples for a patient in the practice who is enrolled in a clinical trial at the Cancer Center	ANA guidelines in the conduct, dissemination and implementation of nursing research ANA guideline for reporting incompetent, unethical or illegal practices
Confidentiality	You overhear two residents discussing Mrs. Jay's medical condition and prognosis with her employer who is visiting	*Patient's Bill of Rights*
Advance directives	You are making your fourth home visit with Mrs. Roy who has ovarian cancer. She describes her recent hospitalization and recounts how upset she was that the staff asked her to sign an advance directive form.	The 1991 Patient Self Determination Act *Patient's Bill of Rights*

dence areas where nurses caring for cancer patients should be prepared for ethical dilemmas.

Assisted Suicide

The media are replete with examples of "terminal" patients seeking physician-assisted suicide. The national media attention has helped to shift discussions regarding death and dying from a private issue into the public light (Haisfeld-Wolfe, 1996). This public debate creates opportunities for nurses to participate in the discussion. A recent survey of oncology nurses in the New England region revealed that physicians were more likely than nurses (11% versus 1%) to assist in a patient's suicide, and that nurses were more likely than physicians to perform patient-requested euthanasia (4% versus 1%; LaPorte Matzo & Emanual, 1997). Despite the limitations of this survey, the authors call for further research into this area. The authors further recommend that this survey be conducted with a more diverse group of physicians and nurses. Both the Oncology Nursing Society (ONS, 1997) and the American Nurses Association (ANA, 1994a; ANA, 1994b) state that nurses should not participate in assisted suicide or active euthanasia, and both identify the nurse's obligation to provide comprehensive and compassionate end of life care.

End of Life Care

End of life care encompasses a host of clinically relevant ethical dilemmas, including one of the other nine high-priority ethical areas for oncology practice—advance directives. Patient and family issues regarding truth telling, effective symptom management, spiritual care, and comprehensive palliative care are clinical examples in which ethical dilemmas might occur. Nurses working with patients and families in this part of the health continuum face special issues concerning dealing with patients and families who are having difficulty "letting go." This may be evident by family members blocking or interfering with the administration of narcotic analgesics or questioning why intravenous hydration has not been initiated (Edwards, 1994; Zerwekh, 1997). Strategies for dealing with these difficult and sometimes painful situations include establishing and maintaining a relationship with the patient and family, asking

difficult questions to qualify values and beliefs, encouraging and providing for the patient and family to have as much contact as is comfortable for both, eliciting facts, and dealing only with facts. Nurses should provide pertinent information based on the clinical situation (e.g., decisions regarding beginning or stopping hydration, increasing/changing analgesia), always maintaining an open line of communication with the patient and family unit. Finally, the nurse may consider consultation with the bioethics or medical ethics committees to avoid staff and family polarization and the "us and them" scenario (Zerwekh, 1994). The nurse in direct contact with the patient, whether in a hospice, hospital, or in the patient's home, has an irreplaceable role in promoting open communication between the patient and family and in ensuring the patient's final months, weeks, and hours are comfortable.

Pain Management

Effective and appropriate pain management in cancer patients has been a clinical concern in cancer care for a long time. In 1994, the publication of the Agency for Health Care Policy and Research (AHCPR) guidelines for management of cancer pain established national standards of care for managing cancer pain (Jacox et al., 1994). These guidelines address the assessment of pain and the use of non-narcotic and narcotic analgesics. After obtaining these guidelines, a review and discussion of them at staff or interdisciplinary meetings help identify clinical situations where they can be applied (McCaffery & Ferrell, 1994). The area of the use of placebos in the management of cancer pain is fraught with ethical conflict and dilemmas (Fox, 1994; McCaffery, Ferrell & Turner, 1996). Some clinicians believe that placebos are useful in determining if the pain is "real" or not, and believe pain can be relieved without associated harmful side effects. Nurses may be asked to administer placebos because there is a medical order and the physician believes that a placebo may provide useful information. This misconception is acutely at odds with the ethical principle of veracity, which is the act of being truthful. Unless the patient gives informed consent to use a placebo, nurses are being dishonest despite their best intentions if they administer a placebo. Given this background, the ONS in 1996 took a bold step stating that "placebos should not be used in the assessment and management of cancer pain" (McCafferey et al., 1996, p. 1589). Nurses should request and review this position statement within their clinical practice settings with interdisciplinary groups like the pharmacy and therapeutics committee, bioethics committee, and cancer committee. The purposes would be to (1) revise or develop policies that address the use of placebos and to prohibit their use in the assessment and management of cancer pain, (2) design interdisciplinary educational programs for health care providers, and (3) establish the ethics committee as the forum to discuss and resolve clinical/ethical dilemmas regarding placebos.

Health Care Reform and Access to Care

The fourth and fifth priority ethical areas in cancer care are health care reform and access to care. With over 43 million Americans without health insurance, and current national legislative attention focused on health maintenance organization (HMO) reform, ensuring access to care for oncology patients remains a paramount concern for nurses. On a daily basis, nurses work with patients and families who describe situations in which they were not able to access care. Examples include insurance denials for bone marrow transplantation or denials for payment for a chemotherapeutic agent being used outside its official labeling. In 1997, the ONS published a position paper on quality cancer care (ONS, 1997). One of the major tenets of this position paper is that cancer patients have access to care that includes a multidisciplinary team. This care should be reimbursable and include the entire cancer continuum: prevention, early detection services, treatment (including participation in clinical trials), supportive follow-up, and end of life care. A patient's inability to self-refer to a cancer specialist or to receive a particular narcotic analgesic or antiemetic not on the HMO's formulary represents an ethical dilemma regarding access to care. These are common occurrences for nurses in clinical practice.

In 1996, oncology specialty groups formed a coalition called the American Federation of Clinical Oncologic Societies (AFCOS). This coalition, which includes patient advocacy groups, recently published a consensus statement on access to quality cancer care, which establishes sixteen elements of quality cancer care (AFCOS, 1998).

Registered nurses can use both documents to begin interdisciplinary discussions regarding the provision of cancer care to patients within their treatment area. These tools can also be used to design specific outcome studies. Nurses should participate with professional associations and patient advocacy groups to continue to identify barriers to quality cancer care. Through active participation with these organizations, nurses can identify access issues for discussion and resolution.

Truth Telling

The sixth priority ethical area for cancer patients is truth telling and making informed choices. The *Patient's Bill of Rights* and the Patient's Self-Determination Act, as well as professional codes for ethical behavior, explicitly call for truthful behavior. How then can nurses experience ethical dilemmas within this area? Daily clinical situations emerge where there may be conflict in truth telling, either between the patient and family or the family/patient and staff. An example might be a situation in which family dynamics suggest that the husband has been the primary decision maker for the family for the past 25 years. The wife's breast cancer has now recurred or progressed. The husband asks the nurse not to tell the patient that her cancer has spread but that the change in chemotherapy represents the newest medication with the best chance for cure. Although the husband may have the best intentions in protecting his wife from frustrating and depressing news, the proposed untruth does create an ethical dilemma. Many nurses will face these types of situations on a daily basis when managing important medical information regarding the patient's disease status and treatment. Using a multidisciplinary case presentation and the nursing process (see Box 30-1) in roundtable discussions is an intervention that can address day-to-day clinical practice dilemmas (Ferrell & Rivera, 1995; Heitman & Robinson, 1997). Informed choice refers not only to treatment decisions, but also refers to how providers inform patients regarding their therapeutic options. This can include selecting a specialist for their particular cancer who may not be in the insurance or provider network. Are patients informed regarding their rights in the appeal process for services, or denied claims? Can the patient request and receive medications that may not be available in that office practice or on the HMO or local hospital formulary? How do we discuss these issues with patients? As managed care continues to penetrate our society, truth telling and informed choices may extend beyond health care providers (physicians and nurses) to truth telling by providers and insurers regarding reimbursement and coverage for a wide spectrum of cancer care services.

Scientific Integrity

The seventh ethical priority area for cancer care is scientific integrity. The clinical care of many oncology patients includes providing care to patients enrolled in clinical trials. Before initiating any trial, informed consent must be received (Berry et al., 1996). Informed consent represents communication and agreement between individuals at a particular point in time. It extends well beyond a simple signature on a consent form. Nurses are frequently key in the informed consent process by providing supportive information and education (Table 30-4) and in validating the patient's understanding and knowledge regarding a particular treatment choice. Scientific integrity includes collecting and managing data, accurately reporting results, and maintaining compliance with all regulatory agencies (institutional review boards, cooperative groups, and federal agencies such as the National Cancer Institute [NCI] or the Food and Drug Administration [FDA]). The same standards of ethical scientific integrity apply to nurses participating in or conducting nursing research (Silva, 1995). Although reporting unethical be-

TABLE 30-4	
SELECTED MATERIALS ADDRESSING HIGH-PRIORITY ETHICAL AREAS	

The National Cancer Institutes
1998 Publication Catalogue
Call the NCI's information service
1-800-4 Cancer
NCI's web site *http://www.nci.nih.gov*
	Patient to Patient Clinical Trials and You
	    (Video) (Pub. V112)
	Taking Part in Clinical Trials: What Cancer
	    Patients Need to Know (Pub. 148)
	Understanding Gene Testing (Pub. T922)

**Agency for Health Care Policy and
    Research (AHPCR)**
AHCPR Publication Clearinghouse
PO Box 8547
Silver Spring, MD 20907
(800-358-9295)
	AHCPR Guidelines for Cancer Pain
	Clinical Practice Guidelines
	Quick Reference Guides
	    (children and adults)
	Patient Guide (children and adults)

American Nurses Association
American Nurses Publishing
9 Jay Gould Ct.,
Waldorf MD 20602-2741
(800-637-0323)
	Code for Nurses with Interpretive State-
	    ments (Pub. #G-56)
	Ethical Guidelines in the Conduct, Dissemi-
	    nation and Implementation of Nursing
	    Research (Pub. #D-95)
	Guidelines on Reporting Incompetent,
	    Unethical, or Illegal Practices (Pub. #NP91)

Oncology Nursing Society 501 Holiday Drive Pittsburgh, PA 15220-2749 (412-921-7373) Fax: (412-921-6565) member@ons.org (e-mail) *www.ons.org* (Web site)	Selected Position Papers: Assisted Suicide/Euthanasia Placebos in Pain Management Genetic Testing Quality Cancer Care
Cancer Resources in the United States Oncology Nursing Forum (1997) 24 (9) 1607-1620.	Annual update of national resources for cancer patients (reprints free to ONS members)

havior is uncomfortable, nurses have a professional obligation to do so (ANA, 1994). At a local level, state nursing associations can be helpful to nurses who find themselves in situations in which they believe reporting unethical behavior ("whistle-blowing") puts them at risk professionally or personally.

Confidentiality

Confidentiality is the eighth high-priority ethical area in cancer care. Information is power, and in this day and age of electronic databases, it is increasingly imperative that private health information remain secure and under the control of the individual patient. This is particularly necessary with genetic testing and risk identification for disease. One very real concern about genetic testing is that family members who undergo testing and are identified as possessing a gene associated with a particular malignancy run the risk of employment and insurance discrimination (Engleking, 1995). This is an emerging field, and many questions remain unanswered. For example: Who should be tested? When? What are the consequences for the family member who is identified as carrying a gene associated with a particular cancer? Once a family member is identified as carrying a gene associated with a particular cancer, what do we do with that information? Is there any efficacy in educating this person about prevention and early detection? Are there any therapeutic interventions, and what are the consequences of those interventions? Nurses can play a key role in developing systems that protect this type of sensitive data. This will be of paramount importance as our knowledge and understanding of the genetic causes and treatment of cancer expand.

Advance Directives

The final priority ethical area for cancer care is advance directives. Nurses providing care to cancer patients, regardless of the setting (hospital, private practice, home care), have a unique opportunity to put into operation the federal Patient Self-Determination Act. This can be accomplished by using the nursing process and through day-to-day therapeutic communication with patients. Signing an advance directive is the final step in a long process

of communication. The nurse should explore with patients their values and beliefs regarding the end of life. Through clarification and providing information, the nurse can promote patient comfort with decisions concerning advance directives. Another important component of advance directives is ensuring that all health care members are informed regarding patient choices. The complexity of our current health care system requires that nurses participate in systems that promote accurate communication across treatment settings. The goal would be that nurses in office, hospital, and home care settings share information regarding advance directives as well as other pertinent clinical information.

Conclusion

As cancer care evolves in this changing and complex health care system, registered nurses in all settings will face ethical dilemmas. In the future, we can expect to see more cancer patients cured and many others to live longer. As a result, in practice we will experience ethical dilemmas regardless of where the patient is on the cancer continuum. Nine ethical high-priority areas have been identified, and this list is by no means exhaustive. These nine areas help to guide nurses to focus on "high incidence areas" in which ethical dilemmas are expected to emerge. The tools that nurses can use to ensure ethical practice include basic ethical principles as well as professional nursing guidelines for practice. Once the ethical dilemma is identified, the nurse will work toward solutions by using the nursing process in the context of an interdisciplinary discussion to address and resolve ethical dilemmas. Registered nurses providing care to cancer patients remain in pivotal roles focusing on patients and families to ensure the delivery of ethically competent, compassionate, and quality cancer care.

REFERENCES

American Federation of Clinical Oncologic Societies. (1998). Access to quality cancer care: Consensus statement. *Journal of Clinical Oncology, 16*(4), 1628–1630.
American Hospital Association. (1992). *A patient's bill of rights*. Chicago, IL: Author.

American Nurses Association. (1994a). *ANA position statement on active euthanasia.* Washington, DC: Author.

American Nurses Association. (1994b). *ANA position statement on assisted suicide.* Washington, DC: Author.

American Nurses Association. (1994c). *Guidelines on reporting incompetent, unethical, or illegal practices.* Washington, DC: American Nurses Publishing (Publication # NP-91).

American Nurses Association. (1992). *Code for nurses with interpretive statements.* Washington DC: Author.

American Nurses Association and Oncology Nursing Society. (1987). *Standards of oncology nursing practice.* Washington, DC: Author.

American Nurses Association and Oncology Nursing Society. (1979). *Outcome standards for cancer nursing practice.* Kansas City, MO: The Association.

Berrio, M. W., & Levesque, M. E. (1996). Advance directives: Most patients don't have one. Do yours? *American Journal of Nursing, 96*(8), 25–29.

Berry, D. L., Dodd, M. J., Hinds, P. S., et al. (1996). Informed consent: Process and clinical issues. *Oncology Nursing Forum, 23*(3), 507–512.

Edwards, B. S. (1994). When the family can't let go. *American Journal of Nursing, 94*(1), 52–56.

Engleking, C. (1995). Genetics in cancer care: Confronting a Pandora's Box of dilemmas. *Oncology Nursing Forum, 22*(Suppl. 2), 27–34.

Ersek, M., Scanlon, C., Glass, E., et al. (1995). Priority ethical issues in oncology nursing: Current approaches and future directions. *Oncology Nursing Forum, 22*(5), 803–807.

Ferrell, B. R., & Rivera, L. M. (1995). Ethical decision making in oncology. *Cancer Practice, 3*(2), 94–99.

Ferrell, B. R., & Winter, G. (1993). Ethics and oncology nursing: Report of the Ethics Task Force. *Oncology Nursing Forum, 20*(10), 3–56.

Fox, A. E. (1994). Confronting the use of placebos for pain. *American Journal of Nursing, 94*(9), 42–46.

Fry, S. T. (1991). Conceptual themes basic to cancer nursing. In S. B. Baird, R. McCorkle & M. Grant (Eds.), *Cancer nursing* (pp. 31–37). Philadelphia: W. B. Saunders.

Haisfeld-Wolfe, M. E. (1996). End of life care: Evolution of the nurse's role. *Oncology Nursing Forum, 22*(6), 931–935.

Heitman, L. K., & Robinson, B. E. S. (1997). Developing a nursing ethics roundtable. *American Journal of Nursing, 97,* 36–38.

Jacox, A., Carr, D. B., Payne, R., et al. (1994). *Management of cancer pain: Adults quick reference guide* (AHCPR Publication No. 94-0594). Rockville, MD: Agency for Health Care Policy and Research. U.S. Department of Health and Human Services, Public Health Service.

Jonsen, A. R., Siegler, M., & Winslade, W. J. (1998). *Clinical ethics.* New York: McGraw-Hill.

LaPorte Matzo, M., & Emanual, E. J. (1997). Oncology nurses' practices of assisted suicide and patient-requested euthanasia. *Oncology Nursing Forum, 24(10),* 1725–1732.

McCaffery, M., & Ferrell, B. R. (1994). How to use the new AHCPR cancer pain guidelines. *American Journal of Nursing, 94*(7), 42–47.

McCaffery, M., Ferrell, B. R., & Turner, M. (1996). Ethical issues in the use of placebos in cancer pain management. *Oncology Nursing Forum, 23*(10), 1587–1593.

McCash, K. E. (1996). Nursing process. In S. M. Lewis, I. C. Collier & M. M. Heitkemper (Eds.), *Medical surgical nursing* (pp. 3–13). St. Louis: Mosby.

Meares, C. J. (1997). A case study application of the integrated ethical/clinical judgment model. *Oncology Nursing Forum, 24*(3), 513–518.

Oncology Nursing Society. (1997a). Oncology Nursing Society's position paper on quality cancer care. *Oncology Nursing Forum, 24*(6), 951–953.

Oncology Nursing Society. (1997b). *ONS's endorsement of the ANA position statements on active euthanasia and assisted suicide.* Pittsburgh: Author.

Scanlon, C. (1998). Unraveling ethical issues in palliative care. *Seminars in Oncology Nursing, 14*(2), 137–144.

Scanlon, C., & Glover, J. (1995). A professional code of ethics: Providing a moral compass for turbulent times. *Oncology Nursing Forum, 22*(10), 1515–1521.

Silva, M. (1995). *Ethical guidelines in the conduct and dissemination and implementation of nursing research.* Washington, DC: American Nurses Publishing (Publication # D-95).

Thomasma, D. C. (1997). Ethical issues in cancer nursing practice. In S. L. Groenwald, M. H. Frogge, M. Goodman & C. H. Yarbro (Eds.), *Cancer nursing principles and practice* (pp. 1608–1624). Boston: Jones and Bartlett.

Winters, G., Glass, E., & Sakuri, C. (1993). Ethical issues in oncology nursing practice: An overview of topics and strategies. *Oncology Nursing Forum, 20*(Suppl. 10), 21–34.

Zerwekh, J. (1994). The truth tellers: How hospice nurses help patients confront death. *American Journal of Nursing, 94*(2), 31–34.

Zerwekh, J. V. (1997). Do dying patients really need IV fluids? *American Journal of Nursing, 97*(3), 26–31.

The Challenges of Cultural Diversity in Patient Care

Rosemary Mackey

As health care providers, we are probably exposed to more different aspects of cultural diversity than are most people. "Culture" is a difficult concept to define. Perhaps one way to think of it is all the baggage that we carry with us from our birth to our death—baggage that includes skin color, social behaviors, values, habits, likes, dislikes, religious beliefs, and regional customs and rituals that we learn first from our families and then, through experiences, to which we are exposed as we travel through life.

The United States of America is a nation of immigrants and the descendants of immigrants. It is common to think of the United States as a "melting pot" in which peoples of many races, backgrounds, and nationalities have become homogenized into "Americans." It is true that those who constituted successive waves of immigration gradually became assimilated into the mainstream culture of America. However, as those immigrants have contributed to the culture of their adopted country, many have maintained some of the ethnic characteristics that they or their forebears brought to it.

Patients come in all shapes, sizes, and colors, as do caregivers and, indeed, Americans in general. Although tensions in various parts of the world produced incentives for mass migration of Irish, Italians, Eastern Europeans, and (involuntarily) Africans, there have always been smaller numbers coming from many other countries. More recently, the United States has absorbed large numbers of Hispanics and Asians, as a result of either political unrest or economic hardship in parts of Latin America and Asia. Each of these population groups has individual cultures, although it is usual that their particular characteristics become diluted and less prominent in the second and third generations. Still, people of Northern European descent are likely to appear much more stoic in their responses to stress than those of Mediterranean, African, or Latin backgrounds, who may seem much more excitable and dramatic as they deal with pain and/or loss.

Although national characteristics may become attenuated, there are regional differences within the United States (e.g., residents of the deep South may appear "foreign" to New Englanders, and New Yorkers have speech and behavioral traits that makes them stand out in the Midwest). In our need and desire to treat all people equally, it is important also to observe cultural differences, at the same time avoiding offensive stereotyping. It can be a fine line. The guiding principle, transcending racial, national, regional, and religious classification, is the requirement to consider and treat people as individuals. It has been said that the secret of the care of the patient is caring for the patient!

KEY CONCEPT

We are a nation of diverse origins, cultures, and beliefs. Treat patients equally, observe cultural requirements, and avoid stereotyping.

In health care, as in many other activities, the increase in ease of communication and airline transportation and the perceived excellence of American medicine also bring a steady flow of international patients to our hospitals and clinics. Ethnic and cultural differences may be more marked among these visitors than among "average Americans." Coping with these differences can be a challenging but necessary adaptation for all members of the health team.

By taking time to learn about different cultures, a health care provider can directly facilitate the provider–patient relationship. A cultural assessment completed at the time of registration as an outpatient or admission as an inpatient can provide a great deal of the information that will facilitate a patient's course of care. The specific factors that require understanding or discussion include the more obvious ones of ethnic origin, language preference, diet, dress, and religion, and also those relating to family structure and dynamics, appropriate forms of address, socioeconomic influences, and beliefs about patients' rights.

Ethnic Origin

Knowledge of a patient's ethnic origin is important in that it provides clues to his or her geographic origin, race, language, religious beliefs, values, traditions, and dietary preferences or requirements. However, it is important not to stereotype a person based on ethnic origin or racial background alone. Just as not everyone in the United States shares all the same elements of a common culture, so too people from another country will have individual beliefs and value systems.

> **KEY CONCEPT**
>
> Understand that your personal beliefs and values may differ significantly from those of your patient from another country. Because this may ultimately affect the delivery of the person's health care, take the time to learn about and appreciate those cultural differences.

Language

Language is one of the initial factors to evaluate because the ability to communicate effectively will also have direct implications on health care delivery. English, even if spoken loudly, cannot penetrate the consciousness of someone who simply does not know English. A common mistake is to assume that limited use of English guarantees complete comprehension. Good communication is absolutely essential if we are to understand a patient's problem and, conversely, if the patient is to understand our instructions. Most major medical centers have adequate resources for interpretation, and it is necessary to call upon these freely. For smaller institutions that may not have available to them easy access to interpreters or may require such services infrequently, the use of a commercial service such as AT&T's Language Line is recommended.

The employment of an interpreter can be extremely valuable; however, it is necessary to remember that the interpreter is a tool that we use to converse with a patient. We must look at and address the patient, not the interpreter. In turn, the interpreter must respond in the patient's and the health care professional's words—in fact, he or she is a translator, not a conveyer of what he or she thinks the patient meant to say or what the patient would like to hear.

Finally, where possible, avoid the use of local expressions and jargon because they are generally difficult to translate in a meaningful way.

Written materials (financial expectations, informed consent for surgical and nonsurgical treatment or experimental procedures) must be provided to the patient in his or her own language. Therefore, it is extremely important to ascertain that the patient is literate in that language.

>
>
> **KEY CONCEPTS**
>
> Determine which language(s) the patient speaks or reads.
>
> If the patient does *not* understand, speak, or read English, obtain the services of an accredited health care interpreter. Don't

rely solely on a family member to translate because they may use their own "interpretation."

Always address the patient directly—*not* the interpreter.

Speak clearly and simply—don't use local expressions or jargon.

Diet

Dietary requirements are important to many: Orthodox Jews do not eat pork or shellfish and do not mix meat and dairy products; Muslims do not eat pork and, during the month of Ramadan, eat nothing between sunrise and sunset; and Hindus do not eat beef. Others, because of religious strictures or conviction, are vegetarian. If there are sound medical reasons for recommending modification of these rules, that may be done in some instances but only after serious discussion with the patient and often with the concurrence of his or her religious counselor. Other dietary preferences, while not carrying the mandate of religion, are quite fixed. Many Asians regard rice as a staple of diet and require it as part of nearly every meal. Similarly, Italians will be much more comfortable if they are offered a simple pasta dish rather than our typical American fare.

KEY CONCEPTS

A good understanding of cultural preferences and religious stipulations for specific foods is essential.

If not detrimental to the patient's health and/or contrary to the physician's orders, encourage the family to bring in the patient's favorite ethnic food if it is not available in the hospital.

Dress

The most superficial way in which international visitors differ from "average Americans" is in

dress. Certainly in many of the larger medical centers throughout the country, we are no longer surprised to see men and women wearing Arab or African dress, and it requires no particular adaptation for us to accept that. Increasingly, as visitors and immigrants travel throughout the United States and use health care services, the staffs of community hospitals will also be exposed to people in national dress, and it will be important to educate staffs to the meaning of and requirements for specific clothes and head-coverings. For example, men in Saudi Arabia wear a head covering called a *ghotra* and white flowing robes called *thobe*. Because the temperature is hot in the desert, these loose-fitting garments make sense. Women, on the other hand, wear a black, tentlike covering called an *abaya* with an accompanying black veil. These garments are required to maintain a woman's modesty and, because of religious prohibitions, it is improper for her to have any body part exposed while she is out in public.

KEY CONCEPT

Understand the meaning of special garments and that there may be a great reluctance on the part of the patient to be disrobed in front of a caregiver—physician or nurse—of the opposite sex.

Religion

Religious diversity is a hallmark of America; it is unlikely that any religion in the world will not also be encountered in the United States. When examining different religions, it becomes clear that for many people their everyday lives—eating, dressing, bathing, praying—are governed by beliefs and customs that are outcomes of those religions.

Whether caring for international visitors or Americans, our health institutions must be prepared to understand and accommodate a patient's religious requirements. Many hospitals now have ecumenical chapels, and many have established specific places of worship for specific religious groups. For example, small Moslem mosques or prayer rooms with the appropriate signage noting the direction of Mecca in the East are common-place. What is equally important is the education of the staff regarding the required times and necessary preparations for prayer—particularly those relating to ritual washing and cleanliness. Schedules for appointments with doctors, for treatments, or for diagnostic tests will need to be made around mandatory prayer times.

In hot climates, such as the Middle East, where meticulous hygiene is a deterrent to the spread of disease and where eating from a communal dish is commonplace, it is customary to use the right hand for eating and the left hand for cleansing oneself after going to the bathroom. It would, therefore, be insensitive to put food into an Arab's left hand or suggest that he wash himself with his right one.

An Indian man wearing a turban is most likely an Orthodox Sikh who considers it contrary to his religion to cut any of his body hair. This will be important when preparing him for a surgical procedure that would normally require shaving of hair or for a chemotherapy treatment that will result in hair loss. Bringing this to the attention of the surgeon before preoperative preparation or to the oncologist before commencement of chemotherapy may provide the opportunity to explore alternatives and thus save the patient from experiencing the additional trauma of doing something that is against his religion.

An orthodox Hasidic Jewish woman will, most likely, wear a wig to cover her bald head when she is out in public. Do not assume that her baldness results from chemotherapy or alopecia; she is wearing a wig because she keeps her head shaved in accord with her religious beliefs. Similarly, the clothes the Hasidim wear may seem heavy, particularly on a hot day or if the patient has a fever. Suggest tactfully that such clothing be removed, but do not be surprised if your suggestion is received with reluctance.

One particularly complex issue is the transfusion of blood and blood products for some religious groups. For example, for Jehovah's Witnesses these transfusions are absolutely prohibited, and many members of this denomination refuse to violate that prohibition, even as a life-saving measure. Because, in general, the courts have upheld the right of adults to refuse transfusion, any discussions to the contrary should involve the hospital's legal counsel.

KEY CONCEPTS

Whatever a patient's religious persuasion, prayer can play an important role in a person's life, particularly at a time of crisis such as illness.

Be familiar with holy days and the restrictions and requirements surrounding them.

Recognize that preparations for a surgical procedure should be made in the context of the patients religious and cultural practices.

Never assume that a person's appearance results from illness or stupidity; if in doubt, ask the patient or his or her family if there are religious aspects to be considered.

Accept gracefully a circumstance that you may not understand but are powerless to change.

Forms of Address

American informality is not always welcome or acceptable to people of other backgrounds. The tendency in the United States to address others by their first names is not always acceptable to Americans and may very definitely be offensive to others. Unless specifically invited to do otherwise, one should always address the patient and family members as Mr., Mrs., or Ms. Smith, not John or Mary. Elderly patients are not children and should be accorded the same respect as other adults.

It is desirable to follow the custom of the visitor's culture in addressing him or her. For example, Mr. Juan Fernandez Lopez from Mexico is Mr. Fernandez, not Mr. Lopez; Lopez is his mother's name. Arabic names are particularly confusing to Western cultures. If a patient's name is *Sheikh* Mohammed *bin* Sultan *al* Saud, it literally translates as follows: *Sheikh* means he is a member of the royal family; Mohammed is his first name; *bin* Sultan means he is "from" Sultan, which could be either his father's name or his hometown; and *al* Saud tells us that he is from the house or family of Saud. One thing to keep in mind is that the royal families in the Middle East are very large, so a *Sheikh* could be a pretty distant relative to the ruler of the country. If in doubt, one should ask the patient or family member for the correct term of address.

Because we are rather an informal nation when it comes to forms of address, an excellent teaching tool for all members of the professional and support staff is a popular movie entitled "The Doctor." The story of a physician who is diagnosed and treated for nasopharyngeal cancer, it clearly demonstrates the issue of addressing a patient appropriately and has a number of other "customer service" messages related to health care.

KEY CONCEPTS

Always show respect by referring to the patient by his or her formal name until requested to do otherwise.

Ask family members, the patient, or an interpreter the correct pronunciation of the patient's name.

Gender Issues

The United States has moved far toward the ideal and practice of female/male equality, but that is not a universal concept. In many parts of the world, women are considered distinctly inferior to and dominated by men. Although that may be distasteful to many American medical personnel, it is not the role of the health provider to attempt to alter that relationship. The perceived inferiority of women may cause some international patients to have difficulty in accepting the role of women in health care in our hospitals; that is not to say that women should forego their roles, but the issue should be faced diplomatically.

A corollary of the attitudes of some cultures toward women is the marked protectiveness that they may display toward their female family members. That may cause some hesitancy in allowing women to be examined or treated by male medical

personnel. At the very least, such encounters must be well chaperoned. The converse can also be true in that a male patient may reject care by female physicians.

KEY CONCEPTS

Understand that in many cultures it is perfectly normal for the male head of the household to speak and make decisions for his wife, children, and other female relatives.

Female purity and modesty may result from deep-seated religious and cultural beliefs. This may extend to requiring same-sex health care providers for both female and male patients.

Patients' Rights

The health care professions in the United States are very concerned with the patient's right to know everything about his or her diagnosis, treatment, and prognosis. That has not always been the case in the United States, and it is almost the antithesis of practice in many parts of the world where patients and their relatives try to shield each other from the unpleasant realities of death and dying.

In many cultures, there is a sense that the patient should not be told that he has a serious, life-threatening disease. That can create serious difficulties in obtaining the patient's "informed consent" to a diagnostic or therapeutic procedure with family members demanding that the patient not be told of either the potential diagnosis or of any possible complications from treatment. In most instances, discussion with the family will eliminate that barrier, but it must be done diplomatically.

KEY CONCEPT

Never plunge into a discussion of diagnosis or prognosis without understanding the cultural and religious implications.

Death and Dying

A very specific issue in this regard deals with poor prognoses and potential deaths. Particularly in the field of oncology, this is an issue that must be addressed upon diagnosis or admission.

In the event that an international patient is near death or dies suddenly, it is imperative that staff members are aware of the religious and cultural practices that will be attendant with that death. Just as there is no one approach to death in the United States, so too people from different countries and religions will approach this difficult time in different ways. For some, the relatives' wailing and loud crying may be quite normal, although it will undoubtedly be very traumatic for the staff and the rest of the patients; for others, tending to the soul or "spirit" of the patient who has died may be of paramount importance and may require having a window open to set the spirit free.

One major area that requires upfront discussion is the desire or requirement for autopsy. Although postmortems are carried out less frequently than they were in the past, there may be times when they are legally necessary. The hospital chaplain or rabbi can be enormously helpful in serving as the liaison between the family members and the professional staff if circumstances require an autopsy that is contrary to the patient's religious or cultural beliefs but may themselves be unwilling to endorse a position in conflict with their belief.

KEY CONCEPTS

Cultural issues surrounding death and dying of an international patient may be even more sensitive than is the norm for an American patient.

Seek the information and help from an appropriate minister or rabbi if particular rites and traditions are unfamiliar to you.

Conclusion

Probably the very best way to approach the care of the international patient is to try to put oneself in his or her place. Imagine that you are on holiday in a foreign country—for example, Greece. You are away from a major city, such as Athens, and you wake up one morning knowing that you have appendicitis. The hotel arranges for you to see a physician who speaks limited English, and he admits you to the local hospital where the nurses are friendly but speak only Greek, which you do not. You have the surgery, but when you wake up you are in pain and cannot communicate even your smallest needs. Once you are allowed food, you are given local Greek food, which probably will not be nearly as comforting as beef broth and Jello or a baked potato! Now you can *begin* to imagine how the patient from Saudi Arabia who has come for complex cancer treatment feels. He or she not only is a long way from home without the ability to communicate well but also has a life-threatening disease and is undergoing difficult and sometimes painful treatment.

As transportation and communication systems become more sophisticated, health care providers will come into contact with people of different backgrounds, cultures, and faiths with increasing frequency. The issues raised in this chapter have been discussed briefly; there is much more that the individual practitioner can learn about the people with whom he or she shares this world. The other major concepts to understand as you care for patients from different countries are summarized as follows:

- They are individuals just like you and me who have beliefs, values, and traditions that they have learned over a lifetime.
- Their beliefs, values, and customs may be different from ours, but they are no less genuine.
- Learn as much as you can about the parts of the world from which your patients come. With access to the Internet or even the local public library, you have a wealth of information regarding religious beliefs and cultural norms at your fingertips.

- If the patient is alone, try to find a community resource to help with language and to serve as a support system.
- We are a nation in a hurry; take that extra moment with patients from abroad—they are probably used to a more leisurely pace.
- The idea of the extended "family" is probably stronger outside the United States. We are, in general, a transient society, whereas, in many countries, large families stay close together in their original hometowns, caring for and supporting each other in times of need and illness.
- Treat the patient with the same dignity that you would expect and hope to receive in another country.

BIBLIOGRAPHY

Galanti, G. (1997). *Caring for patients from different cultures: Case studies from American hospitals.* Philadelphia: University of Pennsylvania Press.

Gladson, I., & Nwanna, G. I. (1998). *Do's and don'ts around the world: A country guide to cultural and social taboos and etiquette—The Middle East.* Baltimore: World Travel Institute.

Gladson, I., & Nwanna, G. I. (1998). *Do's and don'ts around the world: A country guide to cultural and social taboos and etiquette—South America.* Baltimore: World Travel Institute.

Morrison, T., Conaway, W. A., & Borden, G. A. (1994). *Kiss, bow or shake hands: How to do business in sixty countries.* Holbrook, MA: Adams Media Corporation.

Spector, R. E. (1996). *Cultural diversity in health and illness.* Stamford, CT: Appleton & Lange.

INDEX

Page numbers followed by *t* denote tables; those followed by *f* denote figures; those followed by *b* denote boxes